COMPREHENSIVE SERIES IN PHOTOCHEMISTRY AND PHOTOBIOLOGY

Series Editors

Donat P. Häder
Professor of Botany

and

Giulio Jori
Professor of Chemistry

European Society for Photobiology

COMPREHENSIVE SERIES IN PHOTOCHEMISTRY AND PHOTOBIOLOGY

Series Editors: Donat P. Häder and Giulio Jori

Titles in this Series:

Volume 1 UV Effects in Aquatic Organisms and Ecosystems
Edited by E.W. Helbling and H. Zagarese

Volume 2 Photodynamic Therapy
Edited by T. Patrice

Volume 3 Photoreceptors and Light Signalling
Edited by A. Batschauer

Volume 4 Lasers and Current Optical Techniques in Biology
Edited by G. Palumbo and R. Pratesi

Volume 5 From DNA Photolesions to Mutations, Skin Cancer and Cell Death
Edited by É. Sage, R. Drouin and M. Rouabhia

Volume 6 Flavins: Photochemistry and Photobiology
Edited by E. Silva and A.M. Edwards

Volume 7 Photodynamic Therapy with ALA: A Clinical Handbook
Edited by R. Pottier, B. Krammer, R. Baumgartner, H. Stepp

Volume 8 Primary Processes of Photosynthesis, Part 1: Principles and Apparatus
Edited by G. Renger

Volume 9 Primary Processes of Photosynthesis, Part 2: Principles and Apparatus
Edited by G. Renger

Visit our website at http://www.rsc.org/Publishing/Books/PPS

COMPREHENSIVE SERIES IN PHOTOCHEMISTRY AND
PHOTOBIOLOGY–VOLUME 9

Primary Processes of Photosynthesis, Part 2
Principles and Apparatus

Editor

Gernot Renger
Technische Universität Berlin
Max-Volmer-Laboratorium für Biophysikalische Chemie
Sekr. PC 14
Strasse des 17. Juni 135
D–10623 Berlin, Germany

RSCPublishing

ISBN: 978-0-85404-236-4

ISBN of set: 978-0-85404-364-4

A catalogue record for this book is available from the British Library

© European Society of Photobiology 2008

All rights reserved

Apart from fair dealing for the purposes of research for non-commercial purposes or for private study, criticism or review, as permitted under the Copyright, Designs and Patents Act 1988 and the Copyright and Related Rights Regulations 2003, this publication may not be reproduced, stored or transmitted, in any form or by any means, without the prior permission in writing of The Royal Society of Chemistry, or in the case of reproduction in accordance with the terms of licences issued by the Copyright Licensing Agency in the UK, or in accordance with the terms of the licences issued by the appropriate Reproduction Rights Organization outside the UK. Enquiries concerning reproduction outside the terms stated here should be sent to The Royal Society of Chemistry at the address printed on this page.

Published by The Royal Society of Chemistry,
Thomas Graham House, Science Park, Milton Road,
Cambridge CB4 0WF, UK

Registered Charity Number 207890

For further information see our web site at www.rsc.org

Preface for the ESP Series in Photochemical and Photobiological Sciences

"Its not the substance, it's the dose which makes something poisonous!" When Paracelsius, a German physician of the 14th century made this statement he probably did not think about light as one of the most obvious environmental factors. But his statement applies as well to light. While we need light, for example for vitamin D production, too much light might cause skin cancer. The dose makes the difference. These diverse findings of light effects have attracted the attention of scientists for centuries. The photosciences represent a dynamic multidisciplinary field that includes such diverse subjects as behavioral responses of single cells, cures for certain types of cancer and the protective potential of tanning lotions. It also includes photobiology and photochemistry, photomedicine as well as the technology for light production, filtering and measurement. Light is a common theme in all these areas. In recent decades a more molecular centered approach has changed both the depth and the quality of the theoretical as well as the experimental foundation of photosciences.

An example of the relationship between global environment and the biosphere is the recent discovery of ozone depletion and the resulting increase in high-energy ultraviolet radiation. The hazardous effects of high-energy ultraviolet radiation on all living systems is now well established. This discovery of the result of ozone depletion put photosciences at the center of public interest with the result that, in an unparalleled effort, scientists and politicians worked closely together to come to international agreements to stop the pollution of the atmosphere.

The changed recreational behavior and the correlation with several diseases in which sunlight or artificial light sources play a major role in the causation of clinical conditions (e.g., porphyrias, polymorphic photodermatoses, *Xeroderma pigmentosum* and skin cancers) have been well documented. As a result, in some countries (e.g., Australia) public services inform people about the potential risk of extended periods of sun exposure every day. The problems are often aggravated by the phototoxic or photoallergic reactions produced by various environmental pollutants, food additives or therapeutic and cosmetic drugs. However, if properly used, light-stimulated processes can induce important beneficial effects in biological systems, such as the elucidation of several aspects of cell structure and function. Novel developments are centered around photodiagnostic and phototherapeutic modalities for the treatment of cancer, arthrosclerosis, several autoimmune diseases, neonatal jaundice and others. In addition, classic research areas such as vision and photosynthesis are still very active. Some of these developments are unique to photobiology, since the peculiar physicochemical properties of electronically excited biomolecules often lead to the promotion of reactions that are characterized by high levels of selectivity in space and time. Besides the biologically centered areas, technical developments have paved the way for the harnessing of solar energy to produce warm water and electricity or the development of environmentally friendly techniques for addressing problems of large social impact (e.g., the decontamination of polluted waters). While also in use in Western countries, these techniques are of great interest for developing countries.

The European Society for Photobiology (ESP) is an organization that aims to develop and coordinate the very different fields of photosciences in terms of public knowledge and scientific interests. Owing to the ever increasing demand for a comprehensive overview of the photosciences the ESP decided to initiate an encyclopedic series, the "Comprehensive Series in Photochemical and Photobiological Sciences". This series is intended to give an in-depth coverage over all the very different fields related to light effects. It will allow investigators, physicians, students, industry and laypersons to obtain an updated record of the state-of-the-art in specific fields, including ready access to the recent literature. Most importantly, such reviews give a critical evaluation of the directions that the field is taking, outline hotly debated or innovative topics and even suggest a redirection if appropriate. It is our intention to produce the monographs at a sufficiently high rate to generate a timely coverage of both well established and emerging topics. As a rule, the individual volumes are commissioned; however, comments, suggestions or proposals for new subjects are welcome.

Donat-P. Häder and Giulio Jori
Spring 2002

Volume Preface

The interaction of living matter with electromagnetic radiation in the near-ultraviolet (NUV), visible (Vis) and near-infrared (NIR) regions is a most important topic in life sciences. The radiation from a huge extraterrestrial fusion reactor, the sun, not only provides the unique Gibbs energy for the development and sustenance of almost all forms of life on our planet but also plays a key role in several regulatory functions such as synchronizing biological clocks and information transfer processes (e.g., vision, photomorphogenesis, phototaxis, communication via bioluminescence signals).

It is, therefore, not surprising that the sun played a central role in mankind's cultural development and religious admiration throughout the world, ranging from the great Aton hymn of the old Egyptians, to the worshippers of the sun in India and to the highly advanced ancient Indian societies (Mayas and Incas) in the Western hemisphere.

Among the different light-induced processes, photosynthesis is fundamental and unique because it enables the biological transformation of solar radiation into (electro)chemical Gibbs energy. Furthermore, it is the most abundant chemical reaction on the earth's surface (land and oceans), with an estimated turnover of 300–500 billion tons of CO_2 per year, converted into carbohydrates and subsequent products. The crucial role of photosynthesis can be best summarized in only four words: "Life is bottled sunshine" [Wynword Read, *Martyrdom of Man*, 1924].

Studies on photosynthesis date back to the early days of the development of natural sciences. The fundamental principles of energy transformation in general and photosynthesis in particular, described by the first and second law of thermodynamics, were outlined in the nineteenth century by R. J. Mayer and L. Boltzmann, respectively (Chapter 1). Nowadays, the unraveling of the underlying structural and functional organization of photosynthesis focuses on intensive research activities. The high scientific relevance of topics related to the subject is best illustrated by the impressive list of about 20 Nobel laureates that were awarded the Prize for their work performed in this field, starting with Richard Willstätter in 1915 and Hans Fischer in 1930 and their pioneering studies on the chemistry of chlorophylls as the key pigments of the photosynthetic apparatus [for an excursion into the history of photosynthesis research, I recommend the excellent book *Discoveries in Photosynthesis* (Govindjee, J. T. Beatty, H. Gest, J. F. Allen, eds.), Springer, 2005].

The overall process of photosynthesis consists of several reactions, which take place in quite different time domains, covering a range from femtoseconds (light absorption) up to hours (long-term acclimation) and even days or months (plant growth). Within this wide time region the light-driven reactions leading to the primary metabolites ("energy rich" bound hydrogen and ATP) are the fastest reactions, which are accomplished within milliseconds and referred to as "Primary Processes of Photosynthesis". Research on this topic is not only a fascinating part of pure science but it can also offer nature's masterpiece for solar energy exploitation as a blueprint for the technical development of devices aiming at contributing to solutions of mankind's Gibbs energy demands.

This edition of two volumes is restricted to topics on the "Primary Processes of Photosynthesis". As several books in this field already exist (see, for example, *Advances in Photosynthesis and Respiration*, Series editor Govindjee, Springer), one might ask: Why publish another two? The major reason for doing so is the enormous progress achieved in molecular biology and X-ray diffraction crystallography of membrane proteins during the last two decades, which has enabled, in combination with developments of sophisticated spectroscopic methods of very high time resolution, much deeper insight into the mechanisms and structure of the apparatus down to the level of atomic dimensions. Furthermore, significant advances in the methodology of theory (quantum chemistry, molecular mechanics) offer a new basis for a better understanding of structure–function relationships, including the role of dynamic processes.

This publication is an ambitious attempt to provide a synoptic state-of-the-art picture of the primary processes of photosynthesis by casting together the mosaics of detailed knowledge described by leading experts in the field. Twenty two chapters have been written by 42 authors from Europe, USA, Japan and Australia. The wealth of information appears to be best presented in two different volumes (Parts 1 and 2). Part 1 describes the photophysical principles, photosynthetic pigments and light harvesting/adaptation/stress. It is divided into five sections: Section I is an introduction to the field, giving an overview on the primary processes of photosynthesis in a single chapter presented by G. Renger. Section II also contains a single chapter, by T. Renger, which provides the basic theoretical background of the underlying photophysical principles (excitation energy and electron transfer) for light harvesting and the electron transport chain. Section III describes the properties of the main pigments in two chapters, i.e. the chlorophylls in Chapter 3 by H. Scheer and the carotenoids in Chapter 4 by Koyama et al. In Section IV, five chapters deal with light harvesting, regulatory control of excitation energy fluxes and Chapter 5, presented by Law and Cogdell, provides an insight into the structure and function of the antenna system of anoxygenic photosynthetic bacteria, and in Chapter 6, presented by Mimuro et al., the properties of the antenna system of oxygenic cyanobacteria are Morosinotto and Bassi, in Chapter 7, and van Amerongen and Croce, in Chapter 8, summarize our knowledge on the antenna systems of Photosystem I and Photosystem II, respectively, of higher plants.

Chapter 9, by Gilmore and Li, presents information on the regulatory control of the antenna function in plants. Section V describes, in a single Chapter 10 by Vass and Aro, the effects induced by light stress.

Part 2 is divided into three sections: Section VI (the numbering is continued from Part 1) is devoted to the structure and function of reaction centers in anoxygenic photosynthetic bacteria and the two photosystems of oxygen evolving organisms. Lancaster in Chapter 11 and Parson in the complementary Chapter 12 summarize the current state of knowledge on the structure and the functional pattern, respectively, of reaction centers in anoxygenic bacteria. Analogously, structure and functional pattern of Photosystem I (PS I) and Photosystem II (PS II) in oxygen-evolving organisms are described in the following five chapters presented by Fromme et al. (Chapter 13: structure of PS I), Setif and Leibl (Chapter 14: functional pattern of PSI), Zouni (Chapter 15: structure of PS II), G. Renger (Chapter 16: functional pattern of PS II) and J. Messinger and G. Renger (Chapter 17: oxygen evolution). Section VII on electron transport chains and photophosphorylation contains four chapters: anoxygenic bacteria are described by Verméglio (Chapter 18), oxygen-evolving cyanobacteria by Peschek (Chapter 19), the cytochrome b_6f complex by Cramer et al. (Chapter 20), and in Chapter 21 Junge summarizes our knowledge on photophosphorylation. In Section VIII, Larkum describes, in Chapter 22, the evolution of photosynthetic organisms.

All the chapters in these two parts provide a modern and updated view of the corresponding topics. Accordingly, this edition is not only a most valuable text for graduate students but it is also addressed to all scientists who are interested in the field of the primary processes of photosynthesis. It is my sincere hope that these two books will entice young people into this exciting research area with the aim of addressing successfully the challenging problems of high relevance that are still awaiting a satisfactory answer.

I have many people to thank. First of all, the authors for their efforts to offer the reader excellent chapters and for their positive responses to my suggestions. Without their invaluable cooperation there would be no books. My thanks also go to Susanne Renger and Solweig Nothing for their continuous help in the preparation of electronic versions of figures and typing of manuscripts, respectively.

I am most grateful to my wife Eva for all her enthusiasm in supporting this work and her invaluable help during periods of frustration and disappointment by sharing her optimism in finally reaching the desired goal.

I wish all readers a pleasant and stimulating journey through the fascinating "world" of the primary processes of photosynthesis.

Gernot Renger

Contents

Part 1: Photophysical Principles, Pigments and Light Harvesting/Adaptation/ Stress

I. Introduction

Chapter 1	Overview of Primary Processes of Photosynthesis *Gernot Renger*	5

II. Basic Photophysical Principles

Chapter 2	Absorption of Light, Excitation Energy Transfer and Electron Transfer Reactions *Thomas Renger*	39

III. Pigments

Chapter 3	Chlorophylls *Hugo Scheer*	101
Chapter 4	Photophysical Properties and Light-Harvesting and Photoprotective Functions of Carotenoids in Bacterial Photosynthesis: Structural Selections *Yasushi Koyama, Yoshinori Kakitani and Yasutaka Watanabe*	151

IV. Structure and Function of Antenna Systems

Chapter 5	The Light-Harvesting System of Purple Anoxygenic Photosynthetic Bacteria *Christopher J. Law and Richard J. Cogdell*	205
Chapter 6	Oxygen-Evolving Cyanobacteria *Mamoru Mimuro, Masami Kobayashi, Akio Murakami, Tohru Tsuchiya and Hideaki Miyashita*	261

Chapter 7	Antenna System of Higher Plants' Photosystem I and Its Interaction with the Core Complex *Tomas Morosinotto and Roberto Bassi*	301
Chapter 8	Structure and Function of Photosystem II Light-Harvesting Proteins (Lhcb) of Higher Plants *Herbert van Amerongen and Roberta Croce*	329
Chapter 9	Regulatory Control of Antenna Function in Plants *Adam M. Gilmore and Xiao-Ping Li*	369

V. Light Stress

Chapter 10	Photoinhibition of Photosynthetic Electron Transport *Imre Vass and Eva-Mari Aro*	393
Subject Index		427

Part 2: Reaction Centers/Photosystems, Electron Transport Chains, Photophosphorylation and Evolution

VI. Structure and Function of Reaction Centers and Photosystems

Chapter 11	Structures of Reaction Centers in Anoxygenic Bacteria *C. Roy D. Lancaster*	5
Chapter 12	Functional Pattern of Reaction Centers in Anoxygenic Photosynthetic Bacteria *William W. Parson*	57
Chapter 13	Structure and Function of Photosystem I *Raimund Fromme, Ingo Grotjohann and Petra Fromme*	111
Chapter 14	Functional Pattern of Photosystem I in Oxygen Evolving Organisms *Pierre Sétif and Winfried Leibl*	147
Chapter 15	From Cell Growth to the 3.0 Å Resolution Crystal Structure of Cyanobacterial Photosystem II *Athina Zouni*	193
Chapter 16	Functional Pattern of Photosystem II *Gernot Renger*	237

CONTENTS

Chapter 17	Photosynthetic Water Splitting *Johannes Messinger and Gernot Renger*	291

VII. Electron Transport Chains and Phosphorylation

Chapter 18	Anoxygenic Bacteria *André Verméglio*	351
Chapter 19	Electron Transport Chains in Oxygenic Cyanobacteria *Günter A. Peschek*	383
Chapter 20	Structure–Function of the Cytochrome $b_6 f$ Complex: A Design that has Worked for Three Billion Years *William A. Cramer, Huamin Zhang, Jivsheny Yan, Genji Kurisu, Eiki Yamashita, Naranbaatar Dashdorj, Hanyovp Kim and Sergei Savikhin*	417
Chapter 21	Photophosphorylation *Wolfgang Junge*	447

VIII. Evolution

Chapter 22	The Evolution of Photosynthesis *Anthony W.D. Larkum*	489

Subject Index   523

Contributors

Eva-Mari Aro, *Department of Biology, University of Turku, Turku, Finland*
Roberto Bassi, *Dipartimento Scientifico e Tecnologico, Università di Verona. Strada Le Grazie, 15-37134 Verona, Italy*
Richard J. Cogdell, *Microbial Photosynthesis Laboratory, Division of Biochemistry & Molecular Biology, Institute of Biomedical and Life Sciences, University of Glasgow, Glasgow G12 8QQ, UK*
W. A. Cramer, *Department of Biological Sciences, Purdue University, West Lafayette, IN 47907, USA*
Roberta Croce, *Institute of Biophysics CNR, C/o ITC. 38100 Povo, Trento, Italy Present address: Biophysical Chemistry, University of Groningen, Nijenborg 4, 9747 AG Groningen, The Netherlands*
N. Dashdorj, *Department of Physics, Purdue University, West Lafayette, IN 47907, USA*
Petra Fromme, *Department of Chemistry and Biochemistry, Arizona State University, Box 871604, 85287-1607 Tempe, Arizona, USA*
Raimund Fromme, *Department of Chemistry and Biochemistry, Arizona State University, Box 871604, 85287-1607 Tempe, Arizona, USA*
Adam M. Gilmore, *Fluorescence Division, Horiba Jobin Yvon Inc., 3880 Park Avenue, Edison, NJ 08820, USA*
Ingo Grotjohann, *Department of Chemistry and Biochemistry, Arizona State University, Box 871604, 85287-1607 Tempe, Arizona, USA*
Wolfgang Junge, *Department of Biophysics, University of Osnabrück, 49069 Osnabrück, Germany*
Yoshinori Kakitani, *Faculty of Science and Technology, Kwansei Gakuin University, 2-1 Gakuen, Sanda 669-1137, Japan*
H. Kim, *Department of Physics, Purdue University, West Lafayette, IN 47907, USA*
Masami Kobayashi, *Institute of Materials Science, University of Tsukuba, Tsukuba, Ibaraki 305–8573, Japan*
Yasushi Koyama, *Faculty of Science and Technology, Kwansei Gakuin University, 2-1 Gakuen, Sanda 669-1337, Japan*
G. Kurisu, *Department of Biological Sciences, Purdue University, West Lafayette, IN 47907, USA*

Present address: Department of Life Sciences, Graduate School of Arts and Sciences, University of Tokyo, Komaba 3-8-1, Meguro-ku, Tokyo 153–8902, Japan

C. Roy D. Lancaster, Max Planck Institute of Biophysics, Department of Molecular Membrane Biology, P.O. Box 55 03 53, D-60402, Frankfurt am Main, Germany

Anthony W.D. Larkum, School of Biological Sciences, University of Sydney and Sydney University Biological Information and Technology Centre (SUBIT), Medical Foundation Building, University of Sydney, NSW 2006, Australia

Christopher J. Law, Microbial Photosynthesis Laboratory, Division of Biochemistry & Molecular Biology, Institute of Biomedical and Life Sciences, University of Glasgow, Glasgow G12 8QQ, UK

Winfried Leibl, Service de Bioénergétique and URA CNRS 2096, Département de Biologie Joliot-Curie, CEA Saclay, 91191 Gif sur Yvette, France

Xiao-Ping Li, Biotechnology Center for Agriculture and the Environment, Foran Hall, Cook Campus, Rutgers, The State University of New Jersey, 59 Dudley Road, New Brunswick, NJ 08901–8520, USA

Johannes Messinger, Max-Planck-Institut für Bioanorganische Chemie, Stiftstrasse 34–36, D-45470 Mülheim an der Ruhr, Germany

Mamoru Mimuro, Department of Technology and Ecology, Hall of Global Environmental Research, and Graduate School of Human and Environmental Studies, Kyoto University, Yoshida-Honmachi, Sakyo-ku, Kyoto 606–8501, Japan

Hideaki Miyashita, Department of Technology and Ecology, Hall of Global Environmental Research, and Graduate School of Human and Environmental Studies, Kyoto University, Yoshida-Honmachi, Sakyo-ku, Kyoto 606–8501, Japan

Tomas Morosinotto, Dipartimento Scientifico e Tecnologico, Università di Verona. Strada Le Grazie, 15-37134 Verona, Italy
Present address: Dipartmento di Biologia, Università di Padova, Via Ugo Bassi 58 B, 35131 Padova, Italy

Akio Murakami, Kobe University Research Center for Inland Seas, Iwaya, Awaji, Hyogo 656–2401, Japan

William W. Parson, Department of Biochemistry, Box 35–7350, University of Washington, Seattle, WA 98195–7350, USA

Günter A. Peschek, Molecular Bioenergetics Group, Institute of Physical Chemistry, University of Vienna, Althanstrasse 14, A-1090 Wien, Austria

Gernot Renger, Technische Universität Berlin, Institut für Chemie, Max-Volmer-Laboratorium für Biophysikalische Chemie, Straße des 17. Juni 135, D-10623 Berlin, Germany

Thomas Renger, Institut für Chemie (Kristallographie), Freie Universität Berlin, Takustrasse 6, D-14195 Berlin, Germany

S. Savikhin, Department of Physics, Purdue University, West Lafayette, IN 47907, USA

H. Scheer, Dept. Biologie I-Bereich Botanik, Universität München, Menzinger Str. 67, D-80638 München, Germany

CONTRIBUTORS

Pierre Sétif, *Service de Bioénergétique and URA CNRS 2096, Département de Biologie Joliot-Curie, CEA Saclay, 91191 Gif sur Yvette, France*

Tohru Tsuchiya, *Department of Technology and Ecology, Hall of Global Environmental Research, and Graduate School of Human and Environmental Studies, Kyoto University, Yoshida-Honmachi, Sakyo-ku, Kyoto 606–8501, Japan*

Herbert van Amerongen, *Laboratory of Biophysics, Wageningen University, P.O. Box 8128, 6700 ET Wageningen, The Netherlands*

Imre Vass, *Institute of Plant Biology, Biological Research Center, Hungarian Academy of Sciences, 6726 Szeged, Temesvári krt. 62, Hungary*

André Verméglio, *Laboratoire de Bioénergétique Cellulaire, UMR 6191 CNRS-CEA-Aix-Marseille II DEVM CEA, Cadarache 13108, Saint Paul lez Durance, France*

Yasutaka Watanabe, *Faculty of Science and Technology, Kwansei Gakuin University, 2-1 Gakuen, Sanda 669–1137, Japan*

E. Yamashita, *Department of Biological Sciences, Purdue University, West Lafayette, IN 47907, USA*

J. Yan, *Department of Biological Sciences, Purdue University, West Lafayette, IN 47907, USA*
Present address: Department of Pharmacology, University of California-Davis, Davis, CA 95616, USA

H. Zhang, *Department of Biological Sciences, Purdue University, West Lafayette, IN 47907, USA*

Athina Zouni, *Institute for Chemistry/Max Volmer Laboratory for Biophysical Chemistry, Technical University Berlin, Strasse des 17. Juni 135, D-10623 Berlin, Germany*

Abbreviations and Symbols

A or A_0, special chlorophyll a molecules acting as electron acceptors in type I RCs
A, antheraxanthin
A_1, special phylloquinone molecule(s) acting as electron acceptor in PS I (see also PhQ_A and PhQ_B)
aa or AA, amino acid
Acc, electron acceptor
ALA, 5-aminolevulinic acid
APC, allophycocyanin
ATP, adenosine triphosphate
B_A, B_B, "accessory" BChls in proteobacterial RCs
BC, before Christ
(B)Chl, (bacterio)chlorophyll
(B)Pheo or (B)Phe, (bacterio)pheophytin
BIC, butyl isocyanide
B_X, B_y, higher energy optical absorption bands (Soret bands) of (bacterio)chlorins and porphyrins
CAB, chlorophyll a/b binding protein
CAC, chlorophyll a/c binding protein
CAM crassulacean acid metabolism
Car, carotenoid
CcO, cytochrome c oxidase
CD, circular dichroism
CM, cytoplasmic or plasma membrane(s)
CPX, chlorophyll binding protein of molecular mass X
cyt, cytochrome
d.w., dry weight
D1, D2, central polypeptides of PS II RCs
DBMIB, 2,5-dibromo-3-methyl-6- isopropyl-p-benzoquinone
DCCD, dicyclohexylcarbodiimide
DCMU, 3-(3,4-dichlorophenyl)-1,1-dimethylurea
DGDG, digalactosyldiacylglycerol
DOPC, dioleoyl-phosphatidylcholine
EET, excited state energy transfer (excitation energy transfer)

ELIP, early light induced protein
EM, electron microscopy
E_m, midpoint oxidation–reduction potential
ENDOR, electron nuclear double resonance
EPR, electron paramagnetic resonance
ER, endoplasmatic reticulum
ESEEM, electron spin echo envelope modulation
ESR, electron spin resonance
ET, electron transfer
ETC, Electron transport chain
ETP, electron transport phosphorylation
EXAFS, extended X-ray absorption fine structure
F_A, F_B, F_x, Iron-sulfur centers in PS I and chlorobial RCs
F_{AB} protein, subunit PsaC of photosystem I which binds the two iron-sulfur clusters F_A and F_B
FCWD, Franck–Condon weighted density of states
Fd or fd, ferredoxin
FDP, flavo-diiron proteins
FIOP, flash-induced oxygen evolution pattern
Fld, flavodoxin
FNR, ferredoxin-$NADP^+$-oxidoreductase
FTIR, Fourier-transform infrared
FWHM, full-width at half-maximum
Ga, giga years ago
GAP, glyceraldehyde 3-phosphate
GAP-DH, glyceraldehyde 3-phosphate dehydrogenase
H_A, H_B, bacteriopheophytins in proteobacterial RCs
HiPIP, high-potential iron-sulfur protein
HLIP, high light-induced protein
IC, internal conversion
ICM, intracytoplasmic membrane
IChM, inner chloroplast membrane
IEF, isoelectric focusing
IEP, (pH of) isoelectric point
IR, infrared
ISC, intersystem crossing
isiA, iron stress-induced protein A
ISP, iron-sulfur protein
ISP-s, 139 residue p-side soluble domain of the ISP
K_z, equilibrium binding (association) constant between Z (or A) and one PS II unit;
L, lutein
L, M, H, subunits of proteobacterial RCs
LD, linear dichroism
LH, light harvesting

ABBREVIATIONS AND SYMBOLS

LHC I, II (or Lhc I, II), light-harvesting chlorophyll complexes of Photosystem I, II
LH(C)P, light harvesting (chlorophyll) protein
MDGD, monogalactosyldiacylglycerol
MgDVP, Mg-2, 4-divinyl phaeoporphyrin methyl ester
MIMS, membrane inlet mass spectrometry
MK, MKH_2, menaquinone, menaquinol
MSH, membrane spanning helix (see also TMH)
N, neoxanthin
NAD^+, NADH, nicotinamide adenine dinucleotide (oxidized and reduced, respectively)
NHFe, nonheme iron
NIR, near-infrared spectral range (700–1200 nm)
NMR, nuclear magnetic resonance
NPQ, nonphotochemical quenching (of PS II chlorophyll fluorescence)
NQNO, 2-n-nonyl-4-hydroxyquinoline N-oxide
OChM, outer chloroplast membrane
OEC oxygen evolving complex
p- and n-, electrochemically positive and negative sides of the membrane
P, special pair, photochemically active pigment of bacterial RCs
P870, special pair in proteobacterial RCs
p.m.f., proton motive force
P680 (or P_{680}), photochemically active pigment of PS II
P700, photochemically active pigment (or electron donor) in PS I
P798, photochemically active pigment in heliobacterial RCs
P840, photochemically active pigment in chlorobial RCs
PAR, photosynthetically active radiation
PBRC (or PbRC), purple bacteria reaction center
PC, phycocyanin
PC, also used as abbreviation for plastocyanin
pcb, prochlorophyte chlorophyll binding protein
PCET, proton coupled electron transfer
PE, phycoerythrin
PEC, phycoerythrocyanin
PET, photosynthetic electron transport
PG, Phosphatidylglycerol
PhQ_A and PhQ_B, the two phylloquinones A- of PS I associated to the A- and B-branches of electron transfer
PQ, plastoquinone
(P)Chlide, (Proto)Chlorophyllide
Proto, protoporphyrin IX
PS I (or PS1), Photosystem I (1)
PS II (or PS2), Photosystem II (2)
PS II CC, PS II core complex
PsaA, PsaB, subunits of PS I RCs
PsbS (also called CP22), 22 kDa PS II protein

PscA, PscB, polypeptides of chlorobial RCs
Q_A, primary quinone electron acceptor of type II RCs
Q_B, secondary plastoquinone acceptor of type II RCs
Q_x, Q_y, low energy optical absorption bands of (bacterio)chlorins and porphyrins
RC, reaction centre
RET, respiratory electron transport
RIXS, resonant inelastic x-ray scattering
ROS reactive oxygen species
rRNA ribosomal ribose nucleic acid
S (or S_i) states, formal oxidation states of the water-oxidizing complex
SDS-PAGE, sodium dodecyl sulfate polyacrylamide gel electrophoresis
SQDG, sulfoquinovosyldiacylglycerol
TA, transient absorption
TDS, tridecyl-stigmatellin
TMH, trans-membrane helix (see also MSH)
TRO, terminal respiratory oxidase
T-S, triplet minus singlet
UQ, ubiquinone (coenzyme Q)
UV, ultraviolet spectral range (200–400 nm)
V, violaxanthin
VDE, violaxanthin de-epoxidase
Vis, Visible spectral range (400–700 nm)
W_f, W_s, fast and slowly exchanging substrate (water) molecules bound to the WOC
WOC, water-oxidizing complex (= OEC, oxygen-evolving complex)
WT, wild type
XANES, X-ray absorption near edge structure
Xanth, xanthophyll
XRD(C), X-ray diffraction (crystallography)
Y_Z, Y_D, redox active tyrosine of polypeptides D1 and D2, respectively, in PS II
Z, zeaxanthin
ΔpH, trans-membrane difference of pH
$\Delta \tilde{\mu}_H^+$, trans-membrane proton electrochemical potential difference
ε, molar extinction coefficient ($M^{-1}\ cm^{-1}$)
λ, wavelength (nm)
μE, micro Einstein (Einstein is the unit for one mole photons)

Part 2: Reaction Centers/Photosystems, Electron Transport Chains, Photophosphorylation and Evolution

VI. Structure and Function of Reaction Centers and Photosystems

Chapter 11

Structures of Reaction Centers in Anoxygenic Bacteria

C. Roy D. Lancaster

Table of Contents

11.1	Introduction.	7
11.2	Structural Overview	9
	11.2.1 Subunit Composition and Molecular Characterization	9
	11.2.2 Crystallization	12
	11.2.3 X-Ray Crystal Structures of the RCs from Anoxygenic Purple Bacteria.	13
11.3	Arrangement of the Cofactors.	18
11.4	Structure of the Protein Subunits.	18
	11.4.1 L Subunit.	18
	11.4.2 M Subunit.	20
	11.4.3 H Subunit.	21
	11.4.4 C Subunit.	21
11.5	Cofactor Conformation and Protein–Cofactor Interactions.	21
	11.5.1 Primary Electron Donor.	21
	11.5.2 Accessory Bacteriochlorophylls.	25
	11.5.3 Bacteriopheophytins.	25
	11.5.4 The Primary Electron Acceptor Q_A and the Non-Heme Iron.	25
	11.5.5 Heme-Iron Site Geometries.	28
11.6	Substrate Binding Sites.	29
	11.6.1 The Electron-Acceptor Substrate Q_B and the Binding of Inhibitors.	29
	11.6.2 The Electron-Donor Substrate, Cytochrome c_2 or HiPiP.	32
11.7	Aspects of Membrane Protein Structure.	34
	11.7.1 Side-Chain Distributions.	34
	11.7.2 Bound Water.	36
	11.7.3 Phospholipid Binding.	37

11.8 Structures of Modified Reaction Centers 39
      11.8.1 Variant Reaction Centers 39
      11.8.2 Dark-Adapted Versus Light-Adapted Reaction Centers ... 43
11.9 Comparison with Photosystem II 44
11.10 Conclusions and Future Perspectives 45
References 45

Abstract

Photosynthetic reaction centers from anoxygenic bacteria are the best-characterized membrane protein complexes. This chapter compares over 50 X-ray crystal structures of reaction centers from *Rhodopseudomonas* (*Blastochloris*) *viridis*, *Rhodobacter sphaeroides*, and *Thermochromatium tepidum* on the basis of data quality and quantity, maximum resolution limits, and structural features. Not only the overall architecture of the reaction centers and the relevant positions and orientations of the prosthetic groups, but also specific structural features are conserved. Small structural differences might provide a basis for the explanation of the observed spectral and functional discrepancies between the three species. Particular points of focus in this chapter are, first, the site of binding of the secondary quinone (Q_B) where electron transfer is coupled to the uptake of protons from the cytoplasm; second, the respective binding sites of the electron donor proteins; third the increasing number of structures of variant reaction centers; and, fourth, the binding of phospholipids to these membrane protein complexes. Finally, recent progress in the structure determination of Photosystem II allows a comparison of the structures of bacterial RCs to that of Photosystem II.

11.1 Introduction

A large proportion of photosynthetically active organisms consists of anoxygenic photosynthetic bacteria. Purple bacteria find their ecological niche in deeper layers of stagnant bodies of water. In all purple bacteria, the photosynthetic pigments and the photosynthetic apparatus are located within a more or less extended system of invaginated intracytoplasmic membranes. Located within these photosynthetic membranes, reaction centers (RCs) [1–8] are defined as the minimal functional units that can catalyze light-induced electron transfer reactions, thus stabilizing the separation of charged species across the membrane. In contrast to the higher plants, algae, and cyanobacteria of oxygenic photosynthesis, which contain the two membrane-bound Photosystems I and II, each of the anoxygenic photosynthetic bacteria has only one type of reaction center. While the iron-sulfur type RCs of heliobacteria and anaerobic green sulfur bacteria resemble that of Photosystem I, the pheophytin-quinone type RCs of purple bacteria are more similar to the RC of Photosystem II. The RC essentially functions as a [reduced soluble electron carrier protein]:quinone photo-oxidoreductase (Figure 1).

The absorption of two photons of light leads to two one-electron oxidations of a soluble electron carrier protein in the periplasm and to the two-electron reduction of a quinone, which is coupled to the uptake of two protons from the cytoplasm. The resulting quinol then leaves its binding site, diffuses in the photosynthetic membrane and is reoxidized by a second membrane protein complex, the cytochrome bc_1 complex, which results in proton release to the periplasm. The electrons are transferred to re-reduce the soluble electron carrier protein in the periplasm. This net proton transport produces a transmembrane electrochemical proton potential that can drive ATP synthesis [9] through a third membrane-spanning complex, the ATP synthase (see Chapter 21 for details).

Unlike Photosystem II, however, the purple bacterial RC is incapable of extracting electrons from water. Instead it must oxidize inorganic or organic molecules available in the environment. According to their electron donor requirements, sulfur and non-sulfur purple bacteria have traditionally been

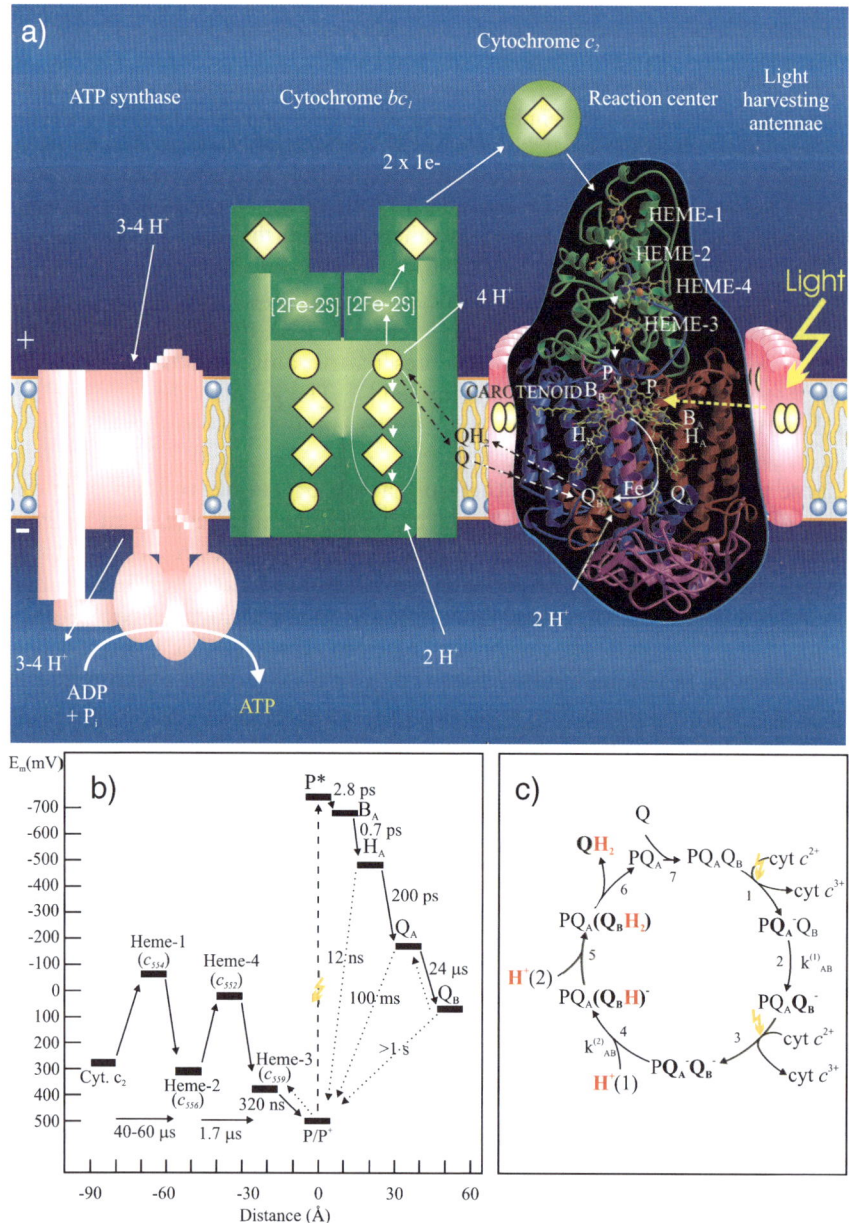

distinguished. In contrast to sulfur purple bacteria (Chromatiaceae, Ectothiorhodospira), non-sulfur purple bacteria (Rhodospirillaceae) do not require inorganic sulfur compounds, such as hydrogen sulfide, but instead use organic electron donors such as malate or succinate as electron donors. Most of what is known today about purple bacterial RCs results from studies on RCs from non-sulfur purple bacteria. These are currently the best characterized membrane protein complexes [1–8].

11.2 Structural Overview

11.2.1 Subunit Composition and Molecular Characterization

Most bacterial reaction centers contain four protein subunits (Figure 2), referred to as H, M, L, and C (a tetraheme cytochrome c). Some, however, such as the RCs of *Rhodobacter* (*Rb.*) *sphaeroides*, *Rb. capsulatus*, and *Rhodospirillum* (*Rs.*) *rubrum*, contain only the H, M, and L subunits. The related RC of the green aerobic thermophilic bacterium *Chloroflexus* (*Cf.*) *aurantiacus* lacks the H subunit. References to representative amino acid sequence information of RC subunits have been compiled [7]. The gene for the H subunit lies on a different operon than those for the other subunits and has been examined less frequently.

Generally, RCs from purple bacteria have been isolated and characterized from *Rhodopseudomonas* (*Rp.*) *viridis* [10], more recently referred to as *Blastochloris* (*Bl.*) [11] *viridis*, *Rb. sphaeroides* [12], *Thermochromatium* (*Tc.*) *tepidum* [13], *Rb. capsulatus* and several other purple bacteria [12,14]. Variant RCs have been isolated and characterized from *Rb. capsulatus* [15–17], *Rb. sphaeroides* [18,19], and *Bl. viridis* mutants [20–23]. The methods for isolation (and

---

Figure 1. Structure and function of the photosynthetic RC. (a) Light-induced cyclic electron flow and the generation and utilization of a transmembrane electrochemical potential in the purple bacterium *Bl. viridis*. The structure of the *Bl. viridis* RC is represented schematically, showing the heterotetramer of C, L, M, and H subunits as Cα traces in green, brown, blue, and purple, respectively, plus the 14 cofactors, which have been projected on to the molecule for better visibility. Also for the sake of clarity, the quinone tails are truncated after the first isoprenoid unit and the phytyl side-chains of the bacteriochlorophyll and bacteriopheophytin molecules have been omitted, as have those atoms of the carotenoid molecule not observed in the electron density and assigned zero occupancy in the PDB entry 2PRC (see Table 2 for reference). Carbon, nitrogen, and oxygen atoms are drawn in yellow, blue, and red, respectively. Prepared with programs MolScript [168] and Raster3D [169]. [Adapted from [170]]. (b) Equilibrium oxidation–reduction potentials of the *Bl. viridis* RC cofactors as reported in [22,117,171–174] as a function of inter-cofactor distance. The soluble electron donor protein cytochrome c_2 has been included as suggested by [175] and [176]. The photochemical excitation is indicated by a dashed arrow and unphysiological charge recombination reactions are shown as dotted arrows. [Adapted from [7]]. (c) Quinone reduction cycle. Reduced quinones are in bold. Steps 2, 4, 5, and 6 are reversible. See text for details.

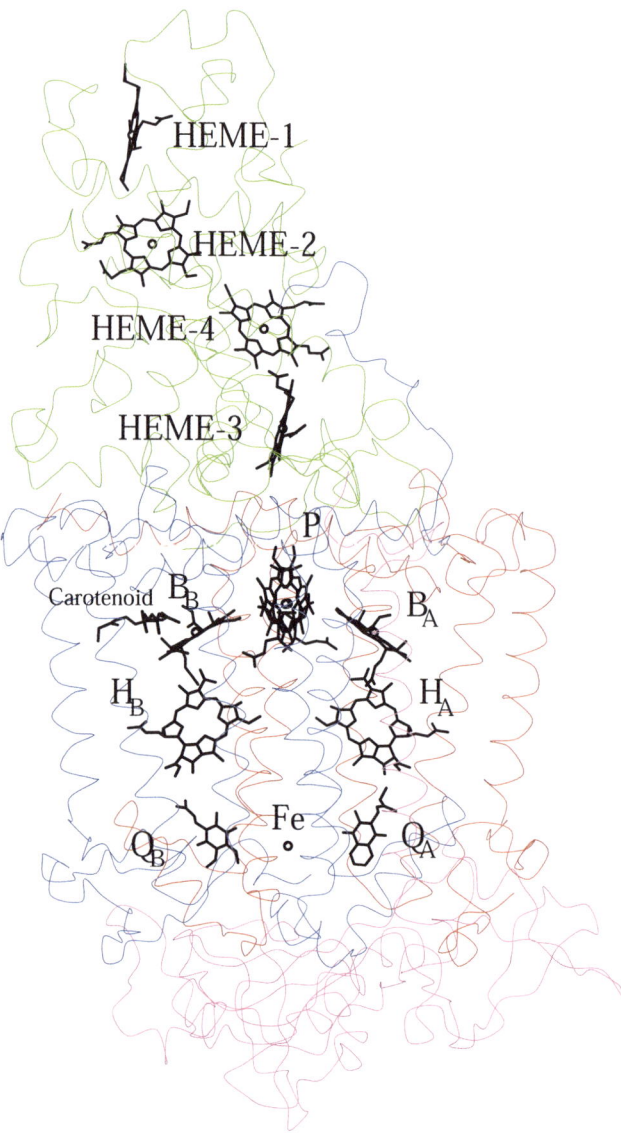

Figure 2. Subunit and cofactor arrangement in the photosynthetic RC from *Bl. viridis*: Schematic representation of the structure of the *Bl. viridis* RC, showing the heterotetramer of C, L, M, and H subunits as Cα traces in green, brown, blue, and purple, respectively, plus the 14 cofactors. For the sake of clarity, the quinone tails are truncated after the first isoprenoid unit and the phytyl side-chains of the bacteriochlorophyll and bacteriopheophytin molecules have been omitted, as have those atoms of the carotenoid molecule not observed in the electron density and assigned zero occupancy. PDB entry 2PRC.

crystallization) of the RCs from *Rb. sphaeroides* and *Bl. viridis* have been reviewed [7,24]. The purification procedures consist of disrupting the bacteria by ultrasonication, isopycnic centrifugation of the chromatophores in a sucrose gradient, and solubilization of the RCs with the detergent *N,N*-dimethyldodecylamine *N*-oxide (LDAO) at concentrations of 6% (*Bl. viridis*) and of 0.5% (*Rb. sphaeroides*), respectively. The RCs are further purified by a combination of column chromatography steps. In the case of *Bl. viridis* RCs, molecular sieve chromatography is used exclusively [25]. For the RCs of *Rb. sphaeroides*, various modifications of a combination of anion exchange chromatography and molecular sieve chromatography [26] have been employed. A procedure for the rapid isolation using Ni^{2+}-nitrilotriacetic acid (NTA) affinity chromatography of *Rb. sphaeroides* RCs with an engineered poly-histidine tag fused to the C terminus of the M subunit has been published [27], and successful crystallization of the isolated material has been reported [28]. A procedure with an engineered His_6-tag fused to the C-terminus of the C subunit of recombinant *Bl. viridis* RC has yielded material that could be crystallized [23].

The L, M, and H subunits of the *Bl. viridis* RC contain 273, 323, and 258 amino acid residues ($M_r = 30.5$, 35.9, 28.3 kDa), respectively [29,30]. The C subunit of *Bl. viridis* (336 residues, $M_r = 40.5$ kDa) [31] is a lipoprotein and is anchored in the membrane by a diacylglycerol moiety, which is covalently bound to the N-terminal Cys side-chain via a thioether bond [32]. A recognition site for the covalent attachment of a diglyceride and removal of the signal peptide by signal peptidase II is present in *Bl. viridis* and *Rv. gelatinosus* but not in *Cf. aurantiacus*.

RC preparations have a non-heme iron and four magnesium-containing bacteriochlorophyll cofactors per RC [12], as measured by atomic absorption spectroscopy [33]. In *Rb. sphaeroides* and *Bl. viridis*, these are bacteriochlorophyll *a* and bacteriochlorophyll *b*, respectively (Figure 3). Those preparations with a tightly bound C subunit have four iron-containing heme groups that are covalently bound to the protein. Apart from these four *c*-type heme groups, all other cofactors are non-covalently bound by the L and M subunits. In addition to the metal-containing cofactors, these comprise two bacteriopheophytin groups, a carotenoid, and two quinones. In *Rb. sphaeroides*, these are bacteriopheophytin *a*, spheroidene, and ubiquinone-10, respectively, whereas *Bl. viridis* contains bacteriopheophytin *b*, 1,2-dihydroneurosporene, menaquinone-9 and ubiquinone-9. Similar to the *Rb. sphaeroides* RC, the *Tc. tepidum* RC contains four bacteriochlorophyll *a* and two bacteriopheophytin *a* groups. Similar to the *Bl. viridis* RC, the *Tc. tepidum* RC contains four *c*-type heme groups, menaquinone-8 and ubiquinone-8. The carotenoid in the *Tc. tepidum* RC is spirilloxanthin.

Apart from the availability of high resolution crystal structures discussed below, one major reason why, despite its complexity, the purple bacterial RC has become the "hydrogen atom of protein electron transfer" ([34], see also [35,36]) is the richness of its characterization by optical absorption, electron paramagnetic resonance (EPR), electron-nuclear double resonance (ENDOR), Fourier-transform infrared (FTIR), resonance Raman (RR), fluorescence, Stark effect, and other types of spectroscopy; comprehensively reviewed in [1–8].

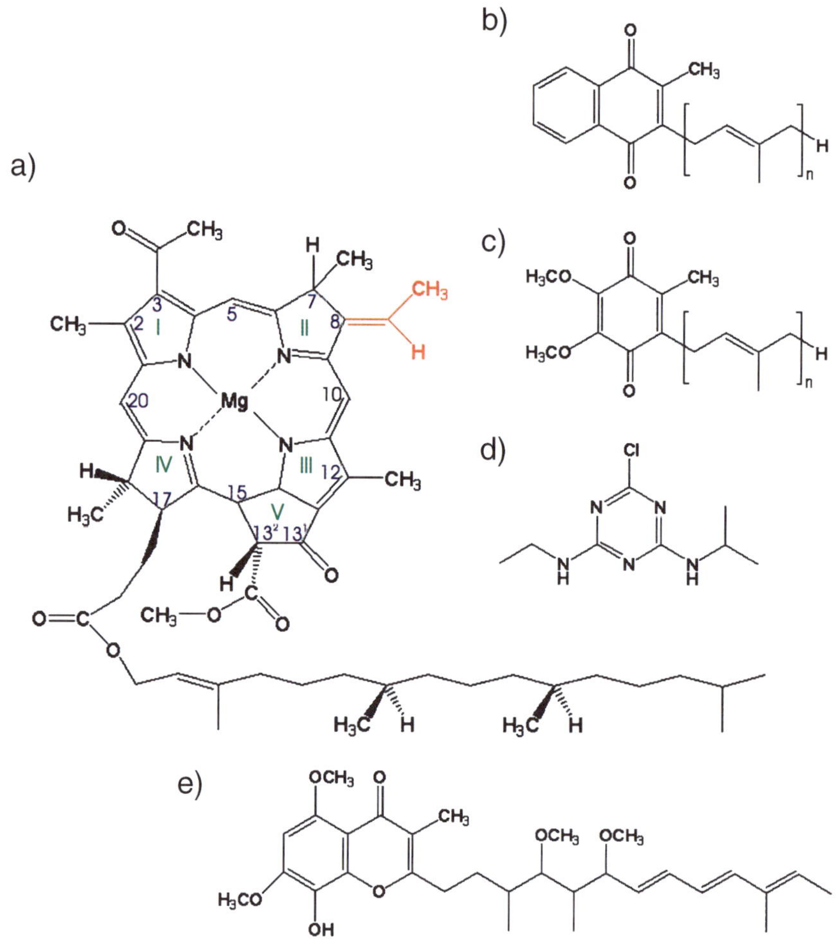

Figure 3. Chemical structures of RC cofactors (a–c) and inhibitors at the Q_B site (d, e). (a) Bacteriochlorophyll b, as bound in the *Bl. viridis* RC. The bacteriochlorophyll a bound in the *Rb. sphaeroides* RC differs by the presence of a C8 ethyl group instead of the C8 ethylidene group indicated in red. Bacteriopheophytins (a or b) are the metal-free variants of the bacteriochlorophylls (a or b) with two protons bonded to the nitrogens of the unsaturated pyrrole rings A and C. (b) Menaquinone-n. The native Q_A in the *Bl. viridis* RC is menaquinone-9. In the *Tc. tepidum* RC, Q_A is menaquinone-8. (c) Ubiquinone-n. The native Q_B in the *Bl. viridis* RC is ubiquinone-9. In the *Tc. tepidum* RC, Q_B is ubiquinone-8. In the *Rb. sphaeroides* RC, both Q_A and Q_B are ubiquinone-10. (d) Atrazine (2-chloro-4-ethylamino-6-isopropylamino-*s*-triazine). (e) Stigmatellin A.

11.2.2 Crystallization

Crystals of the *Bl. viridis* RC were first grown by vapor diffusion from a protein droplet containing 1.5 M $(NH_4)_2SO_4$, 0.1% *N,N*-dimethyldodecylamine *N*-oxide (lauryl-*N,N*-dimethyl *N*-oxide, LDAO) and 3% heptane-1,2,3-triol against a reservoir containing 2–3 M $(NH_4)_2SO_4$ [25]. They are tetragonal, space group $P4_32_12$ with $a = b = 223.5$ Å, $c = 113.6$ Å [37], and one molecule per asymmetric unit (crystal form "A" in Table 1). Using these crystals, the structure of the *Bl. viridis* RC was solved by multiple isomorphous replacement [37,38] and refined to a crystallographic *R*-factor of 19.3% up to a resolution of 2.3 Å [39,40]. More recent crystals diffract to at least 1.8 Å resolution (CRD Lancaster, unpublished observations), and the structure has been refined with complete data to 2.0 Å resolution (see Table 2 below) [41].

Three kinds of well-diffracting crystals have been obtained of the *Rb. sphaeroides* RC (as reviewed by Fritzsch [24]). They are orthorhombic, [42–45] trigonal [46] and tetragonal [47] (crystal forms "B", "C", and "D", respectively, in Table 1). Orthorhombic crystals are grown in the presence of 10–12% poly(ethylene glycol) 4000 (PEG4000), 0.06% LDAO and 3.5–3.9% heptane-1,2,3-triol or 0.8% *n*-octyl-ß-D-glucopyranoside against a reservoir buffer containing 18–25% PEG4000. The space group is $P2_12_12_1$. The best resolution is 2.8 Å in the direction of the long axis, but worse in the other directions. Using a partially refined coordinate set of the *Bl. viridis* RC for molecular replacement, three different groups used these orthorhombic crystal forms with slightly different cell dimensions to determine the structure of the *Rb. sphaeroides* RC. As discussed earlier [48], for all RC structures based on these orthorhombic crystals, the number of observed unique reflections, n_{obs}, is less than the number of parameters, n_{par}, required to define the model (cf. Tables 2 and 3 below).

Trigonal crystals can be obtained in the presence of 0.5–1.0 M potassium phosphate, pH 6.5–7.5, 0.06–0.15% LDAO and 1.8–3.0% heptane-1,2,3-triol against a reservoir buffer containing 1.4–1.7 M potassium phosphate. The space group is $P3_121$. The best crystals diffract to 1.8 Å [49]. To date, this is the crystal form of the *Rb. sphaeroides* RC, which has yielded by far the largest number of well-defined structures (cf. Tables 2 and 3 below).

Tetragonal crystals are grown in the presence of 6% PEG4000, 0.85% *n*-octyl-β-D-glucopyranoside, 2.5% heptane-1,2,3-triol and 0.4% benzamidine hydrochloride against a reservoir solution containing 32% PEG4000 [47]. Crystals belong to the space group $P4_32_12$ with two RCs per asymmetric unit. Data from these crystals have been collected to 2.2 Å resolution [50].

More recently, crystals of the *Rb. sphaeroides* RC have been obtained using the cubic lipid phase technique [51] of membrane protein crystallization (crystal form "E" in Table 1). Data from these crystals have been collected to 2.35 Å resolution [52].

For the *Tc. tepidum* RC, orthorhombic crystals have been obtained in the presence of 47% (w/v) PEG4000 as a precipitant in a 15 mM phosphate buffer, pH 7.0, together with 0.36 M NaCl, 0.1% (w/v) NaN_3, and 0.1 mM EDTA (crystal form "H" in Table 1) [53]. Data from these crystals have been collected to 2.2 Å resolution [54].

11.2.3 X-Ray Crystal Structures of the RCs from Anoxygenic Purple Bacteria

Tables 2 and 3 list the coordinate sets of those RC structures deposited in the PDB as of 1 August, 2005. Table 3 (below) contains all coordinate sets of variant

Table 1. Crystal forms of bacterial reaction centers

Crystal form	Sample	Space group	a (Å)	b (Å)	c (Å)	α (°)	β (°)	γ (°)	No. of PDB depositions	References[a]
A	*Blastochloris viridis* RC	$P4_32_12$	223.5	223.5	113.6	90	90	90	10	[25]
B	*Rhodobacter sphaeroides* RC	$P2_12_12_1$	143.7	139.8	78.7	90	90	90	5	[42–45]
C	*Rhodobacter sphaeroides* RC	$P3_121$	141.3	141.3	187.2	90	90	120	26	[46]
D	*Rhodobacter sphaeroides* RC	$P4_32_12$	140.1	140.1	271.6	90	90	90	7	[47]
E	*Rhodobacter sphaeroides* RC *in cubo*	$P4_22_12$	100.0	100.0	237.2	90	90	90	3	[52]
F	*Rhodobacter sphaeroides* variant RC with PSII-like Mn^{2+}-binding site	$P4_222$	203.8	203.8	119.9	90	90	90	1	[152]
G	*Rhodobacter sphaeroides* variant RC with PSII-like Mn^{2+}-binding site	$P4_222$	207.8	207.8	107.5	90	90	90	1	[152]
H	*Thermochromatium tepidum* RC	$P2_12_12_1$	133.3	196.6	84.2	90	90	90	1	[53]
X	*Rhodobacter sphaeroides* RC-cyt c_2 complex	$P2_1$	78.2	115.7	79.7	90	110.3	90	1	[153]
Y	*Rhodobacter sphaeroides* RC-cyt c_2 complex	$P2_1$	77.9	80.3	246.6	90	92.4	90	1	[153]
Z	*Rhodopseudomonas palustris* RC-LH1 core complex	$P1$	76.0	119.0	130.4	69.3	72.7	66.5	1	[154]

[a]In general, only the first publication is cited, although the precise crystallization conditions and unit cell dimensions may vary in subsequent publications.

Table 2. Reaction center structures (excluding *Rb. sphaeroides* RC variants)[a]

PDB ID	Remarks (if any)	Crystal form[b]	High-resolution limit (Å)	R_{cryst}^{c} (%)	R_{free}^{d} (%)	n_{obs}/n_{par}^{e}	Reference
Blastochloris viridis							
1DXR	His L168 → Phe variant; terbutryn complex	A	2.00	19.4	21.8	4.44	[41]
1VRN		A	2.20	19.1	21.2	2.78	[135]
2JBL	Stigmatellin complex (replaces 4PRC)	A	2.40	19.0	20.6	2.46	[155]
6PRC	Triazine DG-420314 complex	A	2.30	18.4	22.5	2.43	[58]
1PRC		A	2.30	19.3	n/a	2.38	[40]
5PRC	Atrazine complex	A	2.35	19.0	23.6	2.20	[58]
3PRC	Q_B-depleted	A	2.40	17.8	21.5	2.07	[66]
2PRC	Ubiquinone-2 complex	A	2.45	18.2	22.9	1.89	[66]
4PRC	Stigmatellin complex	A	2.40	19.1	24.1	1.82	[66]
7PRC	Triazine DG-420315 complex	A	2.65	18.4	23.1	1.73	[58]
1R2C		A	2.86	20.2	22.8	1.58	[156]
Rhodobacter sphaeroides							
1RG5	Carotenoidless RC	C	2.50	15.5	18.2	2.51	[157]
1M3X		C	2.55	18.5	20.9	2.34	[158]
1AIJ	Ground state	D	2.20	21.6	27.0	1.95	[50]
1PCR		C	2.65	18.6	n/a	1.91	[55]
1RQK	Carotenoidless RC reconstituted with 3, 4-dihydrospheroidene	C	2.70	16.4	19.4	1.82	[157]
1OGV	Lipid cubic phase crystal	E	2.35	21.4	24.4	1.74	[52]
1DV6	Zn^{2+}-complex; ground state	D	2.50	23.8	26.5	1.65	[92]
1DV3	Cd^{2+}-complex; charge-separated state	D	2.50	22.6	25.2	1.61	[92]
1DS8	Cd^{2+}-complex; ground state	D	2.50	22.7	25.6	1.61	[92]
1L9B	Cytochrome c_2-RC complex	X	2.40	22.0	26.4	1.55	[153]
1RGN	Carotenoidless RC reconstituted with spheroidene	C	2.80	19.1	23.2	1.48	[157]
2BNS	Lipid cubic phase crystal; charge-separated state	E	2.50	21.1	24.7	1.41	[136]

Table 2 (continued)

PDB ID	Remarks (if any)	Crystal form[b]	High-resolution limit (Å)	R_{cryst}^{c} (%)	$R_{free}^{f\ d}$ (%)	n_{obs}/n_{par}^{e}	Reference
1AIG	Charge-separated state	D	2.60	21.5	29.9	1.26	[50]
2BNP	Lipid cubic phase crystal; ground state	E	2.70	21.2	24.9	1.16	[136]
1K6L		C	3.10	19.3	19.4	1.08	[28]
4RCR		B	2.80	22.7	n/a	0.81	[159,160,161]
1PSS		B	3.00	22.3	n/a	0.79	[109]
1L9J	Cytochrome c_2-RC complex	Y	3.25	24.8	28.7	0.77	[153]
1YST		B	3.00	23.4	n/a	0.69	[162]
2RCR		B	3.10	22.0	n/a	0.64	[163]
1Z9K		G	4.60	33.0	33.0	0.57	[152]
Thermochromatium tepidum							
1EYS		H	2.20	23.1	28.7	2.37	[54]
Rhodopseudomonas palustris							
1PYH	RC-LH1 core complex	Z	4.80	46.9	49.1	n/a	[154]

[a]Continuously updated versions of Tables 1–3 will be provided online at http://www.mpibp-frankfurt.mpg.de/lancaster/rc/. Statistics are quoted as supplied with the PDB entries and are not necessarily consistent with the respective publications.
[b]As defined in Table 1.
[c]$R_{cryst} = \Sigma_{(hkl)} ||F_o| - |F_c|| / \Sigma_{(hkl)} |F_o|$.
[d]$R_{free} = \Sigma_{(hkl)\ \in\ T} ||F_o| - |F_c|| / \Sigma_{(hkl)\ \in\ T} |F_o|$, where T is the test set [164].
[e]n_{obs} = number of observed unique reflections used in the working set; n_{par} = number of parameters necessary to define the model; this includes three to four parameters (x, y, z coordinates, plus an isotropic atomic B factor, where applicable) per atom.

STRUCTURES OF REACTION CENTERS

Table 3. *Rb. sphaeroides* RC variant structures; see Table 2 footnotes for details

PDB ID	Remarks	Crystal form	High resolution limit (Å)	R_{cryst} (%)	R_{free} (%)	n_{obs}/n_{par}	Reference
1RZH	Asp L213 → Asn/Arg M233 → Cys variant	C	1.80	22.1	23.3	6.21	[49]
1QOV	Ala M260 → Trp variant	C	2.10	16.9	18.6	4.27	[114,165]
1RY5	Asp L213 → Asn variant	C	2.10	21.1	22.6	3.96	[49]
1E6D	Trp M115 → Phe/Phe M197 → Arg variant	C	2.30	17.4	20.0	3.10	[166]
1YF6	Quintuple variant (Phe L181 → Tyr/Gly M203 → Asp/ Tyr M210 → Phe/Leu M214 → His/Ala M260 → Trp)	C	2.25	19.7	21.6	2.82	[115]
2BOZ	Gly M203 → Leu variant	C	2.40	17.5	19.8	2.55	[102]
1FNQ	Pro L209 → Glu variant	C	2.60	21.7	24.7	2.16	[119]
1FNP	Pro L209 → Phe variant	C	2.60	21.6	24.8	2.14	[119]
1KBY	His M202 → Leu variant	C	2.50	19.5	22.4	2.00	[106]
1MPS	Tyr M177 → Phe/Phe M197 → Arg variant	C	2.55	19.4	21.7	1.92	[110]
1E14	Phe M197 → Arg/Gly N203 → Asp variant	C	2.70	22.6	26.8	1.85	[167]
1RVJ	Asp L213 → Asn/Arg H177 → His variant	C	2.75	21.8	23.7	1.84	[49]
1JGW	Thr M21 → Leu variant	C	2.80	21.1	23.7	1.81	[126]
1RZZ	Asp L213 → Asn/Arg N233 → Cys variant; Ground state	D	2.40	21.6	23.8	1.81	[49]
1UMX	Arg M267 → Leu variant	C	2.80	22.5	24.9	1.79	[125]
1F6N	Pro L209 → Tyr variant	C	2.80	22.1	25.0	1.75	[119]
1JGZ	Tyr M76 → Lys variant	C	2.70	21.5	24.9	1.56	[126]
1JGX	Thr M21 → Asp variant	C	3.01	21.1	24.9	1.44	[126]
1S00	Asp L213 → Asn/Arg M233 → Cys variant; charge-separated state	D	2.60	22.6	26.8	1.38	[49]
1JGY	Tyr M76 → Phe variant	C	2.70	21.8	25.7	1.32	[126]
1K6N	Glu L212 → Ala/Asp L213 → Ala variant	C	3.10	20.3	20.7	1.02	[28]
1JH0	Glu L205 → Leu	C	3.50	22.5	26.9	0.99	[126]
1PST	His M202 → Leu variant	E	3.00	21.8	n/a	0.82	[109]
1Z9J	Multiple variant (Leu L131 → His/Leu M160 → His/Arg M164 → Tyr/Met M168 → Glu/Phe M197 → His/Gly M288 → Asp) with PSII-like Mn^{2+}-binding site	F	4.50	29.9	33.8	0.59	[152]

Rb. sphaeroides RC structures, while Table 2 list all other coordinate sets. Coordinate sets are ordered by their ratio of the number of observed unique reflections, n_{obs}, to the number of parameters required to define the respective atomic model, n_{par}. The structures based on the trigonal crystal form satisfy these criteria best, so we shall primarily refer to these when comparing the RC structure from this species to that of Bl. viridis. The structure of the four-subunit Bl. viridis RC is shown schematically in Figures 1 and 2. The RC from Rb. sphaeroides would appear almost identical except for the cytochrome subunit at the top, which would be missing. The Rb. sphaeroides and Bl. viridis RC structures have been compared in detail previously [55,56].

The Bl. viridis RC has an overall length of 130 Å in the direction perpendicular to the membrane. Parallel to the membrane, the maximum width is about 70 Å. The central core of the RC is formed by the L subunit and the M subunit, which possess five membrane-spanning segments each. Both subunits are closely associated and non-covalently bind ten cofactors as detailed above and shown in Figures 1 and 2. Large parts of the L and M subunits and their associated cofactors are related by a two-fold axis of symmetry perpendicular to the plane of the membrane. The H subunit is anchored to the membrane by a single membrane-spanning helix and is attached to the LM core on the cytoplasmic side. On the periplasmic side, the C subunit with its four covalently bound heme groups is attached. The N-terminal diacylglycerol moiety is not visible in the electron density map.

11.3 Arrangement of the Cofactors

The pigments form two symmetry-related branches, also shown in Figure 2, each consisting of two bacteriochlorophylls, one bacteriopheophytin and one quinone, which both cross the membrane starting from the "special pair" P of two closely associated bacteriochlorophylls near the periplasmic side, followed by the "accessory" bacteriochlorophyll, B, one bacteriopheophytin, H, and a quinone, Q. As indicated in Figure 1, only the branch more closely associated with L subunit is used in the light-driven electron transfer. It is called the A-branch, the inactive one the B-branch. The active branch ends with the primary quinone Q_A, the inactive one with the secondary quinone Q_B. Halfway between both quinones, a non-heme iron is located. The carotenoid, which has a cis double bond at the 15–15' position in its RC-bound state [57,58], is in van der Waals contact with B_B and disrupts the two-fold symmetry. In both species the crystallographic temperature factors, which are a measure for the rigidity of the structure, are considerably higher along the B-branch than along the A-branch.

11.4 Structure of the Protein Subunits

11.4.1 L Subunit

Figure 4(a) shows the Cα trace of the L subunit of the Bl. viridis RC. The dominant features are the five long membrane-spanning helices (A–E). They

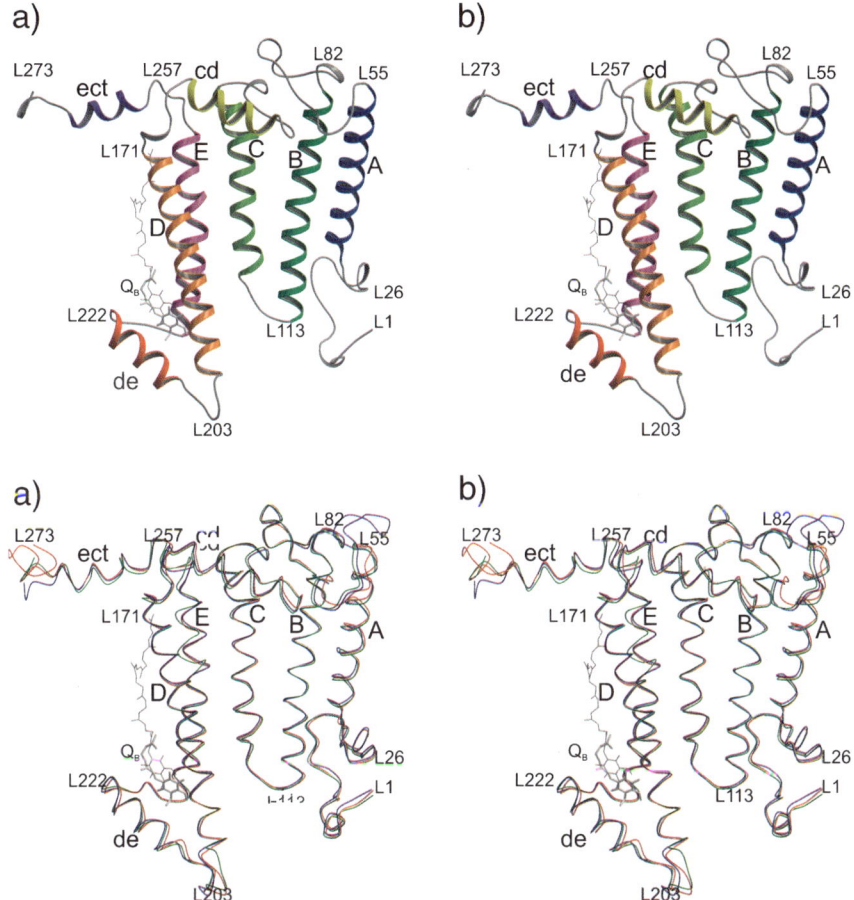

Figure 4. Stereo views: The Cα trace of the L subunit of the *Bl. viridis* RC (a) and its comparison with those of the *Tc. tepidum* and *Rb. sphaeroides* RCs (b). The letters "A" to "E" designate the five transmembrane helices. The additional helices "cd", "de", and "ect" are detailed in the text (PDB entries used: 2PRC, 1EYS, 1PCR).

are 21 (helix A), 24 (helices C and E), or 28 (helices B and D) residues long [39]. On the periplasmic side, the connection of transmembrane helices C and D contains a helix ("cd") of eleven residues and the connection between transmembrane helix E and the C-terminus a helix ("ect") of nine residues. On the cytoplasmic side, the connection of transmembrane helices D and E contains a helix ("de") of twelve residues. This region of the structure forms the binding site of the secondary electron acceptor Q_B, which is also included in Figure 4(a). In projection, viewed from the top of the membrane, the transmembrane helices form a semicircular arrangement in the order A, B, C, E, and D [39]. Transmembrane helices A, B, and D are straight, helix E is smoothly curved, and helix C possesses a kink of more than 30°. When the L subunits from *Bl. viridis*, *Tc. tepidum*, and *Rb. sphaeroides* are compared (Figure 4b), an additional eight amino acid residues are found at the C-terminus in the *Rb. sphaeroides* RC [56].

11.4.2 M Subunit

The M subunit of the *Bl. viridis* RC is displayed in Figure 5(a). As indicated already by the sequence identity of around 30% between the L and M subunits, the overall protein fold is very similar. The five transmembrane helices of the M subunit are 24 (C), 25 (A,E), 26 (D) or 27 (B) residues long. The connecting helices "cd" (twelve residues) and "ect" (seven residues) on the periplasmic side as well as "de" (14 residues) on the cytoplasmic side, forming part of the Q_A site, are also present. Accompanied by an insertion of seven amino acids (compared with the L subunit), short additional helices are found in the

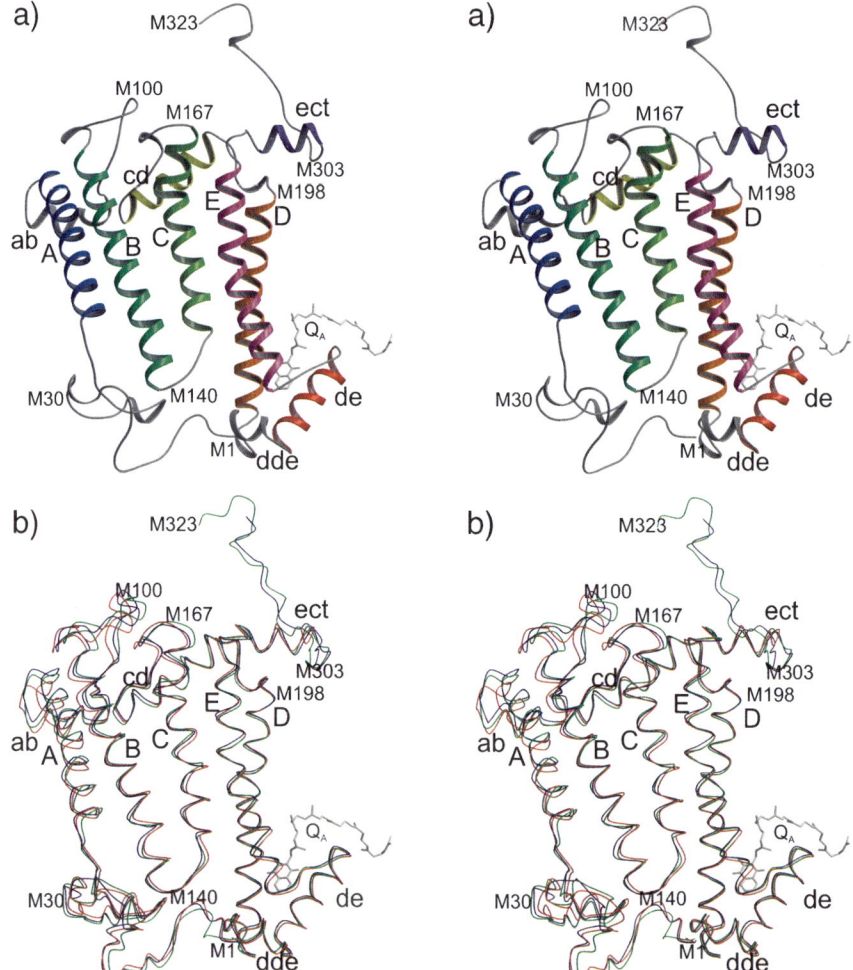

Figure 5. Stereo views: Cα trace of the M subunit of the *Bl. viridis* RC (a) and its comparison with those of the *Tc. tepidum* and *Rb. sphaeroides* RCs (b). "A"–"E" designate the five transmembrane helices. The additional helices "ab", "cd", "dde", "de", and "ect" are detailed in the text (PDB entries 2PRC, 1EYS, 1PCR).

connections of transmembrane helices A and B (helix "ab", seven residues) on the periplasmic side, and between transmembrane helix D and the connecting helix "de" on the cytoplasmic side (helix "dde", six residues).

On the cytoplasmic side, the L and M subunits are tightly interwoven. When the L and M subunits are compared, the M subunits are 26 (*Bl. viridis*) or 25 (*Rb. sphaeroides*, Figure 5b) residues longer at the N-termini than the L subunits. At the C terminus, the M subunit from *Rb. sphaeroides* is nine amino acids shorter than the L subunit. The M subunit from *Bl. viridis* possesses an additional 18 amino acids at the C-terminus, which interact with the C subunit (see also Figures 1 and 2).

11.4.3 H Subunit

The N-terminus of the H subunit (Figure 6) is located on the periplasmic side of the membrane. Residues H12 to H35 form a membrane-spanning helix (Figure 6a), which is an α-helix at its beginning but a π-helix at its very end. The next 70 residues are preferentially in contact with the LM complex. A globular region follows that has been referred to as the "PRC barrel" [59] and contains an extended system of antiparallel and parallel β-sheets. Close to the C-terminus, an α-helix is found.

11.4.4 C Subunit

The structure of the tetraheme cytochrome or C subunit (Figure 7) has been described in detail [40]. It is not related to other known tetraheme protein structures and consists of five segments, an N-terminal segment (C1–C66), the first heme-binding segment (C67–C142), a connecting segment (C143–C225), a second heme-binding segment (C226–C315), and the C-terminal segment(C316–C336). Apart from an α-helix (C25–C34) in the N-terminal segment, the three non-heme-binding segments contain little regular secondary structure. The four hemes and the two heme-binding segments make up the core of the cytochrome subunit. The first heme-binding segment contains the binding sites for heme-1 (c_{554}) and heme-2 (c_{556}), the second those for heme-3 (c_{559}) and heme-4 (c_{552}). Each heme-binding site consists of an α-helix that runs parallel to the heme plane, a loop, and the heme attachment site with the sequence Cys-X-Y-Cys-His.

11.5 Cofactor Conformation and Protein–Cofactor Interactions

11.5.1 Primary Electron Donor

The primary electron donor ("special pair") is located at the interface of the L and M subunits near the periplasmic side (Figures 1, 2, and 8). It interacts with residues of the transmembrane helices C, D, E and the connections of helices C

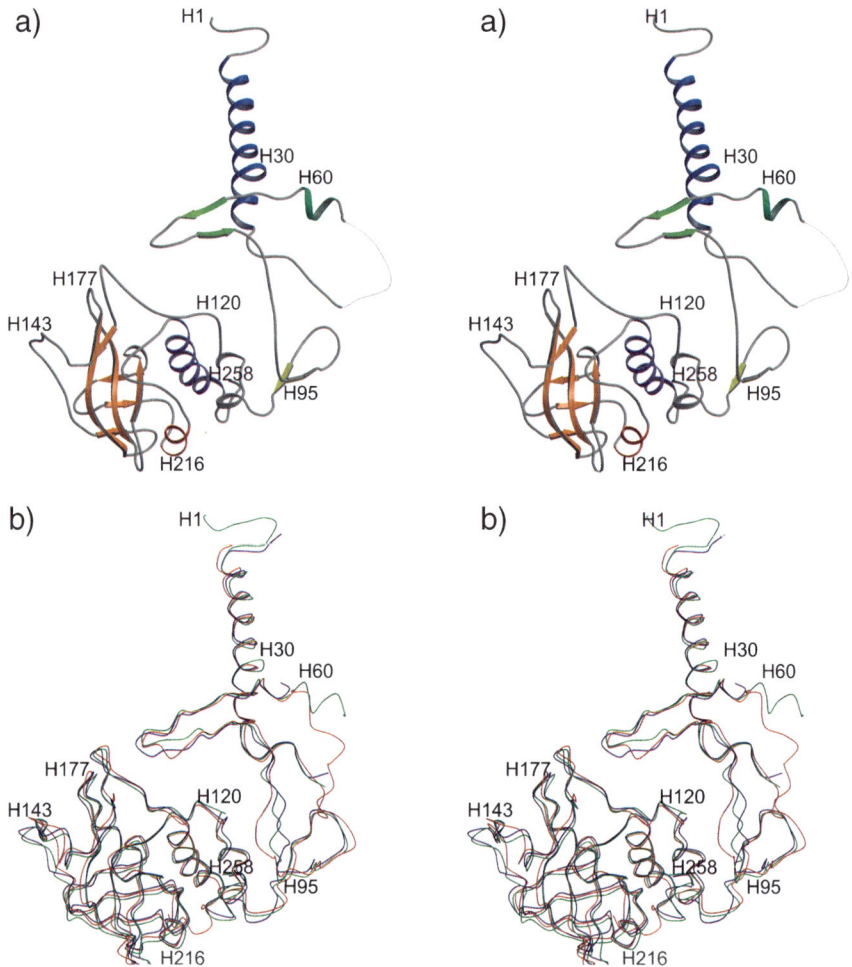

Figure 6. Stereo views: Cα trace of the H subunit of the *Bl. viridis* RC (a) and its comparison with those of the *Tc. tepidum* and *Rb. sphaeroides* RCs (b). Residues H47 to H53 (on the right) are not observed in the electron density. This region is included as a very thin line to facilitate chain tracing (PDB entries 2PRC, 1EYS, 1PCR).

and D. The special pair bacteriochlorophylls are held in their position by specific interactions with the protein matrix (Figure 8). The first four ligands to the five-coordinated bacteriochlorophyll magnesium are provided by the bacteriochlorin ring nitrogen atoms, and the fifth ligand is provided by the Nε atom of a His side-chain (Figure 8). For the "special pair" bacteriochlorophylls, these His residues (L173 and M200) are close to the N-terminal ends of the L and M subunit transmembrane helices D, respectively. Apart from binding the Mg^{2+} ion, the protein displays several hydrogen bonding interactions with the bacteriochlorophyll molecules, as deduced from the structures [55,60] (Figure 8). The ring I acetyl group (Figure 3a) of P_L is hydrogen bonded to a His residue

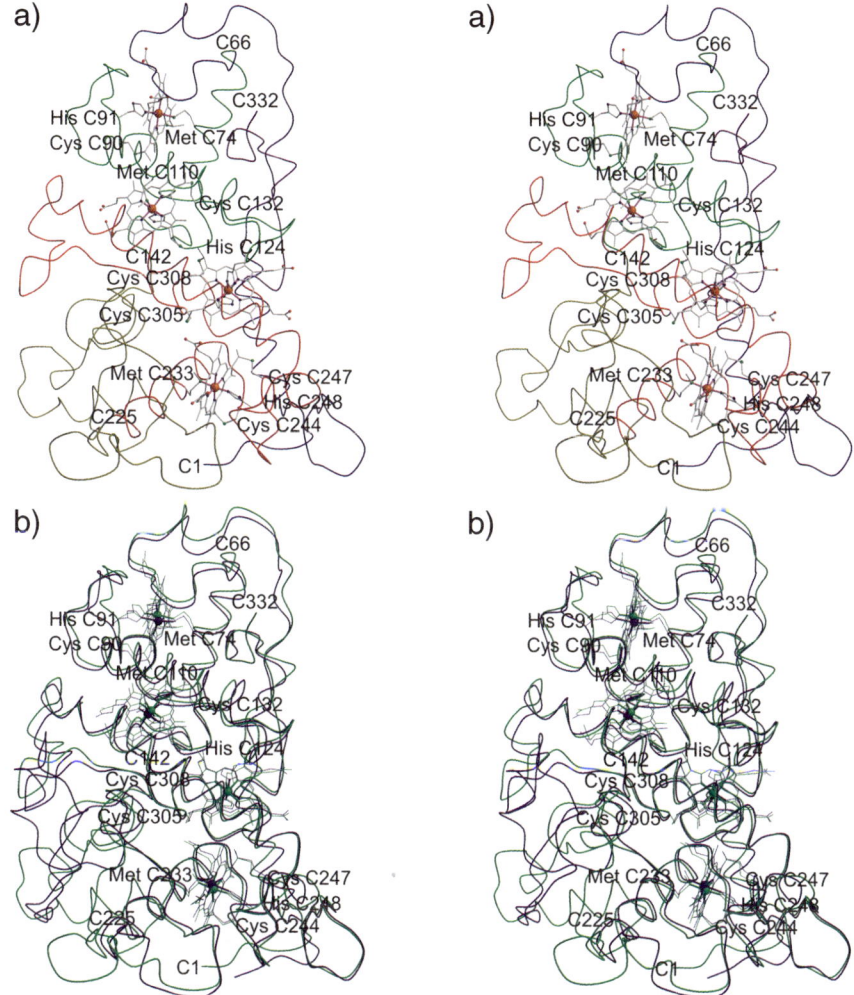

Figure 7. Stereo views: Cα trace of the C subunit of the *Bl. viridis* RC (a) and its comparison with those of the *Tc. tepidum* RC (b). The N-terminal segment drawn in blue, the first heme-binding segment in green, the connecting segment in yellow, the second heme-binding segment in red, and the C-terminal segment in purple. The cofactor heme groups and the side-chains of their ligands are displayed as atomic models (PDB entries 1PRC, 1EYS).

(His L168 in both the *Bl. viridis* and *Rb. sphaeroides* RC, His L176 in the *Tc. tepidum* RC) in all three RCs. The symmetry-related amino-acid residue near P_M is Phe M197 in *Rb. sphaeroides*. Thus, no hydrogen bond can be formed. In *Bl. viridis* and *Tc. tepidum*, the respective residues are Tyr M195 and Tyr M196, which donate hydrogen bonds to the acetyl carbonyl oxygen of ring I.

Thr L248 donates a hydrogen bond to the ring V keto carbonyl (Figure 3a) of P_L in *Bl. viridis*, which, in combination with the presence of the bulky Met L127

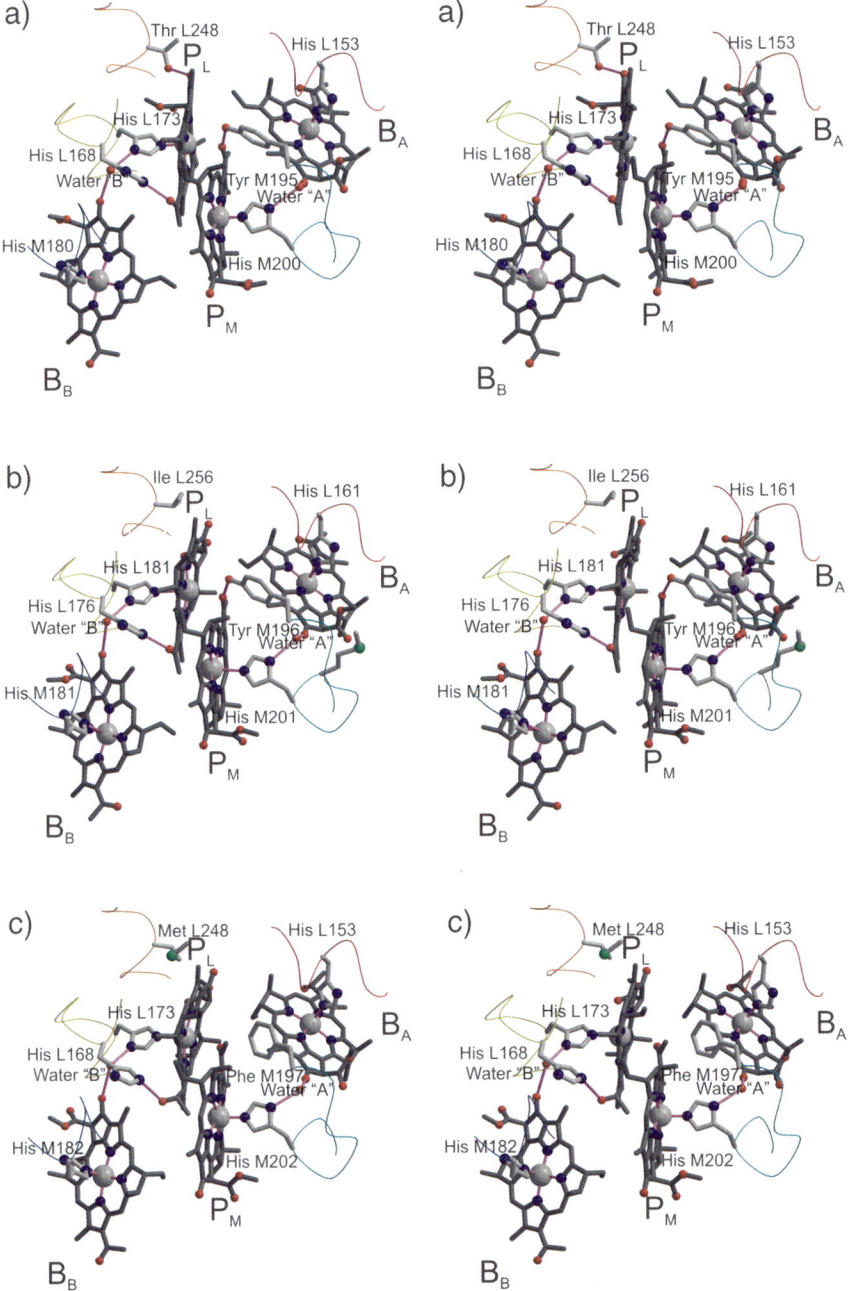

Figure 8. Stereo pairs of the regions of the special pair and the accessory bacteriochlorophyll molecules of the *Bl. viridis* RC (a), *Tc. tepidum* RC (b), and *Rb. sphaeroides* RC (c). Hydrogen bonds and ligand binding Mg-His are indicated as purple lines. (PDB entries 2PRC, 1EYS, 1PCR.)

on the opposite side of the ring, results in ring V being bent towards Thr L248 (Figure 8a). This ring is oriented in the opposite direction in *Tc. tepidum* and *Rb. sphaeroides*, where Ala residues are found at the position of the *Bl. viridis* Met L127, and the *Bl. viridis* residues Gly L247 and Thr L248 correspond to Cys L247 and Met L248 in *Rb. sphaeroides*, and to Cys L255 and Ile L256 in *Tc. tepidum*.

11.5.2 Accessory Bacteriochlorophylls

The accessory bacteriochlorophylls B_A and B_B are located between P and the respective bacteriopheophytins H_A and H_B and are in van der Waals contact with both respective neighboring cofactors. The His ligands for the accessory bacteriochlorophylls, L153 (L161 in *Tc. tepidum*) and M180 (M181 in *Tc. tepidum* and M182 in *Rb. sphaeroides*), are situated close to the N-terminal end of the L and M subunit periplasmic helices "cd", respectively. The average His $N\varepsilon$–Mg distance is 2.1 Å, as is the average distance between the bacteriochlorin N atoms and the respective Mg^{2+}. Significant conformational differences between the reaction centers are found only at the ethyl groups – caused by the structural difference between the ethyl group of bacteriochlorophyll *a* and the ethylidene group of bacteriochlorophyll *b* (Figure 3a). In all three RCs, the ring V carbonyl oxygen atoms are hydrogen-bonded via a water molecule ("water A") to His M200 (M201 in *Tc. tepidum*, M202 in *Rb. sphaeroides*) and (via "water B") to His L173, respectively (Figure 8).

11.5.3 Bacteriopheophytins

Figure 9 shows the location of the bacteriopheophytin H_A between B_A and Q_A for all three reaction centers. At the top, Tyr M208 (M209, M210) appears to be of importance since it is in van der Waals contact with P_M, P_L, and B_A. The symmetry-related residue in the L subunit is Phe L181 (L189, L181). The pattern of hydrogen bonding formed by H_A and H_B with the protein matrix is identical in both species. Trp L100 (L108, L100) and Trp M127 (M128, M129), respectively, donate a hydrogen bond to the ester carbonyls of ring V of H_A and H_B. The carboxyl group of Glu L104 (L112, L104) is calculated [63,77,78] to be protonated and donates a hydrogen bond to the H_A ring V keto group (Figure 9) [60]. This is responsible for the 10 nm redshift of the H_A Q_x band compared with the H_B Q_x band [61], but is not a dominant contributor to the directionality of electron transfer in RCs. The bacteriopheophytin H_A is surrounded by a significant number of Phe residues (Figure 9). Around H_B, these bulky residues are replaced to a large extent by smaller amino acid residues. As seen in Figures 9 and 10, Trp M250 (M251, M252), with its large aromatic side-chain, bridges the gap between H_A and Q_A in all three reaction centers.

11.5.4 The Primary Electron Acceptor Q_A and the Non-Heme Iron

Figure 10 shows the binding site of the primary electron acceptor quinone Q_A for all three reaction centers. Q_A is located on the A side where the L subunit

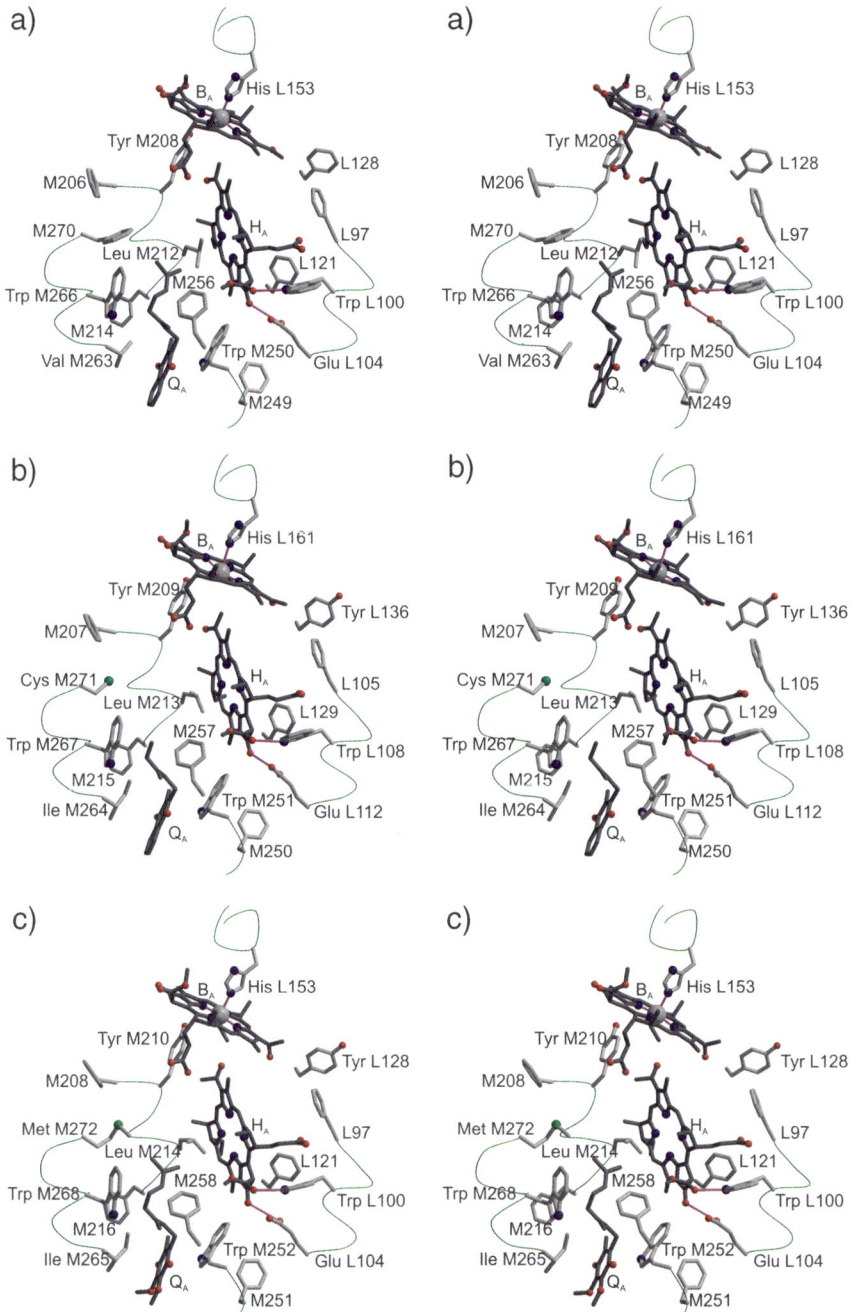

Figure 9. Stereo pairs of the regions of the bacteriopheophytin molecules H$_A$ of the *Bl. viridis* RC (a), *Tc. tepidum* RC (b), and *Rb. sphaeroides* RC (c). (PDB entries 1DXR, 1EYS, 1PCR.)

STRUCTURES OF REACTION CENTERS

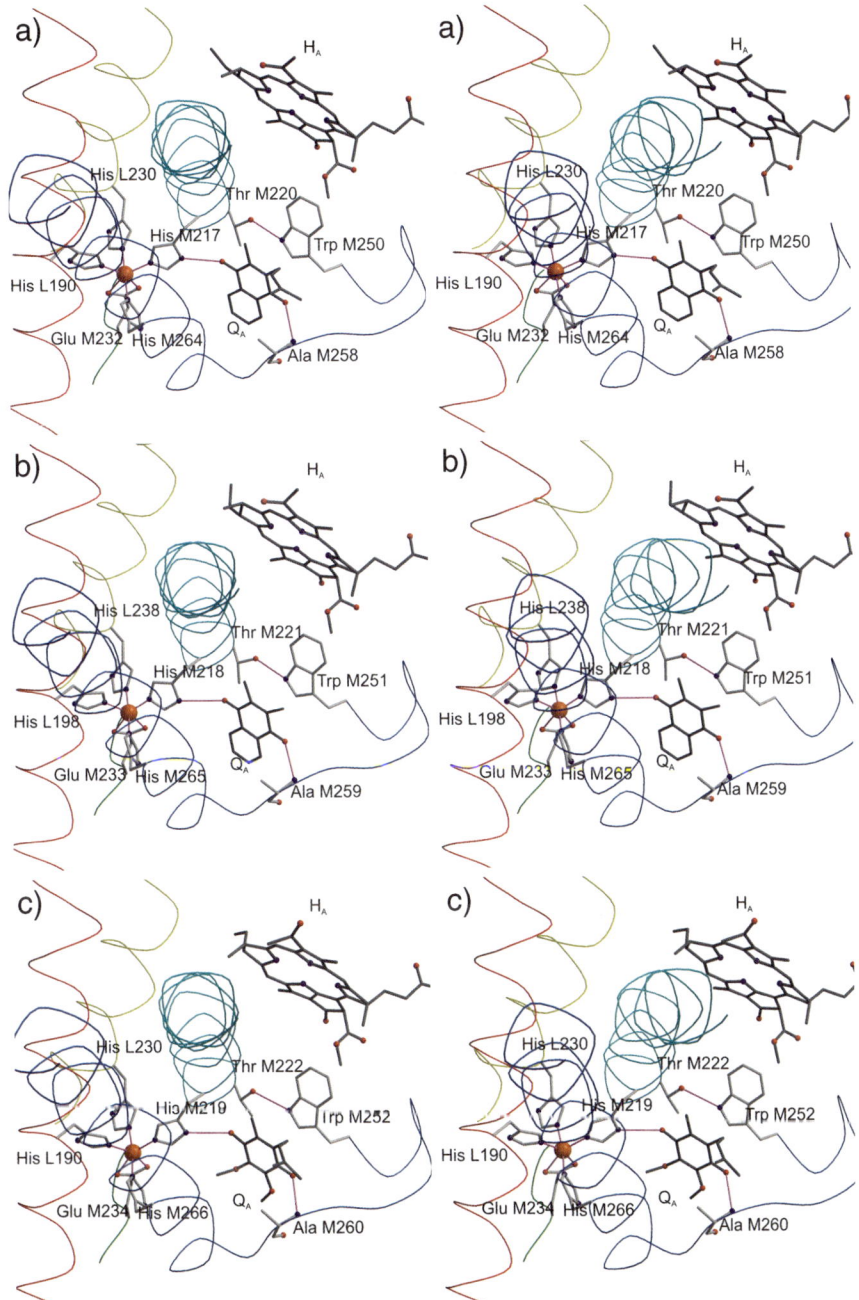

Figure 10. Stereo pairs of the regions of the Q_A molecules and the non-heme iron atoms of the RCs of *Bl. viridis* (a), *Tc. tepidum* (b), and *Rb. sphaeroides* (c). (PDB entries 1DXR, 1EYS, 1PCR.)

dominates (Figure 2), but the quinone ring interacts exclusively with residues of the M subunit. The Q_A-binding site is clearly more hydrophobic than the Q_B-binding site. A major part of the Q_A-binding site is formed by Trp M250 (M251, M252). The ring systems of the tryptophan and Q_A are parallel. Trp M250 (M251, M252) donates a hydrogen bond to Thr M220 (M221, M222). The structural difference between menaquinone as Q_A in *Bl. viridis* and *Tc. tepidum* and ubiquinone as Q_A in *Rb. sphaeroides* causes only minor rearrangements of the Q_A-binding site, which are not shown in Figure 10 for clarity.

The six-coordinate non-heme ferrous iron (Figure 10) is in a distorted octahedron environment, the base plane of which is formed by the three Nε atoms of His L190 (L198, L190), His L230 (L238, L230), and His M217 (M218, M219), and by one carboxyl Oε of Glu M232 (M233, M234). The apices of the octahedron are formed by the Nε atom of His M264 (M265, M266) and the second carboxyl Oε atom of Glu M232 (M233, M234). Such a distorted octahedral coordination had been predicted from Mössbauer and EXAFS results, as reviewed by Feher and Okamura [62]. The average ligand–Fe distances are 2.2 ± 0.2 Å. The four His ligands are located four to eight residues away from the cytoplasmic ends of transmembrane helices D and E of the L and M subunits. The Glu ligand is situated at the N-terminal end of the cytoplasmic helix "dde", which is only present in the M, but not in the L subunit (see above). The flanking residues Asp M230 (M231, Glu M232), Arg M231 (M232, M233, see also Figure 13 below), and Glu M234 (Asp M235, Glu M236), are important constituents of the "Q_B cluster", a group of electrostatically strongly interacting, protonatable residues calculated [63] to be important for proton uptake and transfer to the Q_B site coupled to quinone reduction. The His ligands M217 (M218, M219) and L190 (L198, L190) also provide, with their Nδ atoms, the proximal hydrogen bonding partners to the quinones Q_A and Q_B, respectively. The non-heme Fe^{2+} ion can be removed and replaced with Fe^{2+}, Mn^{2+}, Co^{2+}, Ni^{2+}, Cu^{2+}, and Zn^{2+} in the RC of *Rb. sphaeroides* [64] and with Zn^{2+} in the RC of *Bl. viridis* [65]. Apparently, neither Fe^{2+} nor any divalent cation is required for rapid electron transfer from Q_A^- to Q_B [64]. However, the presence of a metal ion in the Fe site appears to be necessary to establish the characteristic electron transfer properties of Q_A [64].

11.5.5 Heme-Iron Site Geometries

The first four ligands to the six-coordinated heme iron are provided by the porphyrin ring nitrogen atoms. The Cys residues of the heme attachment site sequences Cys-X-Y-Cys-His (C87-C91; C132-C136; C244-C248; C305-C309 in *Bl. viridis*, C85-C89, C130-C134, C225-C229, C285-C289 in *Tc. tepidum*) form thioether bonds with the heme groups and the His is the fifth ligand to the heme iron. The Met residues C74, C110, and C233 in *Bl. viridis* (C72, C108, C214 in *Tc. tepidum*) in the respective parallel helices are the sixth ligands to heme-1, heme-2, and heme-3 (Figure 11a), whereas the sixth ligand to heme-4 is His C124 in *Bl. viridis* (C122 in *Tc. tepidum*), which is located in the loop region of the heme-2 binding site (Figure 11b). The average His Nε–Fe distance is 2.0 Å;

STRUCTURES OF REACTION CENTERS

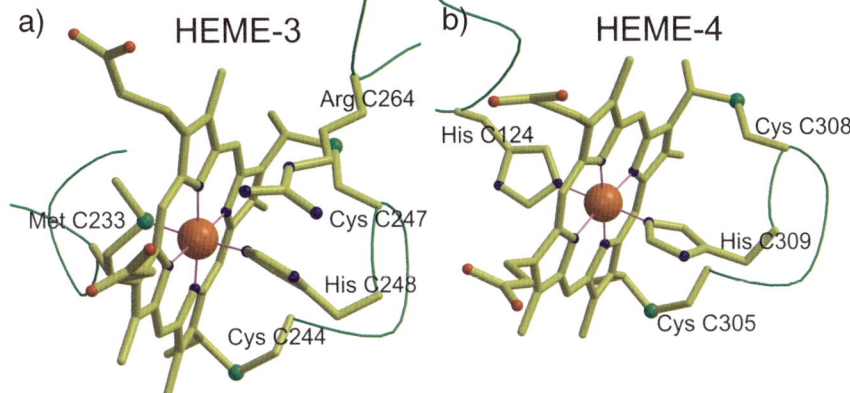

Figure 11. Heme iron site geometries in the *Bl. viridis* RC (PDB entry 2PRC). (a) The binding site of heme-3 as an example for a His-Met ligated heme iron. The binding sites for heme-1 and heme-2 are similar except for the close proximity of Arg C264, which has been shown both theoretically [177] and experimentally [23] to strongly modulate the redox potential of heme-3. (b) The binding site of heme-4 as a His-His ligated heme iron.

the average distance between the porphyrin N atoms and the respective Fe^{2+} is 2.05 Å. The average Met Sδ–Fe distance is 2.3 Å.

11.6 Substrate Binding Sites

11.6.1 The Electron-Acceptor Substrate Q_B and the Binding of Inhibitors

In the original *Bl. viridis* RC structure, the Q_B site was poorly defined because it was only partially occupied with the native ubiquinone-9 in the standard RC crystals. However, ubiquinone-2-reconstitution experiments have yielded crystals with full quinone occupancy of the Q_B site [66]. Subsequent X-ray diffraction analysis and refinement has led to a well-defined Q_B-site model (PDB entry 2PRC), with the quinone bound in the "proximal" position, i.e., close to the non-heme iron (hydrogen-bonded to its ligand His L190, see Figure 12a). In the RC structure with a Q_B-depleted Q_B site (3PRC, Figure 12b), refined at 2.4 Å, apparently five, possibly six, water molecules are bound instead of the ubiquinone head group, and a detergent molecule binds in the region of the isoprenoid tail [66]. Using the structures 2PRC and 3PRC as references, the original data set 1PRC [40] was re-examined. While not excluding the presence of a minor fraction of the quinone in the proximal site, this resulted in the suggestion [66] of a "distal" dominant Q_B-binding position for the native ubiquinone-9 (1PRC$_{new}$), not hydrogen-bonded to His L190 and further away from the non-heme iron (Figure 12a). A more quantitative analysis [67] of the original data resulted in 20% of the Q_B sites being occupied with quinone in the proximal site, 30% having quinone bound in the distal site, and half of the Q_B

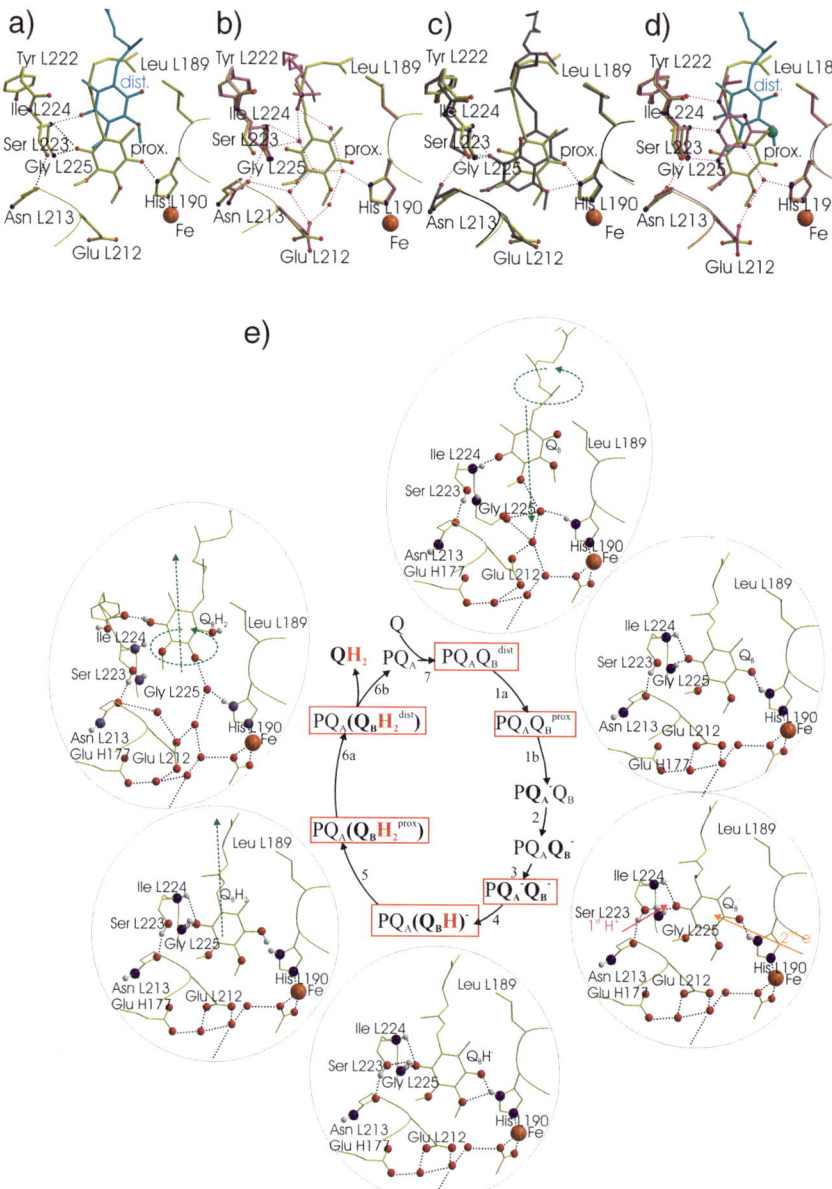

Figure 12. Derivatives at the Q_B site of the *Bl. viridis* RC. (a) Comparison of distal (1PRC$_{new}$, cyan) and proximal (2PRC, yellow) ubiquinone-binding sites. (b) Comparison of Q_B-depleted (3PRC, pink) and ubiquinone-2-occupied (2PRC, yellow) Q_B sites. (c) Comparison of stigmatellin binding (4PRC, gray) and ubiquinone-2 binding (2PRC, yellow). (d) Atrazine binding (5PRC, pink) compared with distal (1PRC$_{new}$, cyan) and proximal (2PRC, yellow) ubiquinone-binding sites. (e) Mechanistic implications of the structures 2PRC, 3PRC, 4PRC, and the revised model 1PRC$_{new}$ for the events at the Q_B site within the reduction cycle of quinone to quinol. The numbering of the steps is analogous to that in Figure 1(c). Hydrogen atoms are drawn as small light gray spheres. Dashed green arrows symbolize quinone movements.

sites being empty or having the quinone unaccounted for. A further structure, the RC complex with the inhibitor stigmatellin (4PRC), refined at 2.4 Å, indicates that additional hydrogen bonds stabilize the binding of stigmatellin over that of ubiquinone-2 (Figure 12c). The binding pattern observed for the stigmatellin complex can be viewed as a model for the stabilization of a monoprotonated reduced intermediate (Q_BH or Q_BH^-) [48,66,68]. This indicates that the Q_B site is not optimized for Q_B binding, but for Q_B reduction to the quinol [68]. In combination with the results of electrostatic calculations, these crystal structures can provide models for intermediates in the reaction cycle of ubiquinone reduction to ubiquinol, as discussed below.

The Q_B site is also a well-established site of herbicide action. Over half [69] of the commercially available herbicides function by inhibition of higher plants at the Q_B site of the D1 polypeptide of the Photosystem II RC (see Section 11.9 for a comparison of the Q_B sites from the bacterial RC and Photosystem II). A commercially very important class of herbicides are the triazines, which were introduced by J.R. Geigy S.A. in the 1950s [70]. A prominent example is atrazine (Figure 3d), first reported in 1957 [71]. According to statistics from 1995, atrazine was used on approximately 67% of all U.S. corn acreage, 65% of sorghum acreage, and 90% of sugarcane acreage. Another well known triazine is terbutryn (2-*t*-butylamino-4-ethylamino-6-methylthio-*s*-triazine). X-Ray crystal structures of complexes of the RC with atrazine (PDB entry 5PRC) [58] and terbutryn (PDB entry 1DXR [41]) have been determined at 2.35 and 2.00 Å resolution, respectively (see Table 2). In both cases, three hydrogen bonds bind the distal side of the inhibitors to the protein, and four additional hydrogen bonds, mediated by two tightly-bound water molecules, are apparent on the proximal side, as shown for atrazine in Figure 12(d). In contrast to the proximal binding of stigmatellin (Figure 12c), the triazine inhibitor partially overlaps with both the distal and the proximal ubiquinone binding sites (Figure 12d).

Both Q_A and Q_B sites are buried deep within the photosynthetic reaction center complex, approximately 15 Å from the cytoplasmic surface. Proton transfer to the reduced quinone within the Q_B site could occur by protons moving along a chain of proton donors and acceptors by a "proton wire", or hydrogen-bonded chain mechanism [72–74]. Possible proton donors and acceptors are protonatable amino acid residues and water molecules (see also Figure 13 below). Several the protonatable residues between the Q_B site and the cytoplasmic surface have been shown to be functionally relevant to the proton transfer process by analysis of site-directed mutations, reviewed in [18,19], and second site revertants [15,75]. The observed effects can be due to the modification of the kinetics and thermodynamics of electron or proton transfer. Electrostatic calculations on the RCs of *Rb. sphaeroides* [76–78] and *Bl. viridis* [63,79] led to the identification of residues that can contribute to the changes in equilibrium distributions of protons in the different redox states of the protein, thus helping to determine the role of the functionally important residues.

In combination with the results of electrostatic calculations [63] the crystal structures 3PRC, $1PRC_{new}$, 2PRC, and 4PRC discussed above (cf. Figure 12) can provide models for intermediates in the reaction cycle of ubiquinone reduction to ubiquinol (Figure 12e) [66,68]. The binding of the incoming Q_B to the distal site displaces some of the water molecules present in the "empty" pocket. The quinone ring is flipped around the isoprenoid tail and further water molecules are displaced for the Q_B to occupy the proximal position. This is the position in which neutral Q_B accepts an electron from Q_A^-. The hydrogen bonds donated to the quinone will automatically lead to a tighter binding of the negatively charged semiquinone Q_B^- compared with the neutral Q_B. Additionally, the side-chain of Ser L223 can reorient by rotation of its χ_2 (Cα-Cβ-Oγ-Hγ) torsional angle, thus establishing an additional hydrogen bond to Q_B^- [7,66]. Coupled to the transfer of the second electron, the first proton is transferred, possibly via a transiently protonated Ser L223-OH$_2^+$ [63], thus forming the monoprotonated, doubly reduced intermediate Q_BH^-. After transfer of the second proton, movement of the quinol from the proximal to the distal position may be facilitated by increased stacking interactions of the aromatic ring systems with the Phe L216 ring and the diffusion of water molecules back into the pocket. The structures of these intermediates provide explanations for their relative binding affinities, as required for proper enzymatic function of the Q_B site. A rearrangement of hydrogen bonds, most prominently the reorientation of the Ser L223 side-chain for Q_B reduction, as suggested by the scenario in Figure 12, is also calculated to be necessary to make Q_B reduction more favorable than Q_A reduction [78]. These local rearrangements may constitute the conformational changes deduced to be required for function by various experiments [80–83]. A similar mechanism has been proposed for the *Rb. sphaeroides* RC [84].

The addition of Cd^{2+} or Zn^{2+} decreases the apparent transfer rates of both the first electron from Q_A^- to Q_B ($k^{(1)}_{AB}$ Figure 1c) and the second electron from Q_A^- to Q_B^- ($k^{(2)}_{AB}$, Figure 1c) 10-fold and 20-fold, respectively [83,85–88]. Three mechanisms of inhibition by Cd^{2+} or Zn^{2+} binding have been proposed. These are not mutually exclusive, but highlight the respective dominant effect. First, based on the decrease of $k^{(1)}_{AB}$ upon Zn^{2+} binding, Utschig *et al.* [83] proposed a gating inhibition mechanism, because the rate-limiting step for $k^{(1)}_{AB}$ was considered to be a conformational gating step, governed by RC dynamics [89]. However, subsequent studies on a Glu L212 → Asn *Rb. sphaeroides* variant RC [87] indicated that the inhibiting step in Cd^{2+} is proton uptake, leading to the second proposal, namely, His-entry inhibition as the key inhibition mechanism [90,91]. This mechanism is consistent with the location of the Cd^{2+} or Zn^{2+} binding site in the crystal structure (PDB entry 1DV6, Table 2) of the respective complexes of the *Rb. sphaeroides* RC (cf. Figure 13) [92]. However, the only four-fold decrease in $k^{(2)}_{AB}$ in the His H126 → Ala/His H128 → Ala is much less pronounced than the 20-fold decrease observed upon Cd^{2+} binding. Therefore, Gerencsér and Maróti [88] have proposed that proton transfer inhibition by metal binding is caused by induced pK_a shifts of residues along proton transfer pathways.

11.6.2 The Electron-Donor Substrate, Cytochrome c_2 or HiPiP

The electrons used to re-reduce the photo-oxidized special pair P^+ are provided by soluble electron carrier proteins, such as cytochrome c_2 in the case of *Bl.*

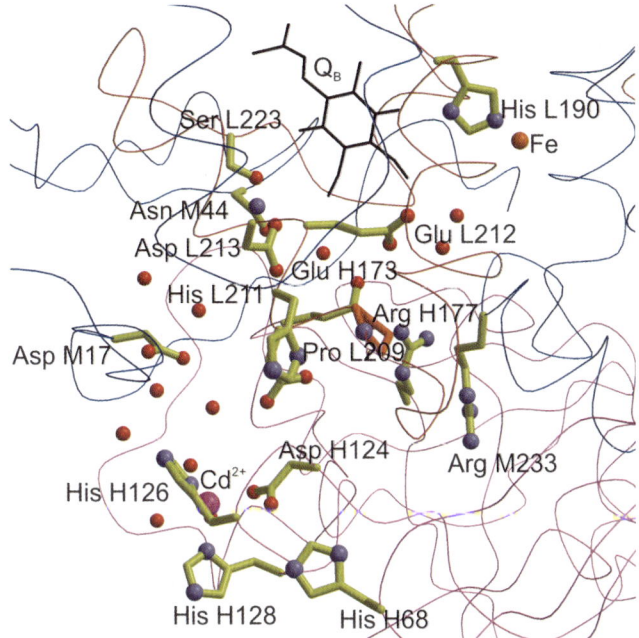

Figure 13. Selected residues of the "Q_B cluster" in the *Rb. sphaeroides* RC. Residues shown are located between the cytoplasmic surface of the protein and the Q_B site (PDB entry 1DV3). Also shown, in purple, is the binding of Cd^{2+}. This binding site is not conserved in the RCs of *Tc. tepidum* and *Bl. viridis*.

viridis and *Rb. sphaeroides*, and a high-potential iron-sulfur protein (HiPiP) in the case of *Tc. tepidum*.

All four hemes of the *Bl. viridis* RC tetraheme C subunit are located close enough to the surface of the protein to accept electrons from soluble cytochrome c_2. Site-directed mutagenesis in another non-sulfur purple bacterium, *Rubrivivax gelatinosus*, has led to the identification of a patch of acidic residues immediately surrounding the distal low-potential heme-1 of the tetraheme C subunit that apparently forms an electrostatically favorable binding site for soluble cytochromes. Thus, all four hemes in the C subunit appear to be directly involved in the electron transfer towards the photo-oxidized special pair. Based on these findings, a model was proposed for the transient cytochrome c_2-RC complex for *Bl. viridis* (Figure 14a). Also, in the case of the *Tc. tepidum* RC, the surface around heme-1 was found to be the best candidate for a binding site of HiPiP. However, with HiPiP, electrostatic interactions appear to have a negligible influence [93,94] on the binding to the tetraheme cytochrome c subunit. Instead hydrophobic interactions are apparently responsible for docking HiPiP and the C subunit of the RC in *Tc. tepidum*.

With the *Rb. sphaeroides* RC, which lacks the C subunit, the photo-oxidized special pair P^+ is directly re-reduced by cytochrome c_2. The structure of the co-complex of the *Rb. sphaeroides* RC and cytochrome c_2 has been determined by

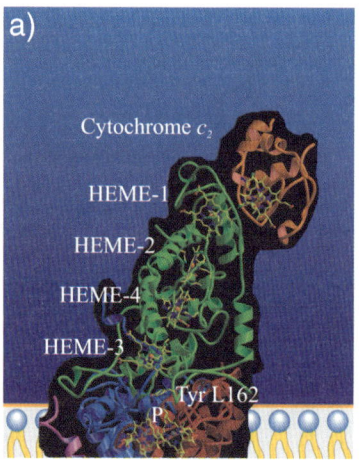 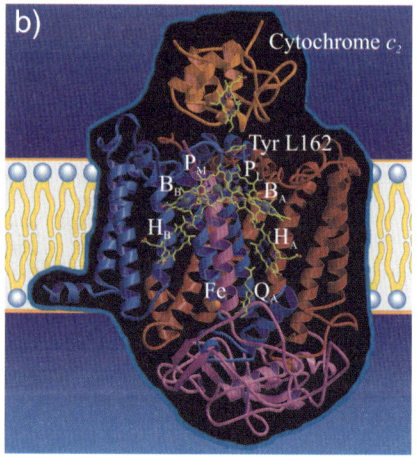

Figure 14. Cytochrome c_2 oxidation by the photosynthetic RCs of *Bl. viridis* and *Rb. sphaeroides*. (a) Reduction of the photo-oxidized tetraheme C subunit of the *Bl. viridis* RC (color-coding as in Figure 1a) by *Bl. viridis* cytochrome c_2 (orange). Theoretical docking as suggested from mutagenesis experiments. (b) Reduction of the special pair P in the *Rb. sphaeroides* RC (color coding of the L, M, and H subunits analogous to Figure 1a) by *Rb. sphaeroides* cytochrome c_2 (orange) as determined by X-ray crystal structure analysis (PDB entry 1L9B).

X-ray crystallography at 2.4 Å resolution (cf. Figure 14b). In these crystals, P^+ is reduced by cytochrome c_2 at the same rate as measured in solution, indicating that the structure of the complex in the region of electron transfer is the same in the crystal and in solution. The binding interface can be divided into two domains. The first domain contributes to the strength and specificity of cytochrome c_2 binding and is a short-range interaction domain that includes Tyr L162 (cf. Figure 14b), and groups exhibiting non-polar interactions, hydrogen bonding, and a cation–π interaction. The second is a long-range, electrostatic interaction domain that contains complementary charges on the RC and cytochrome c_2. In addition to contributing to the binding, this domain may help steer the unbound proteins into the right orientation.

11.7 Aspects of Membrane Protein Structure

11.7.1 Side-Chain Distributions

The distributions within the L and M subunits of the strongly basic amino acid residues, Arg and Lys, and of the strongly acidic residues, Glu and Asp, is shown in Figure 15(a, c, e), for the RCs from *Bl. viridis*, *Tc. tepidum*, and *Rb. sphaeroides*, respectively. Based on electrostatic calculations, only very few of these residues are considered not to be fully ionized, most notably Glu L104 (cf. Figure 9), which is fully protonated, and Glu L212 (cf. Figures 12 and 13),

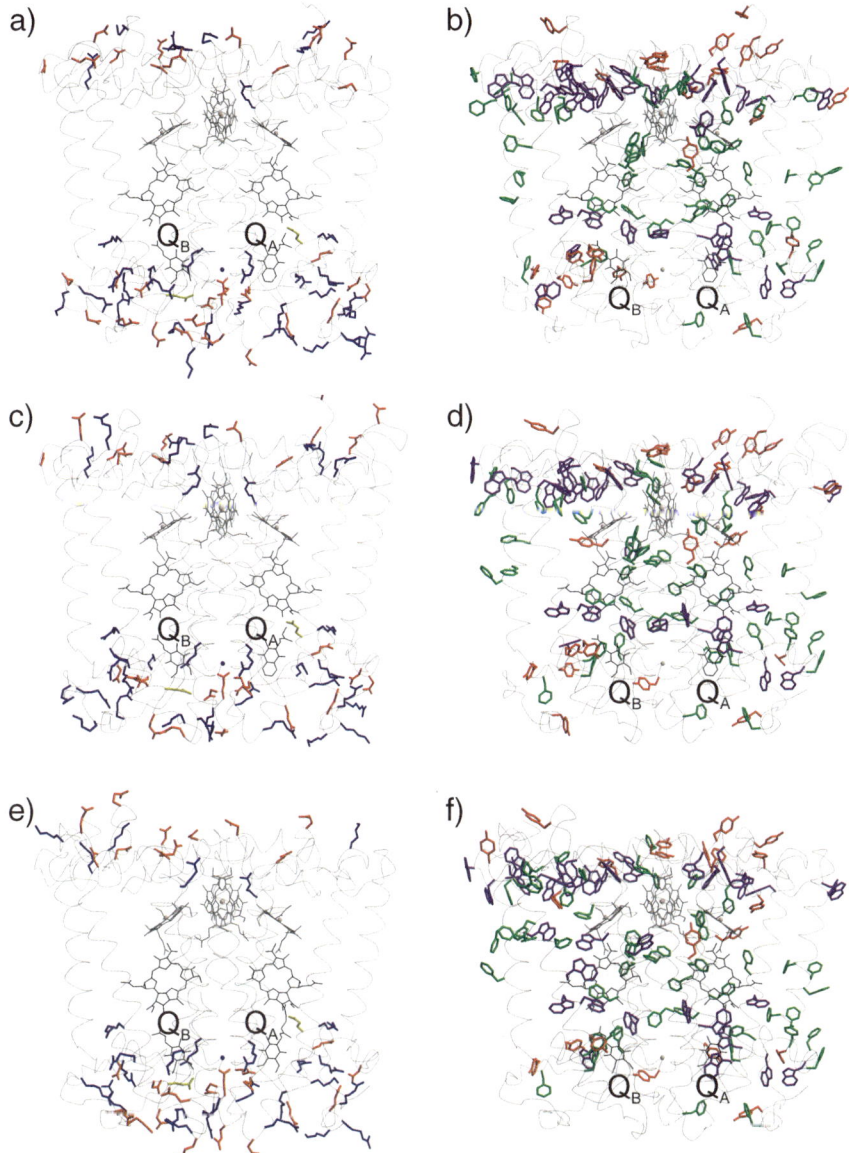

Figure 15. Side-chain distribution of selected amino acid residues in the RCs of *Bl. viridis* (a,b), *Tc. tepidum* (c,d), and *Rb. sphaeroides* (e,f): (a), (c), (e) Distribution of Arg, Lys (in blue), Asp, Glu (in red) residues. Glu residues calculated [63,77,78] to be (predominantly) neutral (L212 near Q_B, L104 near H_A) are drawn in yellow. (b), (d), (f) Distribution of Trp (purple), Tyr (red), and Phe (green) residues in the L and M subunits.

which is predominantly protonated. The residues shown in Figure 15 exhibit an asymmetrical distribution with respect to the cytoplasmic and periplasmic sides. Whereas positively charged residues Arg and Lys predominate on the cytoplasmic, negatively charged residues, Asp and Glu, predominate on the periplasmic side. This observation, as discussed for the *Bl. viridis* RC [29] is conserved not only in the case of the other RCs (Figure 15), but has since led to the formulation of the "positive-inside" rule [95], which was found to be valid not only for bacterial inner membrane proteins, but also for eukaryotic proteins from the endoplasmic reticulum, the plasma membrane, the inner mitochondrial membrane, and the chloroplast thylakoid membrane and across a wide range of organisms [96].

The L and M subunits display a remarkably uneven distribution of Trp side-chains, compared with those of Tyr and Phe side-chains (Figure 15b, d, f). About two-thirds of the Trp residues are found in the hydrophobic surface-to-polar transition zone on the periplasmic side of the complex [39,97]. On the surface of the molecules, they are correctly positioned to form hydrogen bonds with the lipid head groups while their hydrophobic rings are immersed in the lipid part of the bilayer. It has been suggested that Trp residues are involved in the translocation of protein through the membrane and that, following translocation, Trp residues serve as anchors on the periplasmic side of the membrane [97,98].

11.7.2 Bound Water

The original *Bl. viridis* RC crystal structure (1PRC) contained 201 tentative, ordered water molecules [37]. In more recent structures (cf. Figure 16), between 114 [66] and 384 [41] additional water molecules were assigned, based on electron density maps and local chemistry. Calculation of the water quality factor (*QualWat*), as introduced by Arnold and Rossmann [99], indicated that the average crystallographic quality of the additionally fitted water molecules was similar to that of the original ones [66]. Generally in proteins, internal water not only fills structural cavities, but it is also necessary to stabilize three-dimensional folding [100,101]. In particular, several water molecules have been described that mediate hydrogen bonding between transmembrane helices in the hydrophobic region of the membrane. Originally, two water molecules were described [39] that mediate hydrogen bonding between transmembrane helices C and E of the L subunit and between transmembrane helix D of the L subunit and transmembrane helix D of the M subunit. The binding of a third water molecule in the transmembrane region was described subsequently [66], mediating hydrogen bonding between transmembrane helices C and E of the M subunit. Recently, a water molecule, referred to as "water A" and located within hydrogen bonding distance of the keto carbonyl of the accessory bacteriochlorophyll B_A (cf. Figure 8), has been shown [102] to have strong effects on the rate of primary electron transfer [103] from the excited primary donor P* (Section 11.8.1). In addition, the participation of water molecules is

STRUCTURES OF REACTION CENTERS

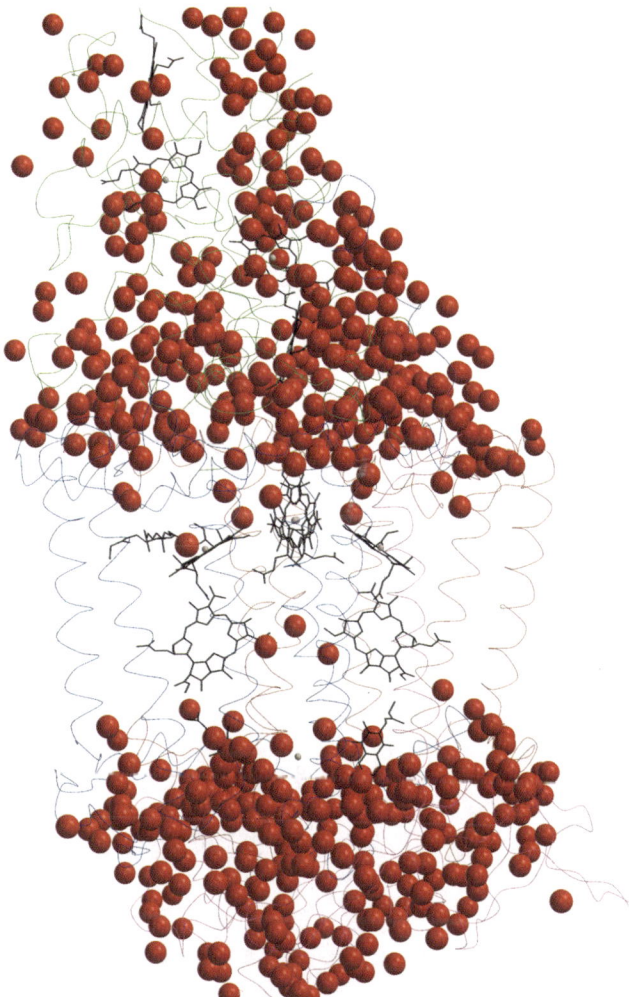

Figure 16. Bound water: Distribution of 585 bound water molecules in the *Bl. viridis* RC (PDB entry 1DXR).

apparently essential [66,104,105,] for the pathways and kinetics of proton transfer to the Q_B site.

11.7.3 Phospholipid Binding

The advent of more refined purification strategies, reviewed earlier [7], in particular involving significantly lower concentrations of detergent used to solubilize the photosynthetic membranes of *Rb. sphaeroides* and *Tc. tepidum*, has led to the identification of motionally-restricted phospholipid molecules on the intramembrane surface (Figure 17). Using the standard purification protocol for the *Bl. viridis* RC with high detergent concentrations [7], no

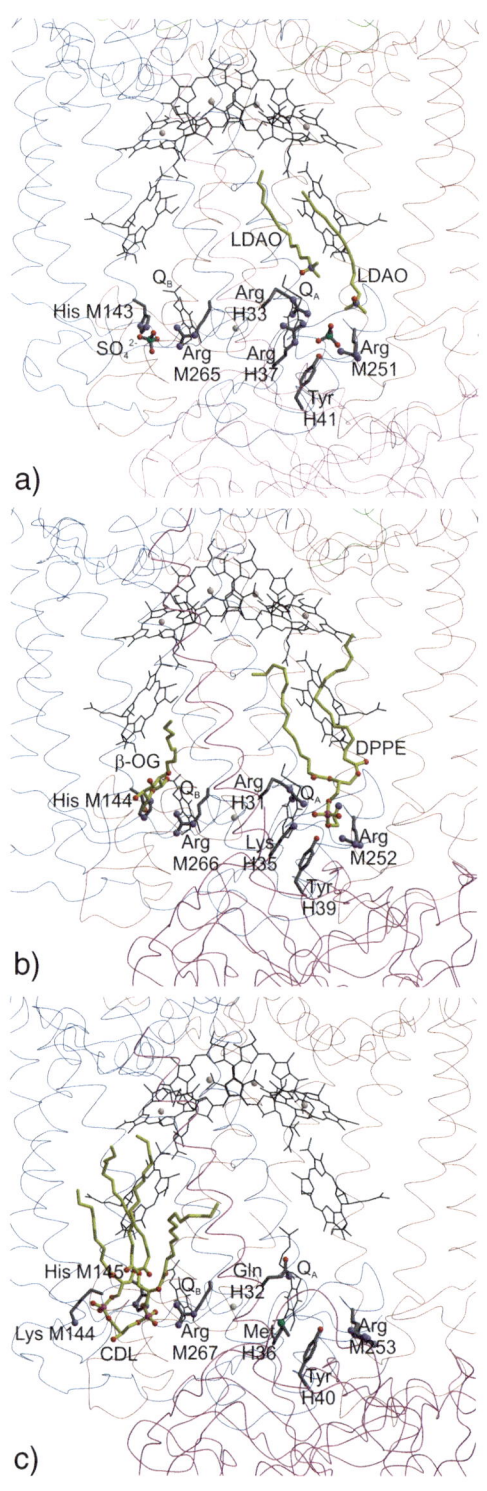

phospholipid is retained (H. Michel, personal communication). However, the binding of two molecules of the detergent LDAO and of a sulfate ion in the *Bl. viridis* RC (Figure 17a) is clearly analogous to the binding of dipalmitoylphosphatidylethanolamine (DPPE) described for the *Tc. tepidum* RC (Figure 17b). In turn, the binding site of a β-octyl glucoside molecule in the *Tc. tepidum* RC (Figure 17b) is occupied by a cardiolipin molecule in the case of the *Rb. sphaeroides* RC (Figure 17c). The role of Arg M267 (Figure 17c) has been investigated (PDB entry 1UMX, Table 3, Section 11.8.1).

11.8 Structures of Modified Reaction Centers

11.8.1 Variant Reaction Centers

Work on site-directed mutagenesis of photosynthetic reaction centers started with the RC from *Rb. capsulatus* (see [15,16] for early reviews). This species is genetically very well characterized and able to grow non-photosynthetically under aerobic conditions, as well as under anaerobic conditions using, for example, dimethyl sulfoxide as an electron acceptor. Most importantly, under these latter conditions, the photosynthetic apparatus is fully induced. Unfortunately, the RC from *Rb. capsulatus* could not be crystallized, thus thwarting proper inspection for structural changes.

The closely related *Rb. sphaeroides* can be grown under similar non-photosynthetic conditions, so that site-directed mutagenesis is also straightforward. As detailed above, this RC is amenable to inspection by X-ray crystallography for structural changes. Many amino acids that were considered to be of importance for pigment binding, electron transfer [60], in particular the directionality of electron transfer along the A branch, proton transfer to Q_B, phospholipid binding or crystal packing were changed in *Rb. sphaeroides* RCs, in some cases after the corresponding replacements in the *Rb. capsulatus* RC had been shown to be important.

When the residues His L173 and His M202 (corresponding to M200 in *Bl. viridis*, Figure 8) liganded to the special pair bacteriochlorophylls P_L and P_M are replaced by Leu residues, bacteriopheophytins are incorporated as P_L and P_M, respectively. In addition to being analyzed by X-ray crystallography of the orthorhombic crystal form ("B") at 3 Å resolution (PDB entry 1PST, Table 3), the structure of the "heterodimer" *Rb. sphaeroides* RC variant His M202 → Leu has subsequently been determined in the trigonal crystal form ("C") at higher resolution [106] (PDB entry 1KBY). This has allowed a more detailed description of the structural changes associated with this amino acid

---

Figure 17. Phospholipid binding: Binding of selected detergent and/or phospholipid molecules in the RCs from *Bl. viridis* (a, PDB entry 3PRC), *Tc. tepidum* (b, PDB entry 1EYS), and *Rb. sphaeroides* (c, PDB entry 1QOV). The Q_B models provided in (a) and (b) to facilitate orientation are from PDB entry 2PRC, the Q_A model in (c) is from PDB entry 1PCR.

replacement, which include the loss of water "A", which, in the wild-type RC, is hydrogen-bonded both to His M202 and the bacteriochlorophyll monomer B_A (Figure 8). Based on the structural (PDB entry 2BOZ) and functional characterization of the *Rb. sphaeroides* RC variant Gly M203 → Leu, this water molecule "A" has recently been shown to have a strong effect on the rate of light-driven charge separation, in that its removal leads to an approximately eight-fold slowing of the rate of decay of P* [102].

Also remarkable is the replacement of Tyr M210 (Figure 9) with a Phe, taking into account that the symmetry-related residue in the L subunit is Phe L181. In the Tyr M210 → Phe variant RC the rate of initial electron transfer is slowed by a factor of 4–6 [107,108]. X-Ray crystallographic analysis [109] using the orthorhombic crystal form ("B") did not reveal any significant structural changes except for the absence of the O atom, which appears to be the reason for the decreased observed rate of electron transfer.

Several the *Rb. sphaeroides* variant RC structures listed in Table 3 involve the replacement of Phe M197, close to P_M (cf. Figure 8c), with Arg. These were combined with the replacement of residues in the carotenoid-binding pocket (Tyr M177, Trp M115) with Phe (PDB entries 1MPS and 1E6D, respectively) [110,111]. The structure of the Phe M197 → Arg/Tyr M177 → Phe variant RC shows an unexpected change in the structure, with a reorientation of the new arginine, the incorporation of a new water molecule into the structure, and the rotation of the P_M ring I acetyl group. The replacement of Phe M197 with Arg was also combined with the replacement of the nearby residue Gly M203 with Asp (PDB entry 1E14). This replacement and the analogous replacement (Gly M201 → Asp) in *Rb. capsulatus* have been shown to inhibit electron transfer along the A branch. The residue Phe M197 in *Rb. sphaeroides* corresponds to a Tyr in *Bl. viridis* and *Tc. tepidum* (Figure 8). The structure of a Phe M197 → Tyr mutant has also been described [112]. In combination with electrochemically induced FTIR spectra, there is clear evidence for the existence of a newly established hydrogen bond between Tyr M197 and the P_M ring I acetyl group. The residue corresponding to Phe M197 in the L subunit is His L168. Its replacement will be discussed below in the context of *Bl. viridis* variant RCs.

In the Leu M214 → His variant, corresponding to residue M212 in *Bl. viridis* (Figure 9) and *Rb. capsulatus* [113], a bacteriochlorophyll, termed β, is incorporated as H_A instead of a bacteriopheophytin [109]. A very interesting Q_A cofactor exclusion variant RC, involving the replacement of Ala M260 (Figure 10) with a Trp residue, has been structurally described at 2.1 Å resolution (PDB entry 1QOV) [114]. In the Ala M260 → Trp variant, there is no space left in the former Q_A binding pocket for the binding of the native ubiquinone. Instead, in addition to the Trp side-chain, a Cl^- ion is found at this position. A recent quintuple variant, combining previously discussed amino acid replacements to inhibit electron transfer via the A-branch (Gly M203 → Asp, Tyr M210 → Phe, Leu M 214 → His), to promote electron transfer via the B-branch (Phe L181 → Tyr), and to exclude the Q_A cofactor (Ala M260 → Trp), has been shown to reduce Q_B via the B-branch and its structure, based on crystal form "C", has been described at 2.25 Å resolution (PDB entry 1YF6) [115]. A further multiple variant of the *Rb.*

sphaeroides RC containing three replacements (Leu L131 → His/Leu M160 → His/Phe M197 → His) designed to increase the P/P^+ midpoint potential [116], one replacement (Arg M164 → Tyr) for the incorporation of a Tyr near P, and two replacements (Gly M288 → Asp/Met M168 → Glu), designed to introduce a Mn^{2+} binding-site, has been shown to possess a redox-active Mn^{2+}-site, mimicking that of Photosystem II. X-Ray structure analysis of this variant based on crystal form "F" (Table 1) has, however, been limited to 4.5 Å resolution (Table 3). In addition to mutagenesis, cofactors may be removed or replaced chemically with a wide range of similar compounds – reviewed by Gunner [117] in the case of quinones and by Scheer and Struck [118] for bacteriochlorins.

Residues that are either part of or in close proximity to the "Q_B cluster" of interacting residues considered to be relevant for proton transfer to the Q_B site (cf. Figures 12 and 13) have also been replaced by site-directed mutagenesis. Using the orthorhombic crystal form "B", mutations such as those involving protonatable residues Glu L212 → Gln and Asp L213 → Asn, and a ligand to the non-heme iron His M219 → Cys (corresponding to residue M217 in *Bl. viridis*, Figure 10), do not lead to detectable structural changes [109]. However, the resolution of the respective data sets was limited to 3.3, 3.0, and 4 Å. Using the trigonal crystal form "C", the structure of the Asp L213 → Asn variant was more recently shown at 2.1 Å resolution (PDB entry 1RY5, Table 3) [49] to be very similar to that of the wild-type RC, with the exception of the nearby residue Glu H173, which was found in two alternate conformations. Also using the trigonal crystal form, the reaction center double variant Glu L212 → Ala/Asp L213 → Ala has been described at 3.1 Å resolution, revealing unexpected changes in main chain positions (PDB entry 1K6N) [28]. RC variants involving replacement of the nearby residue Pro L209 (Figure 13), with Tyr, Phe or Glu (PDB entries 1F6N, 1FNP, and 1FNQ, respectively) have been determined at 2.6–2.8 Å resolution [119].

In addition, interesting second-site replacements that restore photosynthetic competence have been obtained both for *Rb. capsulatus* [75,120–122] and *Rb. sphaeroides* [123,124]. The structures of the Asp L213 → Asn/Arg M233 → Cys and Asp L213 → Asn/Arg H177 → His *Rb. sphaeroides* RC variants have been determined on the basis of crystal form "C" at 1.8 and 2.75 Å, respectively (PDB entries 1RZH and 1RVJ) [49]. From the structures, alternate proton transfer pathways could be delineated, the main changes occurring near Glu H173 (Figure 13).

The residue Arg M267, found to be involved in cardiolipin binding (Figure 17), has been replaced with a Leu residue and the structure of the corresponding variant RC has been determined at 2.8 Å resolution (PDB entry 1UMX, cf. Table 3) [125]. Instead of cardiolipin, only a phosphate ion was bound by the side-chains of Tyr H30, Trp M271, and His M145. Other than the M267 side-chain, the structure of the protein cofactor system remained unaltered. The mutation did not affect the rate of photosynthetic growth or the functional properties of the RC. However, the thermal stability of the RC was compromised by this amino acid replacement.

The role of crystal contact interactions has been assessed by replacement of amino-acid residues on the surface of the *Rb. sphaeroides* RC and subsequent crystallization and X-ray structure analysis (PDB entries 1JGW, 1JGX, 1JGY, 1JGZ, 1JH0, cf. Table 3). Depending on the crystal form, significant differences in the resolution limits were associated with the loss of specific interactions between neighboring proteins [126].

Site-directed mutagenesis of the RC from *Bl. viridis* is possible [127] but more difficult. *Bl. viridis* can grow only under photosynthetic and, very slowly, under microaerophilic conditions. However, under microaerophilic conditions, the photosynthetic apparatus is not induced and photosynthetic growth conditions exert a selection pressure for revertants and suppressor mutants if the RCs are functionally impaired. In contrast, very interesting herbicide-resistant mutants were obtained by classical selection procedures, with mutations, some of which would not have been made by site-directed mutagenesis [20,128].

Some of these herbicide resistant mutants of the *Bl. viridis* RC have also been analyzed by X-ray crystallography. In the double mutant Arg L217 → His/Ser L223 → Ala, the side-chain of Asn L213, which is hydrogen-bonded to Ser L223 in the wild type, is rotated towards the cavity that is created by the replacement of Arg L217 by the smaller His [129]. At the same time, Q_B becomes more firmly bound [20]. The mutation Tyr L222 → Phe unexpectedly leads to resistance against the herbicide terbutryn. In the wild type, Tyr L222 forms a hydrogen bond with the peptide carbonyl oxygen of Asp M43. Since this hydrogen bond is now missing, a stretch of the M subunit (M25–50) moves into a new position. The side-chain of Phe L222 rotates by 90° into the herbicide binding site (see above), thereby preventing the binding of terbutryn by steric hindrance [130].

Using site-directed mutagenesis, the highly conserved Tyr L162, positioned halfway between P and the proximal heme-3 (cytochrome c_{559}) in the *Bl. viridis* RC, was exchanged against several amino acids. All mutants grew photosynthetically. The redox potentials of P and c_{559} were changed by the mutations. The structures of two mutants (Tyr L162 → Phe and Tyr L162 → Thr) were determined and found not to differ significantly from the wild-type structure [21]. Analysis of the kinetics of electron transfer led to the conclusion that the tyrosine residue at position L162 is not required for fast electron transfer from c_{559} to P^+ [21].

Replacement of His L168, which donates a hydrogen bond to the ring I acetyl group of P_L (Figure 8), with Phe leads to a more than three-fold acceleration of the rate of initial electron transfer from the excited primary donor P*. This is associated with the lowering of the oxidation–reduction midpoint potential of P/P^+ by 80 mV [131]. The structure of the His L168 → Phe variant RC, refined at 2.0 Å resolution (PDB entry 1DXR, cf. Table 2), provides an explanation for these properties. Compared with the wild-type RC, the hydrogen bond to the ring I acetyl group of P_L is removed, the acetyl group is rotated and its acetyl oxygen is found 1.1 Å closer to the bacteriochlorophyll-Mg^{2+} of P_M. Similar findings were subsequently reported for the same amino acid replacement in the *Rb. sphaeroides* RC [132].

A replacement of Arg C264 by Lys decreases the midpoint potential of heme-3 (cytochrome c_{559}) from +380 to +270 mV, i.e., below that of heme-2 (+320 mV, see Figures 11a and 1b) [23]. In the structure of the variant RC at 2.46 Å

STRUCTURES OF REACTION CENTERS

resolution, no remarkable differences were found apart from the replaced residue itself [23]. The halftime of electron transfer between heme-2 and heme-3 was the same as in the wild-type, indicating that the observed reaction rate is limited by the very uphill electron transfer from heme-2 to heme-4 (Figure 1b) [23].

11.8.2 Dark-Adapted Versus Light-Adapted Reaction Centers

Previous attempts to determine the structural changes of the RC protein upon illumination of dark-adapted, detergent-grown RC crystals were inconclusive [50,133–135]. Recently, Katona and colleagues [136] grew *Rb. sphaeroides* RC crystals from a lipidic cubic phase and could describe structural changes at 100 K in the form of a subdomain movement of the H subunit, involving large parts of the PRC barrel, by up to 0.7 Å (Figure 18). The full conformational change

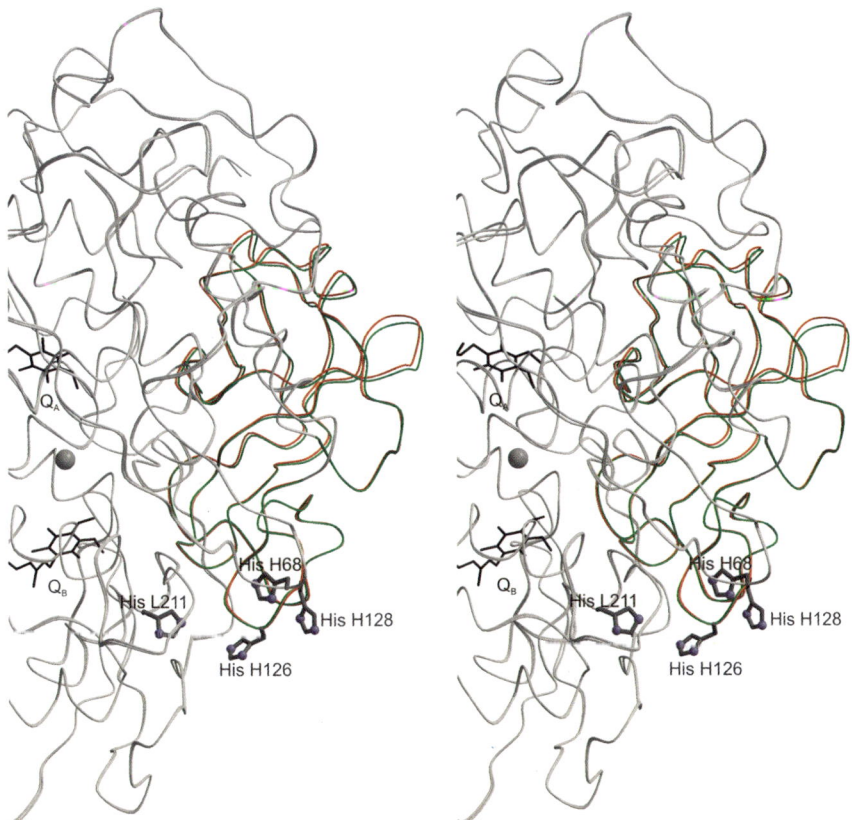

Figure 18. Light-induced structural changes. Comparison of Cα traces of the *Rb. sphaeroides* RC in the dark-adapted state (PDB entry 2BNP, red) and in the illuminated state (2BNS, green). The secondary quinone Q_B (from 2PRC), Q_A, the non-heme iron, and the four His residues L211, H68, H126, and H128 are drawn to facilitate the orientation relative to the previous figures.

is not expected at the low temperature of this experiment. Crystals illuminated at room temperature do not diffract. The observation of this structural change was apparently obscured previously in the case of the other crystal forms due to crystal packing constraints.

11.9 Comparison with Photosystem II

Based on the determined structure of the purple bacterial RC, very specific sequence homologies, and azidoatrazine labeling, the RC core of higher plant photosystem (PS) II was proposed to be similar to the LM core of the bacterial RC, with the D1 and D2 proteins corresponding to the L and M subunits, respectively [137–141]. This proposal could be verified experimentally [142]. Similar to the processes discussed in Section 11.6.1 for the bacterial RC, indirect lines of evidence indicate that the reoxidation of Q_A^- by Q_B (Q_B^-) is a conformationally triggered reaction in PS II ([143,144]; for details, see Chapter 16) Suitably designed, modified bactcrial RCs mimic tyrosine oxidation [145] and mimic redox-active Mn^{2+} in PS II [146]. Atomic models of the structure of Photosystem II, as determined by X-ray crystallography at 3.5, 3.2, and 3.0 Å resolution, have been presented [147–149]. Each of the D1 and D2

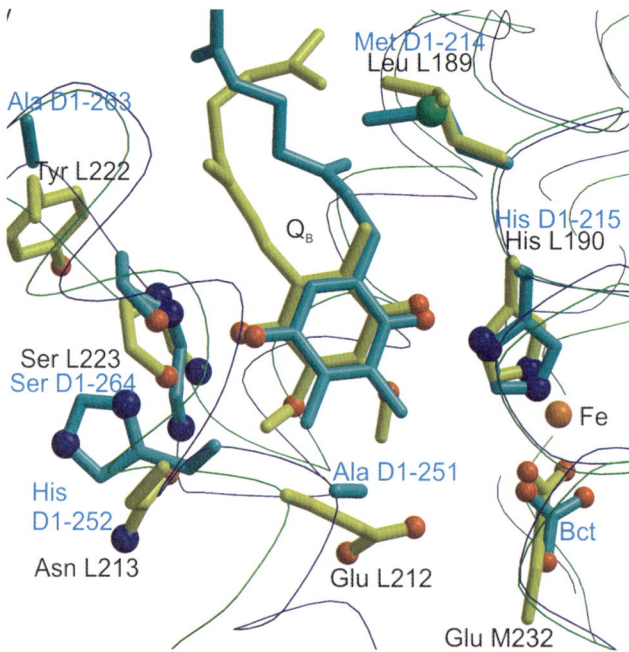

Figure 19. Comparison of the Q_B site of Photosystem II. The Cα trace of the *Bl. viridis* RC (PDB entry 2PRC) is drawn in green, individual bonds involving C atoms are depicted in yellow. The Cα trace of Photosystem II (PDB entry 2AXT [149]) is drawn in blue, the respective bonds involving C atoms are shown in light blue.

subunits consists of five transmembrane helices organized in a manner almost identical to that of the L and M subunits of the bacterial RC, with a root-mean-square deviation of 1.9 Å for 395 Cα atoms [147]. The Q_B site appears slightly wider in PSII due to the insertion of a residue in the loop connecting the de helix and transmembrane helix E and containing Ser D1–264 (corresponding to Ser L223 of the RC, cf. Figure 19), which may explain the difference in herbicide specificity [150]. Nevertheless, in the case of the inhibitors of both the RC and Photosystem II, such as stigmatellin, atrazine, and terbutryn, the crystal structures of the complexes of these inhibitors with the *Bl. viridis* RC [41,58,66,130] can serve as useful models of PS II inhibition.

11.10 Conclusions and Future Perspectives

Over 20 years after the publication of the first crystal structure of the *Bl. viridis* RC, reaction centre crystallography has come of age, providing, in particular, structures of variants and other modified RCs at, generally, higher resolution and quality. These structures, and those of further modified RCs, still to be determined, are prerequisites for an atomic-level understanding of the function and mechanism of action of these fascinating membrane protein complexes. In addition, the improved perspectives for time-resolved X-ray crystallography (see [151] for a recent review) are expected to provide further insight into the dynamical aspects of RC structures.

References

1. J. Deisenhofer, J.R. Norris (eds.), *The Photosynthetic Reaction Center*, (1993) Academic Press, San Diego, Vols I and II.
2. R.E. Blankenship, M.T. Madigan and C.E. Bauer (eds.), *Anoxygenic Photosynthetic Bacteria* (1995) Kluwer Academic Publishers, Dordrecht.
3. M.-E. Michel-Beyerle, (ed.), *The Reaction Center of Photosynthetic Bacteria. Structure and Dynamics* (1996) Springer-Verlag, Berlin.
4. J. Amesz, A.J. Hoff (eds.), *Biophysical Techniques in Photosynthesis* (1996) Kluwer Academic Publishers, Dordrecht.
5. A. J. Hoff, J. Deisenhofer, Photophysics of photosynthesis – structure and spectroscopy of reaction centers of purple bacteria. *Phys. Rep.* **287** (1997) 1–247.
6. J. Breton, E. Nabedryk, A. Vermeglio (eds.), Special issue on reaction centers of photosynthetic purple bacteria-structure, spectroscopy, dynamics, *Photosynth. Res.* **55** (1998) 117–378.
7. C.R.D. Lancaster, H. Michel, Photosynthetic reaction centers of purple bacteria, in: *Handbook of Metalloproteins* (1997) (A. Messerschmidt, R. Huber, T. Poulos, K. Wieghardt, eds.), J. Wiley & Sons, Chichester, Vol. 1, pp. 119–135.
8. C.C. Moser, C.C. Page, R.J. Cogdell, J. Barber, C.A. Wraight, P.L. Dutton, Length, time, and energy scales of photosystems, in: *Advances in Protein Chemistry* (2003) (D.C. Rees, ed.), Elsevier, San Diego, Vol. 63, pp. 71–109.

9. P. Mitchell, Keilin's respiratory chain concept and its chemiosmotic consequences. *Science* **206** (1979) 1148–1159.
10. J.P. Thornber, R.J. Cogdell, R.E.B. Seftor, G.D. Webster, Further studies on the composition and spectral properties of the photochemical reaction centers of bacteriochlorophyll *b*-containing bacteria. *Biochim. Biophys. Acta* **593** (1980) 60–75.
11. A. Hiraishi, Transfer of the bacteriochlorophyll *b*-containing phototrophic bacteria *Rhodopseudomonas viridis* and *Rhodopseudomonas sulfoviridis* to the genus *Blastochloris* gen. Nov. *Int. J. Syst. Bacteriol.* **47** (1997) 217–219.
12. G. Feher, M.Y. Okamura, Chemical composition and properties of reaction centers, in: *The Photosynthetic Bacteria* (1978) (R.K. Clayton, W.R. Sistrom, eds.), Plenum Press, New York, pp. 349–386.
13. T. Nozawa, J.T. Trost, T. Fukada, M. Hatano, J.D. McManus, R.E. Blankenship, Properties of the reaction center of the thermophilic purple photosynthetic bacterium *Chromatium tepidum*. *Biochim. Biophys. Acta* **894** (1987) 468–476.
14. J.M. Olson, J.P. Thornber, Photosynthetic reaction centers, in: *Membrane Proteins in Energy Transduction* (1979) (R.A. Capaldi, ed.), Marcel Dekker, New York, pp. 279–340.
15. W.J. Coleman, D.C. Youvan, Spectroscopic analysis of genetically modified photosynthetic reaction centers. *Annu. Rev. Biophys. Biophys. Chem.* **19** (1990) 333–367.
16. B.A. Diner, P.J. Nixon, J.W. Farchaus, Site-directed mutagenesis of photosynthetic reaction centers. *Curr. Opin. Struct. Biol.* **1** (1991) 546–554.
17. P. Sebban, P. Maroti, D.K. Hanson, Electron and proton transfer to the quinones in bacterial photosynthetic reaction centers–Insight from combined approaches of molecular genetics and biophysics. *Biochimie* **77** (1995) 677–694.
18. E. Takahashi, C.A. Wraight, Molecular genetic manipulation and characterization of mutant photosynthetic reaction centers from purple nonsulfur bacteria. *Adv. Mol. Cell Biol.* **10** (1994) 197–251.
19. M.Y. Okamura, G. Feher, Proton-coupled electron transfer reactions of Q_B in reaction centers from photosynthetic bacteria, in: *Anoxygenic Photosynthetic Bacteria* (1995) (R.E. Blankenship, M.T. Madigan, C.E. Bauer, eds.), Kluwer Academic Publishers, Dordrecht, pp. 577–594.
20. I. Sinning, H. Michel, P. Mathis, A.W. Rutherford, Characterization of four herbicide-resistant mutants of *Rhodopseudomonas viridis* by genetic analysis, electron paramagnetic resonance, and optical spectroscopy. *Biochemistry* **28** (1989) 5544–5553.
21. B. Dohse, P. Mathis, J. Wachtveitl, E. Laussermair, S. Iwata, H. Michel, D. Oesterhelt, Electron transfer from the tetraheme cytochrome to the special pair in the *Rhodopseudomonas viridis* reaction center: effect of mutations of tyrosine L162. *Biochemistry* **34** (1995) 11335–11343.
22. T. Arlt, B. Dohse, S. Schmidt, J. Wachtveitl, E. Laussermair, W. Zinth, D. Oesterhelt, Electron transfer dynamics of *Rhodopseudomonas viridis* reaction centers with a modified binding site for the accessory bacteriochlorophyll. *Biochemistry* **35** (1996) 9235–9244.
23. I.-P. Chen, P. Mathis, J. Koepke, H. Michel, Uphill electron transfer in the tetraheme cytochrome subunit of the *Rhodopseudomonas viridis* photosynthetic reaction center: Evidence from site-directed mutagenesis. *Biochemistry* **39** (2000) 3592–3602.
24. G. Fritzsch, Obtaining crystal structures from bacterial photosynthetic reaction centers. *Methods Enzymol.* **297** (1998) 57–77.

25. H. Michel, Three-dimensional crystals of a membrane protein complex. The photosynthetic reaction centre from *Rhodopseudomonas viridis*. *J. Mol. Biol.* **158** (1982) 567–572.
26. J.P. Allen, G. Feher, Crystallization of reaction centers from *Rhodobacter sphaeroides*, in: *Crystallization of Membrane Proteins* (1991) (H. Michel, ed.), CRC Press, Boca Raton, FL, pp. 137–153.
27. J.O. Goldsmith, S.G. Boxer, Rapid isolation of bacterial photosynthetic reaction centers with an engineered poly-histidine tag. *Biochim. Biophys. Acta* **1276** (1996) 171–175.
28. P.R. Pokkuluri, P.D. Laible, Y.-L. Deng, T.N. Wong, D.K. Hanson, M. Schiffer, The structure of a mutant photosynthetic reaction center shows unexpected changes in main chain orientations and quinone position. *Biochemistry* **41** (2002) 5998–6007.
29. H. Michel, K.A. Weyer, H. Gruenberg, I. Dunger, D. Oesterhelt, F. Lottspeich, The light and medium subunits of the photosynthetic reaction center from *Rhodopseudomonas viridis*–Isolation of the genes, nucleotide and amino acid sequence. *EMBO J.* **5** (1986) 1149–1158.
30. H. Michel, K.A. Weyer, H. Gruenberg, F. Lottspeich, The 'heavy' subunit of the photosynthetic reaction centre from *Rhodopsedomonas viridis*: isolation of the gene, nucleotide and amino acid sequence. *EMBO J.* **4** (1985) 1667–1672.
31. K.A. Weyer, F. Lottspeich, H. Gruenberg, F.S. Lang, D. Oesterhelt, H. Michel, Amino acid sequence of the cytochrome subumit of the photosynthetic reaction center from the purple bacterium *Rhodopseudomonas viridis*. *EMBO J.* **6** (1987) 2197–2202.
32. K.A. Weyer, W. Schäfer, F. Lottspeich, H. Michel, The cytochrome subunit of the photosynthetic reaction center from *Rhodopseudomonas viridis* is a lipoprotein. *Biochemistry* **26** (1987) 2909–2914.
33. G. Feher, Some chemical and physical properties of a bacterial reaction center particle and its primary photochemical reactants. *Photochem. Photobiol.* **14** (1971) 373–387.
34. W.W. Parson, Photosynthetic reaction centers, in: *Protein Electron Transfer* (1996) (D.S. Bendall, ed.), BIOS Scientific Publishers, Oxford, pp. 125–160.
35. C.C. Moser, J.M. Keske, K. Warncke, R.S. Farid, P.L. Dutton, Nature of biological electron transfer. *Nature* **355** (1992) 796–802.
36. C.C. Page, C.C. Moser, X. Chen, P.L. Dutton, Natural engineering principles of electron tunnelling in biological oxidation-reduction. *Nature* **402** (1999) 47–52.
37. J. Deisenhofer, O. Epp, K. Miki, R. Huber, H. Michel, X-ray structure analysis of a membrane protein complex. Electron density map at 3 Å resolution and a model of the chromophores of the photosynthetic reaction center from *Rhodopseudomonas viridis*. *J. Mol. Biol.* **180** (1984) 385–398.
38. J. Deisenhofer, O. Epp, K. Miki, R. Huber, H. Michel, Structure of the protein subunits in the photosynthetic reaction center of *Rhodopseudomonas viridis* at 3 Å resolution. *Nature* **318** (1985) 618–624.
39. J. Deisenhofer, H. Michel, The photosynthetic reaction centre from the purple bacterium *Rhodopseudomonas viridis*. *EMBO J.* **8** (1989) 2149–2170.
40. J. Deisenhofer, O. Epp, I. Sinning, H. Michel, Crystallographic refinement at 2.3 Å resolution and refined model of the photosynthetic reaction centre from *Rhodopseudomonas viridis*. *J. Mol. Biol.* **246** (1995) 429–457.
41. C.R.D. Lancaster, M.V. Bibikova, P. Sabatino, D. Oesterhelt, H. Michel, Structural basis of the drastically increased initial electron transfer rate in the reaction

center from a *Rhodopseudomonas viridis* mutant described at 2.00-Å resolution. *J. Biol. Chem.* **275** (2000) 39364–39368.
42. J.P. Allen, G. Feher, Crystallization of reaction center from *Rhodopseudomonas sphaeroides* – preliminary characterization. *Proc. Natl. Acad. Sci U.S.A.* **81** (1984) 4795–4799.
43. C.-H. Chang, M. Schiffer, D. Tiede, U. Smith, J. Norris, Characterization of bacterial photosynthetic reaction center crystals from *Rhodopseudomonas sphaeroides* R-26 by X-ray diffraction. *J. Mol. Biol.* **186** (1985) 201–203.
44. A. Ducruix, F. Reiss-Husson, Preliminary characterization by X-ray diffraction of crystals of photochemical reaction centers from wild-type *Rhodopseudomonas sphaeroides*. *J. Mol. Biol.* **193** (1987) 419–421.
45. H.A. Frank, S.S. Taremi, J.R. Knox, Crystallization and preliminary X-ray and optical spectroscopic characterization of the photochemical reaction center from *Rhodobacter sphaeroides* strain 2.4.1. *J. Mol. Biol.* **198** (1987) 139–141.
46. S.K. Buchanan, G. Fritzsch, U. Ermler, H. Michel, New crystal form of the photosynthetic reaction centre from *Rhodobacter sphaeroides* of improved diffraction quality. *J. Mol. Biol.* **230** (1993) 1311–1314.
47. J.P. Allen, Crystallization of the reaction center from Rhodobacter sphaeroides in a new tetragonal form. *Proteins* **20** (1994) 283–266.
48. C.R.D. Lancaster, H. Michel, New insights into the X-ray structure of the reaction center from *Rhodopseudomonas viridis*, in: *The Reaction Center of Photosynthetic Bacteria. Structure and Dynamics* (1996) (M.-E. Michel-Beyerle, ed.), Springer-Verlag, Berlin, pp. 23–35.
49. Q. Xu, H.L. Axelrod, E.C. Abresch, M.L. Paddock, M.Y. Okamura, G. Feher, X-Ray structure determination of three mutants of the bacterial photosynthetic reaction centers from *Rb. sphaeroides:* Altered proton transfer pathways. *Structure* **12** (2004) 703–715.
50. M.H.B. Stowell, T.M. McPhillips, D.C. Rees, S.M. Soltis, E. Abresch, G. Feher, Light-induced structural changes in photosynthetic reaction center: implications for mechanism of electron-proton transfer. *Science* **276** (1997) 812–816.
51. E.M. Landau, J.P. Rosenbusch, Lipidic cubic phases: a novel concept for the crystallization of membrane proteins. *Proc. Natl Acad. Sci. U.S.A.* **93** (1996) 14532–14535.
52. G. Katona, U. Andreasson, E.M. Landau, L.E. Andreasson, R. Neutze, Lipidic cubic phase crystal structure of the photosynthetic reaction centre from *Rhodobacter sphaeroides* at 2.35 Å resolution. *J. Mol. Biol.* **331** (2003) 681–692.
53. N. Katayama, M. Kobayashi, F. Motojima, K. Inaka, T. Nozawa, K. Miki, Preliminary X-ray crystallographic studies of photosynthetic reaction center from a thermophilic sulfur bacterium, *Chromatium tepidum*. *FEBS Lett.* **348** (1994) 158–160.
54. T. Nogi, I. Fathir, M. Kobayashi, T. Nozawa, K. Miki, Crystal structures of photosynthetic reaction center and high-potential iron-sulfur protein from *Thermochromatium tepidum:* Thermostability and electron transfer. *Proc. Natl. Acad. Sci. U.S.A.* **97** (2000) 13561–13566.
55. U. Ermler, G. Fritzsch, S.K. Buchanan, H. Michel, Structure of the photosynthetic reaction centre from *Rhodobacter sphaeroides* at 2.65 Å resolution: cofactors and protein-cofactor interactions. *Structure* **2** (1994) 925–936.
56. C.R.D. Lancaster, U. Ermler, H. Michel, The structures of photosynthetic reaction centers from purple bacteria as revealed by X-ray crystallography, in: *Anoxygenic Photosynthetic Bacteria* (1995) (R.E. Blankenship, M.T. Madigan, C.E. Bauer, eds.), Kluwer Academic Publishers, Dordrecht, pp. 503–526.

57. M. Lutz, W. Szponarski, G. Berger, B. Robert, J.-M. Neumann, The stereoisomerism of bacterial, reaction-center-bound carotenoids revisited: an electronic absorption resonance Raman and ^{1}H-NMR study. *Biochim. Biophys. Acta* **894** (1987) 423–433.
58. C.R.D. Lancaster, H. Michel, Refined crystal structures of reaction centres from *Rhodopseudomonas viridis* in complexes with the herbicide atrazine and two chiral atrazine derivatives also lead to a new model of the bound carotenoid. *J. Mol. Biol.* **286** (1999) 883–898.
59. V. Anantharaman, L. Aravind, The PRC-barrel: a widespread, conserved domain shared by photosynthetic reaction center subunits and proteins of RNA metabolism. *Genome Biol.* **3** (2002) research006.1–006.9.
60. H. Michel, O. Epp, J. Deisenhofer, Pigment protein interactions in the photosynthetic reaction center from *Rhodopseudomonas viridis*. *EMBO J.* **5** (1986) 2445–2451.
61. E.J. Bylina, C. Kirmaier, L. McDowell, D. Holten, D.C. Youvan, Influence of an amino acid residue on the optical properties and electron transfer dynamics of a photosynthetic reaction center complex. *Nature* **336** (1988) 182–184.
62. G. Feher, M.Y. Okamura, The primary and secondary acceptors in bacterial photosynthesis: II. The structure of the Fe^{2+}-Q^- complex. *Appl. Magn. Reson.* **16** (1999) 63–100.
63. C.R.D. Lancaster, H. Michel, B. Honig, M.R. Gunner, Calculated coupling of electron and proton transfer in the photosynthetic reaction center of *Rhodopseudomonas viridis*. *Biophys. J.* **70** (1996) 2469–2492.
64. R.J. Debus, G. Feher, M.Y. Okamura, Iron-depleted reaction centers from *Rhodopseudomonas sphaeroides* R-26.1–Characterization and reconstitution with Fe^{2+}, Mn^{2+}, Co^{2+}, Ni^{2+}, Cu^{2+}, and Zn^{2+}. *Biochemistry* **25** (1986) 2276–2287.
65. A.T. Gardiner, S.G. Zech, F. MacMillan, H. Kass, R. Bittl, E. Schlodder, F. Lendzian, W. Lubitz, Electron paramagnetic resonance studies of zinc-substituted reaction centers from *Rhodopseudomonas viridis*. *Biochemistry* **38** (1999) 11773–11787.
66. C.R.D. Lancaster, H. Michel, The coupling of light-induced electron transfer and proton uptake as derived from crystal structures of reaction centres from *Rhodopseudomonas viridis* modified at the binding site of the secondary quinone, Q_B. *Structure* **5** (1997) 1339–1359.
67. C.R.D. Lancaster, Quinone binding sites in membrane proteins - what can we learn from the *Rhodopseudomonas viridis* reaction centre? *Biochem. Soc. Trans.* **27** (1999) 591–596.
68. C.R.D. Lancaster, Ubiquinone reduction and protonation in photosynthetic reaction centres from *Rhodopseudomonas viridis* - X-ray structures and their functional implications. *Biochim. Biophys. Acta* **1365** (1998) 143–150.
69. M.P. Percival, N.R. Baker, Herbicides and photosynthesis, in: *Herbicides* (1991) (N.R. Baker, M.P. Percival, eds.), Elsevier Science Publishers B. V, Amsterdam, pp. 1–26.
70. J.R. Bowyer, P. Camilleri, W.F.J. Vermaas, Photosystem II and its interaction with herbicides, in: *Herbicides* (1991) (N.R. Baker, M.P. Percival, eds.), Elsevier Science Publishers B. V, Amsterdam, pp. 27–85.
71. H. Gysin, E. Knüsli, Triazinderivate als herbizide, in: *Proceedings 4th International Congress Crop Protection, Hamburg 1957* (1959), Selbstverlag des IV Internationalen Pflanzenschutzkongresses, Braunschweig, Vol. 1, pp. 549–553.
72. C.J.T. von Grotthuss, Mémoire sur la decomposition de l'eau et des corps qu'elle tient en dissolution à l'aide de l'electricité galvanique. *Ann. Chim. Phys. (Paris)* **58** (1806) 54–74.

73. J.F. Nagle, S. Tristam-Nagle, Hydrogen-bonded chain mechanisms for proton conduction and proton pumping. *J. Membr. Biol.* **74** (1983) 1–14.
74. N. Agmon, The Grotthuss mechanism. *Chem. Phys. Lett.* **244** (1995) 456–462.
75. D.K. Hanson, D.M. Tiede, S.L. Nance, C.-H. Chang, M. Schiffer, Site-specific and compensatory mutations imply unexpected pathways for proton delivery to the Q_B binding site of the photosynthetic reaction center. *Proc. Natl. Acad. Sci. U.S.A.* **90** (1993) 8929–8933.
76. M.R. Gunner, B. Honig, Calculations of proton uptake in *Rb. sphaeroides* reaction centers, in: *The Photosynthetic Bacterial Reaction Center II* (1992) (J. Breton, A. Verméglio, eds.), Plenum Press, New York, pp. 403–410.
77. P. Beroza, D.R. Fredkin, M.Y. Okamura, G. Feher, Electrostatic calculations of amino acid titration and electron transfer, $Q_A^{-\cdot} Q_B$ to $Q_A Q_B^{-\cdot}$, in the reaction center. *Biophys. J.* **68** (1995) 2233–2250.
78. E.G. Alexov, M.R. Gunner, Calculating protein and proton motions coupled to electron transfer: The electron transfer from Q_A^- to Q_B in photosynthetic reaction centers from *Rb. sphaeroides*. *Biochemistry* **38** (1999) 8253–8270.
79. B. Rabenstein, G.M. Ullmann, E.W. Knapp, Calculation of protonation patterns in proteins with structural relaxation and molecular ensembles – application to the photosynthetic reaction center. *Eur. Biophys. J. Biophys. Lett.* **27** (1998) 626–637.
80. D. Kleinfeld, M.Y. Okamura, G. Feher, Electron-transfer kinetics in photosynthetic reaction centers cooled to cryogenic temperatures in the charge-separated state: Evidence for light-induced structural changes. *Biochemistry* **23** (1984) 5780–5786.
81. O.A. Gopta, D.A. Bloch, D.A. Cherepanov, A.Y. Mulkidjanian, Temperature dependence of the electrogenic reaction in the Q_B site of the *Rhodobacter sphaeroides* photosynthetic reaction center: the $Q_A^- Q_B \rightarrow Q_A Q_B^-$ transition. *FEBS Lett.* **412** (1997) 490–494.
82. J. Li, D. Gilroy, D.M. Tiede, M.R. Gunner, Kinetic phases in the electron transfer from $P^+ Q_A^- Q_B$ to $P^+ Q_A Q_B^-$ and the associated processes in *Rhodobacter sphaeroides* R-26 reaction centers. *Biochemistry* **37** (1998) 2818–2829.
83. L.M. Utschig, Y. Ohigashi, M.C. Thurnauer, D.M. Tiede, A new metal-binding site in photosynthetic bacterial reaction centers that modulates Q_A to Q_B electron transfer. *Biochemistry* **37** (1998) 8278–8281.
84. A.Y. Mulkidjanian, M.A. Kozlova, D.A. Cherepanov, Ubiquinone reduction in the photosynthetic reaction centre of *Rhodobacter sphaeroides:* interplay between electron transfer, proton binding and flips of the quinone ring. *Biochem. Soc. Trans.* **33** (2005) 845–850.
85. M.L. Paddock, M.S. Graige, G. Feher, M.Y. Okamura, Identification of the proton pathway in bacterial reaction centers: inhibition of proton transfer by binding of Zn^{2+} or Cd^{2+}. *Proc. Natl. Acad. Sci. U.S.A.* **96** (1999) 6183–6188.
86. M.L. Paddock, G. Feher, M.Y. Okamura, Identification of the proton pathway in bacterial reaction centers: replacement of Asp-M17 and Asp-L210 with Asn reduces the proton transfer rate in the presence of Cd^{2+}. *Proc. Natl. Acad. Sci. U.S.A.* **97** (2000) 1548–1553.
87. P. Ädelroth, M.L. Paddock, L.B. Sagle, G. Feher, M.Y. Okamura, Identification of the proton pathway in bacterial reaction centers: both protons associated with reduction of Q_B to $Q_B H_2$ share a common entry point. *Proc. Natl. Acad. Sci. U.S.A.* **97** (2000) 13086–13091.
88. L. Gerencsér, P. Maróti, Retardation of proton transfer caused by binding of transition metal ion to bacterial reaction center is due to pKa-shifts of key protonatable residues. *Biochemistry* **40** (2001) 1850–1860.

89. M.S. Graige, G. Feher, M.Y. Okamura, Conformational gating of the electron transfer reaction $Q_A^{-\cdot}Q_B \to Q_A Q_B^-$ in bacterial reaction centers of *Rhodobacter sphaeroides* determined by a driving force assay. *Proc. Natl. Acad. Sci. U.S.A.* **95** (1998) 11679–11684.

90. P. Ädelroth, M.L. Paddock, A. Tehrani, J.T. Beatty, G. Feher, M.Y. Okamura, Identification of the proton pathway in bacterial reaction centers: Decrease of proton transfer rate by mutation of surface histidines at H126 and H128 and chemical rescue by imidazole identifies the initial proton donors. *Biochemistry* **40** (2001) 14538–14546.

91. M.L. Paddock, L. Sagle, A. Tehrani, J.T. Beatty, G. Feher, M.Y. Okamura, Mechanism of proton transfer inhibition by Cd^{2+} binding to bacterial reaction centers: determination of the pKa of functionally important histidine residues. *Biochemistry* **42** (2003) 9626–9632.

92. H.L. Axelrod, E.C. Abresch, M.L. Paddock, M.Y. Okamura, G. Feher, Determination of the binding sites of the proton transfer inhibitors Cd^{2+} and Zn^{2+} in bacterial reaction centers. *Proc. Natl. Acad. Sci. U.S.A.* **97** (2000) 1542–1547.

93. A. Osyczka, K.V. Nagashima, K. Shimada, K. Matsuura, Interaction site for high-potential iron-sulfur protein on the tetraheme cytochrome subunit bound to the photosynthetic reaction center of *Rubrivivax gelatinosus*. *Biochemistry* **38** (1999) 2861–2865.

94. A. Osyczka, K.V. Nagashima, S. Sogabe, K. Miki, K. Shimada, K. Matsuura, Comparison of the binding sites for high-potential iron-sulfur protein and cytochrome c on the tetraheme cytochrome subunit bound to the bacterial photosynthetic reaction center. *Biochemistry* **38** (1999) 15779–15790.

95. G. von Heijne, The distribution of positively charged residues in bacterial inner membrane proteins correlates with the trans-membrane topology. *EMBO J.* **5** (1986) 3021–3027.

96. J. Nilsson, B. Persson, G. von Heijne, Comparative analysis of amino acid distributions in integral membrane proteins from 107 genomes. *Proteins* **60** (2005) 606–616.

97. M. Schiffer, C.H. Chang, F.J. Stevens, The functions of tryptophan residues in membrane proteins. *Protein Eng.* **5** (1992) 213–214.

98. P. Braun, G. von Heijne, The aromatic residues Trp and Phe have different effects on the positioning of a transmembrane helix in the microsomal membrane. *Biochemistry* **38** (1999) 9778–9782.

99. E. Arnold, M.G. Rossmann, Analysis of the structure of a common cold virus, human rhinovirus 14, refined at a resolution of 3.0 Å. *J. Mol. Biol.* **211** (1990) 763–801.

100. G.A. Jeffrey, W. Saenger, *Hydrogen Bonding in Biological Structures* (1991) Springer-Verlag, Berlin.

101. E. Meyer, Internal water molecules and H-bonding in biological macromolecules: a review of structural features with functional implications. *Protein Sci.* **1** (1992) 1543–1562.

102. J.A. Potter, P.K. Fyfe, D. Frolov, M.C. Wakeham, R. van Grondelle, B. Robert, M.R. Jones, Strong effects of an individual water molecule on the rate of light-driven charge separation in the *Rhodobacter sphaeroides* reaction center. *J. Biol. Chem.* **280** (2005) 27155–27164.

103. A.G. Yakovlev, A.Y. Shkuropatov, V.A. Shuvalov, Nuclear wavepacket motion between P* and $P^+B_A^-$ potential surfaces with subsequent electron transfer to H_A in bacterial reaction centers. 1. Room temperature. *Biochemistry* **41** (2002) 2667–2674.

104. M.Y. Okamura, M.L. Paddock, M.S. Graige, G. Feher, Proton and electron transfer in bacterial reaction centers. *Biochim. Biophys. Acta* **1458** (2000) 148–163.
105. C.A. Wraight, Proton and electron transfer in the acceptor quinone complex of photosynthetic reaction centers from *Rhodobacter sphaeroides*. *Front. Biosci.* **9** (2004) 309–337.
106. A. Camara-Artigas, C. Magee, A. Goetsch, J.P. Allen, The structure of the heterodimer reaction center from *Rhodobacter sphaeroides* at 2.55Å resolution. *Photosynth. Res.* **74** (2002) 87–93.
107. U. Finkele, C. Lauterwasser, W. Zinth, K.A. Gray, D. Oesterhelt, The role of tyrosine M210 in the initial charge separation of reaction centers of *Rhodobacter sphaeroides*. *Biochemistry* **29** (1990) 8517–8521.
108. V. Nagarajan, W.W. Parson, D. Gaul, C.C. Schenk, Effect of specific mutations of tyrosine-(M)210 on the primary photosynthetic electron-transfer process in *Rhodobacter sphaeroides*. *Proc. Natl. Acad. Sci. U.S.A.* **87** (1990) 7888–7892.
109. A.J. Chirino, E.J. Lous, M. Huber, J.P. Allen, C.C. Schenk, M.L. Paddock, G. Feher, D. Rees, Crystallographic analyses of site-directed mutants of the photosynthetic reaction center from *Rhodobacter sphaeroides*. *Biochemistry* **33** (1994) 4584–4593.
110. K.E. McAuley-Hecht, P.K. Fyfe, J.P. Ridge, S.M. Prince, C.N. Hunter, N.W. Isaacs, R.J. Cogdell, M.R. Jones, Structural studies of wild-type and mutant reaction centers from an antenna-deficient strain of *Rhodobacter sphaeroides:* Monitoring the optical properties of the complex from bacterial cell to crystal. *Biochemistry* **37** (1998) 4740–4750.
111. P.K. Fyfe, K.E. McAuley-Hecht, J.P. Ridge, S.M. Prince, N.W. Isaacs, R.J. Cogdell, M.R. Jones, Crystallographic studies of mutant reaction centres from *Rhodobacter sphaeroides*. *Photosynth. Res.* **55** (1998) 133–140.
112. A. Kuglstatter, P. Hellwig, G. Fritzsch, J. Wachtveitl, D. Oesterhelt, W. Mäntele, H. Michel, Identification of a hydrogen bond in the Phe M197 → Tyr mutant reaction center of the photosynthetic purple bacterium *Rhodobacter sphaeroides* by X-ray crystallography and FTIR spectroscopy. *FEBS Lett.* **463** (1999) 169–174.
113. B.A. Heller, D. Holten, C. Kirmaier, Control of electron transfer on the L- and M-sides of photosynthetic reaction centers. *Science* **269** (1995) 940–945.
114. K.E. McAuley, P.K. Fyfe, J.P. Ridge, R.J. Cogdell, N.W. Isaacs, M.R. Jones, Ubiquinone binding, ubiquinone exclusion, and detailed cofactor conformation in a mutant bacterial reaction center. *Biochemistry* **39** (2000) 15032–15043.
115. M.L. Paddock, C. Chang, Q. Xu, E.C. Abresch, H.L. Axelrod, G. Feher, M.Y. Okamura, Quinone (Q_B) reduction by B-branch electron transfer in mutant bacterial reaction centers from *Rhodobacter sphaeroides:* Quantum efficiency and X-ray structure. *Biochemistry* **44** (2005) 6920–6928.
116. N.W. Woodbury, J.P. Allen, The pathway, kinetics and thermodynamics of electron transfer in wild type and mutant reaction centers of purple nonsulfur bacteria, in: *Anoxygenic Photosynthetic Bacteria* (1995) (R.E. Blankenship, M.T. Madigan, C.E. Bauer, eds.), Kluwer Academic, Dordrecht, pp. 527–557.
117. M.R. Gunner, The reaction center protein from purple bacteria: structure and function. *Curr. Top. Bioenerg.* **16** (1991) 319–367.
118. H. Scheer, A. Struck, in: *The Photosynthetic Reaction Center* (1993) (J. Deisenhofer, J.R. Norris, eds.), Academic Press, San Diego, Vol. I, pp. 157–192.
119. A. Kuglstatter, U. Ermler, H. Michel, L. Baciou, G. Fritzsch, X-Ray structure analyses of photosynthetic reaction center variants from *Rhodobacter sphaeroides*:

Structural changes induced by point-mutations at position L209 modulate electron and proton transfer. *Biochemistry* **40** (2001) 4253–4260.
120. D.K. Hanson, L. Baciou, D.M. Tiede, S.L. Nance, M. Schiffer, P. Sebban, In bacterial reaction centers protons can diffuse to the secondary quinone by alternative pathways. *Biochim. Biophys. Acta* **1102** (1992) 260–265.
121. J. Tandori, L. Baciou, E. Alexov, P. Maroti, M. Schiffer, D.K. Hanson, P. Sebban, Revealing the involvement of extended hydrogen-bond networks in the cooperative function between distant sites in bacterial reaction centers. *J. Biol. Chem.* **276** (2001) 45513–45515.
122. P. Maroti, D.K. Hanson, M. Schiffer, P. Sebban, Long-range electrostatic interaction in the bacterial photosynthetic reaction center. *Nat. Struct. Biol.* **2** (1995) 1057–1059.
123. S.H. Rongey, M.L. Paddock, G. Feher, M.Y. Okamura, Pathway of proton transfer in bacterial reaction centers: second site mutation Asn-M44 → Asp restores electron and proton transfer in reaction centers from the photosynthetically deficient Asp-L213→Asn mutant of *Rhodobacter sphaeroides*. *Proc. Natl. Acad. Sci. U.S.A.* **90** (1993) 1325–1329.
124. M.L. Paddock, M.E. Senft, M.S. Graige, S.H. Rongey, T. Turanchik, G. Feher, M.Y. Okamura, Characterization of second site mutations show that fast proton transfer to Q_B^- is restored in bacterial reaction centers of *Rhodobacter sphaeroides* containing the Asp-L213→Asn lesion. *Photosynth. Res.* **55** (1998) 281–291.
125. P.K. Fyfe, N.W. Isaacs, R.J. Cogdell, M.R. Jones, Disruption of a specific molecular interaction with a bound lipid affects the thermal stability of the purple bacterial reaction center. *Biochim. Biophys. Acta* **1608** (2004) 11–22.
126. A. Camara-Artigas, C.L. Magee, J.C. Williams, J.P. Allen, Individual interactions influence the crystalline order for membrane proteins. *Acta Crystallogr. D Biol. Crystallogr.* **57** (2001) 1281–1286.
127. E. Laussermair, D. Oesterhelt, A system for site-specific mutagenesis of the photosynthetic reaction center in *Rhodopseudomonas viridis*. *EMBO J.* **11** (1992) 777–783.
128. G. Ewald, C. Wiessner, H. Michel, Sequence analysis of four atrazine-resistant mutants from *Rhodopseudomonas viridis*. *Z. Naturforsch., Teil C* **45** (1990) 459–462.
129. I. Sinning, J. Koepke, H. Michel, Recent advances in the structure analysis of *Rhodopseudomonas viridis* reaction center mutants, in: *Reaction Centers of Photosynthetic Bacteria* (1990) (M.-E. Michel-Beyerle, ed.), Springer-Verlag, Berlin, pp. 199–208.
130. I. Sinning, Herbicide binding in the bacterial photosynthetic reaction center. *Trends Biochem. Sci.* **17** (1992) 150–154.
131. T. Arlt, M. Bibikova, H. Penzkofer, D. Oesterhelt, W. Zinth, Strong acceleration of primary photosynthetic electron transfer in a mutated reaction center of *Rhodopseudomonas viridis*. *J. Phys. Chem.* **100** (1996) 12060–12065.
132. D. Spiedel, A.W. Roszak, K. McKendrick, K.E. McAuley, P.K. Fyfe, E. Nabedryk, J. Breton, B. Robert, R.J. Cogdell, N.W. Isaacs, M.R. Jones, Tuning of the optical and electrochemical properties of the primary donor bacteriochlorophylls in the reaction centre from *Rhodobacter sphaeroides*: spectroscopy and structure. *Biochim. Biophys. Acta* **1554** (2002) 75–93.
133. S.K. Buchanan, *Light-Induced Conformational Changes in the Reaction Center from Rhodopseudomonas viridis Measured by X-Ray Diffraction Analysis and*

FTIR Difference Spectroscopy (1990), Doctoral Thesis, J. W. Goethe University, Frankfurt am Main.

134. G. Fritzsch, J. Koepke, R. Diem, A. Kuglstatter, L. Baciou, Charge separation induces conformational changes in the photosynthetic reaction centre of purple bacteria. *Acta Crystallogr. D Biol. Crystallogr.* **58** (2002) 1660–1663.

135. R.H. Baxter, B.L. Seagle, N. Ponomarenko, J.R. Norris, Cryogenic structure of the photosynthetic reaction center of *Blastochloris viridis* in the light and dark. *Acta Crystallogr. D Biol. Crystallogr.* **61** (2005) 605–612.

136. G. Katona, A. Snijder, P. Gourdon, U. Andreasson, O. Hansson, L.E. Andreasson, R. Neutze, Conformational regulation of charge recombination reactions in a photosynthetic bacterial reaction center. *Nat. Struct. Mol. Biol.* **12** (2005) 630–631.

137. H. Michel, J. Deisenhofer, X-ray diffraction studies on a crystalline bacterial photosynthetic reaction center: a progress report and conclusions on the structure of Photosystem II reaction centers, in: *Encyclopedia of Plant Physiology New Series Vol. 19, Photosynthesis III* (1986) (L.A. Staehelin, C.J. Arntzen, eds.), Springer, Berlin, pp. 371–381.

138. J.E. Hearst, Primary structure and function of the reaction center polypeptides of Rhodopseudomonas capsulata - the structural and functional analogies with the Photosystem II polypeptides of plants, in: *Encyclopedia of Plant Physiology New Series Vol. 19, Photosynthesis III* (1986) (L.A. Staehelin, C.J. Arntzen, eds.), Springer, Berlin, pp. 382–389.

139. A. Trebst, The topology of the plastoquinone and herbicide binding peptides of Photosystem II in the thylakoid membrane. *Z. Naturforsch., Teil C* **41** (1986) 240–245.

140. A. Trebst, The three-dimensional structure of the herbicide binding niche on the reaction center polypeptides of Photosystem II. *Z. Naturforsch., Teil C* **42** (1987) 742–750.

141. H. Michel, J. Deisenhofer, Relevance of the photosynthetic reaction center from purple bacteria to the structure of Photosystem II. *Biochemistry* **27** (1988) 1–7.

142. O. Nanba, K. Satoh, Isolation of a Photosystem II reaction center consisting of D-1 and D-2 polypeptides and cytochrome b_{559}. *Proc. Natl. Acad. Sci. U.S.A.* **84** (1987) 109–112.

143. F. Reifarth, G. Renger, Indirect evidence for structural changes coupled with $Q_B^{-\bullet}$ formation in Photosystem II. *FEBS Lett.* **428** (1998) 123–126.

144. A. Garbers, F. Reifarth, J. Kurreck, G. Renger, F. Parak, Correlation between protein flexibility and electron transfer from $Q_A^{-\bullet}$ to Q_B in PSII membrane fragments from spinach. *Biochemistry* **37** (1998) 11399–11404.

145. L. Kálmán, R. LoBrutto, J.P. Allen, J.C. Williams, Modified reaction centres oxidize tyrosine in reactions that mirror Photosystem II. *Nature* **402** (1999) 696–699.

146. L. Kálmán, M.C. Thielges, J.C. Williams, J.P. Allen, Proton release due to manganese binding and oxidation in modified bacterial reaction centers. *Biochemistry* **44** (2005) 13266–13273.

147. K.N. Ferreira, T.M. Iverson, K. Maghlaoui, J. Barber, S. Iwata, Architecture of the photosynthetic oxygen-evolving center. *Science* **303** (2004) 1831–1838.

148. J. Biesiadka, B. Loll, J. Kern, K.-D. Irrgang, A. Zouni, Crystal structure of cyanobacterial Photosystem II at 3.2 Å resolution: a closer look at the Mn-cluster. *Phys. Chem. Chem. Phys.* **6** (2004) 4733–4736.

149. B. Loll, J. Kern, W. Saenger, A. Zouni, J. Biesiadka, Towards complete cofactor arrangement in the 3.0 Å resolution structure of Photosystem II. *Nature* **438** (2005) 1040–1044.

150. W. Oettmeier, Herbicides and Photosystem II, in: *The Photosystems: Structure, Function, and Molecular Biology* (1992) (J. Barber, ed.), pp. 349–408.
151. D. Bourgeois, A. Royant, Advances in kinetic protein crystallography. *Curr. Opin. Struct. Biol.* **15** (2005) 538–547.
152. M. Thielges, G. Uyeda, A. Camara-Artigas, L. Kalman, J.C. Williams, J.P. Allen, Design of a redox-linked active metal site: Manganese bound to bacterial reaction centers at a site resembling that of Photosystem II. *Biochemistry* **44** (2005) 7389–7394.
153. H.L. Axelrod, E.C. Abresch, M.Y. Okamura, A.P. Yeh, D.C. Rees, G. Feher, X-ray structure determination of the cytochrome c_2: reaction center electron transfer complex from *Rhodobacter sphaeroides*. *J. Mol. Biol.* **319** (2002) 501–515.
154. A.W. Roszak, T.D. Howard, J. Southall, A.T. Gardiner, C.J. Law, N.W. Isaacs, R.J. Cogdell, Crystal structure of the RC-LH1 core complex from *Rhodopseudomonas palustris*. *Science* **302** (2003) 1969–1972.
155. C.R.D. Lancaster, C. Hunte, J. Kelley III, B.L. Trumpower, R. Ditchfield, A comparison of stigmatellin conformations, free and bound to the photosynthetic reaction center and the cytochrome bc_1 complex. *J. Mol. Biol.* **368** (2007) 197–208.
156. R.H. Baxter, N. Ponomarenko, V. Srajer, R. Pahl, K. Moffat, J.R. Norris, Time-resolved crystallographic studies of light-induced structural changes in the photosynthetic reaction center. *Proc. Natl. Acad. Sci. U.S.A* **101** (2004) 5982–5987.
157. A.W. Roszak, K. McKendrick, A.T. Gardiner, I.A. Mitchell, N.W. Isaacs, R.J. Cogdell, H. Hashimoto, H.A. Frank, Protein regulation of carotenoid binding: Gatekeeper and locking amino acid residues in reaction centers of *Rhodobacter sphaeroides*. *Structure* **12** (2004) 765–773.
158. A. Camara-Artigas, D. Brune, J.P. Allen, Interactions between lipids and bacterial reaction centers determined using protein crystallography. *Proc. Natl. Acad. Sci. U.S.A.* **99** (2002) 11055–11060.
159. J.P. Allen, G. Feher, T.O. Yeates, D.C. Rees, J. Deisenhofer, H. Michel, R. Huber, Structural homology of reaction centers from *Rhodopseudomonas sphaeroides* and *Rhodopseudomonas viridis* as determined by X-ray diffraction. *Proc. Natl. Acad. Sci. U.S.A.* **83** (1986) 8589–8593.
160. J.P. Allen, G. Feher, T.O. Yeates, H. Komiya, D.C. Rees, Structure of the reaction center from *Rhodobacter sphaeroides* R-26: the cofactors. *Proc. Natl. Acad. Sci. U.S.A.* **84** (1987) 5730–5734.
161. T.O. Yeates, H. Komiya, A. Chirino, D.C. Rees, J.P. Allen, G. Feher, Structure of the reaction center from *Rhodobacter sphaeroides* R-26 and 2.4.1: Protein-cofactor interactions (bacteriochlorophyll, bacteriopheophytin, and carotenoid) interactions. *Proc. Natl. Acad. Sci. U.S.A.* **85** (1988) 7993–7997.
162. B. Arnoux, J. F. Gaucher, A. Ducruix, F. Reiss-Husson, Structure of the photochemical reaction centre of a spheroidene containing purple bacterium, *Rhodobacter sphaeroides* Y, at 3 Å resolution. *Acta Crystallogr. D Biol. Crystallogr.* **51** (1995) 368–379.
163. C.-H. Chang, O. El-Kabbani, D. Tiede, J. Norris, M. Schiffer, Structure of the membrane-bound protein photosynthetic reaction center from *Rhodobacter sphaeroides*. *Biochemistry* **30** (1991) 5352–5360.
164. A.T. Brünger, Free R value, A novel statistical quantity for assessing the accuracy of crystal structures. *Nature* **355** (1992) 472–475.
165. K.E. McAuley, P.K. Fyfe, J.P. Ridge, N.W. Isaacs, R.J. Cogdell, M.R. Jones, Structural details of an interaction between cardiolipin and an integral membrane protein. *Proc. Natl. Acad. Sci. U.S.A.* **96** (1999) 14706–14711.

166. J.P. Ridge, P.K. Fyfe, K.E. McAuley, M.E. van Brederode, B. Robert, R. van Grondelle, N.W. Isaacs, R.J. Cogdell, M.R. Jones, An examination of how structural changes can affect the rate of electron transfer in a mutated bacterial photoreaction center. *Biochem J.* **351** (2000) 567–578.
167. P.K. Fyfe, J.P. Ridge, K.E. McAuley, R.J. Cogdell, N.W. Isaacs, M.R. Jones, Structural consequences of the replacement of glycine M203 with aspartic acid in the reaction center from *Rhodobacter sphaeroides. Biochemistry* **39** (2000) 5953–5960.
168. P.J. Kraulis, MolScript: a program to produce both detailed and schematic plots of protein structures. *J. Appl. Crystallogr.* **24** (1991) 946–950.
169. E.A. Merritt, D.J. Bacon, Raster3D: Photorealistic molecular graphics. *Methods Enzymol.* **277** (1997) 505–524.
170. C.R.D. Lancaster, Purple bacteria: Photosynthetic reaction centers, in: *Encyclopedia of Biological Chemistry* (2004) (W.J. Lennarz, M.D. Lane, eds.), Elsevier, Oxford, pp. 586–594.
171. G.W. Pettigrew, R. Bartsch, T. Meyer, M.D. Kamen, Redox potentials of the photosynthetic bacterial cytochrome c_2 and the structural bases for variability. *Biochim.Biophys. Acta* **503** (1978) 509–523.
172. S.M. Dracheva, L.A. Drachev, A.A. Konstantinov, A.Y. Semenov, V.P. Skulachev, A.M. Arutjunjan, V.A. Shuvalov, S.M. Zaberezhnaya, Electrogenic steps in the redox reactions catalyzed by photosynthetic reaction-centre complex from *Rhodopseudomonas viridis. Eur. J. Biochem.* **171** (1988) 253–264.
173. R.C. Prince, J.S. Leigh, P.L. Dutton, Thermodynamic properties of the reaction center of *Rhodopseudomonas viridis.* In vivo measurement of the reaction center bacteriochlorophyll - primary acceptor intermediary electron carrier. *Biochim. Biophys. Acta* **440** (1976) 622–636.
174. G. Alegria, P.L. Dutton, I. Langmuir-Blodgett, monolayer films of bacterial photosynthetic membranes and isolated reaction centers: Preparation, spectrophotometric and electrochemical characterization. *Biochim. Biophys. Acta* **1057** (1991) 239–257.
175. A. Osyczka, K.V.P. Nagashima, S. Sogabe, K. Miki, M. Yoshida, K. Shimada, K. Matsuura, Interaction site for soluble cytochromes on the tetraheme cytochrome subunit bound to the bacterial photosynthetic reaction center mapped by site-directed mutagenesis. *Biochemistry* **37** (1998) 11732–11744.
176. J.M. Ortega, F. Drepper, P. Mathis, Electron transfer between cytochrome c_2 and the tetraheme cytochrome c in *Rhodopseudomonas viridis. Photosynth. Res.* **59** (1999) 147–157.
177. M.R. Gunner, B. Honig, Electrostatic control of midpoint potentials in the cytochrome subunit of the *Rhodopseudomonas viridis* reaction center. *Proc. Natl. Acad. Sci. U.S.A.* **88** (1991) 9151–9155.

Chapter 12

Functional Patterns of Reaction Centers in Anoxygenic Photosynthetic Bacteria

William W. Parson

Table of Contents

12.1 Introduction	59
12.1.1 The Four Groups of Anoxygenic Photosynthetic Bacteria	59
12.1.2 Electron Carriers	61
12.1.3 Structural Features of Type I and Type II RCs	63
12.2 Purple Photosynthetic Bacteria (Proteobacteria)	67
12.2.1 Structures of Proteobacterial Reaction Centers	67
12.2.2 Kinetics and Energetics of the Initial Electron-Transfer Steps	69
12.2.3 Secondary Electron-Transfer Reactions	72
12.2.4 Directionality (Asymmetry) of the Initial Steps in Type II RCs	74
12.2.5 Alternative Pathways	75
12.3 Green Non-Sulfur Bacteria (Chloroflexi)	75
12.3.1 Structures of RCs in Green Non-Sulfur Bacteria	75
12.3.2 Electron-Transfer Kinetics and Energetics	76
12.4 Green Sulfur Bacteria (Chlorobi)	77
12.4.1 Structures of Chlorobial RCs	77
12.4.2 Electron-Transfer Kinetics and Energetics	79
12.4.3 Directionality (Asymmetry) of Electron Transfer in Type I RCs	81
12.5 Heliobacteria (Firmicutes)	82
12.5.1 Structures of Heliobacterial Reaction Centers	82
12.5.2 Electron-Transfer Kinetics and Energetics	83
12.6 Concluding Remarks	84
Acknowledgements	85
References	85

FUNCTIONAL PATTERNS OF REACTION CENTERS

Abstract

Photosynthetic organisms that do not evolve oxygen are found in four of the 24 phyla of bacteria: Proteobacteria (purple bacteria), Chloroflexi (green, non-sulfur bacteria), Chlorobi (green, sulfur bacteria) and Firmicutes (Heliobacteria). The reaction centers (RCs) of photosynthetic Chlorobi and Firmicutes (Type I reaction centers) are structurally and functionally similar to the RC of Photosystem I in oxygenic organisms, while those of Proteobacteria and Chloroflexi (Type II reaction centers) resemble Photosystem II. Reaction centers of Type I transfer electrons from a c-type cytochrome or plastocyanin to bound [4Fe-4S] iron-sulfur centers, which then reduce the soluble iron-sulfur protein ferredoxin. Type II RCs transfer electrons from c-type cytochromes to a quinone that picks up protons and dissociates from the RC as the fully reduced quinol. This chapter describes the patterns of electron transfer through the RCs of the four families of bacteria, with an emphasis on the relationships between function and structure. These functional patterns are reasonably clear in proteobacterial RCs, but much remains to be learned about them in some of the other families.

12.1 Introduction

12.1.1 The Four Groups of Anoxygenic Photosynthetic Bacteria

Anoxygenic photosynthetic bacteria make up a diverse collection of organisms that spread over four of the 24 phyla of bacteria [1–5]. In addition to numerous species of purple bacteria from the phylum Proteobacteria, they include green sulfur bacteria (phylum Chlorobi), filamentous green nonsulfur bacteria (phylum Chloroflexi), and Heliobacteria (phylum Firmicutes or "Gram-positive Bacteria"). Table 1 lists some of the most commonly studied species. The

Table 1. Commonly studied species of anoxygenic photosynthetic bacteria

Phylum	Species
Proteobacteria	*Blastochloris viridis*
	Rhodobacter sphaeroides
	Rhodobacter capsulatus
	Rhodospirillum rubrum
	Allochromatium vinosum
	Thermochromatium tepidum
Chloroflexi	*Chloroflexus aurantiacus*
Chlorobi	*Chlorobium limicola*
	Chlorobium tepidum
	Chlorobium vibrioforme
	Prosthecochloris aestuarii
Firmicutes	*Heliobacillus mobilis*
	Heliobacterium chlorum

photosynthetic organisms in the different phyla are not closely related in any major respect other than their ability to carry out photosynthesis [1,6–8]. Purple photosynthetic bacteria and green nonsulfur bacteria, for example, are facultative photoautotrophs that can live under either aerobic or anaerobic conditions, whereas heliobacteria and green sulfur bacteria are obligate photoautotrophs and anaerobes. Green sulfur bacteria and some proteobacteria (the purple sulfur bacteria) use H_2S or elemental sulfur as an electron donor and thrive in the presence of high concentrations of sulfide that are lethal for most other organisms. The initial steps of photosynthesis, however, are basically the same in all these organisms. The underlying principle is simply that when chlorophyll (Chl) or bacteriochlorophyll (BChl) is raised to the excited electronic state it can transfer an electron to or from another nearby molecule, launching a series of secondary electron-transfer reactions that separate electrical charge across a membrane.

Taxonomists regard bacteria, or "Eubacteria" as they formerly were called, as one of three basic kingdoms of living things, the other two being Archaea and Eukaryotes [1,6]. Some archaeal species, such as *Halobacterium salinarium*, can perform a type of photosynthesis based on photoisomerization of a retinylidine Schiff base rather than electron-transfer reactions. This process has little in common with photosynthesis based on electron transfer, and the two approaches probably arose independently after the bacterial and archaeal lineages had diverged. The archaeal process is less efficient, and may serve mainly as a back-up to respiration. In both cases, however, the reactions driven by light create a transmembrane electrochemical potential gradient, and a proton-conducting ATP synthase uses this gradient to drive the synthesis of ATP. The basic chemiosmotic mechanism of ATP synthesis thus probably antedates the divergence of Bacteria and Archaea. Several structural features of redox proteins also appear to have arisen before this division [9].

Unlike plants, algae and cyanobacteria, which have two photosystems that operate in series to move electrons from water to NADP, anoxygenic photosynthetic bacteria have only one photosystem. The photosynthetic reaction centers (RCs) of heliobacteria and green sulfur bacteria resemble Photosystem I (PS I) of plants and cyanobacteria in transferring electrons to the soluble iron-sulfur protein ferredoxin via bound iron-sulfur centers (Figure 1A). They therefore are commonly called "Type I" or "iron-sulfur-type" RCs [10,11]. The RCs of purple bacteria and green nonsulfur bacteria ("Type II" or "quinone-type" RCs) resemble plant and cyanobacterial Photosystem II (PS II) in reducing a quinone that dissociates from the RC and diffuses to a separate cytochrome complex for reoxidation (Figure 1B). Type I RCs generate a stronger reductant, but a weaker oxidant than Type II RCs. The arrangement of the pigments that participate in the initial charge-separation steps, however, is essentially the same in both types of RC. The core polypeptides of the two types of RCs also have many primary and secondary structural features in common, particularly in the transmembrane α-helices that house the electron carriers [12].

FUNCTIONAL PATTERNS OF REACTION CENTERS 61

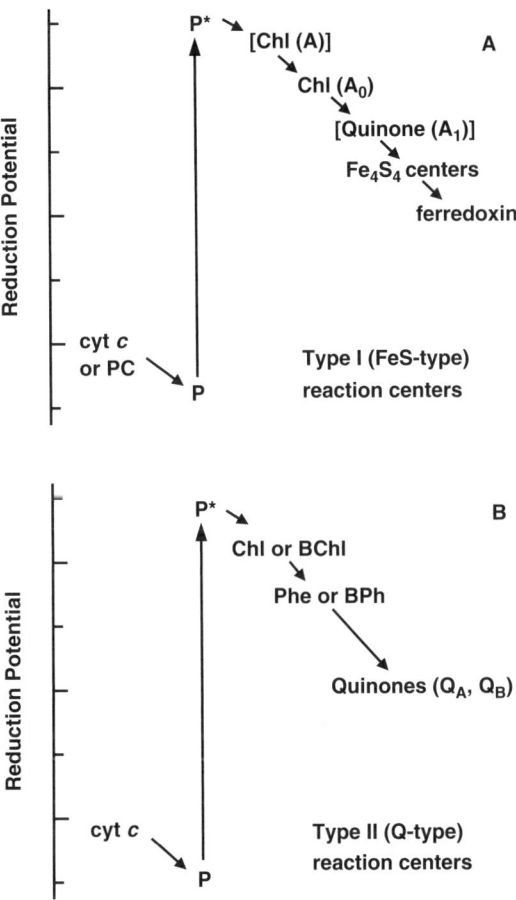

Figure 1. Electron-transfer schemes of Type I (FeS-type) reaction centers (A) and Type II (Q-type) reaction centers (B). BChl=bacteriochlorophyll; BPh=bacteriopheophytin; Chl=chlorophyll; cyt c=c-type cytochrome (with multiple hemes in some cases); P=BChl dimer; PC=plastocyanin; Phe=pheophytin. Chl A and quinone A_1 are shown in brackets in (A) because their participation in some RCs is uncertain (see text).

12.1.2 Electron Carriers

Figure 2 shows the structures of the main types of BChl found in anoxygenic bacterial RCs. Bacteriochlorophylls differ from Chls primarily in being reduced in ring B as well as ring D. Proteobacteria, Chlorobi and Chlorofexi use a dimer of BChl *a* or *b* as the photochemical electron donor, while heliobacteria use a dimer of BChl *g*. Type II RCs also contain small amounts of bacteriopheophytin (BPh), which differs from the corresponding BChl in having two hydrogens in place of the central Mg. Pheophytins (Phes) and BPhs generally have less negative midpoint reduction potential (E_m) values for one-electron reduction

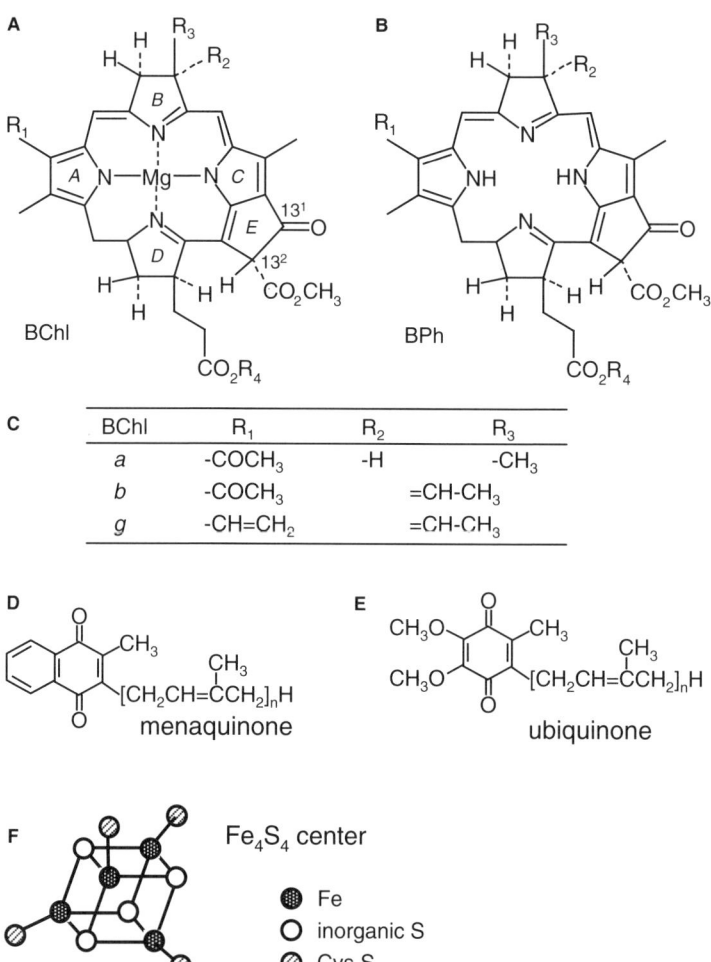

Figure 2. Structures of BChls (A), BPh's (B), quinones (D, E) and iron-sulfur centers (F) found in reaction centers of anoxygenic bacteria. The five rings (*A, B, C, D* and *E*) and the IUPAC-IUB numbering of carbons 13^1 and 13^2 of Bchl are labeled. (In the older Fischer nomenclature, the rings are numbered I–IV, and C-13^1 and C-13^2 are called C-9 and C-10.) The table (C) gives the substituents (R_1, R_2 and R_3) on rings *A* and *B* in BChls *a*, *b* and *g*. The alcohol in the propionyl ester attached to ring *D* (HO-R_4) usually is phytol, farnesol or geranylgeraniol. Type-1 RCs of anoxygenic bacteria typically contain menaquinone (D). Type-2 RCs can contain either ubiquinone (E), menaquinone, or both. The number of isoprenoid (five-carbon) units in the side-chain of the quinone (*n*) varies from 7 to 10. Bacteriochlorophylls with inverted stereochemistry at C-13^2 occur in reaction centers of some bacterial species and are denoted with a prime following the name (e.g., BChl *a'*). Bacteriochlorophyll containing Zn in place of Mg occurs in some bacterial species that live under strongly acidic conditions [368,369]. For further information on Chl and BChl structures see Scheer [370].

FUNCTIONAL PATTERNS OF REACTION CENTERS 63

than the corresponding Chls and BChls, and they play special roles as electron acceptors.

Figure 2 also shows the structures of the quinones and iron-sulfur centers found in RCs of anoxygenic bacteria. Type I RCs from these species usually contain menaquinone (MK), while Type II RCs contain either ubiquinone (UQ), menaquinone or both, depending on the species. Menaquinone has a more negative E_m than UQ, in keeping with the generalization that Type I RCs produce stronger reductants than Type II RCs. However, as we discuss below, the role of quinones in the RCs of heliobacteria and green sulfur bacteria is less clear than it is in Photosystem I. The iron-sulfur centers (Figure 2F) contain four iron atoms bound to the thiol groups of four cysteine residues of the protein and four inorganic sulfur atoms [13].

The pigments that serve as early electron donors and acceptors in RCs of the four phyla of anoxygenic photosynthetic bacteria are listed in Table 2. The table also gives the subunit compositions of the RCs and the E_m values of the primary electron donors.

12.1.3 Structural Features of Type I and Type II RCs

The main structural features of the two types of RC are illustrated beautifully in the crystal structures of Photosystems I and II from the thermophilic cyanobacterium *Synechococcus* (*S.*) *elongatus*, an oxygenic organism that also is known as *Thermosynechococcus* (*Ths.*) *elongatus* [14–16] (see Chapters 13 and 15 for details). A crystal structure of PS II at somewhat lower resolution also has been obtained from a closely related species, *Ths. vulcanus* [17]. Each of the cyanobacterial RCs is constructed around a dimer of two homologous polypeptides. In PS I (Figure 3A), these are referred to as subunits PsaA and PsaB; in PS II (Figure 3B) they are called D1 and D2. D1 and D2 each has five transmembrane α-helices; PsaA and PsaB each has eleven, of which the C-terminal five are structurally homologous to the five helices in D1 or D2. The core polypeptides bind a Chl dimer that serves as an electron donor (P700

Table 2. RC components and thermodynamic properties

Phylum	Protein subunits	Primary donor[a]	Electron acceptors
Proteobacteria	L, M, H; C (cyt) in some species	P870 (BChl *a* or *b*) [0.50 V]	BChl *a* or *b*, BPh *a* or *b*, UQ or both UQ and MK
Chloroflexi	L, M	P870 (BChl *a*) [0.36 V]	BChl *a*, BPh *a*, UQ
Chlorobi	PscA dimer, PscB (Fe-S), PscC (cyt), PscD	P840 (BChl *a'*) [0.25 V]	Chl *a*, MK[b], Fe-S
Firmicutes	PshA dimer, cyt	P798 (BChl *g'*) [0.23 V]	8-OH-Chl *a*, MK[b], Fe-S

[a]Common name (pigment composition) and [E_m].
[b]The role of MK in these RCs is unclear (see text).

in PS I or P680 in PS II), along with four pigments that serve as either actual or potential electron acceptors. In PS I, the set of acceptors consists of four Chls; in PS II, it consists of two Chls and two Phes. The electron carriers are arranged in two branches on either side of a two-fold rotational axis of pseudosymmetry that passes between the two Chls of P700 or P680 and also relates the two central polypeptides. Each of the electron-acceptor branches terminates in a quinone. PS I uses phylloquinone, a naphthoquinone, while PS II uses plastoquinone, a benzoquinone.

Photosystem I RCs also have three [4Fe-4S] iron-sulfur centers, one of which (center F_X) is bound near the phylloquinones on the symmetry axis between the

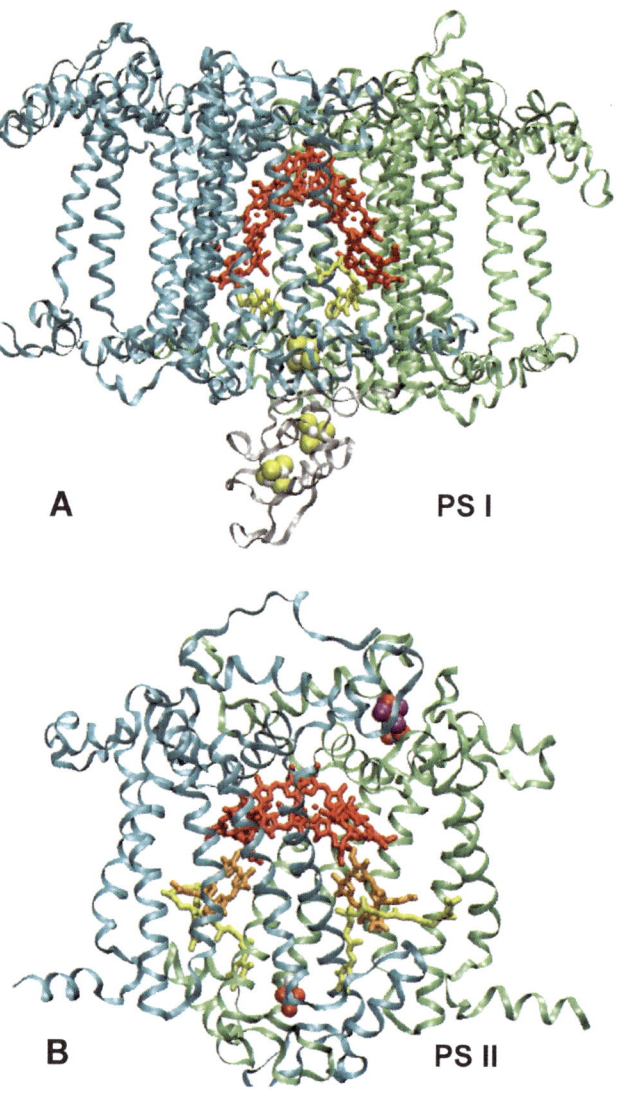

PsaA and PsaB subunits. The other two iron-sulfur centers (F_A and F_B) reside in a separate, small subunit (PsaC) that binds to the RC on the side facing the chloroplast matrix. Another small subunit (PsaD, not shown in Figure 3) is situated close to PsaC, and appears to participate in the binding of ferredoxin [18]. Spectroscopic studies of wild-type and mutant RCs have shown that electrons move from the quinones to iron-sulfur center F_X, and through F_A and F_B to ferredoxin in the sequence $F_x \to F_A \to F_B \to$ ferredoxin [13,19]. Photosystem II RCs lack the iron-sulfur centers, but have a single nonheme iron atom on the symmetry axis between the two quinones. A bicarbonate ion and four histidine residues of the D1 and D2 subunits serve as ligands for this iron [15,20].

Phylloquinone was identified as an electron acceptor in PS I before the structure of the RC was known, and because it was the first such acceptor to be recognized it was called "A_1". This name now is used generically to refer to both phylloquinones, or with extra characters in the subscript to refer specifically to one molecule or the other. The pair of acceptor Chls that sit closer to P700 (Figure 3A) are called "A", and the pair of Chls located closer to the phylloquinones are called "A_0".

The oxygen-evolving center is a complex of four Mn atoms and a Ca^{2+} ion located on the side of the PS II RC that faces the thylakoid lumen, or in cyanobacteria, the intracellular space (see Figure 3B and Chapter 16). The oxidized Chl dimer ($P680^{\cdot+}$) extracts electrons from the Mn complex by way of a tyrosine residue in the D1 subunit (Chapter 17). PS I has a putative binding site for a *c*-type cytochrome or the copper-protein plastocyanin in the corresponding region of the structure (Chapter 13) [18].

In addition to Chls mentioned above, the PsaA-PsaB dimer binds approximately 79 molecules of Chl *a* and 22 carotenoids that serve as antenna pigments by absorbing light and transferring energy to P700 or one of the

---

Figure 3. (A) Crystal structure of the PS-I RC from the oxygenic bacterium *S. elongatus* [14]. The PsaA, PsaB and PsaC subunits are represented as ribbons in green, cyan and silver, respectively; the six Chls that act as electron donors or acceptors are shown in red, and the two phylloquinones in yellow. Iron-sulfur centers F_X, F_A and F_B are shown in space-filling representations with CPK colors (yellow and white). The other subunits, antenna pigments, and phytyl side chains of the Chls are omitted for clarity. (B) Crystal structure of the PS II RC from *S. elongatus* [15]. The D1 and D2 subunits are represented in green and cyan, respectively. The central four Chls, two Phes and two plastoquinones bound to these subunits are shown in red, orange and yellow, respectively. Space-filling representations with CPK colors are used for the nonheme iron with bound CO_2 and the oxygen-evolving center (modeled as a Mn_3CaO_4 cluster with a fourth Mn linked by a μ-oxo bridge). The other subunits, two peripheral Chls, carotenoid, and phytyl side chains of the Chls are omitted. The figure was drawn with the program VMD [371], using the Protein Data Bank [372] structure files 1jb0.pdb [14] and 1fe1.pdb [15]. The structures are viewed parallel to the surface of the photosynthetic membrane and are oriented to put the cytosolic side of the membrane at the bottom. (The corresponding side of the thylakoid membrane in plants faces the chloroplast lumen.)

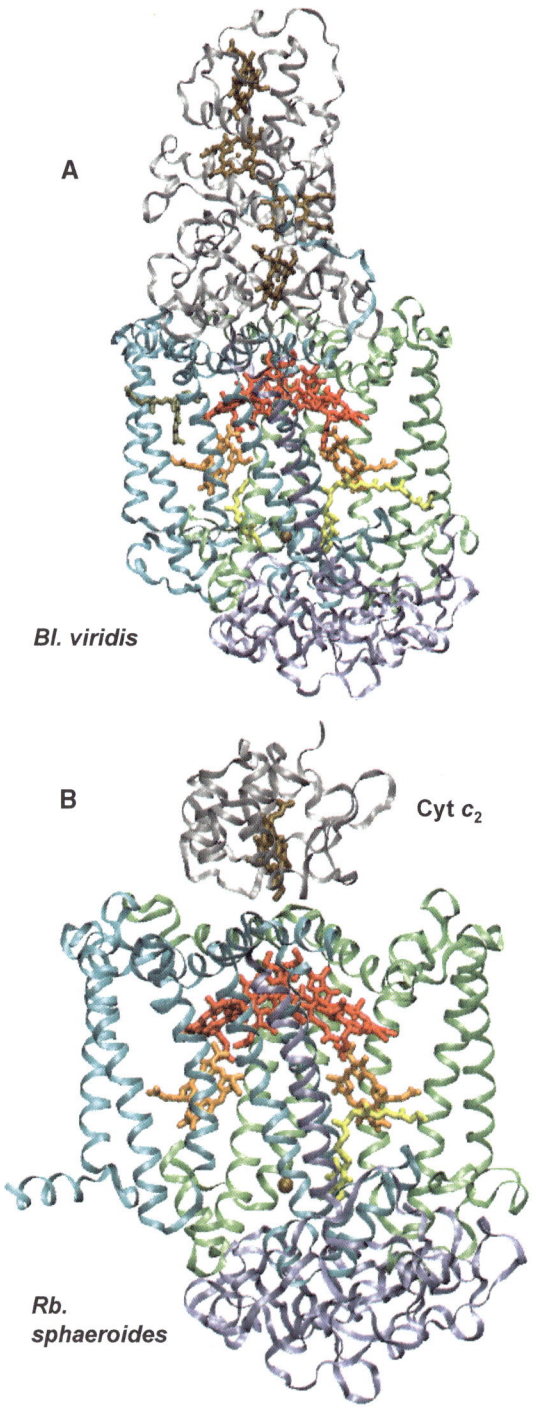

Bl. viridis

B Cyt c_2

Rb. sphaeroides

other electron carriers. The antenna pigments have been removed from Figure 3(A) to show the electron carriers more clearly. The D1 and D2 subunits of PS II are considerably smaller than PsaA and PsaB and do not bind such antennas. They do, however, have two additional molecules of Chl a (Chl$_{ZD1}$ and Chl$_{ZD2}$) and a heme (cytochrome b559) that are not in the main electron-transfer pathway but can be oxidized by P680$^{\cdot+}$ under some circumstances (Chapter 16). These molecules also have been left out of Figure 3(B). Other subunits of PS II bind antenna Chls and carotenoids in an array that is structurally homologous to the antenna array in PS I [15] (Chapter 15).

Although their structural similarities argue strongly that Type I and Type II RCs had a common evolutionary origin, gene duplication, loss and lateral transfer have made the phylogenetic relationships among contemporary organisms difficult to trace (Chapter 10) [2,8,11,21–29]. As understanding of these relationships has improved, species names have undergone multiple revisions, making some of the literature in the field also hard to follow. The widely studied protobacterial species *Rhodobacter* (*Rb.*) *capsulatus*, for example, was formerly called *Rhodopseudomonas* (*Rps.*) *capsulata*. *Rb. sphaeroides* and *Blastochloris* (*Bl.*) *viridis* also previously were classified in the genus *Rhodopseudomonas*, and *Thermochromatium* (*Tch.*) *tepidum* and *Allochromatium* (*Ach.*) *vinosum* were both in the genus *Chromatium* [3,30].

12.2 Purple Photosynthetic Bacteria (Proteobacteria)

12.2.1 Structures of Proteobacterial Reaction Centers

All the known photosynthetic proteobacteria have Type II RCs that contain four molecules of BChl a or b, two molecules of BPh a or b, two quinones (either ubiquinone, menaquinone or one of each), and a nonheme iron atom. High-resolution crystal structures have been obtained for RCs from the purple, nonsulfur bacteria *Bl. viridis* [31–33] and *Rb. sphaeroides* [34–41], and from the purple sulfur bacterium *Tch. tepidum* [42,43] Figure 4(A) shows the *Bl. viridis* structure, and Figure 4(B) shows the *Rb. sphaeroides* structure in complex with cytochrome c_2. Figure 5 shows expanded views of the electron carriers in the *Bl. viridis* structure (for further details see Chapter 12). As in PS II of oxygenic

---

Figure 4. (A) Crystal structure of the *Bl. viridis* RC. The L, M, H and C subunits are represented as ribbons in green, cyan, ice-blue, and silver, respectively; the four BChls and two BPh's are shown in red and orange, respectively; menaquinone (Q_A) and ubiquinone (Q_B) are in yellow; the hemes and nonheme iron atom are in ochre; and the carotenoid (dihydroneurosporene) is in tan. (B) Crystal structure of the RC from *Rb. sphaeroides* in complex with cytochrome c_2. The subunits and prosthetic groups are colored as in (A). The strain of *Rb. sphaeroides* used for this structure lacks carotenoids, and ubiquinone Q_B is missing from the crystal structure. The figure was drawn with VMD [371] using structure files 2prc.pdb [33] and 1lb9.pdb and [373]. The side chains of the BChls and BPh's are omitted for clarity.

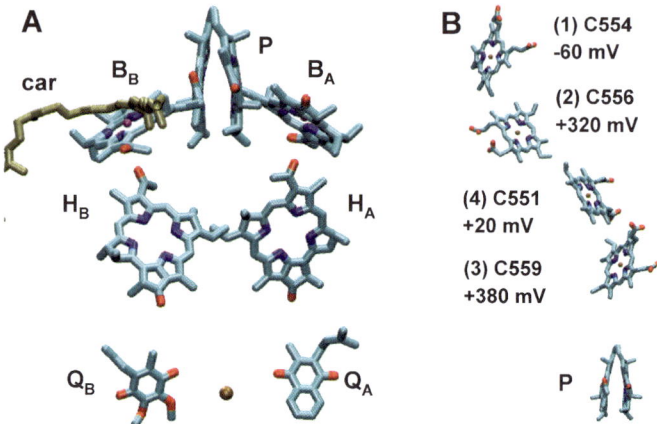

Figure 5. Electron carriers in the *Bl. viridis* RC. (A) The BChls (P, B_A and B_B), BPh's (H_A and H_B), quinones (Q_A and Q_B), nonheme Fe atom (ochre sphere), and carotenoid (car) are seen from a viewpoint approximately 90° around the pseudosymmetry axis of the L and M subunits relative to the viewpoint in Figure 4(A). The side chains of the BChls, BPh's and quinones are truncated. (B) The four hemes and the two BChls of P from the same viewpoint. The hemes are numbered 1–4 according to the positions of their His axial ligands in the protein sequence. They also are named C554, C556, C551 and C559 to indicate the position of the alpha absorption maximum in nm. The midpoint reduction potential (E_m) of each heme is indicated [374–376]. [The figure was drawn with VMD [371] using structure file 2prc.pdb [33].]

organisms, the pigments are bound to two homologous polypeptides (L and M), each of which has five transmembrane α-helices. A third polypeptide (H) is located mainly on the cytosolic side of the cell membrane, but also has one transmembrane α-helix. Two of the BChls sit close together, forming the "special pair" (P) that serves as the primary electron donor. The other BChls (B_A and B_B in one widely-used nomenclature, B_L and B_M in another), the BPhs (H_A and H_B, or H_L and H_M) and the quinones (Q_A and Q_B) sit in two branches on either side of the pseudosymmetry axis, with B_A and B_B situated close to P, and H_A and H_B located between the BChls and the quinones. A rotation by 180° about the symmetry axis interchanges the corresponding pigments on the two branches along with the homologous amino acid residues of L and M. A single carotenoid molecule sits near BChl B_B, breaking the symmetry of the pigments.

The structural similarity of these RCs to the PS II RC of *S. elongatus* is apparent from a comparison of Figures 4 and 5 with Figure 3(B). Though not shown in Figure 3(B), the PS II RC also has a carotenoid in a similar position (Chapter 15). The most obvious difference between the two structures is the absence of the Mn_4 center in anoxygenic organisms. The anoxygenic RC also lacks the two Chls farthest from the symmetry axis of the PS II RC, and has the other pigments packed somewhat closer together. The nonheme Fe atom is bound to four histidine residues as in PS II, but also to a glutamic acid residue rather than CO_2 (Chapter 11).

In addition to the L, M and H subunits, RCs from many photosynthetic proteobacteria have a tightly bound cytochrome subunit with four c-type hemes [44]. These organisms include the purple non-sulfur bacteria *Bl. viridis* [45,46], *Rubrivivax* (formerly *Rhodocyclus*) *gelatinosus* [47], *Rhodocyclus tenuis* [48], *Roseobacter denitrificans* [49,50], and *Rhodoferax fermentans* [51], and the purple sulfur bacteria *Ach. vinosum* and *Tch. tepidum* [52]. The cytochrome provides an electron to return the oxidized special pair ($P^{·+}$) to its resting state after the initial photooxidation. In the crystal structures of *Bl. viridis* and *Tch. tepidum* RCs, the cytochrome subunit is located on the periplasmic side of the membrane, with the hemes stretching out in a line from P (Figures 4A and 5B). The midpoint reduction potentials (E_ms) of the hemes alternate, with the heme closest to P having a relatively high potential, the next heme having a much lower potential, and the third and fourth hemes repeating this pattern (Figure. 5B). *Rhodovulvum sulfidophilum* has a similar cytochrome with three hemes instead of four [53,54]. Some photosynthetic proteobacteria, including *Rb. sphaeroides*, use a small, single-heme cytochrome (cytochrome c_2), which associates more loosely with the same region of the RC (Figure 4B). Cytochrome c_2 has an E_m of about 300 mV when it is bound to the RC [55].

The absorption spectra of proteobacterial RCs containing BChl *a* and BPh *a*, such as those of *Rb. sphaeroides* and *Rb. capsulatus*, have three strong bands in the near-infrared (Figure 6A). P contributes a broad band in the region 860–880 nm, which bleaches when the special pair is oxidized or raised to an excited singlet or triplet state. The large shift of this band to the red relative to the lowest-energy (Q_y) absorption band of monomeric BChl *a* in solution (760–780 nm) can be explained by a combination of exciton interactions and mixing with charge-transfer transitions in which an electron moves from one of the two BChls to the other [56–58]. A narrower band in the region of 800 nm is assigned primarily to the "accessory" BChls (B_A and B_A) with contributions from an exciton state of P on the red side of the band; and a band at 760 nm is attributed mainly to the BPh's (H_A and H_B). The absorption spectra of RCs containing BChl *b* and BPh *b*, such as those of *Bl. viridis*, are qualitatively similar except that the long-wavelength band of P is shifted even farther to the red (960 nm). The absorption bands of the other BChls and the BPh's appear in the region of 830 nm and are less well resolved than in RCs containing BChl *a* and BPh *a*.

12.2.2 Kinetics and Energetics of the Initial Electron-Transfer Steps

The kinetics and energetics of the initial charge-separation steps have been explored by pump–probe measurements of stimulated emission and transient changes in the absorption bands of the pigments. When the RC is excited with a short pulse of light, the excitation energy flows to P within about 0.1 ps [59–62]. The excited dimer (P*) then transfers an electron to BPh H_A, forming the radical-pair state $P^{·+}H_A^{·-}$ with an overall time constant of about 3.5 ps at room temperature [59–60,63–74]. $H_A^{·-}$ passes an electron on to Q_A with a time

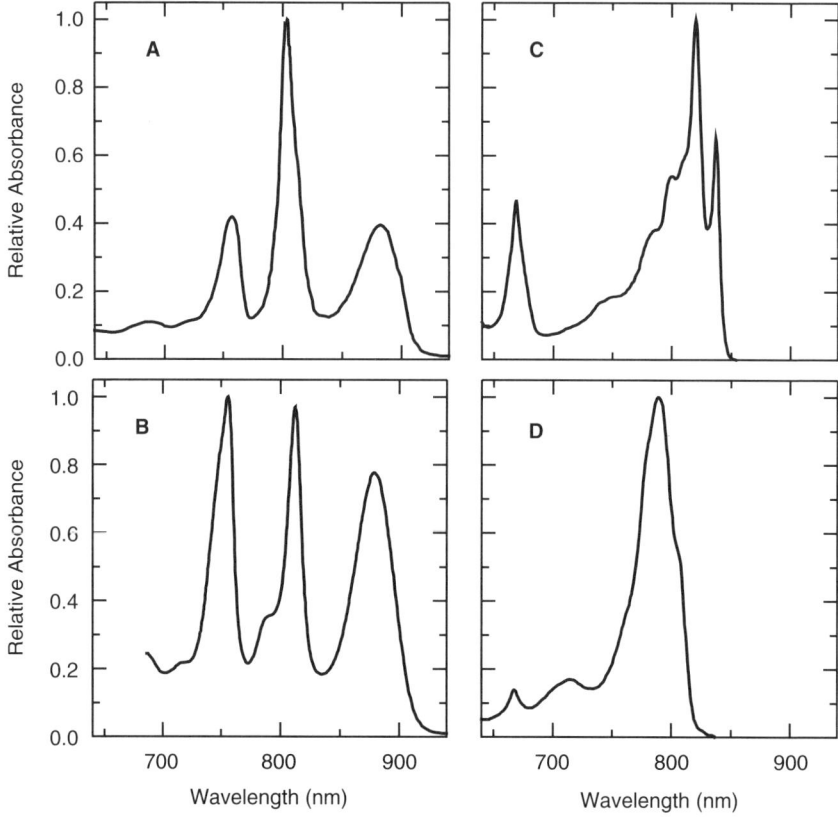

Figure 6. Near-IR absorption spectra of RCs at low temperatures. (A) *Rb. sphaeroides* RCs in a poly(vinyl alcohol) (PVA) film at 5 K [198]. (B) *Cfl. aurantiacus* RCs in a PVA film at 80 K [253]. (C) *Psc. aestuarii* RCs in aqueous glycerol at 10 K [299]. (D) *Hba. mobilis* in aqueous glycerol at 6 K [359]. Spectra are replotted from the original publications and normalized at their peaks to facilitate comparisons. The absorption bands are sharper and better resolved at low temperatures than they are at room temperature, and the long-wavelength absorption band is usually shifted farther to the red.

constant of about 200 ps [75–77]. These reactions occur with a quantum yield of essentially 100% [78,79]. They also have the curious property of increasing in rate with decreasing temperature [60,65,67,74,80–87].

Electron transfer from $^1P^*$ to H_L probably occurs in two discrete steps, with an electron moving first to BChl B_A to create an intermediate $P^{·+}B_A^{·-}$ radical-pair, and $B_A^{·-}$ then passing an electron on to H_A [66,69,73,88–98]. Assuming that both steps are irreversible, Zinth and co-workers obtained time constants of 3.5 ps for electron transfer from $^1P^*$ to B_A and 0.9 ps for electron transfer from $B_A^{·-}$ to H_A [66,73,95]. Holzwarth and Müller [69] suggested a model in which both steps are reversible and have time constants of approximately 2.5 ps. Such schemes are necessarily tentative, because the spectroscopic signals assigned to $P^{\cdot+}B_A^{\cdot-}$ are small and short-lived and the apparent time constants depend on the model. An alternative to the two-step pathway is a "superexchange" mechanism, in which $P^{\cdot+}B_A^{\cdot-}$ serves only as a virtual intermediate that mixes quantum mechanically with $^1P^*$ and $P^{\cdot+}H_A^{\cdot-}$. The main distinction between real and virtual intermediates in this context is that a real intermediate has a long lifetime relative to the time required for the loss of electronic coherence, which probably is on the order of 10–100 fs.

For the two-step mechanism to work at low temperatures, $P^{\cdot+}B_A^{\cdot-}$ must lie close to or below $^1P^*$ in energy. The superexchange mechanism would allow $P^{\cdot+}B_A^{\cdot-}$ to be farther above $^1P^*$, although the rate would fall off as the energy difference increases. Most recent estimates put $P^{\cdot+}B_A^{\cdot-}$ below $^1P^*$ by several kcal mol^{-1}, in accord with the two-step mechanism [93–94,99–101], but are not sufficiently accurate to settle this point definitively.

The restrictions on the energy of $P^{\cdot+}B_A^{\cdot-}$ in the two-step mechanism actually may not be very stringent, because electron transfer probably occurs partly from excited vibrational levels of $^1P^*$ that are populated by the excitation flash [85,102]. Judging from the damping of coherent vibrational oscillations that are set in motion by excitation with short flashes, vibrational equilibration of $^1P^*$ with the surroundings requires 1–2 ps, which is comparable to the time constants for electron transfer [96,103–116]. The dependence of the electron-transfer kinetics on temperature and the energy of $P^{\cdot+}B_A^{\cdot-}$ cannot, therefore, be treated reliably by theories that assume rapid vibrational thermalization in $^1P^*$ and rapid vibrational relaxations in $P^{\cdot+}B_A^{\cdot-}$. However, more complex treatments using a density matrix formalism have been developed and appear to account for the observed kinetics reasonably well [102,117,118]. Almost all the parameters needed for a density-matrix model with multiple vibrational modes can be obtained from molecular dynamics simulations based on the crystal structure of the RC [102,117].

Transient spectroscopic signals indicative of $P^{\cdot+}B_A^{\cdot-}$ become more prominent if RCs are modified in ways that should increase the energy of $P^{\cdot+}H_A^{\cdot-}$ and thus slow electron transfer from $B_A^{\cdot-}$ to H_A. One way to do this is to replace H_A by Phe or BChl, both of which have more negative reduction potentials than BPh [119–124,97]. Measurements of the amount of $P^{\cdot+}B_A^{\cdot-}$ in equilibrium with $P^{\cdot+}Phe^{\cdot-}$ in such modified RCs suggest that $P^{\cdot+}B_A^{\cdot-}$ lies about 1 kcal mol^{-1} below $^1P^*$ [97,122,123]. The lifetime of $P^{\cdot+}B_A^{\cdot-}$ also can be increased by site-directed mutations that raise the energy of $P^{\cdot+}H_A^{\cdot-}$ or lower that of $P^{\cdot+}B_A^{\cdot-}$ [97,119,120,123–129]. Reaction centers in which BChl B_A is replaced by BPh also give long-lived signals consistent with a $P^{\cdot+}Phe^{\cdot-}$ radical pair [125].

Mutations that raise the energy of $P^{\cdot+}B_A^{\cdot-}$ slow charge separation and make the rate more dependent on temperature. Increasing the number of hydrogen bonds between the protein and the BChls of P, for example, destabilizes $P^{\cdot+}$ and generally slows the initial electron-transfer reaction, while decreasing the number of hydrogen bonds has the opposite effect [74,130–134]. Mutations that introduce negatively charged residues near P also speed up the reaction [85]. Replacing a tyrosine residue near B_A (Tyr M210 in *Rb. sphaeroides* or the homologous M208 in *Rb. capsulatus*) by phenylalanine, tryptophan or other amino acids also slows charge separation, probably in large part because the loss of the phenolic –OH group destabilizes both $P^{\cdot+}$ and $B_A^{\cdot-}$ [82,92,135–143], although the mutation may also affect the electronic coupling of B_A with P [144]; replacing Phe by Tyr at the homologous position in the L subunit has the opposite effect [138,142].

12.2.3 Secondary Electron-Transfer Reactions

Following the formation of $P^{\cdot+}Q_A^{\cdot-}$, an electron moves from $Q_A^{\cdot-}$ to the second quinone (Q_B) with multiphasic kinetics that spread over the time range of 10 to several hundred microseconds [145–156]. The kinetics of this step have been probed by double-flash techniques in which one measures the photochemical reactions or fluorescence yield on a second pulse of light as a function of the time between the two pulses, and by following shifts in the absorption spectra of other pigments near the two quinones. They also can be measured more directly in RCs containing spectroscopically distinguishable quinones as Q_A and Q_B. The kinetics appear not to be determined by the rate of electron transfer per se, but rather by conformational changes in the protein or proton uptake onto amino acid residues near Q_B [155–158]. This was demonstrated by substituting quinones with different E_m values for Q_A and showing that the rate of electron transfer did not depend on the free energy change [155]. The nature of the gating, however, is not yet clear. Crystallographic studies have shown that Q_B can bind to the RC in two different sites [159], but the gating does not appear to involve movement of the quinone from one of these sites to the other [160,161].

Although the nonheme iron atom is situated between the two quinones, there is no indication that it undergoes transient reduction or oxidation during the reaction. Removing the iron atom or replacing it by Zn^{2+} slows electron transfer from $H_A^{\cdot-}$ to Q_A but has little or no effect on the rate of electron transfer from $Q_A^{\cdot-}$ to Q_B [162,163]. It thus seems likely that the iron plays mainly a structural or electrostatic role in the RC. Binding of Zn^{2+}, Cd^{2+} or Cu^{2+} to a nearby site in the H subunit does slow electron transfer from $Q_A^{\cdot-}$ to Q_B, possibly by disrupting the path by which protons move from the solution to Q_B [153,154,158,164].

While electron transfer between the quinones is occurring on one side of the RC, the cytochrome on the other side supplies an electron to $P^{\cdot+}$. In RCs with a four-heme cytochrome, such as those of *Bl. viridis* or *Ach. vinosum*, electron transfer from the proximal heme (C559 in Figure 5B) to $P^{\cdot+}$ typically occurs with a time constant of 0.2–1 µs if the adjacent heme (C551) is in its reduced state, and somewhat more slowly if the latter heme is oxidized [45–46,50,52,77,165–179]. The electronic hole in the proximal heme is quickly refilled by an electron from one of the other hemes. In species that have only the single-heme, soluble cytochrome c_2, such as *Rb. sphaeroides* (Figure 4B), bound cytochrome c_2 reduces $P^{\cdot+}$ with a time constant on the order of 1 µs. The kinetics in these species often include a slower, second-order component that reflects diffusion and binding of the free cytochrome [172,179–184]. In some species, notably *Rb. capsulatus*, a membrane-bound monoheme cytochrome (cytochrome c_y) takes the place of, or augments, the soluble cytochrome c_2 [185–187].

With P and Q_A back in their resting states, the RC is ready to accept another excitation. The kinetics of the ensuing progression through $^1P^*$, $P^{·+}B_A^{·-}$ and $P^{·+}H_A^{·-}$ to $P^{·+}Q_A^{·-}$ are essentially the same as following the first excitation. In species with a four-heme cytochrome, reduction of $P^{·+}$ also proceeds with similar, though generally not identical, kinetics as after the first turnover [45,52,169]. This step is slower in species that use cytochrome c_2, in which the cytochrome oxidized on the first turnover first must dissociate from the RC and be replaced by a fresh molecule. Electron transfer from $Q_A^{·-}$ to Q_B also exhibits different kinetics on the second pass, because now Q_B starts mainly in its anionic semiquinone state ($Q_B^{·-}$) (Figure 7). The reaction probably is preceded by rapid, reversible protonation of the semiquinone [146,147]. Reduction of the neutral semiquinone (Q_BH) generates the quinol anion (Q_BH^-), which picks up a second proton to give the neutral quinol or dihydroquinone

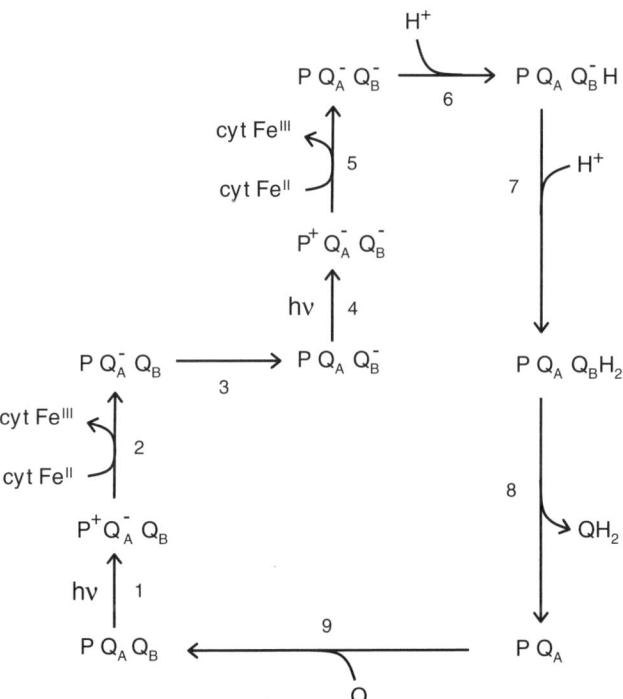

Figure 7. The quinone cycle in Type-II RCs. Steps 1 and 2 represent photochemical electron transfer from P to Q_A followed by reduction of $P^{·+}$ by a c-type cytochrome. These reactions can be repeated (steps 4 and 5) after an electron moves from $Q_A^{·-}$ to Q_B (step 3). Transfer of the second electron from $Q_A^{·-}$ to Q_B^- (step 6) requires uptake of a proton. Uptake of another proton (step 7) generates the quinol (QH_2), which dissociates from the RC and is replaced by a fresh quinone (steps 8 and 9).

(Q_BH_2). The quinol then dissociates from the RC and diffuses in the membrane to the cytochrome bc_1 complex [188–190], where it is reoxidized.

Several different carriers can ferry electrons from the cytochrome bc_1 complex back to the RC, depending on the bacterial species [191–194]. Cytochrome c_2 does this in *Rb. sphaeroides* and *Rb. capsulatus*, passing an electron directly to $P^{\cdot+}$ as described above. The soluble "high-potential iron-sulfur protein" (HiPIP) plays a similar role in some species that have a four-heme cytochrome bound to the RC, such as *Rf. fermentans* and *Ach. vinosum*, where it probably passes an electron to the heme farthest from P [192,194–196]. *Bl. viridis* uses a soluble cytochrome that, though called cytochrome c_2, is structurally more related to mitochondrial cytochrome *c* [197]. Another soluble cytochrome (cytochrome c_8) appears to replace HiPIP in *Ach. vinosum* under some growth conditions [194].

12.2.4 Directionality (Asymmetry) of the Initial Steps in Type II RCs

One of the most intriguing features of the electron-transfer reactions in proteobacterial RCs is their directionality. Despite the symmetry of the structure (Figures 4 and 5A), electron transfer from P to H_A is at least 100 × faster than transfer to the corresponding BPh on the "*B*" side, H_B [80,198–200]. The two BPh's can be distinguished experimentally because a hydrogen bond from a Glu side chain to the keto group of H_A shifts the Q_x absorption band of this pigment to the red [201]. The functional asymmetry also appears to result at least partly from electrostatic interactions of B_A and B_B with the protein. Although it has not yet been possible to reverse the specificity entirely, mutations designed to raise the energy of $P^{\cdot+}B_A^{\cdot-}$ and/or lower the energy of $P^{\cdot+}B_B^{\cdot-}$ usually increase electron transfer to H_B [202–211]. Excitation with blue light or multiple photons also can result in electron transfer to H_B [212,213], which also seems qualitatively consistent with the idea that electron transfer in this direction is limited by an energy barrier between $^1P^*$ and $P^{\cdot+}B_B^{\cdot-}$.

Attempts to calculate the relative energies of $P^{\cdot+}B_A^{\cdot-}$ and $P^{\cdot+}B_B^{\cdot-}$ based on the structure of the RC have given mixed results. While several authors have found $P^{\cdot+}B_B^{\cdot-}$ to be significantly higher in energy than $P^{\cdot+}B_A^{\cdot-}$ [92,101,214], a more recent study led to the opposite conclusion [100], and another study found only a small difference between the energies [215]. The variability of opinion reflects the difficulty of evaluating both the vacuum energies of the ion-pair states and the screening of electrostatic interactions with the protein. A stronger electronic coupling of P to H_A probably contributes to the specificity [216–219], although the coupling appears to be strong enough to make kinetics relatively insensitive to changes in this parameter [102].

The highly directional pattern of electron transfer in Type II RCs can be related to their overall function of transferring two electrons to a quinone and releasing the fully reduced quinol. As discussed above, the binding sites for the two quinones are specialized for different reactions. Q_A cycles only between the oxidized quinone and the unprotonated semiquinone and remains tightly bound to the RC; Q_B successively accepts two electrons and two protons and then dissociates. The transfer of electrons from $^1P^*$ specifically to the acceptors on the A side presumably allows the binding sites for Q_A and Q_B to be optimized independently for these different processes.

12.2.5 Alternative Pathways

The foregoing description of the initial steps leading from $^1P^*$ to $P^{\cdot+}H_A^{\cdot-}$ emphasizes the role of P as the primary electron donor. In this picture, excitation energy absorbed by B_A, B_B, H_A or H_B flows rapidly to P, which then transfers an electron to B_A. Pump–probe signals seen in the 800-nm region following excitation of B_A suggest that $B_A^{\cdot+}H_A^{\cdot-}$ or $P^{\cdot+}B_A^{\cdot-}$ may also form directly from $^1B_L^*$, particularly in mutants in which the pathway via $^1P^*$ is slowed [220–223]. In addition, the action spectrum for electron transfer differs from the excitation spectrum for fluorescence from $^1P^*$: exciting RCs in the 800-nm absorption band of B_A appears to give more electron transfer relative to $^1P^*$ fluorescence than excitation in the 870-nm absorption band of P [224,225]. The absorption spectrum in the 800-nm region also exhibits a large "resonance" Stark effect that can be explained by coupling of $^1B^*$ with $B_A^{\cdot+}H_A^{\cdot-}$ [226,227]. However, the quantitative importance of these alternative pathways remains unclear. From an analysis of the resonance Stark effects, Zhou and Boxer [226,227] concluded that the direct formation of $B_A^{\cdot+}H_A^{\cdot-}$ is an order of magnitude slower than energy transfer from $^1B_A^*$ to P in wild-type *Rb. sphaeroides* RCs but can be sped up by mutations that lower the energy of the $B_A^{\cdot+}H_A^{\cdot-}$ radical pair. Lin et al. [228] have suggested that some of the anomalous pump–probe signals reflect heterogeneity of the RCs rather than direct electron transfer to or from $^1B_A^*$. No direct electron transfer reactions involving $^1B_A^*$ were detected in mutant RCs that lack P [229].

12.3 Green Non-Sulfur Bacteria (Chloroflexi)

12.3.1 Structures of RCs in Green Non-Sulfur Bacteria

The best studied species of the green non-sulfur bacteria, *Chloroflexus aurantiacus*, is a thermophile that grows optimally at temperatures of 52–60 °C and survives even at 70 °C. It is found in hot springs, where its flexible, multicellular filaments typically form orange mats underneath a layer of cyanobacteria [5,230]. The bacteria can move on solid surfaces in the direction of the filament axis by a mysterious process called "gliding", which may be driven extension and retraction of pili or possibly by expulsion of slime in the opposite direction [231]. Most, but not all, green non-sulfur bacteria resemble green sulfur bacteria (Chlorobi) in having chlorosomes, peripheral antenna complexes that contain thousands of molecules of BChl *c* [232]. They lack the Fenna–Mathews–Olson (FMO) protein, which is a small antenna complex containing BChl *a* that is found only in the green sulfur bacteria (Section 12.4) [232].

Chloroflexus aurantiacus has Type II RCs that are functionally similar to those of protobacteria but differ significantly in composition. First, they have only two polypeptide subunits, which are homologous to the L and M subunits of proteobacteria; they have no homolog of the H subunit [233–238]. Second, *Cfl. aurantiacus* RCs have three molecules of BChl-*a* instead of four, three molecules of BPh-*a* instead of two, manganese in place of the nonheme iron, and menaquinones as both Q_A and Q_B instead of two molecules of ubiquinone or one of each type of quinone [235–236,239–241]. The carotenoid located near B_B in proteobacterial RCs also is absent.

Although RCs from *Cfl. aurantiacus* have been crystallized [242–244], a high-resolution structure has not been obtained from this or any other species of Chloroflexi. However, the similarities of the amino acid sequences of the L and M subunits to their proteobacterial homologues suggest that the overall structures of the RCs are much the same as in proteobacteria. The spectroscopic properties of the RCs also are similar to those of *Rb. sphaeroides* RCs, except that the BPh absorption band in the 760-nm region is stronger and the 800-nm band of the BChls is weaker, as would be expected from the different pigment content (Figure 6B). Comparisons of the amino acid sequences and spectroscopic properties indicate that the arrangement of the pigments probably is essentially the same, with the additional BPh in the *Cfl. aurantiacus* RC replacing BChl B_B of proteobacteria [235–236,241,245–251]. The substitution of BPh for BChl evidently results from the loss of a histidine residue that serves as an axial ligand of B_B, which is replaced by leucine in *Cfl. aurantiacus*. As in proteobacteria, electron transfer occurs specifically to the carriers on the *A* side of the RC [252], and the replacement of BChl by BPh on the *B* side seems unlikely to have much effect on this process.

12.3.2 Electron-Transfer Kinetics and Energetics

The E_m for oxidation of P in *Cfl. aurantiacus* is +0.36 V [239], as compared with approximately +0.50 V in proteobacteria. Other things being equal, this would lower the free energy of $P^{\cdot+}B_A^{\cdot-}$ by 0.14 eV. However, *Cfl. aurantiacus* RCs lack the tyrosine residue (Tyr M208 or M210) that stabilizes $P^{\cdot+}B_A^{\cdot-}$ in proteobacterial RCs. They also have glutamine in place of a glutamic acid residue that stabilizes $H_A^{\cdot-}$ in proteobacteria. From an analysis of the decay kinetics of $P^{\cdot+}H_A^{\cdot-}$ in RC preparations lacking quinones, Volk *et al.* [252] conclude that the free energy of $P^{\cdot+}H_A^{\cdot-}$ is 0.04 eV higher in *Cfl. aurantiacus* than in *Rb. sphaeroides*, and that the free energy of $P^{\cdot+}B_A^{\cdot-}$ probably also is higher by a similar or somewhat larger amount.

As in *Rb. sphaeroides*, the quantum yield of charge separation in *Cfl. aurantiacus* RCs is essentially 100% [79]. The initial electron-transfer kinetics, however, are slower. Electron transfer from $^1P^*$ to H_A occurs with a mean time constant of about 10 ps, almost independent of temperature between 10 and 320 K [143,253–259]. The kinetics are multiphasic, possibly because of structural relaxations of the protein or heterogeneity in the redox state of Q_A or the energy of $P^{\cdot+}B_A^{\cdot-}$ or $P^{\cdot+}H_A^{\cdot-}$. There is no clear evidence for a $P^{\cdot+}B_A^{\cdot-}$

intermediate in the reaction, although the participation of such an intermediate seems likely in the light of the other similarities to proteobacterial RCs.

Electron transfer from $H_A^{\cdot-}$ to Q_A occurs with a time constant of about 320 ps in *Cfl. aurantiacus* at room temperature [260], as compared with 200 ps in *Rb. sphaeroides* or *Rb. capsulatus*. In intact cells, an electrogenic event with a time constant of 100 ps has been assigned to formation of $P^{\cdot+}H_A^{\cdot-}$, and a component with a time constant of 530 ps to formation of $P^{\cdot+}Q_A^{\cdot-}$ [261].

Chloroflexus aurantiacus RCs have a tightly bound, four-heme cytochrome that is functionally homologous to the four-heme cytochrome of *Bl. viridis* and *Ach. vinosum* [191,239,262–264]. Other than in the heme-binding sites, however, the amino acid sequence of the *Cfl. aurantiacus* cytochrome is very different from those of the protobacterial cytochromes [262], and the hemes span a smaller E_m range (0 to +280 mV compared with −60 to +380 mV) [264]. All the hemes except the one with the highest E_m can be photooxidized at 4 K [264].

Electrons returning from to the four-heme cytochrome from the menaquinol (MKH_2) that dissociates from the RC are carried by a small, "blue" copper protein, auracyanin, rather than by another cytochrome or HiPIP as in proteobacteria [265–267]. Auracyanin is structurally similar to the blue copper protein plastocyanin that carries electrons from the cytochrome b_6f complex to $P700^{\cdot+}$ in chloroplasts and many cyanobacteria. But how electrons move from MKH_2 to auracyanin is not entirely clear. *Chloroflexus aurantiacus* has membrane-bound *b*- and *c*-type cytochromes and a Rieske-type iron-sulfur center [268–270], but these apparently do not form a cytochrome *bc* complex resembling the b_6f complex or the cytochrome bc_1 complexes found in proteobacteria, green sulfur bacteria and heliobacteria [27,270].

In addition to *Chloroflexus*, the phylum Chloroflexi includes the genera *Oscillochloris*, *Chloronema*, *Oscillochloris*, *Heliothrix* and *Roseiflexus*, all of which consist of filamentous, gliding photosynthetic bacteria. Little is known about the RCs of any of these organisms other than *Cfl. aurantiacus*. Many of the species that have been isolated, including *Cfl. aggregans* [271], *Heliothrix oregonensis* [272] and *Roseiflexus castenholzii* [273], resemble *Cfl. aurantiacus* in being thermophiles, but some, such as *Oscillochloris trichoides*, are mesophiles [274]. *Roseiflexus castenholzii* and *Heliothrix oregonensis* lack the chlorosomes found in most other Chloroflexi, and their antenna complexes contain only BChl *a*

12.4 Green Sulfur Bacteria (Chlorobi)

12.4.1 Structures of Chlorobial RCs

Green sulfur bacteria typically live in brackish mud flats under a layer of purple sulfur bacteria. They use sulfide as an electron donor, depositing elemental sulfur outside the cells as a waste product. Unlike the green nonsulfur bacteria (Chloroflexi), most green sulfur bacteria are not motile. The available information on their RCs pertains almost entirely to organisms of the genera *Chlorobium* (*Cl.*) and *Prosthecochloris* (*Pcl.*), particularly *Cl. limicola*, *Cl. tepidum*, *Cl. vibrioforme* and *Pcl. aestuarii*, and little is known about the organisms in the other two genera in the phylum (*Pelodictyon* and *Clathrochloris*). "*Chloropseudomonas ethylica*," which was the subject of much of the early work in the field, proved to be a syntrophic culture of *Pcl. aestuarii* and a nonphotosynthetic organism [275]. *Chlorobium tepidum* has become the organism of choice for many studies because the cells can be grown and transformed relatively easily and its complete genome has been sequenced [276].

Green sulfur bacteria have Type I RCs with three iron-sulfur centers that are functionally very similar to those of PS I [13,29,277–281]. However, the RC differs from that of PS I in containing a homodimer of a single 82-kDa subunit (PscA) in place of the PsaA-PsaB heterodimer [282–284]. PscA is homologous to PsaA and PsaB in its amino acid sequence and predicted secondary structure, particularly in the C-terminal domains, where PsaA and PsaB each has five transmembrane α-helices. As in PS I, the PscA homodimer probably holds the primary electron donor (P840), the initial electron acceptors, and one [4Fe-4S] iron-sulfur center (F_X).

In addition to the PscA dimer, chlorobial RCs have a second, smaller peptide (PscB) that is homologous to PsaC and holds two additional [4Fe-4S] iron-sulfur centers (F_A and F_B). Another peptide, PscC, carries a single *c*-type heme. Two copies of PscC subunit probably bind near P840 in the region corresponding to the docking site for plastocyanin or cytochrome c_6 in PS I [284]. A fourth peptide (PscD) is homologous to PsaD, which sits next to PsaC in PS I and appears to assist in the binding of ferredoxin. Seven subunits that form the hydrophobic periphery of the cyanobacterial PS I (PsaE, PsaF, PsaI, PsaJ, PsaK, PsaL and PsaM) are missing in chlorobial RCs, as are three other subunits that have been found only in chloroplasts (PsaG, PsaN and PsaH) [29,285,286].

In contrast to the PsaA-PsaB dimer in PS I, which features 90 antenna Chl molecules and 22 carotenoids along with the six chlorophylls that serve as electron carriers (Chapter 13), the PscA dimer has a total of only 16 BChl *a*, four Chl *a* and two carotenoids [287]. Assuming that the Chl *a*s and two of the BChl *a*s are electron carriers, the central antenna of the core complex thus amounts to only 14 molecules of BChl *a* and two carotenoids. To survive below layers of organisms that absorb most of the incident sunlight, green sulfur bacteria rely on large peripheral antennas. Most of the antenna pigments are found in chlorosomes, vesicular structures that contain extended oligomers of BChl *c*, *d* or *e*. Energy of light absorbed in a chlorosome flows to smaller antenna complexes containing BChl *a* [the "baseplate" and the Fenna–Mathews–Olson (FMO) protein], and from there to antenna BChls in the RC [232]. It is the Chl *c*, *d* or *e* of the chlorosomes that confers the emerald green color that is characteristic of most green sulfur bacteria.

Crystal structures have not been obtained for chlorobial RCs. However, low-resolution models have been obtained by electron microscopy [288], and Heathcote *et al.* [280] have described a homology model of the *Cl. limicola*

RC based on the crystal structure of PS I from *S. elongatus*. An alignment of the amino acid sequences [29] shows that the PscA dimer has conserved histidine residues in positions to provide axial ligands for 14 antenna BChls and the two BChls of the primary electron donor (P840). In addition, lysine residues occur in positions where they could serve as axial ligands for the first Chl (A) in each of the putative chains of electron acceptors branching out from P840, and there are glutamic acid residues where they could be ligands of the second Chl in each chain (A_0) [280]. (As discussed in Chapter 13, the axial ligand of A in PS I is a molecule of water that is hydrogen bonded to an asparagine side chain, and the ligand of A_0 is a methionine [14].) Residues that could form hydrogen bonds with the A_0 Chls also are found at positions where there are similar, though not identical, amino acids in PS I. The model accommodates menaquinones at sites corresponding to the phylloquinone (A_1) binding sites in PS I, although tryptophan residues that contribute to the quinone binding pockets in PS I are replaced by arginines. The homology model is, thus, consistent with a very similar arrangement of the initial electron donor and acceptors in the two RCs, but suggests that the quinones would not bind as tightly in chlorobial RCs as they do in PS I.

12.4.2 Electron-Transfer Kinetics and Energetics

The primary electron donor in green sulfur bacteria (P840) has an E_m of +245 mV [289–291]. P840 may consist of a dimer of Bchl a' (the 13^2 epimer of the more common BChl a), which accounts for two of the 14 bacteriochlorins in the RC [292] (P700 contains one Chl a'). Because of the other structural and functional homologies to PS I, it seems likely that the four Chl a molecules serve as initial electron acceptors and are arranged similarly to the corresponding Chl a molecules in the PS I RC (Figure 3A). The use of Chl rather than BChl as an electron acceptor is consistent with the generation of a strong reductant, because the E_m of Chl a in solution (approx. -1.0 V) is about 0.25 V more negative than that of BChl a [293]. The earliest acceptor that has been detected in time-resolved spectroscopic measurements (A_0) has an absorption band at 663 nm [294–299] (Figure 6C), and a pigment with such a band has been extracted from the RCs and identified as Chl a ligated to 2,6-phytanediol [292,300,301]. The ENDOR spectrum of the reduced species that accumulates during continuous illumination at low temperatures ($A_0^{\cdot-}$) also supports the identification of the electron acceptor as a Chl [302]. As in PS I, A_0 probably is the second Chl in one or both of the putative chains of electron carriers extending out from P840 (Figure 3A).

The presence of antenna pigments makes measurements of the initial electron-transfer kinetics more difficult in Type-I RCs than in Type II. Because the absorption bands of the antenna BChls and the electron carriers overlap, it is difficult to excite the primary donor selectively, and absorbance changes reflecting the electron-transfer reactions can be confused with signals from excited singlet or triplet states in the antenna. When the antenna BChls of *Pcl. aestuarii* RCs are excited with a subpicosecond flash at either room temperature or 10 K, a quasi-equilibrium among excited states of the antenna pigments appears to be established within several picoseconds; absorbance changes indicative of oxidation of P840 and reduction of Chl A_0 then occur with a time constant of about 25 ps [297–299,303]. However, the latter time constant may represent the rate of energy transfer from the antenna BChls to P840, rather than the intrinsic rate of electron transfer from ^{1}P840* to A_0 [299].

Similar biphasic kinetics are seen when the RC is excited in the 670-nm absorption band of the four Chls (A and A_0); however, the final yield of $P^{\cdot+}A_0^{\cdot-}$ then is higher, suggesting that electron transfer occurs more efficiently from ^{1}A* or $^1A_0$* than from ^{1}P840* [298,299]. Green sulfur bacteria thus appear to resemble the purple photosynthetic bacteria in being able to accomplish the initial charge separation in several different ways (Section 12.2.5).

Absorbance changes reflecting transient reduction or oxidation of a Chl between P840 and A_0 (A) have not been resolved in RCs from green sulfur bacteria, or in any other Type-I RCs.

Reoxidation of the photoreduced Chl ($A_0^{\cdot-}$) occurs with a time constant of about 600 ps in *Cl. limicola* [261,294,304] and 700 ps in *Pcl. aestuarii* [297]. This is slower than electron transfer from $A_0^{\cdot-}$ to A_1 (phylloquinone) in PS I, which has a time constant of 20–50 ps [305–308], but faster than electron transfer from the reduced phylloquinone ($A_1^{\cdot-}$) to F_X, which takes 20–200 ns (see Chapter 14 for further details) [309–311]. Although the participation of phylloquinone as an electron carrier between $A_0^{\cdot-}$ and F_X is well established for PS I, the role of quinones in chlorobial RCs is unclear. Green sulfur bacteria contain menaquinone-7 and chlorobiumquinone, an unusual quinone in which the first methylene group of the isoprenoid side chain of menaquinone is replaced by a keto group. Chlorobiumquinone is found exclusively in chlorosomes, where it participates in a regulatory mechanism that prevents overloading RCs with excitation energy under aerobic conditions [232,312]. Menaquinone-7 is found in RCs and elsewhere in cytoplasmic membranes as well as in chlorosomes, but the amount measured in purified RCs has varied from undetectable [287,313] to approximately two molecules per P840 [314]. Kusumoto *et al.* [315] found approximately one molecule of menaquinone per P840 in *Cl. tepidum* RCs, but were unable to detect absorbance changes characteristic of transient reduction of menaquinone when they excited the RCs with a short flash. EPR signals indicative of menasemiquinone are, however, seen when RCs of *Cl. vibrioforme* or *limicola* are illuminated continuously at low temperatures [314,316]. Electron transfer from $A_0^{\cdot-}$ directly to F_X without the intercession of a quinone or another intermediate carrier probably would take considerably more than 600 ps, considering that the shortest edge-to-edge distance between A_0 and F_X is probably about 17 Å [280,315]. The difficulty of detecting transient reduction of the quinone could mean simply that the semiquinone is reoxidized as rapidly as it is formed [315].

The three [4Fe-4S] iron-sulfur centers of chlorobial RCs have been studied by both EPR and optical spectroscopy [13,317–322]. All three centers can be photoreduced at both room temperature and low temperatures, but the kinetics of electron transfer between the different iron-sulfur centers are largely unknown. One of the three, presumably F_B as in PS I, is more accessible to external oxidants than the others, and can transfer electrons to several different [2Fe-2S] ferredoxins [319,323].

In the homology model of *Cl. limicola* RCs, there are no suitable amino acid side-chains in position to form a hydrogen bond to either BChl of P840 [280]. This is in accord with studies of FTIR difference spectra of P840 in its oxidized, reduced, and triplet states, which show that the C-13^1 carbonyl groups of both BChls are free of hydrogen bonds [324]. In PS I, by contrast, the protein appears to form three hydrogen bonds to one of the Chls of P700, but no such bonds to the other Chl [325]. P840 thus appears to be more symmetrical than P700, as one would anticipate from the fact that the protein core consists of a homodimer.

12.4.3 Directionality (Asymmetry) of Electron Transfer in Type I RCs

The symmetry of the chlorobial RC raises the question of whether electron transfer from P840 to F_X proceeds equally well along either branch of acceptors, or preferentially along one branch as in Type-II RCs. Because soluble ferredoxins, the ultimate electron acceptors from Type I RCs, normally accept only a single electron, there would be no clear benefit in specializing the two quinone-binding sites for different processes. Unlike Type-II RCs, where $Q_B^{\cdot-}$ accepts a second electron and leaves the RC as the fully reduced quinol, neither of the two quinones found in most Type-I RCs ($A_{1(A)}$ and $A_{1(B)}$) usually proceeds beyond the semiquinone, except possibly on continued illumination under strongly reducing conditions [326]. But the quasi-symmetry of the PsaA-PsaB heterodimer in PS I RCs is broken to some extent by interactions with subunits that are present in single copies, and the same could be true in Chlorobi. Chlorobi have a menaquinone oxidoreductase that resembles the cytochrome bc_1 and b_6f complexes [191,327,328], and the electron-transfer pathways connecting this complex to the RC are largely unknown.

The relative contributions of the two branches of electron carriers have been investigated extensively in PS I. In the green alga *Chlorella sorokiniana*, flash-induced absorbance changes assigned to a phylloquinone semiquinone ($A_1^{\cdot-}$) decay in two phases with time constants of approximately 15 and 150 ns, which appear to reflect electron transfer to F_X from the two phyllosemiquinones on the two sides of the RC ($A_{1(A)}^{\cdot-}$ and $A_{1(B)}^{\cdot-}$) [311]. Replacing the tryptophan residue near the quinone on the *A* side by phenylalanine affects only the slower decay component, whereas replacing the tryptophan on the *B* side affects only the faster component and a double mutation alters both components [329–331]. Similarly, mutations of the methionine that serves as an axial ligand of Chl A_0 on the *A* side appear to block or slow photoreduction of $A_{1(A)}$ but allow electron transfer to $A_{1(B)}$, while mutations of the homologous residue on the *B* side affect electron transfer to $A_{1(B)}$ but not to $A_{1(A)}$ [332–334]. ^{1}P700*, thus, evidently can launch an electron down either branch of carriers, though not necessarily with equal probabilities. From the relative magnitudes of the signals assigned to the two quinones, electron transfer along the *A* branch appears to predominate strongly over that on the *B* branch, at least at room temperature [330,334]. Mutations of residues near the carriers on the *A* side seem to have more disruptive effects on phototrophic growth than homologous mutations on the *B* side [332,334], although the opposite is true in some cases [333]. Similar studies in RCs from green sulfur bacteria have not been described, but should be interesting if distinguishable menaquinones can be identified as electron carriers between A_0 and F_X.

As mentioned above, RCs from green sulfur bacteria probably bind two copies of a single-heme cytochrome (PscC) [283–284,287,290,315,320,321, 327,335–337]. This cytochrome, which is called variously $c551$ and $c553$, has an E_m of approximately $+160\,mV$ [289–290,338]. The kinetics of electron transfer to $P840^{\cdot+}$ are often found to be biphasic, with time constants ranging from 7 to several hundred μs [284,289,315,320,327,336], but some of the variability of the kinetics probably reflects reactions of cytochromes other than PscC. Green sulfur bacteria also contain a membrane-bound, *c*-type cytochrome with multiple hemes, which appears to be similar to the four-heme cytochrome of photosynthetic proteobacteria and green non-sulfur bacteria, and they have a soluble *c*-type cytochrome (c_z) that may be functionally similar to cytochrome c_y of *Rb. capsulatus* [191,327,328,338–341]. Both these cytochromes apparently can bind to the RC. The physiological roles of the different cytochromes are presently unclear.

12.5 Heliobacteria (Firmicutes)

12.5.1 Structures of Heliobacterial Reaction Centers

Heliobacteria were discovered more recently than the other groups of anoxygenic photosynthetic bacteria [342,343], and although a large number of species have now been described, their photosynthetic RCs and electron-transfer pathways are still poorly understood [344]. Almost all the studies of heliobacterial RCs have focused on the species *Heliobacterium* (*Hbt*.) *chlorum* and *Heliobacillus* (*Hba*.) *mobilis*.

Heliobacteria are strict anaerobes that typically are brownish-green in color. They differ from other known photosynthetic organisms in lacking extrinsic antenna systems; all their light-harvesting pigments are in the RCs, which contain approximately 35 molecules of the unusual BChl *g* [345–347]. Like the RCs of green sulfur bacteria, heliobacterial RCs contain a homodimer of a single core polypeptide (PshA, 68 kDa) with sequence homologies to the PsaA and PsaB subunits of PS I [21,348]. The PshA dimer has a single putative [4Fe-4S] iron-sulfur center homologous to center F_x of PS I and Chlorobial RCs [348]. Purified RCs contain about nine atoms of iron per RC [347], and at least two iron-sulfur centers undergo reduction when heliobacterial RCs or membrane fragments are illuminated [349–351]. Heliobacterial RCs thus clearly are of Type I. However, an iron-sulfur subunit comparable to PsaC of PS I and

PscB of green sulfur bacteria has not been identified in the purified RCs, and no gene coding for such a protein was found in the cluster of genes for other photosynthetic proteins [21].

12.5.2 Electron-Transfer Kinetics and Energetics

As in other anoxygenic photosynthetic bacteria, FTIR [325,352] and EPR [353] studies have shown that the positive charge and unpaired electron spin of the oxidized primary electron donor in heliobacterial RCs (P798) is delocalized over two molecules of BChl. Each of the subunits in the putative PshA dimer has a conserved histidine at a position homologous to the histidine that probably provides an axial ligand to P840 in green sulfur bacteria [348]. Purified reaction centers from *Hbt. chlorum* and *Hba. mobilis* contain two molecules of the 13^2 epimer of BChl g, BChl g', which by analogy to BChl a' in green sulfur bacteria (Section 12.4) may form the active dimer [346]. P798 has an E_m of +225 mV [353], which is comparable to the +250 mV E_m of P840.

In addition to BChl g and BChl g', which absorb in the region of 800 nm, heliobacterial RCs contain two molecules of 8^1-hydroxychlorophyll a, which absorb at 670 nm [354] (Figure 6D). At least one of the hydroxychlorophyll a molecules appears to act as an initial electron acceptor and is commonly called A_0 although there is no direct evidence that its location in the RC corresponds to that of A_0 in PS I and green sulfur bacteria. Formation of the $P798^{\cdot +}A_0^{\cdot -}$ ion pair can be seen by bleaching of the 798-nm absorption band of the electron donor and the 670-nm band of A_0 when RCs of *Hbt. chlorum* or *Hba. mobilis* are excited with short flashes of light [355–359]. The kinetics of this process are multiphasic, with time constants that range from 1 to 50 ps or longer depending on the excitation wavelength. As in Chlorobi, the observed kinetics probably reflect convolution of the intrinsic rate of electron transfer with the dynamics of energy equilibration among antenna BChl-g molecules, P798 and A_0. Considering the number and spectral properties of the antenna pigments, and assuming that energy equilibration among these pigments occurs rapidly, Lin *et al.* [356] estimate that electron transfer from ^{1}P798* to A_0 has an intrinsic time constant of approximately 1 ps. The time constant is only weakly dependent on temperature.

The efficiency of forming $P798^+$ appears to be higher if A_0 is excited directly in the 670-nm absorption band than it is when the antenna BChl-g is excited in the region of 800 nm [359]. This suggests that electron transfer to or from $^1A_0^*$ can compete effectively with energy transfer from $^1A_0^*$ to P798, as appears to be the case in green sulfur bacteria.

If the locations of the 8^1-hydroxychlorophyll a molecules in heliobacterial RCs correspond to those of the two A_0 chlorophyll molecules in PS I and green sulfur bacteria, one might expect to find another chlorophyll derivative (A) between P798 and each of the hydroxychlorophylls, one in each of the PshA subunits. Apart from the presumed structural homology to other Type-I RCs, an intermediate acceptor or a superexchange mediator seems needed in order for electron transfer from ^{1}P798* to A_0 to occur on the time scale of 1 ps at low temperatures. It is questionable whether BChl g could serve as this intermediate in heliobacteria because, as mentioned above, the E_m values for reduction of BChls generally are less negative than those of Chls. An acceptor whose reduction is too facile would act as a trap, preventing an electron from reaching A_0. This argument is not particularly compelling, however, because, as discussed in Section 12.2, the effective reduction potential of an electron carrier in situ depends strongly on interactions of the pigment with the protein. No chlorophylls other than the two 8^1-hydroxychlorophylls have been detected.

$P798^{·+}A_0^{·-}$ decays with a time constant of about 600 ps at room temperature [349,355,356,360,361], and about twice as rapidly at 15 K [360]. As in Chlorobi (Section 12.4), the identity of the secondary acceptor that removes an electron from $A_0^{·-}$ is unclear. Purified heliobacterial RCs contain approximately one molecule of menaquinone (MK) [347], which becomes reduced if the RCs are illuminated at low temperatures in the presence of a reductant [316,362]. Added MK also can be photoreduced efficiently [363]. However, several investigators have reported finding no sign of transient reduction of MK after excitation of RCs with short pulses of light, suggesting that the electron released by $A_0^{·-}$ might jump directly to F_x [349,361].

The major c-type cytochrome in cell membranes of heliobacteria, cytochrome c553, is a single-heme cytochrome with an E_m of +250 mV, whose amino acid sequence is not closely related to the chlorobial cytochrome with the same name [21,364]. Cytochrome c553 carries electrons to $P798^{·+}$ from a cytochrome bc complex that oxidizes menaquinol (MKH_2) [365,366]. Electron transfer from the cytochrome to $P798^{·+}$ occurs with a time constant of several hundred microseconds in intact cells, but becomes considerably slower if the cells are disrupted [366]. At least three other c-type cytochromes with various E_m values also appear to be able to reduce $P798^{·+}$ [366,367], and the physiological roles of these different cytochromes are largely unexplored. Kramer et al. [365] have suggested that heliobacteria carry out a cyclic electron-transfer process in which ferredoxin reduced by the RC transfers electrons to NAD, NADH reduces MK to MKH_2 via a hypothetical NADH:MK oxidoreductase, the cytochrome bc complex transfers electrons from MKH_2 to cytochrome c553, and the cytochrome returns electrons to P798.

12.6 Concluding Remarks

Because of their comparative simplicity, the reaction centers of anoxygenic bacteria have served as important model systems for the RCs of oxygenic organisms. They also have lent themselves to a broad range of biophysical studies of membrane protein structure, molecular spectroscopy, and electron-transfer dynamics. These studies have focused largely on proteobacterial RCs, leaving much still to be learnt about the Type I RCs of Chlorobi and heliobacteria. Among the many questions that beg for answers concerning chlorobial and heliobacterial RCs are the mechanism and kinetics of the initial electron-transfer step, the roles of MK and the Fe-S centers, and the physiological roles of the various c-type cytochromes that ferry electrons to the RC. High-resolution crystal structures of these RCs would be extremely helpful and, undoubtedly, would lead to renewed interest in these remarkable complexes.

Acknowledgements

Preparation of this chapter was supported by research grant MCB-9904618 from the National Science Foundation.

References

1. C.R. Woese, Prokaryote systematics: the evolution of a science, in: *The Prokaryotes* (1992) (A. Balows, H.G. Trüper, M. Dworkin, W. Harder, K.-H. Schleifer, eds.), Springer-Verlag, New York, pp. 3–18.
2. R.E. Blankenship, Protein structure, electron transfer and evolution of prokaryotic photosynthetic reaction centers. *Antonie v. Leeuwenhoek. Int. J. Gen. Mol. Microbiol.* **65** (1994) 311–329.
3. J.F. Imhoff, Taxonomy and physiology of phototrophic purple bacteria and green sulfur bacteria, in: *Anoxygenic Photosynthetic Bacteria* (1995) (R.E. Blankenship, M.T. Madigan, C.E. Bauer, eds.), Kluwer Academic Publishers, Dordrecht, pp. 1–15.
4. M.T. Madigan, J.G. Ormerod, Taxonomy, physiology and ecology of heliobacteria, in: *Anoxygenic Photosynthetic Bacteria* (1995) (R.E. Blankenship, M.T. Madigan, C.E. Bauer, eds.), Kluwer Academic Publishers, Dordrecht, pp. 17–30.
5. B.K. Pierson, R.W. Castenholz, Taxonomy and physiology of filamentous anoxygenic phototrophs, in: *Anoxygenic Photosynthetic Bacteria* (1995) (R.E. Blankenship, M.T. Madigan, C.E. Bauer, eds.), Kluwer Academic Publishers, Dordrecht, pp. 31–47.
6. C.R. Woese, O. Kandler, M.L. Wheelis, Towards a natural system of organisms: proposal for the domains Archaea, Bacteria, and Eucarya. *Proc. Natl. Acad. Sci. U.S.A.* **87** (1990) 4576–4579.
7. B. Alexander, J.H. Andersen, R.P. Cox, J.F. Imhoff, Phylogeny of green sulfur bacteria on the basis of gene sequences of 16s rRNA and of the Fenna-Matthews-Olson protein. *Arch. Microbiol.* **178** (2002) 131–140.
8. E. Stackebrandt, F.A. Rainey, N. WardRainey, Anoxygenic phototrophy across the phylogenetic spectrum: current understanding and future perspectives. *Arch. Microbiol.* **166** (1996) 211–223.
9. F. Baymann, E. Lebrun, M. Brugna, B. Schoepp-Cothenet, M.T. Giudici-Orticoni, W. Nitschke, The redox protein construction kit: pre-last universal common ancestor evolution of energy-conserving enzymes. *Phil. Trans. R. Soc. London Ser. B Biol. Sci.* **358** (2003) 267–274.
10. B.K. Pierson, J.M. Olson, Evolution of photosynthesis in anoxygenic photosynthetic prokaryotes, in: *Microbial Mats* (1987) (Y. Cohen, E. Rosenberg, eds.), American Society Microbiologists, Washington, pp. 402–427.

11. R.E. Blankenship, Origin and early evolution of photosynthesis. *Photosynth. Res.* **33** (1992) 91–111.
12. W.D. Schubert, O. Klukas, W. Saenger, H.T. Witt, P. Fromme, N. Krauss, A common ancestor for oxygenic and anoxygenic photosynthetic systems: a comparison based on the structural model of Photosystem I. *J. Mol. Biol.* **280** (1998) 297–314.
13. I.R. Vassiliev, M.L. Antonkine, J.H. Golbeck, Iron-sulfur clusters in Type I reaction centers. *Biochim. Biophys. Acta* **1507** (2001) 139–160.
14. P. Jordan, P. Fromme, H.T. Witt, O. Klukas, W. Saenger, N. Krauss, Three-dimensional structure of cyanobacterial Photosystem I at 2.5 Å resolution. *Nature* **411** (2001) 909–917.
15. K.N. Ferreira, T.M. Iverson, K. Maghlaoui, J. Barber, S. Iwata, Architecture of the photosynthetic oxygen-evolving center. *Science* **303** (2004) 1831–1838.
16. A. Zouni, H.T. Witt, J. Kern, P. Fromme, N. Krauss, W. Saenger, P. Orth, Crystal structure of Photosystem II from *Synechococcus elongatus* at 3.8 Å resolution. *Nature* **409** (2001) 739–743.
17. N. Kamiya, J.R. Shen, Crystal structure of oxygen-evolving Photosystem II from *Thermosynechococcus vulcanus* at 3.7-Å resolution. *Proc. Natl. Acad. Sci. U.S.A.* **100** (2003) 98–103.
18. P. Fromme, A. Melkozernov, P. Jordan, N. Krauss, Structure and function of Photosystem I: interaction with its soluble electron carriers and external antenna systems. *FEBS Lett.* **555** (2003) 40–44.
19. J.H. Golbeck, The binding of cofactors to Photosystem I analyzed by spectroscopic and mutagenic methods. *Annu. Rev. Biophys. Biomol. Struct.* **32** (2003) 237–256.
20. C. Berthomieu, R. Hienerwadel, Iron coordination in Photosystem II: interaction between bicarbonate and the QB pocket studied by Fourier transform infrared spectroscopy. *Biochemistry* **40** (1995) 4044–4052.
21. J. Xiong, K. Inoue, C.E. Bauer, Tracking molecular evolution of photosynthesis by characterization of a major photosynthesis gene cluster from *Heliobacillus mobilis*. *Proc. Natl. Acad. Sci. U.S.A.* **95** (1998) 14851–14856.
22. R.S. Gupta, T. Mukhtar, B. Singh, Evolutionary relationships among photosynthetic prokaryotes (*Heliobacterium chlorum*, *Chloroflexus aurantiacus* cyanobacteria, *Chlorobium tepidum* and proteobacteria): implications regarding the origin of photosynthesis. *Mol. Microbiol.* **32** (1999) 893–906.
23. R.S. Gupta, Evolutionary relationships among photosynthetic bacteria. *Photosynth. Res.* **76** (2003) 173–183.
24. J. Raymond, O. Zhaxybayeva, J.P. Gogarten, R.E. Blankenship, Evolution of photosynthetic prokaryotes: a maximum likelihood mapping approach. *Philos. Trans. R. Soc. London Ser. B Biol. Sci.* **358** (2003) 223–230.
25. J. Raymond, O. Zhaxybayeva, J.P. Gogarten, S.Y. Gerdes, R.E. Blankenship, Whole-genome analysis of photosynthetic prokaryotes. *Science* **298** (2002) 1616–1620.
26. W.F. Vermaas, Evolution of heliobacteria: implications for photosynthetic reaction center complexes. *Photosynth. Res.* **41** (1994) 285–294.
27. J. Xiong, W.M. Fischer, K. Inoue, M. Nakahara, C.E. Bauer, Molecular evidence for the early evolution of photosynthesis. *Science* **289** (2000) 1724–1730.
28. G.J. Olsen, C.R. Woese, R. Overbeek, The winds of (evolutionary) change: breathing new life into microbiology. *J. Bacteriol.* **176** (1994) 1–6.
29. F. Baymann, M. Bruga, U. Muhlenhoff, W. Nitschke, Daddy, where did (PS)I come from? *Biochim. Biophys. Acta* **1507** (2001) 291–310.

30. J.F. Imhoff, J. Suling, R. Petri, Phylogenetic relationships among the *Chromatiaceae* their taxonomic reclassification and description of the new genera *Allochromatium, Halochromatium, Isochromatium, Marichromatium, Thiococcus, Thiohalocapsa* and *Thermochromatium*. *Int. J. Syst. Bact.* **48** (1998) 1129–1143.
31. J. Deisenhofer, O. Epp, I. Sinning, H. Michel, Crystallographic refinement at 2.3 Å resolution and refined model of the photosynthetic reaction centre from *Rhodopseudomonas viridis*. *J. Mol. Biol.* **246** (1995) 429–457.
32. J. Deisenhofer, O. Epp, K. Miki, R. Huber, H. Michel, Structure of the protein subunits in the photosynthetic reaction centre of *Rhodopseudomonas viridis* at 3 Å resolution. *Nature* **318** (1985) 618–624.
33. C.R. Lancaster, H. Michel, Refined crystal structures of reaction centres from *Rhodopseudomonas viridis* in complexes with the herbicide atrazine and two chiral atrazine derivatives also lead to a new model of the bound carotenoid. *J. Mol. Biol.* **286** (1999) 883–898.
34. J.P. Allen, G. Feher, T.O. Yeates, H. Komiya, D.C. Rees, Structure of the reaction center from *Rhodobacter sphaeroides* R-26: the protein subunits. *Proc. Natl. Acad. Sci. U.S.A.* **84** (1987) 6162–6166.
35. J.P. Allen, G. Feher, T.O. Yeates, H. Komiya, D.C. Rees, Structure of the reaction center from *Rhodobacter sphaeroides* R-26: the cofactors. *Proc. Natl. Acad. Sci. U.S.A.* **84** (1987) 5730–5734.
36. C.H. Chang, O. El-Kabbani, D. Tiede, J. Norris, M. Schiffer, Structure of the membrane-bound protein photosynthetic reaction center from *Rhodobacter sphaeroides*. *Biochemistry* **30** (1991) 5352–5360.
37. O. El-Kabbani, C.H. Chang, D. Tiede, J. Norris, M. Schiffer, Comparison of reaction centers from *Rhodobacter sphaeroides* and *Rhodopseudomonas viridis*: overall architechture and protein-pigment interactions. *Biochemistry* **30** (1991) 5361–5369.
38. U. Ermler, G. Fritzsch, S.K. Buchanan, H. Michel, Structure of the photosynthetic reaction centre from *Rhodobacter sphaeroides* at 2.65 Å resolution: cofactors and protein-cofacter interactions. *Structure* **2** (1994) 925–936.
39. K.E. McAuley-Hecht, P.K. Fyfe, J.P. Ridge, S.M. Prince, C.N. Hunter, N.W. Isaacs, R.J. Cogdell, M.R. Jones, Structural studies of wild-type and mutant reaction centers from an antenna-deficient strain of *Rhodobacter sphaeroides*: monitoring the optical properties of the complex from bacterial cell to crystal. *Biochemistry* **37** (1998) 4740–4750.
40. P.K. Fyfe, K.E. McAuley-Hecht, J.P. Ridge, S.M. Prince, G. Fritzsch, N.W. Isaacs, R.J. Cogdell, M.R. Jones, Crystallographic studies of mutant reaction centres from *Rhodobacter sphaeroides*. *Photosynth. Res.* **55** (1998) 133–140.
41. P.K. Fyfe, M.R. Jones, Re-emerging structures: continuing crystallography of the bacterial reaction center. *Biochim. Biophys. Acta Bioenerg.* **1459** (2000) 413–421.
42. T. Nogi, I. Fathir, M. Kobayashi, T. Nozawa, K. Miki, Crystal structures of photosynthetic reaction center and high-potential iron-sulfur protein from *Thermochromatium tepidum*: Thermostability and electron transfer. *Proc. Natl. Acad. Sci. U.S.A.* **97** (2000) 13561–13566.
43. T. Nogi, K. Miki, Structural basis of bacterial photosynthetic reaction centers. *J. Biochem.* **130** (2001) 319–329.
44. W. Nitschke, S. Dracheva, Reaction center associated cytochromes, in: *Anoxygenic Photosynthetic Bacteria* (1995) (R.E. Blankenship, M.T. Madigan, C.E. Bauer, eds.), Kluwer Academic Publishers, Dordrecht, pp. 775–805.

45. J.M. Ortega, P. Mathis, Electron transfer from the tetraheme cytochrome to the special pair in isolated reaction centers of *Rhodopseudomonas viridis*. *Biochemistry* **32** (1993) 1141–1151.
46. I.P. Chen, P. Mathis, J. Koepke, H. Michel, Uphill electron transfer in the tetraheme cytochrome subunit of the *Rhodopseudomonas viridis* photosynthetic reaction center: evidence from site-directed mutagenesis. *Biochemistry* **39** (2000) 3592–3602.
47. I. Agalidis, S. Othman, A. Boussac, F. Reiss-Husson, A. Desbois, Purification, redox and spectroscopic properties of the tetraheme cytochrome c isolated from *Rubrivivax gelatinosus*. *Eur. J. Biochem.* **261** (1999) 325–336.
48. L. Menin, B. Schoepp, D. Garcia, P. Parot, A. Verméglio, Characterization of the reaction center bound tetraheme cytochrome of *Rhodocyclus tenuis*. *Biochemistry* **36** (1997) 12175–12182.
49. D. Garcia, P. Richaud, J. Breton, A. Verméglio, Structure and function of the tetraheme cytochrome associated to the reaction center of *Roseobacter denitrificans*. *Biochimie* **76** (1994) 666–673.
50. D. Garcia, P. Mathis, A. Vermeglio, Kinetics of electron transfer between the tetrahemic cytochrome and the special pair in isolated reaction centers of *Roseobacter denitrificans*. *Photosynth. Res.* **55** (1998) 331–335.
51. A. Hochkoeppler, G. Moschettini, D. Zannoni, The electron transport system of the facultative phototroph Rhodoferax fermentans. 1. A functional, thermodynamic and spectroscopic study of the respiratory chain of dark-grown and light-grown cells. *Biochim. Biophys. Acta* **1229** (1995) 73–80.
52. F. Drepper, T. Saito, M. Kobayashi, T. Nozawa, P. Mathis, Electron transfer reactions of high-potential cytochromes in the reaction centre of *Chromatium tepidum*. *Photosynth. Res.* **55** (1998) 325–330.
53. S. Masuda, M. Yoshida, K.V. Nagashima, K. Shimada, K. Matsuura, A new cytochrome subunit bound to the photosynthetic reaction center in the purple bacterium, *Rhodovulum sulfidophilum*. *J. Biol. Chem.* **274** (1999) 10795–10801.
54. J. Alric, Y. Tsukatani, M. Yoshida, K. Matsuura, K. Shimada, R. Hienerwadel, B. Schoepp-Cothenet, W. Nitschke, K.V. Nagashima, A. Vermeglio, Structural and functional characterization of the unusual triheme cytochrome bound to the reaction center of rhodovulum sulfidophilum. *J. Biol. Chem.* **279** (2004) 26090–26097.
55. P.L. Dutton, K.M. Petty, H.S. Bonner, S.D. Morse, Cytochrome c2 and reaction center of *Rhodopseudomonas spheroides* membranes. Extinction coefficients, content, half-reduction potentials, kinetics, and electric field alterations. *Biochim. Biophys. Acta* **387** (1975) 536–556.
56. W.W. Parson, A. Warshel, Spectroscopic properties of photosynthetic reaction centers. 2. Application of the theory to *Rhodopseudomonas viridis*. *J. Am. Chem. Soc.* **109** (1987) 6152–6163.
57. L.J. Moore, H. Zhou, S.G. Boxer, Excited-state electronic asymmetry of the special pair in photosynthetic reaction center mutants: absorption and Stark spectroscopy. *Biochemistry* **38** (1999) 11949–11960.
58. J. Breton, Orientation of the chromophores in the reaction center of *Rhodopseudomonas viridis*. Comparison of low-temperature linear dichroism spectra with a model derived from X-ray crystallography. *Biochim. Biophys. Acta* **810** (1985) 235–245.
59. J. Breton, J.-L. Martin, A. Migus, A. Antonetti, A. Orszag, Femtosecond spectroscopy of excitation electron transfer and initial charge separation in the reaction

center of the photosynthetic bacterium *Rhodopseudomonas viridis*. *Proc. Natl. Acad. Sci. U.S.A.* **83** (1986) 5121–5175.
60. J. Breton, J.-L. Martin, G.R. Fleming, J.-C. Lambry, Low temperature femtosecond spectroscopy of the initial step of electron transfer in reaction centers from photosynthetic purple bacteria. *Biochemistry* **27** (1988) 8276–8284.
61. Y.W. Jia, D.M. Jonas, T.H. Joo, Y. Nagasawa, M.J. Lang, G.R. Fleming, Observation of ultrafast energy-transfer from the accessory bacteriochlorophylls to the special pair in photosynthetic reaction centers. *J. Phys. Chem.* **99** (1995) 6263–6266.
62. B.A. King, T.B. McAnaney, A. deWinter, S.G. Boxer, Excited state energy transfer pathways in photosynthetic reaction centers. 3. Ultrafast emission from the monomeric bacteriochlorophylls. *J. Phys. Chem. B* **104** (2000) 8895–8902.
63. V.Z. Paschenko, B.N. Korvatovskii, A.A. Kononenko, S.K. Chamorovsky, A.B. Rubin, Estimation of the rate of photochemical charge separation in *Rhodopseudomonas spheroides* reaction centers by fluorescence and absorption picosecond spectroscopy. *FEBS Lett.* **191** (1985) 245–248.
64. D. Holten, C. Hoganson, M.W. Windsor, G.C. Schenck, W.W. Parson, A. Migus, R.L. Fork, C.V. Shank, Subpicosecond and picosecond studies of electron transfer intermediates in *Rhodopseudomonas sphaeroides* reaction centers. *Biochim. Biophys. Acta* **592** (1980) 461–477.
65. N.W. Woodbury, M. Becker, D. Middendorf, W.W. Parson, Picosecond kinetics of the initial photochemical electron-transfer reaction in bacterial photosynthetic reaction center. *Biochemistry* **24** (1985) 7516–7521.
66. W. Holzapfel, U. Finkele, W. Kaiser, D. Oesterhelt, H. Scheer, H.U. Stilz, W. Zinth, Initial electron transfer in the reaction center from *Rhodobacter sphaeroides*. *Proc. Natl. Acad. Sci. U.S.A.* **87** (1990) 5168–5172.
67. C. Lauterwasser, U. Finkele, H. Scheer, W. Zinth, Temperature dependence of the primary electron transfer in photosynthetic reaction centers from *Rhodobacter sphaeroides*. *Chem. Phys. Lett.* **183** (1991) 471–477.
68. C. Kirmaier, D. Holten, Subpicosecond spectroscopy of charge separation in *Rhodobacter capsulatus* reaction centers. *Isr. J. Chem.* **28** (1988) 79–85.
69. A.R. Holzwarth, M.G. Müller, Energetics and kinetics of radical pairs in reaction centers from *Rhodobacter sphaeroides*. A femtosecond transient absorption study. *Biochemistry* **35** (1996) 11820–11831.
70. J.M. Peloquin, J.C. Williams, X. Lin, R.G. Alden, A.K.W. Taguchi, J.P. Allen, N.W. Woodbury, Time-dependent thermodynamics during early electron transfer in reaction centers from *Rhodobacter sphaeroides*. *Biochemistry* **33** (1994) 8089–8100.
71. P. Huppmann, S. Sporlein, M. Bibikova, D. Oesterhelt, J. Wachtveitl, W. Zinth, Electron transfer in reaction centers of *Blastochloris viridis*: Photosynthetic reactions approximating the adiabatic regime. *J. Phys. Chem. A* **107** (2003) 8302–8309.
72. J.-L. Martin, J. Breton, A.J. Hoff, A. Migus, A. Antonetti, Femtosecond spectroscopy of electron transfer in the reaction center of the photosynthetic bacterium *Rhodopseudomonas sphaeroides* R-26: direct electron transfer from the dimeric bacteriochlorophyll primary donor to the bacteriopheophytin acceptor with a time constant of 2.8 ± 0.2 psec. *Proc. Natl. Acad. Sci. U.S.A.* **83** (1986) 957–961.
73. W. Holzapfel, U. Finkele, W. Kaiser, D. Oesterhelt, H. Scheer, H.U. Stilz, W. Zinth, Observation of a bacteriochlorophyll anion radical during the primary charge separation in a reaction center. *Chem. Phys. Lett.* **160** (1989) 1–7.
74. N.W. Woodbury, J.M. Peloquin, R.G. Alden, X. Lin, A.K.W. Taguchi, J.C. Williams, J.P. Allen, Relationship between thermodynamics and mechanism

during photoinduced charge separation in reaction centers from *Rhodobacter sphaeroides*. *Biochemistry* **33** (1994) 8101–8112.

75. K.J. Kaufmann, K.M. Petty, P.L. Dutton, P.M. Rentzepis, Picosecond kinetics of events leading to reaction center bacteriochlorophyll oxidation. *Science* **188** (1975) 1301–1304.

76. M.G. Rockley, M.W. Windsor, R.J. Cogdell, W.W. Parson, Picosecond detection of an intermediate in the photochemical reaction of bacterial photosynthesis. *Proc. Natl. Acad. Sci. U.S.A.* **72** (1975) 2251–2255.

77. D. Holten, M.W. Windsor, W.W. Parson, J.P. Thornber, Primary photochemical processes in isolated reaction centers of *Rhodopseudomonas viridis*. *Biochim. Biophys Acta* **501** (1978) 112–126.

78. C.A. Wraight, R.K. Clayton, The absolute quantum efficiency of bacteriochlorophyll photooxidation in reaction centres of *Rhodopseudomonas spheroids*. *Biochim. Biophys. Acta* **333** (1974) 246–260.

79. M. Volk, G. Scheidel, A. Ogrodnik, R. Feick, M.E. Michel-Beyerle, High quantum yield of charge separation in reaction centers of *Chloroflexus aurantiacus*. *Biochim. Biophys. Acta* **1058** (1991) 217–224.

80. C. Kirmaier, D. Holten, W.W. Parson, Temperature and detection-wavelength dependence of the picosecond electron-transfer kinetics measured in *Rhodopseudomonas sphaeroides* reaction centers. Resolution of new spectral and kinetic components in the primary charge-separation process. *Biochim. Biophys. Acta* **810** (1985) 33–48.

81. G.R. Fleming, J.-L. Martin, J. Breton, Rates of primary electron transfer in photosynthetic reaction centers and their mechanistic implications. *Nature* **333** (1988) 190–192.

82. V. Nagarajan, W.W. Parson, D. Davis, C.C. Schenck, Kinetics and free energy gaps of electron-transfer reactions in *Rhodobacter sphaeroides* reaction centers. *Biochemistry* **32** (1993) 12324–12336.

83. P. Huppman, T. Arlt, H. Penzkofer, S. Schmidt, M. Bibikova, B. Dohse, D. Oesterhelt, J. Wachtveit, W. Zinth, Kinetics, energetics, and electronic coupling of the primary electron transfer reactions in mutated reaction centers of *Blastochloris viridis*. *Biophys. J.* **82** (2002) 3186–3197.

84. Y. Jia, T.J. DiMagno, C.-K. Chan, Z. Wang, M. Du, D.K. Hanson, M. Schiffer, J.R. Norris, G.R. Fleming, M.S. Popov, Primary charge separation in mutant reaction centers of *Rhodobacter capsulatus*. *J. Phys. Chem.* **97** (1993) 13180–13191.

85. A.L.M. Haffa, S. Lin, E. Katilius, J.C. Williams, A.K.W. Taguchi, J.P. Allen, N.W. Woodbury, The dependence of the initial electron-transfer rate on driving force in *Rhodobacter sphaeroides* reaction centers. *J. Phys. Chem. B* **106** (2002) 7376–7384.

86. C.C. Schenck, W.W. Parson, D. Holten, M.W. Windsor, A. Sarai, Temperature dependence of electron transfer between bacteriopheophytin and ubiquinone in protonated and deuterated reaction centers of *Rhodopseudomonas sphaeroides*. *Biophys. J.* **36** (1981) 479–489.

87. M.R. Gunner, P.L. Dutton, Temperature and ΔG° dependence of the electron transfer from BPh^- to Q_A in reaction center protein from *Rhodobacter sphaeroides* with different quinones as Q_A. *J. Am. Chem. Soc.* **111** (1989) 3400–3412.

88. M. Bixon, J. Jortner, M.E. Michel-Beyerle, On the mechanism of the primary charge separation in bacterial photosynthesis. *Biochim. Biophys. Acta* **1056** (1991) 301–315.

89. N. Makri, E. Sim, D.E. Makarov, M. Topaler, Long-time quantum simulation of the primary charge separation in bacterial photosynthesis. *Proc. Natl. Acad. Sci. U.S.A.* **93** (1996) 3926–3931.
90. E. Sim, N. Makri, Path integral simulation of charge transfer dynamics in photosynthetic reaction centers. *J. Phys. Chem. B* **101** (1997) 5446–5458.
91. C.K. Chan, T.J. DiMagno, L.X.Q. Chen, J.R. Norris, G.R. Fleming, Mechanism of the initial charge separation in bacterial photosynthetic reaction centers. *Proc. Natl. Acad. Sci. U.S.A.* **88** (1991) 11202–11206.
92. W.W. Parson, Z.T. Chu, A. Warshel, Electrostatic control of charge separation in bacterial photosynthesis. *Biochim. Biophys. Acta* **1017** (1990) 251–272.
93. R.G. Alden, W.W. Parson, Z.T. Chu, A. Warshel, Calculations of electrostatic energies in photosynthetic reaction centers. *J. Am. Chem. Soc.* **117** (1995) 12284–12298.
94. A. Warshel, W.W. Parson, Dynamics of biochemical and biophysical reactions insight from computer simulations. *Q. Rev. Biophys.* **34** (2001) 563–679.
95. T. Arlt, S. Schmidt, W. Kaiser, C. Lauterwasser, M. Meyer, H. Scheer, W. Zinth, The accessory bacteriochlorophyll: a real electron carrier in primary photosynthesis. *Proc. Natl. Acad. Sci. U.S.A.* **90** (1993) 11757–11762.
96. A.G. Yakovlev, A.Y. Shkuropatov, V.A. Shuvalov, Nuclear wavepacket motion between P* and $P^+B_A^-$ potential surfaces with subsequent electron transfer to H_A in bacterial reaction centers. 1. Room temperature. *Biochemistry* **41** (2002) 2667–2674.
97. J.T. Kennis, A.Y. Shkuropatov, I.H.M. van Stokkum, P. Gast, A.J. Hoff, V.A. Shuvalov, T.J. Aartsma, Formation of a long-lived $P^+B_A^-$ state in plant pheophytin-exchanged reaction centers of *Rhodobacter sphaeroides* R26 at low temperature. *Biochemistry* **36** (1997) 16231–16238.
98. I.H.M. van Stokkum, L.M.P. Beekman, M.R. Jones, M.E. van Brederode, R. van Grondelle, Primary electron transfer kinetics in membrane-bound *Rhodobacter sphaeroides* reaction centers: a global and target analysis. *Biochemistry* **36** (1997) 11360–11368.
99. M.R.A. Blomberg, P.H.M. Siegbahn, Modeling electron transfer in biochemistry: a quantum chemical study of charge separation in *Rhodobacter sphaeroides* and Photosystem II. *J. Am. Chem. Soc.* **120** (1998) 8812–8824.
100. M. Ceccarelli, M. Marchi, Simulation and modeling of the *Rhodobacter sphaeroides* bacterial reaction center II: primary charge separation. *J. Phys. Chem. B* **107** (2003) 5630–5641.
101. M. Gunner, A. Nichols, B. Honig, Electrostatic potentials in *Rhodopseudomonas viridis* reaction centers: implications for the driving force and directionality of electron transfer. *J. Phys. Chem.* **100** (1996) 4277–4291.
102. W.W. Parson, A. Warshel, Dependence of photosynthetic electron-transfer kinetics on temperature and energy in a density-matrix model. *J. Phys. Chem. B* **108** (2004) 10474–10483.
103. M.H. Vos, J.C. Lambry, S.J. Robles, D.C. Youvan, J. Breton, J.L. Martin, Direct observation of vibrational coherence in bacterial reaction centers using femtosecond absorption spectroscopy. *Proc. Natl. Acad. Sci. U.S.A.* **88** (1991) 8885–8889.
104. M.H. Vos, J.C. Lambry, S.J. Robles, D.C. Youvan, J. Breton, J.L. Martin, Femtosecond spectral evolution of the excited state of bacterial reaction centers at 10 K. *Proc. Natl. Acad. Sci. U.S.A.* **89** (1992) 613–617.

105. M.H. Vos, F. Rappaport, J.-H. Lambry, J. Breton, J.-L. Martin, Visualization of coherent nuclear motion in a membrane protein by femtosecond spectroscopy. *Nature* **363** (1993) 320–325.
106. M.H. Vos, M.R. Jones, C.N. Hunter, J. Breton, J.-C. Lambry, J.-L. Martin, Coherent dynamics during the primary electron-transfer reaction in membrane-bound reaction centers of *Rhodobacter sphaeroides*. *Biochemistry* **33** (1994) 6750–6757.
107. M.H. Vos, M.R. Jones, C.N. Hunter, J. Breton, J.-L. Martin, Coherent nuclear dynamics at room temperature in bacterial reaction centers. *Proc. Natl. Acad. Sci. U.S.A.* **91** (1994) 12701–12705.
108. M.H. Vos, M.R. Jones, J. Breton, J.C. Lambry, J.-L. Martin, Vibrational dephasing of long- and short-lived primary donor excited states in mutant reaction centers of *Rhodobacter sphaeroides*. *Biochemistry* **35** (1996) 2687–2692.
109. M.H. Vos, C. Rischel, M.R. Jones, J.-L. Martin, Electrochromic detection of a coherent component in the formation of the charge pair $P^+H_L^-$ in bacterial reaction centers. *Biochemistry* **39** (2000) 8353–8361.
110. S. Spörlein, W. Zinth, J. Wachtveitl, Vibrational coherence in photosynthetic reaction centers observed in the bacteriochlorophyll anion band. *J. Phys. Chem. B* **102** (1998) 7492–7496.
111. A.M. Streltsov, T.J. Aartsma, A.J. Hoff, V.A. Shuvalov, Oscillations within the B_L absorption band of *Rhodobacter sphaeroides* reaction centers upon 30 femtosecond excitation at 865 nm. *Chem. Phys. Lett.* **266** (1997) 347–352.
112. A.M. Streltsov, S.I.E. Vulto, A.Y. Shkuropatov, A.J. Hoff, T.J. Aartsma, V.A. Shuvalov, B_A and B_B absorbance perturbations induced by coherent nuclear motions in reaction centers from *Rhodobacter sphaeroides* upon 30-fs excitation of the primary donor. *J. Phys. Chem. B.* **102** (1998) 7293–7298.
113. V.A. Shuvalov, A.G. Yakovlev, Coupling of nuclear wavepacket motion and charge separation in bacterial reaction centers. *FEBS Lett.* **540** (2003) 26–34.
114. A.G. Yakovlev, A.C. Shkuropatov, A.V. Shuvalov, Nuclear wavepacket motion producing a reversible charge separation in bacterial reaction centers. *FEBS Lett.* **466** (2000) 209–212.
115. A.G. Yakovlev, V.A. Shuvalov, Formation of bacteriochlorophyll anion band at 1020 nm produced by nuclear wavepacket motion in bacterial reaction centers. *J. Chin. Chem. Soc.* **47** (2000) 1–6.
116. S. Lin, A.K.W. Taguchi, N.W. Woodbury, Excitation wavelength dependence of energy transfer and charge separation in reaction centers from *Rhodobacter sphaeroides*: evidence for adiabatic electron transfer. *J. Phys. Chem.* **100** (1996) 17067–17078.
117. W.W. Parson, A. Warshel, A density-matrix model of photosynthetic electron transfer with microscopically estimated vibrational relaxation times. *Chem. Phys.* **296** (2004) 201–206.
118. V.I. Novoderezhkin, A.G. Yakovlev, R. van Grondelle, V.A. Shuvalov, Coherent nuclear and electronic dynamics in primary charge separation in photosynthetic reaction centers: a Redfield theory approach. *J. Phys. Chem. B* **108** (2004) 7445–7457.
119. C. Kirmaier, L. Laporte, C.C. Schenck, D. Holten, The nature and dynamics of the charge-separated intermediate in reaction centers in which bacteriochlorophyll replaces the photoactive bacteriopheophytin. 1. Spectral characterization of the transient state. *J. Phys. Chem.* **99** (1995) 8903–8909.
120. C. Kirmaier, L. Laporte, C.C. Schenck, D. Holten, The nature and dynamics of the charge-separated intermediate in reaction centers in which bacteriochlorophyll

replaces the photoactive bacteriopheophytin. 2. The rates and yields of charge separation and recombination. *J. Phys. Chem.* **99** (1995) 8910–8917.
121. L. Laporte, C. Kirmaier, C.C. Schenck, D. Holten, Free-energy dependence of the rate of electron transfer to the primary quinone in beta-type reaction centers. *Chem. Phys.* **197** (1995) 225–237.
122. S. Schmidt, T. Arlt, P. Hamm, H. Huber, T. Nägele, J. Wachtveitl, M. Meyer, H. Scheer, W. Zinth, Primary electron-transfer dynamics in modified bacterial reaction centers containing pheophytin-a instead of bacteriopheophytin-a. *Spectrochim. Acta A* **51** (1995) 1565–1578.
123. A.Y. Shkuropatov, V.A. Shuvalov, Electron transfer in pheophytin a-modified reaction centers from *Rhodobacter sphaeroides* (R-26). *FEBS. Lett.* **322** (1993) 168–172.
124. S. Spörlein, W. Zinth, M. Meyer, H. Scheer, J. Wachtveitl, Primary electron transfer in modified bacterial reaction centers: optimization of the first events in photosynthesis. *Chem. Phys. Lett.* **322** (2000) 454–464.
125. T. Arlt, B. Dohse, S. Schmidt, J. Wachtveitl, E. Laussermaier, W. Zinth, D. Oesterhelt, Electron transfer dynamics of *Rhodopseudomonas viridis* reaction centers with a modified binding site for the accessory bacteriochlorophyll. *Biochemistry* **35** (1996) 9235–9244.
126. S. Schmidt, T. Arlt, P. Hamm, H. Huber, T. Naegele, J. Wachtveitl, M. Meyer, H. Scheer, W. Zinth, Energetics of the primary electron transfer reaction revealed by ultrafast spectroscopy on modified bacterial reaction centers. *Chem. Phys. Lett.* **223** (1994) 116–120.
127. B.A. Heller, D. Holten, C. Kirmaier, Effects of Asp residues near the L-side pigments in bacterial reaction centers. *Biochemistry* **35** (1996) 15418–15427.
128. J.A. Roberts, D. Holten, C. Kirmaier, Primary events in photosynthetic reaction centers with multiple mutations near the photoactive electron carriers. *J. Phys. Chem. B* **105** (2001) 5575–5584.
129. N.W. Woodbury, J.P. Allen, The pathway, kinetics and thermodynamics of electron transfer in wild type and mutant reaction centers of purple nonsulfur bacteria, in: *Anoxygenic Photosynthetic Bacteria* (1995) (R.E. Blankenship, M.T. Madigan, C.E. Bauer, eds.), Kluwer Academic Publishers, Dordrecht, pp. 527–557.
130. J.C. Williams, R.G. Alden, H.A. Murchison, J.M. Peloquin, N.W. Woodbury, J.P. Allen, Effects of mutations near the bacteriochlorophylls in reaction centers from *Rhodobacter sphaeroides*. *Biochemistry* **31** (1992) 11029–11037.
131. J.P. Allen, J.C. Williams, M.S. Graige, M.L. Paddock, A. Labahn, G. Feher, M.Y. Okamura, Free energy dependence of the direct charge recombination from the primary and secondary quinones in reaction centers from *Rhodobacter sphaeroides*. *Photosynth. Res.* **55** (1998) 227–233.
132. X. Lin, H.A. Murchison, V. Nagarajan, W.W. Parson, J.P. Allen, J.C. Williams, Specific alteration of the oxidation potential of the electron donor in reaction centers from *Rhodobacter sphaeroides*. *Proc. Natl. Acad. Sci. U.S.A.* **91** (1994) 10265–10270.
133. T.A. Mattioli, J.C. Williams, J.P. Allen, B. Robert, Changes in primary donor hydrogen bonding interactions in mutant reaction centers from *Rhodobacter sphaeroides*: identification of the vibrational frequencies of all the conjugated carbonyl groups. *Biochemistry* **33** (1994) 1636–1643.
134. T. Arlt, M. Bibikova, H. Penzkofer, D. Oesterhelt, W. Zinth, Strong acceleration of primary photosynthetic electron transfer in a mutated reaction center of *Rhodopseudomonas viridis*. *J. Phys. Chem.* **100** (1996) 12060–12065.

135. R.G. Alden, W.W. Parson, Z.T. Chu, A. Warshel, Orientation of the OH dipole of tyrosine (M)210 and its effect on electrostatic energies in photosynthetic bacterial reaction centers. *J. Phys. Chem.* **100** (1996) 16761–16770.
136. U. Finkele, C. Lauterwasser, W. Zinth, K.A. Gray, D. Oesterhelt, Role of tyrosine M210 in the initial charge separation of reaction centers of *Rhodobacter sphaeroides*. *Biochemistry* **29** (1990) 8517–8521.
137. V. Nagarajan, W.W. Parson, D. Gaul, C. Schenck, Effect of directed mutations of the tyrosine at site (M)210 on the primary photosynthetic electron transfer process in *Rhodobacter sphaeroides*. *Proc. Natl. Acad. Sci. U.S.A.* **87** (1990) 7888–7892.
138. C.K. Chan, L.X.Q. Chen, T.J. Dimagno, D.K. Hanson, S.L. Nance, M. Schiffer, J.R. Norris, G.R. Fleming, Mechanism of the initial charge separation in photosynthetic bacterial reaction centers. *Chem. Phys. Lett.* **176** (1991) 366–372.
139. K.A. Gray, J. Wachtveitl, D. Oesterhelt, Photochemical trapping of a bacteriopheophytin anion in site-specific reaction-center mutants from the photosynthetic bacterium *Rhodobacter sphaeroides*. *Eur. J. Biochem.* **207** (1992) 723–731.
140. L.M.P. Beekman, I.H.M. van Stokkum, R. Monshouwer, A.J. Rijnders, P. McGlynn, R.W. Visschers, M.R. Jones, R. van Grondelle, Primary electron transfer in membrane-bound reaction centers with mutations at the M210 position. *J. Phys. Chem.* **100** (1996) 7256–7268.
141. S. Shochat, T. Arlt, C. Francke, P. Gast, P.I. van Noort, S.C. Otte, H.P.M. Schelvis, S. Schmidt, E. Vijgenboom, J. Vrieze, W. Zinth, A.J. Hoff, Spectroscopic characterization of reaction centers of the (M)Y210W mutant of the photosynthetic bacterium *Rhodobacter sphaeroides*. *Photosynth. Res.* **40** (1994) 55–66.
142. C. Kirmaier, P.D. Laible, D.K. Hanson, D. Holten, B-side charge separation in bacterial photosynthetic reaction centers: Nanosecond time scale electron transfer from H_B^- to Q_B. *Biochemistry* **42** (2003) 2016–2024.
143. A.G. Yakovlev, L.G. Vasilieva, A.Y. Shkuropatov, T.I. Bolgarina, V.A. Shkuropatova, V.A. Shuvalov, Mechanism of charge separation and stabilization of separated charges in reaction centers of *Chloroflexus aurantiacus* and of YM210W(L) mutants of *Rhodobacter sphaeroides* excited by 20 fs pulses at 90 K. *J. Phys. Chem. A* **107** (2003) 8330–8338.
144. K.E. McAuley, P.K. Fyfe, R.J. Cogdell, N.W. Isaacs, M.R. Jones, X-ray crystal structure of the YM210W mutant reaction centre from *Rhodobacter sphaeroides*. *FEBS Lett.* **467** (2000) 285–290.
145. W.W. Parson, The reaction between primary and secondary electron acceptors in bacterial photosynthesis. *Biochim. Biophys. Acta* **189** (1969) 384–396.
146. M.S. Graige, M.L. Paddock, J.M. Bruce, G. Feher, M.Y. Okamura, Mechanism of proton-coupled electron transfer for quinone (Q_B) reduction in reaction centers of *Rb. Sphaeroides*. *J. Am. Chem. Soc.* **118** (1996) 9005–9016.
147. M.Y. Okamura, M.L. Paddock, M.S. Graige, G. Feher, Proton and electron transfer in bacterial reaction centers. *Biochim. Biophys. Acta* **1458** (2000) 148–163.
148. D.M. Tiede, L. Utschig, D.K. Hanson, D.M. Gallo, Resolution of electron and proton transfer events in the electrochromism associated with quinone reduction in bacterial reaction centers. *Photosynth. Res.* **55** (1998) 267–273.
149. J.L. Li, D. Gilroy, D.M. Tiede, M.R. Gunner, Kinetic phases in the electron transfer from $P^+Q_A^-Q_B$ to $P^+Q_AQ_B^-$ and the associated processes in *Rhodobacter sphaeroides* R-26 reaction centers. *Biochemistry* **37** (1998) 2818–2829.
150. J. Li, E. Takahashi, M.R. Gunner, -DG_{AB} and pH dependence of the electron transfer from $P^+Q_A^-Q_B$ to $P^+Q_AQ_B^-$ in *Rhodobacter sphaeroides* reaction centers. *Biochemistry* **39** (2000) 7445–7454.

151. Q. Xu, M.R. Gunner, Exploring the energy profile of the Q_A^- to Q_B electron transfer reaction in bacterial photosynthetic reaction centers: pH dependence of the conformational gating step. *Biochemistry* **41** (2002) 2694–2701.
152. P. Maróti, D.K. Hanson, L. Baciou, M. Schiffer, P. Sebban, Proton conduction within the reaction centers of *Rhodobacter capsulatus*: the electrostatic role of the protein. *Proc. Natl. Acad. Sci. U.S.A.* **91** (1994) 5617–5621.
153. L.M. Utschig, Y. Ohigashi, M.C. Thurnauer, D.M. Tiede, A new metal-binding site in photosynthetic bacterial reaction centers that modulates Q_A to Q_B electron transfer. *Biochemistry* **37** (1998) 8278–8281.
154. M.L. Paddock, M.S. Graige, G. Feher, M.Y. Okamura, Identification of the proton pathway in bacterial reaction centers: inhibition of proton transfer by binding of Zn^{2+} or Cd^{2+}. *Proc. Natl. Acad. Sci. U.S.A.* **96** (1999) 6183–6188.
155. M.S. Graige, G. Feher, M.Y. Okamura, Conformational gating of the electron transfer reaction $Q_A-Q_B- > Q_AQ_B-$ in bacterial reaction centers of *Rhodobacter sphaeroides* determined by a driving force assay. *Proc. Natl. Acad. Sci. U.S.A.* **95** (1998) 11679–11684.
156. D.M. Tiede, J. Vazquez, J. Cordova, P.A. Marone, Time-resolved electrochromism associated with the formation of quinone anions in the *Rhodobacter sphaeroides* R26 reaction center. *Biochemistry* **35** (1996) 10763–10775.
157. E.G. Alexov, M.R. Gunner, Calculated protein and proton motions coupled to electron transfer: electron transfer from Q_A- to Q_B in bacterial photosynthetic reaction centers. *Biochemistry* **38** (1999) 8253–8270.
158. H.L. Axelrod, E.C. Abresch, M.L. Paddock, M.Y. Okamura, G. Feher, Determination of the binding sites of the proton transfer inhibitors $CD2^+$ and Zn^{2+} in bacterial reaction centers. *Proc. Natl. Acad. Sci. U.S.A.* **97** (2000) 1542–1547.
159. M.H.B. Stowell, T.M. McPhillips, D.C. Rees, S.M. Soltis, E. Abresch, G. Feher, Light-induced structural changes in photosynthetic reaction center: Implications for mechanism of electron-proton transfer. *Science* **276** (1997) 812–816.
160. J. Breton, Absence of large-scale displacement of quinone Q_B in bacterial photosynthetic reaction centers. *Biochemistry* **43** (2004) 3318–3326.
161. R.H.G. Baxter, N. Ponomarenko, V. Srajer, R. Pahl, K. Moffat, J.R. Norris, Time-resolved crystallographic studies of light-induced structural changes in the photosynthetic reaction center. *Proc. Natl. Acad. Sci. U.S.A.* **101** (2004) 5982–5987.
162. C. Kirmaier, D. Holten, R.J. Debus, G. Feher, M.Y. Okamura, Primary photochemistry of iron-depleted and zinc-reconstituted reaction centers from *Rhodopseudomonas sphaeroides*. *Proc. Natl. Acad. Sci. U.S.A.* **83** (1986) 6407–6411.
163. G. Feher, M.Y. Okamura, The primary and secondary acceptors in bacterial photosynthesis: II. The structure of the Fe^{2+}-Q^- complex. *Appl. Magn. Reson.* **16** (1999) 63–100.
164. L.M. Utschig, O. Poluektov, S.L. Schlesselman, M.C. Thurnauer, D.M. Tiede, Cu^{2+} site in photosynthetic bacterial reaction centers from *Rhodobacter sphaeroides*, *Rhodobacter capsulatus* and *Rhodopseudomonas viridis*. *Biochemistry* **40** (2001) 6132–6141.
165. J.M. Ortega, B. Dohse, D. Oesterhelt, P. Mathis, Very fast electron transfer from cytochrome to the bacterial photosynthetic reaction center at low temperature. *FEBS Letts.* **401** (1997) 153–157.
166. W. Nitschke, I. Agalidis, A.W. Rutherford, The reaction-center associated cytochrome subunit of the purple bacterium *Rhodocyclus gelatinosus*. *Biochim. Biophys. Acta* **1100** (1992) 49–57.

167. W. Nitschke, M. Jubaultbregler, A.W. Rutherford, The reaction-center associated tetraheme cytochrome subunit from *Chromatium vinosum* revisited. A reexamination of its EPR properties. *Biochemistry* **32** (1993) 8871–8879.
168. W. Nitschke, A.W. Rutherford, The tetraheme cytochromes associated with photosynthetic reaction centers. A model system for intraprotein redox center interactions. *Biochem. Soc. Trans.* **22** (1994) 694–699.
169. W.W. Parson, Cytochrome photooxidations in *Chromatium* chromatophores. Each P870 oxidizes two cytochrome C422 hemes. *Biochim. Biophys. Acta* **189** (1969) 397–403.
170. W.W. Parson, G.D. Case, In *Chromatium* a single photochemical reaction center oxidizes both cytochrome C552 and cytochrome C555. *Biochim. Biophys. Acta* **205** (1970) 232–245.
171. G.D. Case, W.W. Parson, J.P. Thornber, Photooxidations of cytochromes in reaction center preparations from *Chromatium* and *Rhodopseudomonas viridis*. *Biochim. Biophys. Acta* **223** (1970) 122–128.
172. M. Tetreault, S.H. Rongey, G. Feher, M.Y. Okamura, Interaction between cytochrome c(2) and the photosynthetic reaction center from *Rhodobacter sphaeroides*: Effects of charge-modifying mutations on binding and electron transfer. *Biochemistry* **40** (2001) 8452–8462.
173. D. DeVault, B. Chance, Studies of photosynthesis using a pulsed laser. I. Temperature dependence of cytochrome oxidation rate in *chromatium*. Evidence for tunneling. *Biophys. J.* **6** (1966) 825–847.
174. D. DeVault, J.H. Parkes, B. Chance, Electron tunnelling in cytochromes. *Nature* **215** (1967) 642–644.
175. M. Seibert, D. DeVault, Relations between the laser-induced oxidations of the high and low potential cytochromes of *ChromatiumD*. *Biochim. Biophys. Acta* **205** (1970) 220–231.
176. W.W. Parson, The role of P870 in bacterial photosynthesis. *Biochim. Biophys. Acta* **153** (1968) 248–259.
177. B. Chance, M. Nishimura, On the mechanism of chlorophyll-cytochrome interaction: the temperature insensitivity of light-induced cytochrome oxidation in *Chromatium*. *Proc. Natl. Acad. Sci. U.S.A.* **46** (1960) 19–25.
178. J.M. Olson, B. Chance, Cytochrome reactions in *Chromatium*. *Biochim. Biophys. Acta* **28** (1958) 227–228.
179. C.C. Moser, P.L. Dutton, Cytochrome c and c2 binding dynamics and electron transfer with photosynthetic reaction center protein and other integral membrane redox proteins. *Biochemistry* **27** (1988) 2450–2461.
180. R.E. Overfield, C.A. Wraight, D. Devault, Microsecond photooxidation kinetics of cytochrome c2 from *Rhodopseudomonas sphaeroides*: in vivo and solution studies. *FEBS Lett.* **105** (1979) 137–142.
181. G. Venturoli, A. Mallardi, P. Mathis, Electron transfer from cytochrome c2 to the primary donor of *Rhodobacter sphaeroides* reaction centers. A temperature dependence study. *Biochemistry* **32** (1993) 13245–13253.
182. D.M. Tiede, A.C. Vashishta, M.R. Gunner, Electron-transfer kinetics and electrostatic properties of the *Rhodobacter sphaeroides* reaction center and soluble c-cytochromes. *Biochemistry* **32** (1993) 4515–4531.
183. R.E. Overfield, C.A. Wraight, Oxidation of cytochromes c and c_2 by bacterial photosynthetic reaction centers in phospholipid vesicles. 1. Studies with neutral membranes. *Biochemistry* **19** (1980) 3322–3327.

184. D. Rosen, M.Y. Okamura, G. Feher, Interaction of cytochrome c with reaction centers of *Rhodopseudomonas sphaeroides* R-26: determination of number of binding sites and dissociation constants by equilibrium dialysis. *Biochemistry* **19** (1980) 5687–5692.

185. F.E. Jenney, R.C. Prince, F. Daldal, Roles of the soluble cytochrome c_2 and membrane-associated cytochrome c_y of *Rhodobacter capsulatus* in photosynthetic electron transfer. *Biochemistry* **33** (1994) 2496–2502.

186. T.E. Meyer, T.J. Donohue, Cytochromes, iron-sulfur, and copper proteins mediating electron transfer from the cyt bc_1 complex to photosynthetic reaction center complexes, in: *Anoxygenic Photosynthetic Bacteria* (1995) (R.E. Blankenship, M.T. Madigan, C.E. Bauer, eds.), Kluwer Academic Publishers, Dordrecht, pp. 725–745.

187. H. Myllykallio, F.E. Jenny, C.R. Moomaw, C.A. Slaughter, F. Daldal, Cytochrome c_y of *Rhodobacter capsulatus* is attached to the cytoplasmic membrane by an uncleaved signal sequence-like anchor. *J. Bacteriol.* **179** (1997) 2623–2631.

188. L. Yu, Q.C. Mei, C.A. Yu, Characterization of purified cytochrome bc_1 complex from *Rhodopseudomonas sphaeroides* R-26. *J. Biol. Chem.* **259** (1984) 5752–5760.

189. P.O. Ljungdahl, J.D. Pennoyer, D.E. Robertson, B.L. Trumpower, Purification of highly active cytochrome bc_1 complexes from phylogenetically diverse species by a single chromatographic procedure. *Biochim. Biophys. Acta* **891** (1987) 227–241.

190. B.L. Trumpower, Cytochrome bc_1 complexes of microorganisms. *Microbiol. Rev.* **54** (1990) 101–129.

191. T.E. Meyer, M.A. Cusanovich, Discovery and characterization of electron transfer proteins in the photosynthetic bacteria. *Photosynth. Res.* **76** (2003) 111–126.

192. G. van Driessche, I. Vandenberghe, B. Devreese, B. Samyn, T.E. Meyer, R. Leigh, M.A. Cusanovich, R.G. Bartsch, U. Fischer, J.J. van Beeumen, Amino acid sequences and distribution of high-potential iron-sulfur proteins that donate electrons to the photosynthetic reaction center in phototropic proteobacteria. *J. Mol. Evol.* **57** (2003) 181–199.

193. K.V. Nagashima, K. Matsuura, K. Shimada, A. Vermeglio, High-potential iron-sulfur protein (HiPIP) is the major electron donor to the reaction center complex in photosynthetically growing cells of the purple bacterium *Rubrivivax gelatinosus*. *Biochemistry* **41** (2002) 14028–14032.

194. A. Vermeglio, J. Li, B. Schoepp-Cothenet, N. Pratt, D.B. Knaff, The role of high-potential iron protein and cytochrome c(8) as alternative electron donors to the reaction center of *Chromatium vinosum*. *Biochemistry* **41** (2002) 8868–8875.

195. G. Venturoli, M.D. Mamedov, S.S. Mansy, F. Musiani, M. Strocchi, F. Francia, A.Y. Semenov, J.A. Cowan, S. Ciurli, Electron transfer from HiPIP to the photooxidized tetraheme cytochrome subunit of allochromatium vinosum reaction center: new insights from site-directed mutagenesis and computational studies. *Biochemistry* **43** (2004) 437–445.

196. A. Hochkoeppler, D. Zannoni, S. Ciurli, T.E. Meyer, M.A. Cusanovich, G. Tollin, Kinetics of photo-induced electron transfer from high potential iron-sulfur protein to the photosynthetic reaction center of the purple phototroph *Rhodoferax fermentans*. *Proc. Natl. Acad. Sci. U.S.A.* **93** (1996) 6998–6702.

197. S. Sogabe, T. Ezoe, N. Kasai, M. Saeda, A. Uno, M. Miki, K. Miki, Structural similarity of cytochrome c_2 from *Rhodopseudomonas viridis* to mitochondrial cytochromes c revealed by its crystal structure at 2.7 Å resolution. *FEBS Lett.* **345** (1994) 5–8.

198. C. Kirmaier, D. Holten, W.W. Parson, Picosecond photodichroism studies of the transient states in *Rhodopseudomonas sphaeroides* reaction centers at 5 K: effects of electron transfer on the six bacteriochlorin pigments. *Biochim. Biophys. Acta* **810** (1985) 49–61.
199. E.C. Kellog, S. Kolaczkowski, M.R. Wasielewski, D.M. Tiede, Measurement of the extent of electron transfer to the bacteriopheophytin in the M-subunit in reaction centers of *Rhodopseudomonas viridis*. *Photosynth. Res.* **22** (1989) 47–59.
200. T. Mar, G. Gingras, Relative phototrapping rates of the two bacteriopheophytins in the photoreaction center of *Ectothiorhodospira* sp. *Biochim. Biophys. Acta* **1017** (1990) 112–117.
201. E.J. Bylina, C. Kirmaier, L. McDowell, D. Holten, D.C. Youvan, Influence of an amino-acid residue on the optical properties and electron transfer dynamics of a photosynthetic reaction centre complex. *Nature* **336** (1988) 182–184.
202. B.A. Heller, D. Holten, C. Kirmaier, Control of electron transfer between the L- and M-sides of the photosynthetic reaction center. *Science* **269** (1995) 940–945.
203. C. Kirmaier, D. Weems, D. Holten, M-side electron transfer in reaction center mutants with a lysine near the nonphotoactive B bacteriochlorophyll. *Biochemistry* **38** (1999) 11516–11530.
204. C. Kirmaier, C. He, D. Holten, Manipulating the direction of electron transfer in the bacterial reaction center by swapping Phe for Tyr near $BChl_M$ (L181) and Tyr for Phe near $BChl_L$ (M208). *Biochemistry* **40** (2001) 12132–12139.
205. C. Kirmaier, P.D. Laible, K. Czarnecki, A.N. Hata, D.K. Hanson, D.F. Bocian, D. Holten, Comparison of M-side electron transfer in *Rb. sphaeroides* and *Rb. capsulatus* reaction centers. *J. Phys. Chem. B* **106** (2002) 1799–1808.
206. C. Kirmaier, A. Cua, C.Y. He, D. Holten, D.F. Bocian, Probing M-branch electron transfer and cofactor environment in the bacterial photosynthetic reaction center by addition of a hydrogen bond to the M-side bacteriopheophytin. *J. Phys. Chem. B* **106** (2002) 495–503.
207. P.D. Laible, C. Kirmaier, C.S.M. Udawatte, S.J. Hofman, D. Holten, D.K. Hanson, Quinone reduction via secondary B-branch electron transfer in mutant bacterial reaction centers. *Biochemistry* **42** (2003) 1718–1730.
208. E. Katilius, Z. Katiliene, S. Lin, A.K.W. Taguchi, N.W. Woodbury, B-side electron transfer in the HE(M182) reaction center mutant from *Rhodobacter sphaeroides*. *J. Phys. Chem. B* **106** (2002) 12344–12350.
209. E. Katilius, T. Turanchik, S. Lin, A.K.W. Taguchi, N.W. Woodbury, B-side electron transfer in a *Rhodobacter sphaeroides* reaction center mutant in which the B-side monomer bacteriochlorophyll is replaced with bacteriopheophytin. *J. Phys. Chem. B* **103** (1999) 7386–7389.
210. A.Y. Shkuropatov, S. Neerken, H.P. Permentier, R. de Wijn, K.A. Schmidt, V.A. Shuvalov, T.S.J. Aartsma, P. Gast, A.J. Hoff, The effect of exchange of bacteriopheophytin alpha with plant pheophytin alpha on charge separation in Y(M210)W mutant reaction centers of *Rhodobacter sphaeroides* at low temperature. *Biochim. Biophys. Acta* **1557** (2003) 1–12.
211. A.L. de Boer, S. Neerken, R. de Wijn, H.P. Permentier, P. Gast, E. Vijgenboom, A.J. Hoff, B-branch electron transfer in reaction centers of Rhodobacter sphaeroides assessed with site-directed mutagenesis. *Photosynth. Res.* **71** (2002) 221–239.
212. S. Lin, E. Katilius, A.L.M. Haffa, A.K.W. Taguchi, N.W. Woodbury, Blue light drives B-side electron transfer in bacterial photosynthetic reaction centers. *Biochemistry* **40** (2001) 13767–13773.

213. S. Lin, J.A. Jackson, A.K.W. Taguchi, N.W. Woodbury, B-side electron transfer promoted by absorbance of multiple photons in *Rhodobacter sphaeroides* R-26 reaction centers. *J. Phys. Chem. B* **103** (1999) 4757–4763.
214. A. Warshel, P.K. Sharma, M. Kato, W.W. Parson, Modeling electrostatic effects in proteins. *Biochim. Biophys. Acta* **1764** (2006) 1647–1676.
215. J. Hasegawa, H. Nakatsuji, Mechanism and unidirectionality of the electron transfer in the photosynthetic reaction center of Rhodopseudomonas viridis: SAC-CI theoretical study. *J. Phys. Chem. B* **102** (1998) 10420–10430.
216. D. Kolbasov, A. Scherz, Matrix elements play a significant role in asymmetric electron transfer in bacterial reaction centers, in: *Photosynthesis: Mechanisms and Effects* (1998) (G. Garab, ed.), Kluwer Academic Publishers, Dordrecht, Vol. II, pp. 719–722.
217. D. Kolbasov, A. Scherz, Asymmetric electron transfer in reaction centers of purple bacteria strongly depends on different electron matrix elements in the active and inactive branches. *J. Phys. Chem. B* **104** (2000) 1802–1809.
218. L.Y. Zhang, R.A. Friesner, Ab initio calculation of electronic coupling in the photosynthetic reaction center. *Proc. Natl. Acad. Sci. U.S.A.* **95** (1998) 13603–13605.
219. N. Ivashin, B. Källenbring, S. Larsson, Ö. Hansson, Charge separation in photosynthetic reaction centers. *J. Phys. Chem. B* **102** (1998) 5017–5022.
220. M.E. van Brederode, M.R. Jones, F. van Mourik, I.H.M. van Stokkum, R. van Grondelle, A new pathway for transmembrane electron transfer in photosynthetic reaction centers of *Rhodobacter sphaeroides* not involving the excited special pair. *Biochemistry* **36** (1997) 6855–6861.
221. M.H. Vos, J. Breton, J.L. Martin, Electronic energy transfer within the hexamer cofactor system of bacterial reaction centers. *J. Phys. Chem. B* **101** (1997) 9820–9832.
222. M.E. van Brederode, F. van Mourik, I.H.M. van Stokkum, M.R. Jones, R. van Grondelle, Multiple pathways for ultrafast transduction of light energy in the photosynthetic reaction center of *Rhodobacter sphaeroides*. *Proc. Natl. Acad. Sci. U.S.A.* **96** (1999) 2054–2059.
223. M.E. van Brederode, I.H.M. van Stokkum, E. Katilius, F. van Mourik, M.R. Jones, R. van Grondelle, Primary charge separation routes in the BChl:BPhe heterodimer reaction centers of *Rhodobacter sphaeroides*. *Biochemistry* **38** (1999) 7545–7555.
224. M.E. van Brederode, M.R. Jones, R. van Grondelle, Fluorescence excitation spectra of membrane-bound photosynthetic reaction centers of *Rhodobacter sphaeroides* in which the tyrosine M210 residue is replaced by tryptophan: evidence for a new pathway of charge separation. *Chem. Phys. Lett.* **268** (1997) 143–149.
225. M.E. van Brederode, J.P. Ridge, I.H.M. van Stokkum, R. van Mourik, M.R. Jones, R. van Grondelle, On the efficiency of energy transfer and the different pathways of electron transfer in mutant reaction centers of *Rhodobacter sphaeroides*. *Photosynth. Res.* **55** (1998) 141–146.
226. H. Zhou, S.G. Boxer, Probing excited-state electron transfer by resonance Stark spectroscopy. 1. Experimental results for photosynthetic reaction centers. *J. Phys. Chem. B* **102** (1998) 9139–9147.
227. H. Zhou, S.G. Boxer, Probing excited-state electron transfer by resonance Stark spectroscopy. 2. Theory and application. *J. Phys. Chem. B* **102** (1998) 9148–9160.
228. S. Lin, J. Jackson, A.K.W. Taguchi, N.W. Woodbury, Excitation wavelength dependent spectral evolution in *Rhodobacter sphaeroides* R-26 reaction centers at

low temperatures: The Q(y) transition region. *J. Phys. Chem. B* **102** (1998) 4016–4022.
229. J.A. Jackson, S. Lin, A.K.W. Taguchi, J.C. Williams, J.P. Allen, N.W. Woodbury, Energy transfer in *Rhodobacter sphaeroides* reaction centers with the initial electron donor oxidized or missing. *J. Phys. Chem. B* **101** (1997) 5747–5753.
230. B.K. Pierson, Reflections on Chloroflexus. *Photosynth. Res.* **41** (1994) 7–15.
231. M.J. McBride, Bacterial gliding motility: multiple mechanisms for cell movement over surfaces. *Annu. Rev. Microbiol.* **55** (2001) 49–75.
232. R.E. Blankenship, K. Matsuura, Antenna complexes from green photosynthetic bacteria, in: *Light-Harvesting Antennas in Photosynthesis* (2003) (B.R. Green, W.W. Parson, eds.), Kluwer Academic Publishers, Dordrecht, pp. 195–217.
233. B.K. Pierson, J.P. Thornber, R.E.B. Seftor, Partial purification, subunit structure and thermal stability of the photochemical reaction center of the thermophilic green bacterium *Chloroflexus aurantiacus*. *Biochim. Biophys. Acta* **723** (1983) 322–326.
234. B.K. Pierson, J.P. Thornber, Isolation and spectral characterization of photochemical reaction centers from the thermophilic green bacterium *Chloroflexus aurantiacus* strain J10F1. *Proc. Natl. Acad. Sci. U.S.A.* **80** (1983) 80–84.
235. Y.A. Ovchinnikov, N.G. Abdulaev, B.E. Shmuckler, A.A. Zargarov, M.A. Kutuzov, I.N. Telezhinskaya, N.B. Levina, A.S. Zolotarev, Photosynthetic reaction centre of *Chloroflexus aurantiacus*. Primary structure of M-subunit. *FEBS Lett.* **232** (1988) 364–368.
236. J.A. Shiozawa, F. Lottspeich, D. Oesterhelt, R. Feick, The primary structure of the *Chloroflexus aurantiacus* reaction-center polypeptides. *Eur. J. Biochem.* **180** (1989) 75–84.
237. Y.A. Ovchinnikov, N.G. Abdulaev, A.S. Zolotarev, B.E. Shmuckler, A.A. Zargarov, M.A. Kutuzov, I.N. Telezhinskaya, N.B. Levina, Photosynthetic reaction centre of *Chloroflexus aurantiacus* I. Primary structure of L-subunit. *FEBS Lett.* **231** (1988) 237–242.
238. J.A. Shiozawa, F. Lottspeich, R. Feick, The photochemical reaction center of *Chloroflexus aurantiacus* is composed of 2 structurally similar polypeptides. *Eur. J. Biochem.* **167** (1987) 595–600.
239. R.E. Blankenship, R. Feick, B.D. Bruce, C. Kirmaier, D. Holten, R.C. Fuller, Primary photochemistry in the facultative green photosynthetic bacterium Chloroflexus aurantiacus. *J. Cell Biochem.* **22** (1983) 251–261.
240. M.B. Hale, R.E. Blankenship, R.C. Fuller, Menaquinone is the sole quinone in the facultatively aerobic green photosynthetic bacterium *Chloroflexus aurantiacus*. *Biochim. Biophys. Acta* **723** (1983) 376–382.
241. H. Vasmel, J. Amesz, Photoreduction of menaquinone in the reaction center of the green photosynthetic bacterium *Chloroflexus aurantiacus*. *Biochim. Biophys. Acta* **724** (1983) 118–122.
242. R. Feick, A. Ertlmaier, U. Ermler, Crystallization and X-ray analysis of the reaction center from the thermophilic green bacterium *Chloroflexus aurantiacus*. *FEBS Lett.* **396** (1996) 161–164.
243. A.N. Barnakov, V.V. Demin, A.P. Kuzin, A.A. Zargarov, A.S. Zolotarev, N.G. Abdulaev, Two-dimensional crystallization of reaction centers from *Chloroflexus aurantiacus*. *FEBS Lett.* **265** (1990) 126–128.
244. E.V. Yurkova, I.N. Tsygannik, A.A. Zargarov, A.S. Zolotarev, N.G. Abdulaev, V.V. Demin, Crystallization of photosynthetic reaction centers from *Chloroflexus aurantiacus*. *FEBS Lett.* **256** (1989) 167–169.

245. H. Vasmel, R.F. Meiburg, H.J.M. Kramer, L.J. de Vos, J. Amesz, Optical properties of the photosynthetic reaction center of *Chloroflexus aurantiacus* at low temperature. *Biochim. Biophys. Acta* **724** (1983) 333–339.
246. P. Parot, N. Delmas, D. Garcia, A. Verméglio, Structure of *Chloroflexus aurantiacus* reaction center. Photoselection at low temperature. *Biochim. Biophys. Acta* **809** (1995) 137–140.
247. V.A. Shuvalov, A.Y. Shkuropatov, S.M. Kulakova, M.A. Ismailov, V.A. Shkuropatova, Photoreactions of bacteriopheophytins and bacteriochlorophylls in reaction centers of *Rhodopseudomonas sphaeroides* and *Chloroflexus aurantiacus*. *Biochim. Biophys. Acta* **849** (1986) 337–346.
248. H. Vasmel, J. Amesz, A.J. Hoff, Analysis by exciton theory of the optical properties of the *Chloroflexus aurantiacus* reaction center. *Biochim. Biophys. Acta* **852** (1986) 159–168.
249. B.D. Bruce, R.C. Fuller, R.E. Blankenship, Primary photochemistry in the facultatively aerobic green photosynthetic bacterium *Chloroflexus aurantiacus*. *Proc. Natl. Acad. Sci. U.S.A.* **79** (1982) 6532–6536.
250. A. Ivancich, R. Feick, A. Ertlmaier, T.A. Mattioli, Structure and protein binding interactions of the primary donor of the *Chloroflexus aurantiacus* reaction center. *Biochemistry* **35** (1996) 6126–6135.
251. N.J. Cherepy, A.A. Holzwarth, R.A. Mathies, Near-infrared resonance Raman spectra of *Chloroflexus aurantiacus* photosynthetic reaction centers. *Biochemistry* **34** (1995) 5288–5293.
252. M. Volk, G. Aumeier, T. Langenbacher, R. Feick, A. Ogrodnik, M.-E. Michel-Beyerle, Energetics and mechanism of primary charge separation in bacterial photosynthesis. A comparative study on reaction centers of *Rhodobacter sphaeroides* and *Chloroflexus aurantiacus*. *J. Phys. Chem. B* **102** (1998) 735–751.
253. M. Becker, V. Nagarajan, D. Middendorf, W.W. Parson, J.E. Martin, R.E. Blankenship, Temperature dependence of the initial electron-transfer kinetics in photosynthetic reaction centers of *Chloroflexus aurantiacus*. *Biochim. Biophys. Acta* **1057** (1991) 299–312.
254. M.G. Müller, K. Griebenow, A.R. Holzwarth, Primary processes in isolated photosynthetic bacterial reaction centres from *Chloroflexus aurantiacus* studied by picosecond fluorescence spectroscopy. *Biochim. Biophys. Acta* **1098** (1991) 1–12.
255. V.A. Shuvalov, H. Vasmel, J. Amesz, L.N.M. Duysens, Picosecond spectroscopy of the charge separation in reaction centers of *Chloroflexus aurantiacus* with selective excitation of the primary electron donor. *Biochim. Biophys. Acta* **851** (1986) 361–368.
256. P. Hamm, K.A. Gray, D. Oesterhelt, R. Feik, H. Scheer, W. Zinth, Subpicosecond emission studies of bacterial reaction centers. *Biochim. Biophys. Acta* **1142** (1993) 90–105.
257. J.L. Martin, J.C. Lambry, M. Ashokkumar, M.E. Michel-Beyerle, R. Feick, J. Breton, Primary charge separation process in reaction centers from *Chloroflexus aurantiacus* bacterium, in: *Ultrafast Phenomena VII* (1990) (C.B. Harris, E.P. Ippen, G.A. Mourou, A.H. Zewail, eds.), Springer-Verlag, Berlin, pp. 524–528.
258. R. Feick, J.L. Martin, J. Breton, M. Volk, G. Scheidel, T. Langenbacher, C. Urbano, A. Ogrodnik, M.E. Michel-Beyerle, Biexponential charge separation and monoexponential decay of P^+H^- in reaction centers of *Chloroflexus aurantiacus*, in: *Reaction Centers of Photosynthetic Bacteria* (1990) (M.E. Michel-Beyerle, ed.), Springer-Verlag, Berlin, pp. 181–188.

259. G. Schweitzer, M. Hucke, K. Griebenow, M.G. Muller, A.R. Holzwarth, Charge separation kinetics in isolated photosynthetic reaction centers of *Chloroflexus aurantiacus* (with Q_A reduced) at low temperatures. *Chem. Phys. Lett.* **190** (1992) 149–154.
260. C. Kirmaier, R.E. Blankenship, D. Holten, Formation and decay of radical-pair state P^+I^- in *Chloroflexus aurantiacus* reaction centers. *Biochim. Biophys. Acta* **850** (1986) 275–285.
261. K. Schmidt, H.W. Trissl, Trapping and charge stabilization in chlorosome containing bacteria: Comparative study on *Chloroflexus aurantiacus* and *Chlorobium limicola*. *Ber. Bunsen-Gesellschaft Phys. Chem. Chem. Phys.* **100** (1996) 1958–1961.
262. S. Dracheva, J.C. Williams, G. van Driessche, J.J. van Beeumen, R.E. Blankenship, The primary structure of cytochrome c-554 from the green photosynthetic bacterium *Chloroflexus aurantiacus*. *Biochemistry* **30** (1991) 11451–11458.
263. J.C. Freeman, R.E. Blankenship, Isolation and characterization of the membrane-bound cytochrome C-554 from the thermophilic green photosynthetic bacterium *Chloroflexus aurantiacus*. *Photosynth. Res.* **23** (1990) 29–38.
264. P. van Vliet, D. Zannoni, W. Nitschke, A.W. Rutherford, Membrane-bound cytochromes in *Chloroflexus aurantiacus* studied by EPR. *Eur. J. Biochem.* **199** (1991) 317–323.
265. G. van Driessche, W. Hu, G. van de Werken, F. Selvaraj, J.D. McManus, R.E. Blankenship, J.J. van Beeumen, Auracyanin A from the thermophilic green gliding photosynthetic bacterium *Chloroflexus aurantiacus* represents an unusual class of small blue copper proteins. *Protein Sci.* **8** (1999) 947–957.
266. J.D. McManus, D.C. Brune, J. Han, J. Sanders-Loehr, T.E. Meyer, M.A. Cusanovich, G. Tollin, R.E. Blankenship, Isolation, characterization, and amino acid sequences of auracyanins, blue copper proteins from the green photosynthetic bacterium *Chloroflexus aurantiacus*. *J. Biol. Chem.* **267** (1992) 6531–6540.
267. C.S. Bond, R.E. Blankenship, H.C. Freeman, J.M. Guss, M.J. Maher, F.M. Selvaraj, M.C.J. Wilce, K.M. Willingham, Crystal structure of auracyanin, a "blue" copper protein from the green thermophilic photosynthetic bacterium *Chloroflexus aurantiacus*. *J. Mol. Biol.* **306** (2001) 47–67.
268. D. Zannoni, W.J. Ingledew, A thermodynamic analysis of the plasma membrane electron transport components in photoheterotrophically grown cells of *Chloroflexus aurantiacus*. An optical and electron paramagnetic resonance study. *FEBS Lett.* **193** (1985) 93–98.
269. R.M. Wynn, T.E. Redlinger, J.M. Foster, R.E. Blankenship, R.C. Fuller, R.W. Shaw, D.B. Knaff, Electron-transport chains of phototrophically and chemotrophically grown *Chloroflexus aurantiacus*. *Biochim. Biophys. Acta* **891** (1987) 216–226.
270. M.F. Yanyushin, Fractionation of cytochromes of phototrophically grown *Chloroflexus aurantiacus*. Is there a cytochrome *bc* complex among them? *FEBS Lett.* **512** (2002) 125–128.
271. S. Hanada, A. Hiraishi, K. Shimada, K. Matsuura, *Chloroflexus aggregans* sp. nov., a filamentous phototrophic bacterium which forms dense cell aggregates by active gliding movement. *Int. J. Syst. Bacteriol.* **45** (1995) 676–681.
272. B.K. Pierson, S.J. Giovannoni, D.A. Stahl, R.W. Castenholz, *Heliothrix oregonensis* gen. nov., sp. nov., a phototrophic filamentous gliding bacterium containing bacteriochlorophyll a. *Arch. Microbiol.* **142** (1985) 164–167.
273. S. Hanada, S. Takaichi, K. Matsuura, K. Nakamura, *Roseiflexus castenholzii* gen. nov., sp. nov., a thermophilic, filamentous, photosynthetic bacterium that lacks chlorosomes. *Int. J. Syst. Evol. Microbiol.* **52** (2002) 187–193.

274. O.I. Keppen, T.P. Tourova, B.B. Kuznetsov, R.N. Ivanovsky, V.M. Gorlenko, Proposal of *Oscillochloridaceae* fam. nov. on the basis of a phylogenetic analysis of the filamentous anoxygenic phototrophic bacteria, and emended description of *Oscillochloris* and *Oscillochloris trichoides* in comparison with further new isolates. *Int. J. Syst. Evol. Microbiol.* **50** (2000) 1529–1537.
275. J.M. Olson, Confused history of *Chloropseudomonas ethylica* 2K. *Int. J. Syst. Bact.* **28** (1978) 128–129.
276. N.U. Frigaard, A.G.M. Chew, H. Li, J.A. Maresca, D.A. Bryant, *Chlorobium tepidum*: insights into the structure, physiology, and metabolism of a green sulfur bacterium derived from the complete genome sequence. *Photosynth. Res.* **78** (2003) 93–117.
277. G. Hauska, T. Schoedl, H. Remigy, G. Tsiotis, The reaction center of green sulfur bacteria. *Biochim. Biophys. Acta* **1507** (2001) 260–277.
278. H. Sakurai, N. Kusumoto, K. Inoue, Function of the reaction center of green sulfur bacteria. *Photochem. Photobiol.* **64** (1996) 5–13.
279. U. Feiler, G. Hauska, The reaction center from green sulfur bacteria, in: *Anoxygenic Photosynthetic Bacteria* (1995) (R.E. Blankenship, M.T. Madigan, C.E. Bauer, eds.), Kluwer Academic Publishers, Dordrecht, pp. 665–685.
280. P. Heathcote, M.R. Jones, P.K. Fyfe, Type I photosynthetic reaction centers: structure and function. *Philos. Trans. R. Soc. London B Biol. Sci.* **358** (2003) 231–243.
281. W. Nitschke, T. Mattioli, A.W. Rutherford, The FeS-type photosystems and the evolution of photosynthetic reaction centers, in: *Origin and Evolution of Biological Energy Conversion* (1996) (H. Baltscheffsky, ed.), VCH, New York, pp. 177–204.
282. M. Büttner, D.-L. Xie, H. Nelson, W. Pinther, G. Hauska, N. Nelson, Photosynthetic reaction center genes in green sulfur bacteria and in photosystem 1 are related. *Proc. Natl. Acad. Sci. U.S.A.* **89** (1992) 8135–8139.
283. C. Hager-Braun, D.-L. Xie, U. Jarosch, E. Herold, M. Büttner, R. Zimmermann, R. Deutzmann, G. Hauska, N. Nelson, Stable photobleaching of P840 in Chlorobium reaction centre preparations; presence of the 42-kDa bacteriochlorophyll aprotein and a 17-kDa polypeptide. *Biochemistry* **34** (1995) 9617–9624.
284. H. Oh-oka, S. Kamei, H. Matsubara, Two molecules of cytochrome c function as the electron donors to P840 in the reaction center complex isolated from a green bacterium, *Chlorobium tepidum*. *FEBS Lett.* **365** (1995) 30–34.
285. R. Nechushtai, A. Eden, Y. Cohen, J. Klein, Introduction to Photosystem I: reaction center function, composition and structure, in: *Oxygenic Photosynthesis: The Light Reactions* (1996) (D.A. Ort, C.F. Yocum, eds.), Kluwer Academic Publishers, Dordrecht, pp. 298–311.
286. H.V. Scheller, H. Naver, B.L. Møller, Molecular aspects of Photosystem I. *Plant Physiol.* **100** (1997) 842–851.
287. H.P. Permentier, K.A. Schmidt, M. Kobayashi, M. Akiyama, C. Hager-Braun, S. Neerken, M. Miller, J. Amesz, Composition and optical properties of reaction centre core complexes from the green sulfur bacteria *Prosthecochloris aestuarii* and *Chlorobium tepidum*. *Photosynth. Res.* **64** (2000) 27–39.
288. H.W. Remigy, G. Hauska, S.A. Muller, G. Tsiotis, The reaction centre from green sulphur bacteria: progress towards structural elucidation. *Photosynth. Res.* **71** (2002) 91–98.
289. R.C. Prince, J.M. Olson, Some thermodynamic and kinetic properties of the primary photochemical reactants in a complex from a green photosynthetic bacterium. *Biochim. Biophys. Acta* **423** (1976) 357–362.

290. B. Kjaer, H.V. Scheller, An isolated reaction center complex from the green sulfur bacterium *Chlorobium vibrioforme* can photoreduce ferredoxin at high rates. *Photosynth. Res.* **47** (1996) 33–39.
291. C.F. Fowler, N.A. Nugent, R.C. Fuller, The isolation and characterization of a photochemically active complex from *Chloropseudomonas ethylica*. *Proc. Natl. Acad. Sci. U.S.A.* **68** (1971) 2278–2282.
292. M. Kobayashi, H. Oh-oka, S. Akutsu, M. Akiyama, K. Tominaga, H. Kise, F. Nishida, T. Watanabe, J. Amesz, M. Koizumi, N. Ishida, H. Kano, The primary electron acceptor of green sulfur bacteria, bacteriochlorophyll 663, is chlorophyll a esterified with D2,6-phytadienol. *Photosynth. Res.* **63** (2000) 269–280.
293. T. Watanabe, M. Kobayashi, Electrochemistry of chlorophylls, in: *Chlorophylls* (1991) (H. Scheer, ed.), CRC Press, Boca Raton, FL, pp. 287–316.
294. A.M. Nuijs, H. Vasmel, H.L.P. Joppe, L.N.M. Duysens, J. Amesz, Excited states and primary charge separation in the pigment system of the green photosynthetic bacterium *Prosthecochloris aestuarii* as studied by picosecond absorbance difference spectroscopy. *Biochim. Biophys. Acta* **807** (1985) 24–34.
295. A.C. van Bochove, T. Swarthoff, H. Kingma, R.M. Hof, R. van Grondelle, L.N.M. Duysens, J. Amesz, A study of the primary charge separation in green bacteria by means of flash spectroscopy. *Biochim. Biophys. Acta* **764** (1984) 343–346.
296. M. Iwaki, S. Itoh, S. Kamei, H. Matsubara, H. Oh-Oka, Time-resolved spectroscopy of chlorophyll-a like electron acceptor in the reaction center complex of the green sulfur bacterium *Chlorobium tepidum*. *Plant Cell Physiol.* **40** (1999) 1021–1028.
297. V.A. Shuvalov, J. Amesz, L.N.M. Duysens, Picosecond spectroscopy of isolated membranes of the photosynthetic green sulfur bacterium *Prosthecochloris aestuarii* upon selective excitation of the primary electron donor. *Biochim. Biophys. Acta* **851** (1986) 1–5.
298. S. Neerken, H.P. Permentier, C. Francke, T.J. Aartsma, J. Amesz, Excited states and trapping in reaction center complexes of the green sulfur bacterium *Prosthecochloris aestuarii*. *Biochemistry* **37** (1998) 10792–10797.
299. S. Neerken, K.A. Schmidt, T.J. Aartsma, J. Amesz, Dynamics of energy conversion in reaction center core complexes of the green sulfur bacterium *Prosthecochloris aestuarii* at low temperature. *Biochemistry* **38** (1999) 13216–13222.
300. E.J. van de Meent, M. Kobayashi, C. Erkelens, P.A. van Veelen, S.C.M. Otte, K. Inoue, T. Watanabe, J. Amesz, The nature of the primary electron acceptor in green sulphur bacteria. *Biochim. Biophys. Acta* **1102** (1992) 371–378.
301. U. Feiler, D. Albouy, C. Pourcet, T.A. Mattioli, M. Lutz, B. Robert, Structure and binding site of the primary electron acceptor in the reaction center of Chlorobium. *Biochemistry* **33** (1994) 7594–7599.
302. S.E.J. Rigby, I.P. Muhiuddin, S. Santabarbara, M.C.W. Evans, P. Heathcote, Proton ENDOR spectroscopy of the anion radicals of the chlorophyll primary electron acceptors in Type I photosynthetic reaction centers. *Chem. Phys.* **294** (2003) 319–328.
303. H. Kramer, T.J. Aartsma, J. Amesz, Excited states and charge separation in membranes of the green sulfur bacterium *Prosthecochloris aestuarii*. *Photochem. Photobiol.* **64** (1996) 26–31.
304. K.A. Schmidt, H.-W. Trissl, Combined fluorescence and photovoltage studies on chlorosome containing bacteria. *Photosynth. Res.* **71** (1998) 71–80.
305. K. Brettel, Electron transfer and arrangement of the redox cofactors in Photosystem I. *Biochim. Biophys. Acta* **1318** (1997) 322–373.

306. K. Brettel, W. Leibl, Electron transfer in Photosystem I. *Biochim. Biophys. Acta* **1507** (2001) 100–114.
307. S. Itoh, M. Iwaki, I. Ikegami, Modification of Photosystem I reaction center by the extraction and exchange of chlorophylls and quinines. *Biochim. Biophys. Acta* **1507** (2001) 115–138.
308. S. Kumazaki, M. Iwaki, I. Ikegami, H. Kandori, K. Yoshihara, S. Itoh, Rates of primary electron transfer reactions in the Photosystem I reaction center reconstituted with different quinones as the secondary acceptor. *J. Phys. Chem.* **98** (1994) 11220–11225.
309. P. Mathis, P. Sétif, Kinetic studies on the function of A1 in the Photosystem I reaction center. *FEBS Lett.* **237** (1988) 65–68.
310. K. Brettel, Electron transfer from A^-_1 to an iron-sulfur center with $t_{1/2}=200$ ns at room temperature in Photosystem I. Characterization by flash absorption spectroscopy. *FEBS Lett.* **239** (1988) 93–98.
311. P. Joliot, A. Joliot, In vivo analysis of the electron transfer within Photosystem I: are the two phylloquinones involved? *Biochemistry* **38** (1999) 11130–11136.
312. N.U. Frigaard, K. Matsuura, Oxygen uncouples light absorption by the chlorosome antenna and photosynthetic electron transfer in the green sulfur bacterium *Chlorobium*. *Biochim. Biophys. Acta* **1412** (1999) 108–117.
313. N. Frankenberg, C. HagerBraun, U. Feiler, M. Fuhrmann, H. Rogl, N. Schneebauer, N. Nelson, G. Hauska, P840-reaction centers from *Chlorobium tepidum*. Quinone analysis and functional reconstitution into lipid vesicles. *Photochem. Photobiol.* **64** (1996) 14–19.
314. B. Kjaer, N.U. Frigaard, F. Yang, B. Zybailov, M. Miller, J.H. Golbeck, H.V. Scheller, Menaquinone-7 in the reaction center complex of the green sulfur bacterium *Chlorobium vibrioforme* functions as the electron acceptor A_1. *Biochemistry* **37** (1998) 3237–3242.
315. N. Kusumoto, P. Setif, K. Brettel, D. Seo, H. Sakurai, Electron transfer kinetics in purified reaction centers from the green sulfur bacterium *Chlorobium tepidum* studied by multiple-flash excitation. *Biochemistry* **38** (1999) 12124–12137.
316. I.P. Muhiuddin, S.E.J. Rigby, M.C.W. Evans, J. Amesz, P. Heathcote, ENDOR and special TRIPLE resonance spectroscopy of photoaccumulated semiquinone electron acceptors in the reaction centers of green sulfur bacteria and heliobacteria. *Biochemistry* **38** (1999) 7159–7167.
317. C. Hager-Braun, U. Jarosch, G. Hauska, W. Nitschke, A. Riedel, EPR studies of the terminal electron acceptors of the green sulfur bacterial reaction centre revisited. *Photosynth. Res.* **51** (1997) 127–136.
318. I.R. Vassiliev, M.T. Ronan, G. Hauska, J.H. Golbeck, The bound electron acceptors in green sulfur bacteria resolution of the g-tensor for the F^X iron-sulfur cluster in *Chlorobium tepidum*. *Biophys. J.* **78** (2000) 3160–3169.
319. P. Sétif, D. Seo, H. Sakurai, Photoreduction and reoxidation of the three iron-sulfur clusters of reaction centers of green sulfur bacteria. *Biophys. J.* **81** (2001) 1208–1219.
320. H. Oh-oka, S. Kakutani, H. Matsubara, R. Malkin, S. Itoh, Isolation of the photoreactive reaction center complex that contains 3 types of Fe-S centers and a cytochrome-c subunit from the green sulfur bacterium *Chlorobium limicola f.thiosulfatophilum* strain Larsen. *Plant Cell Physiol.* **34** (1993) 93–101.
321. N. Kusumoto, K. Inoue, H. Nasu, H. Sakurai, Preparation of a photoactive reaction center complex containing photoreducible Fe-S centers and photooxidizable cytochrome-c from the green sulfur bacterium *Chlorobium tepidum*. *Plant Cell Physiol.* **35** (1994) 17–25.

322. W. Nitschke, U. Feiler, A.W. Rutherford, Photosynthetic reaction center of green sulfur bacteria studied by EPR. *Biochemistry* **29** (1990) 3834–3842.
323. D. Seo, A. Tomioka, N. Kusumoto, M. Kamo, I. Enami, H. Sakurai, Purification of ferredoxins and their reaction with purified reaction center complex from the green sulfur bacterium *Chlorobium tepidum*. *Biochim. Biophys. Acta* **1503** (2001) 377–384.
324. A. Mezzetti, D. Seo, W. Leibl, H. Sakurai, J. Breton, Time-resolved step-scan FTIR investigation on the primary donor of the reaction center from the green sulfur bacterium *Chlorobium tepidum*. *Photosynth. Res.* **75** (2003) 161–169.
325. J. Breton, Fourier transform infrared spectroscopy of primary electron donors in Type I photosynthetic reaction centers. *Biochim. Biophys. Acta* **1507** (2001) 180–193.
326. P. Setif, H. Bottin, Identification of electron transfer reactions involving the acceptor A_1 of Photosystem I at room temperature. *Biochemistry* **28** (1989) 2689–2697.
327. H. Oh-Oka, M. Iwaki, S. Itoh, Membrane-bound cytochrome c_z couples quinol oxidoreductase to the P840 reaction center complex in isolated membranes of the green sulfur bacterium *Chlorobium tepidum*. *Biochemistry* **37** (1998) 12293–12300.
328. D. Albouy, P. Joliot, B. Robert, W. Nitschke, Electron transfer towards the RCI-type photosystem in the green sulphur bacterium *Chlorobium limicola* forma thiosulphatophilum studied by time-resolved optical spectroscopy in vivo. *Eur. J. Biochem.* **249** (1997) 630–636.
329. M. Guergova-Kuras, B. Boudreaux, A. Joliot, P. Joliot, K. Redding, Evidence for two active branches for electron transfer in Photosystem I. *Proc. Natl. Acad. Sci. U.S.A.* **98** (2001) 4437–4442.
330. W. Xu, P.R. Chitnis, A. Valieva, A. van der Est, K. Brettel, M. Guergova-Kuras, Y.N. Pushkar, S.G. Zech, D. Stehlik, G.Z. Shen, B. Zybailov, J.H. Golbeck, Electron transfer in cyanobacterial Photosystem I-II. Determination of forward electron transfer rates of site-directed mutants in a putative electron transfer pathway from A_0 through A_1 to F-x. *J. Biol. Chem.* **278** (2003) 27876–27887.
331. W. Xu, P. Chitnis, A. Valieva, A. van der Est, Y.N. Pushkar, M. Krzystyniak, C. Teutloff, S.G. Zech, R. Bittl, D. Stehlik, B. Zybailov, G.Z. Shen, J.H. Golbeck, Electron transfer in cyanobacterial Photosystem I-I. Physiological and spectroscopic characterization of site-directed mutants in a putative electron transfer pathway from A_0 through A_1 to F-x. *J. Biol. Chem.* **278** (2003) 27864–27875.
332. W.V. Fairclough, A. Forsyth, M.C.W. Evans, S.E.J. Rigby, S. Purton, P. Heathcote, Bidirectional electron transfer in Photosystem I: electron transfer on the PsaA side is not essential for phototrophic growth in Chlamydomonas. *Biochim. Biophys. Acta* **1606** (2003) 43–55.
333. V.M. Ramesh, K. Gibasiewicz, S. Lin, S.E. Bingham, A.N. Webber, Bidirectional electron transfer in Photosystem I: accumulation of A_0^- in A-side or B-side mutants of the axial ligand to chlorophyll A_0. *Biochemistry* **43** (2004) 1369–1375.
334. R.O. Cohen, G.Z. Shen, J.H. Golbeck, W. Xu, P.R. Chitnis, A.I. Valieva, A. van der Est, Y. Pushkar, D. Stehlik, Evidence for asymmetric electron transfer in cyanobacterial Photosystem I: Analysis of a methionine-to-leucine mutation of the ligand to the primary electron acceptor A_0. *Biochemistry* **43** (2004) 4741–4754.
335. N. Kusumoto, K. Inoue, H. Sakurai, Spectroscopic studies of bound cytochrome-c and an iron-sulfur center in a purified reaction center complex from the green sulfur bacterium *Chlorobium tepidum*. *Photosynth. Res.* **43** (1995) 107–112.

336. J.S. Okkels, B. Kjaer, O. Hansson, I. Svendsen, B.L. Moller, H.V. Scheller, A membrane-bound monoheme cytochrome-c551 of a novel type is the immediate electron donor to P840 of the *Chlorobium vibrioforme* photosynthetic reaction center complex. *J. Biol. Chem.* **267** (1992) 21139–21145.
337. B. Kjaer, Y.-S. Jung, L. Yu, J.H. Golbeck, H.V. Scheller, Iron-sulfur centers in the photosynthetic reaction center complex from *Chlorobium vibrioforme*. Differences from and similarities to the iron-sulfur centers in Photosystem I. *Photosynth. Res.* **41** (1994) 105–114.
338. M.Y. Okamura, K. Shimada, K. Matsuura, Photooxidation of membrane-bound and soluble cytochrome c in the green sulfur bacterium *Chlorobium tepidum*. *Photosynth. Res.* **41** (1994) 125–134.
339. U. Feiler, W. Nitschke, H. Michel, Characterization of an improved reaction center preparation from the photosynthetic green sulfur bacterium *Chlorobium* containing the FeS centers F_A and F_B and a bound cytochrome subunit. *Biochemistry* **31** (1992) 2608–2614.
340. M. Miller, X.M. Liu, S.W. Snyder, M.C. Thurnauer, J. Biggins, Photosynthetic electron transfer reactions in the green sulfur bacterium *Chlorobium vibrioforme*. Evidence for the functional involvement of iron-sulfur redox centers on the acceptor side of the reaction center. *Biochemistry* **31** (1992) 4354–4363.
341. D. Albouy, J.N. Sturgis, U. Feiler, W. Nitschke, B. Robert, Membrane-associated c-type cytochromes from the green sulfur bacterium *Chlorobium limicola* forma thiosulfatophilum: purification and characterization of cytochrome c(553). *Biochemistry* **36** (1997) 1927–1932.
342. H. Gest, Discovery of the heliobacteria. *Photosynth. Res.* **41** (1994) 17–21.
343. H. Gest, J.L. Favinger, *Heliobacterium chlorum* an anoxygenic brownish-green bacterium containing a "new" form of bacteriochlorophyll. *Arch. Microbiol.* **136** (1983) 11–16.
344. S. Neerken, J. Amesz, The antenna reaction center complex of heliobacteria: composition, energy conversion and electron transfer. *Biochim. Biophys. Acta* **1507** (2001) 278–290.
345. E.J. van de Meent, F.A.M. Kleinherenbrink, J. Amesz, Purification and properties of an antenna-reaction center complex from heliobacteria. *Biochim. Biophys. Acta* **1015** (1990) 223–230.
346. M. Kobayashi, E.J. van de Meent, C. Erkelens, J. Amesz, I. Ikegami, T. Watanabe, Bacteriochlorophyll-g epimer as a possible reaction center component of *Heliobacteria*. *Biochim. Biophys. Acta* **1057** (1991) 89–96.
347. J.T. Trost, R.E. Blankenship, Isolation of a photoactive photosynthetic reaction center-core antenna complex from *Heliobacillus mobilis*. *Biochemistry* **28** (1989) 9898–9904.
348. U. Liebl, M. Mockensturmwilson, J.T. Trost, D.C. Brune, R.E. Blankenship, W. Vermaas, Single core polypeptide in the reaction center of the photosynthetic bacterium *Heliobacillus mobilis*. Structural implications and relations to other photosystems. *Proc. Natl. Acad. Sci. U.S.A.* **90** (1993) 7124–7128.
349. S. Lin, H.C. Chiou, R.E. Blankenship, Secondary electron transfer processes in membranes of *Heliobacillus mobilis*. *Biochemistry* **34** (1995) 12761–12767.
350. F.A.M. Kleinherenbrink, H.C. Chiou, R. Lobrutto, R.E. Blankenship, Spectroscopic evidence for the presence of an iron-sulfur center similar to F_x of Photosystem I in *Heliobacillus mobilis*. *Photosynth. Res.* **41** (1994) 115–123.
351. W. Nitschke, P. Setif, U. Liebl, U. Feiler, A.W. Rutherford, Reaction center photochemistry of *Heliobacterium chlorum*. *Biochemistry* **29** (1990) 11079–11088.

352. T. Noguchi, Y. Fukami, H. Oh-Oka, Y. Inoue, Fourier transform infrared study on the primary donor P798 of *Heliobacterium modesticaldum* cysteine: S-H coupled to P798 and molecular interactions of carbonyl groups. *Biochemistry* **36** (1997) 12329–12336.

353. R.C. Prince, H. Gest, R.E. Blankenship, Thermodynamic properties of the photochemical reaction center of *Heliobacterium chlorum*. *Biochim. Biophys. Acta* **810** (1985) 377–384.

354. E.J. van de Meent, M. Kobayashi, C. Erkelens, P.A. van Veelen, J. Amesz, T. Watanabe, Identification of 8^1-hydroxychlorophyll-a as a functional reaction center pigment in *Heliobacteria*. *Biochim. Biophys. Acta* **1058** (1991) 356–362.

355. A.M. Nuijs, R.J. van Dorssen, L.N.M. Duysens, J. Amesz, Excited states and primary photochemical reactions in the photosynthetic bacterium *Heliobacterium chlorum*. *Proc. Natl. Acad. Sci. U.S.A.* **82** (1985) 6865–6868.

356. S. Lin, H.C. Chiou, F.A.M. Kleinherenbrink, R.E. Blankenship, Time-resolved spectroscopy of energy and electron transfer processes in the photosynthetic bacterium *Heliobacillus mobilis*. *Biophys. J.* **66** (1994) 437–445.

357. U. Liebl, J.C. Lambry, W. Leibl, J. Breton, J.L. Martin, M.H. Vos, Energy and electron transfer upon selective femtosecond excitation of pigments in membranes of *Heliobacillus mobilis*. *Biochemistry* **35** (1996) 9925–9934.

358. H.C. Chiou, S. Lin, R.E. Blankenship, Time-resolved spectroscopy of energy transfer and trapping upon selective excitation in membranes of Helicobacillus mobilis at low temperature. *J. Phys. Chem. B* **101** (1997) 4136–4141.

359. S. Neerken, T.J. Aartsma, J. Amesz, Pathways of energy transformation in antenna reaction center complexes of *Heliobacillus mobilis*. *Biochemistry* **39** (2000) 3297–3303.

360. P.J.M. van Kan, T.J. Aartsma, J. Amesz, Primary photosynthetic processes in *Heliobacterium chlorum* at 15 K. *Photosynth. Res.* **22** (1989) 61–68.

361. K. Brettel, W. Leibl, U. Liebl, Electron transfer in the heliobacterial reaction center: evidence against a quinone-type electron acceptor functioning analogous to A_1 in Photosystem I. *Biochim. Biophys. Acta* **1363** (1998) 175–181.

362. M. Brok, H. Vasmel, J.T.C. Horikx, A.J. Hoff, Electron transport components of *Heliobacterium chlorum* investigated by EPR spectroscopy at 9 and 35 GHz. *FEBS Lett.* **194** (1986) 322–326.

363. F.A.M. Kleinherenbrink, J. Amesz, Stoichiometries and rates of electron transfer and charge recombination in *Heliobacterium chlorum*. *Biochim. Biophys. Acta* **1143** (1993) 77–83.

364. I. Albert, A.W. Rutherford, H. Grav, J. Kellermann, H. Michel, The 18 kDa cytochrome c553 from *Heliobacterium gestii*: gene sequence and characterization of the mature protein. *Biochemistry* **37** (1998) 9001–9008.

365. D.M. Kramer, B. Schoepp, U. Liebl, W. Nitschke, Cyclic electron transfer in *Heliobacillus mobilis* involving a menaquinol-oxidizing cytochrome bc complex and an RCI-type reaction center. *Biochemistry* **36** (1997) 4203–4211.

366. W. Nitschke, U. Liebl, K. Matsuura, D.M. Kramer, Membrane-bound c-type cytochromes in *Heliobacillus mobilis*. *In vivo* study of the hemes involved in electron donation to the photosynthetic reaction center. *Biochemistry* **34** (1995) 11831–11839.

367. W. Nitschke, B. Schoepp, B. Floss, A. Schricker, A.W. Rutherford, U. Liebl, Membrane-bound c-type cytochromes in *Heliobacillus mobilis*. Characterisation by EPR and optical spectroscopy in membranes and detergent-solubilised material. *Eur. J. Biochem.* **242** (1996) 695–702.

368. M. Mimuro, M. Kobayashi, K. Shimada, K. Uezono, T. Nozawa, Magnetic circular dichroism properties of reaction center complexes isolated from the zinc-bacteriochlorophyll a-containing purple bacterium *Acidiphilium rubrum*. *Biochemistry* **39** (2000) 4020–4027.
369. A. Hiraishi, K. Shimada, Aerobic anoxygenic photosynthetic bacteria with zinc-bacteriochlorophyll. *J. Gen. Appl. Microbiol.* **47** (2001) 161–180.
370. H. Scheer, The pigments, in: *Light-Harvesting Antennas in Photosynthesis* (2003) (B.R. Green, W.W. Parson, eds.), Kluwer Academic Publishers, Dordrecht, pp. 29–81.
371. W. Humphrey, A. Dalke, K. Schulten, VMD: visual molecular dynamics. *J. Mol. Graph.* **14** (1996) 33–38.
372. H.M. Berman, J. Westbrook, Z. Feng, G. Gilliland, T.N. Bhat, H. Weissig, I.N. Shindyalov, P.E. Bourne, The protein data bank. *Nucleic Acids Res.* **28** (2000) 235–242.
373. H.L. Axelrod, E.C. Abresch, M.Y. Okamura, A.P. Yeh, D.C. Rees, G. Feher, X-Ray structure determination of the cytochrome c_2:reaction center electron transfer complex from *Rhodobacter sphaeroides*. *J. Mol. Biol.* **319** (2002) 501–515.
374. S.M. Dracheva, L.A. Drachev, A.A. Konstantinov, A.Y. Semenov, V.P. Skulachev, A.M. Arutjunjan, V.A. Shuvalov, S.M. Zaberezhnaya, Electrogenic steps in the redox reactions catalyzed by photosynthetic reaction-centre complex from *Rhodopseudomonas viridis*. *Eur. J. Biochem.* **171** (1988) 253–264.
375. G. Fritzsch, S. Buchanan, H. Michel, Assignment of cytochrome hemes in crystallized reaction centers from *Rhodopseudomonas virids*. *Biochim. Biophys. Acta* **977** (1989) 157–162.
376. A. Verméglio, P. Richaud, J. Breton, Orientation and assignment of the 4 cytochrome hemes in *Rhodopseudomonas viridis* reaction centers. *FEBS Lett.* **243** (1989) 259–263.

Chapter 13

Structure and Function of Photosystem I

Raimund Fromme, Ingo Grotjohann and Petra Fromme

Table of Contents

13.1 Introduction... 113
13.2 General Architecture of Photosystem I 114
13.3 Electron Transport Chain................................... 116
    13.3.1 P700: The Primary Electron Donor 117
    13.3.2 A: The Initial Electron Acceptor 118
    13.3.3 A_0: The First Stable Electron Acceptor 118
    13.3.4 A_1: The Phylloquinone 119
    13.3.5 F_X: The First FeS Cluster 120
    13.3.6 F_A and F_B: The Terminal FeS Clusters 121
13.4 Protein Subunits of PS I.................................... 121
    13.4.1 Core of PS I: The Large Subunits PsaA and PsaB 122
    13.4.2 Stromal Hump of PS I: PsaC, PsaD and PsaE 123
        13.4.2.1 Subunit PsaC........................... 123
        13.4.2.2 Subunit PsaD 126
        13.4.2.3 Subunit PsaE........................... 127
    13.4.3 Monomer–Monomer Interface: PsaL, PsaI and PsaM...... 128
        13.4.3.1 Subunit PsaL........................... 128
        13.4.3.2 Subunit PsaI 129
        13.4.3.3 Subunit PsaM 130
    13.4.4 Membrane-Exposed Subunits: PsaF, PsaJ, PsaX and PsaK .. 130
        13.4.4.1 Subunit PsaF........................... 130
        13.4.4.2 Subunit PsaJ 132
        13.4.4.3 Subunit PsaX........................... 132
        13.4.4.4 PsaK................................. 132
13.5 Antenna System of PS I 133
    13.5.1 Antenna Chlorophylls............................... 133
    13.5.2 Carotenoids 135

13.6 Lipids in PS I 135
13.7 Concluding Remarks and Future Perspectives 137
Acknowledgements 138
References 138

STRUCTURE AND FUNCTION OF PHOTOSYSTEM I

Abstract

Photosystem I is a large membrane protein complex that catalyzes the first step of light reactions in photosynthesis. It can be regarded as a solar energy converter that captures the light from the sun through a large core-antenna system of chlorophylls and carotenoids. It then transfers the excitation energy into the center of the complex, where this electronic energy is used to catalyze the light-driven transmembrane electron transfer from plastocyanin to ferredoxin. Photosystem I of cyanobacterial origin consists of 12 protein subunits, to which 127 cofactors are non-covalently bound. This chapter describes the structure and function of cyanobacterial Photosystem I, as revealed from the X-ray structure at 2.5 Å resolution.

13.1 Introduction

Oxygenic photosynthesis is the main process on earth that converts the light energy from the sun into chemical energy. The process supplies almost all higher life on earth with food and produces over 99% of the oxygen in the atmosphere. Two large membrane protein complexes, Photosystems I and II, which are embedded in the membrane, catalyze the initial steps of photosynthesis: the light-induced charge separation. A pool of plastoquinones, the cytochrome *b6f* complex, and plastocyanin or cytochrome *c6* functionally couple both photosystems.

Cyanobacterial Photosystem I consists of 12 protein subunits, to which 127 cofactors are non-covalently bound. It catalyzes the light-driven electron transfer from the soluble Cu-containing protein plastocyanin on the lumenal side (i.e., the inside of the thylakoid membrane) to ferredoxin on the stromal side (outside) of the thylakoid membrane.

Cyanobacteria can also use the heme-containing soluble protein cytochrome *c6* as an alternative or unique electron donor to Photosystem I. There is also some flexibility concerning the electron acceptor. In the case of iron deficiency, flavodoxin can act as the electron acceptor instead of ferredoxin.

The first step of the whole process is light capturing, performed by the large antenna system, which consists of 90 antenna chlorophylls and 22 carotenoids. The excitation energy is transferred to the center of the complex, where the electron transport chain is located. When the energy excites a special pair of two chlorophylls, located in the center of the complex, the "action" takes place and charge separation occurs. Owing to its absorption maximum at 700 nm, this pair of chlorophylls was named P700. The electron is transferred from P700 across the membrane by a chain of electron carriers. These electron carriers had been previously identified by spectroscopic investigations, and their historical names have been maintained. The electron transport chain consists of five steps. The electron is stepwise transferred from P700 to A (a chlorophyll *a* molecule), A_0 (also a chlorophyll *a* molecule), A_1 (a phylloquinone molecule) and from there to the three [4Fe4S] clusters, F_X, F_A and F_B. After the docking of the soluble electron carrier ferredoxin, the electron is transferred from Photosystem I to ferredoxin, which subsequently leaves the docking site to bring the electron to the enzyme ferredoxin-$NADP^+$-reductase, which then finally reduces $NADP^+$ to NADPH. After this process has occurred once, $P700^+$ has to be re-reduced to complete the reaction cycle. There is a docking site for soluble electron carrier proteins located on the lumenal side of the complex, just underneath P700. In plants, reduced plastocyanin docks to this site and reduces $P700^+$, whereas cytochrome *c6* can substitute plastocyanin in cyanobacteria.

Detailed structural information is available from the X-ray structure of cyanobacterial Photosystem I from the thermophilic cyanobacterium *Synechococcus elongatus* (now renamed *Thermosynechococcus elongatus*) at 2.5 Å resolution [1] and will be described in this chapter. The structure of plant Photosystem I has been determined at 4.4 Å resolution from pea [2].

13.2 General Architecture of Photosystem I

In cyanobacteria, Photosystem I can exist in trimeric and monomeric forms [3]. In *S. elongatus*, the total amount of PS I and its oligomeric organization depend on the environmental conditions. At low light intensity, the PS I trimer is the most abundant protein in the thylakoid membrane. The amount of PS I present exceeds the amount of PS II by a factor of eight. Under low light conditions, essentially all PS I exists in the membrane in trimeric form. The formation of intact trimers is essential for the growth of cells at low light intensity [125].

The trimer with a molecular weight of 1 056 000 Da has been isolated and crystallized [125,126]. Photosystem I is the largest and most complex membrane protein for which the structure has been determined.

Figure 1 shows a simplified picture of the trimeric complex, pointing out the elaborate organization of this nano-biosolar system. Each monomeric unit contains 12 proteins, 96 chlorophylls, 22 carotenoids, three [4Fe4S] clusters, two phylloquinone molecules and four lipids. This picture of the trimeric PS I visualizes another remarkable feature of PS I: the high content of cofactors. Some 31% of the total mass of PS I consists of cofactors, which are therefore not only important for the function of the protein but also play an essential role in the assembly and structural integrity of PS I.

One monomeric unit of the cyanobacterial Photosystem I consists of 12 different proteins (PsaA, PsaB, PsaC, PsaD, PsaE, PsaF, PsaI, PsaJ, PsaK, PsaL, PsaM and PsaX) to which 127 cofactors are non-covalently bound. In higher plants, the system contains at least four additional subunits, whose functions are still under investigation.

The main proteins, including all cofactor-binding sites, are well conserved between plants and cyanobacteria, whereas PsaX and PsaM may be unique to cyanobacteria, even if the homologous gene for PsaM has been identified in liver moss [4]. The structure of the plant PSI confirms the absence of PsaM and PsaX in higher plants [2].

STRUCTURE AND FUNCTION OF PHOTOSYSTEM I

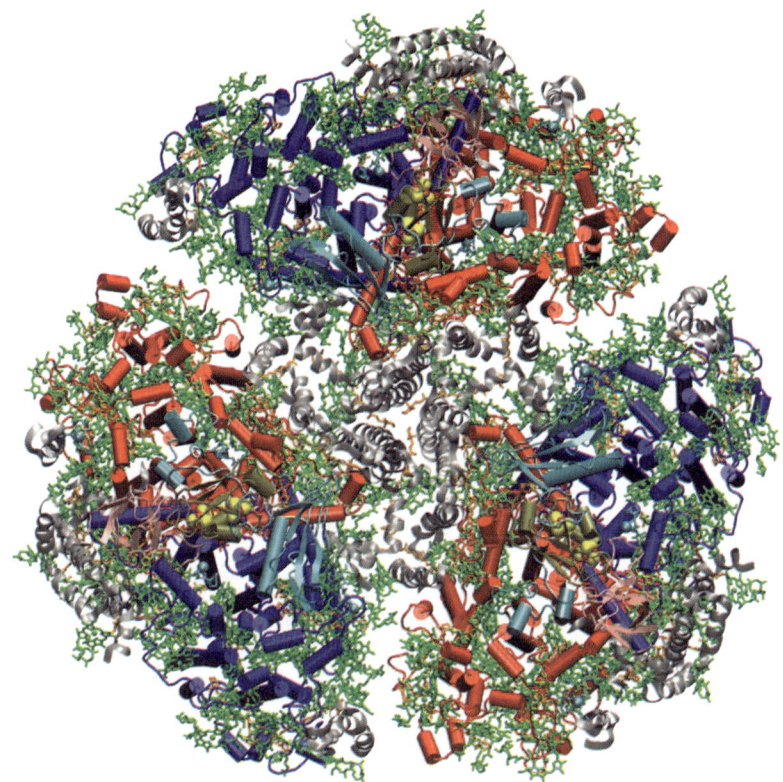

Figure 1. The trimeric structure of Photosystem I from cyanobacteria; the view direction is from the stromal side onto the membrane plane. The 12 proteins are shown in a backbone representation (PsaA, blue; PsaB, red; PsaC, mauve; PsaD, ice blue; PsaE, pink; PsaF, silver; PsaI, silver; PsaJ, gray; PsaK, gray; PsaL, silver; PsaM, silver and PsaX, gray). The head groups of the chlorophylls are shown in green, the chlorophylls of the electron transfer are in red, the phytyl-tails have been omitted for clarity; the carotenoids are depicted in gray and the lipids in dark turquoise.

Figure 4 shows the organization of protein subunits in Photosystem I. The two most important proteins are the large subunits PsaA and PsaB. They harbor most of the antenna system, as well as most of the cofactors of the electron transport chain from P700 to the first FeS cluster, F_X.

All of the small subunits are located at the periphery of PsaA and PsaB. The subunits PsaC, PsaD and PsaE do not contain transmembrane helices. They form the stromal hump of PSI, which extends the membrane by approximately 90 Å. PsaC carries the two terminal FeS clusters, F_A and F_B.

The other small subunits, which contain between one and three transmembrane helices, are located at the periphery of PsaA and PsaB.

These subunits exist in quite different environments. The subunits PsaL and PsaI are located in the center of the trimeric complex (Figure 1) and form the "trimerization domain", while PsaM is located at the interface between the monomers.

PsaJ and PsaF, as well as PsaK and PsaX, are located at the membrane-exposed surface of the trimeric PS I complex. They stabilize the core-antenna system of PS I and may also be involved in the interaction of PS I with its external antenna systems.

13.3 Electron Transport Chain

The electron transport chain is located in the center of the PS I complex, representing the heart of Photosystem I. Figure 2 shows the structural organization of the cofactors of the electron transport chain. It consists of six chlorophylls, two phylloquinones and three [4Fe4S] clusters. The organic cofactors (i.e., the chlorophylls and the phylloquinones) of the electron transfer chain are arranged in two branches. They are named the A and B branches, because most – but not all – cofactors of the A branch and B branch are coordinated by PsaA and PsaB proteins, respectively. Most of the molecules involved in electron transfer were first identified by spectroscopy. Mechanistically, one of the most exciting questions is whether one or both branches are active in electron transfer. First, we discuss the structure and function of the

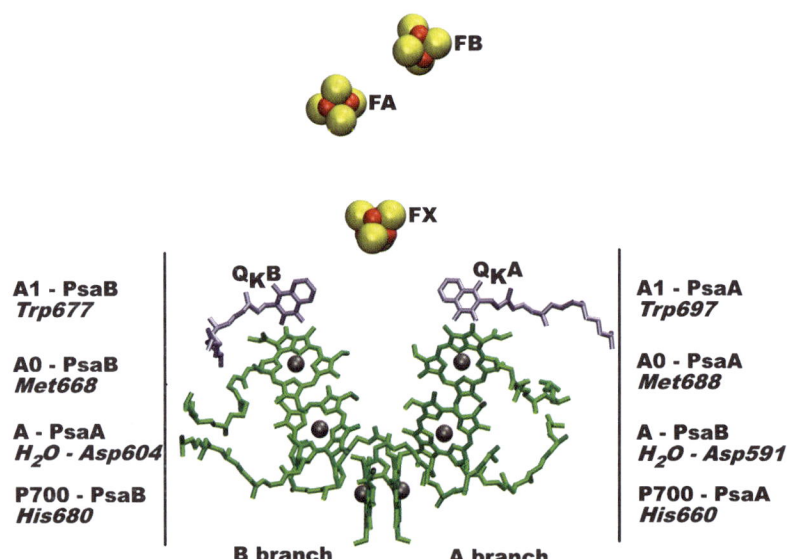

Figure 2. Photosystem I. Depicted is the reaction center from the membrane plane with a focus on non protein compounds. Arrangement of the chlorophylls (in green) relative to the quinones (in ice blue) and Fe_4S_4 clusters (red and yellow). The central Mg^{2+} of the chlorophylls are in silver.

individual cofactors and then come back to the question of whether one or two branches are active when the function of the phylloquinones is discussed.

13.3.1 P700: The Primary Electron Donor

The pair of chlorophylls assigned to P700 is located close to the lumenal surface of Photosystem I. It consists of two chemically different chlorophyll molecules. The chlorophyll on the B-branch is the "common" chlorophyll a molecule, chemically identical to all the other 95 chlorophylls in Photosystem I, whereas the chlorophyll at the A-branch is chlorophyll a', the epimer at the C13 position of the chlorin ring system.

The existence of at least one chlorophyll a' molecule was first suggested by Watanabe and co-workers [5–7,130] on the basis of chlorophyll extraction experiments, but their pioneering findings were questioned until the existence of a Chl a/Chl a' heterodimer was verified by the 2.5 Å crystal structure of cyanobacterial Photosystem I [1].

The chlorophyll on the B-Branch of P700 (eC-B1) is axially coordinated to His B660. No hydrogen bonds are formed between the surrounding protein and the chlorin head group of eC-B1. The chlorophyll on the A-branch of P700 (eC-A1) is the Chl a' molecule; it is axially coordinated by His A680. This Chl a' forms three hydrogen bonds to the side-chains of transmembrane α-helices A-i and A-k and a water molecule.

The distance between the central Mg^{2+} ions of the two chlorophylls assigned to P700 is 6.3 Å, which is shorter than the corresponding distance between the bacteriochlorophylls in the special pair of PbRC. The planes of eC-A1 and eC-B1 are oriented perpendicularly to the membrane plane and parallel to each other, with an interplanar distance of 3.6 Å. The overlap between the ring systems differs between P700 in Photosystem I and the special pair of PbRC. In the bacteriochlorophyll ring system of the special pair, the I rings overlap perfectly [8], whereas rings I and II of the chlorophylls only partially overlap in P700. Electron nuclear double resonance (ENDOR) studies in solution [9] and on single crystals of PS I [10] revealed that the spin density in P700 is asymmetric, with over 85% of the spin density located on the B-branch Chl a of P700. Molecular orbital studies of the electronic structure of P700, based on semi-empirical density functional calculations on the 2.5 Å structure, show that the two chlorophylls are tightly coupled and P700 is a super-molecule [11]. The asymmetry of the spin density can be explained by the interplay between the asymmetric hydrogen bonding, differences in the protein environment and the chemically different nature of the two chlorophyll molecules. Whether the asymmetry is essential for the function of PS I still remains to be proven. However, the fact that Chl a' is a constituent in cyanobacterial, algae and plant PS I may suggest that it plays a key role for the function of PS I. It may be speculated that the asymmetrical spin density distribution could be responsible for the "gating" of the electron along the two cofactor branches; however, there is, thus far, no experimental proof for this suggestion.

The question of how the chlorophyll a' is assembled into the PS I complex or if it may be isomerized by PS I in a photoactivated process also remains unanswered.

13.3.2 A: The Initial Electron Acceptor

Three pairs of chlorophylls are present in the electron transport chain, as found in the X-ray structural model of Photosystem I at 2.5 Å resolution. From electronically excited singlet state ^{1}P700* (represented by the first pair of chlorophylls) the electron is transferred via one of the chlorophylls from the second pair of chlorophylls (A) to the first stable electron acceptor, A_0, which may be located on one of the chlorophylls in the center of the membrane (Figure 2). These first steps of electron transport occur in less than 3 ps; as such the second pair of chlorophylls has not yet been detected by spectroscopy.

The chlorophylls of the second pair (eC-B2 and eC-A2) are often misleadingly named accessory chlorophylls. They have a center-to-center distance of approximately 12 Å to the chlorophylls of P700 and represent the first electron acceptor in PS I. These two chlorophylls are the only cofactors of the electron transport chain (*ETC*) where the coordinating subunit of the A-branch is PsaB and vice versa. In both branches, a water molecule provides the fifth ligand to the central Mg^{2+} ion of the second pair of chlorophylls. The water molecule, which serves as the axial ligand to the chlorophyll a at the A-branch, is bound to asparagine residue AsnB591 via a hydrogen bond and, therefore, this chlorophyll molecule is named eC-B2. The binding pocket of the corresponding chlorophyll in the B-branch is similar, so that AsnA604 is hydrogen bonded to the water molecule, which axially legates the chlorophyll eC-A2. Remarkable differences are observed in the orientation and coordination of the second pair of chlorophylls/bacteriochlorophylls ["accessory (bacterio)chlorophylls"] between Photosystem I and the PbRC, where histidines provide the fifth ligand for the Mg^{2+} [1].

It is remarkable that the "accessory" chlorophylls in PS II match the PbRC with respect to the orientation but resemble PS I in their coordination, because they are not coordinated by an His side-chain [12]. The structure of Photosystem I at 2.5Å resolution strongly supports the idea that the chlorophylls eC-A2 and eC-B2 may be directly involved in electron transfer from P700 to A_0. Results by Holzwarth and co-workers suggest that the charge separation may start from the electronically excited singlet state of the accessory chlorophyll at the B branch rather than from ^{1}P700* [13], but this idea is still a matter of debate [128].

13.3.3 A_0: The First Stable Electron Acceptor

The second pair and third pair of chlorophylls are located in close to each other in PS I (3.8 Å), with a roughly parallel orientation of the chlorin rings of eC-B2 ↔ eC-A3 and eC-A2 ↔ eC-B3. Even if eC-A3 and eC-B3 are supposed to correspond to the spectroscopically identified electron acceptor A_0, it is very likely that the spectroscopic and redox properties of eC-A3 and eC-B3 may be influenced by eC-B2 and eC-A2, respectively. This finding supports the suggestion that the difference spectrum $A_0/A_0^{-\cdot}$ contains contributions from more than one chlorophyll [14]. The chlorophyll molecules eC-A3 and eC-B3 are in the middle of the membrane at a position that exhibits in the spatial position similarities to the (bacterio)pheophytin [(B)Pheo] of both PbRC [8] and PS II [12]. Both chlorophylls constitute one hydrogen bond to the tyrosines A696 and B676, which are direct neighbors to the Trp residues W697 of PsaA and W677 of PsaB that interact via π-stacking with the quinone electron acceptor(s) (see below). The axial ligands of eC-A3 and eC-B3 are unusual. The sulfur atoms of methionine residues A688 and B668 provide the fifth "ligands" of the Mg^{2+} ions. This structural result is remarkable, because the concept of hard and soft acids and bases predicts only weak interactions between the hard acid Mg^{2+} and methionine sulfur as a soft base. Mutation of the methionine AMet688 to AHis688 provides a strong ligand to Mg^{2+} and thereby blocks the electron transfer chain along the A-branch [15]. Remarkably, the cells are not strongly affected in autotrophic growth by this mutation, whereas the mutation of BMet668 into BHis668 leads to severe growth deficits of the green algae, even if the electron transfer along the B-branch is not completely blocked. Recent results of Webber and co-workers [16], who investigated the mutation of the methionines in both branches, also revealed a more pronounced phenotype for the B-site mutation, but both mutants still exhibit some limited photoautotrophic growth. These findings lead to the suggestion that the A-branch is less important than the B-branch at least in green algae. Mutagenesis studies on the cyanobacterial PS I from *Synechocystis PCC 6803* (which unfortunately does not include the His mutant) favor the A-branch over the B-branch [17], so that the question as to whether there are one or two active branches in PS I is still the most controversially discussed topic in PS I. It may even be the case that the branching of the electron along the two chains could differ between different organisms. A detailed sequence comparison and alignment between Photosystem I complexes from cyanobacteria, green algae and higher plants reveals that all amino acids that are involved in axial coordination or hydrogen bonding to the second and third Chl*a* pairs of the ETC are strictly conserved. The conservation of the differences in the axial coordination and hydrogen bonding between the three pairs of chlorophyll molecules throughout evolution could suggest that these protein–chlorophyll interactions are essential for the physicochemical properties (e.g., the redox potentials) of these cofactors. However, the question as to whether the very low redox potential of the electron acceptor, A_0 (−1050 mV), is caused by the absence of a strong fifth ligand to the Mg^{2+} atom of these chlorophylls remains unanswered.

13.3.4 A_1: The Phylloquinone

In the next step of the electron transfer chain the electron is further transferred from A_0 to one of the phylloquinones, which represent the electron acceptor "A_1". The two phylloquinones, QKA and QKB, which may represent A_1, are located at the stromal side of the membrane. The binding pockets are identical on both sites but differ significantly from all other quinone binding pockets found in proteins so far. Both quinones are π-stacked with a tryptophan residue and both show asymmetrical hydrogen bonding: only one of the two oxygen atoms forms a H-bond to an NH backbone group, whereas the other oxygen atom is not hydrogen bonded at all. This could lead to a protein-induced asymmetry in the distribution of the unpaired electron in the radical state $A_1^{-\cdot}$. This may explain why A_1 has the most negative redox potential (−770 mV) of all quinones so far found in nature. The electron proceeds from A_1 to the FeS cluster, F_X.

This is the rate-limiting step of the electron transfer in PS I. Still, a lively scientific discussion continues regarding the question of whether one or both branches are active.

There is experimental evidence that the electron transfer can proceed along both branches, but at different rates. In the green algae *Chlamydomonas reinhardtii*, electron transfer is about a factor of 50 slower on the A- than on the B-branch [18,19].

This could be the result of a higher activation energy barrier on the A- compared with the B-branch. This finding raises the question of the structural reason for this functional difference. There is no significant difference in the protein environments of both branches, but there are two lipid molecules located close to the pathway from A_1 to F_X that could be responsible for the asymmetry. A negatively charged phospholipid, located on the slower A-branch, probably hampers the electron transfer, whereas on the faster B-branch a neutral galactolipid has replaced the phospholipid. This is the most reasonable explanation for the higher activation energy barrier of the electron transfer between QKA and F_X compared with the electron transfer between QKB and F_X.

Another factor, which could lead to a difference in reorganization energy between the two branches, is differences in the water clusters that are located between the quinone binding site and F_X. There are five water molecules located in a pocket at the A-branch, which show a non-specific arrangement. In contrast, five of the total of six water molecules located between the quinone-binding pocket and F_X at the B-branch phylloquinone form the structure of a hexagon, a well-defined low-energy arrangement of a water cluster [20]. Thereby, the hexagon structure of the water cluster at the B-branch may also contribute to the lowering of the reorganization energy and the activation energy barrier at the B-branch. A reasonable explanation was provided for the faster electron transfer along the B-branch compared with the A-branch by the results of Ishikita and Knapp [21]. They calculated the redox potentials of the two active electron transfer quinones in PS I by evaluating the electrostatic energies from the solution of the Poisson–Boltzmann equation based on the crystal structure. The calculated redox potentials are −531 mV for QKA and −686 mV for QKB, which would lead to an uphill electron transfer from QKA to F_X [21].

13.3.5 F_X: The First FeS Cluster

F_X is a rare example of an inter-protein FeS cluster. Histidine ligands are provided by Cys578 and Cys587 of PsaA and Cys565 and Cys574 of PsaB. The ligands are located in the loop connecting helices h and i. This loop is highly conserved and essentially identical in all PS I species from plants, algae and cyanobacteria. It contains two cysteines in the highly conserved sequence (FPCDGPGRGGTCXXSAWDH). In the 1980s, this site was already suggested to be the coordination site for the first [4Fe4S] cluster, F_X [22], which was experimentally supported by mutagenesis studies [23,24]. The structure of cyanobacterial PS I at 2.5 Å resolution confirmed this assignment [1,25].

Electron transfer (ET) from the quinone to F_X is slower than ET from F_X to F_A; therefore, F_X is difficult to detect in intact PS I complexes and, as a consequence, was mainly studied in complexes depleted of the extrinsic subunits or where the terminal FeS clusters are pre-reduced. As both of these procedures can alter the physical and/or chemical parameters of F_X, the value determined for the redox potential of F_X (–710 mV) has to be considered with caution.

In addition to its functional role in electron transfer, F_X also plays an important role in the stabilization and assembly of the PS I complex. The PS I complex can not assemble without the help of proteins that are not a part of PS I, but are found to be attached to the monomeric PS I during assembly. A mutant was described and spectroscopically characterized that lacks the open reading frame for a rubredoxin (rubA) [26]. Shen et al. [26] provided striking evidence that this protein is involved in the assembly of F_X. The mutant PS I assembles all membrane intrinsic subunits but lacks F_X and the extrinsic subunits PsaC, PsaD and PsaE. The assembly of the whole stromal hump may, therefore, depend on the functional assembly of F_X.

13.3.6 F_A and F_B: The Terminal FeS Clusters

The two terminal FeS centers are bound to the extrinsic subunit PsaC. A long standing question was whether F_A or F_B is the terminal FeS cluster that transfers the electron to ferredoxin.

Mutagenesis in combination with EPR investigations [27,28] showed that the cluster in close proximity to F_X (center-to-center distance 14.9 Å), coordinated by the cysteine residues C21, C48, C51 and C54, represents F_A, whereas the cluster coordinated by the cysteine residues C11, C14, C17 and C58 represents the distal cluster F_B [29,30].

Accordingly, F_B is the terminal FeS cluster, with a center-to-center distance of 22 Å to F_X.

A sequential electron transport from F_X to F_A to F_B is also confirmed by numerous spectroscopic and biochemical studies ([31–33] and references therein).

13.4 Protein Subunits of PS I

This section describes the structure and function of the protein subunits in Photosystem I, starting with details on the large subunits PsaA and PsaB.

13.4.1 Core of PS I: The Large Subunits PsaA and PsaB

The major subunits of Photosystem I, PsaA and PsaB, exhibit a large homology to each other and are suggested to have evolved via gene duplication. They each contain eleven transmembrane helices, as evidenced by sequence alignment and folding predictions [34,35]. The arrangement of transmembrane helices in PS I is depicted in Figure 4, in (A) and (B) in the membrane plane and in (C) a top view. The area of transmembrane helices for PsaA/PsaB can be divided into two domains: the five C-terminal α-helices (g to j) surround the electron transfer chain, whereas the N-terminal six helices flank the central region at both sides, forming an arrangement of "trimers of helix-pairs", where the pairs are formed by transmembrane helices a/b, c/d and e/f. The N-terminal domain of PsaA/B is connected to the C-terminal domain by hydrophobic interactions of helix f with helix i, by the fg loop and interaction between the loops, as well as hydrophobic interactions mediated by the cofactors (chlorophylls, carotenoids and lipids). The C-terminal domain shows some similarity to the arrangement of the L and M proteins in bacterial reaction centers [8] and the D1 and D2 proteins in Photosystem II [12,36,37], whereas the N-terminal domain of PsaA and PsaB shows a striking similarity to the arrangement of helices in the core antenna proteins of Photosystem II (PsbB and PsbC) and the peripheral antenna protein IsiA, expressed under iron deficiency [38–40]. It is, therefore, very likely that all photoreaction centers have evolved from a common ancestor and the genes for PsaA and PsaB have evolved by a gene fusion of an ancient RC protein containing five transmembrane helices and an antenna protein consisting of six transmembrane helices, as suggested earlier [41].

Whereas the transmembrane helices nearly perfectly match the two-fold symmetry between PsaA and PsaB, some of the loops show striking differences in sequence, length and secondary structural elements, making the system more asymmetric. The functional reason for this asymmetry is its ability to attach the stromal hump and the small membrane intrinsic subunits at a proper position to the core of PS I. Interestingly, there exist neither barely any hydrogen bonds nor any salt bridges between PsaA/PsaB and the small subunits in the transmembrane regions of PS I [42]. Therefore, analysis of these interactions does not answer the question as to how PS I may be assembled.

Instead, the peripheral membrane intrinsic subunits are attached by hydrophobic interactions with the cofactors and by specific interactions (salt bridges and H-bonds) within the asymmetric parts of the loops of PsaA and PsaB.

PsaA and PsaB coordinate most of the cofactors of the electron transport chain (P700, A, A_0, A_1, and F_X) and 79 of the 90 antenna chlorophylls in PS I. In addition, most of the carotenoids hydrophobically interact with either PsaA or PsaB.

Most, but not all, of the chlorophylls are coordinated by histidines. Interestingly, most of the coordination sites were conserved over millions of years during the evolution from cyanobacteria to plants.

The cofactors of the electron transfer chain from P700 to F_X are coordinated by the C-terminal region of PS I between the end of transmembrane helix h

STRUCTURE AND FUNCTION OF PHOTOSYSTEM I

(corresponding to the 8th transmembrane helix) and the start of transmembrane helix k (corresponding to the 10th transmembrane helix). Details of the ligation of P700, A_0, and A_1 are discussed extensively below.

The helices of the two large subunits are related to each other by a local two-fold symmetry axis running through the FeS cluster, F_X. The iron-sulfur cluster, F_X, is coordinated by two cysteines of the conserved sequence motif of the large subunits PsaA and PsaB. It is a rare example of an inter-protein iron-sulfur cluster. This loop is not only responsible for the coordination of F_X, but also plays an important role in the attachment of PsaC and the whole assembly of the stromal hump (see [43]).

PsaA and PsaB also play an essential role in the docking of the soluble electron donors to PS I. Plastocyanin and cytochrome *c6* bind to Photosystem I at an indentation at the lumenal side to re-reduce the primary electron donor, $P700^+$. The major interaction site is formed by two helices in the loop between helices i and j, located at the lumenal indentation close to $P700^+$. They provide a hydrophobic docking site for plastocyanin and cytochrome *c6*.

Both plastocyanin and cytochrome *c6* have hydrophobic surfaces that match the hydrophobic docking site of Photosystem I. Mutants with distortions of this site are impaired in binding of PC/Cyt c_6 and electron transfer. A further increase in affinity can be provided by positively charged patches of both plastocyanin and cytochrome *c6* that may electrostatically drive their attractive movement toward Photosystem I [44,45].

Two tryptophan residues that are partially exposed to the aqueous phase are other prominent features of the docking site. They may form an important part of the recognition site for the soluble electron donors and may even be involved in the electron transfer from plastocyanin/cytochrome *c6* to P700. Experimental evidence for this hypothesis has been provided by mutagenesis studies on one of these tryptophans [46].

In contrast to cyanobacteria, where only PsaA and PsaB are involved in the docking of plastocyanin, in plants PsaF may also play an important role in the docking of plastocyanin (see below).

13.4.2 Stromal Hump of PS I: PsaC, PsaD and PsaE

Three subunits (the subunits PsaC, PsaD and PsaE) are located at the stromal side of Photosystem I and are involved in the docking of ferredoxin. The structure of the three subunits in the stromal hump and the potential docking site of ferredoxin are shown in Figure 5.

13.4.2.1 Subunit PsaC

Subunit PsaC (8.9 kDa) carries the two terminal FeS clusters F_A and F_B (Figure 3C).

Both clusters are of the [4Fe4S] type. They are defined by distinct lines in the EPR spectra of Photosystem I [47]. The PsaC gene contains two conserved sequence motifs, CXXCXXCXXXCP, with the cysteines providing the ligands

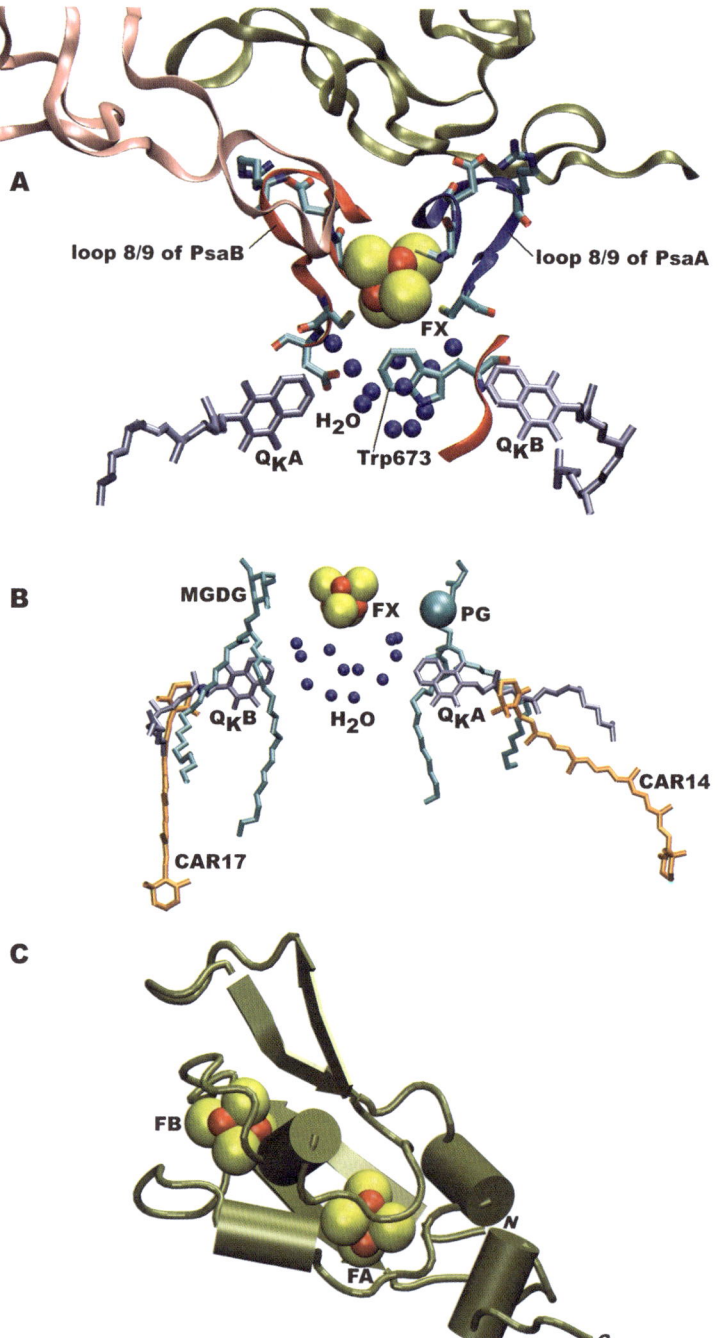

Figure 3. Surrounding of the Fe$_4$S$_4$ clusters. In A the F$_X$ is surrounded by loop 8/9 of PsaB is in red and PsaA in blue. Part B: The quinones in ice blue and the lipids in cyan are emphasized in part B. Part C depicts the subunit PsaC as the main surrounding protein of F$_A$ and F$_B$.

STRUCTURE AND FUNCTION OF PHOTOSYSTEM I

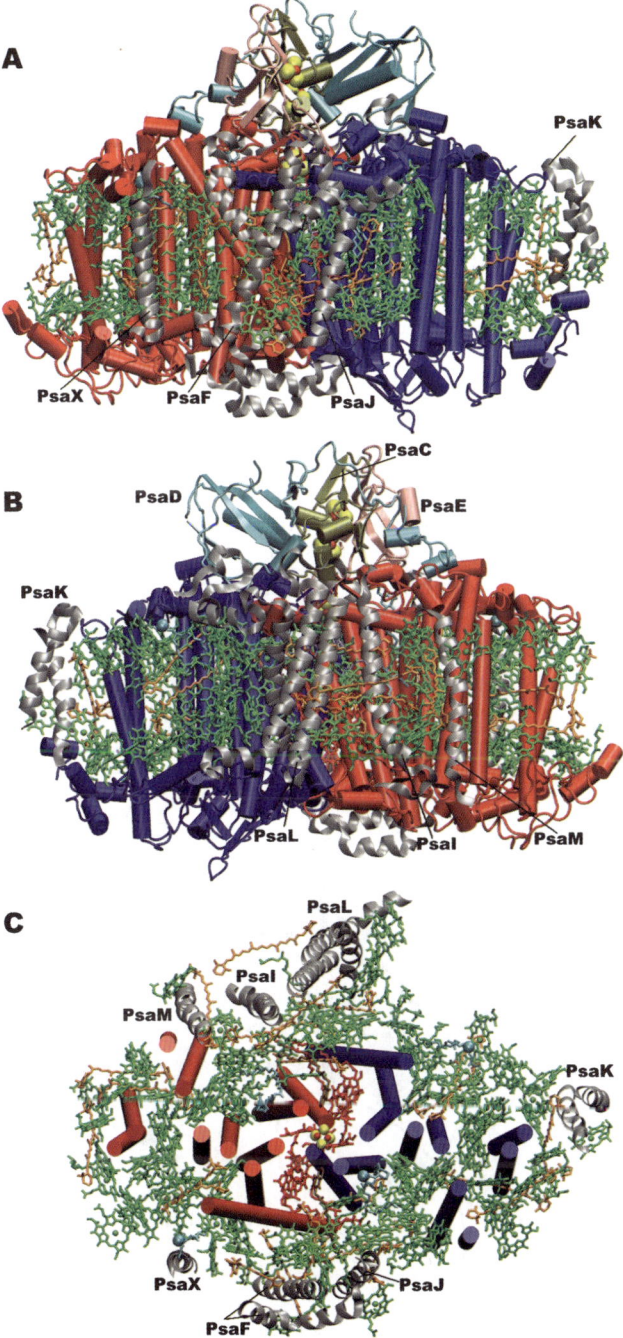

Figure 4. The complete overview of Photosystem I with proteins, chlorophylls, carotenoids and Fe_4S_4 Clusters. Figure A depicts the Photosystem I as seen from the membrane plane in B turned 180 degree to reveal the other subunits. In C the same figure seen from top.

to the Fe atoms. An homology of subunit PsaC to bacterial ferredoxins also containing two [4Fe4S] clusters was suggested from strong sequence similarity and homology models [48,49] and was confirmed by the similarity of both structures [1,50]. Figure 5 shows the structure of PsaC.

The central part of PsaC consists of two short α-helices connecting the two FeS clusters. This part is very similar in PsaC and ferredoxin. The prominent deviations between the two structures are the C- and N-termini, elongated by 14 and two residues, respectively, in PsaC and by an extension of ten residues pointing towards the putative ferredoxin/flavodoxin docking site in the internal loop region exposed to the stroma surface of the PS I complex.

The C-terminus of PsaC is very important for the correct docking of PsaC to the PS I core (for more details see [43]).

13.4.2.2 Subunit PsaD
Subunit PsaD is essential for electron transfer from PS I to ferredoxin [51–55]. It is located at the stromal hump, close to the "connecting domain".

The main part of PsaD consists of a large antiparallel four-stranded β-sheet. The fourth α-strand is connected to the only α-helix of PsaD by a short loop. This helix forms interactions both with PsaC and with PsaA. A short antiparallel β-sheet after the helix is followed by a very prominent and remarkable feature of PsaD: its stromal clamp, consisting of the sequence region between D95 and D123. This part of PsaD wraps around PsaC, forming several contacts between PsaD and both PsaC and PsaE.

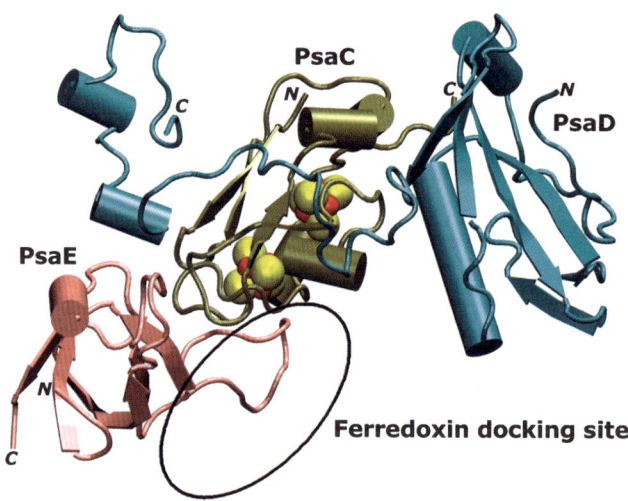

Figure 5. The stromal subunits of Photosystem I. The subunits PsaC, PsaD, and PsaE form a protein cluster on the stromal side of Photosystem I, which harbors the terminal part of the electron transfer chain. PsaC coordinates the FeS clusters F_A and F_B. PsaC is depicted in mauve, PsaD in cyan, and PsaE in pink. View from the stroma on all three stromal subunits of PS I. The possible docking site for Ferredoxin is indicated.

This stromal clamp confirms the important function of PsaD as a critical stabilization factor of the electron acceptor sites in PS I and its important role in keeping PsaC in its correct orientation [56,57].

The C-terminal part of PsaD is close to PsaB and PsaL. The close vicinity of PsaD and PsaL was already suggested from crosslinking and mutagenesis results [58,59]. This interaction may also play an important role in the stabilization of PS I, as the deletion of subunit PsaL de-stabilizes subunit PsaD in cyanobacteria [60]. The C-terminal region of subunit PsaD is exposed on the stromal surface of Photosystem I. This fact was suggested previously by work on the protease accessibility, NHS-biotin labeling, as well as investigations on mutant Photosystem I that lacks the 24 residues from the carboxyl terminus of Photosystem I [58,61].

In addition to its stabilizing function, PsaD is actively involved in the docking of ferredoxin. The direct interaction of these two proteins was shown by chemical crosslinking [62–64]. Lelong et al. [64] showed that the crosslinked complex is fully competent in the transfer of electrons from Photosystem I to ferredoxin. The position of ferredoxin in these crosslinked complexes was identified by electron microscopy [65]. The same docking site was also found for flavodoxin [66,83]. This docking site is indicated in Figure 5. The negatively charged ferredoxin may be guided towards this site by the basic patch provided mainly by PsaD and PsaC. Remarkably, overexpressed PsaD can still bind ferredoxin [67]. Cocrystals between PSI and ferredoxin have been reported that may serve as a basis for a structure of the PS I ferredoxin complex [68].

13.4.2.3 Subunit PsaE
The structure of subunit PsaE (8 kDa) in solution has been determined by ^{1}H and ^{15}N NMR spectroscopy [69]. It shows a compact structure of five antiparallel stranded β-sheets. The core structure of PsaE, consisting of five α-strands, is essentially the same in solution and in PsaE attached to the PS I complex. The main difference between the free and bound PsaE is the conformations of the loops and the C- and N-terminus. The loop connecting the β-sheets β3 (C) and β4 (D) was not well resolved in the NMR structure and, therefore, seems to be flexible and involved in the interaction with the PsaA/PsaB core. This loop has a different conformation and is twisted when PsaE binds to the core complex. The twist of this loop was already reported at 4 Å [70] and is fully confirmed in the structural model at 2.5 Å resolution [71]. This loop is involved in interactions with PsaA, PsaB and PsaC, suggesting a change of the loop conformation during assembly of the Photosystem I complex. More recent studies show that PsaE can assemble into the PS I complex without help of assembly factors and that it is driven by electrostatic interactions [72].

Different functions have been reported for PsaE. It is directly involved in the anchoring of ferredoxin [74,75], plays a role in cyclic electron transport [76], and can be crosslinked in barley with the ferredoxin-NADP$^+$-oxidoreductase (FNR) via its N-terminal extension [77].

The first evidence indicating that the subunit PsaE might be located at the periphery of the stromal hump came from electron microscopy of a mutant lacking the gene of PsaE in cyanobacteria [78]. This was confirmed by the 4 and 2.5 Å structural models of Photosystem I [1,70].

The loop E-β2β3 (BC-loop) connecting strands E-β2 (B) and E-β3 (C), which points towards the putative docking site of ferredoxin, is close to the loop insertion of PsaC.

Interactions between PsaE (loop β1/β2) (AB) and the C-terminal region of the partially membrane integral subunit PsaF also exist, in good agreement with mutagenesis and crosslinking studies [79]. Interactions of PsaE with PsaC and PsaD are relatively weak, which explains the finding that the geometry of the stromal structure formed by PsaC and PsaD is not dramatically changed in the absence of PsaE [53]. However, the C-terminal region of PsaD, which forms a clamp surrounding PsaC, is in direct contact with PsaE (loop β2/β3), confirming previous crosslinking studies [80].

Subunit PsaE, directly involved in anchoring the ferredoxin [73,75,81], plays a role in cyclic electron transport [82] and can be crosslinked in barley with FNR via its N-terminal extension [77]. Site-directed mutagenesis on subunit E in *Synechocystis* shows that the eight C-terminal amino acids are necessary for the precise anchorage of subunit C into Photosystem I. Furthermore, several mutants on PsaE have a dramatic effect on the binding of ferredoxin (for a detailed discussion on the function of subunit E see [54,55]).

The fact that PsaE is involved in the docking of ferredoxin and flavodoxin, [66,84] was questioned by the finding that PsaE deletion mutants are still able to grow photoautotrophically. This contradiction was solved by the discovery that PsaE deletion mutants increased the level of ferredoxin in the cells by orders of magnitude to compensate for defects caused by the lack of PsaE [85].

13.4.3 Monomer–Monomer Interface: PsaL, PsaI and PsaM

PsaL, PsaI and PsaM are located in the region where the adjacent monomers face each other in the trimeric PS I complex. PsaL and PsaI are in the trimerization domain, whereas PsaM is located at the monomer–monomer interface.

13.4.3.1 Subunit PsaL
Location of PsaL in the trimerization domain was first proposed by mutagenesis studies, as no trimers can be detected in PsaL deletion mutants of cyanobacteria [86].

PsaL is close to the C3 axis in the "trimerization domain". It forms most of the contacts between the monomers. Furthermore, PsaL coordinates three antenna Chl *a* and forms hydrophobic contacts with carotenoids and may, therefore, be important for the excitation energy transfer between the monomers.

The structure of PsaL contains three transmembrane helices, named L-d, L-e and L-g, with L-d and L-e forming hydrophobic contact sites between the monomers within the trimer. Most of the other contact sites between the monomers in the trimerization domain are provided by hydrogen bonds and electrostatic interactions within the loop regions. The N-terminal loop is located on the stromal side, harboring three small α-strands and one α-helix. This loop forms various contacts with loop regions of PsaA and is also in contact with PsaD, thereby attaching PsaL to the core of PS I. A short lumenal loop connects the first and second transmembrane α-helices. Likewise, the second and third transmembrane α-helices are connected by a short stromal loop. The C-terminus is folded into a short α-helix located in the lumen. The electron density map suggests that a metal ion, possibly a Ca^{2+}, is coordinated by amino acid side-chains of PsaL in two adjacent PS I monomers and by PsaA. It could possibly be required for the stabilization of the PS I trimer, which is in agreement with observations of *Synechocystis sp. PCC 6803* (P. Chitnis, J. Kruip, personal communication), indicating that the addition of Ca^{2+} stimulates formation of PS I trimers. PsaL forms hydrophobic contacts with three carotenoids, two are located at the interface between PsaL and PsaA and PsaI, while the third is located at the monomer–monomer interface in the trimerization domain. The latter carotenoid may also play an important role in the stabilization of the trimeric PS I complex.

13.4.3.2 Subunit PsaI

PsaI contains one transmembrane helix. It does not bind any Chl *a*, but forms hydrophobic interactions with carotenoid molecules while forming few contacts with the adjacent monomer. PsaI is located between PsaL and PsaM. The close proximity of PsaL and PsaI was first suggested by mutagenesis experiments in which PsaI was deleted. Schluchter *et al.* showed that the deletion of PsaI influences the stability of these two subunits in the PS I complex of *Synechococcus PCC 7002* [87]. These mutants consisted of only 10% trimeric Photosystem I, indicating that PsaI stabilizes PsaL. A close interaction of PsaL and PsaI has also been reported for *Synechocystis PCC 6803* [88] and barley [59]. The crystal structure revealed that PsaI forms various contacts with PsaL, but also forms contacts with PsaM, as already suggested by Schluchter *et al.* in 1996 [87]. The existence of close interactions of PsaI and PsaL in higher plants suggests that the arrangement of these small subunits is a motif that was conserved during evolution [59,89]. The structure of higher plant PS I has been determined at 4.4 Å resolution [2]. Even if the sequence was not assigned due to the limited resolution, the structure shows that PsaI and PsaL also form close contacts in plant Photosystem I. This is remarkable, taking into account the fact that plant PS I is a monomer and the region of PsaI and PsaL (and PsaH) may function in forming interactions with the Light Harvesting Complex II (LHC II) [59,89,90]. This raises questions about the function of the trimer in cyanobacteria. Mutants of *Synechococcus elongatus* lacking PsaL [80] exhibit normal growth at high light intensity, while growth under low light conditions is decreased by a factor of ten compared with the wild type [91].

These results suggest that the trimer is essential for optimal light capturing in cyanobacteria. In plants, an additional subunit (PsaH) is located close to PsaI and PsaL [2]. This region may be the contact site between PS I and the LHC II complex [92]. The idea can be put forward that PsaL stabilized by PsaI might form an entrance gate for the excitation energy from the external antenna complexes in plants. This would correspond to excitation energy transfer between the monomers in the trimeric PS I.

Significant excitation energy transfer between monomers has been spectroscopically determined [93,94] and was also found by theoretical studies [95,124].

13.4.3.3 Subunit PsaM
PsaM (3.4 kDa) is the smallest subunit of Photosystem I. This subunit contains only one transmembrane α-helix, as predicted by Falzone et al. [69]. This subunit is unique to cyanobacterial Photosystem I. Although an open reading frame for this subunit was also found in the liverwort chloroplast genome [4], this subunit has yet to be identified in any preparation of plant Photosystem I and is also not present in the 4.4 Å structure of pea PS I [2]. PsaM is close to the monomer-monomer interface, in the neighborhood of PsaI and PsaB. The N-terminus is located in the lumen, the C-terminus in the stroma.

PsaM forms hydrophobic contacts with a carotenoid molecule and is involved in the coordination of one Chl a. This Chl (M-1) may play an important role in excitation energy transfer between monomers. It is strongly functionally coupled to chlorophylls of the neighboring monomer, i.e., it may be functionally considered as part of the clustered network of this adjacent monomeric unit [124]. In this respect, it is remarkable that the protein side-chains of PsaM do not form direct contacts between monomers. However, it may play a role in the stabilization of the trimeric structure by forming hydrophobic interactions with the carotenoid that is involved in trimerization.

13.4.4 Membrane-Exposed Subunits: PsaF, PsaJ, PsaX and PsaK

Four hydrophobic protein subunits, PsaF, PsaJ, PsaX and PsaK, are located at the detergent-exposed surface of Photosystem I. PsaF and PsaJ are located symmetrically to the trimerization domain and form various contacts with PsaA, PsaB and PsaE, whereas PsaX is at the periphery of PsaA and is only in contact with PsaB and PsaK. All four proteins are involved in the stabilization of the core antenna system of PS I and may play an additional important role in forming interactions with the membrane intrinsic peripheral antenna system, the IsiA ring [105].

13.4.4.1 Subunit PsaF
Regarding its structure, function and import pathway, subunit PsaF is the most astonishing subunit in PS I. It was long thought to be an extrinsic subunit located at the lumenal side of Photosystem I. This assumption was based primarily on the fact that plant PsaF contains two pre-sequences: one for import into the chloroplast and a second for import into the thylakoid lumen. This protein is imported by the same pathway used for the import of

plastocyanin (the soluble lumenal electron carrier) [96–98]. It is still unknown why PsaF, as a transmembrane protein, can be translocated by the Sec pathway like plastocyanin and the 33 kDa protein of Photosystem II.

The structure of subunit PsaF consists of three domains. The N-terminal domain is located in the lumen, followed by a transmembrane domain with one transmembrane helix and two short helical pieces in a V-shaped arrangement. The C-terminus is located in the stroma and is sandwiched between PsaA and PsaE.

The N-terminal domain is located at the lumenal side of the complex, with α-helices F-c and F-d being the most prominent features. These hydrophilic α-helices are parallel to the membrane plane and are approximately 15 Å from the putative docking site of cytochrome $c6$. The function of the N-terminal domain of PsaF is different in plant and cyanobacterial PS I. In plants and green algae, subunit PsaF contains 25 amino acids inserted into its lumenal domain, which is responsible for formation of a tight complex between plastocyanin and Photosystem I [99–101]. This structural region forms an extension of the two lumenal α-helices F-c and F-d in plants [2]. This insertion of PsaF may explain why PsaF is involved in the docking of plastocyanin in plants [99,101–103], but not in cyanobacteria [79]. Although cyanobacterial PsaF is not directly involved in electron transfer from plastocyanin/cytochrome $c6$ to P700, this part of PsaF could play an important role in the stabilization of the lumenal surface of Photosystem I.

The membrane intrinsic domain of PsaF contains only one transmembrane α-helix, F-f, followed by a short hydrophilic helix, F-g, and two shorter hydrophobic α-helices, F-h and F-i. This region of PsaF is very unusual. An α-helix F-h enters the membrane from the stromal side and ends in the first third of the membrane. After a crease, it is followed by α-helix F-i, and runs back to the stromal side, where the C-terminus is located and forms contacts with PsaE, PsaA and PsaB. PsaF does not axially coordinate chlorophylls, but forms hydrophobic interactions with chlorophylls and several carotenoids. A possible role of the transmembrane part of PsaF could be a means by which the carotenoids and chlorophylls are shielded from the lipid phase. A further possible function of PsaF in cyanobacteria could be its structural and functional interaction with the external antenna system of IsiA and the phycobilisomes. Deletion of PsaF in *Synechococcus elongatus* leads to a growth defect at low light intensity, accompanied by a dramatic increase of allophycocyanin, giving the entire cell suspension a turquoise color (P. Jordan, P. Fromme, unpublished), which may support the suggestion that PsaF plays a role in the interaction of the PS I core with the phycobilisomes. Recently, investigations of mutants lacking PsaJ and PsaF found that the acceptor site of PS I was impaired and the cells showed signs of oxidative damage. Furthermore, IsiA is induced in these mutants even in the presence of iron [104]. Boekema and co-workers have used electron microscopy to investigate mutants lacking PsaF and PsaJ under iron deficiency [105].

The mutants form large aggregates of IsiA; however, some PS I–IsiA complexes can still be isolated that contain 17, rather than 19, IsiA proteins attached to the PS I complex.

These results show that PsaF and PsaJ are important but are not absolutely essential for the interaction of PS I with the IsiA ring.

In plants, the direct contact of PsaF with the plant light harvesting systems has been suggested by experiments in which plant subunit PsaF was isolated as a Chl–protein complex with LHCI proteins [106]. Interaction sites between PsaF and the LHC I proteins were also identified in the structure of Photosystem I from pea plants [2].

13.4.4.2 Subunit PsaJ

PsaJ contains one transmembrane α-helix. It binds three chlorophylls and is in hydrophobic contact with carotenoids. The structure is shown in Figure 4(C).

A location of PsaJ close to PsaF was predicted by mutagenesis and cross-linking experiments on the cyanobacterial [79] and plant Photosystem I [31,59]. The N-terminus of PsaJ is in the stroma while the C-terminus is in the lumen. In addition to the coordination of three antenna chlorophylls, PsaJ may play an important role in the stabilization of PsaF and the pigment clusters located at the interface between PsaJ/PsaF and the PsaA/PsaB core. The three chlorophylls that are coordinated by this subunit are supposed to play an important role in the excitation energy transfer from the IsiA ring to the PS I core.

13.4.4.3 Subunit PsaX

A single transmembrane helix found near PsaF was identified as PsaX, a twelfth subunit of PS I. It coordinates one chlorophyll and forms hydrophobic contacts with several carotenoid molecules and one of the lipids. The structure of PsaX is present at the membrane-exposed surface of PS I; therefore, one can speculate that PsaX may also play a role in the interaction of PS I with the IsiA antenna ring formed under iron deficiency.

This protein is not present in plant Photosystem I, as recently shown by the 4.4 Å structure of the PS I from the pea plant [2]. To date, PsaX has been identified only by N-terminal sequencing in PS I from the thermophilic cyanobacteria *Thermosynechococcus vulcanus* and *Anabaena variabilis* [107,108] and in single crystals from *Thermosynechococcus elongatus*. The structural model of PsaX contains 29 residues. The six stromally located N-terminal amino acids were not identified in the structure, possibly because this part of the structure is flexible. Remarkably, not a single gene was assigned to PsaX in the complete genomic sequence of *Thermosynechococcus elongatus* [109]. The could be because the sequence was just not assigned to an open reading frame. Also, a gene sequence for PsaX has yet to be assigned in the mesophilic cyanobacterium *Synechocystis PCC 6803*. The question as to whether PsaX is a unique subunit of thermophilic cyanobacteria, necessary for stability of the PS I complex at higher temperatures, has still to be answered.

13.4.4.4 PsaK

As predicted from the sequence [69] subunit PsaK, which contains two transmembrane α-helices, was found to be located at the periphery of the PS I complex. It only forms protein contacts with PsaA. As indicated by high temperature factors, this subunit seems to be the least ordered subunit in the PS I complex, such that an unambiguous sequence assignment was not possible and the structure was modeled with polyalanine. The two helices are connected in the stroma, so that both the C- and N-terminus are located in the lumen. This topology is also supported by insertion studies performed on in vitro expressed PsaK [110] and meets the "positive inside rule" [111], which was based on the finding that highly positively charged loops connecting transmembrane α-helices are rarely translocated through the membrane during the insertion and assembly of membrane proteins. The protein coordinates two chlorophylls and forms contacts with carotenoids. It may also play an important role in the interaction with the IsiA antenna ring under iron deficiency.

In plants, PsaK has been shown to interact with the LHC I proteins. Furthermore, a role of PsaK in state transitions (for further details, see Chapter 6) has been suggested [112].

Unlike plant PS I, cyanobacterial PS I does not contain a subunit corresponding to PsaG, a plant-PS I subunit that exhibits sequence homology to PsaK. These proteins have the same genetic origin [113] and PsaG has been evolved via gene duplication. The 4.4 Å structure of the pea PS I shows that this subunit is located at a position symmetrical to PsaK in the vicinity of PsaB. It is the only subunit of the plant PS I core that forms direct contacts via a transmembrane helix with the Light Harvesting Complex I (Lhca1) [2].

13.5 Antenna System of PS I

Details of light harvesting by cyanobacteria and PS I of plants are outlined in detail in Chapters 6 and 7, respectively. Here a few considerations will be added. The core antenna system of Photosystem I consists of 90 Chlorophyll *a* molecules and 22 carotenes. Figure 3 shows the arrangement of the central pigments. The function of the antenna chlorophylls (shown in green) is to capture light and transfer the excitation energy to the center of the complex, where the electron transfer takes place. After excitation of any of the antenna chlorophylls, the chance that the energy is successfully transferred to P700 and that subsequent charge separation occurs is 99.98% at room temperature.

13.5.1 Antenna Chlorophylls

The arrangement of the antenna chlorophylls in PS I is unique. Instead of forming a symmetric ring surrounding the reaction center core, as it occurs in the light harvesting systems of purple bacteria, the chlorophylls form a clustered network [114]. Each of the chlorophylls has several neighbors at a center-to-center distance of less than 15 Å – so energy can be efficiently transferred via multiple pathways to the center of the complex. The system can be compared with the nerve-network system in the brain where multiple connections are responsible for the high efficiency of information transfer. The antenna system in Photosystem I is highly optimized for efficiency and robustness [95]. The side view along the membrane plane (Figures 2 and 6) shows that the core antenna system of PS I can be divided into a central domain, which surrounds the electron transfer chain, and two peripheral domains, flanking the core on both sides. In the peripheral domains, the antenna chlorophylls are arranged in two layers, one close to the stromal surface of the membrane and the other close to the lumenal surface of the membrane. When a peripheral antenna chlorophyll becomes electronically excited this energy will first be transferred from this "two-dimensional" layer to the central domain. In the central domain, chlorophylls are distributed over the full depths of the membrane, i.e., the excitation energy can be exchanged between the two layers. The excitation energy is then transferred from the chlorophylls of the central domain to the electron transfer chain. There are two chlorophylls (named "connecting chlorophylls") that seem to be the structural link between the antenna system and the electron transfer chain. Mutagenesis experiments have been performed on the ligands of these connecting chlorophylls [115]. The mutants exhibit minor alterations in the trapping of the excitation energy, but the question as to whether they play a crucial role in excitation energy transfer remains unanswered.

A very exciting topic of PS I is the question of the location and function of the pigments that absorb at $\lambda > 700$ nm. They are called "red" or "long-wavelength" chlorophylls. There are several reasons that can cause a redshift of the chlorophyll absorption: strong excitonic coupling with neighboring chlorophylls may provide the strongest contribution, but the protein environment may also play an important role as the redshift can also be caused by variation of the fifth ligand of the Mg^{2+} or electrostatic fields provided by the protein [127]. The long-wavelength chlorophylls may function in increasing the spectral width of the light absorbed by Photosystem I, which can be used by Photosystem I. Another function of the "red" chlorophylls may be as a means of "funneling" the excitation energy to the center of the complex. The latter function may be provided by chlorophylls that absorb between 685 and 705 nm, which are present in all PS I complexes from plants, algae and cyanobacteria. One very exciting questions is the location of the "red" chlorophylls within the PS I complex. Fleming and co-workers have calculated the effective Hamiltonian for chlorophyll Q(y) excitations, enabling the tentative assignment of red chlorophylls and calculation of the absorption spectrum of PS I [116,117]. The calculations show that the strongly coupled chlorophylls must not be the ones that absorb at the longest wavelength.

The PS I composition's relation to the pigments absorbing at longer wavelengths varies between organisms. The PS I core in cyanobacteria contains more chlorophylls that absorb at wavelengths $\lambda > 705$ nm than the core of plant systems, but the variation between different cyanobacterial species is as high as between plants and cyanobacteria, so that the recent suggestion of a directed evolution from cyanobacteria towards replacement of the long-wavelength chlorophylls [118] seems to be questionable. It is much more likely that cyanobacteria adaptation to low light conditions and the competition among aquatic photosynthetic organisms led to the development of pigments absorbing at longer wavelengths. Based on the structure of Photosystem I, several theoretical studies have investigated the excitation energy transfer and trapping in Photosystem I. These studies show that the excitation energy transfer in PS I is trap limited and is highly optimized for robustness and efficiency [95,119,120,128].

13.5.2 Carotenoids

Twenty two carotenoids have been identified in the cyanobacterial structure of PS I. The carotenoids fulfill three functions in Photosystem I: they play a structural role, function as additional antenna pigments, and prevent the system from damage by over-excitation caused by excess light (photoinhibition). The latter function is absolutely critical to the whole system. Chlorophylls are, in principle, dangerous and reactive molecules. Superfluous excitation can lead to the formation of chlorophyll triplets (^{3}Chl), which react with oxygen to give singlet oxygen ($^1\Delta_g$ O_2), which is a very dangerous cell poison (see also Chapter 16). Multiple interactions can be observed between the carotenoids and the chlorophylls of the antenna system. The carotenoids are distributed over the whole antenna system and prevent photodamage by the quenching of chlorophyll triplet states. The energy from the triplet chlorophylls is transferred to the carotenoids, which form the carotenoids triplet state, ^{3}Car.

The energy of the ^{3}Car is too low to react with O_2 [129]. When the carotenoids return to the ground state they dissipate the energy as heat, thereby preventing photodamage. The system works very efficiently, even under high light conditions, as the ^{3}Chl triplet state cannot be detected in the intact Photosystem I. Despite the important role of carotenoids in photoprotection, structural integrity and light capturing, they might not be directly involved in the electron transfer process. Mutants that completely lack carotenoids [121] still contain some PS I, and charge separation can be detected. Samples lacking all carotenoids and quinones due to extraction with organic solvents are still able to perform electron transfer from P700 to A_0 [122].

An important and still open question is why 17 of the carotenoids are in a trans configuration whereas the other five contain one or two cis-double bonds (Figure 6A–C). The simplest explanation would be that "fit-into-space" considerations lead to the incorporation of the cis carotenoids. However, other possibilities may also have to be taken into account, as there may be a different efficiency for quenching for the cis- and trans-carotenoids (Figure 6), because the energy level for the trans form is lower than that for the cis-carotenoids. The role of the cis-carotenoids is a very interesting subject for further investigations.

13.6 Lipids in PS I

Four lipids have been identified in the structure of PS I at 2.5 Å resolution: three molecules of phosphatidylglycerol (PG) and one of monogalactosyldiacylglycerol

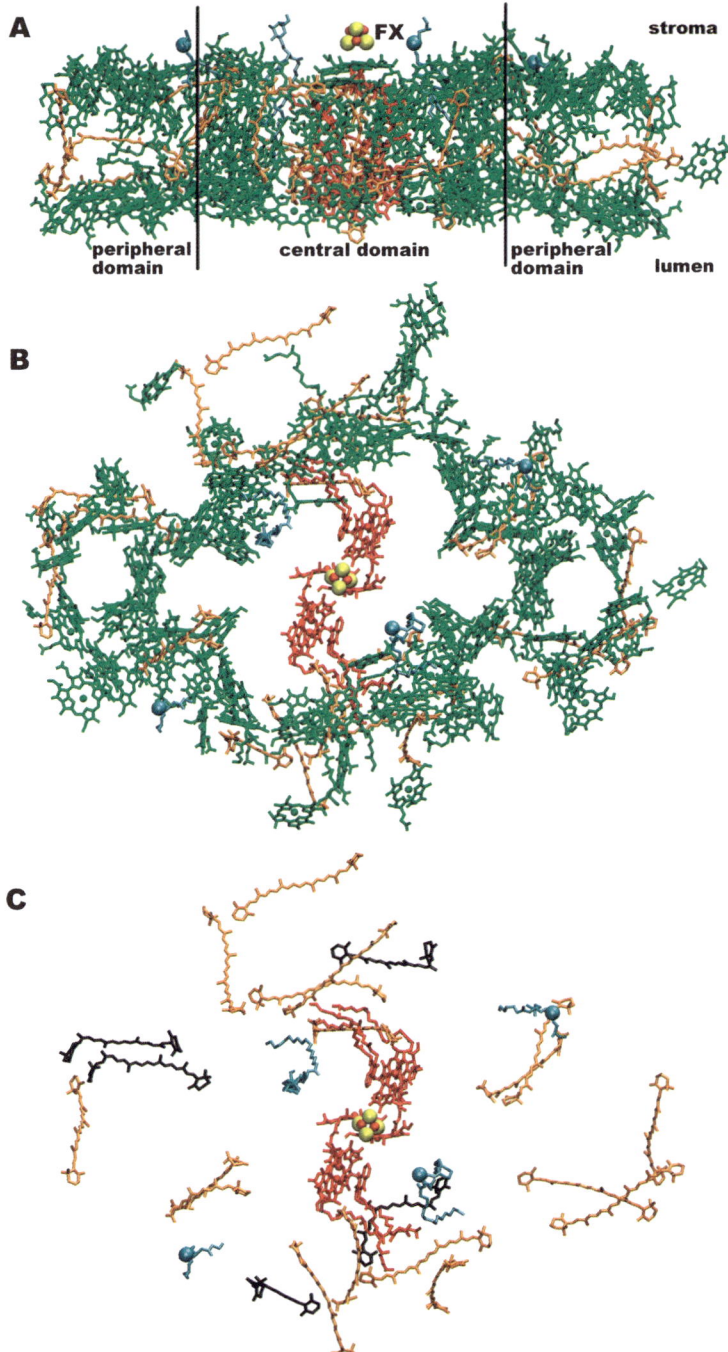

Figure 6. Lipids and carotenoids in Photosystem I. In A seen from the membrane plane. Lipids in cyan, trans-carotenoids in orange, cis-carotenoids in black. Figure B is a top view with lipids and carotenoids and Figure C same only with carotenoids. In this figure the ET Chlorophylls are in red.

(MDGD) (for the lipid arrangement see Figure 6). Two of these lipids are close to the electron transfer chain. They must be incorporated into PS I at a very early stage of the assembly process, because their head groups are not solvent accessible but are covered by the loops of PsaA and PsaB and the three stromal subunits PsaC, PsaD and PsaE. The lipids close to the electron transport chain may even play an important role in the difference in the rates of electron transfer between the two different branches.

Recently, mutants have been described that are impaired in the synthesis of PG [123]. These mutants grow only in the presence of externally added PG, i.e., PG is essential for photoautotrophic growth. When the mutants are depleted of PG, at first PS II activity is inhibited, probably due to the much higher turnover of PS II compared with PS I. In the PG-depleted PS II, the ET from Q_A to Q_B is blocked. This finding is very exciting and raises the question as to whether there might also be lipids in PS II located in a similar position as to those in PSI. The long depletion time ($>$ 10 days) finally leads to the loss of PS I function, which parallels the starvation of the cells, showing that PS I is non-functional or cannot be assembled without the lipids.

The two other PG molecules are at the periphery of PS I, one at the monomer interface, the other at the membrane-exposed surface of PS I, in tight interaction with PsaX. Interaction between PsaX and PG is mainly hydrophobic but both molecules interact so tightly that the role of this PG might be the stabilization of PsaX within the complex.

The lipid at the monomer–monomer interface coordinates one chlorophyll (named PL1). This chlorophyll may contribute to the excitation energy transfer between different monomeric units.

Recently, it was reported that PG may also be involved in trimerization of PSI and that it interacts with PsaL [123]. The electron density map of PS I at 2.5 Å resolution indeed showed a lipid-like structure close to PsaL, with the lipid-head group located in the lumen (Jordan, Fromme, Krauss, unpublished). However, the electron density was not clearly identified as a PG molecule (it looks more like a lipid with four fatty acid chains).

Owing to the unclear assignment, the "fifth" lipid was not included in the published X-ray structure. The function of lipids in PS I is still an exciting topic, with new discoveries and surprises on the way.

13.7 Concluding Remarks and Future Perspectives

Since the structure of Photosystem I has been elucidated at the atomic level, the assigning of compounds to the underlying mechanism has become a driving force. The use of light energy in photosynthesis will be understood in detail on an atomic level. High-resolution structures of Photosystems I and II from variant organisms will be available soon and this will give our knowledge a new solid foundation. The interaction between the photosystems and the LHC complexes may be solved additionally soon with high resolution. Photosynthesis research will, therefore, be a hot topic in the coming years. Indeed, both photosystems are unique highlights in both aesthetics and research.

Acknowledgements

We thank our colleagues at Arizona State University for the pleasant atmosphere and fruitful discussions. We are thankful to Priscilla Benbrook for reading the manuscript and to many colleagues around the world for their enthusiasm and contributions to our understanding of the "green side" of science.

Funding for our research by the United States Department of Agriculture 2003–35318–13573, NIH R01 GM7 1619–01and NSF MCB 04127142 is gratefully acknowledged.

References

1. P. Jordan, P. Fromme, O. Klukas, H.T. Witt, W. Saenger, N. Krauß, Three dimensional structure of cyanobacterial photosystem I at 2.5 Å resolution. *Nature* **411** (2001) 909–917.
2. A. Ben-Shem, F. Frolow, N. Nelson, Crystal structure of plant photosystem I. *Nature* **426** (2003) 630–635.
3. J. Hladik, D. Sofrova, Does the trimeric form of the Photosystem-1 reaction center of cyanobacteria in vivo exist? *Photosynth. Res.* **29** (1991) 171–175.
4. K. Ohyama, H. Fukazawa, T. Kohchi, H. Shirai, S. Tohru, S. Sano, K. Umesono, Y. Shiki, M. Takeuchi, Z. Chang, S.I. Aota, H. Inokuchi, H. Ozeki, Chloroplast gene organization deduced from complete sequence of liverwort *Marchantia polymorpha* chloroplast DNA. *Nature* **322** (1986) 572–574.
5. T. Watanabe, M. Kobayashi, A. Hongu, M. Nakazato, T. Hiyama, Evidence, that a chlorophyll a' dimer constitutes the photochemical reaction centre 1 (P700) in photosynthetic apparatus. *FEBS Lett.* **235** (1985) 252–256.
6. H. Maeda, T. Watanabe, M. Kobayashi, I. Ikegami, Presence of two chlorophyll a' molecules at the core of Photosystem I. *Biochim. Biophys. Acta* **1099** (1992) 74–80.
7. J. Maroc, A. Tremolieres, Chlorophyll a$'$ and pheophytin a, as determined by HPLC, in photosynthesis mutants and double mutants of *Chlamydomonas reinhardtii*. *Biochem. Biophys. Acta* **1018** (1990) 67–71.
8. J. Deisenhofer, O. Epp, I. Sinning, H. Michel, Crystallographic refinement at 2.3 Å resolution and refined model of the photosynthetic reaction centre from *Rhodopseudomonas viridis*. *J. Mol. Biol.* **246** (1995) 429–457.
9. H. Kass, E. Bittersmannweidlich, L.E. Andreasson, B. Bonigk, W. Lubitz, ENDOR and ESEEM of the N-15 labeled radical cations of chlorophyll-*a* and the primary donor P-700 in Photosystem-I. *Chem. Phys.* **194** (1995) 419–432.
10. H. Kass, P. Fromme, H.T. Witt, W. Lubitz, Orientation and electronic structure of the primary donor radical cation P-700(+center dot) in photosystem I: a single crystals EPR and ENDOR study. *J. Phys. Chem. B* **105** (2001) 1225–1239.

11. M. Plato, N. Krauss, P. Fromme, W. Lubitz, Molecular orbital study of the primary elelctron donor P700 of photosystem I based on a recent X-ray single crystal structure analysis. *Chem. Phys.* **294** (2003) 483–499.
12. K.N. Ferreira, T.M. Iverson, K. Maghlaoui, J. Barber, S. Iwata, Architecture of the photosynthetic oxygen-evolving center. *Science* **303** (2004) 1831–1838.
13. M.G. Muller, J. Niklas, W. Lubitz, A.R. Holzwarth, Ultrafast transient absorption studies on Photosystem I reaction centers from Chlamydomonas reinhardtii. 1. A new interpretation of the energy trapping and early electron transfer steps in Photosystem I. *Biophys. J.* **85** (2003) 3899–3922.
14. G. Hastings, S. Hoshina, A.N. Webber, R.E. Blankenship, Universality of energy and electron transfer processes in photosystem I. *Biochemistry* **34** (1995) 15512–15522.
15. W.V. Fairclough, A. Forsyth, M.C. Evans, S.E. Rigby, S. Purton, P. Heathcote, Bidirectional electron transfer in photosystem I: electron transfer on the PsaA side is not essential for phototrophic growth in Chlamydomonas. *Biochim. Biophys. Acta* **1606** (2003) 43–55.
16. V.M. Ramesh, K. Gibasiewicz, S. Lin, S.E. Bingham, A.N. Webber, Bidirectional electron transfer in photosystem I: accumulation of A_0- in A-side or B-side mutants of the axial ligand to chlorophyll A_0. *Biochemistry* **43** (2004) 1369–1375.
17. R.O. Cohen, G. Shen, J.H. Golbeck, W. Xu, P.R. Chitnis, A.I. Valieva, A. van der Est, Y. Pushkar, D. Stehlik, Evidence for asymmetric electron transfer in cyanobacterial photosystem I: analysis of a methionine-to-leucine mutation of the ligand to the primary electron acceptor A_0. *Biochemistry* **43** (2004) 4741–4754.
18. M. Guergova-Kuras, B. Boudreaux, A. Joliot, P. Joliot, K. Redding, Evidence for two active branches for electron transfer in photosystem I. *Proc. Natl. Acad. Sci. U.S.A.* **98** (2001) 4437–4442.
19. B. Boudreaux, F. MacMillan, C. Teutloff, R. Agalarov, F. Gu, S. Grimaldi, R. Bittl, K. Brettel, K. Redding, Mutations in both sides of the photosystem I reaction center identify the phylloquinone observed by electron paramagnetic resonance spectroscopy. *J. Biol. Chem.* **276** (2001) 37299–37306.
20. E.V. Akhmatskaya, M.D. Cooper, N.A. Burton, A.J. Masters, I.H. Hillier, Monte Carlo simulations of water clusters on a parallel computer using an ab initio potential. *Int. J. Quantum Chem.* **74** (1999) 709–719.
21. H. Ishikita, E.W. Knapp, Redox potential of quinones in both electron transfer branches of photosystem I. *J. Biol. Chem.* **278** (2003) 52002–52011.
22. L. Fish, U. Kück, L. Bogorad, Two partially homologous adjacent light-inducible maize chloroplast genes encoding polypeptides of the P700 chlorophyll a protein complex of photosystem I. *J. Biol. Chem.* **260** (1985) 1413–1421.
23. B. Hallahan, S. Purton, A. Ivison, D. Wright, M.C.W. Evans, Analysis of the proposed FeSx binding region of Photosystem I by site directed mutation of PsaA in Chlamydomonas rheinhardtii. *Photosynth. Res.* **46** (1995) 257–264.
24. I.R. Vassiliev, Y.S. Jung, L.B. Smart, R. Schulz, L. McIntosh, J.H. Golbeck, A mixed-ligand iron-sulfur cluster (C556SPaB or C565SPsaB) in the F_X- binding site leads to a decreased quantum efficiency of electron transfer in photosystem I. *Biophys. J.* **69** (1995) 1544–1553.
25. P. Fromme, P. Jordan, N. Krauss, Structure of photosystem I. *Biochim. Biophys. Acta* **1507** (2001) 5–31.
26. G.Z. Shen, M.L. Antonkine, A. van der Est, I.R. Vassiliev, K. Brettel, R. Bittl, S.G. Zech, J.D. Zhao, D. Stehlik, D.A. Bryant, J.H. Golbeck, Assembly of photosystem I. Rubredoxin is required for the in vivo assembly of F-x in

Synechococcus sp PCC 7002 as shown by optical and EPR spectroscopy. *J. Biol. Chem.* **277** (2002) 20355–20366.

27. J. Zhao, N. Li, P.V. Warren, J.H. Golbeck, D.A. Bryant, Site-directed conversion of a cysteine to aspartate leads to the assembly of a [3Fe-4S] cluster in PsaC of photosystem I. The photoreduction of FA is independent of F_B. *Biochemistry* **31** (1992) 5093–5099.
28. T. Mehari, F. Qiao, M.P. Scott, D.F. Nellis, J. Zhao, D.A. Bryant, J.H. Golbeck, Modified ligands to F_A and F_B in photosystem I. I. Structural constraints for the formation of iron-sulfur clusters in free and rebound PsaC. *J. Biol. Chem.* **270** (1995) 28108–28117.
29. L. Yu, D.A. Bryant, J.H. Golbeck, Evidence for a mixed-ligand [4Fe-4S] cluster in the C14D mutant of PsaC. Altered reduction potentials and EPR spectral properties of the F_A and F_B clusters on rebinding to the P700-F_X core. *Biochemistry* **34** (1995) 7861–7868.
30. L. Yu, I.R. Vassiliev, Y.S. Jung, D.A. Bryant, J.H. Golbeck, Modified ligands to F_A and F_B in photosystem I. II. Characterization of a mixed ligand [4Fe-4S] cluster in the C51D mutant of PsaC upon rebinding to P700-F_X cores. *J. Biol. Chem.* **270** (1995) 28118–28125.
31. N. Fischer, P. Setif, J.D. Rochaix, Site-directed mutagenesis of the PsaC subunit of photosystem I. F(b) is the cluster interacting with soluble ferredoxin. *J. Biol. Chem.* **274** (1999) 23333–23340.
32. K.V. Lakshmi, Y.S. Jung, J.H. Golbeck, G.W. Brudvig, Location of the iron-sulfur clusters F_A and F_B in photosystem I: an electron paramagnetic resonance study of spin relaxation enhancement of P700+. *Biochemistry* **38** (1999) 13210–13215.
33. J.H. Golbeck, A comparative analysis of the spin state distribution of in vitro and in vivo mutants of PsaC. *Photosynth. Res.* **61** (1999) 107–144.
34. J.H. Golbeck, in: *Advances in Photosynthesis: The Molecular Biology of Cyanobacteria* (1994) (D.A. Bryant, ed.), Kluwer Academic, Dordrecht, pp. 319–360.
35. H.B. Pakrasi, Genetic analysis of the form and function of Photosystem I and Photosystem II. *Annu. Rev. Genet.* **29** (1995) 755–756.
36. A. Zouni, H.T. Witt, J. Kern, P. Fromme, N. Krauss, W. Saenger, P. Orth, Crystal structure of photosystem II from Synechococcus elongatus at 3.8 A resolution. *Nature* **409** (2001) 739–743.
37. N. Kamiya, J.R. Shen, Crystal structure of oxygen-evolving photosystem II from Thermosynechococcus vulcanus at 3.7-A resolution. *Proc. Natl. Acad. Sci. U.S.A.* **100** (2003) 98–103.
38. T.S. Bibby, J. Nield, J. Barber, Iron deficiency induces the formation of an antenna ring around trimeric photosystem I in cyanobacteria. *Nature* **412** (2001) 743–745.
39. E.J. Boekema, A. Hifney, A.E. Yakushevska, M. Piotrowski, W. Keegstra, S. Berry, K.P. Michel, E.K. Pistorius, J. Kruip, A giant chlorophyll-protein complex induced by iron deficiency in cyanobacteria. *Nature* **412** (2001) 745–748.
40. J. Nield, E.P. Morris, T.S. Bibby, J. Barber, Structural analysis of the photosystem I supercomplex of cyanobacteria induced by iron deficiency. *Biochemistry* **42** (2003) 3180–3188.
41. W.D. Schubert, O. Klukas, W. Saenger, H.T. Witt, P. Fromme, N. Krauss, A common ancestor for oxygenic and anoxygenic photosynthetic systems: a comparison based on the structural model of photosystem I. *J. Mol. Biol.* **280** (1998) 297–314.

42. B. Loll, G. Raszewski, W. Saenger, J. Biesiadka, Functional role of C(alpha)-H ... O hydrogen bonds between transmembrane alpha-helices in photosystem I. *J. Mol. Biol.* **328** (2003) 737–747.

43. M.L. Antonkine, P. Jordan, P. Fromme, N. Krauss, J.H. Golbeck, D. Stehlik, Assembly of protein subunits within the stromal ridge of photosystem I. Structural changes between unbound and sequentially PS I-bound polypeptides and correlated changes of the magnetic properties of the terminal iron sulfur clusters. *J. Mol. Biol.* **327** (2003) 671–697.

44. C. Frazao, C.M. Soares, M.A. Carrondo, E. Pohl, Z. Dauter, K.S. Wilson, M. Hervas, J.A. Navarro, M.A. De la Rosa, G.M. Sheldrick, Ab initio determination of the crystal structure of cytochrome c6 and comparison with plastocyanin. *Structure* **3** (1995) 1159–1169.

45. F.P. Molina-Heredia, A. Diaz-Quintana, M. Hervas, J.A. Navarro, M.A. De La Rosa, Site-directed mutagenesis of cytochrome c(6) from Anabaena species PCC7119. Identification of surface residues of the hemeprotein involved in photosystem I reduction. *J. Biol. Chem.* **274** (1999) 33565–33570.

46. F. Sommer, F. Drepper, M. Hippler, The luminal helix 1of PsaB is essential for recognition of plastocyanin or cytochrome c6 and fast electron transfer to photosystem I in Chlamydomonas reinhardtii. *J. Biol. Chem.* **277** (2002) 6573–6581.

47. M.C.W. Evans, S.G. Reeves, R. Cammack, Determination of oxidation-reduction potential of bound iron-sulfur proteins of primary electron-acceptor complex of Photosystem-I in spinach-chloroplasts. *FEBS Lett.* **49** (1974) 111–114.

48. P.P. Dunn, L.C. Packman, D. Pappin, J.C. Gray, N-terminal amino acid sequence analysis of the subunits of pea photosystem I. *FEBS Lett.* **228** (1988) 157–161.

49. J.H. Golbeck, The structure of Photosystem I. *Curr. Opin. Struct. Biol.* **3** (1993) 508–514.

50. E.T. Adman, L.C. Sieker, L.H. Jensen, The structure of a bacterial ferredoxin. *J. Biol. Chem.* **248** (1973) 3987–3996.

51. V.P. Chitnis, Y.S. Jungs, L. Albee, J.H. Golbeck, P.R. Chitnis, Mutational analysis of photosystem I polypeptides. Role of PsaD and the lysyl 106 residue in the reductase activity of the photosystem I. *J. Biol. Chem.* **271** (1996) 11772–11780.

52. V.P. Chitnis, A. Ke, P.R. Chitnis, The PsaD subunit of photosystem I. Mutations in the basic domain reduce the level of PsaD in the membranes. *Plant Physiol.* **115** (1997) 1699–1705.

53. P. Barth, B. Lagoutte, P. Setif, Ferredoxin reduction by photosystem I from Synechocystis sp. PCC 6803: toward an understanding of the respective roles of subunits PsaD and PsaE in ferredoxin binding. *Biochemistry* **37** (1998) 16233–16241.

54. P. Setif, Ferredoxin and flavodoxin reduction by photosystem I. *Biochim. Biophys. Acta* **1507** (2001) 161–179.

55. P. Setif, N. Fischer, B. Lagoutte, H. Bottin, J.D. Rochaix, The ferredoxin docking site of photosystem I. *Biochim. Biophys. Acta* **1555** (2002) 204–209.

56. N. Li, P.V. Warren, J.H. Golbeck, G. Frank, H. Zuber, D.A. Bryant, Polypeptide composition of the Photosystem I complex and the Photosystem I core protein from Synechococcus sp. PCC 6301. *Biochim. Biophys. Acta* **1059** (1991) 215–225.

57. B. Lagoutte, J. Hanley, H. Bottin, Multiple functions for the C terminus of the PsaD subunit in the cyanobacterial photosystem I complex. *Plant Physiol.* **126** (2001) 307–316.

58. Q. Xu, Y.S. Jung, V.P. Chitnis, J.A. Guikema, J.H. Golbeck, P.R. Chitnis, Mutational analysis of photosystem I polypeptides in Synechocystis sp. PCC

6803. Subunit requirements for reduction of $NADP^+$ mediated by ferredoxin and flavodoxin. *J. Biol. Chem.* **269** (1994) 21512–21518.
59. S. Janson, B. Andersen, H.V. Scheller, Nearest-neighbor analysis of higher-plant photosystem I holocomplex. *Plant. Physiol.* **112** (1996) 409–420.
60. T.S. Armbrust, P.R. Chitnis, J.A. Guikema, Organization of Photosystem I polypeptides examined by chemical crosslinking. *Plant Physiol.* **111** (1996) 1307–1312.
61. P.R. Chitinis, Q. Xu, V.P. Chtinis, R. Nechustai, Function and organization of Photosystem I polypeptides. *Photosynth. Res.* **44** (1995) 23–40.
62. G. Zanetti, G. Merati, Interaction between photosystem I and ferredoxin. Identification by chemical cross-linking of the polypeptide which binds ferredoxin. *Eur. J. Biochem.* **169** (1987) 143–146.
63. M. Zilber, R. Malkin, Ferredoxin cross-links to a 22 kDa subunit of Photosystem I. *Plant Physiol.* **88** (1988) 810–814.
64. C. Lelong, P. Setif, B. Lagoutte, H. Bottin, Identification of the amino acids involved in the functional interaction between photosystem I and ferredoxin from Synechocystis sp. PCC 6803 by chemical cross-linking. *J. Biol. Chem.* **269** (1994) 10034–10039.
65. C. Lelong, E.J. Boekema, J. Kruip, H. Bottin, M. Rögner, P. Setif, Characterization of a redox active cross-linked complex between cyanobacterial photosystem I and soluble ferredoxin. *EMBO J.* **15** (1996) 2160–2168.
66. U. Mühlenhoff, J. Kruip, D.A. Bryant, M. Rögner, P. Setif, E. Boekema, Characterization of a redox-active cross-linked complex between cyanobacterial photosystem I and its physiological acceptor flavodoxin. *EMBO J.* **15** (1996) 488–497.
67. V. Pandini, A. Aliverti, G. Zanetti, Interaction of the soluble recombinant PsaD subunit of spinach photosystem I with ferredoxin I. *Biochemistry* **38** (1999) 10707–10713.
68. P. Fromme, H. Bottin, N. Krauss, P. Setif, Crystallization and EPR characterization of a functional complex of Photosystem I with its natural electron acceptor ferredoxin. *Biophys. J.* **83** (2002) 1760–1773.
69. C.J. Falzone, Y.H. Kao, J. Zhao, D.A. Bryant, J.T. Lecomte, Three-dimensional solution structure of PsaE from the cyanobacterium Synechococcus sp. strain PCC 7002, a photosystem I protein that shows structural homology with SH3 domains. *Biochemistry* **33** (1994) 6052–6062.
70. O. Klukas, W.D. Schubert, P. Jordan, N. Krauss, P. Fromme, H.T. Witt, W. Saenger, Photosystem I, an improved model of the stromal subunits PsaC, PsaD, and PsaE. *J. Biol. Chem.* **274** (1999) 7351–7360.
71. A. Zouni, R. Jordan, E. Schlodder, P. Fromme, H. Witt, First photosystem II crystals capable of water oxidation. *Biochim. Biophys. Acta* **1457** (2000) 103–105.
72. A. Lushy, L. Verchovsky, R. Nechushtai, The stable assembly of newly synthesized PsaE into the photosystem I complex occurring via the exchange mechanism is facilitated by electrostatic interactions. *Biochemistry* **41** (2002) 11192–11199.
73. K. Sonoike, H. Hatanaka, S. Katoh, Small subunits of Photosystem I reaction center complexes from Synechococcus elongatus. II. The psaE gene product has a role to promote interaction between the terminal electron acceptor and ferredoxin. *Biochim. Biophys. Acta* **1141** (1993) 52–57.
74. N. Weber, H. Strotmann, On the function of subunit PsaE in chloroplast Photosystem I. *Biochim. Biophys. Acta* **1143** (1993) 204–210.
75. F. Rousseau, P. Setif, B. Lagoutte, Evidence for the involvement of PSI-E subunit in the reduction of ferredoxin by photosystem I. *EMBO J.* **12** (1993) 1755–1765.

76. J. Zhao, W.B. Snyder, U. Mühlenhoff, E. Rhiel, P.V. Warren, J.H. Golbeck, D.A. Bryant, Cloning and characterization of the psaE gene of the cyanobacterium Synechococcus sp. PCC 7002: characterization of a psaE mutant and overproduction of the protein in Escherichia coli. *Mol. Microbiol.* **9** (1993) 183–194.
77. B. Andersen, H.V. Scheller, B.L. Moller, The PSI-E subunit of photosystem I binds ferredoxin:NADP$^+$ oxidoreductase. *FEBS Lett.* **311** (1992) 169–173.
78. J. Kruip, P.R. Chitnis, B. Lagoutte, M. Rögner, E.J. Boekema, Structural organization of the major subunits in cyanobacterial photosystem 1. Localization of subunits PsaC, -D, -E, -F, and -J. *J. Biol. Chem.* **272** (1997) 17061–17069.
79. Q. Xu, L. Yu, V.P. Chitnis, P.R. Chitnis, Function and organization of photosystem I in a cyanobacterial mutant strain that lacks PsaF and PsaJ subunits. *J. Biol. Chem.* **269** (1994) 3205–3211.
80. U. Muhlenhoff, J. Zhao, D.A. Bryant, Interaction between photosystem I and flavodoxin from the cyanobacterium Synechococcus sp. PCC 7002 as revealed by chemical cross-linking. *Eur. J. Biochem.* **235** (1996) 324–331.
81. H. Strotmann, N. Weber, On the function of PsaE in chloroplast Photosystem I. *Biochim. Biophys. Acta* **1143** (1993) 204–210.
82. L. Yu, J. Zhao, U. Muhlenhoff, D.A. Bryant, J.H. Golbeck, PsaE is required for in vivo cyclic electron flow around Photosystem I in the cyanobacterium Synechococcus sp. PCC 7002. *Plant Physiol.* **103** (1993) 171–180.
83. U. Mühlenhoff, J. Zhao, D.A. Bryant, Interaction between photosystem I and flavodoxin from the cyanobacterium Synechococcus sp. PCC 7002 as revealed by chemical cross-linking. *Eur. J. Biochem.* **235** (1996) 324–331.
84. K. Meimberg, B. Lagoutte, H. Bottin, U. Mühlenhoff, The PsaE subunit is required for complex formation between photosystem I and flavodoxin from the cyanobacterium Synechocystis sp. PCC 6803. *Biochemistry* **37** (1998) 9759–9767.
85. J.J. van Thor, T.H. Geerlings, H.C. Matthijs, K.J. Hellingwerf, Kinetic evidence for the PsaE-dependent transient ternary complex photosystem I/ferredoxin/ferredoxin:NADP($^+$) reductase in a cyanobacterium. *Biochemistry* **38** (1999) 12735–12746.
86. V.P. Chitnis, P.R. Chitnis, PsaL subunit is required for the formation of photosystem I trimers in the cyanobacterium Synechocystis sp. PCC 6803. *FEBS Lett.* **336** (1993) 330–334.
87. W.M. Schluchter, G. Shen, J. Zhao, D.A. Bryant, Characterization of psaI and psaL mutants of Synechococcus sp. strain PCC 7002: a new model for state transitions in cyanobacteria. *Photochem. Photobiol.* **64** (1996) 53–66.
88. Q. Xu, D. Hoppe, V.P. Chitnis, W.R. Odom, J.A. Guikema, P.R. Chitnis, Mutational analysis of photosystem I polypeptides in the cyanobacterium Synechocystis sp. PCC 6803. Targeted inactivation of psaI reveals the function of psaI in the structural organization of psaL. *J. Biol. Chem.* **270** (1995) 16243–16250.
89. B. Andersen, H.V. Scheller (eds.), *Structure, Function and Assembly of Photosystem I* (1993), Academic Press, San Diego.
90. H.V. Scheller, P.E. Jensen, A. Haldrup, C. Lunde, J. Knoetzel, Role of subunits in eukaryotic Photosystem I. *Biochim. Biophys. Acta* **1507** (2001) 41–60.
91. P. Fromme, *Crystallization of Photosystem I for Structural Analysis, Habilitation*, Technical University Berlin, Germany (1998).
92. S.P. Zhang, H.V. Scheller, Light-harvesting complex II binds to several small subunits of photosystem I. *J. Biol. Chem.* **279** (2004) 3180–3187.

93. N.V. Karapetyan, The dynamics of excitation energy in photosystem I of cyanobacteria: transfer in the antenna, capture by the reaction site, and dissipation. *Biofizika* **49** (2004) 212–226.
94. N.V. Karapetyan, V.V. Shubin, R.J. Strasser, Energy exchange between the chlorophyll antennae of monomeric subunits within the Photosystem I trimeric complex of the cyanobacterium Spirulina. *Photosynth. Res.* **61** (1999) 291–301.
95. M. Sener, S. Park, D.Y. Lu, A. Damjanovic, T. Ritz, P. Fromme, K. Schulten, Excitation transfer dynamics in monomeric and trimeric forms of cyanobacterial photosystem I. *Biophys. J.* **84** (2003) 274a.
96. I. Karnauchov, D. Cai, I. Schmidt, R.G. Herrmann, R.B. Klosgen, The thylakoid translocation of subunit 3 of photosystem I, the psaF gene product, depends on a bipartite transit peptide and proceeds along an azide-sensitive pathway. *J. Biol. Chem.* **269** (1994) 32871–32878.
97. M.P. Scott, V.S. Nielsen, J. Knoetzel, R. Andersen, B.L. Moller, Import of the barley PSI-F subunit into the thylakoid lumen of isolated chloroplasts. *Plant Mol. Biol.* **26** (1994) 1223–1229.
98. M. Hugosson, G. Nurani, E. Glaser, L.G. Franzen, Peculiar properties of the PsaF photosystem I protein from the green alga Chlamydomonas reinhardtii: presequence independent import of the PsaF protein into both chloroplasts and mitochondria. *Plant Mol. Biol.* **28** (1995) 525–535.
99. M. Hippler, J. Reichert, M. Sutter, E. Zak, L. Altschmied, U. Schroer, R.G. Herrmann, W. Haehnel, The plastocyanin binding domain of photosystem I. *EMBO J.* **15** (1996) 6374–6384.
100. M. Hippler, A. Riedel, U. Schroer, W. Nitschke, W. Haehnel, Light-induced charge separation between plastocyanin and the iron-sulfur clusters F_A and F_B in the complex of plastocyanin and photosystem I. *Arch. Biochem. Biophys.* **330** (1996) 414–418.
101. M. Hippler, F. Drepper, W. Haehnel, J.D. Rochaix, The N-terminal domain of PsaF: precise recognition site for binding and fast electron transfer from cytochrome c6 and plastocyanin to photosystem I of Chlamydomonas reinhardtii. *Proc. Natl. Acad. Sci. U.S.A.* **95** (1998) 7339–7344.
102. W. Haehnel, T. Jansen, K. Gause, R.B. Klosgen, B. Stahl, D. Michl, B. Huvermann, M. Karas, R.G. Herrmann, Electron transfer from plastocyanin to photosystem I. *EMBO J.* **13** (1994) 1028–1038.
103. J. Farah, F. Rappaport, Y. Choquet, P. Joliot, J.D. Rochaix, Isolation of a psaF-deficient mutant of Chlamydomonas reinhardtii: efficient interaction of plastocyanin with the photosystem I reaction center is mediated by the PsaF subunit. *EMBO J.* **14** (1995) 4976–4984.
104. R. Jeanjean, E. Zuther, N. Yeremenko, M. Havaux, H.C. Matthijs, M. Hagemann, A photosystem 1 psaFJ-null mutant of the cyanobacterium Synechocystis PCC 6803 expresses the isiAB operon under iron replete conditions. *FEBS Lett.* **549** (2003) 52–56.
105. R. Kouril, N. Yeremenko, S. D'Haene, A.E. Yakushevska, W. Keegstra, H.C. Matthijs, J.P. Dekker, E.J. Boekema, Photosystem I trimers from Synechocystis PCC 6803 lacking the PsaF and PsaJ subunits bind an IsiA ring of 17 units. *Biochim. Biophys. Acta* **1607** (2003) 1–4.
106. S. Anandan, A. Vainstein, J.P. Thornber, Correlation of some published amino acid sequences for photosystem I polypeptides to a 17 kDa LHCI pigment-protein and to subunits III and IV of the core complex. *FEBS Lett.* **256** (1989) 150–154.

107. K. Koike, M. Ikeuchi, T. Hiyama, Y. Inoue, Identification of photosystem I components from the cyanobacterium Synechococcus vulcanus by N-terminal sequencing. *FEBS Lett.* **253** (1989) 257–263.
108. M. Ikeuchi, K.J. Nyhus, Y. Inoue, H.B. Pakrasi, Identities of four low-molecular mass subunits of the photosystem I complex from Anabaena variabilis ATCC 29413. Evidence for the presence of the psaI gene product in a cyanobacterial complex. *FEBS Lett.* **287** (1991) 5–9.
109. Y. Nakamura, T. Kaneko, S. Sato, M. Ikeuchi, H. Katoh, S. Sasamoto, A. Watanabe, M. Iriguchi, K. Kawashima, T. Kimura, Y. Kishida, C. Kiyokawa, M. Kohara, M. Matsumoto, A. Matsuno, N. Nakazaki, S. Shimpo, M. Sugimoto, C. Takeuchi, M. Yamada, S. Tabata, Complete genome structure of the thermophilic cyanobacterium Thermosynechococcus elongatus BP-1. *DNA Res* **9** (2002) 123–130.
110. A. Mant, C.A. Woolhead, M. Moore, R. Henry, C. Robinson, Insertion of PsaK into the thylakoid membrane in a "Horseshoe" conformation occurs in the absence of signal recognition particle, nucleoside triphosphates, or functional albino3. *J. Biol. Chem.* **276** (2001) 36200–36206.
111. Y. Gavel, J. Steppuhn, R. Herrmann, G. von Heijne, The "positive inside rule" applies to thylakoid membrane proteins. *FEBS Lett.* **282** (1991) 41–46.
112. C. Varotto, P. Pesaresi, P. Jahns, A. Lessnick, M. Tizzano, F. Schiavon, F. Salamini, D. Leister, Single and double knockouts of the genes for photosystem I subunits G, K, and H of Arabidopsis. Effects on photosystem I composition, photosynthetic electron flow, and state transitions. *Plant Physiol.* **129** (2002) 616–624.
113. S. Kjaerulff, B. Andersen, V.S. Nielsen, B.L. Moller, J.S. Okkels, The PSI-K subunit of photosystem I from barley (Hordeum vulgare L.). Evidence for a gene duplication of an ancestral PSI-G/K gene. *J. Biol. Chem.* **268** (1993) 18912–18916.
114. G. Mcdermott, S.M. Prince, A.A. Freer, A.M. Hawthornthwaitelawless, M.Z. Papiz, R.J. Cogdell, N.W. Isaacs, Crystal-Structure of an Integral Membrane Light-Harvesting Complex from Photosynthetic Bacteria. *Nature* **374** (1995) 517–521.
115. K. Gibasiewicz, V.M. Ramesh, S. Lin, K. Redding, N.W. Woodbury, A.N. Webber, Excitonic interactions in wild-type and mutant PSI reaction centers. *Biophys. J.* **85** (2003) 2547–2559.
116. A. Damjanovic, H.M. Vaswani, P. Fromme, G.R. Fleming, Chlorophyll excitations in photosystem I of Synechococcus elongates. *J. Phys. Chem. B* **106** (2002) 10251–10262.
117. M. Yang, A. Damjanovic, H.M. Vaswani, G.R. Fleming, Energy transfer in photosystem I of cyanobacteria Synechococcus elongates: Model study with structure-based semi-empirical Hamiltonian and experimental spectral density. *Biophys. J.* **85** (2003) 140–158.
118. A. Ben-Shem, F. Frolow, N. Nelson, Evolution of photosystem I-from symmetry through pseudo-symmetry to asymmetry. *FEBS Lett.* **564** (2004) 274–280.
119. L.O. Palsson, C. Flemming, B. Gobets, R. van Grondelle, J.P. Dekker, E. Schlodder, Energy transfer and charge separation in photosystem I: P700 oxidation upon selective excitation of the long-wavelength antenna chlorophylls of Synechococcus elongates. *Biophys. J.* **74** (1998) 2611–2622.
120. M. Byrdin, P. Jordan, N. Krauss, P. Fromme, D. Stehlik, E. Schlodder, Light harvesting in photosystem I: modeling based on the 2.5-A structure of photosystem I from Synechococcus elongates. *Biophys. J.* **83** (2002) 433–457.

121. S. Romer, H. Senger, N. Bishop, Characterization of the carotenoidless strain of Scenedesmus oliquus, mutant C-6E, a living Photosystem I model. *Bot. Acta* **108** (1995) 80–86.
122. I. Ikegami, S. Itoh, M. Iwaki, Selective extraction of antenna chlorophylls, carotenoids and quinones from photosystem I reaction center. *Plant Cell Physiol.* **41** (2000) 1085–1095.
123. I. Domonkos, P. Malec, A. Sallai, L. Kovacs, K. Itoh, G. Shen, B. Ughy, B. Bogos, I. Sakurai, M. Kis, K. Strzalka, H. Wada, S. Itoh, T. Farkas, Z. Gombos, Phosphatidylglycerol is essential for oligomerization of photosystem I reaction center. *Plant Physiol.* **134** (2004) 1471–1478.
124. M.K. Sener, S. Park, D. Lu, A. Damjanovic, T. Ritz, P. Fromme, K. Schulten, Excitation migration in trimeric cyanobacterial photosystem I. *J. Chem. Phys.* **120** (2004) 11183–11195.
125. P. Fromme, A. Melkozernov, P. Jordan, N. Krauss, Structure and function of photosystem I: interaction with its soluble electron carriers and external antenna systems. *FEBS Lett.* **555** (2003) 40–44.
126. P. Fromme, H.T. Witt, Improved isolation and crystallization of Photosystem I for structural analysis. *Biochim. Biophys. Acta* **1365** (1998) 175–184.
127. J.O. Goldsmith, B. King, S. Boxer, Mg coordination by amino acid side-chains is not required for assembly and function of the special pair in bacterial photosynthetic reaction centers. *Biochemistry* **35** (1996) 2421–2428.
128. M.G. Muller, J. Niklas, W. Lubitz, A.R. Holzwarth, Ultrafast transient absorption studies on Photosystem I reaction centers from Chlamydomonas reinhardtii: 1. A new interpretation of the energy trapping and early electron transfer steps in Photosystem I. *Biophys. J.* **85** (2003) 3899–3922.
129. M. Havaux, K.K. Niyogi, The violaxanthin cycle protects plants from photooxidative damage by more than one mechanism. *Proc. Natl. Acad. Sci. U.S.A.* **96** (1999) 8762–8767.
130. A. Nakamura, M. Akai, E. Yoshida, T. Taki, T. Watanabe, Reversed-phase HPLC determination of chlorophyll a' and phylloquinone in Photosystem I of oxygenic photosynthetic organisms. Universal existence of one chlorophyll a' molecule in Photosystem I. *Eur. J. Biochem.* **270** (2003) 2446–2458.

Chapter 14

Functional Pattern of Photosystem I in Oxygen Evolving Organisms

Pierre Sétif and Winfried Leibl

Table of Contents

14.1 Introduction... 149
14.2 General Overview.. 149
    14.2.1 Structure of the PS I Reaction Center 149
    14.2.2 The Electron Transfer Chain................................ 150
14.3 Energetics of Electron Transfer and Redox Potentials of
    Cofactors.. 151
    14.3.1 P700 152
    14.3.2 Initial Charge Separation Leading to Phylloquinone Reduction 153
    14.3.3 Phylloquinones and the Iron-Sulfur Cluster F_X........... 155
    14.3.4 The Terminal Acceptors, F_A and F_B 158
14.4 Electron Transfer: Kinetics and Spectroscopy................. 159
    14.4.1 Primary Electron Transfer P700 → A_0 → A_1............. 159
    14.4.2 Secondary Electron Transfer A_1 → F_X → F_A → F_B 163
14.5 Current Issues and Hot Topics 165
    14.5.1 The Primary Donor P700: Spectroscopy and Structure 165
    14.5.2 The Two-Electron Transfer Branches: Are Both Active?.... 167
14.6 Electron Transfer Out of Photosystem I......................... 171
    14.6.1 Reduction of Ferredoxin and Flavodoxin by
    Photosystem I.. 172
    14.6.2 Photoreduction of $NADP^+$ 173
        14.6.2.1 FNR Association to Photosynthetic Membranes
        and Phycobilisomes 174
        14.6.2.2 Fast Electron Transfer Between Ferredoxin/
        Flavodoxin and FNR....................................... 175
14.7 Concluding Remarks and Future Perspectives 176
Acknowledgements 176
References... 177

Abstract

Photosystem I catalyzes the light-driven transfer of electrons from plastocyanin or cytochrome c_6 located in the lumen to ferredoxin or flavodoxin located in the stroma. This chapter focuses on electron transfer within Photosystem I, with special emphasis on the kinetic and thermodynamic parameters of the different electron transfer steps and on the spectroscopic characterization of the Photosystem I electron-transfer cofactors. The reduction of ferredoxin and flavodoxin by Photosystem I is also briefly reviewed, together with some functional and structural aspects of $NADP^+$ photoreduction.

14.1 Introduction

Photosystem I (PS I), one of the two photosystems involved in the linear electron transfer (ET) chain of oxygenic photosynthesis, is an Fe-S type reaction center. Like its relatives in anoxygenic heliobacteria and green sulfur bacteria, it contains low potential iron-sulfur centers as terminal electron acceptors. Its physiological function is the light-driven transfer of electrons from reduced plastocyanin or cytochrome c_6 in the lumen to ferredoxin in the stroma. The redox span between the external donors ($E_m \approx +360\,mV$) and ferredoxin ($E_m \approx -420\,mV$) is about 780 mV. If the energy of a photon of wavelength 700 nm (1.77 eV) is taken as the minimum energy input, a maximum standard energy conversion yield of about 44% can be estimated for PS I. This is remarkably efficient. PS I delivers electrons at sufficiently low redox potential to allow the reduction of $NADP^+$ to NADPH ($E_m \approx -350\,mV$ at pH 8.0) via ferredoxin and another enzyme, the flavoprotein ferredoxin-$NADP^+$-reductase (FNR). The photooxidized electron donors, plastocyanin or cytochrome, are re-reduced by electrons delivered from Photosystem II (PS II) via the Cyt b_6f complex (Chapter 20).

This chapter complements the previous chapter dedicated to structural aspects of PS I and will present the current picture on functional aspects of PS I that has emerged from spectroscopic and kinetic data. The focus will be on most recent experimental data concerning the ET reactions. For discussion of excitation energy transfer reactions and the antenna system the reader is referred to Chapters 2 and 7.

14.2 General Overview

14.2.1 Structure of the PS I Reaction Center

A detailed description of the structure of PS I is given in Chapter 13 (see also Fromme et al. [1]). Here we restrict ourselves to recall those structural aspects that are basically important for understanding the function of this enzyme, in particular ET in the PS I RC (see earlier reviews [2–5]).

The core of the RC consists of two large membrane-integral protein subunits, PsaA and PsaB, of 80 kDa each, forming a heterodimer. As in all other RC, these two central subunits bind the primary donor and all the redox active cofactors involved in ET across the membrane, with the exception of the terminal electron acceptors F_A and F_B, which are bound to another subunit, PsaC, attached on the stromal side. As in other Fe-S type reaction centers but in contrast to quinone-type reaction centers (PS II, purple bacteria; see Chapters 12 and 16), PS I also binds a large number of chlorophylls (Chl) that serve as undissociable antenna (Chapter 7 gives a description of the antenna system of PS I). The two core protein subunits each contain eleven transmembrane α-helices. Five of these are proposed to be homologous to the five transmembrane helices of the L/M subunits of the purple bacterial RC (Chapter 11) as well as those of the D1/D2 subunits of Photosystem II, whereas the remaining six show homology with the antenna proteins CP43 and CP47 of PS II [6] (Chapter 15). This indicates an evolutionary relationship between the different types of RC and antenna proteins [7–9].

14.2.2 The Electron Transfer Chain

The structure and function of PS I have been studied for nearly 50 years, probably starting with the discovery of "P700" based on reversible photobleaching of a pigment at 700 nm in photosynthetic organisms by Kok [10,11]. Subsequently, the essential redox intermediates have been identified by spectroscopic methods long before the X-ray structure became known. Functional aspects were widely studied by measurements of time-resolved absorption changes in the visible and near-UV region as well as by infrared and magnetic resonance spectroscopy. The latter techniques are mainly employed to characterize redox states that can be populated in a steady-state by light (photoaccumulation) or prepared by redox control of the samples. In this way not only the oxidized state of the primary donor P700 but also paramagnetic states related to reduced acceptors ($A_0^{-\cdot}$, $A_1^{-\cdot}$, F_X^-, etc) have been identified. There are some variations in ET rates between PS I from different organisms or between PS I preparations isolated by different procedures. However, the essential features are rather conserved. In the following, we present our current knowledge on the reaction events occurring upon photoexcitation of PS I.

In PS I, the primary donor[†] is a special pair of one Chl *a* and one Chl *a'* molecule absorbing at 700 nm and, hence, called P700, located on the lumenal side of the complex (for alternative interpretations, see Sections 14.3.2, 14.4.1 and 14.5.1). A more detailed description of the properties of this Chl heterodimer is given below in Section 14.5.1. From P700, two rather symmetrical chains of cofactors, each containing two Chl molecules (A_{-1}, A_0) and one phylloquinone molecule (A_1), extend across the membrane. They build up two potential electron-transfer branches (A-branch and B-branch) that join at the first [4Fe-4S] cluster F_X (Figure 1). The latter is bound to two cysteine residues

---

[†] Defined here as the cofactor that is in the oxidized state during transmembrane electron transfer.

FUNCTIONAL PATTERN OF PHOTOSYSTEM I

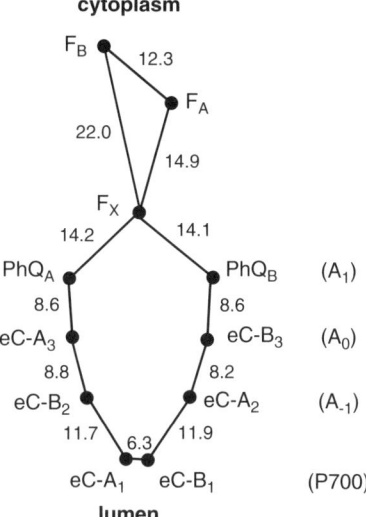

Figure 1. Schematic representation of the ET chain in PS I based on the X-ray structural model of PS I from the thermophilic cyanobacterium *Th. elongatus* [12]. Six Chls (eC-x) and two phylloquinones (PhQ) bound to the PsaA or PsaB subunits form two symmetric branches (A- and B-branches) across the membrane. Center-to-center distances between cofactors are given in Å. The denominations in brackets correspond to the redox intermediates identified by spectroscopic methods (for details on the structure, see Chapter 13).

on each subunit, bridging the two large subunits. Two additional [4Fe-4S] centers, F_A and F_B, are bound to a small, ferredoxin-like protein subunit, PsaC, which is firmly attached to the RC core on its cytoplasmic surface. There is now general agreement that after photoexcitation ET occurs in consecutive steps from P700 through the spectroscopically identified acceptors in the order $A_0^{-\bullet} \to A_1^{-\bullet} \to F_X^- \to F_A^- \to F_B^-$.

To relate the cofactors identified in the X-ray structural model with the spectroscopically identified redox intermediates, we adopt the nomenclature of Jordan et al. [12] to designate the cofactors (Figure 1). Chlorophylls are labeled eC-A(B)x where A(B) designates the protein subunit (PsaA or PsaB) to which the Chl is bound and x numbers the Chl along each branch starting from P700 ($x=1$).

14.3 Energetics of Electron Transfer and Redox Potentials of Cofactors

As introduced in Chapter 2, free energy is a key parameter, together with electronic coupling/distance and reorganization energy, for ET in proteins. Knowing the energetic scheme of PS I would, therefore, be extremely useful to understand in more detail the reaction sequence occurring in this complex system after formation of a high-energy state by light excitation. However, as outlined here, many parameters of this scheme are ill-defined. Brettel has presented an extensive discussion on this matter [3]. The general scheme proposed by Brettel was revised in 2005 in an attempt to model all PS I ET reactions and considering that the two branches are active [13]. In this chapter, we briefly summarize our present knowledge on the PS I ET energetics while focusing on a few important points. All midpoint potentials given are versus SHE [14].

14.3.1 P700

P700 consists of a heterodimer of Chl a and a' (a $C13^2$ epimer of Chl a [15]) that is located around the C_2 pseudo-symmetry axis of the PS I core. P700 is generally considered as the primary electron donor, the excitation of which leads to the primary charge separation (see recent reviews [16,17]). For alternative interpretations, see Sections 14.3.2, 14.4.1 and 14.5.1. This view has been challenged recently, with P700 oxidation following the initial charge separation (see below). To take this possibility into account, one can state conservatively that $P700^{+\bullet}$ is formed rapidly after PS I photoexcitation, in the picosecond time domain.

Early measurements of the ($P700^{+\bullet}$/P700) midpoint potential gave scattered values, ranging from 360 to 520 mV [18]. In recent measurements, data scattering, though still present, is much more restricted, with values in the 420–470 mV range. Different values were thus found for PS I complexes from different organisms: 470 mV for spinach [19], 447 mV and 469 mV for *Chlamydomonas reinhardtii* [20,21], 468 mV for *Synechocystis* PCC 6803 [22] (hereafter named *Syn.* 6803) and 420 mV for *Thermosynechococcus elongatus* [19]. The 50 mV downshift in *Th. elongatus* (420 mV) compared with spinach (470 mV) [19], indicating a significant species-dependence, is remarkable. In this last study, it was also shown that, for PS I from a given species, there is no detergent dependence of the midpoint potential, in disagreement with a previous report [23].

If one assumes that P700 is the primary donor, the initial charge separation proceeds via the singlet excited state $^1P700^*$, which is a very powerful reductant, and the process will depend on the ($P700^{+\bullet}/^1P700^*$) midpoint potential. In turn, this potential depends on the ($P700^{+\bullet}$/P700) midpoint potential and on the energy of the lower exciton state of the special pair, which is given by the main bleaching band associated with P700 oxidation. This bleaching, which does not seem to depend on the timescale of monitoring, has peak positions between 696 and 703 nm (see Witt et al. [24] for a detailed comparison of P700 properties in different species). This makes $^1P700^*$ more reducing than P700 by 1.76–1.78 eV and leads to a midpoint potential for ($P700^{+\bullet}/^1P700^*$) between −1.29 and −1.34 eV. Notably, a similar midpoint potential of −1.34 eV is found for ($P740^{+\bullet}/^1P740^*$) in the cyanobacterium *Acaryochloris marina*, which contains mostly Chl d instead of Chl a. In this organism, the energy of the lower exciton band (740 nm) and the ($P740^{+\bullet}$/P740) midpoint potential (335 mV) are both shifted so as to give ^{1}P740* the same redox energy as ^{1}P700* [25]. Similar redox energies of the excited primary donors are also found in heliobacteria and green sulfur bacteria (Chapter 12).

14.3.2 Initial Charge Separation Leading to Phylloquinone Reduction

The initial charge separation has long been considered to involve P700 as the primary electron donor and a monomeric Chl named A_0 [3], which is generally considered to be eC-A3 (if ET proceeds along the A-branch) or eC-B3 (if ET proceeds along the B-branch) [12] (Figure 1). In this view, the Chls eC-B2 and/or eC-A2 may be transiently reduced (which would make them the real primary electron acceptors, but they would have missed celebrity) or help ET between P700 and A_0 via a superexchange mechanism [26]. However, an alternative possibility in which the primary charge separation produces eC-B2$^{+\cdot}$ eC-A3$^{-\cdot}$ (it may be eC-A2$^{+\cdot}$ eC-B3$^{-\cdot}$ as well) has been proposed recently on the basis of ultrafast absorption and fluorescence measurements [27–30]. Other hypotheses put forward for the primary charge separation include the primary acceptor being a dimer of Chl *a* (eC-B2/eC-A3 for the A-branch and eC-A2/eC-B3 for the B-branch) [13,31]. This last proposal would be in line with point dipole calculations that suggest a rather strong excitonic coupling between Chls eC-B2 and eC-A3 (or eC-A2/eC-B3) [32,33]. However, the site energies (the site energy corresponding to the red absorption maximum that a Chl would exhibit in the absence of excitonic interactions) of the different ET Chls, which are critical for calculations of excitonic couplings, are still rather uncertain. This is illustrated by a recent study that suggested that these energies are quite different for (eC-B2/A2) and (eC-A3/B3) [34]. Kinetic and spectral analyses on a picosecond timescale are also made much more complex if the two ET branches are active, a possibility that has not been fully taken into account up to now in ultrafast measurements. Recent studies also suggest that reversibility between excited states and radical pair(s) should be considered [28,29]. In brief, the exact nature of both the excited state(s) preceding charge separation and the initial radical pair remain, actively investigated as they are, a matter of controversy.

Whatever the nature of the primary acceptor is, its midpoint potential is too low for a direct measurement. However, the free energy of the primary radical pair (named P700$^{+\cdot}$ $A_0^{-\cdot}$, with A_0 taken generally as eC-A3 or eC-B3) has been estimated by several methods. This free energy is more relevant to ET properties than the midpoint potential of $A_0/A_0^{-\cdot}$ due to the electrostatic interaction‡ between P700$^{+\cdot}$ and $A_0^{-\cdot}$ [3]. By measuring the ratio between prompt and delayed fluorescence, the radical pair (P700$^{+\cdot}$ $A_0^{-\cdot}$), presumably in a relaxed state, has been estimated to lie below ^{1}P700* by 0.18–0.28 eV in free energy [35,36]. Previous measurements of activation enthalpies, which were deduced

---

‡Electrostatic interactions with P700$^{+\cdot}$ are probably negligible in the case of PS I iron-sulfur clusters because they are much more distant from P700$^{+\cdot}$ and much closer to the aqueous phase than A_0. For the phylloquinones, a useful comparison can be made with the case of bacterial reaction centers, where a rather small average electrostatic interaction of 20 meV was found between the oxidized primary donor and the anionic semiquinones [232].

from the temperature dependence of different recombination reactions involving iron-sulfur clusters, gave values that are compatible with the last ones [3]. Notably, however, in the case of entropic effects being really associated with reduction of PS I iron-sulfur clusters (see below), a straightforward interpretation of this compatibility is problematic. From ultrafast optical studies, a much smaller value of about 60 meV was recently derived for the free energy gap between the excited singlet state of the reaction center and the primary radical pair [29,37]. These authors propose that charge separation occurs most likely from the excited state ^{1}eC-B2* (it may be ^{1}eC-A2* as well but the authors did not consider a two-branch model) and that the primary radical pair is eC-B2$^{+\cdot}$/eC-A3$^{-\cdot}$ (or eC-A2$^{+\cdot}$/eC-B3$^{-\cdot}$). This model, as well as a more classical one involving ^{1}P700*, are shown together in Figure 2, where, for simplicity, only the A-branch cofactors are indicated.

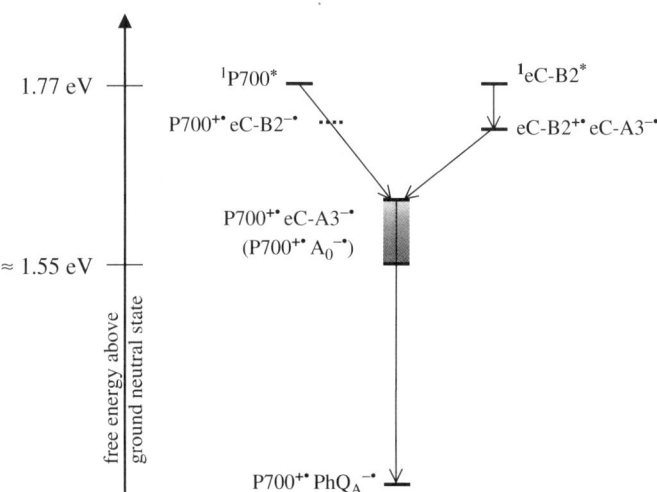

Figure 2. Two possible pathways for the initial steps of charge separation in PS I. For simplicity, only the A-branch cofactors are shown. A similar scheme can be drawn for the B-branch. The left-hand pathway is the "traditional" one starting from ^{1}P700*. In the frame of this pathway, Chl eC-B2 should be involved, but not necessarily as a real intermediate. The free energy of the state (P700$^{+\cdot}$ eC-A3$^{-\cdot}$) is shown as a smeared region as it may be different during the initial charge separation (upper level) or after relaxation, as measured, for example, during its decay via recombination (lower level). The extent of relaxation is not presently known. The right-hand pathway has been proposed more recently (see text), starting from ^{1}eC-B2*, with an excitation energy that is supposedly similar to that of ^{1}P700*. The free-energy scale is only indicative. The only parameters that were experimentally derived are the energy of ^{1}P700* (1.76–1.78 eV above the ground state), the free energy difference between ^{1}P700* and (P700$^{+\cdot}$ A$_0^{-\cdot}$) in its relaxed state (180–280 meV; left-hand pathway) and the free energy difference between ^{1}eC-B2* and (eC-B2$^{+\cdot}$ eC-A3$^{-\cdot}$) (≈ 60 meV; right-hand pathway).

14.3.3 Phylloquinones and the Iron-Sulfur Cluster F_X

As for the Chl acceptor(s), the midpoint potentials of PS I phylloquinones have never been measured directly. For studies before 1997, we will refer to a sentence in a previous review [3]: "In summary, the literature does not provide reliably accurate data on the free energy of the pair $P700^{+\cdot}$ $PhQ^{-\cdot}$ during normal forward ET in PS I". Much has been done in recent years about forward ET involving the PS I phylloquinones (see below), especially with regard to the issue of the relative activity of the two branches. However, the data relevant to quantitative estimates of the phylloquinones midpoint potentials are still rather scarce. We will discuss first these data and then address more specifically two essential issues regarding the energetics of ET involving phylloquinones.

The temperature dependence of $PhQ^{-\cdot}$ reoxidation during forward ET was measured in purified PS I from *Syn.* 6803 [38]. This process exhibits two phases, which were ascribed to the two ET branches [39]. The fast phase, ascribed to the B-branch, is almost temperature independent (activation enthalpy $E_A \approx 15\,\text{meV}$) whereas E_A of the slow phase (A-branch) is about 110 meV. This is smaller by a factor of two than E_A of 220 meV previously found in PS I from *Th. elongatus* [40], where a faster phase was not resolved. A simple interpretation of these data consists in assuming that the ET from $PhQ_B^{-\cdot}$ to F_X is exergonic whereas the ET from $PhQ_A^{-\cdot}$ to F_X is endergonic with $\Delta G^\circ \approx E_A = 110\,\text{meV}$ [38]. The temperature dependence of ET of this process was also studied in PS I from *Syn.* 6803 where phylloquinone was replaced by anthraquinone AQ [41]. These measurements were performed by using transient EPR spectroscopy, which allows a direct resolution of only the slowest component of semiquinone reoxidation in the A-branch. The ET from $AQ_A^{-\cdot}$ to F_X at room temperature was found to be about eight times faster than in normal PS I (with $PhQ_A^{-\cdot}$). This finding is consistent with $AQ_A^{-\cdot}$ being more reducing than $PhQ_A^{-\cdot}$ by about 100 mV, within the frame of the classical Marcus theory. Despite this redox shift, the process is still temperature dependent, with $E_A \approx 60\text{--}120\,\text{meV}$. In the same study, the activation enthalpy of $PhQ_A^{-\cdot}$ reoxidation was taken as 220 mV (as in Schlodder et al. [40]), but this was more an assumption than a precise measurement. In brief, a clear picture about the relationship between midpoint potentials of the quinones and the activation enthalpies of F_X reduction cannot be obtained from these two studies.

A redox gap of 205 mV between the phylloquinone (assumed to be PhQ_A) and (F_A, F_B) was derived in *Syn.* 6803 from modeling recombination reactions in PS I at room temperature. This gap is reduced to 35 mV when phylloquinone is replaced by plastoquinone-9 using a mutant unable to synthesize phylloquinone [42]. From this study, thermal repopulation of the pair ($P700^{+\cdot}$ quinone$^{-\cdot}$) from [$P700^{+\cdot}$ (F_A, F_B)$^-$] followed by a direct recombination within the ($P700^{+\cdot}$ quinone$^{-\cdot}$) pair appears to be the dominant recombination pathway, compared with thermal repopulation of the pair ($P700^{+\cdot}$ $A_0^{-\cdot}$). This interpretation is in accordance with the previous determination of an activation enthalpy of 220 meV for recombination between $P700^{+\cdot}$ and (F_A, F_B)$^-$ [43].

In principle, the redox gap of 200–220 mV between $(P700^{+\cdot}\ PhQ_A^{-\cdot})$ and $[P700^{+\cdot}\ (F_A, F_B)^-]$ can be used to derive the midpoint potential of $(PhQ_A/PhQ_A^{-\cdot})$, if one neglects electrostatic interactions. However, this relies upon the determination of the midpoint potentials of F_A and F_B, for which some uncertainty remains. Taking the generally admitted value of -540 mV for $E_m(F_A/F_A^-)$ [3], a value of $E_m(PhQ_A/PhQ_A^{-\cdot}) \approx -750$ mV is obtained. When using a higher midpoint potential of about -440 mV, which was found more recently for the first reduction of (F_A, F_B) [43], the $E_m(PhQ_A/PhQ_A^{-\cdot})$ is calculated to be about -650 mV.

Former determinations of the F_X/F_X^- midpoint potential, performed either after prereduction or inactivation of F_A and F_B, gave values in the -670 to -730 mV range [44]. From an analysis of recombination reactions in PS I, the redox gap between F_X and F_A was found to be about 100 mV [45]. When comparing this value with the redox gap of 200–220 mV between PhQ_A and F_A (see above), $PhQ_A^{-\cdot}$ is inferred to be more reducing than F_X^- by about 100 mV [42]. From values of $E_m(F_A/F_A^-) = -440$ mV or -540 mV, one gets also $E_m(F_X/F_X^-) \approx -540$ or -640 mV, respectively. Although the analysis by Shinkarev et al. [45] is not affected by electrostatic interactions, it may be biased by the comparison between PS I preparations with different contents of iron-sulfur centers, which may lead to systematic errors.

We now discuss two different issues with regard to the relative midpoint potentials of the phylloquinones and of F_X: (1) what is the midpoint potential difference ΔE_m between the phylloquinones in the two branches and (2) where is E_m of F_X located on this redox scale? Although a significant activity in the B-branch is still disputed (see below), we will assume here that ET occurs in the two branches. Concerning the first issue, there is a general consensus that PhQ_B has a lower midpoint potential than PhQ_A, based on the respective rates (Section 14.4.2) and activation enthalpies [38] of F_X reduction by the two phylloquinones and on electrostatic calculations [46]. From these data, $PhQ_B^{-\cdot}$ appears to be more reducing than $PhQ_A^{-\cdot}$ by about 150 mV. However, unexpectedly, a much smaller difference of 20 mV has been proposed on the basis of ET modeling, where it was concluded that the phylloquinones are almost isoenergetic with F_X [13]. Concerning the second issue, it seems likely that the ET from PhQ_B to F_X is exergonic, as it is a very weakly activated process [38]. In contrast, the relative midpoint potentials of PhQ_A and F_X are far less clear. The ET from PhQ_A to F_X has been concluded to be endergonic as it is strongly activated [38]. However, the activation may result also from a large reorganization energy associated with $\Delta G° < 0$ in terms of classical Marcus theory (see, for example, Pushkar et al. [41]). An entropy increase accompanying ET from PhQ_A to F_X was also recently proposed for reconciling exergonicity and a significant activation enthalpy [47].

Two current observations are relevant to the issue of the relative midpoint potentials of PhQ_A and F_X: Firstly, $PhQ_A^{-\cdot}$ reoxidation exhibits about the same kinetics whether it is measured by time-resolved absorption or EPR spectroscopy; Secondly, when the midpoint potential of PhQ_A is positively shifted by various mutations, the rate of the slow phase decreases (which is quite expected) whereas its relative amplitude (compared with that of the fast phase ascribed to PhQ$_B^{-\cdot}$ decay) is not modified (which is not so expected). For these two observations to be compatible with an endergonic process, the ET from F_X^- to F_A needs to be much faster than that from F_X to PhQ$_A$. If this were not the case, PhQ$_A^{-\cdot}$ should be populated, not only from eC-A3$^{-\cdot}$ but also from the B-branch, so that the A-branch contribution should increase when E_m(PhQ$_A$/PhQ$_A^{-\cdot}$) increases (Figure 3, model A). Moreover, if the ET from F_X^- to F_A is not faster than that from F_X to PhQ$_A$, the apparent PhQ$_A^{-\cdot}$ decay measured by EPR should be faster than its chemical decay, due to a loss of spin polarization in the pair (P700$^{+\cdot}$ PhQ$_A^{-\cdot}$) associated with F_X reduction and back transfer to PhQ$_A^{-\cdot}$.

At present, two antagonistic models are still under debate with regard to the relative midpoint potentials of the phylloquinones and F_X: E_m(PhQ$_B$/PhQ$_B^{-\cdot}$) < E_m(F_X/F_X^-) < E_m(PhQ$_A$/PhQ$_A^{-\cdot}$) (Figure 3, model A) and E_m(PhQ$_B$/PhQ$_B^{-\cdot}$) < E_m(PhQ$_A$/PhQ$_A^{-\cdot}$) < E_m(F_X/F_X^-) (Figure 3, model B). For model B, there is little kinetic constraint on F_A reduction by F_X^-. However, one needs to explain the large differences in the temperature dependences of PhQ$_A^{-\cdot}$ and PhQ$_B^{-\cdot}$ reoxidations. An entropy increase upon F_X reduction, leading to a PhQ$_B^{-\cdot}$ > F_X^- > PhQ$_A^{-\cdot}$ ordering of enthalpies, is one possible explanation. This hypothesis is supported by photoacoustic

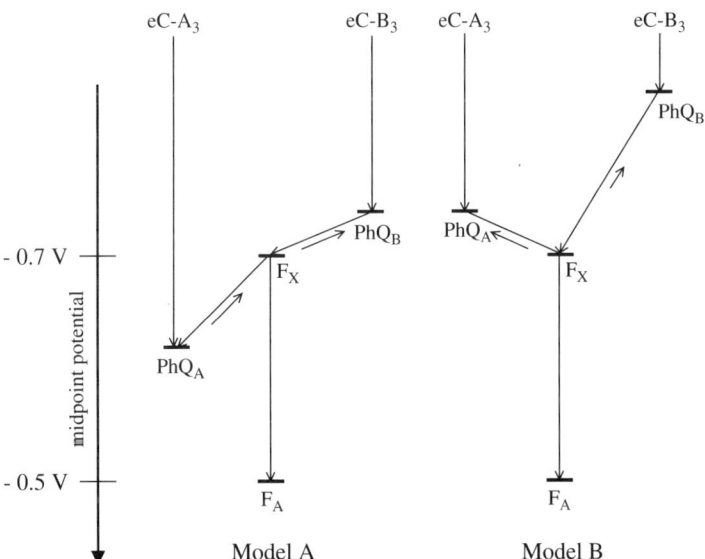

Figure 3. Two possible models for the relative midpoint potentials of the two phylloquinones PhQ$_A$ and PhQ$_B$ and the iron-sulfur center F_X. These midpoint potentials refer to the PhQ$_A$/PhQ$_A^{-\cdot}$, PhQ$_B$/PhQ$_B^{-\cdot}$ and F_X/F_X^- couples. For both models, ET from PhQ$_B$ to F_X is exergonic but the two models differ with regard to the free energy change accompanying ET from PhQ$_A$ to F_X. The redox scale (versus SHE), which exhibits the midpoint potentials measured at physiological pH [14], is only indicative.

measurements that indicate that an entropy increase makes a large contribution to the free energy change associated with $P700^{+\cdot}$ $(F_A, F_B)^-$ formation from $^1P700*$ [48]. One needs also to explain the small equilibrium constants between the states $(P700^{+\cdot}$ PhQ $F_X^-)$ and $(P700^{+\cdot}$ PhQ$^{-\cdot}$ $F_X)$ that are generally found during recombination reactions [3]. Electrostatic interactions (when F_A^- and F_B^- are prereduced) or modifications due to (F_A, F_B) disruption may lead to a decrease in these equilibrium constants. For model A, there is a strong kinetic constraint on F_A reduction by F_X^-, which should be significantly faster than PhQ$_A$ reduction by F_X. Recent data suggest that F_A reduction by F_X^- might not be fast enough (≈ 180 ns [49]; $t_{1/2} \approx 125$ ns, M. Byrdin, personal communication) to be compatible with this redox pattern.

14.3.4 The Terminal Acceptors, F_A and F_B

As noted above and discussed previously [3], the midpoint potential for the first reduction of (F_A, F_B) is in the -440 to -540 mV range. This reduction is considered to be that of F_A, as F_A is generally reduced before F_B during redox titrations, with F_B^- being apparently 25 to 50 mV more reducing than F_A^- [3]. As F_B is the direct partner of ferredoxin (Fd), this would mean that an uphill ET from F_A to F_B is involved during Fd reduction. However, there are at least two main unknown parameters regarding this issue [44,50]: firstly, the electrostatic interaction between F_A and F_B [shift of $E_m(F_B/F_B^-)$ when F_A is reduced] has not been determined and, secondly, docking of the negatively charged Fd to PS I should shift the midpoint potentials of F_A and F_B, to an extent that is still unknown.

Photoacoustic measurements have shown that the enthalpy of the reaction [$^1P700* \rightarrow P700^{+\cdot}$ $(F_A, F_B)^-$] is -0.39 ± 0.1 eV (measured in purified PS I complexes from *Syn.* 6803 [48]; see also Boichenko et al. [51]). Accordingly, the entropy increase $T\Delta S°$ is 0.35 ± 0.1 eV for the same reaction, when values of $E_m[(F_A, F_B)/(F_A, F_B)^-]$ are assumed to be in the lower range. Entropy changes associated with the reduction of small electron carriers, which include solvent reorganization effects and changes in protein flexibility, can be very large ($|T\Delta S°|$ up to 0.8 eV [52]). For iron-sulfur proteins, which are generally negatively charged, entropic contributions are most often negative [52,53], with $T\Delta S°$ in the range -0.45 to $+0.1$ eV for reduction of [4Fe-4S] clusters. However, the stromal side of cyanobacterial PS I exhibits an excess of positive charges [48]. Conceivably, therefore, (F_A, F_B) reduction in the absence of Fd, which should lead to a decrease in the positive electrostatic potential on the PS I stromal side, is associated with a release of counter-ions, thus giving rise to a positive entropy change [48]. The value of $T\Delta S°$ found by Hou et al. [48] would make ET from phylloquinone to (F_A, F_B) almost isoenthalpic, if one assumes that there is little entropy change associated with $(P700^{+\cdot}$ PhQ$^{-\cdot})$ formation. This should favor recombination between $P700^{+\cdot}$ and $(F_A, F_B)^-$ at low temperature due to population of PhQ$^{-\cdot}$, which is contrary to observations (the recombination is blocked at low temperature). Obviously, entropy changes associated with PS I charge separation deserve further consideration. Entropy effects may also contribute to the decrease in efficiency of charge separation in PS I at low temperature [40] (reviewed by Brettel [3]).

As a conclusion to this section, one can state that there are still many uncertainties with regard to the energetics of charge separation in PS I. This is, firstly, related to uncertainties in the ET pathways, especially for the primary steps of charge separation (Figure 2), and, secondly, to the large uncertainties that emerge from the available data for the midpoint potentials of the secondary acceptors (Figure 3). Regardless of these problems, one firm and basic conclusion can be drawn: Two forward ET steps are essentially irreversible due to a large decrease in free energy ($\Delta G° < -100$ meV). These steps are the reduction of the phylloquinone(s) by the Chl acceptor(s) A_0 and the reduction of F_A by F_X.

14.4 Electron Transfer: Kinetics and Spectroscopy

14.4.1 Primary Electron Transfer $P700 \rightarrow A_0 \rightarrow A_1$

The primary photochemical events in PS I follow the universal scheme that is valid for all types of photosynthetic RCs (Chapter 1). Transfer of excitation energy from the antenna (see Chapter 7 for a description of the Photosystem I antenna of plants) results in an excited state of one or several coupled cofactors within the RC. The excitation equilibrates within some picoseconds [54] and leads to primary charge separation, i.e., formation of the primary radical pair, a process called "trapping". In PS I the primary radical pair detected by fast spectroscopy is the state $P700^{+\cdot} A_0^{-\cdot}$ where A_0, the primary electron acceptor, is a Chl species (see below for a recently proposed alternative model where this radical pair is formed only in the second ET step). Spectral characterization of $A_0^{-\cdot}/A_0$ was first obtained by subtraction of $P700^{+\cdot}/P700$ difference spectra from $P700^{+\cdot} A_0^{-\cdot}$ spectra in preparations where the forward ET was blocked by extraction or reduction of the phylloquinones [55,56], and also by time resolved pump–probe experiments [57–59]. The $A_0^{-\cdot}/A_0$ difference spectrum is characterized by an absorption decrease at ~680–690 and 430 nm and an absorption increase around 760 and 460 nm. These features are compatible with its identification as a Chl *a* species. Proton ENDOR spectroscopy of A_0 provided hyperfine coupling constants and methyl group anisotropy of the $A_0^{-\cdot}$ radicals in PS I from spinach [60]. Comparison with the corresponding spectra obtained in the related RC of *C. limicola* and *H. chlorum* where A_0 is the only Chl *a*-type pigment present showed that the photoaccumulation procedure does not cause photoreduction of other pigments. Spectroscopic studies of site-directed mutants [59,61,62] identified A_0 as the Chl *a* molecules eC-A3/eC-B3 (Figure 1) although it cannot be excluded that A_0 is actually a coupled pair of Chls, eC-B2/eC-A3 in the A-branch or/and eC-A2/eC-B3 in the B-branch [13,63].

Direct measurements of the intrinsic time constant of the charge separation reaction are hampered by difficulties in isolation of an intact PS I RC core that is deprived of antenna pigments. Therefore, excitation energy transfer (EET) from the antenna to the RC proper, which occurs on a similar time scale, interferes with the primary ET reactions. In particular, interference by slower phases due to EET is a problem in strains that contain far-red forms of antenna Chls (see Gobets and Van Grondelle [54] for a review). In PS I particles containing only 12–13 Chl per P700, a rate constant of 1.2–2 ps^{-1} was estimated from femtosecond transient absorption spectroscopy [64]. To extract spectral features related to charge separation within more intact reaction centers many ultrafast studies make use of a comparison between transients recorded in "open" (P700 reduced) and "closed" (P700 oxidized) reaction centers, with the implicit assumption that the redox state of P700 has no significant effect on EET [58,65]. In other studies the spectral evolution was compared at different excitation wavelengths, exciting preferentially the antenna or RC pigments [37]. In any case extraction of the intrinsic rate of primary charge separation from apparent rates (decay of the excited state or formation of the primary radical pair) depends on the model for the trapping mechanism, i.e., whether the latter is considered trap-limited or transfer-to-trap limited (see, for example, Müller et al. [37]). The intrinsic rate of primary charge separation in PS I was generally believed to be similar to the rate observed in RC from purple photosynthetic bacteria, i.e., $>10\,ps^{-1}$ [58,66]. This was confirmed by a combined study of time-resolved absorption and fluorescence on PS I from *C. reinhardtii* [29,37]. The data obtained in these studies were found to be compatible only with a "charge recombination" model with effective rate constants of 438 and 52 ns^{-1} for primary charge separation and recombination to the excited state, respectively, yielding an intrinsic rate constant for charge separation of about 2 ps^{-1} [29]. The fact that the measured apparent lifetime of charge separation (8 ps) was slower by a factor of four was ascribed to an "antenna effect".

When forward ET is blocked, the primary radical pair ($P700^{+\cdot}\,A_0^{-\cdot}$) decays in 20–30 ns at room temperature by charge recombination, leading to a high yield of triplet state formation [67,68]. The acceptor Chl A_0 thus plays a similar role as the bacteriopheophytin BPhe H_L in purple photosynthetic bacteria. In the classical model, primary charge separation starts from the state $^1P700^*$ and the Chl cofactor positioned between P700 and A_0 (A_{-1} in Figure 1) is thought to mediate ET as the "accessory" BChl B_L does in the purple bacterial RC. In contrast to RC from purple bacteria (Chapter 12), there is no spectroscopic evidence for A_{-1} transient reduction. Therefore, this compound might be involved in a superexchange mechanism. Recently, a fundamentally different mechanism for primary charge separation has been put forward where oxidation of P700 does not occur on the first ET step [37,69]. This model is based on results of time-resolved ultrafast absorption changes on PS I reaction centers from *C. reinhardtii*, where energy trapping is fast compared with other systems. The new mechanism implies that the charge separation starts from the excited state $^1A_{-1}^*$, yielding the state $A_{-1}^{+\cdot}\,A_0^{-\cdot}$ as the first radical pair, which is formed with an intrinsic rate constant of charge separation of $<1\,ps^{-1}$. The state $P700^{+\cdot}\,A_0^{-\cdot}$ forms only on the second ET step on a timescale of about 10 ps (Figure 2, right-hand side). Thus, the role of the "accessory" Chl(s) A_{-1} in the traditional and this new alternative models is very different as this cofactor becomes a reduced or an oxidized intermediate, respectively. Besides the transient redox state of A_{-1}, the models differ in the localization of the equilibrated excited state RC^* leading to primary charge separation. Whether the excited state should be considered as localized (on $P700^*$ or A_{-1}^*) or more or less delocalized over the six Chl cofactors is not yet clear from the presently available data. The issue of the identity of the primary electron donor seems to be unimportant for secondary ET reactions occurring after $P700^{+\cdot}\ A_0^{-\cdot}$ formation, but it is certainly relevant to the question of symmetric or asymmetric ET along both branches of cofactors.

Under normal conditions, the primary charge separation in PS I is stabilized by ET from A_0 to A_1, forming the radical pair $P700^{+\cdot}\ A_1^{-\cdot}$. As illustrated in Figure 4, this step is characterized by the largest driving force and can, therefore, be considered to be essentially irreversible. A_1 has been identified as phylloquinone [70–72]. Since one of the two phylloquinone molecules present in PS I could be removed without impairing ET [73], it has been thought that the PS I RC has one active and one inactive branch, like the RC of purple photosynthetic bacteria. However, in recent years this model has been questioned and evidence is increasing that both branches are active (see below). With a halftime of 15–30 ps [57,74–77], reduction of A_1 is nearly an order of

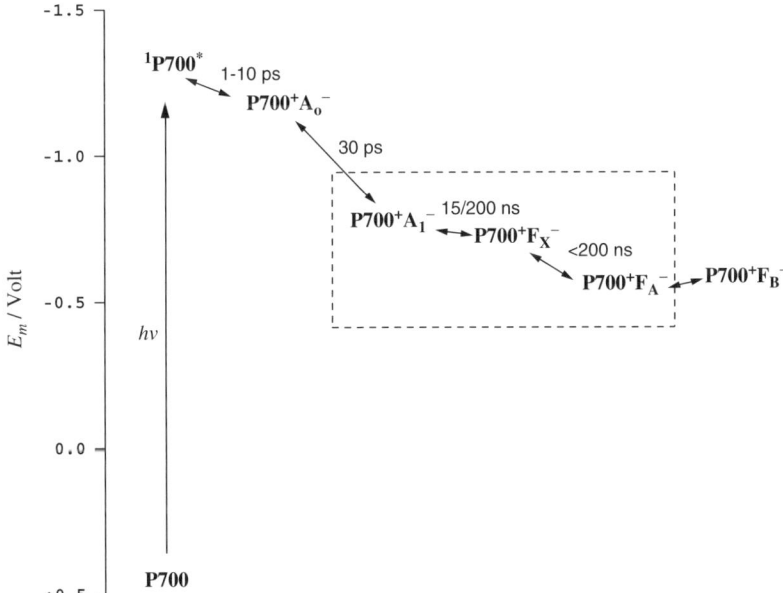

Figure 4. Simplified energetic and kinetic scheme of ET events in PS I. Approximate midpoint potentials (versus SHE) for the different electron acceptors are derived from currently available data obtained by redox titrations or kinetic modeling. The time constants indicate the measured apparent rates for ET steps. The dashed box outlines secondary ET reactions, the energetics of which are discussed in detail in Section 14.3.3 (see also Figure 3).

magnitude faster than charge stabilization on Q_A in quinone-type RCs of purple bacteria and PS II (Chapters 12 and 16) and twenty times faster than reoxidation of $A_0^{-\cdot}$ in other Fe-S-type RCs, possibly due to a lower dielectric protein environment [78]. The quinone A_1 has a much lower midpoint potential (between −500 and −800 mV; see Section 14.3.3) than the quinone acceptors Q_A in quinone-type RCs, which implies a special protein environment. The importance of the protein environment is clearly demonstrated in quinone exchange experiments in which the midpoint potentials of the same quinone in different reaction centers are compared. Such experiments yielded differences of up to 700 mV [79]. Several factors, like proximity of negative charges (especially on F_X), pattern of H-bonding interactions, polarity of the environment and π-stacking interactions with aromatic amino acids have been suggested to be responsible for tuning of the midpoint potentials [46,80]. In a quantum chemical study [81], the importance of an extended side-chain of the quinone was pointed out – it prevents the semiquinone form from reorientation and T-stacking with close by Trp residues, thereby lowering the midpoint potential. This is in line with earlier suggestions of Iwaki and Itoh [82]. Like Q_A in quinone-type RC, A_1 normally accepts only one electron but it can be doubly reduced under artificial, highly reducing conditions [83,84]. When forward ET is blocked by removal of the terminal electron acceptors (F_X, F_A, F_B), the state $P700^{+\cdot}A_1^{-\cdot}$ disappears by direct charge recombination to the ground state with a halftime of about 10 μs [85,86]. When the Fe-S centers are prereduced, recombination occurs via repopulation of the primary radical pair $P700^{+\cdot}A_0^{-\cdot}$ and leads to formation of the triplet state of the primary donor [83,87,88].

A_1 has been characterized by optical, EPR and infrared (IR) spectroscopy. In the visible and near-UV, $A_1^{-\cdot}/A_1$ difference spectra were obtained by transient absorption [89,90]. The obtained spectrum agreed well with that of the model compound $PhyQ^-/PhQ$ in vitro in the spectral range 250–500 nm. The main spectral features of A_1 reduction are a pronounced absorption decrease at 450 nm and a broad absorption increase around 380 nm. In EPR measurements $A_1^{-\cdot}$ displays an asymmetric signal ($g = 2.0048$) that was detected in photoaccumulation experiments at defined temperatures and reducing conditions and confirmed by experiments with deuterated phylloquinone and ^{13}C-labeled naphthoquinones [91–93]. The highly asymmetric electron spin density distribution is attributed to asymmetric hydrogen bonding not only in the neutral [12] but also the reduced state $A_1^{-\cdot}$ [93,94]. Another probe for detection of A_1 is the electron spin polarized signal from the radical pair $P700^{+\cdot}A_1^{-\cdot}$, which is obtained by pulsed or transient EPR [95,96]. With the sensitivity of transient EPR spectroscopy to orientation and dipolar coupling of the radicals, important and precise structural information can be obtained by this method in addition to information on the kinetics and pathway of ET. Other recent transient absorption and EPR studies, which focused mainly on the problem of involvement of both phylloquinones in ET to F_X, are discussed below. Very few studies have been published concerning IR spectroscopy data on A_1. Recent work on A_1 reduction in cyanobacterial PS I at low temperature by time-resolved FTIR spectroscopy afforded $A_1^{-\cdot}/A_1$ difference spectra by subtraction of a $P700^{+\cdot}F_X^-/P700F_X$ difference spectrum from the $P700^{+\cdot}A_1^{-\cdot}/P700A_1$ difference spectra, assuming that contributions related to a F_X^-/F_X redox change can be neglected [97]. As the authors point out, these spectra are very different from earlier photoaccumulated $A_1^{-\cdot}/A_1$ FTIR difference spectra of samples depleted of iron-sulfur centers [98], suggesting that removal of F_X considerably affects the A_1 binding site.

The phylloquinone A_1 is firmly bound to the RC but can be extracted with organic solvents [73,99–101] and replaced by phylloquinones, thus restoring the ET function [99,100,102–104]. This finding strongly supports the identification of A_1 as a phylloquinone. Alternatively, other quinones with different midpoint potentials can be reconstituted in vitro in the phylloquinone binding site [105–108]. This approach has been used to study the structure of the phylloquinone binding site [80] as well as the energetics of ET reactions involving A_1 [78,101]. However, solvent extraction is a rather harsh method (in addition to the two phylloquinones a significant fraction of carotenoids, lipids and antenna Chls are extracted) that potentially induces other structural modifications. As a gentler alternative, incubation/exchange processes without solvent extraction have been described [109]. More recently, methods have been developed for replacement of the A_1 phylloquinones in vivo, based on genetic approaches [110,111]. When the phylloquinone biosynthetic pathway is interrupted, PS I recruits into the A_1 site plastoquinone-9, which can be displaced by addition of other quinones [41,112]. This offers a mild reconstitution method, in particular also for incorporation of isotopically labeled quinones into PS I [79,109,113]. Furthermore, foreign quinones are incorporated more efficiently in mutants that lack the iron-sulfur centers [112].

On the basis of a large body of experimental data demonstrating that A_1 is an intermediate acceptor in the ET pathway to F_X, it was proposed that A_1 is located between A_0 and F_X. When the phylloquinones were resolved in the X-ray structural model, it turned out that their position within PS I was fully compatible with the position of A_1 deduced from various techniques, such as transient and pulsed EPR as well as photovoltage measurements [4,95,96,114]. The clear identification of a quinone as the electron acceptor in the second radical pair is in contrast to the situation in the related reaction centers of heliobacteria and green sulfur bacteria, where participation of a quinone as intermediary acceptor between the primary acceptor A_0 and F_X could not be established, neither by optical nor by EPR spectroscopy experiments [115,116].

14.4.2 Secondary Electron Transfer $A_1 \rightarrow F_X \rightarrow F_A \rightarrow F_B$

From $A_1^{-\cdot}$, the electron is transferred to the three [4Fe-4S] centers F_X, F_A and F_B that function as terminal RC-bound electron acceptors in PS I. These iron-sulfur centers are mainly characterized by their different low-temperature EPR spectra observed upon reduction. Of the three, F_X has the lowest redox midpoint potential (about $-700\,\text{mV}$) and cannot be chemically reduced, although F_X^- can be photoaccumulated under reducing conditions. The study of ET between the Fe-S centers is difficult because their absorption difference spectra are so similar. However, the establishment of biochemical procedures for removal and more or less selective destruction of some of these clusters followed by their subsequent reconstitution has significantly facilitated functional characterization under physiological conditions at room temperature. For example, the F_{AB} protein (PsaC) is readily removed by treatment with chaotropic agents [117], F_X can be oxidatively denatured after removal of the F_{AB} protein [118] and F_B is most susceptible to destruction by Hg [119]. The back reaction kinetics of $P700^{+\cdot}Acc^{-\cdot}$ depend strongly on the terminal acceptor (Acc), which is present in the preparation, and can be easily measured by disappearance of the absorption increase due to $P700^{+\cdot}$ in the near-infrared, thus allowing a clear characterization of the samples. Typical values are ~ 50 ms for back reaction from F_A^- or F_B^- and ~ 1 ms for back reaction from F_X^- (or an equilibrium between $A_1^{-\cdot}$ and F_X^-) in the absence of F_A and F_B [18].

The forward ET from $A_1^{-\cdot}$ has been studied by several techniques, including transient EPR, absorption spectroscopy and photovoltage measurements. Early measurements reported halftimes of about 15 and 200 ns for the reoxidation of $A_1^{-\cdot}$ in PS I from two different species [89,120]. This intriguing difference in rates for the same reaction was resolved when it became clear that reoxidation of $A_1^{-\cdot}$ exhibits, in general, biphasic kinetics with a fast (ca. 25 ns) and slow (ca. 150 ns) phase and relative amplitudes that varied among different preparations [90]. In PS I from cyanobacteria the slow phase of $A_1^{-\cdot}$ reoxidation was largely dominant. In transient EPR measurements of the spin polarized pair $P700^{+\cdot}A_1^{-\cdot}$ and in time-resolved photovoltage measurements, the time resolution did not allow a resolution of the fast phase and, therefore, halftimes of 200 ns were reported for PS I from different species [121–123]. The fact that the 200 ns phase of $A_1^{-\cdot}$ reoxidation was found to be independent of the presence of the F_{AB} protein was taken as evidence that F_X functions as an intermediate electron acceptor that is reduced within 200 ns after excitation of PS I [122–125]. However, a slight but significant enhancement has been reported for the forward ET to F_X after removal of the PsaC subunit by urea treatment. This effect was attributed to a modification of the energetics of this reaction [126]. A much stronger modification was observed in a PsaC-deficient mutant where photoreduction of F_X was largely inhibited. The same study showed, for the first time, that modifications of residues in the F_X binding domain affected forward ET: Replacement of a cysteine ligand to F_X by serine caused a ten-fold decrease of the rate of ET from $A_1^{-\cdot}$ to F_X [126].

The finding by optical spectroscopy that the reoxidation rate of $A_1^{-\cdot}$ is biphasic, not only in preparations of spinach but also in whole cells of the algae *Chlorella* [127], excludes the possibility that this biphasicity was due to a preparation artifact and has led to two interesting hypotheses. The biphasicity can be explained either by the establishment of an equilibrium between the states $A_1^{-\cdot}F_X$ and $A_1F_X^-$, which is close to one [90] followed by ET to F_A and F_B, or by two classes of phylloquinones, which differ in the reoxidation rates of their semiquinone states [127]. Obviously it is appealing to identify the two classes of phylloquinones with PhQ_A and PhQ_B, implying that in PS I both branches of cofactors are active and differ with respect to the kinetics of ET from A_1 to F_X. This topic is still under intensive research and is discussed in more detail below.

Concerning the pathway of electron flow towards and between the two Fe-S centers F_A and F_B, there is now general agreement for electron flow along the sequence $F_X \rightarrow F_A \rightarrow F_B \rightarrow$ Fd (ferredoxin) [44]. Studies on PS I complexes with destroyed F_B suggested that F_A reduction was not affected whereas Fd reduction was [128]. These observations strongly favor the assignments of F_A as the proximal and F_B as the distal center (Figure 1). This assignment agrees with the conclusions derived from X-ray crystallography [1].

14.5 Current Issues and Hot Topics

14.5.1 The Primary Donor P700: Spectroscopy and Structure

As mentioned above, P700 was the first component of PS I to be identified. It was first characterized by differential absorption and magnetic spectroscopy and named after the maximum of bleaching observed upon (photo)oxidation. The fact that the EPR line-width associated with $P700^{+\cdot}$ was narrower than for a Chl monomer was the first evidence that P700 (or more precisely $P700^{+\cdot}$) is a Chl dimer [129]. The main features of the optical $P700^{+\cdot}/P700$ difference spectrum, a broad bleaching at 695 nm and a narrow positive band at 690 nm, were also interpreted as due to a (weakly) coupled dimer [130].

Extensive studies of the primary electron donor of PS I in its active states (oxidized, triplet) have been performed by advanced spectroscopic methods like magnetic resonance and vibrational spectroscopy to get inside into the electronic coupling and electronic structure of the dimer as well as its interactions with the protein. A systematic screening of the $P700^{+\cdot}/P700$ FTIR difference spectra in mutants of conserved His pairs has permitted identification of PsaA-His676 and PsaB-His656 as the axial ligands of the Chls of P700 in *C. reinhardtii*, as this was the only pair of residues that, upon mutation to Gln, perturbed the $P700^{+\cdot}/P700$ light-induced FTIR difference spectrum, the EPR line-widths of $P700^{+\cdot}$ signals and the P700 visible difference spectrum [131]. A PsaB-His656 mutant had already been shown to affect spectroscopic features and midpoint potential of $P700^{+\cdot}/P700$ [132,133]. To investigate cofactor–protein interactions on a molecular level, FTIR difference spectroscopy has proven to be a particularly valuable tool. A comparison of the light-induced steady-state difference spectra due to $P700^{+\cdot}/P700$ and $^3P700/P700$ combined with global isotope labeling allowed the interaction with the protein of the 13^1-keto C=O and 13^3-ester C=O groups (IUPAC numbering scheme) of the two Chls in the neutral, oxidized and triplet state of P700 [16,134] to be identified. One Chl of the dimer was found to be strongly hydrogen-bonded, displaying an extreme downshift of about $60\,\text{cm}^{-1}$ of the 13^1-keto C=O vibration compared with the other Chl of the dimer (which was free from H-bonding). These results are in excellent agreement with later results from X-ray crystallography [12], which showed that the 13^1-keto group of eC-A1 (the Chl a' molecule P_A) forms a hydrogen bond to a Thr residue in PsaA (Chapter 13). The upshift of the C=O bands upon photooxidation of P700 by about $20\,\text{cm}^{-1}$, confirmed by a time-resolved IR study in which the absorption changes in the visible were recorded as a control [135], indicated that in the state $P700^{+\cdot}$ the positive charge is distributed about equally between the two halves of the dimer (with slightly more charge on the Chl that is free from H-bonding), in agreement with the observation of an electronic transition in the mid-IR (4500–$2000\,\text{cm}^{-1}$) in *Syn.* 6803 and spinach PS I [134]. This electronic transition, also called a hole-transfer band, had already been observed in RC from purple bacteria [136] and is characteristic of the delocalization of the positive charge over the two halves of a dimer. Further evidence from FTIR difference spectroscopy that more than one Chl is involved in $P700^{+\cdot}$ was obtained by selective isotope labeling of the 13^3-ester groups of Chl, which led to perturbation upon oxidation of P700 of two Chl ester carbonyl vibrations [137]. The finding by IR spectroscopy of a rather symmetric charge distribution in the state $P700^{+\cdot}$ is in contrast to the conclusion drawn from ENDOR measurements on single crystals and frozen solution that the charge in $P700^{+\cdot}$ is essentially localized on only one half of the dimer [138]. As pointed out by Webber and Lubitz [17], this discrepancy could be because an assignment of hyperfine coupling constants to *both* dimer halves has not yet been achieved for $P700^{+\cdot}$ and, thus, the interpretation of ENDOR data relies on comparison with hfcs of monomeric Chl $a^{+\cdot}$ in organic solvents, which are known to be influenced by the surrounding environment. Interestingly, the enhanced resolution of high-field EPR measurements combined with a comparative analysis of the g-values of $P700^{+\cdot}$ and Chl $a^{+\cdot}$ led to the conclusion that the spin density of the unpaired electron is delocalized between the two Chl molecules at 70 K [139]. To reconcile the results from magnetic resonance and FTIR spectroscopy, a different interpretation of the $P700^{+\cdot}/$P700 FTIR difference spectra was proposed [140,141] (see Pantelidou et al. [142] for a discussion of the different models for interpretation of $P700^{+\cdot}/$P700 FTIR data). However, further FTIR work reported that the vibrations of the axial His ligands of the two Chls of P700 are similarly perturbed upon $P700^{+\cdot}$ formation in *Synechocystis* [143], thereby confirming the original interpretation that the charge is essentially delocalized. It seems that the spectral features detected by IR spectroscopy are more direct probes of the spin or charge distribution on P700 than the small changes in the hyperfine couplings of the methyl groups that are the bases for interpretation of magnetic resonance data in terms of spin density distribution.

As far as the triplet state of P700 is concerned, EPR experiments indicate that the triplet state is delocalized at room temperature but localized at one Chl at low temperature [144–146]. At low temperature, both ADMR and FTIR indicate an almost exclusive localization on one half of the dimer [20,134]. However, the triplet is localized on P_B (which is free from H-bonding) according to ADMR measurements [17,20], whereas it is localized on P_A (which is strongly H-bonded) according to FTIR [16,134]. As was pointed out by Witt and co-workers [21], interpretation of ADMR T-S spectra suffers from difficulties arising from band assignment, which requires taking into account at least the two A_{-1} Chls besides P_A and P_B, thus preventing straightforward conclusions concerning the localization of the triplet state.

When the high-resolution X-ray structure of PS I was obtained it became clear that the geometry of P700 showed striking similarity with the well studied primary donor of purple bacteria. In both cases, two pigments form a special pair in a similar arrangement with the planes perpendicular to the membrane. However, as judged from the larger distance between the two Chls, this special pair is less strongly coupled in PS I than its counterpart in purple photosynthetic bacteria. The structure also confirmed earlier evidence that P700 was a heterodimer consisting of one Chl a and one Chl a' molecule. But, most importantly, the X-ray structural model provided information about amino acids that potentially interacted with P700 and the other cofactors, opening the way for useful site-directed mutagenesis. Since then, numerous mutants have been designed with the aim of either introducing new hydrogen bonds to the Chl a half of the P700 dimer (P_B), which is free from hydrogen bonds in wild type, or removing the hydrogen bonding that exists in the wild type to the Chl a' half (P_A). Several groups characterized the effect of replacement of ThrA739, the residue that is the donor of a hydrogen bond to the 13^1-keto carbonyl of P_A. Loss of this hydrogen bond led to an upshift of the $\sim 1637\,cm^{-1}$ band in FTIR $P700^{+\cdot}/P700$ difference spectra by 24–$39\,cm^{-1}$, depending on the mutation [21,142,147], thus confirming the attribution of this band to the 13^1-keto C=O of P_A. Similarly to observations on the primary donor in purple bacteria [148], mutations of ThrA739 led to a decrease in the $P700^{+\cdot}/P700$ midpoint potential compared with wild type, and the extent of the decrease (-9 to $-60\,mV$) varied with the nature of the residue that replaced Thr[§] [21,147]. The effect of the hydrogen bond to the 13^1-keto group of P_A on distribution of the spin/charge density over the $P700^{+\cdot}$ dimer was found to be small, with some relocation from P_B onto P_A [21,142,147,149]. Another approach to make P700 more symmetric is the introduction of a H-bond to P_B absent in the wild type. A mutant was constructed in which Tyr718 in PsaB was changed to Thr and the formation of $P700^{+\cdot}$ was characterized by FTIR spectroscopy [150]. It was concluded that the mutation led to hydrogen bonding in a significant (40%) fraction of the RCs but this change had only a minor effect on the relative charge distribution between $P_A^{+\cdot}$ and $P_B^{+\cdot}$.

14.5.2 The Two-Electron Transfer Branches: Are Both Active?

The first indication for the existence of two ET branches in the PS I reaction center came from EPR measurements. Heathcote and co-workers [91] found that four spins per $P700^{+\cdot}$ could be photoaccumulated at 230 K, two $A_0^{-\cdot}$ and two $A_1^{-\cdot}$.[¶] This was taken as evidence that PS I exhibits the same pseudo-C_2 symmetry as purple bacterial RC. In the latter case, the existence of two

---
[§]The midpoint potential of $P700^{+\cdot}/P700$ is much more affected in mutants of the axial ligands of the chlorophylls [20,132].
[¶]Recent evidence suggests that the ENDOR spectra of the two reduced phylloquinones are significantly different [233].

symmetric ET branches was clearly established by spectroscopy and X-ray crystallography but only one was found to be active in ET. A rationale for this functional asymmetry was found in the function of the quinone acceptor complex as a two-electron gate, where a recombination pathway from the second quinone acceptor, Q_B, has to be minimized for the semiquinone form to be sufficiently stable for double reduction during a second turnover of the RC. This is achieved by inactivity of the ET branch that contains Q_B (Chapter 13). This constraint is absent in PS I-type RC where electrons are transferred to the terminal acceptors and exported one-by-one. The first X-ray structural model of PS I confirmed the presence of two symmetric branches, consisting of three Chl molecules each, but the quinones were only later positioned in the electron density map [151]. The high-resolution X-ray structural model [1,12] confirmed the presence of two highly symmetric branches, including the two phylloquinones, and raised the question as to whether both branches are active in ET to F_X – a question that cannot be answered by X-ray crystallography.

Functional involvement of phylloquinones in the two branches is supported by recent low-temperature EPR measurements of the polarized signals due to the radical pair(s) ($P700^{+\cdot}\ A_1^{-\cdot}$), which decay(s) by recombination. At 100 K, two kinetic components were observed in PS I from *C. reinhardtii*, with lifetimes of 2.5 and 27 µs. The contribution of the fast phase increased together with photoaccumulation of $PhQ_A^{-\cdot}$ whereas a single fast phase was observed in a mutant where the Trp residue near PhQ_A was replaced by His. This finding led to the conclusion that the fast and slow phases correspond to the decay of ($P700^{+\cdot}\ PhQ_B^{-\cdot}$) and ($P700^{+\cdot}\ PhQ_A^{-\cdot}$), respectively [152]. In a more recent study, two signals with different lifetimes (6 and 60 µs) were observed for the ($P700^{+\cdot}\ A_1^{-\cdot}$) decay at 100 K in PS I from the cyanobacterium *Synechococcus lividus*, the fast phase being observed under highly reducing conditions, leading, presumably, to photoaccumulation of reduced PhQ_A [153]. Moreover, the use of high-field EPR and perdeuterated PS I revealed strongly different line shapes for the two signals in the $A_1^{-\cdot}$ regions of the spectra. These line shapes could be simulated with known magnetic and geometric parameters of PS I, thus showing that the fast and slow signals are due to ($P700^{+\cdot}\ PhQ_B^{-\cdot}$) and ($P700^{+\cdot}\ PhQ_A^{-\cdot}$), respectively [153]. Furthermore, pulsed EPR studies at 100 K were performed on PS I mutants from *C. reinhardtii* where histidine was substituted for methionine as the A_0 axial ligand. Substitution in either the A- or the B-branch allowed a selective observation of the unaffected branch, leading to different decay lifetimes and interspin distances for the radical pairs ($P700^{+\cdot}\ A_1^{-\cdot}$). These observations, together with the wild type spectral and kinetic characteristics, which are a mixture of those of the two mutants, provide support for bidirectional ET in PS I at low temperature [154].

As mentioned before, biphasic reoxidation kinetics of $A_1^{-\cdot}$ were observed by time-resolved optical spectroscopy. The possibility that the biphasic nature had its origin in preparation-induced heterogeneity was eliminated by measurements on whole cells [127] in which the earlier determined half times of 15 and 150 ns were confirmed. It is now generally accepted as an intrinsic feature of PS I that the reoxidation of $A_1^{-\cdot}$ is (at least) biphasic, although the relative amplitude of phases are to some degree species and preparation dependent. Several models, which are not exclusive, have been proposed to explain the multiphasic reoxidation kinetics of $A_1^{-\bullet}$. Firstly, it had been pointed out that the difference in free energy between the states $A_1^{-\bullet} F_X$ and $A_1 F_X^-$ is small [90], which implies that the transition between these states is essentially reversible and thus described by two apparent rates. Approximately, one rate describes the establishment of the (quasi)equilibrium between the two states and the second the depopulation of this equilibrium by forward ET to F_A. The problem is that the rate of the latter reaction, i.e., the ET from F_X^- to F_A, is not well known. Secondly, reoxidation of $A_1^{-\bullet}$ is expected to be multiphasic if either two semiquinones (differing in their reoxidation rates‖) or two (or more) different conformational states of one quinone are involved. At present, no indications for the latter possibility exist. Taking into consideration the involvement of both phylloquinones in quasi-equilibrium with F_X makes the analysis and interpretation of apparent $A_1^{-\bullet}$ reoxidation kinetics particularly complex. The puzzle is not yet completely sorted out and in the following we discuss the experimental evidences obtained so far concerning this reaction step in PS I.

The strongest support for the activity of both ET branches in PS I comes from the effect on the kinetics of $A_1^{-\bullet}$ reoxidation induced by specific point mutations. The first targets for mutagenesis were residues near the two quinones. Mutation of a Trp residue involved in π–π stacking with PhQ_A slowed the slow phase of $A_1^{-\bullet}$ reoxidation in *C. reinhardtii*, as measured by time-resolved absorption spectroscopy, whereas mutation of the symmetric Trp residue near PhQ_B slowed the fast phase of $A_1^{-\bullet}$ reoxidation [39]. Both mutations did not change the relative amplitudes of the two phases, suggesting an efficiency of about 60% and 40% for the ET along the A- and B-branches, respectively. The slowing of the rates was interpreted to be due to an increase of the midpoint potential of the nearby quinone induced by the mutation. Accordingly, if ET to F_X is exergonic, this increase should give the reaction a smaller driving force. Transient EPR spectroscopy can directly resolve only the slow phase of $A_1^{-\bullet}$ reoxidation but qualitative information about the fast phase, at least in mutants where it is slowed down, can be obtained indirectly through its influence on the spin polarization pattern (see van der Est [155] and references therein). Such experiments on the Trp mutants gave results that were consistent with the optical measurements, confirming that the slow phase can be ascribed to ET along the PsaA-side branch of cofactors in PS I [156,157]. Similar mutants in PS I from *Syn.* 6803 showed that forward ET in cyanobacterial PS I is also predominantly (>70%) along the A-branch [158,159]. The effect of mutations in PsaB on the fast phase was not clearly resolved in these studies and it was argued that some mutations might affect predominantly F_X [159]. Removal of PsaE and PsaF (and isolation of PS I using Triton X-100) in *Synechococcus* induced a much larger fraction of fast ET to the iron sulfur

---

‖ The difference in oxidation rates of the two phylloquinones has been proposed to be caused by a difference in a single residue, Trp673 in PsaB (acting as an intermediate acceptor between PhQ_B and F_X) versus Gly693 in PsaA [234]. This proposal needs to be substantiated by characterizing mutants targeted at this residue.

centers [155]. As these subunits are much closer to PsaA than to PsaB it was proposed that this was due to changes in the ET in the A-branch, rather than to redirection of electrons along the B-branch, thereby questioning the attribution of the fast phase of $A_1^{-\bullet}$ reoxidation uniquely to ET along the B-branch.

Another complementary approach to test the model of bidirectional ET in PS I is to create mutations that affect the relative yield of ET along one branch with respect to the other. In the framework of the bidirectional model this should affect the relative amplitudes but not the rates of the two phases of phyllosemiquinone reoxidation. The relative yield of ET along both branches is determined by the efficiency of primary charge separation in both branches and thus the six Chl cofactors upstream of the phylloquinones are potential targets.

The only evident asymmetry revealed by the X-ray structural model is at the level of the special pair P700, where P_A (eC-A1) is a Chl a' molecule and forms two hydrogen bonds to the protein, whereas P_B (eC-B1) is a Chl a molecule and free from hydrogen bonding interactions. To investigate the influence of the hydrogen bonds, the residue donating a hydrogen bond to the 13^1-keto group of P_A was converted into alanine in *C. reinhardtii* [147]. The mutation led to a 60 mV downshift of the $P700^{+\bullet}/P700$ midpoint potential and changes in the visible and IR spectra of the primary donor that are consistent with a removal of the hydrogen bond to P_A. The changes in the $P700^{+\bullet}/P700$ FTIR difference spectrum were interpreted to indicate a 14–18% shift of positive charge density from P_B to P_A. However, the mutation did not cause an observable change in the directionality of ET along the two branches as measured by UV/Vis absorption spectroscopy of $A_1^{-\bullet}$ reoxidation [147]. Thus, there is, up to now, no evidence that the branching ratio of ET is governed by properties of P700.

Several studies have investigated the effect of modifications of the energetics of the A_0 Chls. Replacement of the axial ligand methionine by histidine in *C. reinhardtii* [61], which is expected to alter the midpoint potential of A_0 on the A-branch, blocked the ET to PhQ_A but did not prevent photoautotrophic growth. The corresponding mutation on the B-branch blocked the ET to PhQ_B (at 100 K) and prevented photoautotrophic growth. It was concluded that both branches are active but the B-branch is essential (and sufficient) for photoautotrophic growth. Ramesh et al. [59] studied the same mutants by ultrafast transient absorbance measurements and found also that in either branch the ET between $A_0^{-\bullet}$ and A_1 was blocked when the axial ligand to A_0 was mutated to His. This finding indicates that in *C. reinhardtii* both branches are active, at least through to A_0. However, in this study [59], the PsaB-side Met → His mutant was found to grow anaerobically, in contrast to the results of Fairclough et al. [61]. Notably, the failure of photosynthetic growth of such RC mutants is usually interpreted as an increased sensitivity to photooxidative damage caused by inhibition of normal electron flow. The axial ligands to A_0 were also targeted in *Syn.* 6803 and ET dynamics studied by ultrafast pump–probe spectroscopy [65]. Mutations in the B-branch did not alter ET dynamics, whereas a mutation of the axial Met ligand to Arg or Leu in the A-branch slowed primary charge separation and secondary ET. The latter reaction, ET from A_0 to A_1, occurred with an intrinsic time constant of about 100 ps. The authors concluded that in cyanobacterial PS I ET occurs primarily along the A-branch. From these studies it is unclear whether the mutation caused any redirection of electron flow along the two branches (besides the effect on the kinetics in the A-branch). Obviously, experimental determination of the reoxidation kinetics of $A_1^{-\bullet}$ in such mutants is necessary to clarify this interesting point. One such study has been published [49], using samples from mutants where the axial Met ligands of both A_0 Chls were changed either to His (whole cells from *C. reinhardtii*) or to Leu (PS I particles from *Syn.* 6803). These mutants had been already characterized by EPR techniques [61,62]. Absorbance changes at 380 nm showed that the B-side mutation diminished the amplitude of the fast kinetic phase of $A_1^{-\bullet}$ reoxidation while the A-side mutation diminished the amplitude of the slow phase. The rates of both phases were rather unchanged in the mutants compared with wild type. These findings were taken as further confirmation that ET occurs along both branches, both in cyanobacteria and green algae. However, at other wavelengths the effect of the mutations was much less clear and a refined analysis of absorption transients at 440 nm revealed a third kinetic phase in a A_1 mutant that displayed a significantly retarded slow phase. This new "intermediate" phase (lifetime ~180 ns) was attributed to ET from F_X to (F_A, F_B) and it was suggested that absorbance changes at 340 nm reflect mainly features of iron-sulfur clusters rather than of phylloquinone. This could explain why the effect of mutations near A_0 or A_1 appears rather weak at this wavelength. The implications of the case where the rates of ET from F_X to (F_A, F_B) and of reoxidation of the phyllosemiquinones are comparable are discussed in Section 14.3.3.

The previous discussion shows that, in recent years, a considerable amount of experimental data have been obtained that are relevant to the question of the ET pathways within PS I. The issue of an involvement of both ET branches has been addressed by using various mutants. Conclusions derived from these studies depended on the detection method and the species. One problem with such complicated systems like PS I is that interpretation of kinetic data is often model-dependent. In most recent studies, the possibility of unidirectional or bidirectional ET was explicitly considered but mostly in the framework of irreversible ET steps. However, especially for the problem of phyllosemiquinone reoxidation, reversibility has to be considered [13]. This leads to even more complex models with an increased number of parameters to be determined. However, useful additional information can be obtained, e.g., by studies of the temperature dependence of ET reactions (see Agalarov and Brettel [38]). Such studies should be interesting for analysis of the mutants described above.

14.6 Electron Transfer Out of Photosystem I

Photosystem I drives the reduction of ferredoxin, a small acidic protein of 11 kDa. This protein contains a [2Fe-2S] cluster of low midpoint potential, ranging from −455 to −310 mV [160]. Different structures of plant-type Fds have been determined by X-ray crystallography and by NMR (see Fish et al.

[161] and references therein). These structures are very similar, as expected from the high conservation of their primary sequences [162]. Multiple ferredoxin isoforms are found in most organisms [163]. These isoforms appear to exhibit different midpoint potentials E_m that are adapted to their particular physiological function [164,165]. When the function requires Fd to be reduced by PS I, the midpoint potential of this Fd generally lies in the lower range, i.e., around $-400\,mV$ or below. After reduction by PS I, Fd delivers its electron to many different partners [166]. Most of the reducing equivalents are used for $NADP^+$ reduction, for nitrogen and sulfur assimilation and in cyclic ET. Ferredoxin is also involved in redox regulation of the Calvin cycle and in several other processes [167,168]. In many cyanobacteria and in some algae, flavodoxin (Fld), an FMN containing protein, can substitute Fd under conditions of iron deprivation [169,170]. However, this substitution is not complete because Fd appears to be essential for cell survival, at least in cyanobacteria [171,172]. The Fd function(s) that cannot be fulfilled by Fld has (have) not been identified yet. In cyanobacteria, Fld expression is also induced in the presence of iron in salt-, high light- and oxidative-stress conditions [173–175]. Recent evidence also suggests that iron starvation of cyanobacteria leads to oxidative stress [176].

14.6.1 Reduction of Ferredoxin and Flavodoxin by Photosystem I

Structures of PS I-Fd and PS I-Fld complexes have been obtained at very low resolution [177,178] whereas the PS I docking site for Fd has been modeled on the basis of the PS I structure at 6 Å resolution [179]. These studies concurred to identify the PS I docking region for both partners as a concave site located at the stromal ridge made by the three extrinsic subunits PsaC, PsaD and PsaE [180,181] (see also Chapter 13). Several mutations in these three PS I subunits led to distinct modifications in Fd/Fld affinity and reduction kinetics, which give strong support to this docking site [180,181]. A detailed account of the kinetic effects on photoreduction of Fd/Fld by PS I brought about by these mutations, as well as those by mutations of Fd/Fld, is beyond the scope of the present chapter, but is outlined in detail elsewhere [181]. When docked to PS I, the ET cofactors of Fd/Fld are presumably located at the interface between the partners, thus minimizing the distance between these cofactors and cluster F_B. On the basis of the structure of cyanobacterial PS I at 2.5 Å resolution [12], F_B has been shown to be the most exposed [4Fe-4S] cluster of PS I. A detailed structure of a complex between PS I and Fd (or Fld) is still awaited from cocrystals diffracting to a higher resolution than available to date [182].

In vitro ET kinetics from PS I to Fd and Fld have been measured directly only by flash-absorption spectroscopy. A very brief summary of these studies, which have been reviewed recently [50,181], is given here. The kinetics of Fd photoreduction have been measured essentially with PS I/Fd from either *Syn.* 6803 or *C. reinhardtii*. A common feature of the kinetics observed in both systems is the presence of several first-order phases and a second-order phase in the submillisecond to millisecond time range. Dissociation constants for PS I-Fd complexes in the micromolar range were obtained from these measurements ($K_d = 0.2$–0.4

and 6–9 μM in *Syn.* 6803 and *C. reinhardtii*, respectively). The second-order phase (rate constants = 2–4 × 10^8 M^{-1} s^{-1}) corresponds to a diffusion-limited process between oxidized Fd and PS I with a reduced terminal acceptor. The first-order phases correspond to ET from (F$_A$, F$_B$)$^-$ to Fd in PS I-Fd complexes that are preformed before flash excitation. Two ($t_{1/2}$ < 1 μs, 3–6 μs) and three ($t_{1/2}$ ≈ 0.5, 13–20, 85–120 μs) first-order phases were observed in *C. reinhardtii* [183] and *Syn.* 6803 [184], respectively. Fd reduction is preceded by a lag lasting for about 200 ns, which has been ascribed to the time required for the terminal PS I acceptors to be reduced after flash excitation [185]. The exact origin of the multiple first-order components is not fully clarified [50]: The fastest component is consistent with submicrosecond reduction of F$_B$ in part of the PS I-Fd complexes. The microsecond component(s) may either reflect Fd reduction per se, in a conformation of the PS I-Fd complex that does not allow submicrosecond reduction of Fd, or a rate-limiting ET from F$_A$ to F$_B$ when Fd is bound to PS I in a specific conformation of the complex. The kinetics of Fd dissociation from PS I following its photoreduction were determined recently from ET transfer studies involving the reconstitution of the ET cascade from Photosystem I to FNR, with Fd as an electron shuttle [167]. Reduced Fd was found to dissociate from PS I with a dissociation rate constant of 800 s^{-1}. It was also proposed that either dissociation or association (or both) of Fd from (to) PS I are redox dependent. Fd reduction may thus enhance its dissociation from PS I, thereby favoring the turnover of Fd reduction [167]. Noteworthy in this context, a comparison of the X-ray structures of *Anabaena* Fd in its oxidized and reduced forms revealed a significant conformational change in the vicinity of the [2Fe-2S] cluster, close to the molecular surface [186].

The FMN cofactor of Fld is first reduced to a protonated semiquinone form (E_m = −240 to −180 mV at pH 7) and then to a fully reduced form (E_m = −470 to −370 mV) [187]. The second reduction occurs, therefore, at about the same potential as that of Fd reduction and may be the only one that is physiologically relevant, though involvement of the first reduction cannot be excluded at high stromal pH [169]. The photoreduction kinetics of oxidized Fld by PS I are rather slow, with no evidence for fast intracomplex ET and with limiting ET rates of 300–700 s^{-1} measured at saturating concentrations of oxidized Fld (see, for example, Casaus et al. [188] and Sétif for a review [181]). When measurements are performed with PS I and Fld from the same organism, the photoreduction of semireduced Fld exhibits two phases [189,190]: (i) fast first-order kinetics ($t_{1/2}$ = 10–13 μs) are ascribed to ET within a preformed PS I-Fld complex; (ii) slow second-order kinetics presumably reflect a diffusion-limited process (rate constant ≈ 2 × 10^8 M^{-1} s^{-1}).

14.6.2 Photoreduction of NADP$^+$

NADPH is required for CO$_2$ assimilation in oxygen-evolving organisms. Ferredoxin-NADP$^+$-reductase (FNR) catalyzes the reduction of NADP$^+$, using the electrons provided by (photo)reduced Fd (Fd$_{red}$), according to the global reaction: 2Fd$_{red}$ + NADP$^+$ → 2Fd$_{ox}$ + NADPH. The catalytic process involves two steps of FNR reduction: oxidized FNR (FNR_{ox}) → semireduced FNR (FNR_{sq}) → fully reduced FNR (FNR_{red}). Each of these two steps involves Fd_{red} as a reductant that can bind to FNR at a single site. The reverse reaction (ET from NADPH to Fd catalyzed by FNR) can occur as well, e.g., in nonphotosynthetic tissues of plants and in heterocysts of cyanobacteria. Several recent reviews on ferredoxin-$NADP^+$-reductase deal with functional [191–193], physiological [194] and structural aspects [195], and structures of Fd/FNR cocrystals are now available [196–198]. Structures of Fd/FNR [199,200] and Fld/FNR [201] complexes are also available from NMR data and model calculations. In this chapter, we restrict ourselves to only two aspects of FNR function, firstly its involvement in supramolecular organization and, secondly, the kinetics of ET from Fd/Fld to FNR.

14.6.2.1 FNR Association to Photosynthetic Membranes and Phycobilisomes
There is much experimental evidence for the involvement of FNR in supramolecular organization both in chloroplasts and in cyanobacteria. However, both cases are very different and need to be discussed separately. In chloroplasts, essentially a single form of FNR is found with a MW of about 35 kDa. However, a post-translational modification of unknown role has been found in *C. reinhardtii* [202]. Chloroplastic FNR can be also subjected to N-terminus proteolysis but this is ascribed to purification and storage artifacts (see, for example, Shin [194]). Most FNR is thought to be associated with the thylakoid membrane [203], except for some localizations in the pyrenoid [204] and the inner envelope membrane [205]. A small part of FNR is also found in soluble form in the stroma (see, for example, Hanke et al. [206]). It remains to be confirmed that this is not due to preparation artifacts, e.g., from disruption of a loosely bound form. A physiological role of soluble FNR is supported by the observation that FNR is solubilized from the thylakoid membranes under conditions of oxidative stress [207]. Different modes of FNR association to the thylakoid membrane have been found: FNR has been reported to be membrane-associated either via a small protein called connectein [194] (the gene of which has not been identified yet) or via a protein of approx. 17 kDa. However, the latter result is a matter of controversy, as this protein is identical to a component of the oxygen-evolving complex [208]. From the structure of spinach FNR, it was hypothesized that an unusual hydrophobic cavity is involved in the attachment to the membrane [209]. FNR has been also found to be associated with NADPH dehydrogenase [210,211], with Photosystem I via the stromal subunit PsaE [212] and with the cytochrome b_6f complex [213] (former evidence for this association has been reviewed by Carrillo and Vallejos [203]). Fd was also found to be involved in restricting rotational diffusion of FNR [214]. In this study, it was hypothesized that Fd mediates the formation of a ternary complex PS I-Fd-FNR, though there was no direct evidence for the involvement of PS I in restricting FNR mobility. The different modes of association involving FNR mentioned above may be physiologically regulated and correspond to different ET pathways, e.g., binding of FNR to NADPH dehydrogenase or cytochrome b_6f should favor cyclic ET. However, much work

is still needed before the physiological relevance and the functional significance of these different binding modes are established.

In most cyanobacteria, FNR possesses a N-terminal extension compared with chloroplastic FNR, resulting in a MW of 45–50 kDa [215]. This extension is similar to CpcD, a phycocyanin-associated linker polypeptide of the phycobilisomes (PBS). This extension was shown to localize FNR to the PBS [216], which was found to contain 2.4 [216] or 1–1.6 [217] FNR per PBS. The exact localization of FNR in the PBS is still disputed [215,216] but recent evidence suggested that FNR binds preferentially to the distal ends of the peripheral rods of the PBS [217]. Short forms of cyanobacterial FNRs, of similar size to that of chloroplastic FNR, can be purified and these forms are generally thought to result from proteolytic cleavage following dissociation of FNR from PBS [218]. It is not yet clarified whether short FNR forms are present in significant amounts in vivo in cyanobacteria and, if this is the case, what might be their specific function. It was proposed, for example, that short FNR forms might be unable to sustain cyclic electron flow [219] and are, therefore, involved only in linear electron flow. It was also hypothesized that the N-terminal extension of the high-MW FNR serves to bind FNR to the cyanobacterial membrane in the absence of PBS [220]. Along this line, it was postulated, on the basis of indirect evidence, that the product of the gene *ycf33* is involved in FNR binding in the cyanobacterium *Syn.* 6803 [221]. Indirect evidence suggested that the stromal subunit PsaE of PS I is involved in a ternary complex, PS I/Fd/FNR [222], but this was not confirmed by later in vitro experiments [167].

14.6.2.2 Fast Electron Transfer Between Ferredoxin/Flavodoxin and FNR
To our knowledge, the kinetics of ET from reduced Fld to oxidized FNR, starting from either singly or doubly reduced Fld, have never been measured. However, in the opposite direction, fast ET has been observed from the FNR semiquinone to oxidized flavodoxin. This experiment was performed by single reduction of FNR that follows photoexcitation of an exogenous flavin (5-deazariboflavin) in the presence of EDTA [223,224]. In these studies, a first-order rate of about 7000 s^{-1} was determined for intracomplex ET from the FNR semiquinone to oxidized flavodoxin.

In the following, we discuss fast ET (millisecond and submillisecond) from reduced Fd to FNR with a brief overview of the Fd residues found to be essential for this process. Many FNR residues were also found to be important for the interactions or ET between Fd (or Fld) and FNR but this topic is outside the scope of the present chapter (reviewed by Hurley et al. [191]; see Nogues et al. [225] for a recent reference).

Fast ET from reduced Fd to FNR has been studied by flash-absorption spectroscopy using two different methods: (a) a series of studies was performed using 5-deazariboflavin as a photosensitizer. The rates of ET from Fd_{red} to FNR_{ox} (leading to FNR_{sq}) were determined by using proteins either from spinach [226,227] or from the cyanobacterium *Anabaena* [227–229]. The ET rates within the Fd-FNR complex were also deduced from the rates observed at large FNR concentrations or extrapolated to infinite FNR concentrations

($k_{ET} \approx 3000$–7000 s^{-1}). Second-order rate constants of 1–1.5×10^8 M^{-1} s^{-1} were obtained under conditions where ET is diffusion-limited according to the process [226,228]: Fd$_{red}$ + FNR$_{ox}$ → Fd$_{ox}$ + FNR$_{sq}$. Many Fd mutants from *Anabaena* have been studied as well, allowing the identification of three residues that are essential for ET from Fd$_{red}$ to FNR$_{ox}$ [191,230,231]: F65, E94 and S47. These three highly conserved residues are located at the Fd surface close to its [2Fe-2S] cluster. Non-conservative substitutions at these three sites, which give rise to significant increases of the Fd midpoint potential (50–90 mV for *Anabaena* Fd), lead to a decrease in ET rate constant by four orders of magnitude (reviewed in Hurley et al. [191]). Mutations at other Fd sites lead to minor effects [191]. Most of the above studies were made at various ionic strengths at pH 7.0 in the absence of the NADP$^+$ substrate of FNR. (b) In the second type of experiments, the ET cascade PS I → Fd → FNR was reconstituted in vitro both in the absence and in the presence of NADP$^+$, and the ET kinetics were studied at pH 8.0 following charge separation within PS I [167]. ET within the Fd-FNR complex could not be measured by this method as all reducing equivalents were provided by Fd, which needs to be bound to PS I for its reduction. However, many other kinetic parameters could be obtained, such as second-order rate constants for FNR$_{ox}$ reduction by Fd$_{red}$ both in the absence and in the presence of NADP$^+$ (4.1 and 3.3×10^8 M^{-1} s^{-1}, respectively), the kinetics of FNR$_{sq}$ reduction by Fd$_{red}$ in the absence of NADP$^+$ (second-order rate constant similar to that of FNR$_{ox}$ reduction) and the duration of a single catalytic turnover.

14.7 Concluding Remarks and Future Perspectives

Our knowledge of electron transfer and electron-transfer cofactors in PS I is continuously improving thanks to the availability of many different mutants and to the use of various and state-of-the-art spectroscopic methods. The availability of a detailed structural model of PS I from the cyanobacterium *Th. elongatus* was instrumental in devising many of the site-directed mutants [12]. Despite recent progress, several important issues (e.g., the initial charge separation process, the key factors influencing the activity of the two branches, the redox scale of the cofactors) are far from fully understood. As discussed in this chapter, it is anticipated that combining different methodological approaches while taking fully into account the inherent high complexity of the PS I ET pathway will help in solving these issues. With regard to the processes of ferredoxin/flavodoxin reduction and NADP$^+$ photoreduction, many functional and structural issues remain unexplored, e.g., the in vivo kinetics of electron transfer and the involvement of supramolecular organization in regulating these processes.

Acknowledgements

We are grateful to Dr Martin Byrdin for discussions and to Dr Fabrice Rappaport for giving us access to unpublished data.

References

1. P. Fromme, P. Jordan, N. Krauss, Structure of Photosystem I. *Biochim. Biophys. Acta* **1507** (2001) 5–31.
2. J.H. Golbeck, D.A. Bryant, Photosystem I. *Curr. Top. Bioenerg.* **16** (1991) 83–177.
3. K. Brettel, Electron transfer and arrangement of the redox cofactors in Photosystem I. *Biochim. Biophys. Acta* **1318** (1997) 322–373.
4. K. Brettel, W. Leibl, Electron transfer in Photosystem I. *Biochim. Biophys. Acta* **1507** (2001) 100–114.
5. P.R. Chitnis, Photosystem I: Function and physiology. *Annu. Rev. Plant Physiol. Plant Mol. Biol.* **52** (2001) 593–626.
6. W.D. Schubert, O. Klukas, W. Saenger, H.T. Witt, P. Fromme, N. Krauss, A common ancestor for oxygenic and anoxygenic photosynthetic systems: A comparison based on the structural model of Photosystem I. *J. Mol. Biol.* **280** (1998) 297–314.
7. J. Barber, W. Kühlbrandt, Photosystem II. *Curr. Opin. Struct. Biol.* **9** (1999) 469–475.
8. D. Baymann, M. Brugna, U. Mühlenhoff, W. Nitschke, Daddy, where did (PS)I come from? *Biochim. Biophys. Acta* **1507** (2001) 291–310.
9. P. Fromme, H.T. Witt, W.D. Schubert, O. Klukas, W. Saenger, N. Krauss, Structure of Photosystem I at 4.5 Å resolution: A short review including evolutionary aspects. *Biochim. Biophys. Acta* **1275** (1996) 76–83.
10. B. Kok, On the reversible absorption change at 705 mµ in photosynthetic organisms. *Biochim. Biophys. Acta* **22** (1956) 399–401.
11. B. Kok, Absorption changes induced by the photochemical reaction of photosynthesis. *Nature* **179** (1957) 583–584.
12. P. Jordan, P. Fromme, H.T. Witt, O. Klukas, W. Saenger, N. Krauss, Three-dimensional structure of cyanobacterial Photosystem I at 2.5 Å resolution. *Nature* **411** (2001) 909–917.
13. S. Santabarbara, P. Heathcote, M.C.W. Evans, Modelling of the electron transfer reactions in Photosystem I by electron tunnelling theory: The phylloquinones bound to the PsaA and the PsaB reaction centre subunits of PSI are almost isoenergetic to the iron-sulfur cluster F_x. *Biochim. Biophys. Acta* **1708** (2005) 283–310.
14. P.L. Dutton, Redox potentiometry: determination of midpoint potentials of oxidation-reduction components of biological electron-transfer systems. *Methods Enzymol.* **54** (1978) 411–435.
15. A. Nakamura, M. Akai, E. Yoshida, T. Taki, T. Watanabe, Reversed-phase HPLC determination of chlorophyll a' and phylloquinone in Photosystem I of oxygenic photosynthetic organisms-Universal existence of one chlorophyll a' molecule in Photosystem I. *Eur. J. Biochem.* **270** (2003) 2446–2458.
16. J. Breton, Fourier transform infrared spectroscopy of primary electron donors in type I photosynthetic reaction centers. *Biochim. Biophys. Acta* **1507** (2001) 180–193.
17. A.N. Webber, W. Lubitz, P700: the primary electron donor of Photosystem I. *Biochim. Biophys. Acta* **1507** (2001) 61–79.
18. J.H. Golbeck, Structure, function and organization of the Photosystem I reaction center complex. *Biochim. Biophys. Acta* **895** (1988) 167–204.
19. A. Nakamura, T. Suzawa, Y. Kato, T. Watanabe, Significant species-dependence of P700 redox potential as verified by spectroelectrochemistry: comparison of spinach and *Theromosynechococcus elongates*. *FEBS Lett.* **579** (2005) 2273–2276.

20. L. Krabben, E. Schlodder, R. Jordan, D. Carbonera, G. Giacometti, H. Lee, A.N. Webber, W. Lubitz, Influence of the axial ligands on the spectral properties of P700 of Photosystem I: A study of site-directed mutants. *Biochemistry* **39** (2000) 13012–13025.
21. H. Witt, E. Scholdder, C. Teutloff, J. Niklas, E. Bordignon, D. Carbonera, S. Kohler, A. Labahn, W. Lubitz, Hydrogen bonding to P700: Site-directed mutagenesis of threonine A739 of Photosystem I in *Chlamydomonas reinhardtii*. *Biochemistry* **41** (2002) 8557–8569.
22. E. Hamacher, J. Kruip, M. Rögner, W. Maentele, Characterization of the primary electron donor of Photosystem I, P700, by electrochemistry and Fourier transform infrared (FTIR) difference spectroscopy. *Spectrochim. Acta Part A* **52** (1996) 107–121.
23. P. Sétif, P. Mathis, The oxidation-reduction potential of P-700 in chloroplast lamellae and subchloroplast particles. *Arch. Biochem. Biophys.* **204** (1980) 477–485.
24. H. Witt, E. Bordignon, D. Carbonera, J.P. Dekker, N. Karapetyan, C. Teutloff, A. Webber, W. Lubitz, E. Schlodder, Species-specific differences of the spectroscopic properties of P700-Analysis of the influence of non-conserved amino acid residues by site-directed mutagenesis of Photosystem I from *Chlamydomonas reinhardtii*. *J. Biol. Chem.* **278** (2003) 46760–46771.
25. Q. Hu, H. Miyashita, I. Iwasaki, N. Kurano, S. Miyachi, M. Iwaki, S. Itoh, A Photosystem I reaction center driven by chlorophyll d in oxygenic photosynthesis. *Proc. Natl. Acad. Sci. U.S.A.* **95** (1998) 13319–13323.
26. M. Bixon, J. Jortner, M.E. Michel-Beyerle, A. Ogrodnik, A superexchange mechanism for the primary charge separation in photosynthetic reaction centers. *Biochim. Biophys. Acta* **977** (1989) 273–286.
27. S. Kumazaki, K. Abiko, I. Ikegami, M. Iwaki, S. Itoh, Energy equilibration and primary charge separation in chlorophyll d-based Photosystem I reaction center isolated from *Acaryochloris marina*. *FEBS Lett.* **530** (2002) 153–157.
28. M.G. Müller, J. Niklas, W. Lubitz, A.R. Holzwarth, Ultrafast transient absorption studies on Photosystem I reaction centers from *Chlamydomonas reinhardtii*. 1. A new interpretation of the energy trapping and early electron transfer steps in Photosystem I. *Biophys. J.* **85** (2003) 3899–3922.
29. A.R. Holzwarth, M.G. Müller, J. Niklas, W. Lubitz, Charge recombination fluorescence in Photosystem I reaction centers from *Chlamydomonas reinhardtii*. *J. Phys. Chem. B* **109** (2005) 5903–5911.
30. A.R. Holzwarth, M.G. Muller, J. Niklas, W. Lubitz, Ultrafast transient absorption studies on Photosystem I reaction centers from *Chlamydomonas reinhardtii*. 2: Mutations near the P700 reaction center chlorophylls provide new insight into the nature of the primary electron donor. *Biophys. J.* **90** (2006) 552–565.
31. G. Hastings, S. Hoshina, A.N. Webber, R.E. Blankenship, Universality of energy and electron transfer processes in Photosystem I. *Biochemistry* **34** (1995) 15512–15522.
32. M. Byrdin, P. Jordan, N. Krauss, P. Fromme, D. Stehlik, E. Schlodder, Light harvesting in Photosystem I: Modeling based on the 2.5-Å structure of Photosystem I from *Synechococcus elongates*. *Biophys. J.* **83** (2002) 433–457.
33. K. Gibasiewicz, V.M. Ramesh, S. Lin, K. Redding, N.W. Woodbury, A.N. Webber, Excitonic interactions in wild-type and mutant PS I reaction centers. *Biophys. J.* **85** (2003) 2547–2559.
34. E. Schlodder, E. Bordignon, T. Renger, Spectral properties of the PS I reaction center from *T. elongatus*: structure-based modelling of optical spectra,

in: *Photosynthesis: Fundamental aspects to Global Perspectives* (2004) (A. van der Est, D. Bruce, eds), Allen Press, Montreal, pp. 61–63.
35. F.A.M. Kleinherenbrink, G. Hastings, B.P. Wittmershaus, R.E. Blankenship, Delayed fluorescence from Fe-S type photosynthetic reaction centers at low redox potential. *Biochemistry* **33** (1994) 3096–3105.
36. Y. Shibata, T. Kasahara, S. Akai, S. Itoh, I. Ikegami, Energy gap between $P700^+$ - A_0^- and P700 in Photosystem I determined by delayed fluorescence at 270–77 K, in: *Photosynthesis: Fundamental Aspects to Global Perspectives* (2004) (A. van der Est, D. Bruce, eds), Allen Press, Montreal, pp. 92–94.
37. M.G. Müller, J. Niklas, W. Lubitz, A.R. Holzwarth, Ultrafast transient absorption studies on Photosystem I reaction centers from *Chlamydomonas reinhardtii*. 1. A new interpretation of the energy trapping and early electron transfer steps in Photosystem I. *Biophys. J.* **85** (2003) 3899–3922.
38. R. Agalarov, K. Brettel, Temperature dependence of biphasic forward electron transfer from the phylloquinone(s) A_1 in Photosystem I: only the slower phase is activated. *Biochim. Biophys. Acta* **1604** (2003) 7–12.
39. M. Guergova-Kuras, B. Boudreaux, A. Joliot, P. Joliot, K. Redding, Evidence for two active branches for electron transfer in Photosystem I. *Proc. Natl. Acad. Sci. U.S.A.* **98** (2001) 4437–4442.
40. E. Schlodder, K. Falkenberg, M. Gergeleit, K. Brettel, Temperature dependence of forward and reverse electron transfer from A_1^-, the reduced secondary electron acceptor in Photosystem I. *Biochemistry* **37** (1998) 9466–9476.
41. Y.N. Pushkar, I. Karyagina, D. Stehlik, S. Brown, A. van der Est, Recruitment of a foreign quinone into the A_1 site of Photosystem I. Consecutive forward electron transfer from A_0 TO A_1 to F_X with anthraquinone in the A_1 site as studied by transient EPR. *J. Biol. Chem.* **280** (2005) 12382–12390.
42. V.P. Shinkarev, B. Zybailov, I.R. Vassiliev, J.H. Golbeck, Modeling of the $P700^+$ charge recombination kinetics with phylloquinone and plastoquinone-9 in the A_1 site of Photosystem I. *Biophys. J.* **83** (2002) 2885–2897.
43. R. Jordan, U. Nessau, E. Schlodder, Charge recombination between the reduced iron-sulphur clusters and $P700^+$, in: *Photosynthesis: Mechanisms and Effects* (1998) (G. Garab, ed.), Kluwer Academic Publishers, Dordrecht, pp. 663–666.
44. I.R. Vassiliev, M.L. Antonkine, J.H. Golbeck, Iron-sulfur clusters in type I reaction centers. *Biochim. Biophys. Acta* **1507** (2001) 139–160.
45. V.P. Shinkarev, I.R. Vassiliev, J.H. Golbeck, A kinetic assessment of the sequence of electron transfer from F_X to F_A and further to F_B in Photosystem I: the value of the equilibrium constant between F_X and F_A. *Biophys. J.* **78** (2000) 363–372.
46. H. Ishikita, E.W. Knapp, Redox potential of quinones in both electron transfer branches of Photosystem I. *J. Biol. Chem.* **278** (2003) 52002–52011.
47. F. Rappaport, B.A. Diner, K. Redding, Optical measurements of secondary electron transfer in Photosystem I, in: *Photosystem I: The Plastocyanin:Ferredoxin Oxidoreductase in Photosynthesis* (2006) (J.H. Golbeck, ed.), Kluwer Academic Publishers, Dordrecht.
48. J.M. Hou, V.A. Boichenko, Y.C. Wang, P.R. Chitnis, D. Mauzerall, Thermodynamics of electron transfer in oxygenic photosynthetic reaction centers: a pulsed photoacoustic study of electron transfer in Photosystem I reveals a similarity to bacterial reaction centers in both volume change and entropy. *Biochemistry* **40** (2001) 7109–7116.
49. M. Byrdin, R. Cohen, W. Fairclough, F. Gu, J. Golbeck, P. Heathcote, K. Redding, F. Rappaport, Secondary electron transfer in Photosystem I: what

transient absorption can tell, in: *Photosynthesis: Fundamental Aspects to Global Perspectives* (2004) (A. van der Est, D. Bruce, eds), Allen Press, Montreal, pp. 36–38.
50. P. Sétif, Ferredoxin and flavodoxin reduction by Photosystem I. *Biochim. Biophys. Acta* **1507** (2001) 161–179.
51. V.A. Boichenko, J.M. Hou, D. Mauzerall, Thermodynamics of electron transfer in oxygenic photosynthetic reaction centers: volume change, enthalpy, and entropy of electron-transfer reactions in the intact cells of the cyanobacterium *Synechocystis* PCC 6803. *Biochemistry* **40** (2001) 7126–7132.
52. G. Battistuzzi, M. Borsari, G. Di Rocco, A. Ranieri, M. Sola, Enthalpy/entropy compensation phenomena in the reduction thermodynamics of electron transport metalloproteins. *J. Biol. Inorg. Chem.* **9** (2004) 23–26.
53. G. Battistuzzi, M. D'Onofrio, M. Borsari, M. Sola, A.L. Macedo, J.J.G. Moura, P. Rodrigues, Redox thermodynamics of low-potential iron-sulfur proteins. *J. Biol. Inorg. Chem.* **5** (2000) 748–760.
54. B. Gobets, R. Van Grondelle, Energy transfer and trapping in Photosystem I. *Biochim. Biophys. Acta* **1507** (2001) 80–99.
55. A.M. Nuijs, V.A. Shuvalov, H.J. Van Gorkom, J.J. Plijter, L.N.M. Duysens, Picosecond absorbance difference spectroscopy on the primary reactions and the antenna-excited states in Photosystem I particles. *Biochim. Biophys. Acta* **850** (1986) 310–318.
56. P. Mathis, I. Ikegami, P. Sétif, Nanosecond flash studies of the absorption spectrum of the Photosystem I primary acceptor A_0. *Photosynth. Res.* **16** (1988) 203–210.
57. G. Hastings, F.A. Kleinherenbrink, S. Lin, T.J. McHugh, R.E. Blankenship, Observation of the reduction and reoxidation of the primary electron acceptor in Photosystem I. *Biochemistry* **33** (1994) 3193–3200.
58. S. Savikhin, W. Xu, P. Martinsson, P.R. Chitnis, W.S. Struve, Kinetics of charge separation and $A_0^- \rightarrow A_1$ electron transfer in photosystem reaction centers. *Biochemistry* **40** (2001) 9282–9290.
59. V.M. Ramesh, K. Gibasiewicz, S. Lin, S.E. Bingham, A.N. Webber, Bidirectional electron transfer in Photosystem I: accumulation of A_0^- in A-side or B-side mutants of the axial ligand to chlorophyll A_0. *Biochemistry* **43** (2004) 1369–1375.
60. S.E.J. Rigby, I.P. Muhiuddin, S. Santabarbara, M.C.W. Evans, P. Heathcote, Proton ENDOR spectroscopy of the anion radicals of the chlorophyll primary electron acceptors in type I photosynthetic reaction centers. *Chem. Phys.* **294** (2003) 319–328.
61. W.V. Fairclough, A. Forsyth, M.C.W. Evans, S.E.J. Rigby, S. Purton, P. Heathcote, Bidirectional electron transfer in Photosystem I: electron transfer on the PsaA side is not essential for phototrophic growth in *Chlamydomonas*. *Biochim. Biophys. Acta* **1606** (2003) 43–55.
62. R.O. Cohen, G.Z. Shen, J.H. Golbeck, W. Xu, P.R. Chitnis, A.I. Valieva, A. van der Est, Y. Pushkar, D. Stehlik, Evidence for asymmetric electron transfer in cyanobacterial Photosystem I: Analysis of a methionine-to-leucine mutation of the ligand to the primary electron acceptor A_0. *Biochemistry* **43** (2004) 4741–4754.
63. G. Hastings, S. Hoshina, A.N. Webber, R.E. Blankenship, Universality of energy and electron transfer processes in Photosystem I. *Biochemistry* **34** (1995) 15512–15522.
64. S. Kumazaki, I. Ikegami, H. Furusawa, S. Yasuda, K. Yoshihara, Observation of the excited state of the primary electron donor chlorophyll (P700) and the ultrafast charge separation in the spinach Photosystem I reaction center. *J. Phys. Chem. B* **105** (2001) 1093–1099.

65. N. Dashdorj, W. Xu, R.O. Cohen, J.H. Golbeck, S. Savikhin, Asymmetric electron transfer in cyanobacterial Photosystem I: charge separation and secondary electron transfer dynamics of mutations near the primary electron acceptor A_0. *Biophys. J.* **88** (2005) 1238–1249.
66. B. Gobets, I.H.M. van Stokkum, M. Rögner, J. Kruip, E. Schlodder, N.V. Karapetyan, J.P. Dekker, R. Van Grondelle, Time-resolved fluorescence emission measurements of Photosystem I particles of various cyanobacteria: a unified compartmental model. *Biophys. J.* **81** (2001) 407–424.
67. P. Sétif, H. Bottin, P. Mathis, Absorption studies of primary reactions in Photosystem I. Yield and rate of formation of the P-700 triplet state. *Biochim. Biophys. Acta* **808** (1985) 112–122.
68. K. Brettel, P. Sétif, Magnetic-field effects on primary reactions in Photosystem I. *Biochim. Biophys. Acta* **893** (1987) 109–114.
69. A.R. Holzwarth, M.G. Muller, J. Niklas, W. Lubitz, Ultrafast transient absorption studies on Photosystem I reaction centers from *Chlamydomonas reinhardtii*. 2: Mutations near the P700 reaction center chlorophylls provide new insight into the nature of the primary electron donor. *Biophys. J.* **90** (2006) 552–565.
70. Y. Takahashi, K. Hirota, S. Katoh, Multiple forms of P700-chlorophyll a-protein complexes from *Synechococcus* sp.: the iron, quinone and carotenoid contents. *Photosynth. Res.* **6** (1985) 183–192.
71. R.W. Mansfield, M.C.W. Evans, UV optical difference spectrum associated with the reduction of electron acceptor A_1 in Photosystem I of higher plants. *FEBS Lett.* **203** (1986) 225–229.
72. H.U. Schoeder, W. Lockau, Phylloquinone copurifies with the large subunit of Photosystem I. *FEBS Lett.* **199** (1986) 23–27.
73. R. Malkin, On the function of two vitamin K_1 molecules in the PS I electron acceptor complex. *FEBS Lett.* **208** (1986) 343–346.
74. B. Hecks, K. Wulf, J. Breton, W. Leibl, H.W. Trissl, Primary charge separation in Photosystem I: a two-step electrogenic charge separation connected with $P700^+A_0^-$ and $P700^+A_1^-$ formation. *Biochemistry* **33** (1994) 8619–8624.
75. S. Kumazaki, M. Iwaki, I. Ikegami, H. Kandori, K. Yoshihara, S. Itoh, Rates of primary electron transfer reactions in the Photosystem I reaction center reconstituted with different quinones as the secondary acceptor. *J. Phys. Chem.* **98** (1994) 11220–11225.
76. K. Brettel, M.H. Vos, Spectroscopic resolution of the picosecond reduction kinetics of the secondary electron acceptor A_1 in Photosystem I. *FEBS Lett.* **447** (1999) 315–317.
77. G. Hastings, F.A. Kleinherenbrink, S. Lin, R.E. Blankenship, Time-resolved fluorescence and absorption spectroscopy of Photosystem I. *Biochemistry* **33** (1994) 3185–3192.
78. M. Iwaki, S. Kumazaki, K. Yoshihara, T. Erabi, S. Itoh, ΔG_0 dependence of the electron transfer rate in the photosynthetic reaction center of plant Photosystem I: Natural optimization of reaction between chlorophyll a (A_0) and quinone. *J. Phys. Chem.* **100** (1996) 10802–10809.
79. A.Y. Semenov, I.R. Vassiliev, A. van der Est, M.D. Mamedov, B. Zybailov, G.Z. Shen, D. Stehlik, B.A. Diner, P.R. Chitnis, J.H. Golbeck, Recruitment of a foreign quinone into the A_1 site of Photosystem I-Altered kinetics of electron transfer in phylloquinone biosynthetic pathway mutants studied by time-resolved optical, EPR, and electrometric techniques. *J. Biol. Chem.* **275** (2000) 23429–23438.

80. M. Iwaki, S. Itoh, Structure of the phylloquinone-binding (Q_ϕ) site in green plant Photosystem I reaction centers: the affinity of quinones and quinonoid compounds for the Q_ϕ site. *Biochemistry* **30** (1991) 5347–5352.
81. M. Kaupp, The function of Photosystem I. Quantum chemical insight into the role of tryptophan-quinone interactions. *Biochemistry* **41** (2002) 2895–2900.
82. M. Iwaki, S. Itoh, Function of quinones and quinonoids in green-plant Photosystem I reaction center. *Adv. Chem. Ser.* **228** (1991) 163–178.
83. P. Sétif, H. Bottin, Identification of electron-transfer reactions involving the acceptor A_1 of Photosystem I at room temperature. *Biochemistry* **28** (1989) 2689–2697.
84. H. Bottin, P. Sétif, Inhibition of electron transfer from A_0 to A_1 in Photosystem I after treatment in darkness at low redox potential. *Biochim. Biophys. Acta* **1057** (1991) 331–336.
85. P.V. Warren, J.H. Golbeck, J.T. Warden, Charge recombination between $P700^+$ and A_1^- occurs directly to the ground state of P700 in a Photosystem I core devoid of F_X, F_B, and F_A. *Biochemistry* **32** (1993) 849–857.
86. K. Brettel, J.H. Golbeck, Spectral and kinetic characterization of electron acceptor A_1 in a Photosystem I core devoid of iron-sulfur centers F_X, F_B and F_A. *Photosynth. Res.* **45** (1995) 183–193.
87. P. Sétif, K. Brettel, Photosystem I photochemistry under highly reducing conditions: study of the P700 triplet state formation from the secondary radical pair ($P700^+$-A_1^-). *Biochim. Biophys. Acta* **1020** (1990) 232–238.
88. M. Polm, K. Brettel, Secondary pair charge recombination in Photosystem I under strongly reducing conditions: temperature dependence and suggested mechanism. *Biophys. J.* **74** (1998) 3173–3181.
89. K. Brettel, Electron transfer from A_1^- to an iron-sulfur center with $t_{1/2} = 200$ ns at room temperature in Photosystem I. Characterization by flash absorption spectroscopy. *FEBS Lett.* **239** (1988) 93–98.
90. P. Sétif, K. Brettel, Forward electron transfer from phylloquinone A_1 to iron-sulfur centers in spinach Photosystem I. *Biochemistry* **32** (1993) 7846–7854.
91. P. Heathcote, J.A. Hanley, M.C.W. Evans, Double-reduction of A_1 abolishes the EPR signal attributed to A_1^-: Evidence for C_2 symmetry in the Photosystem I reaction center. *Biochim. Biophys. Acta* **1144** (1993) 54–61.
92. P. Heathcote, P. Moeenne-Loccoz, S.E.J. Rigby, M.C.W. Evans, Photoaccumulation in Photosystem I does produce a phylloquinone ($A_1^{\cdot -}$) radical. *Biochemistry* **35** (1996) 6644–6650.
93. Y.N. Pushkar, J.H. Golbeck, D. Stehlik, H. Zimmermann, Asymmetric hydrogen-bonding of the quinone cofactor in Photosystem I probed by ^{13}C-labeled naphthoquinones. *J. Phys. Chem. B* **108** (2004) 9439–9448.
94. Y.N. Pushkar, D. Stehlik, M. van Gastel, W. Lubitz, An EPR/ENDOR study of the asymmetric hydrogen bond between the quinone electron acceptor and the protein backbone in Photosystem I. *J. Mol. Struct.* **700** (2004) 233–241.
95. R. Bittl, S.G. Zech, Pulsed EPR spectroscopy on short-lived intermediates in Photosystem I. *Biochim. Biophys. Acta* **1507** (2001) 194–211.
96. A. van der Est, Light-induced spin polarization in type I photosynthetic reaction centers. *Biochim. Biophys. Acta* **1507** (2001) 212–225.
97. V. Sivakumar, R. Wang, G. Hastings, A_1 reduction in intact cyanobacterial Photosystem I particles studied by time-resolved step-scan Fourier transform infrared difference spectroscopy and isotope labeling. *Biochemistry* **44** (2005) 1880–1893.

98. G. Hastings, V. Sivakumar, A Fourier transform infrared absorption difference spectrum associated with the reduction of A_1 in Photosystem I: are both phylloquinones involved in electron transfer? *Biochemistry* **40** (2001) 3681–3689.
99. S. Itoh, M. Iwaki, I. Ikegami, Extraction of vitamin K-1 from Photosystem I particles by treatment with diethyl ether and its effects on the A_1^- EPR signal and system I photochemistry. *Biochim. Biophys. Acta* **893** (1987) 508–516.
100. J. Biggins, P. Mathis, Functional role of vitamin K_1 in Photosystem I of the cyanobacterium *Synechocystis* 6803. *Biochemistry* **27** (1988) 1494–1500.
101. S. Itoh, M. Iwaki, I. Ikegami, Modification of Photosystem I reaction center by the extraction and exchange of chlorophylls and quinines. *Biochim. Biophys. Acta* **1507** (2001) 115–138.
102. S. Itoh, M. Iwaki, Vitamin K_1 (phylloquinone) restores the turnover of FeS centers in the ether-extracted spinach PSI particles. *FEBS Lett.* **243** (1989) 47–52.
103. R.R. Rustandi, S.W. Snyder, L.L. Feezel, T.J. Michalski, J.R. Norris, M.C. Thurnauer, J. Biggins, Contribution of vitamin K_1 to the electron spin polarization in spinach Photosystem I. *Biochemistry* **29** (1990) 8030–8032.
104. I. Sieckman, A. van der Est, H. Bottin, P. Sétif, D. Stehlik, Nanosecond electron transfer kinetics in Photosystem I following substitution of quinones for vitamin K_1 as studied by time resolved EPR. *FEBS Lett.* **284** (1991) 98–102.
105. M. Iwaki, S. Itoh, Electron transfer in spinach Photosystem I reaction center containing benzo-, naphtho- and anthraquinones in place of phylloquinone. *FEBS Lett.* **256** (1989) 11–16.
106. S. Itoh, M. Iwaki, Full replacement of the function of the secondary electron acceptor phylloquinone (=vitamin K_1) by non-quinone carbonyl compounds in green plant Photosystem I photosynthetic reaction centers. *Biochemistry* **30** (1991) 5340–5346.
107. R.R. Rustandi, S.W. Snyder, J. Biggins, J.R. Norris, M.C. Thurnauer, Reconstitution and exchange of quinones in the A_1 site of Photosystem I. An electron spin polarization electron paramagnetic resonance study. *Biochim. Biophys. Acta* **1101** (1992) 311–320.
108. M. Iwaki, S. Itoh, Reaction of reconstituted acceptor quinone and dynamic equilibration of electron transfer in the Photosystem I reaction center. *Plant Cell Physiol.* **35** (1994) 983–993.
109. A.E. Ostafin, S. Weber, Quinone exchange at the A_1 site in Photosystem I in spinach and cyanobacteria. *Biochim. Biophys. Acta* **1320** (1997) 195–207.
110. T.W. Johnson, G.Z. Shen, B. Zybailov, D. Kolling, R. Reategui, S. Beauparlant, I.R. Vassiliev, D.A. Bryant, A.D. Jones, J.H. Golbeck, P.R. Chitnis, Recruitment of a foreign quinone into the A_1 site of Photosystem I-I. Genetic and physiological characterization of phylloquinone biosynthetic pathway mutants in *Synechocystis* sp PCC 6803. *J. Biol. Chem.* **275** (2000) 8523–8530.
111. T.W. Johnson, S. Naithani, C. Stewart, B. Zybailov, A.D. Jones, J.H. Golbeck, P.R. Chitnis, The menD and menE homologs code for 2-succinyl-6-hydroxyl-2,4-cyclohexadiene-1-carboxylate synthase and O-succinylbenzoic acid-CoA synthase in the phylloquinone biosynthetic pathway of *Synechocystis* sp PCC 6803. *Biochim. Biophys. Acta* **1557** (2003) 67–76.
112. Y. Sakuragi, B. Zybailov, G.Z. Shen, D.A. Bryant, J.H. Golbeck, B.A. Diner, I. Karygina, Y. Pushkar, D. Stehlik, Recruitment of a foreign quinone into the A_1 site of Photosystem I - Characterization of a *menB rubA* double deletion mutant in *Synechococcus* sp PCC 7002 devoid of F_X, F_A, and F_B and containing plastoquinone or exchanged 9,10-anthraquinone. *J. Biol. Chem.* **280** (2005) 12371–12381.

113. B. Zybailov, A. van der Est, S.G. Zech, C. Teutloff, T.W. Johnson, G.Z. Shen, R. Bittl, D. Stehlik, P.R. Chitnis, J.H. Golbeck, Recruitment of a foreign quinone into the A_1 site of Photosystem I-II. Structural and functional characterization of phylloquinone biosynthetic pathway mutants by electron paramagnetic resonance and electron-nuclear double resonance spectroscopy. *J. Biol. Chem.* **275** (2000) 8531–8539.
114. Y. Deligiannakis, A.W. Rutherford, Electron spin echo envelope modulation spectroscopy in Photosystem I. *Biochim. Biophys. Acta* **1507** (2001) 226–246.
115. K. Brettel, W. Leibl, U. Liebl, Electron transfer in the heliobacterial reaction center: evidence against a quinone-type electron acceptor functioning analogous to A_1 in Photosystem I. *Biochim. Biophys. Acta* **1363** (1998) 175–181.
116. N. Kusumoto, P. Sétif, K. Brettel, D. Seo, H. Sakurai, Electron transfer kinetics in purified reaction centers from the green sulfur bacterium *Chlorobium tepidum* studied by multiple-flash excitation. *Biochemistry* **38** (1999) 12124–12137.
117. J.H. Golbeck, K.G. Parrett, T. Mehari, K.L. Jones, J.J. Brand, Isolation of the intact Photosystem I reaction center core containing P700 and iron-sulfur center F_X. *FEBS Lett.* **228** (1988) 268–272.
118. P.V. Warren, K.G. Parrett, J.T. Warden, J.H. Golbeck, Characterization of a Photosystem I core containing P700 and intermediate electron acceptor A_1. *Biochemistry* **29** (1990) 6545–6550.
119. T. Fujii, E. Yokoyama, K. Inoue, H. Sakurai, The sites of electron donation of Photosystem I to methyl viologen. *Biochim. Biophys. Acta* **1015** (1990) 41–48.
120. P. Mathis, P. Sétif, Kinetic studies on the function of A_1 in the Photosystem I reaction center. *FEBS Lett.* **237** (1988) 65–68.
121. C.H. Bock, A.J. Van der Est, K. Brettel, D. Stehlik, Nanosecond electron transfer kinetics in Photosystem I as obtained from transient EPR at room temperature. *FEBS Lett.* **247** (1989) 91–96.
122. A. van der Est, C. Bock, J. Golbeck, K. Brettel, P. Sétif, D. Stehlik, Electron transfer from the acceptor A_1 to the iron-sulfur centers in Photosystem I as studied by transient EPR spectroscopy. *Biochemistry* **33** (1994) 11789–11797.
123. W. Leibl, B. Toupance, J. Breton, Photoelectric characterization of forward electron transfer to iron-sulfur centers in Photosystem I. *Biochemistry* **34** (1995) 10237–10244.
124. J. Lüneberg, P. Fromme, P. Jekow, E. Schlodder, Spectroscopic characterization of PS I core complexes from thermophilic *Synechococcus* sp. Identical reoxidation kinetics of A_1^- before and after removal of the iron-sulfur-clusters F_A and F_B. *FEBS Lett.* **338** (1994) 197–202.
125. P. Moenne-Loccoz, P. Heathcote, D.J. Maclachlan, M.C. Berry, I.H. Davis, M.C.W. Evans, Path of electron transfer in photosystem 1: Direct evidence of forward electron transfer from A_1 to Fe-S_X. *Biochemistry* **33** (1994) 10037–10042.
126. X.M. Gong, R. Agalarov, K. Brettel, C. Carmeli, Control of electron transport in Photosystem I by the iron-sulfur cluster F_X in response to intra- and intersubunit interactions. *J. Biol. Chem.* **278** (2003) 19141–19150.
127. P. Joliot, A. Joliot, In vivo analysis of the electron transfer within Photosystem I: are the two phylloquinones involved? *Biochemistry* **38** (1999) 11130–11136.
128. A. Diaz-Quintana, W. Leibl, H. Bottin, P. Sétif, Electron transfer in Photosystem I reaction centers follows a linear pathway in which iron-sulfur cluster F_B is the immediate electron donor to soluble ferredoxin. *Biochemistry* **37** (1998) 3429–3439.
129. J.R. Norris, R.A. Uphaus, H.L. Crespi, J.J. Katz, Electron spin resonance of chlorophyll and the origin of signal I in photosynthesis. *Proc. Natl. Acad. Sci. U.S.A.* **68** (1971) 625–628.

130. H. Schaffernicht, W. Junge, Analysis of the complex band spectrum of P700 based on photoselection studies with Photosystem I particles. *Photochem. Photobiol.* **34** (1981) 223–232.
131. K. Redding, F. MacMillan, W. Leibl, K. Brettel, J. Hanley, A.W. Rutherford, J. Breton, J.D. Rochaix, A systematic survey of conserved histidines in the core subunits of Photosystem I by site-directed mutagenesis reveals the likely axial ligands of P700. *EMBO J.* **17** (1998) 50–60.
132. A.N. Webber, H. Su, S.E. Bingham, H. Käss, L. Krabben, M. Kuhn, R. Jordan, E. Schlodder, W. Lubitz, Site-directed mutations affecting the spectroscopic characteristics and midpoint potential of the primary donor in Photosystem I. *Biochemistry* **35** (1996) 12857–12863.
133. A.N. Melkozernov, H. Su, S. Lin, S. Bingham, A.N. Webber, R.E. Blankenship, Specific mutation near the primary donor in Photosystem I from *Chlamydomonas reinhardtii* alters the trapping time and spectroscopic properties of P700. *Biochemistry* **36** (1997) 2898–2907.
134. J. Breton, E. Nabedryk, W. Leibl, FTIR study of the primary electron donor of Photosystem I (P700) revealing delocalization of the charge in P700$^+$ and localization of the triplet character in ^{3}P700. *Biochemistry* **38** (1999) 11585–11592.
135. G. Hastings, Time-resolved step-scan Fourier transform infrared and visible absorption difference spectroscopy for the study of Photosystem I. *Appl. Spectrosc.* **55** (2001) 894–900.
136. J. Breton, E. Nabedryk, W.W. Parson, A new infrared electronic transition of the oxidized primary electron donor in bacterial reaction centers: a way to assess resonance interactions between the bacteriochlorophylls. *Biochemistry* **31** (1992) 7503–7510.
137. S. Kim, B.A. Barry, Identification of carbonyl modes of P-700 and P-700$^+$ by in situ chlorophyll labeling in Photosystem I. *J. Am. Chem. Soc.* **122** (2000) 4980–4981.
138. H. Käss, P. Fromme, H.T. Witt, W. Lubitz, Orientation and electronic structure of the primary donor radical cation P-700$^+$ in Photosystem I: a single crystals EPR and ENDOR study. *J. Phys. Chem. B* **105** (2001) 1225–1239.
139. O.G. Poluektov, L.M. Utschig, S.L. Schlesselman, K.V. Lakshmi, G.W. Brudvig, G. Kothe, M.C. Thurnauer, Electronic structure of the P-700 special pair from high-frequency electron paramagnetic resonance spectroscopy. *J. Phys. Chem. B* **106** (2002) 8911–8916.
140. G. Hastings, V.M. Ramesh, R.L. Wang, V. Sivakumar, A. Webber, Primary donor photo-oxidation in Photosystem I: a re-evaluation of (P700$^+$-P700) Fourier transform infrared difference spectra. *Biochemistry* **40** (2001) 12943–12949.
141. R.L. Wang, V. Sivakumar, T.W. Johnson, G. Hastings, FTIR difference spectroscopy in combination with isotope labeling for identification of the carbonyl modes of P700 and P700$^+$ in Photosystem I. *Biophys. J.* **86** (2004) 1061–1073.
142. M. Pantelidou, P.R. Chitnis, J. Breton, FTIR spectroscopy of *Synechocystis* 6803 mutants affected on the hydrogen bonds to the carbonyl groups of the PsaA chlorophyll of P700 supports an extensive delocalization of the charge in P700. *Biochemistry* **43** (2004) 8380–8390.
143. J. Breton, W. Xu, B.A. Diner, P.R. Chitnis, The two histidine axial ligands of the primary electron donor chlorophylls (P700) in Photosystem I are similarly perturbed upon P700$^+$ formation. *Biochemistry* **41** (2002) 11200–11210.
144. H.A. Frank, M.B. McLean, K. Sauer, Triplet states in Photosystem I of spinach chloroplasts and subchloroplast particles. *Proc. Natl. Acad. Sci. U.S.A.* **76** (1979) 5124–5128.

145. A.W. Rutherford, P. Sétif, Orientation of P700, the primary electron donor of Photosystem I. *Biochim. Biophys. Acta* **1019** (1990) 128–132.
146. I. Sieckmann, K. Brettel, C. Bock, A. van der Est, D. Stehlik, Transient electron paramagnetic resonance of the triplet state of P700 in Photosystem I: evidence for triplet delocalization at room temperature. *Biochemistry* **32** (1993) 4842–4847.
147. Y.J. Li, M.G. Lucas, T. Konovalova, B. Abbott, F. MacMillan, A. Petrenko, V. Sivakumar, R.L. Wang, G. Hastings, F.F. Gu, J. van Tol, L.C. Brunel, R. Timkovich, F. Rappaport, K. Redding, Mutation of the putative hydrogen-bond donor to P-700 of Photosystem I. *Biochemistry* **43** (2004) 12634–12647.
148. X. Lin, H.A. Murchison, V. Nagarajan, W.W. Parson, J.P. Allen, J.C. Williams, Specific alteration of the oxidation potential of the electron donor in reaction centers from *Rhodobacter sphaeroides*. *Proc. Natl. Acad. Sci. U.S.A.* **91** (1994) 10265–10269.
149. R.L. Wang, V. Sivakumar, Y.J. Li, K. Redding, G. Hastings, Mutation induced modulation of hydrogen bonding to P700 studied using FTIR difference spectroscopy. *Biochemistry* **42** (2003) 9889–9897.
150. J. Breton, P.R. Chitnis, M. Pantelidou, Evidence for hydrogen bond formation to the PsaB chlorophyll of P700 in Photosystem I mutants of *Synechocystis* sp PCC 6803. *Biochemistry* **44** (2005) 5402–5408.
151. O. Klukas, W.D. Schubert, P. Jordan, N. Krauss, P. Fromme, H.T. Witt, W. Saenger, Localization of two phylloquinones, Q_K and Q_K', in an improved electron density map of Photosystem I at 4-Å resolution. *J. Biol. Chem.* **274** (1999) 7361–7367.
152. I.P. Muhiuddin, P. Heathcote, S. Carter, S. Purton, S.E.J. Rigby, M.C.W. Evans, Evidence from time resolved studies of the $P700^+/A_1^-$ radical pair for photosynthetic electron transfer on both the PsaA and PsaB branches of the Photosystem I reaction center. *FEBS Lett.* **503** (2001) 56–60.
153. O.G. Poluektov, S.V. Paschenko, L.M. Utschig, K.V. Lakshmi, M.C. Thurnauer, Bidirectional electron transfer in Photosystem I: direct evidence from high-frequency time-resolved EPR spectroscopy. *J. Am. Chem. Soc.* **127** (2005) 11910–11911.
154. S. Santabarbara, I. Kuprov, W.V. Fairclough, S. Purton, P.J. Hore, P. Heathcote, M.C.W. Evans, Bidirectional electron transfer in Photosystem I: Determination of two distances between $P-700^+$ and A_1^- in spin correlated radical pairs. *Biochemistry* **44** (2005) 2119–2128.
155. A. van der Est, A.I. Valieva, Y.E. Kandrashkin, G.Z. Shen, D.A. Bryant, J.H. Golbeck, Removal of PsaF alters forward electron transfer in Photosystem I: evidence for fast reoxidation of Q_K-A in subunit deletion mutants of *Synechococcus* sp PCC 7002. *Biochemistry* **43** (2004) 1264–1275.
156. B. Boudreaux, F. MacMillan, C. Teutloff, R. Agalarov, F.F. Gu, S. Grimaldi, R. Bittl, K. Brettel, K. Redding, Mutations in both sides of the Photosystem I reaction center identify the phylloquinone observed by electron paramagnetic resonance spectroscopy. *J. Biol. Chem.* **276** (2001) 37299–37306.
157. S. Purton, D.R. Stevens, I.P. Muhiuddin, M.C.W. Evans, S. Carter, S.E.J. Rigby, P. Heathcote, Site-directed mutagenesis of PsaA residue W693 affects phylloquinone binding and function in the Photosystem I reaction center of *Chlamydomonas reinhardtii*. *Biochemistry* **40** (2001) 2167–2175.
158. W. Xu, P. Chitnis, A. Valieva, A. van der Est, Y.N. Pushkar, M. Krzystyniak, C. Teutloff, S.G. Zech, R. Bittl, D. Stehlik, B. Zybailov, G.Z. Shen, J.H. Golbeck, Electron transfer in cyanobacterial Photosystem I-I. Physiological and

spectroscopic characterization of site-directed mutants in a putative electron transfer pathway from A_0 through A_1 to F_X. *J. Biol. Chem.* **278** (2003) 27864–27875.
159. W. Xu, P.R. Chitnis, A. Valieva, A. van der Est, K. Brettel, M. Guergova-Kuras, Y.N. Pushkar, S.G. Zech, D. Stehlik, G.Z. Shen, B. Zybailov, J.H. Golbeck, Electron transfer in cyanobacterial Photosystem I-II. Determination of forward electron transfer rates of site-directed mutants in a putative electron transfer pathway from A_0 through A_1 to F_X. *J. Biol. Chem.* **278** (2003) 27876–27887.
160. R. Cammack, K.K. Rao, C.P. Bargeron, K.G. Hutson, P.W. Andrew, L.J. Rogers, Midpoint redox potentials of plant and algal ferredoxins. *Biochem. J.* **168** (1977) 205–209.
161. A. Fish, T. Danieli, I. Ohad, R. Nechushtai, O. Livnah, Structural basis for the thermostability of ferredoxin from the cyanobacterium *Mastigocladus laminosus*. *J. Mol. Biol.* **350** (2005) 599–608.
162. I. Bertini, C. Luchinat, A. Provenzani, A. Rosato, P.R. Vasos, Browsing gene banks for Fe_2S_2 ferredoxins and structural modeling of 88 plant-type sequences: An analysis of fold and function. *Proteins: Struct. Funct. Genet.* **46** (2002) 110–127.
163. K. Fukuyama, Structure and function of plant-type ferredoxins. *Photosynth. Res.* **81** (2004) 289–301.
164. H. Böhme, B. Schrautemeier, Comparative characterization of ferredoxins from heterocysts and vegetative cells of *Anabaena variabilis*. *Biochim. Biophys. Acta* **891** (1987) 1–7.
165. G.T. Hanke, Y. Kimata-Ariga, I. Taniguchi, T. Hase, A post genomic characterization of *ArabidoPSIs* ferredoxins. *Plant Physiol.* **134** (2004) 255–264.
166. D.B. Knaff, Ferredoxin and ferredoxin-dependent enzymes, in: *Oxygenic Photosynthesis: The Light Reactions* (1996) (D.R. Ort, C. Yocum, eds), Kluwer Academic Publishers, Dordrecht, pp. 333–361.
167. N. Cassan, B. Lagoutte, P. Sétif, Ferredoxin-$NADP^+$ reductase: kinetics of electron transfer, transient intermediates, and catalytic activities studied by flash-absorption spectroscopy with isolated Photosystem I and ferredoxin. *J. Biol. Chem.* **280** (2005) 25960–25972.
168. F. Seeber, A. Aliverti, G. Zanetti, The plant-type ferredoxin-$NADP^+$ reductase/ferrodoxin redox system as a possible drug target against apicomplexan human parasites. *Curr. Pharmaceut. Design* **11** (2005) 3159–3172.
169. L.J. Rogers, Ferredoxins, flavodoxins and related proteins: structure, function and evolution, in: *The Cyanobacteria* (1987) (P. Fay, C. Van Baalen, eds), Elsevier, Amsterdam, pp. 35–67.
170. N.A. Straus, Iron deprivation: physiology and gene regulation, in: *The Molecular Biology of Cyanobacteria* (1994) (D.A. Bryant, ed.), Kluwer Academic Publishers, Dordrecht, pp. 731–750.
171. M. Poncelet, C. Cassier-Chauvat, X. Leschelle, H. Bottin, F. Chauvat, Targeted deletion and mutational analysis of the essential (2Fe-2S) plant-like ferredoxin in *Synechocystis* PCC 6803 by plasmid shuffling. *Mol. Microbiol.* **28** (1998) 813–821.
172. S. Sandström, A.G. Ivanov, Y.I. Park, G. Oquist, P. Gustafsson, Iron stress responses in the cyanobacterium *Synechococcus* sp PCC7942. *Physiol. Plant.* **116** (2002) 255–263.
173. M. Hagemann, R. Jeanjean, S. Fulda, M. Havaux, F. Joset, N. Erdmann, Flavodoxin accumulation contributes to enhanced cyclic electron flow around Photosystem I in salt-stressed cells of *Synechocystis* sp strain PCC 6803. *Physiol. Plant.* **105** (1999) 670–678.

174. R. Jeanjean, E. Zuther, N. Yeremenko, M. Havaux, H.C.P. Matthijs, M. Hagemann, A photosystem 1 psaFJ-null mutant of the cyanobacterium *Synechocystis* PCC 6803 expresses the isiAB operon under iron replete conditions. *FEBS Lett.* **549** (2003) 52–56.
175. M. Havaux, G. Guedeney, M. Hagemann, N. Yeremenko, H.C.P. Matthijs, R. Jeanjean, The chlorophyll-binding protein IsiA is inducible by high light and protects the cyanobacterium *Synechocystis* PCC6803 from photooxidative stress. *FEBS Lett.* **579** (2005) 2289–2293.
176. A. Latifi, R. Jeanjean, S. Lemeille, M. Havaux, C.C. Zhang, Iron starvation leads to oxidative stress in *Anabaena* sp strain PCC 7120. *J. Bacteriol.* **187** (2005) 6596–6598.
177. C. Lelong, E.J. Boekema, J. Kruip, H. Bottin, M. Rögner, P. Sétif, Characterization of a redox active crosslinked complex between cyanobacterial Photosystem I and soluble ferredoxin. *EMBO J.* **15** (1996) 2160–2168.
178. U. Mühlenhoff, J. Kruip, D.A. Bryant, M. Rögner, P. Sétif, E. Boekema, Characterization of a redox-active cross-linked complex between cyanobacterial Photosystem I and its physiological acceptor flavodoxin. *EMBO J.* **15** (1996) 488–497.
179. P. Fromme, W.D. Schubert, N. Krauss, Structure of Photosystem I: Suggestions on the docking sites for plastocyanin and ferredoxin, and the coordination of P700. *Biochim. Biophys. Acta* **1187** (1994) 99–105.
180. P. Sétif, N. Fischer, B. Lagoutte, H. Bottin, J.D. Rochaix, The ferredoxin docking site of Photosystem I. *Biochim. Biophys. Acta* **1555** (2002) 204–209.
181. P. Sétif, Electron transfer from the bound iron-sulfur clusters to ferredoxin/flavodoxin: kinetic and structural properties of ferredoxin/flavodoxin reduction by Photosystem I, in: *Photosystem I: The Plastocyanin:Ferredoxin Oxidoreductase in Photosynthesis* (2006) (J.H. Golbeck, ed.), Kluwer Academic Publishers, Dordrecht.
182. P. Fromme, H. Bottin, N. Krauss, P. Sétif, Crystallization and electron paramagnetic resonance characterization of the complex of Photosystem I with its natural electron acceptor ferredoxin. *Biophys. J.* **83** (2002) 1760–1773.
183. N. Fischer, M. Hippler, P. Sétif, J.-P. Jacquot, J.-D. Rochaix, The PsaC subunit of Photosystem I provides an essential lysine residue for fast electron transfer to ferredoxin. *EMBO J.* **17** (1998) 849–858.
184. P. Sétif, H. Bottin, Laser flash absorption spectroscopy study of ferredoxin reduction by Photosystem I: spectral and kinetic evidence for the existence of several Photosystem I-ferredoxin complexes. *Biochemistry* **34** (1995) 9059–9070.
185. P. Sétif, H. Bottin, Laser flash absorption spectroscopy study of ferredoxin reduction by Photosystem I in *Synechocystis* sp. PCC 6803: Evidence for submicrosecond and microsecond kinetics. *Biochemistry* **33** (1994) 8495–8504.
186. R. Morales, M.H. Charon, G. Hudry-Clergeon, Y. Pétillot, S. Norager, M. Medina, M. Frey, Refined X-ray structures of the oxidized, at 1.3 Å, and reduced, at 1.17 Å, [2Fe-2S] ferredoxin from the cyanobacterium *Anabaena* PCC7119 show redox-linked conformational changes. *Biochemistry* **38** (1999) 15764–15773.
187. G.A. Sykes, L.J. Redox, potentials of algal and cyanobacterial flavodoxins, *Biochem. J.* **217** (1984) 845–850.
188. J.L. Casaus, J.A. Navarro, M. Hervas, A. Lostao, M.A. De la Rosa, C. Gomez-Moreno, J. Sancho, A. Medina, *Anabaena* sp. PCC 7119 flavodoxin as electron carrier from Photosystem I to ferredoxin-$NADP^+$ reductase-role of TRP^{57} and TYR^{94}. *J. Biol. Chem.* **277** (2002) 22338–22344.
189. U. Mühlenhoff, P. Sétif, Laser flash absorption spectroscopy study of flavodoxin reduction by Photosystem I in *Synechococcus* sp. PCC 7002. *Biochemistry* **35** (1996) 1367–1374.

190. K. Meimberg, B. Lagoutte, H. Bottin, U. Mühlenhoff, The PsaE subunit is required for complex formation between Photosystem I and flavodoxin from the cyanobacterium *Synechocystis* sp. PCC 6803. *Biochemistry* **37** (1998) 9759–9767.
191. J.K. Hurley, R. Morales, M. Martinez-Julvez, T.B. Brodie, M. Medina, C. Gomez-Moreno, G. Tollin, Structure-function relationships in *Anabaena* ferredoxin/ferredoxin: $NADP^+$ reductase electron transfer: insights from site-directed mutagenesis, transient absorption spectroscopy and X-ray crystallography. *Biochim. Biophys. Acta* **1554** (2002) 5–21.
192. N. Carrillo, E.A. Ceccarelli, Open questions in ferredoxin-$NADP^+$ reductase catalytic mechanism. *Eur. J. Biochem.* **270** (2003) 1900–1915.
193. M. Medina, C. Gomez-Moreno, Interaction of ferredoxin-$NADP^+$ reductase with its substrates: optimal interaction for efficient electron transfer. *Photosynth. Res.* **79** (2004) 113–131.
194. M. Shin, How is ferredoxin-NADP reductase involved in the NADP photoreduction of chloroplasts? *Photosynth. Res.* **80** (2004) 307–313.
195. P.A. Karplus, H.R. Faber, Structural aspects of plant ferredoxin: $NADP^+$ oxidoreductases. *Photosynth. Res.* **81** (2004) 303–315.
196. R. Morales, M.H. Charon, G. Kachalova, L. Serre, M. Medina, C. Gomez-Moreno, M. Frey, A redox-dependent interaction between two electron-transfer partners involved in photosynthesis. *EMBO Rep.* **1** (2000) 271–276.
197. G. Kurisu, M. Kusunoki, E. Katoh, T. Yamazaki, K. Teshima, Y. Onda, Y. Kimata-Ariga, T. Hase, Structure of the electron transfer complex between ferredoxin and ferredoxin-$NADP^+$ reductase. *Nat. Struct. Biol.* **8** (2001) 117–121.
198. G.T. Hanke, G. Kurisu, M. Kusunoki, T. Hase, Fd:FNR electron transfer complexes: evolutionary refinement of structural interactions. *Photosynth. Res.* **81** (2004) 317–327.
199. M. Maeda, Y.H. Lee, T. Ikegami, K. Tamura, M. Hoshino, T. Yamazaki, M. Nakayama, T. Hase, Y. Goto, Identification of the N- and C-terminal substrate binding segments of ferredoxin-$NADP^+$ reductase by NMR. *Biochemistry* **44** (2005) 10644–10653.
200. P.N. Palma, B. Lagoutte, L. Krippahl, J.J.G. Moura, F. Guerlesquin, *Synechocystis* ferredoxin/ferredoxin-$NADP^+$-reductase/$NADP^+$ complex: structural model obtained by NMR-restrained docking. *FEBS Lett.* **579** (2005) 4585–4590.
201. T. Mayoral, M. Martinez-Julvez, I. Perez-Dorado, J. Sanz-Aparicio, C. Gomez-Moreno, M. Medina, J.A. Hermoso, Structural analysis of interactions for complex formation between ferredoxin-$NADP^+$ reductase and its protein partners. *Proteins: Struct. Funct. Bioinf.* **59** (2005) 592–602.
202. P. Decottignies, V. Flesch, C. Gerard-Hirne, P. Le Maréchal, Role of positively charged residues in *Chlamydomonas reinhardtii* ferredoxin-$NADP^+$-reductase. *Plant Physiol. Biochem.* **41** (2003) 637–642.
203. N. Carrillo, R.H. Vallejos, Ferredoxin-$NADP^+$ oxidoreductase, in: *The Light Reactions* (1987) (J. Barber, ed.), pp. 527–560.
204. K.H. Süss, I. Prokhorenko, K. Adler, In situ association of Calvin cycle enzymes, ribulose-1,5-bisphosphate carboxylase/oxygenase activase, ferredoxin-$NADP^+$ reductase, and nitrite reductase with thylakoid and pyrenoid membranes of *Chlamydomonas reinhardtii* chloroplasts as revealed by immunoelectron microscopy. *Plant Physiol.* **107** (1995) 1387–1397.
205. M. Küchler, S. Decker, F. Hormann, J. Soll, L. Heins, Protein import into chloroplasts involves redox-regulated proteins. *EMBO J.* **21** (2002) 6136–6145.

206. G.T. Hanke, S. Okutani, Y. Satomi, T. Takao, A. Suzuki, T. Hase, Multiple isoproteins of FNR in *ArabidoPS Is*: evidence for different contributions to chloroplast function and nitrogen assimilation. *Plant Cell Environ.* **28** (2005) 1146–1157.
207. J.F. Palatnik, E.M. Valle, N. Carrillo, Oxidative stress causes ferredoxin-NADP$^+$ reductase solubilization from the thylakoid membranes in methyl viologen-treated plants. *Plant Physiol.* **115** (1997) 1721–1727.
208. F.C. Soncini, R.H. Vallejos, The chloroplast reductase-binding protein is identical to the 16.5-kDa polypeptide described as a component of the oxygen-evolving complex. *J. Biol. Chem.* **264** (1989) 21112–21115.
209. C.M. Bruns, P.A. Karplus, Refined crystal structure of spinach ferredoxin reductase at 1.7 Å resolution: oxidized, reduced and 2′-phospho-5′-AMP bound states. *J. Mol. Biol.* **247** (1995) 125–145.
210. G. Guedeney, S. Corneille, S. Cuine, G. Peltier, Evidence for an association of ndh B, ndh J gene products and ferredoxin-NADP-reductase as components of a chloroplastic NAD(P)H dehydrogenase complex. *FEBS Lett.* **378** (1996) 277–280.
211. D. Rumeau, N. Becuwe-Linka, A. Beyly, M. Louwagie, J. Garin, G. Peltier, New subunits NDH-M, -N, and –O, encoded by nuclear genes, are essential for plastid Ndh complex functioning in higher plants. *Plant Cell* **17** (2005) 219–232.
212. B. Andersen, H.V. Scheller, B.L. Moeller, The PS I-E subunit of Photosystem I binds ferredoxin:NADP$^+$ oxidoreductase. *FEBS Lett.* **311** (1992) 169–173.
213. H.M. Zhang, J.P. Whitelegge, W.A. Cramer, Ferredoxin:NADP$^+$ oxidoreductase is a subunit of the chloroplast cytochrome b$_6$f complex. *J. Biol. Chem.* **276** (2001) 38159–38165.
214. R. Wagner, N. Carrillo, W. Junge, R.H. Vallejos, On the conformation of reconstituted ferredoxin-NADP$^+$ oxidoreductase in the thylakoid membrane. Studies via triplet lifetime and rotational diffusion with eosine isothiocyanate as label. *Biochim. Biophys. Acta* **680** (1982) 317–330.
215. W.M. Schluchter, D.A. Bryant, Molecular characterization of ferredoxin-NADP$^+$ oxidoreductase in cyanobacteria: cloning and sequence of the petH gene of *Synechococcus* sp. PCC 7002 and studies on the gene product. *Biochemistry* **31** (1992) 3092–3102.
216. J.J. van Thor, O.W.M. Gruters, H.C.P. Matthijs, K.J. Hellingwerf, Localization and function of ferredoxin:NADP$^+$ reductase bound to the phycobilisomes of *Synechocystis*. *EMBO J.* **18** (1999) 4128–4136.
217. C. Gomez-Lojero, B. Perez-Gomez, G.Z. Shen, W.M. Schluchter, D.A. Bryant, Interaction of ferredoxin:NADP$^+$ oxidoreductase with phycobilisomes and phycobilisome substructures of the cyanobacterium *Synechococcus* sp strain PCC 7002. *Biochemistry* **42** (2003) 13800–13811.
218. M. Nakajima, T. Sakamoto, K. Wada, The complete purification and characterization of three forms of ferredoxin-NADP$^+$ oxidoreductase from a thermophilic cyanobacterium *Synechococcus elongatus*. *Plant Cell Physiol.* **43** (2002) 484–493.
219. J.J. van Thor, R. Jeanjean, M. Havaux, K.A. Sjollema, F. Joset, K.J. Hellingwerf, H.C.P. Matthijs, Salt shock-inducible Photosystem I cyclic electron transfer in *Synechocystis* PCC6803 relies on binding of ferredoxin:NADP$^+$ reductase to the thylakoid membranes via its CpcD phycobilisome-linker homologous N-terminal domain. *Biochim. Biophys. Acta* **1457** (2000) 129–144.
220. H.C.P. Matthijs, R. Jeanjean, N. Yeremenko, J. Huisman, F. Joset, K.J. Hellingwerf, Hypothesis: versatile function of ferredoxin-NADP$^+$ reductase in cyanobacteria provides regulation for transient Photosystem I-driven cyclic electron flow. *Funct. Plant Biol.* **29** (2002) 201–210.

221. M. Ohtsuka, J. Oyabu, Y. Kashino, K. Satoh, H. Koike, Inactivation of ycf33 results in an altered cyclic electron transport pathway around Photosystem I in *Synechocystis* sp PCC6803. *Plant Cell Physiol.* **45** (2004) 1243–1251.
222. J.J. van Thor, T.H. Geerlings, H.C.P. Matthijs, K.J. Hellingwerf, Kinetic evidence for the PsaE-dependent transient ternary complex Photosystem I/ferredoxin/ferredoxin:NADP$^+$ reductase in a cyanobacterium. *Biochemistry* **38** (1999) 12735–12746.
223. M.C. Walker, J.J. Pueyo, C. Gomez-Moreno, G. Tollin, Comparison of the kinetics of reduction and intramolecular electron transfer in electrostatic and covalent complexes of ferredoxin-NADP$^+$ reductase and flavodoxin from *Anabaena* PCC 7119. *Arch. Biochem. Biophys.* **281** (1990) 76–83.
224. M. Medina, C. Gomez-Moreno, G. Tollin, Effects of chemical modification of *Anabaena* flavodoxin and ferredoxin-NADP$^+$ reductase on the kinetics of interprotein electron transfer reactions. *Eur. J. Biochem.* **210** (1992) 577–583.
225. I. Nogues, J. Tejero, J.K. Hurley, D. Paladini, S. Frago, G. Tollin, S.G. Mayhew, C. Gomez-Moreno, E.A. Ceccarelli, N. Carrillo, M. Medina, Role of the C-terminal tyrosine of ferredoxin-nicotinamide adenine dinucleotide phosphate reductase in the electron transfer processes with its protein partners ferredoxin and flavodoxin. *Biochemistry* **43** (2004) 6127–6137.
226. A.K. Bhattacharyya, T.E. Meyer, G. Tollin, Reduction kinetics of the ferredoxin-ferredoxin-NADP$^+$ reductase complex: a laser flash photolysis study. *Biochemistry* **25** (1986) 4655–4661.
227. M.C. Walker, J.J. Pueyo, J.A. Navarro, C. Gomez-Moreno, G. Tollin, Laser flash photolysis studies of the kinetics of reduction of ferredoxins and ferredoxin-NADP$^+$ reductases from *Anabaena* PCC 7119 and spinach: electrostatic effects on intracomplex electron transfer. *Arch. Biochem. Biophys.* **287** (1991) 351–358.
228. J.K. Hurley, Z. Salamon, T.E. Meyer, J.C. Fitch, M.A. Cusanovich, J.L. Markley, H. Cheng, B. Xia, Y.K. Chae, Amino acid residues in *Anabaena* ferredoxin crucial to interaction with ferredoxin-NADP$^+$ reductase: Site-directed mutagenesis and laser flash photolysis. *Biochemistry* **32** (1993) 9346–9354.
229. J.K. Hurley, M.F. Fillat, C. Gomez-Moreno, G. Tollin, Electrostatic and hydrophobic interactions during complex formation and electron transfer in the ferredoxin/ferredoxin:NADP$^+$ reductase system from *Anabaena*. *J. Am. Chem. Soc.* **118** (1996) 5526–5531.
230. J.K. Hurley, H. Cheng, B. Xia, J.L. Markley, M. Medina, C. Gomez-Moreno, G. Tollin, An aromatic amino acid is required at position 65 in *Anabaena* ferredoxin for rapid electron transfer to ferredoxin:NADP$^+$ reductase. *J. Am. Chem. Soc.* **115** (1993) 11698–11701.
231. J.K. Hurley, A.M. WeberMain, M.T. Stankovich, M.M. Benning, J.B. Thoden, J.L. Vanhooke, H.M. Holden, Y.K. Chae, B. Xia, H. Cheng, J.L. Markley, M. Martinez-Julvez, C. Gomez-Moreno, J.L. Schmeits, G. Tollin, Structure-function relationships in *Anabaena* ferredoxin: correlations between X-ray crystal structures, reduction potentials, and rate constants of electron transfer to ferredoxin:NADP$^+$ reductase for site-specific ferredoxin mutants. *Biochemistry* **36** (1997) 11100–11117.
232. N. Ginet, J. Lavergne, Interactions between the donor and acceptor sides in bacterial reaction centers. *Biochemistry* **39** (2000) 16252–16262.
233. S.E.J. Rigby, I.P. Muhiuddin, M.C.W. Evans, S. Purton, P. Heathcote, Photoaccumulation of the PsaB phyllosemiquinone in Photosystem I of *Chlamydomonas reinhardtii*. *Biochim. Biophys. Acta* **1556** (2002) 13–20.
234. N. Ivashin, S. Larsson, Electron transfer pathways in Photosystem I reaction centers. *Chem. Phys. Lett.* **375** (2003) 383–387.

Chapter 15

From Cell Growth to the 3.0 Å Resolution Crystal Structure of Cyanobacterial Photosystem II

Athina Zouni

Table of Contents

15.1	Introduction	195
15.2	Arrangement of PS II in the Thylakoid Membrane of Cyanobacteria and Plants	196
15.3	Subunit Composition of PS IIcc	198
15.4	General View of Oxygen Evolving PS IIcc Crystals	200
15.5	Characterization of the Aggregation State of PS IIcc	200
	15.5.1 Gel Permeation Chromatography (GPC)	202
	15.5.2 Dynamic Light Scattering (DLS)	202
	15.5.2.1 A Critical Point of View	203
	15.5.3 Analytical Ultracentrifugation (AUC)	203
15.6	Growing PS IIcc Crystals	204
	15.6.1 Cofactors, Polypeptide Composition and Lipid Content of PS IIcc	204
15.7	Progress in Structure Analysis of PS IIcc	209
	15.7.1 Problems in the Interpretation of Electron Density Maps from *T. elongatus* and *T. vulcanus* PS IIcc at Moderate Resolution	211
15.8	Structure at 3.0 Å Resolution of PS IIcc from *T. elongatus*	212
	15.8.1 Symmetry and Arrangement of Transmembrane α-Helices	213
	15.8.2 Chlorophyll Arrangement in the Proteins CP43 and CP47	213
	15.8.3 Integral Lipids	215
	15.8.4 Electron Acceptor Side and Q_B Diffusion Pathway	218
	15.8.5 Carotenoids	220
	15.8.6 Chlorophyll *a* and Pheophytin *a* in the Electron Transfer Chain (ETC)	222

15.9	General View of the Water Oxidizing Complex (WOC)........ 223
	15.9.1 Environment of the Mn_4O_xCa Cluster 224

15.10 Conclusion and Perspectives 227
Acknowledgements 228
References 229

STRUCTURE OF CYANOBACTERIAL PHOTOSYSTEM II

Abstract

This chapter describes the structure of PS II that was obtained on the basis of an improved protocol for the preparation, purification and crystallization of the dimeric Photosystem II core complex (PS IIcc) from *Thermosynechococcus elongatus* (*T. elongatus*). The individual components of this PS IIcc were biochemically characterized and the aggregation behavior of dimeric PS IIcc, which is crucial for the design of crystallization experiments, was studied using dynamic light scattering, analytical ultracentrifugation and gel permeation chromatography. The new protocols for PS IIcc purification and crystallization are prerequisites for a significantly improved resolution of the crystal structure to 3.0 Å. Critical aspects for the interpretation of the electron density map of PS IIcc at medium resolution (3.8–3.2 Å) are pointed out. The 3.0 Å resolution structure of Photosystem II is an important step towards detailed information on cofactor arrangement. These findings offer a basis for a deeper mechanistic understanding of electron and energy transfer. Likewise, the new assignment of eleven β-carotenes is important for considerations on photoprotection. Fourteen integrally bound lipids were resolved for the first time and their structural and functional importance for flexibility and assembly of PS IIcc are discussed. Of special interest is the discovery of a lipophilic diffusion pathway for plastoquinone Q_B. Limitations of our current structure information are outlined, especially with respect to the nature of the manganese cluster of the water oxidizing complex.

15.1 Introduction

The reactions of direct light transformation into electrochemical Gibbs energy via oxygenic photosynthesis take place in two large multimeric protein–pigment complexes, denoted Photosystem I (PS I) and Photosystem II (PS II), that are anisotropically embedded in the photosynthetic thylakoid membrane of cyanobacteria, green algae and plants. Both photosystems act in series, coupled by a pool of plastoquinone, the cytochrome b_6f complex and the soluble electron carrier plastocyanin or cytochrome c_6, as outlined in Chapter 1. In marked contrast to the close similarity of Photosystem I and II among all oxygen evolving organisms, the antenna system markedly differ between cyanobacteria and plants (Chapters 6–8).

The reaction pattern of these units consists of three different types of reaction sequences: (i) light-induced formation of a "stable" radical ion pair $P_{RC}^{+\cdot}$ $A_{CC}^{-\cdot}$ (stab) where P_{RC} is the photoactive pigment and A_{CC} (stab) the electron acceptor that stabilizes the charge separation; (ii) oxidation reactions with $P_{RC}^{+\cdot}$ as driving force; and (iii) reduction processes with $A_{CC}^{-\cdot}$(stab) as ultimate electron donor. The functional and structural organization of these processes exhibits striking similarities among all photosynthetic organisms, but there is one fundamental difference in PS II, i.e., the capability of oxidative water splitting. This function is of paramount importance for the bioenergetics of living matter and the cornerstone in evolution of all higher forms of life (Chapters 1, 19, 22). Therefore, the structure and function of PS II are of great scientific interest and the subject of world-wide research activities.

Understanding this process requires information on both the structure of the apparatus at atomic resolution and the mechanics of the reactions that lead to oxidative water cleavage by visible light. Our current state of knowledge on the latter is described in Chapters 16 and 17. This chapter presents the state of the art on the PS II structure. Studies on the structure go back to early electron microscopic investigations that led to the discovery of thylakoids [1]. Further advancement of EM techniques revealed the particle structure of different membrane surfaces [2]. Based on functional investigations, PS I and PS II were shown to be anisotropically incorporated into the thylakoid membrane (for a review, see [3] and reference therein)). It was concluded that the photoactive pigment P680 of PS II is located near to lumenal side and the acceptor Q_A on the stroma side of thylakoids in chloroplasts. The possible role of proteins as matrix was analyzed, by using the proteolytic enzyme trypsin, and a preliminary model was proposed for the arrangement of the cofactors [4]. Progress in preparative methodology led to isolation of the PS II core [5–7] and D1/D2/cyt*b*-559 complexes [8]. These achievements were the prerequisite for advanced studies on the structure of PS II by image analyses of EM micrographs [6,9]. As a result, the overall shape of PS II core complexes was resolved and, in particular, a crude picture obtained on the extrusion due to the extrinsic PsbO protein [6]. More structural details could be gathered from using the method of electron diffraction on two-dimensional crystal lattices of D1/D2/CP47/cyt*b*-559 preparation (Section 15.7).

However, all these results were far from offering a structure of the PS II complex that enabled the resolution of the arrangement of the cofactors and the protein matrix with sufficient detail. A breakthrough in structural studies on integral membrane proteins of the photosynthetic apparatus was the crystallization and X-ray structure analyses of isolated reaction centers from the anoxygenic bacterium *Rhodopseudomonas* (now *Blastochloris*) *viridis* by Michel, Deisenhofer and Huber [10,11]. This finding paved the way for corresponding studies on PS I (Chapter 13) and PS II. An essential obstacle was the lack of crystals of sufficient quality for X-ray diffraction patterns. In long-lasting work at the Max-Volmer Institut (now in the Institute for Chemistry/Max Volmer Laboratory for Biophysical Chemistry) of the TU Berlin the thermophilic cyanobacterium *T. elongatus* was found to provide a most suitable material for crystallization of both PS I [12] and PS II [13]. The present chapter describes the progress made in the preparation, characterization and crystallization of PS II core complexes from *T. elongatus* and also presents the most advanced structure.

15.2 Arrangement of PS II in the Thylakoid Membrane of Cyanobacteria and Plants

The thylakoid bilayer membrane consists of four main lipids: digalactosyldiacylglycerol (DGDG), sulfoquinoldiacylglycerol (SQDG), monogalactosyldiacylglycerol (MGDG) and phosphatidylglycerol (PG), which make up about 50% of the thylakoid mass. The other 50% is due to membrane-intrinsic protein complexes. The thylakoid membrane forms a continuous, spatially closed membrane system separating the lumenal (inner) space from the stromal (cytoplasmic) space (Figure 1a).

In higher plants, the photosynthetic process occurs inside specialized organelles, the chloroplasts. The number of chloroplasts per cell varies from 1 to over 100, depending upon the particular plant and on growth conditions (Chapter 1). Internally, the chloroplast contains a system of lamellae or flattened thylakoids that are arranged in stacks in dense green regions known as grana that are interconnected by a system of loosely arranged membranes called the stroma lamellae (see Figure 9, in Chapter 1) (Figure 1b). Each lamella in the chloroplast contains two double-layer membranes, each 5–7 nm thick. The thylakoids are embedded in a colorless matrix called stroma, and the whole chloroplast is surrounded by a bounding bilayer membrane, the chloroplast envelope. The thylakoid membranes of plants contain the light-harvesting complex of Photosystem II (LHCII) that collects solar energy and transmits it to the core complex. LHCII is a trimeric protein largely responsible for the organization of the photosynthetic system by maintaining the tight appression of the thylakoid membranes in chloroplast grana [14]. At 2.5 Å resolution the structure of trimeric LHCII from pea reveals surface charges that probably contribute to the stacking of membranes into grana. This arrangement ensures that the PS II reaction centre is surrounded on all sides by antenna pigments [15].

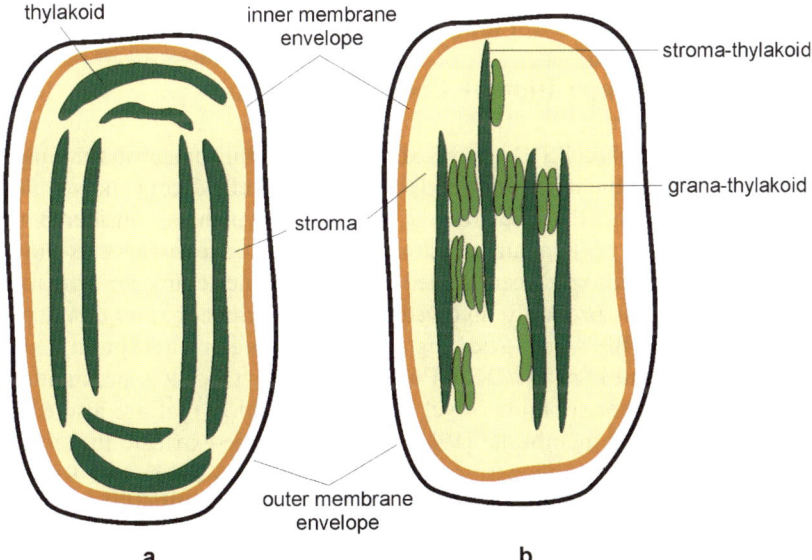

Figure 1. Photosynthetic membrane of (a) cyanobacteria and (b) chloroplasts from higher plants [122]: Outer membrane envelope (black), inner membrane envelope (orange), stroma/cytoplasm (yellow) and thylakoid (green).

The organization of PS I and PS II is different in the stacked grana membrane regions from that in the unstacked stroma lamellae [2,16]. This is explained by the predominance of dimeric Photosystem II in stacked grana while monomeric PS II as well as PS I are located in the stroma lamellae. The space enclosed by the thylakoid bilayer membrane, the intrathylakoid region, is termed the lumen. The lumenal space is about 5–10 nm wide; its full composition is not yet known. During photosynthetic electron transport, protons are transferred from the stroma to the lumenal space through the thylakoid membrane and drive ATP synthase that produces ATP from ADP and inorganic phosphate (Chapter 21).

In PS I and PS II embedded into the lamellae the conversion of light energy take place thus providing the driving force of the associated electron and proton transport reactions of photosynthesis. The stroma (cytosol) contains many soluble proteins, including the enzymes of the Calvin cycle that carry out the dark reactions leading to reduction of CO_2 to carbohydrates.

The overall architecture of the cyanobacterial thylakoid system differs from that of higher plants (Figure 1a). Instead of LHCII, soluble pigment–protein complexes, the phycobilisomes, are the major light-harvesting system. Since the large phycobilisomes are membrane-extrinsic and attached at the stromal surface of PS II, stacking of thylakoids is sterically hindered and not possible (Figure 1a). The photosynthetic material present in the cyanobacteria consists of parallel layers of lamellar thylakoid membranes that traverse the cytoplasm and harbor all the photosynthetic players: PS I, PS II, cytochrome b_6f complex (cyt b_6f), ATP synthase.

15.3 Subunit Composition of PS IIcc

During preparation of PS II complexes, the phycobilisomes of the antenna system are lost and the remaining PS II core complex (PS IIcc) is fully active in all respects [13]. The PS IIcc from *T. elongatus*, which is considered here, contains at least 19 protein subunits, of which 16 that are intrinsic as they are embedded in the thylakoid membrane. The heterodimeric protein cytochrome (cyt) *b-559* [17,18] is probably involved in electron transfer reactions that are switched on when the water oxidizing complex is defective ([18] and Chapter 16). The core assembly of D1/D2, CP43, CP47 and cyt *b-559* is surrounded by at least eleven smaller subunits of yet unknown function that are also embedded in the thylakoid membrane [19]. Three membrane-extrinsic proteins, cyt *c-550* (PsbV), PsbO (manganese stabilizing protein, 33 kDa) and PsbU (12 kDa), are associated at the lumenal side of the core assembly in cyanobacteria (for a review see [20]), and the corresponding membrane-extrinsic in higher plants are the proteins PsbO (33 kDa), PsbP (23 kDa) and PsbQ (16 kDa) are [21]. There are several other subunits in plants but not in cyanobacteria (PsbR, S, T_N, W) (see [19] for a review). A more detailed description of the subunits of PS II is given in Section 15.6.1.

STRUCTURE OF CYANOBACTERIAL PHOTOSYSTEM II

Subunits D1 and D2 form the heterodimeric protein matrix of the reaction center (RC) that binds the chlorophyll *a* molecules (Chl *a*) called P680 and several other redox-active cofactors needed for linear electron flow along the electron transfer chain (ETC) from the lumenal to the stromal side of the membrane. After excitation by light, the electronic excitation energy is transferred from the core antenna proteins CP47 and CP43 (located on both sides of the D1/D2 heterodimes see Fig. 2) to the RC. P680 in its first exicited singlet state P680* is oxidized to the cation radical P680$^{+ \cdot}$, and the electron first transferred to pheophytins *a* (Pheo *a*) and subsequently to a special plastoquinone (Q_A). The $Q_A^{- \cdot}$ is the reductant for PQH_2 formation at the Q_B-site (Figure 2 and Chapter 16). P680$^{+ \cdot}$ is rereduced via redox-active tyrosine Tyr$_Z$ by an electron from the unique Mn_4-Ca-cluster, where the oxidation of water results in the release of molecular oxygen, under the release of protons into the lumen ([22] and Chapter 17). After two cycles, doubly reduced and protonated Q_B is released as plastoquinol (Q_BH_2) into the thylakoid membrane and reoxidized at the membrane-intrinsic cytochrome b_6f complex ([23] and Chapter 20). The electrons are transferred at the lumenal side of the membrane by soluble cytochrome c_6 (in cyanobacteria) or plastocyanin (in plants) to Photosystem I and from there at the stromal side via water-soluble ferredoxin to NADP$^+$-reductase to produce the strongly reducing NADPH (see Chapter 1). This process is coupled with the formation of a proton gradient

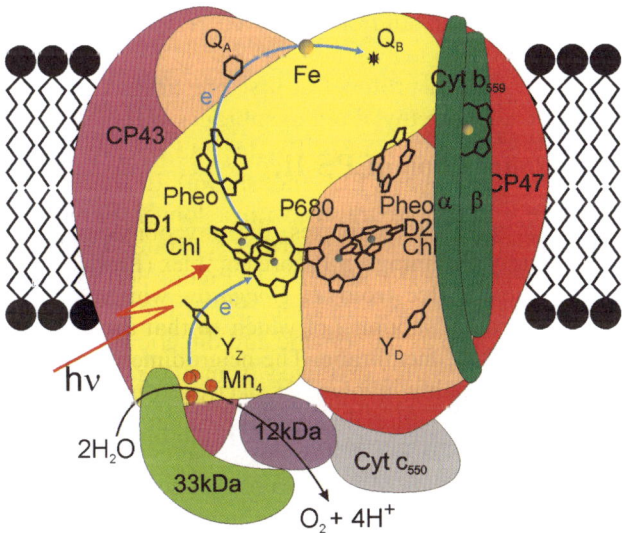

Figure 2. Schematic view of cyanobacterial Photosystem II. For simplicity, small subunits have been omitted and only the major subunits: D1, D2, CP47, CP43, cyt *b-559*, PsbO (33 kDa), PsbU (12 kDa), PsbV (cyt *c-550*) are shown. The redox active cofactors of water plastoquinone oxidoreductase are non-covalently bound to D1 (yellow) and D2 (orange) or a constituent of these polypeptides (Y_Z, Y_D). The pathway of light-induced electron transfer from water to plastoquinone is indicated by colored arrows.

across the membrane that drives ATP synthase and the formation of ATP (Chapter 21). Finally both ATP and NADPH reduce CO_2 to carbohydrates in the Calvin cycle [23].

15.4 General View of Oxygen Evolving PS IIcc Crystals

Several preparation procedures are known for the PS II core complexes (PS IIcc) from the thermophilic cyanobacterium *T. elongatus* [9,24–34].

Three groups have isolated, purified and crystallized oxygen-evolving PS IIcc from *T. elongatus* and the related *T. vulcanus* and derived the PS IIcc structure by X-ray diffraction pattern analysis at resolutions (in Å) of 3.8 [35], 3.7 [36], 3.5 [37] and 3.2 [38]. The most detailed structure of cyanobacterial PS IIcc obtained so far has a resolution of 3.0 Å [39]. The prerequisite for X-ray structure analysis of high resolution are crystals of sufficient quality.

A novel photobioreactor (Figure 3a) and recent improvements in growth conditions of *T. elongatus* permitted us to obtain reproducible high cyanobacterial density with a yield of about 4 g cells per liter of culture. Figure 3(b) shows a typical cell growth diagram.

To obtain large amounts of crystallizable PS IIcc it was necessary to develop a fast, large-scale purification method. Previously published procedures used either time-consuming density gradient centrifugations for the separation of limited amounts of protein and/or employed a mixture of detergents for solubilization.

In our recently developed protocol, a first preparative purification step of crude protein extracted from thylakoid membranes with *n*-dodecyl-β-D-maltoside (β-DM) separates phycobilisomes, PS IIcc and PS I by preparative anion exchange chromatography using FPLC (not shown). In a second step, using the same anion exchange chromatography with a longer, slimmer column, the PS IIcc fraction from the first step is further separated into phycobilisomes, monomeric and dimeric PS IIcc and PS I (Figure 3c). With the described extraction and purification procedure about 5% of protein-bound Chl *a* in the crude cell extract is purified as monomeric and dimeric PS IIcc, corresponding to a total of *ca*. 200 mg PS IIcc extracted from 100 g of cells. These refined purification and crystallization procedures led to high quality crystals that gave X-ray diffraction patterns extending to 3.0 Å resolution [39].

15.5 Characterization of the Aggregation State of PS IIcc

The oligomerization state of PS II from both cyanobacteria and higher plants, and, in particular, the molecular weight of PS IIcc, were a matter of controversy in the literature. In a series of reports, PS IIcc was claimed to exist as monomer with an effective molecular mass of 318 ± 50 kDa [40–43]. In many other studies, however, PS IIcc appears as a dimer [34,37,44–52] with an effective

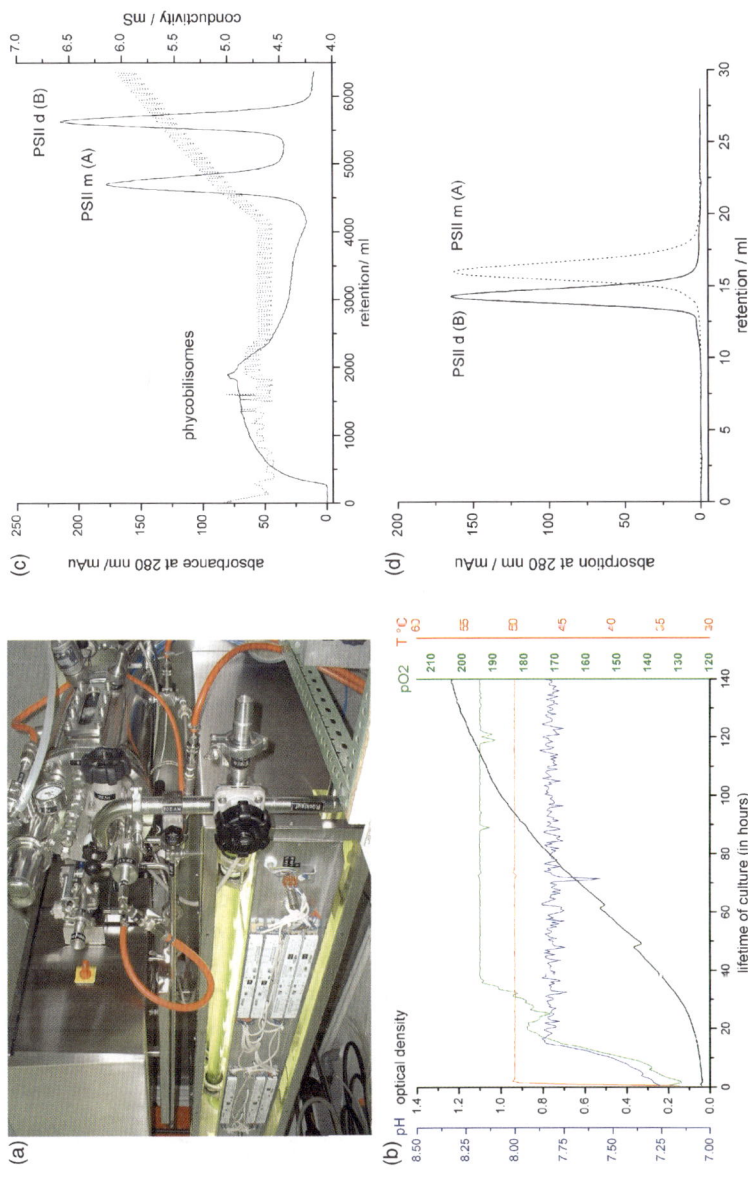

Figure 3. (a) Commercial Photobioreactor (IGV-Potsdam). (b) Parameters during a 7-day growth of a batch of cells (100 g wet weight) in a culture of 32 liters. During *T. elongatus* cell growth [122] the following parameters were kept constant: pH at 7.8 (blue curve) through automatic addition of CO_2; oxygen partial pressure (green curve), temperature at 56 °C (red curve). (c) Course of the second preparative anion-exchange chromatography step of PS IIcc purification [13], leading to the separation of monomeric fraction A (PS IIm) and dimeric fraction B (PS IId). Solid line: absorption at 280 nm; dotted line: conductivity. (d) Course gel permeation chromatography (GPC) of monomeric-fraction A (PS IIm dotted line) and dimeric-fraction B (PS IId solid line) using a Superose 6 gel-filtration column [13].

molecular mass in the range between 450 kDa [9,53] and 812 kDa [46]. The obtained molecular mass of PS IIcc depends on the preparation conditions (e.g., the detergent used [43,54]) and on the analytical methods employed [e.g., electron microscopy image analysis, gel permeation chromatography (GPC)].

The aggregation behavior of PS IIcc from *T. elongatus* in solution is crucial for the design of successful crystallization experiments. Therefore, we studied this property carefully, using GPC combined with dynamic light scattering (DLS) and analytical ultracentrifugation (UC). The various methods yield different aggregation states of PS IIcc in solution [55,56]. In the following they are discussed with respect to the requirements for crystallization.

15.5.1 Gel Permeation Chromatography (GPC)

After purification with anion exchange chromatography, two PS IIcc fractions A and B were separated (Figure 3c) and further analyzed with GPC. Based on the clearly different retention times, PS IIcc fractions A and B could be assigned to monomeric and dimeric PS IIcc, respectively (Figure 3d). The GPC column was not calibrated with soluble proteins as had been done thus far, but with the following membrane proteins as this appeared to be more appropriate: CP29 (28 kDa), CP47 (56 kDa) and LHCII (152 kDa) from *Spinacia oleracea* (*S. oleracea*) and trimeric (1068 kDa) and monomeric (356 kDa) *T. elongatus* Photosystem I (PS I*Te*). The latter two complexes were purified as described in [12,57]. CP47 and LHCII were isolated and purified from spinach [58–60]. CP29 was isolated and purified from spinach chloroplasts by a modification of the protocol in [61], as described in [62].

The molecular mass of PS IIcc determined by GPC with membrane proteins for column calibration corresponds to the protein, including the detergent belt that renders the protein soluble [63]. The molecular masses of monomeric (fraction A) and dimeric (fraction B) PS IIcc from *T. elongatus* were estimated to be 400 ± 20 kDa and 740 ± 55 kDa, respectively, corresponding to calculated molecular masses of 433 kDa for PS IIcc monomer and 805 kDa for PS IIcc dimer including detergent [56]. In contrast to our studies, all other GPC studies [9,33,34,51] determined the molecular masses of monomeric and dimeric PS IIcc by using soluble proteins for calibration and ignored the contribution of the detergent belt. These results differed markedly, far beyond the error limits. Therefore, the use of membrane protein standards is recommended in the mass determination of membrane protein by GPC.

15.5.2 Dynamic Light Scattering (DLS)

The molecular mass determination, based on measurements of dynamic light scattering (DLS) of diluted solutions of monomeric and dimeric PS IIcc, was made to determine the diffusion coefficient D_Z, which leads by use of the Stokes–Einstein equation to the hydrodynamic radius, R_H. The latter parameter allows the calculation of the molar mass under the assumption that the particle of interest is spherical. These measurements revealed aggregation and that the hydrodynamic radius R_H of PS IIcc depends on the concentration of PS IIcc, thus indicating aggregate formation of dimeric PS IIcc particles (fraction B) in solution [56].

At low PS IIcc concentrations (≤ 0.5 mg mL^{-1}) a molecular weight of 400 ± 20 kDa was determined. At higher PS IIcc concentration (≥ 3.3 mg mL^{-1}) these particles still persist but dimeric PS IIcc (see next subsection) and larger aggregates with molecular masses of about 3600 kDa are formed, reflecting the presence of various, but well-defined aggregation forms of PS IIcc, ranging from monomer to nonamer. At higher PS IIcc concentrations, the light absorption increased nonlinearly due to inner filter effects that became so strong that DLS experiments had to be abolished.

Since crystallization with poly(ethylene glycol) as precipitating agent requires PS IIcc concentrations of at least 10 mg mL^{-1} [13,31] it is concluded that formation of larger aggregates is considerable under crystallization conditions, and that larger aggregates dissociate when dimeric PS IIcc is consumed by growing nuclei.

In essence, these experiments show that PS IIcc occurs predominantly as relatively small, well-defined aggregates in solution. This is in line with the general behavior of well-crystallizing proteins [64–66] and can be taken as prerequisite for successful crystallization experiments.

15.5.2.1 A Critical Point of View
In DLS experiments the calculation of the hydrodynamic radius, R_H, from the measured diffusion coefficient, D_Z, assumes that the macromolecules under study are spherical. For monomeric and dimeric PS IIcc it is important to know that DLS experiments are not suited to distinguish between monomer and dimer forms of a protein because the increase in the hydrodynamic radius of a sphere with twice the molecular mass (or volume) is only 20% larger. This difference is of the same order of magnitude as the experimental error typical for DLS experiments.

15.5.3 Analytical Ultracentrifugation (AUC)

In contrast to DLS experiments, the molar weight (MW) determined by sedimentation equilibrium centrifugation does not depend on the shape of the molecules. The results of AUC experiments have clearly demonstrated that the PS IIcc form dimers even at concentrations below 0.2 mg mL^{-1}. This method is superior to DLS if accurate molar masses have to be determined [55,56].

If diluted to protein concentrations below 0.2 mg mL^{-1}, fraction B contains PS IIcc dimers with a molar mass of 756 ± 18 kDa. This corresponds to a MW of 805 kDa calculated from the amino acid composition of the subunits of PS IIcc deposited in cyanobase (http://www.kazusa.or.jp/cyanobase/) and including the molar mass of cofactors and detergent [56]. Importantly, dimeric PS IIcc partially (20–30%) dissociates into monomers at concentrations around and below 0.05 mg mL^{-1}. The resulting monomers are unstable under these conditions and aggregate to form heterogeneous (polydisperse) particles.

AUC experiments with monomeric PS IIcc (fraction A) at low protein concentrations (0.1 mg mL^{-1}) indicated a molar mass of 441 ± 10 kDa, which is virtually the same as the calculated value of 433 kDa, including cofactors and detergent. At higher PS IIcc concentrations (0.65–0.9 mg mL^{-1}) the monomers transformed into higher aggregates (1215 kDa), in agreement with DLS studies for monomeric PS IIcc (fraction A) [56]. The formation of higher aggregates of monomeric PS IIcc even at low protein concentration indicates that crystallization of monomeric PS IIcc might be difficult and, indeed, no 3D crystals have been reported so far.

15.6 Growing PS IIcc Crystals

Using the micro-batch crystallization method, crystals of dimeric PS IIcc were obtained within 2–3 days at room temperature (Figure 4a) that were fully active in oxygen evolution [13,31,67]. Crystals used for X-ray diffraction studies had a size of 0.5–0.8 mm in the longest dimension and about 0.1 and 0.02 mm in the two other dimensions (Figure 4a). The space group is orthorhombic ($P2_12_12_1$), and unit cell constants are $a = 127.5$ Å, $b = 224.6$ Å, $c = 305.6$ Å, as described previously [38]. The diffraction limit of these crystals under cryogenic conditions is 2.9 Å (Figure 4b), but due to anisotropy in the X-ray diffraction pattern the complete data sets were collected at lower (3.2 Å) resolution at the ESRF beamline ID14–2 [38]. Further improvement steps in purification and crystallization of PS IIcc led to crystals that diffracted to 3.0 Å resolution [39].

The interpretation of the electron density maps requires detailed knowledge of the subunit composition, the stoichiometry of pigments, cofactors, lipids and the polypeptide composition. Therefore, thorough biochemical analyses were performed to characterize the PS IIcc preparations and on the crystals obtained from the material.

15.6.1 Cofactors, Polypeptide Composition and Lipid Content of PS IIcc

Before and after crystallization of dimeric PS IIcc the oxygen evolution activity, pigment stoichiometry, as well as lipid and detergent composition were analyzed.

Dimeric PS IIcc proved to be very stable and highly active in oxygen evolution and, consequently, suitable for crystallization [13,31,67]. The light-induced average oxygen yield per flash was determined by a method originally described in [68]. The values obtained cover the range 40–55 Chl *a* per oxygen evolving center for dimeric PS IIcc in solution and are comparable to values obtained for redissolved crystals of PS IIcc. Corresponding values were obtained for the quantification by light-induced Q_A^- formation measured via absorption changes at 320 nm [67].

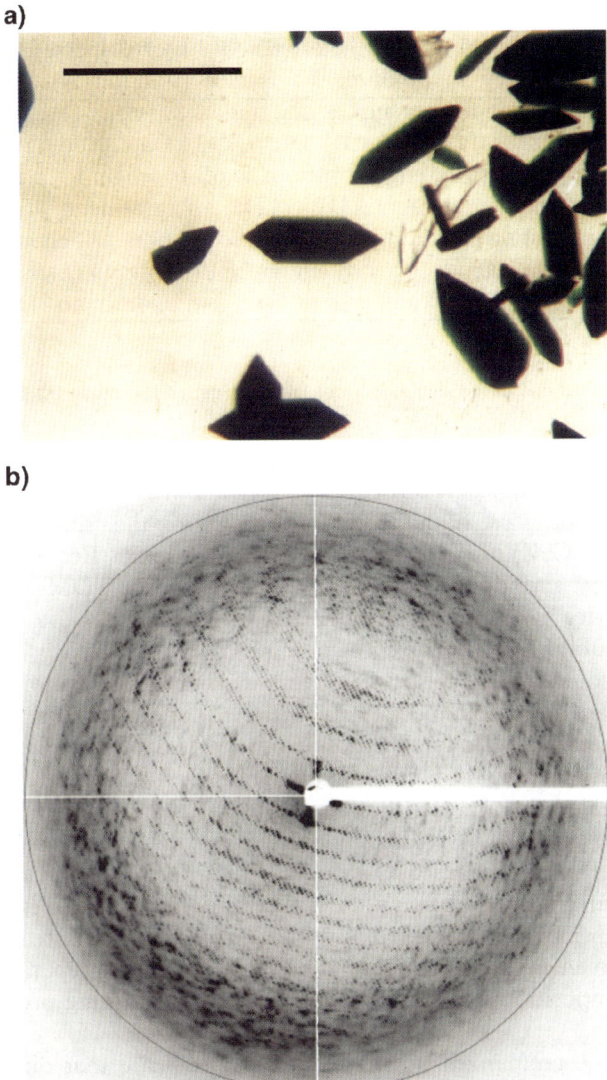

Figure 4. (a) Crystals of dimeric PS IIcc from *T. elongatus* [13], bar = 1 mm. (b) X-Ray diffraction pattern of a PS IIcc crystal at 100 K; maximum resolution of the pattern corresponds to 2.9 Å (measured at ESRF, Grenoble) [Adapted from Kern et al. 2005 [13].]

The content of organic cofactors in dimeric PS IIcc was determined by extraction with organic solvents (acetone or methanol) and subsequent analyses with a combination of UV/Vis absorption spectroscopy and reversed-phase chromatography [13]. These studies yielded 34 Chl *a* (Chl), 2 pheophytin *a* (Pheo), 9 β-carotene (Car), 2.9 plastoquinone9 (PQ9) per active center of PS IIcc (Table 1). The fatty acid (lipid) content was quantified with gas

Table 1. Cofactor and lipid stoichiometry of dimeric PS IIcc measured after purification and from redissolved crystals. Numbers in parentheses indicate number of independent experiments

	Dimeric PS IIcc before crystallization	Redissolved PS IIcc crystals
Chl a^a	34 ± 2.1 (8)	34 ± 2.2 (3)
Car^b	9.1 ± 1 (10)	9.1 ± 0.8 (5)
PQ9^a	2.9 ± 0.8 (6)	2.2 ± 0.2 (3)
Mn^b	3.8 ± 0.5 (4)	3.6 ± 0.5 (4)
Lipids^b	10 ± 4 (6)	Nd^c
β-DM^b	110 ± 20 (6)	Nd^c

^{a}Values are per two Pheo a.
^{b}Values are per 36 Chl a.
^{c}Nd: not determined due to the high amount of protein required for measurement.

chromatography and the detergent (β-DM) content by 2D thin-layer chromatography. For one dimeric PS II core complex about 20 lipid and 220 detergent (β-DM) molecules were found [13,56]. Furthermore, the critical solubilization concentration (CSC) of β-DM, necessary to keep the PS IIcc in solution, was determined by turbidimetric titrations. At least 190 β-DM molecules per dimeric PS IIcc in excess of the CSC of 0.16 ± 0.03 mM are necessary for complete solubilization of this core complex [69].

The Mn-content of dimeric PS IIcc was analyzed by atom absorption spectroscopy (AAS), yielding 3.8 ± 0.5 Mn per monomer before and 3.6 ± 0.5 Mn per monomer after crystallization (from redissolved crystals) (Table 1).

These data, resulting from different analytical methods on several batches of PS IIcc, revealed that PS IIcc from *T. elongatus* is a highly stable and active multi-subunit protein–cofactor complex.

MALDI-TOF MS was used as a rapid method for routine quality checks of PS IIcc preparations before and after crystallization, and SDS-PAGE was used to detect high molecular weight impurities [55,70]. The main reason for these checks was to ensure that PS IIcc obtained from different preparations were of the same composition and that no subunits were lost during preparation and crystallization.

The results, summarized in Table 2, clearly indicate that dimeric PS IIcc exhibit basically the same MALDI-TOF MS spectra before and after crystallization. In summary, the following 16 subunits could be unambiguously identified from the mass spectra to be present in dimeric *T. elongatus* PS IIcc: Psb A (D1), B (CP47), C (CP43), D (D2), E (α-cyt*b-559*), F (β-cyt*b-559*), H, I, K, L, O (33 kDa), T, U (12 kDa), V (17 kDa, cyt*c-550*), X, and Z (YCF9).

The large subunits PsbA to PsbD could not be detected in all preparations with MALDI-TOF MS, because their flight behavior strongly depends on slight variations in the matrix used, possibly due to different grades of crystallization of the matrix from sample to sample. Therefore, their presence was confirmed independently by SDS-Urea-PAGE [71] that was run routinely for all of the samples investigated by MALDI-TOF MS. In the relevant mass region (up to 30 kDa), there were no sharp single spikes but rather broad peaks,

Table 2. Polypeptide composition of dimeric PS IIcc from *T. elongatus* (*Te*) before and after crystallization, as obtained from MALDI-TOF MS spectrometry. Psb: corresponding gene product (protein subunit)

Designation of the gene (cyanobase number)	Protein, trivial names	Theoretically predicted average masses unprocessed/mature form $(M+H)^+$ (Da)	Present in PS IIc*Te* before and after crystallization	Experimentally determined average masses $(M+H)^+ \pm \sigma$ (Da)
psbA1/psbA1 (*tlr1843*), *psbA2* (*tlr1844*) *psbA3* (*tlr1477*)	PsbA, D1-protein	39737.5/38240.9(1–344) 38109.7 (2–344) (psbA1) 39738.8/38201.0 (psbA2) 39757.6/38260.9 (psbA3)	+	38144 ± 224
psbB (*tlr1530*)	PsbB, apoprotein of the core antenna CP47	56603.7 56473.6 (2-end)	+	56485 ± 108
psbC (*tlr1631*)	PsbC, apoprotein of the core antenna CP43	51621.4	+	51704 ± 87
psbD (*tlr0455*)	PsbD, D2 protein	39362.4 (1-end) 39231.2 (2-end)	+	39290 ± 79
psbE (*tsr1541*)	PsbE, α-subunit of cyt*b*-559	9573.9 (1-end) 9442.7 (2-end)	+	9446 ± 6 4724 ± 3
psbF (*tsr1542*)	PsbF, β-subunit of cyt*b*-559	5065.95 4934.7 (2-end)	+	4938 ± 4 4981 ± 5 5070 ± 4
psbH (*tsll386*)	PsbH, phosphoprotein	7355 7223.6 (2-end)	+	7227 ± 5
psbI (*tsr1074*)	PsbI	4406.3	+	4437 ± 4
psbJ (*tsr1544*)	PsbJ	4105.9 3974.8 (2-end)	+	4017 ± 2 4033 ± 2
psbK (*tsl0176*)	PsbK	5027.1 4100.9 (10-end)	+	4103 ± 4
psbL (*tsr1543*)	PsbL	4298.1	+	4301 ± 4
psbM (*tsl2052*)	PsbM	3980.7	+	4011 ± 2 4025 ± 2
psbN (*tsr1387*)	PsbN	4542.1	See text	–

(*Continued*)

Table 2. (*Continued*)

Designation of the gene (cyanobase number)	Protein, trivial names	Theoretically predicted average masses unprocessed/mature form $(M+H)^+$ (Da)	Present in PS IIccTe before and after crystallization	Experimentally determined average masses $(M+H)^+ \pm \sigma$ (Da)
psbO (*t110444*)	PsbO, 33 kDa protein, OEE1, MSP	29607.6	+	26830 ± 30
		26825.0 (27-end)		13415 ± 9
psbT, ycf8 (*tsr1531*)	PsbT	3875.8	+	3906 ± 4
psbU (*t112409*)	PsbU	15018	+	11649 ± 8
		11646 (31-end)		5826 ± 4
psbV (*t111285*)	PsbV, Cytc550	18028	+	15752 ± 11
		15131 (27-end)		7877 ± 6
		15750 (+heme)		
psbX (*tsr2013*)	PsbX	5233.4	+	4192 ± 4
		4189.1 (11-end)		
psbY, ycf 32, orf8, (*ts10836*)	PsbY	4773.9	+	4617 ± 4
		4585.7 (3-end)		
ycf9, orf62 (*tsr1967*)	PsbZ	6765.3	+	6798 ± 5
psbZ, psb27 (*t112464*)	PsbZ-like, Psb27	15101	See text	–

rendering an exact mass determination difficult and resulting in higher standard deviations (σ) (Table 2).

In SDS-Urea-PAGE analysis the large subunits CP47, CP43, D1/D2, PsbO and the smaller PsbE and PsbF were well separated and their identity was confirmed by Western blotting in combination with specific antibodies [55,70]. Up to seven low molecular mass subunits below 10 kDa could be resolved and visualized after silver staining [70]. All PS IIcc subunits smaller than 30 kDa, identified with MALDI-TOF MS, were also found in redissolved crystals (Figure 5a, b). Due to the minor mass differences ($\Delta m = 6$ Da) of some of the small subunits [e.g., (PsbM (4011 $\pm$ 2 Da) and PsbJ (4017 $\pm$ 2 Da)], unambiguous identification was achieved by recording the spectra in linear as well as in reflector mode (Figure 5c). Using the reflector mode spectrum, the various isotopes could be resolved. The presence of PsbY (4617 $\pm$ 4 Da) in the PS IIcc dimer is very probable but it could be confused with PsbN (4542.1 Da) if chemically modified. The assignment of PsbN was based on poor sequencing data and no evidence for its presence in PS IIcc was provided by recent studies [70,72]. Taking these three subunits (PsbJ, PsbM, PsbY) into account yields a total number of 19 subunits in dimeric PS IIcc.

PsbE, H, K, L, U, V and PsbX are all present in unmodified forms. Formylations were identified for PsbM, I, T, Y and Z, whereas for PsbF and PsbJ the N-terminally acetylated forms are present. The larger subunits PsbA (D1) and PsbD (D2) do not allow clear mass assignments since the peaks are very broad, although a loss of methionine (Met1) seems very likely, and in contrast to spinach PS IIcc no phosphorylations at all could be detected [70].

15.7 Progress in Structure Analysis of PS IIcc

Initial information on the structure of PS II from spinach was gathered from electron microscopy in combination with image averaging procedures. These pictures resolved the general shape and also revealed the presence of the membrane-extrinsic PS IIcc proteins. More details were obtained by using the method of electron diffraction. The structural work on a spinach PS II fragment consisting of subunits D1, D2, CP47 by electron diffraction on 2D crystals led to resolutions of about 8 Å [73]. Analyses of intact spinach PS II by electron microscopy yielded structures at 9-10 Å resolution [74].

The arrangement of transmembrane α-helices (TMH) in the heterodimeric protein matrix of the reaction center formed by subunits D1 and D2 and associated cofactors of PS II from spinach was inferred to resemble that of subunits L and M in the purple bacterial reaction center (PBRC) [73], in line with earlier proposals [75]. Structure analyses of PS I revealed that the five carboxy-terminal TMHs of PsaA and PsaB in Photosystem I [76] are similarly organized. This finding supports the hypothesis of the evolution of all photosynthetic reaction centers from one ancestor [75,76].

It was also possible to assign six TMH to CP47 and to show, for the first time, that these helices are arranged in a circular manner as three pairs [73,76].

It was noted that this arrangement is similar to that of the six N-terminal TMH of the PS I RC proteins, which had been revealed by X-ray crystallography initially at 4 Å [77] and, finally, at 2.5 Å resolution [78,79]. The first direct evidence for the same arrangements of transmembrane α-helices TMH of CP43 and CP47 was obtained by low-resolution (12.9 Å) electron crystallography on 2D crystals of dimeric PS II core preparations isolated from spinach [80], and more accurately from the first X-ray crystallographic analysis of *T. elongatus* PS IIcc at 3.8 Å resolution [35]. In the electron crystallography study of PS IIcc,

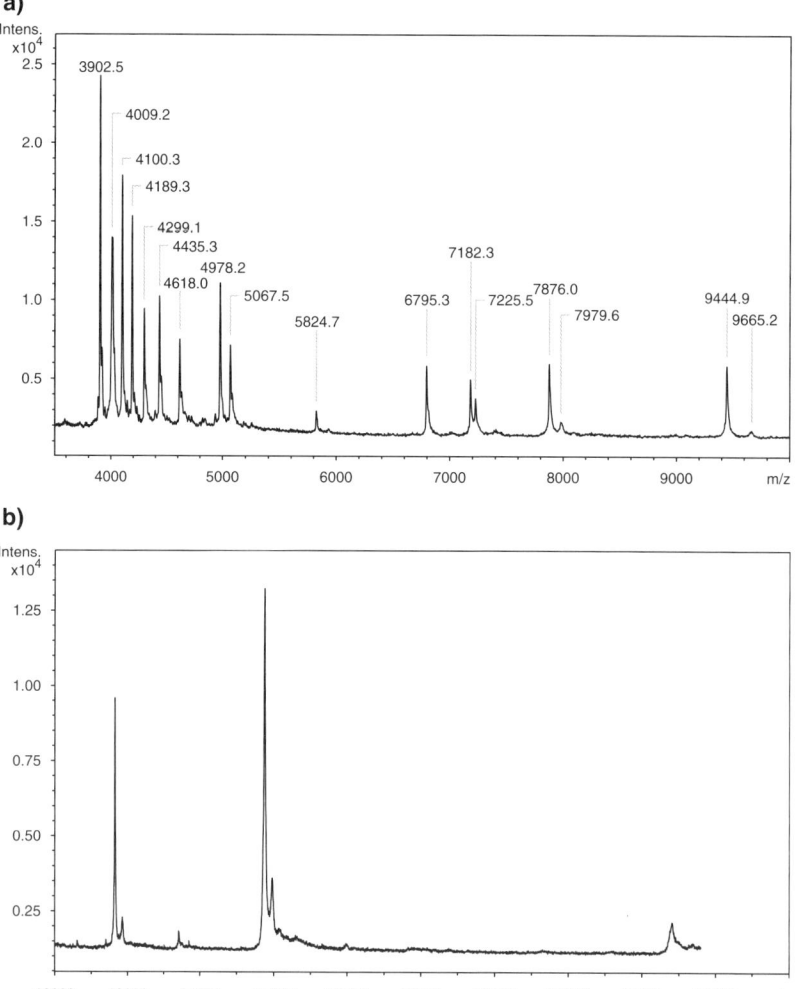

Figure 5. MALDI-TOF MS spectrum in linear mode of redissolved crystals of dimeric PS IIcc [124]. The assignments to PS IIcc subunits are given above the respective peaks. (a) Mass range 3600–10 000 m/z. (b) Mass range 10 000–30 000 m/z. (c) MALDI-TOF MS spectrum of dimeric PS IIcc in reflector mode [123]. Mass range 4005–4056 m/z, the 1st and 4th monoisotopic peaks are labeled, and possible assignments, including proposed modifications, are given in the top line. Ac, acetylation; f, formylation; ox, oxidation.

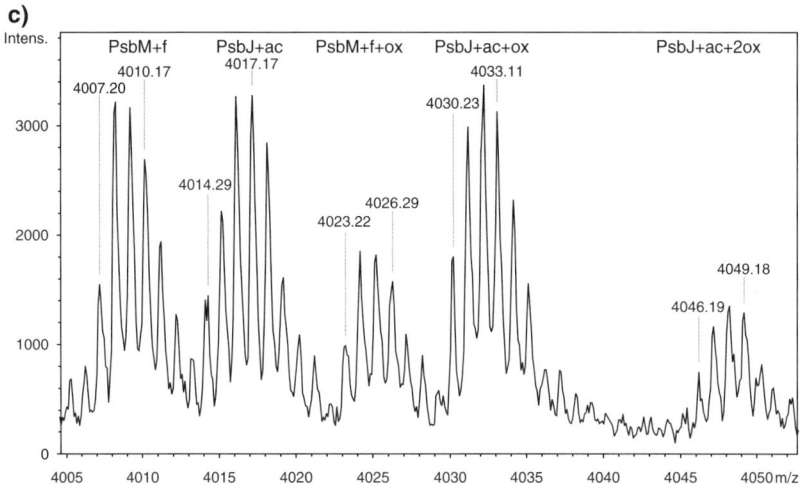

Figure 5. (*Continued*).

seven other TMH were assigned, with two of them tentatively identified as the α and β subunits (PsbE and PsbF proteins, respectively) of cyt*b-559* [81], and later confirmed at 3.8 Å resolution [35].

The X-ray crystal structure of *T. elongatus* PS IIcc at 3.8 Å resolution was derived from crystals that were fully active in oxygen evolution [35]. This breakthrough in PS II structure research stimulated several groups to determine the PS IIcc structure at atomic resolution. The crystal structure of *T. elongatus* PS IIcc was later given at a better resolution of 3.5 Å [37] and that of *T. vulcanus* has been reported at 3.7 Å resolution [36]. The recently published crystal structure of PS IIcc from *T. elongatus* at 3.2 Å resolution [38] represents a moderate improvement in resolution but still with limits in interpretation of cofactors like carotenoids, lipids, quinones Q_A and Q_B, and small subunits. The currently determined structure of PS IIcc at 3.0 Å resolution is a significant step forward towards the desired higher resolution of 2.8 Å, where crystallographers can begin to identify reliably amino acid side-chains from the electron density.

*15.7.1 Problems in the Interpretation of Electron Density Maps from
T. elongatus and T. vulcanus PS IIcc at Moderate Resolution*

Notably, all crystal structures at moderate resolution (3.8–3.2 Å) presented thus far for PS IIcc from *T. elongatus* and *T. vulcanus* have to be considered with caution. Interpretation of the electron density maps at this resolution is reliable only for polypeptide chains, where an unambiguous sequence assignment can be achieved for regions with specific sequence landmarks like bulky amino acid side-chains (tyrosine or tryptophan) and/or coordination sites of cofactors (Chl *a* or Fe^{2+}). Therefore, the best defined sections in the electron density map of PS IIcc are membrane-intrinsic parts of the main subunits D1, D2, CP43, CP47 and cyt*b-559*. By contrast, interpretation of the electron density for the small subunits is ambiguous or even impossible at 3.2 Å resolution, because most of these subunits are located at the periphery of PS IIcc and less well defined in electron density due to thermal vibration and/or disorder. Additional complicating factors for the assignment of these small subunits are the absence of coordination with marker groups (Chl *a*) and the presence of only a few of the aromatic amino acid side-chains that occur more frequently in the large subunits.

These critical aspects suggest that many sections of the 3.5 and 3.7 Å crystal structures [36,37] may have been over-interpreted, especially with respect to loop segments and small subunits. For example, the assignment of carotenoids in *T. vulcanus* [36] was shown to be wrong, and several carotenoids, Chl *a*, and side-chains were erroneously placed in the *T. elongatus* crystal structure at 3.5 Å resolution [37]. In several cases, unconnected patches of electron density were interpreted as Car molecules that could (and did) represent phytyl chains of Chl *a* or lipids, as we know from the improved 3.0 Å resolution crystal structure.

The next section describes the currently most advanced PS IIcc structure at 3.0 Å resolution, with special focus on new insights into the structural array of the 35 Chl *a*, eleven carotenoids (Car), two Pheo, two PQ, two heme groups, bicarbonate, 14 lipid, three detergent molecules (*n*-dodecyl-β-maltoside), four Mn-atoms, and two Ca^{2+} and Fe^{2+} [39].

15.8 Structure at 3.0 Å Resolution of PS IIcc from *T. elongatus*

The combination of biochemically identified protein subunits and structure analysis of dimeric PS IIcc from *T. elongatus* at 3.0 Å resolution [39] leads to the following conclusions: PS IIcc occurs as homodimer with the monomers related by a non-crystallographic pseudo-twofold axis (pseudo-*C2*) located between the monomers and oriented normal to the membrane plane. Two other pseudo-C2 axes, called pseudo-*C2* (Fe^{2+}), are also normal to the membrane plane and located between D1 and D2 subunits of the two monomers and cross the nonheme iron Fe^{2+}. Of the at least 16 membrane-intrinsic protein subunits in the PS IIcc monomer [55] the six largest and functionally most important ones were identified and 24 TMH were assigned to the proteins D1, D2, CP43, CP47, and PsbE and PsbF of cyt*b-559*. The remaining ten membrane intrinsic proteins with mostly unknown function are much smaller, with one or at most two TMH that correspond to a total of 12 TMH in the electron density at 3.0 Å resolution. Low molecular weight subunits PsbH, PsbI, PsbJ, PsbK, PsbZ are located at the periphery, and PsbL, PsbM and PsbT are at the monomer–monomer interface of PS IIcc. Eight of these subunits are folded into a single TMH, and one features two TMH. The latter was assigned to PsbZ based on a combination of MALDI-TOF MS spectroscopy [70] and X-ray analyses [35–39]. The assigned low molecular subunits bind some Chl *a*, Car, and lipid molecules and coordinate a putative Ca^{2+} [39].

Only three TMH are not yet assigned to further low-molecular weight subunits due to poor electron density at 3.0 Å resolution. At present, a 12th TMH in the electron density that probably belongs to one of the small subunits remains unidentified or is a copy of one of the known subunits. PsbN is very likely not an integral subunit of PS IIcc from *T. elongatus*, in contrast to the assignment of Ferriera et al. [37].

The three membrane-extrinsic subunits PsbO, PsbU and PsbV (cyt*c-550*) were localized on the lumenal side of PS IIcc [82]. In total, 19 protein subunits were found in the X-ray structure analysis. This perfectly corresponds with the biochemical data from MALDI-TOF MS and SDS-PAGE [70] (see above) and shows that PS IIcc crystallized as a fully intact particle without loss of subunits.

15.8.1 Symmetry and Arrangement of Transmembrane α-Helices

In the photoactive center of PS IIcc the heterodimeric membrane intrinsic subunits D1/D2 harbor cofactors of the water-plastoquinone oxidoreductase activity. Two groups of five transmembrane α-helices (TMH) of D1 and D2 (**a** to **e**) are arranged in two semicircles interlocked in a handshake motif and related by the local twofold axis [pseudo-*C2* (Fe^{2+})] (Figure 6a). This arrangement of the TMHs belonging to D1 and D2 resembles that of the subunits L and M in the structurally well-resolved (2.3 Å) purple bacterial reaction center (PBRC) [75] (for details, see Chapter 11) and of the five carboxy-terminal helices of PsaA and PsaB in Photosystem I [76] (for details, see Chapter 13). The N- and C-termini of D1 and D2 are exposed to the cytoplasmic and lumenal sides, respectively, and partially folded into α-helices **Na** and **eC**. The loop connecting TMH **d** and **e** is in part folded into short α-helices **de** located on the cytoplasmic side of the membrane and exposed to solvent, whereas loops connecting TMH **a**, **b** and **c**, **d** (α-helices **ab** and **cd**) are on the lumenal side (Figure 6a, b). The pigment containing proteins CP43 and CP47 flank both sides of the heterodimeric subunits D1/D2 and are related by the local twofold axis [pseudo-*C2* (Fe^{2+})]. CP43 and CP47 contain six TMH (**a–f**) each that are arranged as trimers of dimers and the N- and C-termini of both subunits are on the cytoplasmic side. Both core antenna proteins feature short connections between TMH **a** to **e**, of which two are folded into short α-helices **ab** and **de**, connecting TMH **a**, **b** and **d**, **e**, respectively. The unusually large domains **e-f** span 129 and 188 amino acids and feature 4 (CP47) and 2 (CP43) short α-helices **ef**, respectively, that are located on the lumenal side (Figure 6a, b). These large extensions of CP47 and CP43, which have no analogous feature in PsbA and PsbB of PS I, interact with membrane-extrinsic subunits PsbO, PsbU, PsbV (Figure 6b). In contrast to all other subunits in PS IIcc with α-helical structures, PsbO is dominated by β-strands forming a hollow cylinder. PsbO features two large loops, one binding to CP47 of one PS II monomer and the other to D1, D2 and CP47 of the second monomer. These interactions contribute to the stabilization of the two PS II monomers within the homodimer.

15.8.2 Chlorophyll Arrangement in the Proteins CP43 and CP47

As was first shown for PsaA and PsbB in the crystal structure of Photosystem I (PS I) at 4 Å resolution [76] and for CP47 of a spinach PS II fragment by

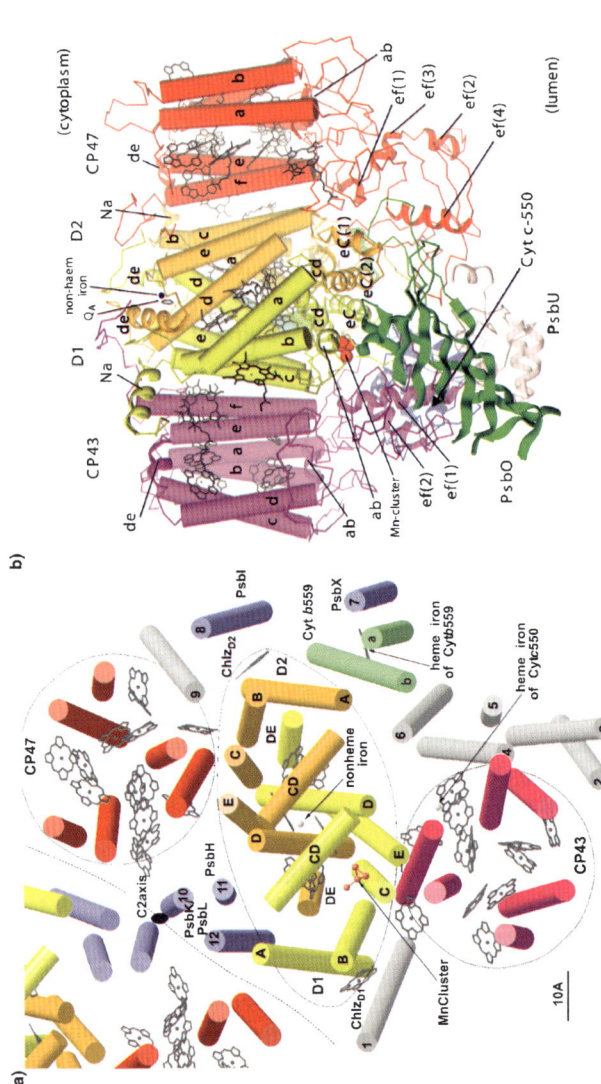

Figure 6. Overall view of the PS IIcc structure [35]. (a) Direction from the lumenal side, perpendicular to the membrane plane. The membrane-extrinsic subunits on the lumenal side and non-helical segments are not shown. One PS IIcc monomer is drawn completely, the other monomer in the dimer (related by the pseudo-C_2 axis, black ellipse) only partially upper left. Chlorine rings and hemes are indicated by black wire drawings. The helices of subunits are colored in magenta (CP43), yellow (D1), orange (D2), red (CP47), green and cyan (cyt b-559, α- and β-subunits). The transmembrane α-helices (TMH) belonging to small unassigned and tentatively assigned subunits (grey) are labeled by numbers (1–12). The local pseudo-$C_2(Fe^{2+})$ axis passes through the nonheme Fe^{2+} site (grey dot) and relates D1 with D2 and CP43 with CP47. (b) Side view of one PS IIcc monomer along the membrane plane [38]. Subunits D1, D2, CP43 and CP47 colored as in (a). For the sake of better illustration, TMHs that belong to small subunits are omitted. TMHs are labeled with letters in sequential order, and loops or α-helices in the loops are denoted with two letters. **ef** indicating the loop connecting TMH **e** and **f** of CP43 or CP47, and numbers **ef(2)** label non-TMH α-helices in sequential order. **Na** and **eC** indicate N- and C-termini, respectively, of D1 and D2. Membrane-extrinsic subunits on the lumenal side are PsbO (green), PsbU (pink) and cyt$c$-550 (blue). The chlorin rings, heme, heme Q_A (quinone head group) and carotenoids are in black.

STRUCTURE OF CYANOBACTERIAL PHOTOSYSTEM II

electron crystallography at 8 Å resolution [73], the Chl *a* molecules in CP43 are also organized in two layers parallel to the membrane plane and close to the stromal and lumenal sides.

The organization of Chl *a* in two layer structures in CP43 and CP47 of PS IIcc was first described for the X-ray structure of PS IIcc from *T. elongatus* at 3.8 Å resolution and later confirmed for *T. vulcanus* and *T. elongatus* at 3.7, 3.5 and 3.2 Å resolution [36–38]. The first structure model of PS IIcc from *T. elongatus* at 3.8 Å resolution reported 26 Chl *a* embedded in the core antenna system, 12 in CP43 and 14 in CP47 [35]. By contrast, 30 chlorophylls were found in the core antenna system of PS IIcc from *T. vulcanus*, 13 in CP43 and 17 in CP47 [36], and in PS IIcc from *T. elongatus* at 3.5 Å resolution [37] 30 Chl *a* were identified, 14 in CP43 and 16 in CP47, all of them in positions similar to the ones described at the lower resolution crystal structures. One of the Chl *a* molecules in CP43 shown by Ferriera et al. [37] and Kamiya and Shen [36] is not present in the 3.2 Å resolution structure [38]. In the 3.0 Å resolution structure of PS IIcc this Chl *a* position is occupied by a lipid [39], yielding a total of 29 Chl *a* molecules.

As described earlier, the 13 Chl *a* molecules in CP43 and 16 Chl *a* molecules in CP47 are arranged in two layers near the cytoplasmic and lumenal sides of the membrane. All Chl *a* molecules within the antennae have neighboring Chl *a* molecules within 16.5 Å. Near the periphery of the lumenal layer of CP47 one more Chl*a* was identified but this is less well defined and appears to be more weakly bound than the other Chl *a* molecules. This Chl *a* was not detected in some of our crystals. A possible explanation for this phenomenon is a partial loss of this Chl *a* during purification on the anion exchange column. We cannot exclude that further Chl *a* molecules located close to the periphery of the two layers are lost in this way and/or are not visible in the electron density due to limitations of current experimental data [38].

15.8.3 Integral Lipids

Although no structural information about lipids bound to PS IIcc was available [35–38,83], various studies indicated the influence of lipids on the assembly and function of PS IIcc [84–86]. The 3.0 Å resolution structure of PS II reveals for the first time the composition of 14 lipids located in the inner part of PS IIcc: four digalactosyldiacylglycerol (DGDG), six monogalactosyldiacylglycerol (MGDG), three sulfoquinovosyldiacylglycerol (SQDG) and one phosphatidyldiacylglycerol (PG) (Figure 7a, b). This lipid composition in PS IIcc corresponds to that found in cyanobacterial thylakoids, containing mainly galactolipids and lower amounts of phospholipids [87]. The lipids are likely an integral part of the PS IIcc structure and not preparation artifacts, since none of the lipid or detergent molecules are bound to the hydrophobic, membrane-exposed side of PS IIcc. Eight and six of the hydrophilic lipid head groups are close to the stromal and lumenal surfaces, respectively, of the membrane embedded subunits of PS IIcc and form hydrogen bonds to the protein, while the hydrophobic fatty acid chains are located between TMH of different subunits (Figure 7b) [39].

On the cytoplasmic side the negatively charged head groups of SQDG and PG are predominant, and one SQDG is located at the cytoplasmic side of the D1/CP43 interface. These findings agree with the binding of SQDG-specific antibodies at the solvent-exposed surface of the D1/D2 complex of PS II from tobacco [88]. Two other SQDG molecules are located at the monomer–monomer interface.

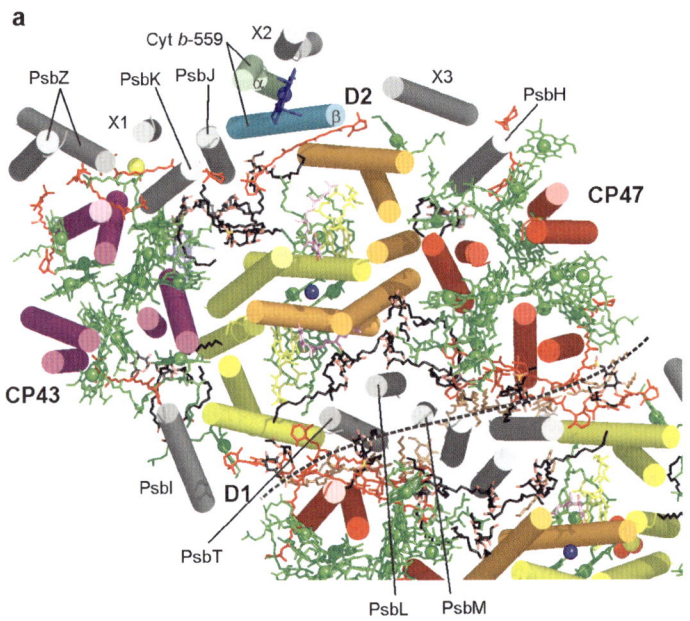

Figure 7. (a) Overall view of one monomer and part of the other monomer of PS IIcc from the cytoplasmic side, showing α-helices as cylinders and cofactors in wire drawing [125]. For simplicity, membrane extrinsic subunits (PsbO, U, V) are omitted. The two monomers of PS IIcc are related by a non-crystallographic twofold axis parallel to the membrane normal. D1, CP43 and D2, CP47 are related by a second non-crystallographic twofold axis [pseudo-$C2(Fe^{2+})$] that passes through the nonheme Fe^{2+} site (blue dot). Subunits are labeled by colors: D1 (yellow), D2 (orange), CP43 (magenta), CP47 (red), α- and β-chain of cyt *b-559* (green and cyan), low molecular weight subunits (grey). Unassigned TMH are labeled X1–X3. Cofactors are in green (Chl *a*), yellow (Pheo), red (Car), blue (heme), violet (quinone), cyan (lipids), and brown (detergent and assigned alkyl chains). (b) Schematic view from the cytoplasmic side of cofactors bound to membrane-intrinsic subunits of PS IIcc, showing one monomer completely and the other monomer only partly (lower right side) [125]. TMHs and cofactors are colored as in (a). Lipid and detergent molecules are drawn with head groups pointing "downwards" (towards the lumenal side) and "upwards" (towards the cytoplasmic/stromal side). Green numbers in the proteins CP43 and CP47 indicate positions of antenna Chl *a*. Chl *a* molecules located towards the cytoplasmic side of the membrane are numbered 11–17 and 33–37 in CP47 and CP43, respectively. The cavity close to the Q_B-pocket is indicated by a dotted line.

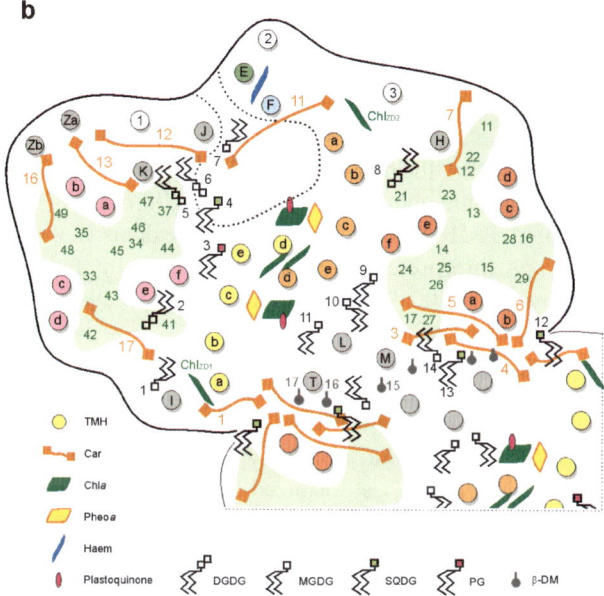

Figure 7. (*Continued*).

The D1/D2 heterodimer is surrounded by a belt of eleven lipids that separate it from antenna and small subunits (Figure 7a, b). The remaining three lipids and three detergent molecules are located in the monomer–monomer interface of PS II.

The function of these integral lipid molecules is probably associated with the protection of the multisubunit protein complex to photodamage. Chl *a* triplet states can be populated at high light intensities and react with molecular triplet oxygen. In this way aggressive singlet oxygen is formed that causes oxidative damage of protein subunits (for details, see Chapters 10 and 16). The preferentially photodamaged component in PS IIcc is the RC protein D1 that undergoes continuous turn-over by exchange with freshly synthesized D1 [89] (Chapter 10). For this exchange process an environment with structural flexibility appears to be required and is provided by the belt of lipids surrounding the RC. In parallel, local mobility of PS IIcc subunits may be necessary to promote subunit–subunit recognition and assembly in analogy to other multimeric membrane complexes, where the role of lipids is to provide a deformable or "lubricant" rather than a rigid interface between subunits [90,91].

Other structurally and functionally important lipid binding sites in PS IIcc are close to those of the primary (Q_A) and secondary quinones (Q_B) where MGDG11 and SQDG4, respectively, are located. The binding of lipids close to quinones is similar to that observed in other membrane protein complexes like PS I ([78] and Chapter 13), cyt b_6f ([92,93] and Chapter 20), cyt bc_1 complex [94], suggesting that lipid binding sites close to quinones in membrane proteins is a general feature. A detailed analysis of lipid-cofactor and lipid-protein interactions in photosynthesis is given in Ref. [95].

15.8.4 Electron Acceptor Side and Q_B Diffusion Pathway

The nonheme Fe^{2+} on the local pseudo-$C2(Fe^{2+})$ axis is coordinated by four histidines of D1/D2 in analogy to PBRC ([96] and Chapter 11) and as found in previously presented PSII structures [35–39]. A peak in the F_0-F_c difference electron density was interpreted as bicarbonate coordinated to Fe^{2+} based on FTIR spectroscopy data [96]. This bicarbonate is hydrogen bonded by D1-Tyr246-OH and D2-Tyr244-OH.

The primary quinone Q_A is sandwiched between D2-Trp253 and D2-Leu267, and the keto oxygens accept hydrogen bonds from D2-His214NεH and D2-Phe261NH. In contrast to the proposal of Ferriera et al. [37], the sidechain of D2-Phe261 points to and not away from the Q_A binding site.

The secondary quinone Q_B is localized in the pseudo-$C2(Fe^{2+})$ related position to Q_A on the D1 side. In agreement with biochemical and spectroscopic data [13,97] the electron density of Q_B is weaker than that of Q_A, with the Q_B binding site being about half-occupied. Q_B is sandwiched between D1-Phe255 and D1-Leu271 and forms hydrogen bonds with D1-His215NεH and/or D1-Ser264OγH or D1-Phe265NH.

The Q_B binding pocket opens into a large cavity located between TMHs of PsbF, J, K, TMH-d and e of D1 and TMH-a of D2 (Figure 8a). The walls of the cavity are coated by phytyl chains of P_{D2}, Chl_{D2}, $Pheo_{D2}$, Chl a37, 44 and 46, and by acyl chains of SQDG4, DGDG4, DGDG5, DGDG6, and MGDG7. The ionone rings of carotenoids Car11 and 12 point into the cavity. Since electron density in the cavity is fragmented and not yet interpretable, the cavity is likely filled by two or more disordered lipophilic molecules. The cavity has two entrances perpendicular to each other: the large one ($\sim 16 \times 16$ Å) opens towards the cytoplasmic side and the smaller one ($\sim 10 \times 20$ Å), flanked by TMHs of cyt b-559 and PsbJ, faces the transmembrane region (Figure 8d).

The Q_B binding pocket forms an antechamber of the large cavity. It is located opposite to the membrane-facing opening, and is filled by the quinone head group, while the isoprenoid chain of Q_B winds along the wall of the cavity. Based on the new structure data, the lipophilic environment in the diffusion pathway of Q_B is inferred to be a prerequisite for effective exchange between its binding site in PS IIcc and the plastoquinone pool in the thylakoid membrane (Figure 8d).

Similar pathways have been postulated for photosynthetic cyt b_6f ([92,93] and chapter 20) and for the respiratory cyt bc_1 complex [94]. The alternative exchange pathway through the larger cytosolic (in chloroplasts the entrance from the stroma side) entrance can possibly be excluded because the hydrophobic plastoquinone molecules would have to pass the cytosol (or stroma) before entering the membrane. Since the subunits PsbJ and cyt b-559 flank the membrane opening, they could likely regulate diffusion of Q_B, and it has

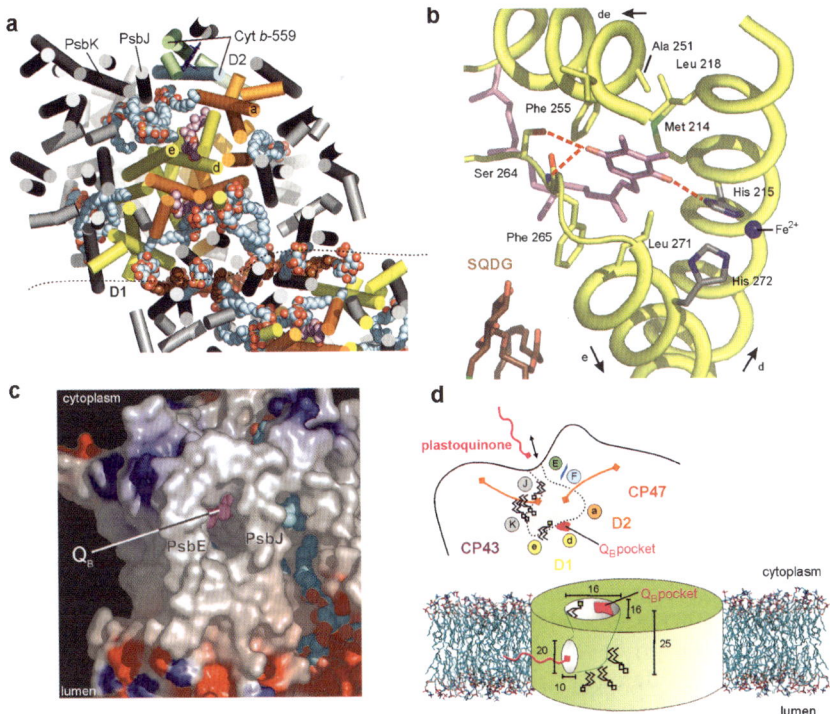

Figure 8. Location of lipids in PS IIcc [128]. (a) Top view from cytoplasmic side as in Figure 7(a) (one monomer is shown completely, the other only partly), the dashed line indicates the monomer–monomer interface. Lipids, detergents and quinones drawn in space filling representation, α-helices of protein subunits as cylinders colored as in Figure 7. The wall of the cavity is formed by labeled TMHs. (b) Plastoquinone (Q_B) binding pocket for side groups of amino acids of D1 interacting with Q_B (violet) are explicitly shown [128]. The orientations of TMH-**d** and TMH-**e** and the connecting α-helix **de** are indicated by arrows. (c) Cavity close to the Q_B pocket and plastoquinone diffusion pathway [128]. View along the membrane plane onto the cavity opening that faces the thylakoid membrane in space-filling presentation with electrostatic potentials marked in colors (red: negative, blue: positive and white: neutral). Lipids are colored cyan; TMH of PsbE and PsbJ are labeled. The Q_B-tail (violet) is nestled in the cavity. (d) Top: Schematic view of the Q_B diffusion pathway in two orientations; same view as in (a). The wall of the cavity (circles) is formed by labeled circles colored by subunits as in Figure 7(a); ionone head groups of Car (orange squares), lipid molecules and the position of the membrane-facing opening are indicated. Bottom: PS IIcc embedded in the thylakoid membrane. The position of the Q_B binding pocket and lipids as well as localization of the two openings of the cavity towards thylakoid membrane and cytoplasm and approximate dimensions of the openings (in Å) are shown.

actually been observed that PsbJ influences the electron transfer between Q_A, Q_B and the plastoquinone pool in tobacco PS II [99,100]. Interestingly, an influence of the cavity on the redox properties of cyt*b-559* can be imagined as the heme group of cyt-*b559* is exposed to the cavity. The existence of a special site denoted Q_C has been proposed that binds PQ/PQH_Z thus modulating the E_m of cyt*b-559* [101].

15.8.5 Carotenoids

Eleven carotenoids in all-trans configuration are detected in the 3.0 Å resolution structure of PS IIcc and are well-defined in the electron density (Figure 7a, b). Five of these are in similar positions as reported by Ferriera et al. [37], whereas six were found at different/novel positions. Predissolved crystals of dimeric PS IIcc contained 9–10 Car per reaction center (Table 1), in agreement with earlier reports [28,102], indicating that no Car were lost upon crystallization (Section 15.6.1, Table 1). Two carotenoids (Car1, 11) are bound to the D1/D2 heterodimer, eight are located around the core antenna subunits (five at CP47, three at CP43), and one (Car12) is nested between small subunits PsbJ, PsbK, PsbZ and X1. Most of the carotenoids are distributed uniformly at the periphery of PS II; only Car 3, 4, 5, and 6 are grouped at the dimer interface and interact with Car1 of the other monomer. In contrast to the pseudo-$C2(Fe^{2+})$ symmetry related location of Chl *a* molecules in the PS IIcc monomer [103], there is no obvious symmetry in the carotenoid substructure (Figure 7a).

The D1/D2 heterodimer of PS IIcc harbors two β-carotenes [104,105]. These carotenoids are differently oriented and, therefore, spectroscopically distinct, as is confirmed by linear dichroism data [106–108]. Owing to these studies, an assignment of Car_{D1} to Car_{498} and of Car_{D2} to Car_{507} is possible.

Car_{D2} is located nearly parallel to the membrane plane, and the protein matrix surrounding it is mainly hydrophobic [109]. This β-carotene electronically connects cyt *b-559* with $Chlz_{D2}$ through Chl_{D2} [38]. Car_{D2} could represent the β-carotene that is suggested to be involved in an electron transfer pathway between the heme group of cyt *b-559* and/or $Chlz_{D2}$ [105,110]. This Car_{D2} is found in a position similar to Car_{48} reported in [37] but differs from the two Car given in [36].

Car_{D1} is located 4.1 Å (edge-to-edge of π-systems) from $Chlz_{D1}$ and oriented perpendicular to the membrane plane, with the isoprenoid segment nearly parallel to TMH-a of D1 (Figure 9a). However, Car_{D1} does not bridge between $Chlz_{D1}$ and other cofactors of the ETC and does, probably, not participate in electron transfer reactions. Its position would rather allow optimal transfer/quenching of triplet states formed on $Chlz_{D1}$ and quenching of singlet oxygen that could be produced by $^3P680$ [104]. This is in contrast with the putative function of Car_{D2} that is not optimized for triplet transfer, indicating a significantly less efficient quenching of triplet states on this side and rather a "molecular wire" role for Car_{D2} [104]. This Car_{D2} functions as redox active component in the putative secondary electron transfer that acts as protective reaction when the Mn_4O_xCa cluster is not active or absent. Estimates of maximal electron transfer rates on the basis of a rate constant-distance relationship in proteins [111] indicate that oxidation of Car_{D2} and $Chlz_{D2}$ by P_{D1} is by orders of magnitude faster than oxidation of Car_{D1} and $Chlz_{D1}$.

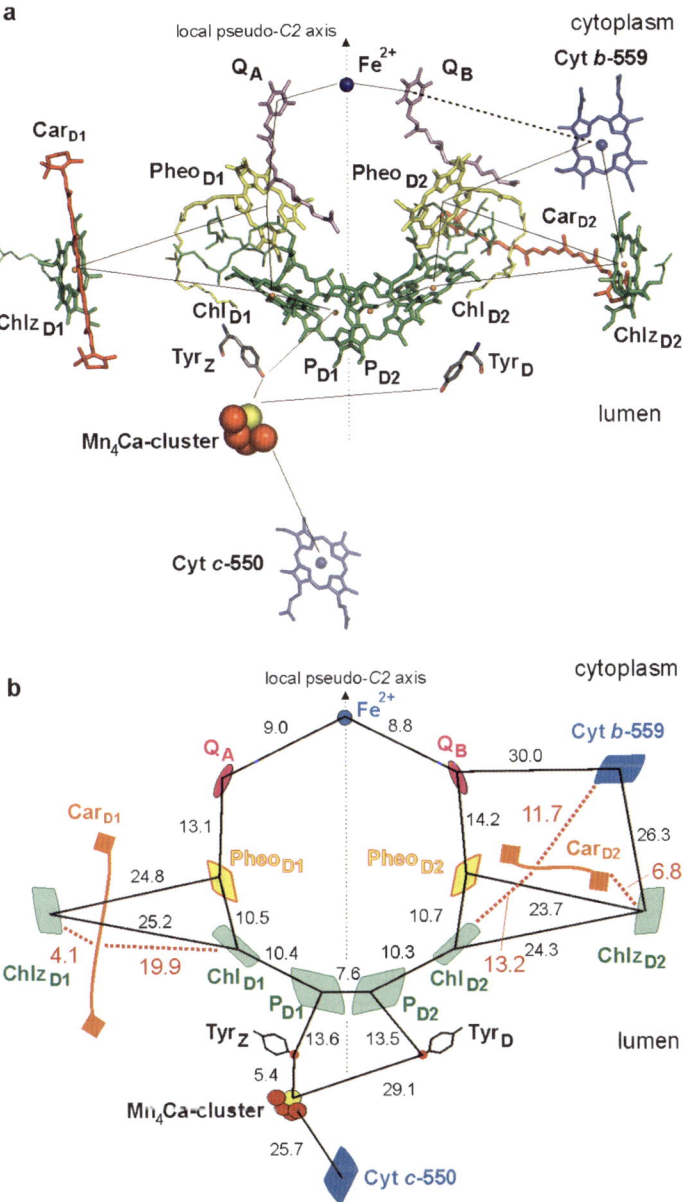

Figure 9. Arrangement of redox-active cofactors and electron transfer chain (ETC) in PS IIcc [128]. (a) View along the membrane plane; the cofactors are colored as in Figure 7(a). The cofactors P_{D1}/P_{D2}, Chl_{D1}/Chl_{D2}, $Pheo_{D1/D2}$, Q_A and Q_B of the ETC are related by the pseudo-$C2$(Fe^{2+}) axis indicated by an arrow and the dotted line. Fe, Mn, and Ca cations are shown as spheres and colored blue, red and yellow, respectively. (b) Schematic view of (a); the symbols of cofactors are as in Figure 7(b). Center-to-center distances between selected cofactor centers (in Å) are symbolized by black lines or edge to edge distances between π-system by red dotted lines.

Consequently, this "protective" electron transfer reaction will predominantly occur on the D2 side.

Car_{D1} in the PS IIcc dimer is close to a cluster consisting of four Car located in the "other" monomer (Car3', 4', 5' and 6') and near CP47'. A coupled group of three Chl a (Ch114', 17', and 26') of CP47' are close to the Car-cluster formed by Car 3', 4', 5', 6'. Three of the clustered Car are at the van der Waals distance to each other, forming a coupled Car trimer that could lead to a broadened absorption spectrum of the core antenna system.

In the subunits CP43 and CP47 most of the Car are located at van der Waals contact with Chl a (edge to edge distance of π-electron-systems < 4 Å). This is a prerequisite for both singlet–singlet excitation energy transfer (EET) from Car to Chl a as well as rapid triplet–triplet transfer from ^{3}Chl to Car as the protection mechanism of PS II to deleterious effects induced by triplet states of Chl a. Although not all Chl a molecules interact directly with Car molecules, excitonically coupled groups of Chl a have at least one Car in close contact. Triplet states can migrate between neighboring Chls a, so that efficient triplet quenching could still be possible if these strongly coupled Chl a molecules are connected to a Car. The two groups strongest coupling (Chl a11, 12, 13 and Chl a14, 25, 26, 27) in CP47 are at van der Waals distance to one Car, while the corresponding groups in CP43 (Chl a34, 46 and Ch145, 47) are more distant to a Car (Figure 7b), which might cause lower triplet quenching efficiency.

15.8.6 Chlorophyll a and Pheophytin a in the Electron Transfer Chain (ETC)

In contrast to the special pair in the purple bacterial reaction centers (PBRCs) the photoactive pigment of PS II, P680, is a multimeric pigment ([112], see Chapter 16). The Chl a molecules P_{D1} and P_{D2} are coordinated by D1-His198Nε and D2-His197Nε, respectively, and the two Mg^{2+} ions are 8.3 Å apart [37,38]. This distance resembles the value reported in [113] and is shorter than the 10 Å reported by [35,36]. The interplanar separation of the chlorin heterocycles is 3.6 Å (Figure 10), and the environment of P_{D1} and P_{D2} is mainly hydrophobic with no evidence for direct hydrogen-bonding to protein. D2-Trp191, shown to be important for the high redox potential of $P680^{+\cdot}$ [114], stacks with D2-His197 and is in van der Waals contact with P_{D2} [38].

Chl_{D1} and Chl_{D2} are found in similar positions as the two accessory bacteriochlorophylls in the PBRC. In contrast to PBRC ([96]; see Chapter 11), however, they are not coordinated by histidines, but probably by water molecules hydrogen-bonded to D1-Thr179Oγ and D2-Val175O, respectively. The binding pockets of Chl_{D1} and Chl_{D2} are both hydrophobic with two notable differences: first, in the Chl_{D1} binding pocket there are three Met residues, but none in the Chl_{D2} pocket and, second, there is no direct hydrogen bond in the Chl_{D1} pocket, but one in the Chl_{D2} pocket formed between D1-Gln199NεH and the carboxymethyl carbonyl oxygen of Chl_{D2} [38].

$Pheo_{D1}$ is located between TMH **c** of D1 and **d** of D2, and $Pheo_{D2}$ between TMH **c** of D2 and **d** of D1 (Figure 6a). Both Pheo a molecules are in van der Waals contact with non-polar side-chains, and $Pheo_{D2}$ is not involved in any

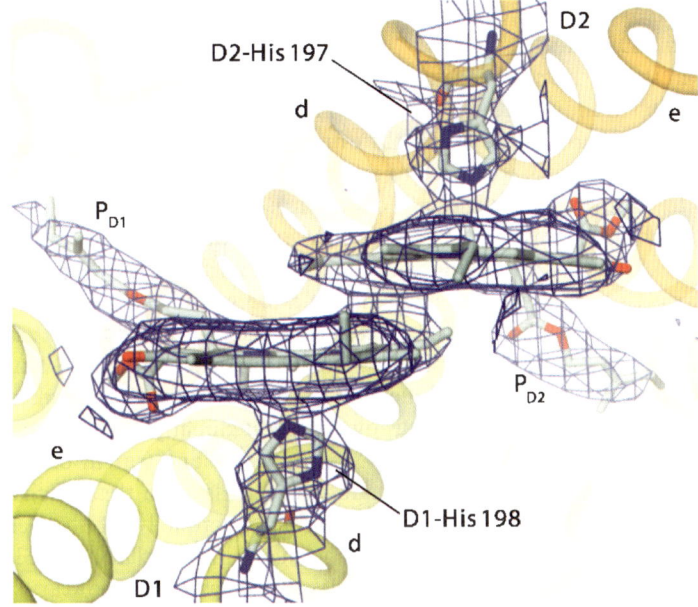

Figure 10. Coordination and environment of the P_{D1}-P_{D2} unit [38]. P_{D1} is coordinated by D1-His198 and its counterpart P_{D2} by D2-His197. Both cofactors are embedded between TMH **d** and **e** of D1 (yellow) and D2 (orange), respectively. Electron density (blue) is contoured at the 1.2 σ level. Amino acid side-chains and phytyl chains of the Chl *a* are clearly defined in the electron density.

direct hydrogen-bond to the protein matrix [38]. By contrast, Pheo$_{D1}$ forms three hydrogen-bonds: between D1-Gln130NεH and the keto oxygen; D1-Tyr126OηH and carboxymethyl carbonyl oxygen; D1-Tyr147OηH and carboxyphytyl carbonyl oxygen.

The arrangement and orientation of the cofactors, which are involved in stable charge separation of PS II, resemble those of the corresponding components in PBRC, but there are some notable differences. The $Mg^{2+}\cdots Mg^{2+}$ distance of 8.3 Å between P_{D1} and P_{D2} in PS IIcc [38], is 0.7 Å longer than that of the two bacteriochlorophyll *b* moieties of P960 (7.6 Å) (Chapter 11) [96] and similar to the PS IIcc structures published at lower resolution [37,113]. Despite some structural similarities between P_{D1}-P_{D2} and the photoactive special pair in PBRCs, P680 is clearly a multichromophoric complex, as discussed in a recent review [112] and outlined in detail in Chapter 16.

15.9 General View of the Water Oxidizing Complex (WOC)

The structure of the WOC and the mechanism by which it catalyzes water oxidation have been widely studied by different biophysical and biochemical methods ([115] and see Chapter 17). The WOC contains a multinuclear metal center with four Mn plus one Ca^{2+} ions that are connected by μ-oxo bridges. This unit, usually symbolized by Mn_4O_xCa, is the catalytic site of oxidative water cleavage (for details, see Chapter 17). The μ-oxo bridges are not resolved in the X-ray structure at 3.0 Å resolution of PS IIcc.

The first X-ray crystal structure of PS IIcc from *T. elongatus* at 3.8 Å resolution [35] provided information on the size, shape and location of the Mn_4O_xCa cluster. This unit is bound close to the lumenal surface at the C-terminus of the D1 protein and near to its non-transmembrane α-helix CD [35]. The electron density of the Mn cluster is bulged in three directions in the shape of a distorted Y and was interpreted as one Mn in the center and three Mn at the ends of the Y arms. The Mn are not coplanar, the central Mn being out of the plane formed by the other three Mn, so that the shape is reminiscent of a tripod with the central Mn pointing toward the lumenal side of the membrane. In PS IIcc from *T. vulcanus* at 3.7 Å resolution a similar location and size of the Mn cluster was found but the shape is described as "pear", and the Mn-cations are coplanar, coordinated by four or five amino acid residues of the D1 protein, the carboxyl group of the C-terminus D1-Ala344, D1-Asp170, D1-Glu333 (or D1-His332) and possibly D1-His337, D1-Asp189 (or His190) that could provide direct ligands to the Mn ions [36]. This proposal was based on mutational studies [116,117], but not on crystallographic data because the resolution was too low to permit an unambiguous assignment of the amino acid side-chains. Nevertheless, the idea that the C-terminus of protein D1 provides ligands for the Mn_4O_xCa cluster is consistent with mutants that are unable to assemble the Mn_4O_xCa cluster [118] and with site-directed mutations in this region [116,117,119].

On the basis of the 3.5 Å resolution structure [37] a model of the manganese cluster was proposed, where three Mn and one Ca^{2+} are arranged in a cubane-like structure linked to a fourth Mn by a mono-μ-oxo bridge; in addition, the nature of the protein ligands and the overall protein environment of the WOC were also specified. This model was used as the basis for the formulation of a molecular mechanism of the water splitting reaction [37]. Our PS IIcc*Te* structure at 3.0 Å resolution indicates that this proposal has to be revised. A different picture emerges, especially concerning the manganese cluster, as outlined in the following section.

15.9.1 Environment of the Mn_4O_xCa Cluster

When analyzing redissolved crystals of dimeric PS IIcc by atom absorption spectroscopy (AAS) the Mn/Chl *a* stoichiometry was found to be 3.6 ± 0.5 Mn/ 36 Chl *a* (Table 1). In combination with oxygen yield measurements this indicates that 90% of the centers in the crystals contain a fully assembled Mn_4-Ca cluster.

The shape of the electron density of the Mn_4O_xCa cluster can be best described by four Mn cations arranged as a "hook" (Figure 11a). This feature partly resembles the previously suggested Y-shaped arrangement [35]. The Mn cations are numbered Mn1–4, starting from the bend of the "hook", where the electron density is highest. Since the Mn–Mn distances could not be resolved directly at 3.0 Å resolution, the following procedure was applied based on the assumption that the distances between the Mn-pairs Mn1–Mn2, Mn2–Mn3, Mn3–Mn4 and Mn1–Mn3 can adopt one of two values gathered from XANES measurements: 2.7 or 3.3 Å for di-μ-oxo or mono-μ-oxo bridging, respectively (for details see Chapter 17). For a detailed description of the refinement procedure to the Mn–Mn distances see [39]. This yielded two types of Mn···Mn pairs in the electron density, one indicating di-μ-oxo bridges spaced by 2.7 Å for Mn1–Mn2 and Mn2–Mn3, and the others spaced by 3.3 Å represent mono-μ-oxo bridges for Mn1–Mn3 and for the terminal Mn3–Mn4. X-ray diffraction data measured at and beyond the Mn-edge confirmed the presence of Ca^{2+} near the larger electron density of Mn, thus enabling an interpretation in terms of a Mn-Ca-heteronuclear cluster [120], with Ca^{2+} located between the Mn cations and redox-active Tyr$_Z$. The Ca^{2+} forms the vertex of a trigonal pyramid and is equidistant (~ 3.4 Å) to the three cations Mn1–3 at the base (Figure 11b). These are typical Mn–Ca distances, as derived by EXAFS studies [121], and correspond to the suggested "3 + 1" Mn-cluster model [122]. This arrangement markedly differs from the cubane-like structure postulated on the basis of the 3.5 Å resolution data, as is illustrated by a comparison of Figure 11(a) and (b) [37].

Importantly, X-ray data obtained for the structure of the Mn_4O_xCa cluster has to be interpreted with caution due to general problems emerging from radiation damage of the cluster caused by manganese reduction during the long exposure of the crystals to X-rays required for data collection. Such damage might be reflected by uneven distribution of the electron density associated with disorder of Mn and Ca^{2+} cations [39]. These difficulties are clearly illustrated by EXAFS studies [123] that showed Mn(III) and Mn(IV) of the Mn_4O_xCa cluster in PS II to be rapidly reduced to Mn(II) by X-rays in both solution and crystals even at low (10 K) temperature [123]. These findings indicate that structural changes have to be expected that are associated with disruption of μ-oxo bridges and of Mn–ligand interactions caused by the reduction of Mn cations.

Mn(III), Mn(IV) and Ca^{2+} cations are coordinated by side-chains of D1 and CP43 (Figure 11b). Other amino acids, i.e., D1-Asp61, D1-Glu165, D1-His337, and CP43-Arg357, are too far from the Mn_4O_xCa cluster (>4.0 Å) to allow direct coordination but are suitable for water-mediated ligation or may provide cation ligation in different redox-states of the Mn_4O_xCa cluster.

In total, 12 oxygen/nitrogen atoms from nearby side-chains and from the carboxy terminus Ala344 of protein D1 were found at distances <3.0 Å from a Mn and Ca^{2+} cation (i.e., an average of 2.4 per metal), in contrast with ten atoms (i.e., two per metal) found at 3.5 Å resolution. Carboxylate groups of two glutamates (Figure 11a, b) (D1-Glu189, D1-Glu333), one aspartate (D1-Asp342), and the C-terminus of D1 (D1-Ala344) could act as bidentate ligands, thereby bridging different metals, whereas in the 3.5 Å structure only one ligand (D1-Glu333) is positioned to coordinate two cations simultaneously. The combination of bidentate ligands could serve to enhance the stability of metal coordination and assist in the rearrangement of μ-oxo and di-μ-oxo bridges during the S-state cycle [124]. This interpretation is consistent with mutational

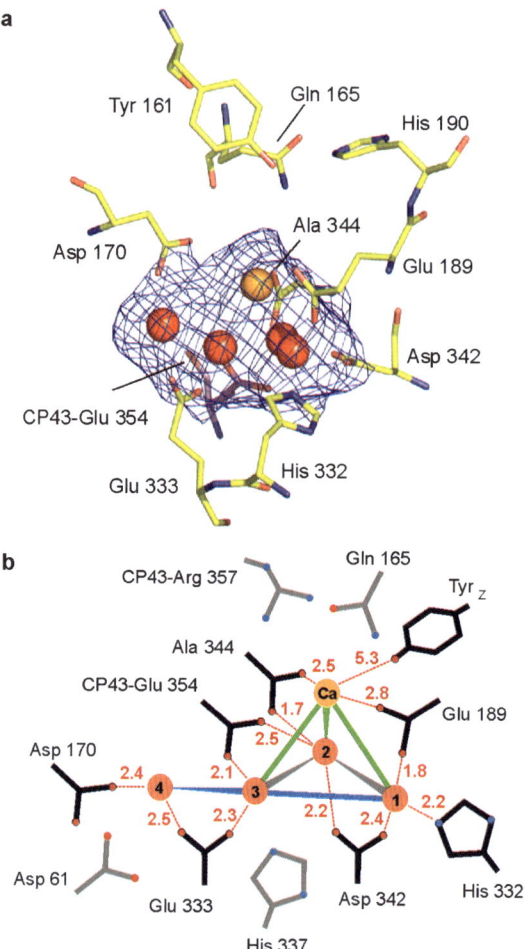

Figure 11. Protein environment and coordination of Mn$_4$O$_x$Ca-cluster and Tyr$_Z$ [128]. (a) Location of the Mn$_4$O$_x$Ca-cluster: view along the membrane plane, similar to Figure 9(a). Relevant surrounding amino acids of D1 and CP43 are marked in yellow and magenta, respectively. Mn and Ca cations are colored red and orange, respectively; the μ-oxo bridges are not resolved and omitted. Electron density of the Mn$_4$O$_x$Ca-cluster is contoured at 1.2 σ level (blue) for its overall shape of the Mn$_4$Ca-cluster. (b) Schematic view of the Mn$_4$O$_x$Ca cluster; the distances between Mn (red) and Ca (orange) cations shown by connecting lines (grey: 2.7 Å; blue: 3.3 Å, green: 3.4 Å; the μ-oxo bridges are not seen). Amino acids colored in black represent members of the first coordination sphere, whereas the second sphere of amino acids is in grey (distances are in Å). (c) Superposition of the current Mn$_4$O$_x$Ca-cluster structure colored as in (a) with the Mn$_4$O$_x$Ca-cluster structure at 3.5 Å resolution as described in [37]; in the latter structure, subunits D1 and CP43 are in green and orange, respectively. Mn and Ca cations are colored in violet and yellow, respectively.

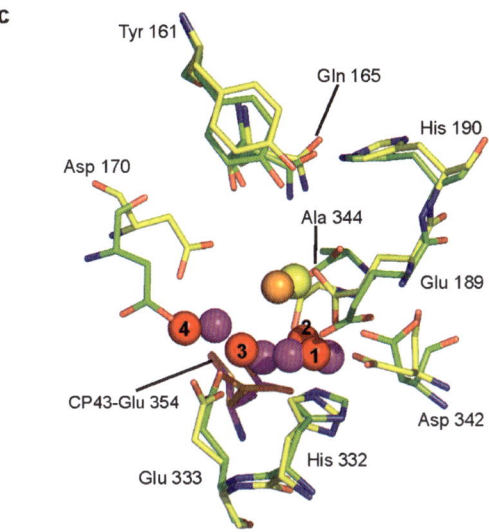

Figure 11. (*Continued*).

replacement of ligating residues by residues with non-ligating groups that in many cases, except for D1-Glu333 and D1-Asp342, led to partially functional Mn_4O_xCa clusters [116,117]. Indeed, in our structure a second ligating group is present in all cases except for Mn4. The second ligand would stabilize the cations in their position, if the other ligands were lost. The C-terminus of D1-Ala344 ligates Mn2 as well as Ca^{2+}, whereas in the 3.5 Å structure this residue is only close to Ca^{2+}.

15.10 Conclusion and Perspectives

The studies described in this chapter have clearly demonstrated that improvement in cultivation of *T. elongatus* cells combined with thorough biochemical characterization of the obtained PS IIcc and refined crystallization protocols are essential to achieve X-ray diffraction data at higher resolution.

The present 3.0 Å resolution structure of PS IIcc provides important and novel information on the location of the phytyl chains of Chl *a* and Pheo *a* and of eleven carotenoids, 14 lipid and three detergent molecules. It also permits a more reliable assignment of several amino acid side-chains. Highlights of the improved resolution are the discovery of intrinsically bound lipids that cover a channel for putative PQ/PQH_2 diffusion between the Q_B binding pocket in PS II and the plastoquinone pool in the thylakoid membrane.

The large number (14) of intrinsic lipid molecules bound to core protein suggests that these molecules play an important structural role, possibly in providing a deformable interface around the cofactor scaffold of D1/D2 and at the dimer interface. These features are assumed to be essential in facilitating the assembly and rearrangement of the PS II complex, especially during the replacement of photodamaged subunit D1 (for PS II repair, see Chapter 10).

The discovery of the diffusion channel for the mobile plastoquinone Q_B in PS II is most important for an understanding of the turnover mechanism of PQ/PQH_2 at PS II (see also Chapter 16). Lipids and carotenoids form a flexible lipophilic cavity that "lubricates" the diffusion of plastoquinone/plastoquinol between its binding pocket in PS II and the plastoquinone pool in the thylakoid membrane.

In addition to this entirely novel finding, the 3.0 Å structure data also unambiguously resolved the arrangement of the two Car molecules in the D1/D2 heterodimer, thereby providing a sound basis for understanding their role in the electron and/or excitation energy transfer. Furthermore, nine Car molecules in the core antenna of CP43 and CP47 were assigned, and their possible participation in light harvesting and efficient triplet quenching has been discussed. The cluster of Cars located at the monomer–monomer interface suggests that excitonically coupled Car multimers could possibly participate in light harvesting.

New information on the structure of the WOC is limited. The "hook" shaped arrangement of the Mn_4O_xCa cluster resembles the $3+1$ models proposed earlier [35,38]. Four Mn and one Ca^{2+} of the cluster are bridged in bidentate mode by carboxylate groups but the μ-oxo bridges postulated from EXAFS data are not yet resolved. Comparative EXAFS studies clearly show that the Mn_4O_xCa cluster is definitely distorted due to radiation damage, which leads to manganese reduction and dismantling. For the unraveling of the undamaged structure of the Mn_4O_xCa cluster at atomic resolution, a combination of X-ray crystallographic studies with dichroic EXAFS measurements at lowest possible doses on PS IIcc single crystals is indispensable at present. These studies are in progress and will, hopefully, provide details on the WOC structure as a new starting point for deeper insight into the mechanism of water oxidation (Chapter 17).

Novel EXAFS experiments on PSII single crystals from *T. elongatus*, which avoided radiation damage and provided a high resoultion structure of the Mn_4-Ca cluster are presented in [126].

Acknowledgements

I highly appreciate the competence of and excellent cooperation with the crystallographic group of Professors W. Saenger, J. Biesiadka and Bernhard Loll, who made our success possible, and last but not least I thank especially J. Kern, K.-D. Irrgang and, for excellent technical assistance, D. DiFiore and C. Lüneberg. I am grateful to Professor Dr. W. Saenger, Dr. F. Müh and Professor Dr. G. Renger for critical reading of the manuscript. This work was supported by Deutsche Forschungsgemeinschaft (SFB 498, TP A4 and C7). Beamtime and support by beamline scientists at the synchrotrons ESRF (Grenoble, France), SLS (Villigen), BESSY (Berlin), and DESY (Hamburg) are gratefully acknowledged.

References

1. W. Menke, Untersuchungen über den Feinbau des Protoplasmas mit dem Universal-elektronenmikroskop. *Protoplasma* **35** 1940, 115–130 [in German].
2. L.A. Staehelin, G.W.M. van der Staay, Structure, composition, functional organization and dynamic properties of thylakoid membranes, in: *Molecular Biology of Cyanobacteria* (1996) (D.A. Bryant, ed.), Kluwer Academic, Dordrecht, pp. 11–30.
3. H.T. Witt, Coupling of quanta, electrons, field ions and phosphorylation in the functional membrane of photosynthesis. *Q. Res. Biophys.* **4** (1971) 365–477.
4. G. Renger, Studies on the structural and functional organization of system II of photosynthesis. The use of tryPS In as a structurally selective inhibitor at the outer surface of the thylakoid membrane. *Biochim Biophys Acta* **440** (1976) 287–300.
5. L.G. Franzen, S. Styring, A.-L. Etienne, Ö. Hansson, C. Vernotte, Spectroscopic and functional characterization of a highly oxygen-evolving Photosystem II reaction center complex from spinach. *Photobiochem. Photobiophys.* **13** (1986) 15–28.
6. E. Haag, K.-D. Irrgang, E.J. Boekema, G. Renger, Functional and structural analysis of Photosystem II core complexes from spinach with high oxygen evolution capacity. *Eur. J. Biochem.* **189** (1990) 47–53.
7. G. Tsiotis, M. Psylinakis, B. Woplensinger, A. Lustig, A. Engel, D. Ghanotakis, Investigation of the structure of spinach Photosystem II reaction center complex. *Eur. J. Biochem.* **259** (1999) 320–324.
8. O. Nanba, K. Satoh, Isolation of a Photosystem II reaction center consisting of D-1 and D-2 polypeptides and cytochrome *b-559*. *Proc. Natl. Acad. Sci. U.S.A.* **84** (1987) 109–112.
9. M. Rögner, J.P. Dekker, E.J. Boekema, H.T. Witt, Size, shape and mass of the oxygen-evolving Photosystem II complex from the thermophilic cyanobacterium *Synechococcus* sp. *FEBS Lett.* **219** (1987) 207–211.
10. J. Deisenhofer, O. Epp, K. Miki, R. Huber, H. Michel, X-ray structure analysis of a membrane protein complex. Electron density map at 3 Å resolution and a model of the chromophores of the photosynthetic reaction center from *Rhodopseudomonas viridis*. *J. Mol. Biol.* **180** (1984) 385–398.
11. J. Deisenhofer, O. Epp, K. Miki, R. Huber, H. Michel, Structure of the protein subunits in the photosynthetic reaction centre of *Rhodopseudomonas viridis* at 3Å resolution. *Nature* **318** (1985) 618–624.
12. P. Fromme, H.T. Witt, Improved isolation and crystallization of Photosystem I for structural analysis. *Biochim. Biophys. Acta* **1365** (1998) 175–184.
13. J. Kern, B. Loll, C. Lüneberg, D. DiFiore, J. Biesiadka, K.D. Irrgang, A. Zouni, Purification, characterisation and crystallisation of Photosystem II from *Thermosynechococcus elongatus* cultivated in a new type of photobioreactor. *Biochim. Biophys. Acta* **1706** (2005) 147–157.
14. J.F. Allen, J. Forsberg, Molecular recognition in thylakoid structure and function. *Trends Pharmacol. Sci.* **6** (2001) 317–326.
15. J. Standfuss, A.C. Terwisscha van Scheltinga, M. Lamborghini, W. Kühlbrandt, Mechanisms of photoprotection and nonphotochemical quenching in pea light-harvesting complex at 2.5 A resolution. *EMBO J.* **24** (2005) 919–928.
16. K.-D. Irrgang, Architecture of the thylakoid membrane, in: *Concepts in Photobiology: Photosynthesis and Photomorphogenesis* (1999) (G.S. Singhal, et al., eds.), Narosa Publishing House & Kluwer Academic Publishers, New Dehli, India and Dordrecht, pp. 139–180.

17. J. Whitmarsh, H.B. Pakrasi, Form and function of cytochrome *b-559*, in: *Oxygenic Photosynthesis: The Light Reactions* (1996) (D.R. Ort, C.F. Yocum, eds.), Kluwer Academic Publishers, Dordrecht, pp. 249–264.
18. D.H. Stewart, G.W. Brudvig, Cytochrome *b-559* of Photosystem II. *Biochim. Biophys. Acta* **1367** (1998) 63–87.
19. L.X. Shi, W.P. Schröder, The low molecular mass subunits of the photosynthetic supracomplex. Photosystem II. *Biochim. Biophys. Acta* **1608** (2004) 75–96.
20. A. Seidler, The extrinsic polypeptides of Photosystem II. *Biochim. Biophys. Acta* **1277** (1996) 35–60.
21. R.K. Mishra, D.F. Ghanotakis, Selective extraction of 22 kDa and 10 kDa polypeptides from Photosystem II without removal of 23 kDa and 17 kDa extrinsic proteins. *Photosynth. Res.* **36** (1993) 11–16.
22. R.J. Debus, The manganese and calcium ions of photosynthetic oxygen evolution. *Biophys. Biochim. Acta* **1102** (1992) 269–352.
23. B. Ke, Photosynthesis - photobiochemistry and photobiophysics, in: *Advances in Photosynthesis and Respiration* (2001) (Govindjee, ed.), Kluwer Academic Publishers, Dordrecht, Vol. 10.
24. S. Miyairi, G.H. Schatz, Oxygen-evolving extracts from a thermophilic cyanobacterium *Synechococcus*, sp. *Z. Naturforsch., Teil C* **38** (1983) 44–48.
25. G.H. Schatz, H.T. Witt, Extraction and characterisation of oxygen-evolving Photosystem II complexes from a thermophilic cyanobacterium *Synechococcus* spec. *Photobiochem. Photobiophys.* **7** (1984) 1–14.
26. K. Satoh, T. Ohno, S. Katoh, An oxygen-evolving complex with a simple subunit structure - 'a water-plastoquinone oxidoreductase' - from the thermophilic cyanobacterium *Synechococcus* sp. *FEBS Lett.* **180** (1985) 326–330.
27. A. Yamagishi, S. Katoh, Further characterization of the two Photosysem II reaction center complex preparations from the thermophilic cyanobacterium *Synechococcus* sp. *Biochim. Biophys. Acta* **807** (1985) 74–80.
28. T. Ohno, K. Satoh, S. Katoh, Chemical composition of purified oxygen-evolving complexes from the thermophilic cyanobacterium *Synechococcus* sp. *Biochim. Biophys. Acta* **852** (1986) 1–8.
29. J.P. Dekker, E.J. Boekema, H.T. Witt, M. Rögner, Refined purification and further characterization of oxygen-evolving and tris-treated Photosystem II particles from the thermophilic cyanobacterium *Synechococcus* sp. *Biochim. Biophys. Acta* **936** (1988) 307–318.
30. P. da Fonseca, K. Maghlaoui, B. Hankamer, C. Büchel, J. Barber, Purification of oxygen evolving PS II complexes from *Synechococcus elongatus* for electron crystallography, in: *Photosynthesis: Mechanisms and Effects* (1998) (G. Garab, ed.), Kluwer Academic Publishers, Dordrecht, pp. 969–972.
31. A. Zouni, C. Lüneberg, P. Fromme, W.D. Schubert, W. Saenger, H.T. Witt, Characterization of single crystals of Photosystem II from the thermophilic cyanobacterium *Synechococcus elongatus*, in: *Photosynthesis: Mechanisms and Effects* (1998) (G. Garab, ed.), Kluwer Academic, Dordrecht, pp. 925–928.
32. E. Setlikova, D. Sofrova, O. Prasil, P. Budac, M. Koblizek, I. Setlik, Integrity and activity of photosystem 2 complexes isolated from the thermophilic cyanobacterium *Synechococcus elongatus* using various detergents. *Photosynthetica* **37** (1999) 183–200.
33. M. Sugiura, Y. Inoue, Highly purified thermo-stable oxygen-evolving Photosystem II core complex from the thermophilic cyanobacterium *Synechococcus elongatus* having His-tagged CP43. *Plant Cell Physiol.* **40** (1999) 1219–1231.

34. H. Kuhl, J. Kruip, A. Seidler, A. Krieger-Liszkay, M. Bunker, D. Bald, A.J. Scheidig, M. Rögner, Towards structural determination of the water-splitting enzyme. Purification, crystallization, and preliminary crystallographic studies of Photosystem II from a thermophilic cyanobacterium. *J. Biol. Chem* **275** (2000) 20652–20659.
35. A. Zouni, H.T. Witt, J. Kern, P. Fromme, N. Krauss, W. Saenger, P. Orth, Crystal structure of Photosystem II from *Synechococcus elongatus* at 3.8 Å resolution. *Nature* **409** (2001) 739–743.
36. N. Kamiya, J.R. Shen, Crystal structure of oxygen-evolving Photosystem II from *Thermosynechococcus vulcanus* at 3.7-Å resolution. *Proc. Natl. Acad. Sci. U. S. A.* **100** (2003) 98–103.
37. K.N. Ferreira, T.M. Iverson, K. Maghlaoui, J. Barber, S. Iwata, Architecture of the photosynthetic oxygen-evolving center. *Science* **303** (2004) 1831–1838.
38. J. Biesiadka, B. Loll, J. Kern, K.-D. Irrgang, A. Zouni, Crystal structure of cyanobacterial Photosystem II at 3.2 Å resolution: a closer look at the Mn-cluster. *Phys. Chem. Chem. Phys.* **6** (2004) 4733–4736.
39. B. Loll, J. Kern, W. Saenger, A. Zouni, J. Biesiadka, Towards complete cofactor arrangement in the 3.0 Å resolution structure of Photosystem II. *Nature* **438** (2005) 1040–1044.
40. A. Lustig, A. Engel, M. Zulauf, Density determination by analytical ultracentrifugation in a rapid dynamical gradient: application to lipid and detergent aggregates containing proteins. *Biochim. Biophys. Acta* **1115** (1991) 89–95.
41. A. Holzenburg, M.C. Bewly, F.H. Wilson, W.V. Nicholson, R. Ford, Three-dimensional structure of Photosystem II. *Nature* **363** (1993) 470–472.
42. R.C. Ford, M.F. Rosenberg, F.H. Shepherd, P. McPhie, A. Holzenburg, Photosystem II 3-D structure and the role of the extrinsic subunits in photosynthetic oxygen evolution. *Micron* **26** (1995) 133–140.
43. G. Tsiotis, G. McDermott, D. Ghanotakis, Progress towards structural elucidation of Photosystem II. *Photosynth. Res.* **50** (1996) 93–101.
44. R. Bassi, A. Ghiretti Magaldi, G. Tognon, G.M. Giacometti, K.R. Miller, Two-dimensional crystals of the Photosystem II reaction center complex from higher plants. *Eur. J. Cell Biol.* **50** (1989) 84–93.
45. G.F. Peter, J.P. Thornber, Biochemical composition and organization of higher plant Photosystem II light-harvesting pigment-proteins. *J. Biol. Chem.* **266** (1991) 16745–16754.
46. M.K. Lyon, K.M. Marr, P.S. Furcinitti, Formation and characterization of two-dimensional crystals of Photosystem II. *J. Struct. Biol.* **110** (1993) 133–140.
47. C. Santini, V. Tidu, G. Tognon, A. Ghiretti Magaldi, R. Bassi, Three-dimensional structure of the higher-plant Photosystem II reaction centre and evidence for its dimeric organization in vivo. *Eur. J. Biochem.* **221** (1994) 307–315.
48. E.J. Boekema, B. Hankamer, D. Bald, J. Kruip, J. Nield, A.F. Boonstra, J. Barber, M. Rögner, Supramolecular structure of the Photosystem II complex from green plants and cyanobacteria. *Proc. Natl. Acad. Sci. U.S.A.* **92** (1995) 175–179.
49. K.M. Marr, D.N. Mastronarde, M.K. Lyon, Two-dimensional crystals of Photosystem II: biochemical characterization, cryoelectron microscopy and localization of the D1 and cytochrome *b-559* polypeptides. *J. Cell Biol.* **132** (1996) 823–833.
50. J. Nield, C. Funk, J. Barber, Supermolecular structure of Photosystem II and location of the PsbS protein. *Philos. Trans. R. Soc. London B Biol. Sci.* **355** (2000) 1337–1344.

51. J.R. Shen, N. Kamiya, Crystallization and the crystal properties of the oxygen-evolving Photosystem II from *Synechococcus vulcanus*. *Biochemistry* **39** (2000) 14739–14744.
52. A.E. Yakushevska, P.E. Jensen, W. Keegstra, H. van Roon, H.V. Scheller, E.J. Boekema, J.P. Dekker, Supermolecular organization of Photosystem II and its associated light harvesting antenna in *ArabidoPS Is thaliana*. *Eur. J. Biochem.* **268** (2001) 6020–6028.
53. M. Rögner, E.J. Boekema, J. Barber, How does photosystem 2 split water? The structural basis of efficient energy conversion. *Trends Biochem. Sci.* **21** (1996) 44–49.
54. D.F. Ghanotakis, G. Tsiotis, T.M. Bricker, Polypeptides of Photosystem II, in: *Concepts in Photobiology: Photosynthesis and Photomorphogenesis* (1999) (G.S. Singhal, et al., eds.), Narosa Publishing House, New Dehli, pp. 264–291.
55. K.-D. Irrgang, Y. Georgalis, P. Franke, J. Behlke, W. Saenger, A. Zouni, Structural comparison of oxygen-evolving Photosystem II core complexes from *Synechococcus elongatus* and *Spinacia oleracea*. in: *12th International Conference on Photosynthesis* (2001 Brisbane, Australia), CSIRO Publishers, Melbourne.
56. A. Zouni, J. Kern, J. Frank, T. Hellweg, J. Behlke, W. Saenger, K.D. Irrgang, Size determination of cyanobacterial and higher plant Photosystem II by gel permeation chromatography, light scattering, and ultracentrifugation. *Biochemistry* **44** (2005) 4572–4581.
57. P. Jekow, P. Fromme, H.T. Witt, W. Saenger, Photosystem I from *Synechococcus elongates*: preparation and crystallization of monomers with varying subunit compositions. *Biochim. Biophys. Acta* **1229** (1995) 115–120.
58. J. Huyer, H.-J. Eckert, K.-D. Irrgang, J. Miao, H.-J. Eichler, G. Renger, Fluorescence decay kinetics of solubilized pigment protein complexes from the distal, proximal, and core antenna of Photosystem II in the range of 10–277 K and absence or presence of sucrose. *J. Phys. Chem. B* **108** (2004) 3326–3334.
59. K.-D. Irrgang, E.J. Boekema, J. Vater, G. Renger, Structural determination of the Photosystem II core complex from spinach. *Eur. J. Biochem.* **178** (1988) 209–217.
60. S. Vasil'ev, K.D. Irrgang, T. Schrötter, A. Bergmann, H.J. Eichler, G. Renger, Quenching of chlorophyll a fluorescence in the aggregates of LHCII: steady state fluorescence and picosecond relaxation kinetics. *Biochemistry* **36** (1997) 7503–7512.
61. T. Henrysson, W.P. Schröder, H.-E. Äklund, M. Spangfort, Isolation and characterization of the Chl a/b protein complex CP29 from spinach. *Biochim. Biophys. Acta* **977** (1998) 301–308.
62. J. Pieper, K.D. Irrgang, M. Ratsep, J. Voigt, G. Renger, G.J. Small, Assignment of the lowest Qy-state and spectral dynamics of the CP29 chlorophyll *a/b* antenna complex of green plants: a hole-burning study. *Photochem. Photobiol.* **71** (2000) 574–581.
63. R.M. Garavito, Z. Markovic-Housley, The growth and characterization of membrane protein crystals. *J. Crystal Growth* **76** (1986) 701–709.
64. S. Veesler, S. Marq, S. Lafont, J.P. Astier, R. Boistelle, Influence of polydispersity on protein crystallization: a quasi-elastic light-scattering study applied to alpha-amylase. *Acta Crystallogr., Sect. D* **50** (1994) 355–360.
65. Y. Georgalis, A. Zouni, W. Eberstein, W. Saenger, Formation dynamics of protein precrystallization fractal clusters. *J. Crystal Growth* **126** (1993) 245–260.
66. W. Eberstein, Y. Geogalis, W. Saenger, The influence of temperature on the dynamics of protein precrystallization clusters, studied by photon correlation spectroscopy. *Eur. Biophys. J.* **22** (1993) 359–366.

67. A. Zouni, R. Jordan, E. Schlodder, P. Fromme, H.T. Witt, First Photosystem II crystals capable of water oxidation. *Biochim. Biophys. Acta* **1457** (2000) 103–105.
68. G. Renger, The action of 2-anilinothiophenes as accelerators of the deactivation reactions in the water splitting enzyme system of photosynthesis. *Biochim. Biophys. Acta* **256** (1972) 428–439.
69. F. Müh, A. Zouni, Extinction coefficients and critical solubilisation concentrations of Photosystems I and II from *Thermosynechococcus elongates*. *Biochim. Biophys. Acta* **1708** (2005) 219–228.
70. A. Zouni, J. Kern, B. Loll, J. Biesiadka, W. Saenger, K.-D. Irrgang, Biochemical and functional analysis of Photosystem II crystals from *Thermosynechococcus elongatus* diffracting to 3.2 Å, in: *13th International Photosynthesis Conference* (2004. Montreal, Canada), Allen Press, Lawrence, Kansas.
71. Y. Kashino, H. Koike, K. Satoh, An improved sodium dodecyl sulfate-polyacrylamide gel electrophoresis system for the analysis of membrane protein complexes. *Electrophoresis* **22** (2001) 1004–1007.
72. Y. Kashino, W.M. Lauber, J.A. Carroll, Q. Wang, J. Whitmarsh, K. Satoh, H.B. Pakrasi, Proteomic analysis of a highly active Photosystem II preparation from the cyanobacterium *Synechocystis* sp. PCC 6803 reveals the presence of novel polypeptides. *Biochemistry* **41** (2002) 8004–8012.
73. K.H. Rhee, E.P. Morris, J. Barber, W. Kühlbrandt, Three-dimensional structure of the plant Photosystem II reaction centre at 8 Å resolution. *Nature* **396** (1998) 283–286.
74. J. Nield, O. Kruse, J. Ruprecht, P. da Fonseca, C. Buchel, J. Barber, Three-dimensional structure of *Chlamydomonas reinhardtii* and *Synechococcus elongatus* Photosystem II complexes allows for comparison of their oxygen-evolving complex organization. *J. Biol. Chem.* **275** (2000) 27940–27946.
75. H. Michel, J. Deisenhofer, Relevance of the photosynthetic reaction center from purple bacteria to the structure of Photosystem II. *Biochemistry* **27** (1988) 1–7.
76. W.D. Schubert, O. Klukas, W. Saenger, H.T. Witt, P. Fromme, N. Krauss, A common ancestor for oxygenic and anoxygenic photosynthetic systems: a comparison based on the structural model of Photosystem I. *J. Mol. Biol.* **280** (1998) 297–314.
77. N. Krauss, W.D. Schubert, O. Klukas, P. Fromme, H.T. Witt, W. Saenger, Photosystem I at 4 Å resolution represents the first structural model of a joint photosynthetic reaction centre and core antenna system. *Nat. Struct. Biol.* **3** (1996) 965–973.
78. P. Jordan, P. Fromme, H.T. Witt, O. Klukas, W. Saenger, N. Krauss, Three-dimensional structure of cyanobacterial Photosystem I at 2.5 Å resolution. *Nature* **411** (2001) 909–917.
79. W. Saenger, P. Jordan, N. Krauß, The assembly of protein subunits and cofactors in Photosystem I. *Curr. Opin. Struct. Biol.* **12** (2002) 244–254.
80. B. Hankamer, E.P. Morris, J. Barber, Cryoelectron microscopy of Photosystem II shows that CP43 and CP47 are located on opposite of the D1/D2 reaction centre proteins. *Nat. Struct. Biol.* **6** (1999) 560–564.
81. K.H. Rhee, Photosystem II: the solid structural era. *Annu. Rev. Biophys. Biomol. Struct.* **30** (2001) 307–328.
82. A. Zouni, J. Kern, B. Loll, P. Fromme, H.T. Witt, P. Orth, N. Krauss, W. Saenger, J. Biesiadka. Biochemical characterization and crystal structure of water oxidizing Photosystem II from *Synechococcus elongatus*. in: *12th International Congress on Photosynthesis* (2001, Brisbane, Australia), CSIRO Publishers, Melbourne.

83. F. Reifarth, G. Christen, A.G. Seeliger, P. Dormann, C. Benning, G. Renger, Modification of the water oxidizing complex in leaves of the dgd1 mutant of *Arabidopsis thaliana* deficient in the galactolipid digalactosyldiacylglycerol. *Biochemistry* **36** (1997) 11769–11776.
84. Z. Gombos, Z. Varkonyi, M. Hagio, M. Iwaki, L. Kovacs, K. Masamoto, S. Itoh, H. Wada, Phosphatidylglycerol requirement for the function of electron acceptor plastoquinone Q(B) in the Photosystem II reaction center. *Biochemistry* **41** (2002) 3796–3802.
85. R. Steffen, A.A. Kelly, J. Huyer, P. Dormann, G. Renger, Investigations on the reaction pattern of Photosystem II in leaves from ArabidoPS Is thaliana wild type plants and mutants with genetically modified lipid content. *Biochemistry* **44** (2005) 3134–3142.
86. N. Sato, M. Aoki, Y. Maru, K. Sonoike, A. Minoda, M. Tsuzuki, Involvement of sulfoquinovosyl diacylglycerol in the structural integrity and heat-tolerance of Photosystem II. *Planta* **217** (2003) 245–251.
87. H. Wada, N. Murata, Membrane lipids in cyanobacteria, in *Lipids in Photosynthesis: Structure, Function and Genetics* (1998) (N. Murata, ed.), Kluwer Academic Publishers, Dordrecht, pp. 65–81.
88. R. Voß, A. Radunz, G.H. Schmid, Binding of lipids onto polypeptides of the thylakoid membrane. I. Galacto-lipids and sulfolipids as prosthetic groups of the core peptides of the Photosystem II complex. *Z. Naturforsch., Teil C* **47** (1992) 406–415.
89. E. Baena-Gonzalez, E.M. Aro, Biogenesis, assembly and turnover of Photosystem II units. *Philos. Trans. Royal Soc. London Ser. B-Biol. Sci.* **357** (2002) 1451–1459.
90. P.K. Fyfe, Probing the interface between membrane proteins and membrane lipids by X-ray crystallography. *Trends Biochem. Sci.* **26** (2001) 106–112.
91. H. Palsdottir, C. Hunte, Lipids in membrane protein structures. *Biochim. Biophys. Acta* **1666** (2004) 2–18.
92. D. Stroebel, Y. Choquet, J.L. Popot, D. Picot, An atypical haem in the cytochrome b_6f complex. *Nature* **426** (2003) 413–418.
93. G. Kurisu, H. Zhang, J.L. Smith, W.A. Cramer, Structure of the cytochrome *b6f* complex of oxygenic photosynthesis: tuning the cavity. *Science* **302** (2003) 1009–1014.
94. C. Lange, J.H. Nett, B.L. Trumpower, C. Hunte, Specific roles of protein-phospholipid interactions in the yeast cytochrome bc_1 complex structure. *EMBO J.* **20** (2001) 6591–6600.
95. B. Loll, J. Kern, W. Saenger, A. Zouni, J. Biesiadka, Lipids in photosystem II: Interactions with protein and cofactors. *Biochom. Biophys. Acta* **1767** (2007) 509–519.
96. J. Deisenhofer, O. Epp, I. Sinning, H. Michel, Crystallographic refinement at 2.3 Å resolution and refined model of the photosynthetic reaction center from *Rhodopseudomonas viridis*. *J. Mol. Biol.* **246** (1995) 429–457.
97. C. Berthomieu, R. Hienerwadel, Iron coordination in Photosystem II: interaction between bicarbonate and the Q(B) pocket studied by Fourier transform infrared spectroscopy. *Biochemistry* **40** (2001) 4044–4052.
98. K. Zimmermann, M. Heck, J. Frank, J. Kern, I. Vass, A. Zouni, Herbicide binding and thermal stability of Photosystem II isolated from *Thermosynechococcus elongatus*. *Biochim. Biophys. Acta* **1757** (2006) 106–114.

99. R.E. Regel, N.B. Ivleva, H. Zer, J. Meurer, S.V. Shestakov, R.G. Herrmann, H.B. Pakrasi, I. Ohad, Deregulation of electron flow within Photosystem II in the absence of the PsbJ protein. *J. Biol. Chem.* **276** (2001) 41473–41478.

100. I. Ohad, C. Dal Bosco, R.G. Herrmann, J. Meurer, Photosystem II proteins PsbL and PsbJ regulate electron flow to the plastoquinone pool. *Biochemistry* **43** (2004) 2297–2308.

101. O. Kaminskaya, V.A. Shuvalov, G. Renger, Evidence for a novel quinone binding site in the PS II (PSII) complex which regulates the redox potential of Cyt b-559. *Biochemistry* **46** (2007) 1091–1105.

102. X.-S. Tang, B.A. Diner, Biochemical and spectroscopic characterization of a new oxygen-evolving Photosystem II core complex from the cyanobacterium *Synechocystis* PCC 6803. *Biochemistry* **33** (1994) 4594–4603.

103. B. Loll, J. Kern, A. Zouni, W. Saenger, J. Biesiadka, K.D. Irrgang, The antenna system of Photosystem II from *Thermosynechococcus elongatus* at 3.2 Å resolution. *Photosynth. Res.* **86** (2005) 175–184.

104. A. Telfer, What is beta-carotene doing in the Photosystem II reaction centre? *Philos. Trans. R. Soc. London Ser. B* **357** (2002) 1431–1440.

105. C.A. Tracewell, G.W. Brudvig, Two redox-active beta-carotene molecules in Photosystem II. *Biochemistry* **42** (2003) 9127–9136.

106. R.J. van Dorssen, J. Breton, J.J. Plijter, K. Satoh, H.J. Van Gorkom, J. Amesz, Spectroscopic properties of the reaction center and of the 47 kDa chlorophyll protein of Photosystem II. *Biochim. Biophys. Acta* **893** (1987) 267–274.

107. S.L.S. Kwa, W.R. Newell, R. van Grondelle, J.P. Dekker, The reaction center of Photosystem II studied with polarized fluorescence spectroscopy. *Biochim. Biophys. Acta* **1099** (1992) 193–202.

108. T. Tomo, M. Mimuro, M. Iwaki, M. Kobayashi, S. Itoh, K. Satoh, Topology of pigments in the isolated Photosystem II reaction center studied by selective extraction. *Biochim. Biophys. Acta* **1321** (1997) 21–30.

109. K.V. Lakshmi, O.G. Poluektov, M.J. Reifler, A.M. Wagner, M.C. Thurnauer, G.W. Brudvig, Pulsed high-frequency EPR study on the location of carotenoid and chlorophyll cation radicals in Photosystem II. *J. Am. Chem. Soc.* **125** (2003) 5005–5014.

110. P. Faller, A. Pascal, A.W. Rutherford, beta-Carotene redox reactions in Photosystem II: electron transfer pathway. *Biochemistry* **40** (2001) 6431–6440.

111. C.C. Moser, J.M. Keske, K. Warncke, R.S. Farid, P.L. Dutton, Nature of biological electron transfer. *Nature* **355** (1992) 796–802.

112. G. Renger, A.R. Holzwarth, Primary electron transfer, in: *Photosystem II: The Water/Plastoquinone Oxido-Reductase in Photosynthesis* (2005) (T. Wydrzynski, K. Satoh, eds.), Kluwer Academic Publishers, Dordrecht, pp. 139–175.

113. S. Vasil'ev, P. Orth, A. Zouni, T.G. Owens, D. Bruce, Excited-state dynamics in Photosystem II: insights from the x-ray crystal structure. *Proc. Natl. Acad. Sci. U.S.A.* **98** (2001) 8602–8607.

114. A.T. Keilty, D.V. Vavilin, W.F. Vermaas, Functional analysis of combinatorial mutants with changes in the C-terminus of the CD loop of the D2 protein in Photosystem II of *Synechocystis* sp. PCC 6803. *Biochemistry* **40** (2001) 4131–4139.

115. J.H.A. Nugent, A.M. Rich, M.C.W. Evans, Photosynthetic water oxidation: towards a mechanism. *Biochim. Biophys. Acta* **1503** (2001) 138–146.

116. R.J. Debus, Amino acid residues that modulate the properties of tyrosine Y(Z) and the manganese cluster in the water oxidizing complex of Photosystem II. *Biochim. Biophys. Acta* **1503** (2001) 164–186.

117. B.A. Diner, Amino acid residues involved in the coordination and assembly of the manganese cluster of Photosystem II. Proton-coupled electron transport of the redox-active tyrosines and its relationship to water oxidation. *Biochim. Biophys. Acta* **1503** (2001) 147–163.
118. J.G. Metz, M. Seibert, Presence in Photosystem-II core complexes of a 34 kilodalton polypeptide required for water photolysis. *Plant Physiol.* **76**(3) (1984) 829–832.
119. B.A. Diner, P.J. Nixon, J.W. Farchaus, Site-directed mutagenesis of photosynthetic reaction centers. *Curr. Opin. Struct. Biol.* **1** (1991) 546–554.
120. R.M. Cinco, K.L. McFarlane Holman, J.H. Robblee, J. Yano, S.A. Pizarro, E. Bellacchio, K. Sauer, V.K. Yachandra, Calcium EXAFS establishes the Mn-Ca cluster in the oxygen-evolving complex of Photosystem II. *Biochemistry* **41** (2002) 12928–12933.
121. J.H. Robblee, R.M. Cinco, V.K. Yachandra, X-ray spectroscopy-based structure of the Mn cluster and mechanism of photosynthetic oxygen evolution. *Biochim. Biophys. Acta* **1503** (2001) 7–23.
122. T.G. Carrell, A.M. Tyryshkin, G.C. Dismukes, An evaluation of structural models for the photosynthetic water-oxidizing complex derived from spectroscopic and X-ray diffraction signatures. *J. Biol. Inorg. Chem.* **7** (2002) 2–22.
123. J. Yano, J. Kern, K.D. Irrgang, M.J. Latimer, U. Bergmann, P. Glatzel, Y. Pushkar, J. Biesiadka, B. Loll, K. Sauer, J. Messinger, A. Zouni, V.K. Yachandra, X-ray damage to the Mn4Ca complex in single crystals of Photosystem II: A case study for metalloprotein crystallography. *Proc. Natl. Acad. Sci. U.S.A.* **102** (2005) 12047–12052.
124. G.S. Tae, M.T. Black, W.A. Cramer, O. Vallon, L. Bogorad, Thylakoid membrane protein topography: Transmembrane orientation of the chloroplast cytochrome *b-559* psbE gene product. *Biochemistry* **27** (1988) 9075–9080.
125. J. Kern, Structural and functional investigestiuns of Photosystem II from *Thermosynechococcus elongatus*, Phd Thesis, Faculty, Math and Science, Technical University, Berlin, 2005, p.161.
126. J. Kern and G. Renger, Photosystem II: Structure and mechanism of the water: plastoquinone oxidoreductase. *Photosynth. Res.* (2007) (in press).
127. S. Bhaduri, M. Pink, G. Christou, Towards a synthetic model of the photosynthetic water oxidizing complex: $Mn_3O_4(O_2CMe)(4)(bpy)(2)$ containing the Mn-3(IV)(mu-O)(4) (4+) core. *Chem. Comm.* (2002), 2352–2353.
128. B. Loll, J. Kern, W. Saenger, A. Zouni, J. Biesiadka, Towards complete cofactor arrangement in the 3.0 Å resolution structure of Photosystem II. *Nature* **438** (2005) 1040–1044.
129. J. Yano, J. Kern, K. Sauer, M.J. Latimer, Y. Pushkar, J. Biesiadka, B. Loll, W. Saenger, J. Messinger, A. Zouni, V.K. Yachandra, Where water is oxidized to dioxygen: Structure of the photosynthetic Mn_4Ca cluster. *Science* **314** (2006) 821–825.

Chapter 16

Functional Pattern of Photosystem II

Gernot Renger

Table of Contents

16.1 Introduction... 239
16.2 Light-Induced Stable Charge Separation in Photosystem II... 241
    16.2.1 Limitations of the "Cofactor-Apoprotein" Concept... 241
    16.2.2 Chemical Nature of Cofactors... 242
    16.2.3 Structural Arrangement of the Cofactors... 243
    16.2.4 Structure and Properties of P680... 244
        16.2.4.1 Structure of the Photochemically Active Pigment Complex... 244
        16.2.4.2 The Electronic State of ^{1}P680*... 247
        16.2.4.3 Triplet State ^{3}P680... 248
        16.2.4.4 Cation Radical P680$^{+\cdot}$... 250
        16.2.4.5 Is P680 Always a Chl a Complex?... 251
    16.2.5 Properties of Pheophytin (Pheo)... 252
    16.2.6 Properties of Q_A... 253
    16.2.7 Mechanism and Kinetics of Charge Separation... 255
        16.2.7.1 Mechanism and Kinetics of P680$^{+\cdot}$Pheo$^{-\cdot}$ Formation... 255
        16.2.7.2 Kinetics of P680$^{+\cdot}$Q$_A^{-\cdot}$ Formation... 257
    16.2.8 Energetics of P680$^{+\cdot}$Q$_A^{-\cdot}$ Formation... 258
        16.2.8.1 Energy Levels of the "Initial" (^{1}P680*) and "Final" (P680$^{+\cdot}$Q$_A^{-\cdot}$) State... 258
        16.2.8.2 Energy Levels of Intermediary States and Role of the Protein Environment (Relaxation Processes)... 259
16.3 Oxidative Reactions Driven by P680$^{+\cdot}$... 262
    16.3.1 P680$^{+\cdot}$ Reduction by Y_Z and Oxidative Water Splitting... 262
    16.3.2 P680$^{+\cdot}$ Reduction by Y_Z in PS II Complexes without Intact WOC... 265
    16.3.3 Recombination Reactions of P680$^{+\cdot}$ with $Q_A^{-\cdot}$ and Pheo$^{-\cdot}$; ^{3}P680 Triplet Formation... 266

16.4 PQH$_2$ Formation 267
    16.4.1 Two-Step Reaction Sequence Induced by Q$_A^{-\cdot}$ 267
    16.4.2 Structure of the Q$_B$ Site and Quinol/Quinone Exchange
           Reactions 270
16.5 Role of Lipids 271
16.6 Concluding Remarks 272
Acknowledgements 272
References 273

Abstract

This chapter reviews our current knowledge on the energetics, kinetics, and mechanism of electron transfer in Photosystem II (PS II), excluding oxidative water splitting, which is outlined in Chapter 17. Similarities of PS II with the reaction centers of anoxygenic (non-oxygen evolving) purple bacteria in the general functional and structural organization of charge separation and quinol formation are outlined. The striking differences are discussed that emerge from the thermodynamic requirements for water oxidation to molecular oxygen and four protons, i.e., the generation of electron holes of sufficiently strong oxidizing power. An understanding of the nature and the properties of the photoactive component P680 as the site of photochemical hole formation is of central relevance. The unique properties of P680 are best described by assigning P680 to a special multichromophoric unit (Chl a)$_4$ Pheo$_x$ with $x=0$, 1 or 2 (the value of x is a matter of controversy), rather than a single chromophore or special pair. The possible electronic structures of ^{1}P680*, ^{3}P680 and P680$^{+\cdot}$ are discussed. It is emphasized that the surrounding protein matrix forms an integral and decisive part of the functional properties of P680, in particular for its extraordinarily high reduction potential. Evidence is presented that in the first electron transfer event of charge separation a "monomeric" type Chl a within P680 transfers an electron from its excited singlet state to an associated pheophytin (Pheo) a molecule, which acts as the primary electron acceptor. This event is followed by rapid spin redistribution, leading to predominant localization of the electron hole on a Chl a in P680$^{+\cdot}$ designated as P$_{D1}$, which is part of a "dimeric" structural motif termed P$_{D1}$P$_{D2}$ and is in close proximity to the redox-active tyrosine Y$_Z$. The subsequent reactions of P680$^{+\cdot}$ reduction by Y$_Z$ and of PQH$_2$ formation via a two-step, one-electron reaction sequence with Q$_A^{-\cdot}$ as reductant are described with special emphasis on the role of the protein dynamics for energetics and kinetics.

16.1 Introduction

The essential steps of photosynthetic water splitting take place in a multimeric pigment–protein complex, referred to as Photosystem II (PS II). This complex acts as a water-plastoquinone-oxidoreductase and is anisotropically incorporated into the thylakoid membrane [1,2]. *In vivo*, PS II exists predominantly as dimers in cyanobacteria, algae and higher plants [3–5]. The PS II contains a core complex that is connected with pigment–proteins acting as peripheral and proximal antennae for light harvesting and adaptation to different illumination conditions. In marked contrast to the great variability of the peripheral and proximal antenna systems (Chapters 6–8), the PS II core complex (PS II CC) of all oxygen-evolving organisms has remained comparatively invariant during evolution, ranging from the "ancient" cyanobacteria up to higher plants (for details, see Chapter 22). This PS II CC is characterized by a unique and unusually complex subunit composition, including over 20 subunits (for a review, see [6] and references therein).

The overall process of water splitting in PS II consists of three types of reaction sequences (for a review see [7]):

(a) light-induced "stable" charge separation:

$$P_{RC}Acc_1Acc_2 \xrightarrow{h\nu} {}^1P_{RC}^*Acc_1Acc_2 \rightarrow P_{RC}^{+\bullet}Acc_1^{-\bullet}Acc_2 \\ \rightarrow P_{RC}^{+\bullet}Acc_1Acc_2^{-\bullet} \quad (1)$$

(b) oxidative water splitting:

$$4\oplus + 2H_2O \rightarrow O_2 + 4H_{Lumen}^+ \quad (2)$$

(c) plastoquinol formation:

$$4\ominus + 4H_{Stroma}^+ + 2PQ \rightarrow 2PQH_2 \quad (3)$$

where P_{RC} denotes the photoactive pigment in the reaction center (RC) that transfers an electron from its lowest excited electronic singlet state to the primary acceptor Acc_1, thus forming the primary cation–anion radical pair $P_{RC}^{+\bullet}Acc_1^{-\bullet}$. A subsequent rapid electron transfer from $Acc_1^{-\bullet}$ to the secondary acceptor Acc_2 is required for a sufficient stabilization of the light-induced charge separation. The symbols $\oplus$ and $\ominus$ represent redox equivalents (including the cofactors involved, see Sections 16.3 and 16.4) that give rise to oxidative water splitting [sequence (b)] and plastoquinol formation [sequence (c)], respectively; H_{Lumen}^+ and H_{Stroma}^+ represent proton release into the thylakoid lumen and uptake from the stroma, respectively.

The performance of oxidative water splitting [reaction sequence (b)] relies on two indispensable prerequisites: (i) an oxidant with a sufficiently positive reduction potential as driving force and (ii) controlled cooperation of four oxidizing redox equivalents. The highly oxidizing species is generated by the light-induced charge separation [reaction sequence (a)] and the cooperation is achieved via a sequence of one-electron oxidation steps that takes place at a specially tailored metalloprotein complex referred to as the water oxidizing complex (WOC). After attaining a formal storage level of four electron holes in the WOC, water oxidation is accomplished and molecular oxygen released [reaction sequence (b)].

This chapter describes the nature, functional properties, and geometrical arrangement of the cofactors that are involved in the reaction pattern of PS II. Reaction sequences (a) and (c) basically resemble the corresponding processes that take place in the reaction centers of anoxygenic purple bacteria (PBRCs) (Chapter 12). The striking difference between PBRCs and PS II CC in reaction sequence (a) is the formation of the strong oxidant that is necessary for oxidative water splitting. Therefore, special emphasis is placed on the peculiarities of light-induced "stable" charge separation in PS II. The subsequent reactions of oxidative water splitting [sequence (b)] and plastoquinol formation [sequence (c)] are described briefly. Structural details of the photosynthetic apparatus and the mechanism of the unique reaction sequence (b) are outlined in Chapters 15 and 17, respectively.

16.2 Light-Induced Stable Charge Separation in Photosystem II

The reaction behavior (energetics and kinetics) of electron transfer cofactors in general and of water splitting by PS II in particular depends on both the chemical nature of a particular cofactor and the specific interaction of the cofactor with the protein environment. We, therefore, start with a brief discussion of the principles of cofactor "functionalizing" and limitations of the conventional "cofactor-apoprotein" concept. Subsequent sections address the following topics on PS II: (i) chemical nature of the cofactors of sequence (a), (ii) arrangement of the cofactors within the protein matrix, (iii) nature and properties of P_{RC}, (iv) properties of Acc_1 and Acc_2, and (v) energetics and kinetics of stable charge separation.

16.2.1 Limitations of the "Cofactor-Apoprotein" Concept

The influence of the protein is often discussed within the framework of the conventional "cofactor-apoprotein" concept. However, in several cases a separation into a functional cofactor and a host apoprotein is too simple and can be even misleading, because it ignores a possible direct functional role of the protein itself. The great variability of proteins in establishing controlled potential energy surfaces permits a precise tuning of the energetics of cofactors and their reaction coordinates. The availability of this "ideal" material has enabled biological systems, during a long lasting process of evolutionary development, to achieve practically any degree of specificity, efficiency and regulatory control that is required for a particular biological function.

The tuning of cofactors, in particular of metal centers, for specific demands in living systems is a "hot" topic of life science research. Deeper insight into the underlying principles will not only shift our state of knowledge to a higher level of understanding but also pave the way for engineering of "molecular machines" of nanoscale dimension for technical purposes (see also Chapter 1). First attempts have been reported on computer-aided design of proteins that specifically bind and "functionalize" non-biological cofactors with the ambitious aim of developing biomimetic catalysts with desired properties [8]. Directed evolution of enzymes for special purposes is an attractive approach [9].

The high relevance of the protein environment for development and assembly of a functionally competent PS II complex is clearly illustrated by the unusually large number of small subunits [6] that are not present in PS I or PBRCs and have not changed significantly during evolution from cyanobacteria to higher plants [10].

16.2.2 Chemical Nature of Cofactors

Equation (1) summarizes the basic principle of light transformation into electrochemical Gibbs energy in the form of a stabilized cation–anion radical pair. This type of reaction takes place in all photosynthesizing organisms but the nature of the cofactors varies among the different types of reaction centers in anoxygenic bacteria and the two photosystems (PS I and PS II) in oxygen evolving organisms. The chemical nature of constituents P_{RC}, Acc_1 and Acc_2 in PS II and the general turnover kinetics of these components were identified and resolved by measuring light-induced absorption changes. Figure 1 summarizes typical difference spectra that characterize the turnover of the individual components P_{RC}, Acc_1 and Acc_2. The spectrum of flash-induced absorption changes that reflect the turnover of the photoactive pigment P_{RC} of PS II is shown in Figure 1(A). Based on its characteristic bleaching bands in the blue (Soret band) and red (Q_y band) regions, P_{RC} was identified as a special chlorophyll a [11]. In analogy to the symbol P700 for P_{RC} of PS I (Chapters 13 and 14) and corresponding symbols for P_{RC} of the reaction centers of anoxygenic photosynthetic bacteria (Chapters 11 and 12), this component is referred to as P680.

Figure 1(B) depicts a difference spectrum of absorption changes due to the turnover of Acc_1. The characteristic features in the blue (Soret band), green (Q_x band) and red (Q_Y band) region led to the assignment of Acc_1 to a pheophytin a (Pheo a) [12].

In marked contrast to the difference spectra of $P680/P680^{+\bullet}$ and $Pheo^{-\bullet}/Pheo$ with their strong bleaching bands $\Delta\varepsilon_\lambda(P680^{+\bullet}/P680)$ and $\Delta\varepsilon_\lambda(Pheo^{-\bullet}/Pheo)$ in the Soret and Q_Y regions, the turnover of the acceptor component Acc_2 leads to relatively small spectral changes $\Delta\varepsilon_\lambda(Q_A^-/Q_A)$ in the visible (Vis) but gives rise to marked absorption changes in the UV region. These characteristic features led to the identification of Acc_2 as a specially bound plastoquinone [13,14]. This component is denoted Q_A. The Q_A in PBRCs is also a quinone (menaquinone or ubiquinone) (Chapter 12). A typical Q_A^-/Q_A difference spectrum is shown in Figure 1(C) [15].

With the identification of the cofactors P_{RC}, Acc_1 and Acc_2 as P680, Pheo and Q_A, respectively, the overall reaction pattern of stable charge separation according to eqn. (1) can be summarized more specifically by the following sequence for PS II:

$$P680\,Pheo\,Q_A \xleftrightarrow{h\nu} {}^1P680^*\,Pheo\,Q_A \underset{k_{-1}}{\overset{k_{PC}}{\rightleftarrows}} P680^{+\bullet}\,Pheo^{-\bullet}\,Q_A \underset{k_{-2}}{\overset{k_{stab}}{\rightleftarrows}} P680^{+\bullet}\,Pheo\,Q_A^{-\bullet} \quad (4)$$

The first step of eqn. (4) summarizes excited singlet state formation either by direct light absorption of P680 or by excitation energy transfer (EET) from electronically excited antenna pigments to P680, the rate constants k_{pc} and k_{stab}

FUNCTIONAL PATTERN OF PHOTOSYSTEM II

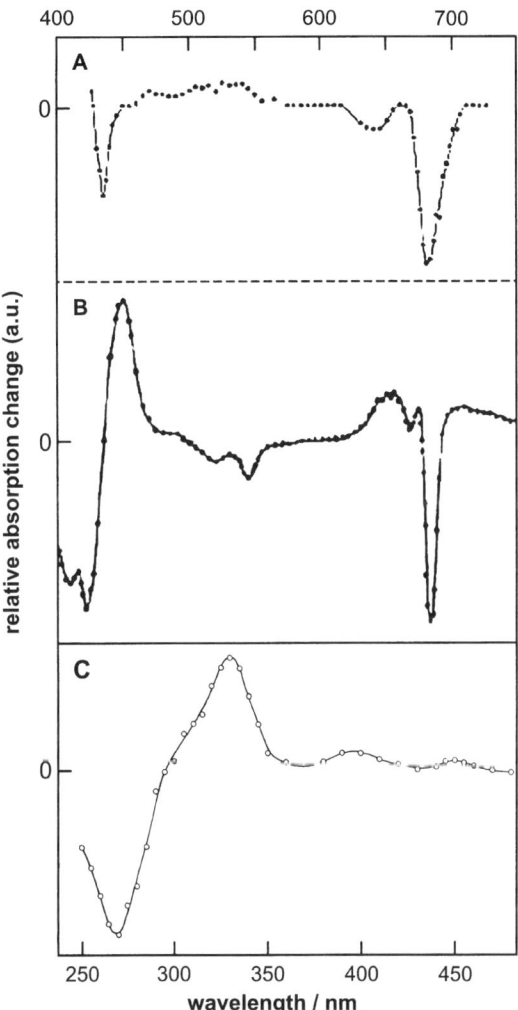

Figure 1. Difference absorption spectra reported for P_{RC} ($P680^{+\cdot}/P680$) (A), Acc_1 ($Pheo^{-\cdot}/Pheo$) (B) and Acc_2 ($Q_A^{-\cdot}/Q_A$) (C) of PS II. The spectra were redrawn from data published in Döring et al. (1969), Klimov et al. (1977), and van Gorkom (1974), respectively ([11,12] and [15], respectively). Top wavelength scale refers to (A) and (B), the bottom scale to (C).

describe the primary charge separation and its stabilization, respectively, and k_{-1} and k_{-2} are the rate constants of the corresponding back reactions.

16.2.3 Structural Arrangement of the Cofactors

The structure of PS II has been resolved by X-ray crystallography [16–20] with a currently available resolution of 3.0 Å (for details, see Chapter 15). The crystal structures show that all cofactors that catalyze reaction sequences (a)–(c) are incorporated into a heterodimeric protein matrix consisting of polypeptide D1 and D2. One exception is the sequence (b). At least one additional polypeptide (CP43) is inferred to provide ligand(s) to the first coordination sphere of the Mn_4CaO_x cluster in the water-oxidizing complex (WOC) (Chapters 15 and 17).

Figure 2 shows the array of the cofactors within the D1/D2 heterodimer. In addition to the Chl *a* and Pheo *a* molecules and Q_A that were identified as the cofactors of stable charge separation, the tetranuclear manganese cluster of the WOC, the redox active tyrosines (Y_Z and Y_D), the nonheme iron center (NHFe) and the two β-carotenes [21–23] are also seen. In addition, the D1/D2 matrix contains lipids that are not shown in Figure 2 (for further details, see [20] and Chapter 15).

An inspection of the arrangement of the eight chlorins reveals a clear structural separation into two peripheral chlorophylls, $Chlz_{D1}$ and $Chlz_{D2}$, and a reaction center pigment complex (RC-PC) consisting of Chl_{D1}, P_{D1}, P_{D2}, Chl_{D2} and the pheophytin *a* molecules $Pheo_{D1}$ and $Pheo_{D2}$. This striking structural feature has important implications for the functions of these Chl *a* molecules (Section 16.2.4).

The chlorophyll molecules $Chlz_{D1}$ and $Chlz_{D2}$ are separated from RC-PC and do not contribute to formation of P680. Interestingly, no corresponding counterparts exist in PBRCs, in contrast to the other six chlorins whose arrangement is strikingly similar to that of the corresponding four bacteriochlorophylls (BChl) and two bacteriopheophytins (BPheo) in the PBRCs (Chapter 11). Therefore, it seems likely that $Chlz_{D1}$ and $Chlz_{D2}$ are of special functional relevance for PS II. This idea is confirmed by studies on mutants of *Chlamydomonas reinhardtii* in which the axial histidine ligands of $Chlz_{D1}$ (H118 of polypeptide D1) and $Chlz_{D2}$ (H117 of polypeptide D2) were replaced by other amino acid residues [25]. The mutants exhibit significant differences in various properties, inter alia in light-harvesting efficiency and sensitivity to photoinhibition [23]. It was suggested that these two pigments could be constituents of the EET pathway from the core antenna pigment–protein complexes CP43 and CP47 to P680 [25]. However, model calculations based on the PS II CC structure revealed that $Chlz_{D1}$ and $Chlz_{D2}$ probably play only a minor role compared with the direct EET from Chls of CP43 and CP47 to the RC-core [26,27].

Therefore, a role in protection to light stress [28,29] appears to be the most likely function of $Chlz_{D1}$ and $Chlz_{D2}$.

16.2.4 Structure and Properties of P680

16.2.4.1 Structure of the Photochemically Active Pigment Complex
The RC-PC contains four Chl *a* molecules that are potential candidates as constituents of P680. Theoretical calculations based on the PS II structure at 3.2 Å resolution [19] revealed that the four Chl *a* and two Pheo molecules are excitonically coupled with values ranging from about 30 up to 160 cm^{-1} and

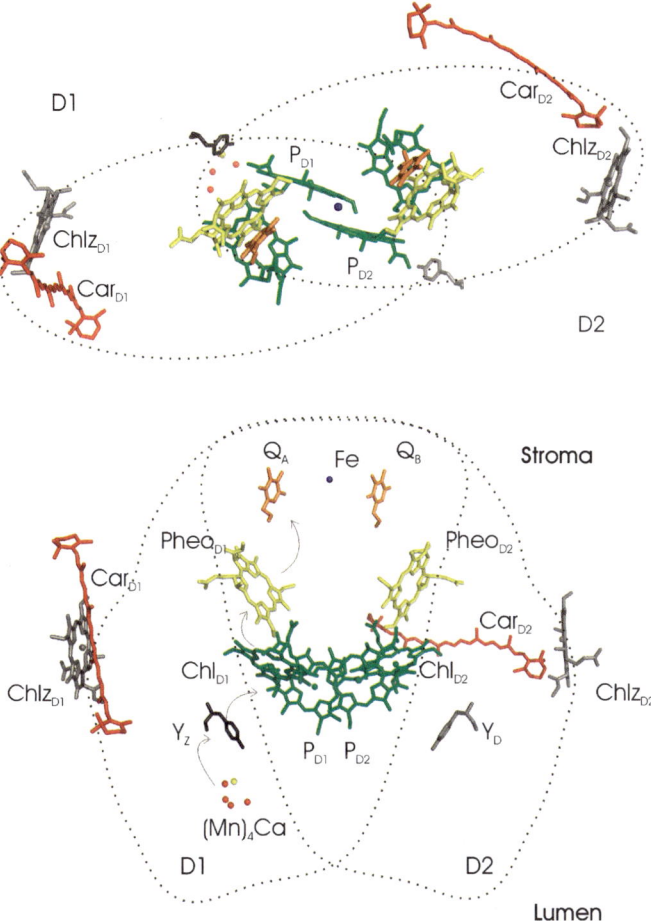

Figure 2. Top view (upper part) and side view (bottom part) of the structural array of the cofactors of PS II within the heterodimer of polypeptides D1 and D2. Chl_{D1}, Chl_{D2}, P_{D1} and P_{D2} (in green) are the four Chl a, and $Pheo_{D1}$ and $Pheo_{D2}$ (in yellow) the two Pheo a molecules of the reaction center core (RC-PC); $Chlz_{D1}$ and $Chlz_{D2}$ (in grey) are the distal Chl a molecules; Q_A (in brown) is the plastoquinone acceptor; $(Mn)_4$ (in red), the tetranuclear manganese cluster of the water-oxidizing complex; and Fe (in blue), the nonheme iron center. Furthermore, the two Car molecules in the D1/D2 heterodimer are also shown (for the sake of simplicity lipid molecules are omitted, see Chapetr 15). The ET of the active branch is symbolized by arrows. The dimensions of D1 and D2 are symbolized by dotted contour lines. [The figure was kindly provided by Dr. Jan Kern. See text for details.]

the strongest coupling was found between the two Chl a molecules P_{D1} and P_{D2} [30]. The structural array of P_{D1} and P_{D2} is similar to that of the special pair P ([31] and Chapter 11) that acts as the photochemically active species for the primary charge separation in PBRCs (Chapter 12). Therefore, at a first glance, it might be attractive to assign P680 to a special pair consisting of P_{D1} and P_{D2}.

The finding that the photochemically active pigment P700 of PS I is also a dimer (for an alternative model, see [32] and Chapter 13) would appear to support this idea. In this case P700 is a heterodimer consisting of one Chl a and one Chl a' molecule [33]. Chl a' is the 13^2 epimer in which the positions of –H and –COOCH$_3$ at the asymmetric C-Atom 13^2 of ring V are exchanged, as outlined in Chapter 3. However, closer inspection reveals that the center-to-center distance between P_{D1} and P_{D2} (8.3 Å) is larger than the 7.6 Å ([31] and Chapter 11) and 6.3 Å ([33] and Chapter 13) between the two BChl molecules in the special pair P of PBRCs and Chl a and Chl a' in P700, respectively.

As a consequence of the larger distance and smaller Q_y transition dipole moments of Chl compared with Bchl, the value of about $160\,\text{cm}^{-1}$ [30] for excitonic coupling between P_{D1} and P_{D2} is lower than values reported for the special pair P of PBRC ([34] and references therein), and the spectral differences between the chlorins of RC-PC in PS II are much less pronounced than the marked difference between P and the four "monomeric" molecules BChl$_A$, BChl$_B$, BPheo$_A$ and BPheo$_B$ in PBRCs (for details of PBRCs, see Chapters 11 and 12).

These considerations reveal that an analogous separation between a "special pair" consisting of P_{D1}/P_{D2} and the remaining four chlorins of the RC-PC is not justified. Accordingly questions arise on the nature of P680.

Apart from problems due to the congestion of the P680 band by the absorption of Chl a molecules of the antenna, another major obstacle hampers a straightforward analysis. In contrast to the well characterized and functionally fully intact isolated PBRCs, a method is missing for isolation of an analogous PS II reaction center preparation that permits stable charge separation according to eqn. (4). An important step forward was achieved by Nanba and Satoh [35] by the isolation of D1/D2/Cyt b559 preparations that carry out charge separation leading to formation of the radical pair $P680^{+\cdot}Pheo^{-\cdot}$ with high yield [36]. However, these preparations lack any oxygen evolution capacity and are completely deprived of both Q_A, which is required for stabilizing the primary charge preparation, and the NHFe [21,35,37,38]. Furthermore, the reaction of $P680^{+\cdot}$ with the redox-active tyrosines (Section 16.3) is also severely modified [23]. Therefore the term "PS II reaction centers" for D1/D2/Cyt b_{559} preparations is highly misleading and should be avoided. Furthermore, it must be carefully analyzed as to what extent the results obtained with these preparations really reflect the properties of an intact PS II. New FTIR measurements clearly show that the properties of P680 in D1/D2/Cyt b559 preparations differ from those of intact PS II core complexes, in particular the E_m value and the charge distribution within the cation radical are significantly changed [39].

Based on a review of the currently available experimental data and theoretical analyses, it seems necessary to assign P680 to the pigment cluster of the RC-PC unit (Chl a)$_4$Pheo$_x$ [40], where index x denotes the number of coupled Pheo molecules. The mode of excitonic coupling of the pheophytins Pheo$_{D1}$ and Pheo$_{D2}$ is a matter of controversy, with values of $x = 0$, 1 or 2 having been reported (for review, see [40]). The close interrelationship among the six pigments of RC-PC is illustrated clearly in a study on a *Chlamydomonas reinhardtii* mutant where Pheo$_{D2}$ was transformed into a Chl *a* by replacement of Leu-210 in polypeptide D1 with a His residue that acts as a ligand for Mg^{2+} in the center of the chlorine ring. Xiong et al. [41] found that PS II core complexes (PS II CC) isolated from the D1-L210H mutant were virtually unable to evolve oxygen [the rate under saturating light was <4% of the value of the wild type (WT)] and to photoaccumulate $Q_A^{-\cdot}$. On the other hand, the kinetics of primary charge separation were not substantially altered in isolated D1/D2/Cyt b559 preparations from this mutant. These results were interpreted on the assumption that the distribution of the excited singlet state energy in ^{1}(RC-PC)* of the mutant differs from that in WT complexes, thus giving rise to a dissipative decay via fluorescence at the expense of charge separations [41].

In marked contrast to the striking modulation of the functional pattern of PS II due to Pheo$_{D2}$ replacement by a Chl molecule, not only the analogous Bpheo$_B$ in PBRCs can be substituted by BChl but it can be even eliminated by suitable site-directed mutagenesis without affecting the kinetics of light-induced ET in the "active A-branch" (Section 16.2.5 and Chapter 12) and the capacity for photoautotrophic growth of the corresponding *Rb. sphaeroides* mutants [42]. This feature clearly illustrates marked differences between PBRCs and PS II with respect to the role of the six chlorines in the reaction center pigment core (Section 16.2.7.1).

The assignment of P680 to Chl$_{D1}$, P$_{D1}$, P$_{D2}$, Chl$_{D2}$, Pheo$_{D1}$, Pheo$_{D2}$ contributes to quite a different extent to the lowest electronically excited singlet state ^{1}P680*, the triplet state ^{3}P680 and the cation radical P680$^{+\cdot}$. The molecular orbital (MO) schemes of ^{1}(RC-PC)*, ^{3}(RC-PC) and (RC-PC)$^{+\cdot}$ do not only depend on the chemical structures of the pigments themselves, but also on both the pigment–pigment and pigment–protein interactions. Detailed quantum chemical calculations are required to unravel the electronic configuration of these states.

Apart from restrictions by the capacity of quantum chemical and molecular mechanics methods due to the size of the system, these studies are also limited by the resolution of the X-ray structure analysis (Chapter 15) and problems arising from spectral overlap. Despite these obstacles important information has been obtained and is summarized below.

16.2.4.2 The Electronic State of ^{1}P680*

A serious problem for straightforward spectral analyses is the strong overlap of the bands in the Q_y region. Multiple attempts have been made to unravel the spectral properties of ^{1}P680*. Most of the studies were performed with D1/D2/Cyt b_{559} preparations (for a review, see [40] and references therein). To cope with the overlapping spectral properties of the eight chlorins in these preparations two different approaches were used for selective modification of individual pigments: (i) site-directed mutagenesis of binding sites and (ii) replacement by other chlorin derivatives.

Modification of the coordination of the central Mg^{2+} of the Chl *a* molecules P$_{D1}$ and P$_{D2}$ is one promising tool that offers, in addition, the possibility of studies on more intact preparations like PS II core complexes or even intact cells. Based on FTIR measurements, Noguchi et al. [43] showed that in P_{D1} and P_{D2} the central Mg^{2+} is pentacoordinated, with His (D1-His-198 and D2-His-197, respectively in *Synechocystis* sp. PCC 6803) as axial ligands [44]. The assembly of functionally competent PS II complexes tolerates replacement of these residues by Gln and Ala whereas a mutation to the larger Leu residue is disastrous and prevents any detectable formation of stable PS II [45]. A thorough analysis of whole cells and of manganese-depleted PS II CC isolated from these mutants and comparison with the corresponding WT samples led to the conclusion that within the (RC-PC) the Q_Y transition with the lowest excitation energy is localized on Chl_{D1} and is characterized by a peak position of 684 nm at 5 K and 681–689 nm at 80 K [46] whereas the Q_Y transition of the native P_{D1} occurs at 673.5 nm [45]. In an alternative interpretation these spectral features have been assigned to exciton bands of the P_{D1}–P_{D2} dimer [47] but this idea is not supported by a theoretical analysis [30].

Complementary information on the spectral features was obtained by using the method of selective replacements of chlorins in D1/D2/Cyt b559 preparations from spinach, where $Pheo_{D2}$ was replaced by the derivative $13'$-deoxy-13^1 hydroxypheophytin [48].

A thorough theoretical analysis [30] has been performed on the basis of experimental spectral data and the X-ray crystallographic structure analysis of PS II at 3.2 Å resolution [19]. This study provides new information on the electronic state of the $^1(RC\text{-}PC)^*$. Figure 3 compares the density of the six exciton states of the strongly coupled RC pigments with the exciton states pigment distribution function. Several interesting features emerge from an inspection of these data. The most striking result is the finding that the lowest exciton state is dominated by Chl_{D1} and not by a "special pair" P_{D1}–P_{D2}. This phenomenon clearly contrasts with the situation in PBRCs where the "red-most" Q_Y transition is associated with the lower exciton state of the special pair. In PS II the 3rd and the 6th exciton states are ascribed to the pair P_{D1}–P_{D2} and characterized by peaks at 675 and 660 nm, respectively.

The second lowest exciton state is dominated by $Pheo_{D2}$, while states 4 and 5 are mainly due to absorption by $Pheo_{D1}$ and Chl_{D2}, respectively.

An inspection of these data shows that the strongest coupling exists between P_{D1} and P_{D2} so that these two molecules might resemble a kind of "special pair" within the RC-PC although its functional role differs drastically from that of the special pair P in PBRCs. In marked contrast to P in PBRCs, the "special pair" P_{D1}-P_{D2} in PS II does not act as either the trap of excitation energy or as the primary electron donor (Section 16.2.7.1). Therefore, the term "special pair" is highly misleading for P680 and should not be used in this connection.

16.2.4.3 Triplet State $^3P680$

A markedly different situation arises for the electronic configuration of the triplet state $^3P680$. In this case the excitonic coupling is vanishingly small due to a spin-forbidden transition [49] and can be ignored. First information on the triplet localization within the state $^3(RC\text{-}PC)$ was obtained from orientation

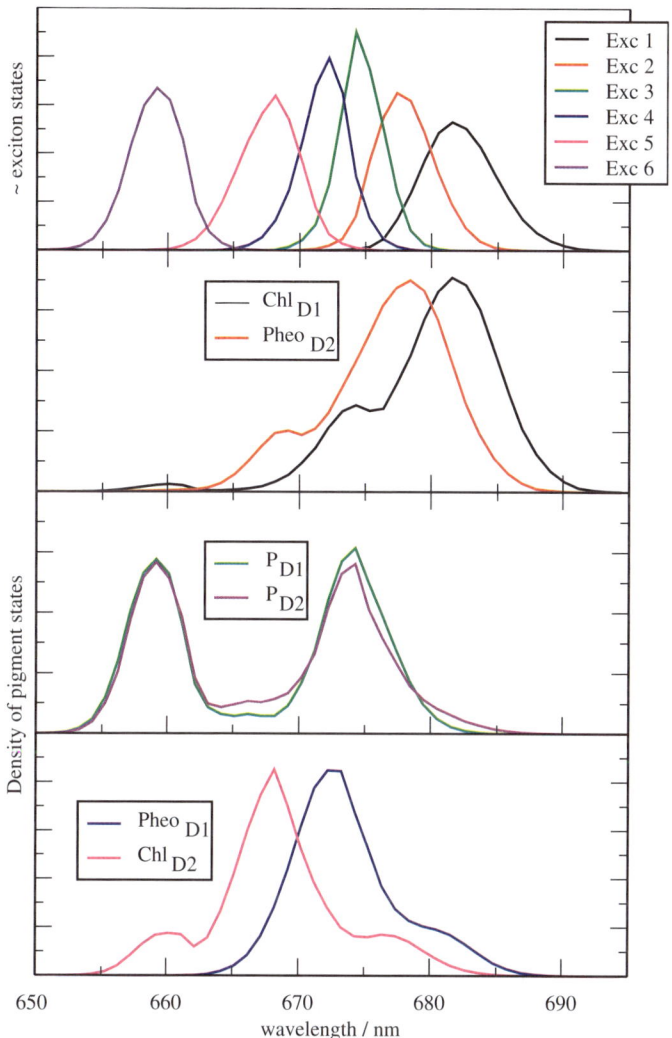

Figure 3. Calculated density of exciton states (top panel) and distribution functions of exciton states (density of exciton states – lower three panels) of the six strongly coupled pigments in the RC-PC unit. See [30] for details of the calculations. [The figure was kindly provided by Dr. T. Renger.]

studies. The plane of the chlorin ring where the triplet resides was shown to deviate drastically from the normal to the thylakoid membrane [50], in marked contrast to the parallel orientation of ^{3}P to the chromatophore membrane in PBRCs [51]. An experimental study on *Synechocystis* sp. PCC 6803 mutants [45] and a theoretical analysis [30] led to the conclusion that at low temperatures the triplet state is located at Chl_{D1}, thus explaining the former results of [50]. At higher temperatures the triplet state becomes delocalized with an energy gap of the order of 10 meV [52].

16.2.4.4 Cation Radical $P680^{+\cdot}$

The cation radical $P680^{+\cdot}$ is one of the strongest oxidants in biology and the energetic prerequisite for the oxidative water splitting into molecular oxygen and four protons. With an estimated reduction potential of $+1.1$ to $+1.26\,\text{V}$ [53–55] $P680^{+\cdot}$ exceeds the oxidizing power of the cation radical $P_{RC}^{+\cdot}$ [see eqn. (1)] in all natural PBRCs and PS I by at least $0.5\,\text{V}$. A comparison with P700, which has been identified as a dimer of Chl a and its 13^2 epimer Chl a' (Section 16.2.4.1 and Chapter 13), shows that the chemical nature of Chl a per se is not the essential point for the unique redox properties of P680. It is, therefore, reasonable to assume that the embedding protein matrix of (RC core) plays the key role in establishing the exceptionally high E_m.

Several factors have been discussed as possibly being responsible for this effect: (i) hydrogen bonding, (ii) distance between the chlorophylls P_{D1} and P_{D2}, (iii) planarity of the chlorine ring, and (iv) dielectric environment.

Experiments on RCs isolated from mutants of anoxygenic purple bacteria reveal that the redox potential of the special pair can be upshifted significantly by introducing additional hydrogen bonds to carbonyl groups of BChl via genetic engineering [56,57]. This mechanism, however, seems to be of minor relevance to P680 because, unlike BChl, Chl a does not contain acetyl groups as a H-bond partner (Chapter 3). Furthermore, the PS II structure models – although currently of limited resolution (Chapter 15) – do not suggest the presence of strong hydrogen bonds to Chl a in (RC-PC).

The first X-ray structure model of PS II at $3.8\,\text{Å}$ resolution led to a center–center distance of about $10\,\text{Å}$ between P_{D1} and P_{D2} [16]. This value is markedly larger than the $7.6\,\text{Å}$ between the two BChls of the special pair in PBRCs ([58] and Chapter 11) and the $6.3\,\text{Å}$ between Chl a and Chl a' of P700 in PS I ([59] and Chapter 13). Based on these striking differences the distance between P_{D1} and P_{D2} was suggested to be an essential prerequisite for establishing a strongly oxidizing $(Chl\,a)^{+\cdot}$ radical. As a corollary of this idea, a mutation of the protein that resulted in the separation of the two pigments in the special Chl a pair was proposed to be the key event in the evolution of an oxygen-evolving PS II [60]. New information on the PS II structure of higher resolution, however, revealed that the center–center distance between P_{D1} and P_{D2} is only 8.2–$8.5\,\text{Å}$ (Chapter 13). Thus, the hypothesis of an evolutionary distance enlargement [60] appears to be less attractive. Furthermore, the magnitude of this effect is comparatively small (about $0.15\,\text{V}$ upshift of E_m at maximum) and does not account for an overall increase of about $0.4\,\text{V}$ for the E_m of P680/ $P680^{+\cdot}$ compared with the E_m of monomeric $(Chl\,a)/(Chl\,a)^{+\cdot}$ in solution [61].

Deviations from chlorin planarity (ring puckering) were shown to reduce E_m [62]. Therefore, it appears reasonable to assume that the protein environment prevents ring puckering. However, the contributions of this effect are comparatively small and cannot explain the large increase of the redox potential.

Our understanding took an essential step forward on the basis of theoretical analyses. Hasegawa and Noguchi showed, by density functional theory (DFT) calculations, that the reduction potential of Chl $a^{+\cdot}$ reaches values of $+1.3\,\text{V}$ within a hydrophobic environment with a dielectric constant of about 2 and (based on the structures gathered from X-ray crystallography) that the protein environment of P680 is more hydrophobic than that of the special pair in PBRCs and of P700 in PS I [63]. These findings provide clear evidence for a low dielectric environment around P680 as a major factor in establishing Chl a species with unusually high redox potentials [63]. Studies on the basis of an electrostatic continuum model and the PS II structure at 3.5 and 3.2 Å resolutions [64] are in good agreement with the idea of an E_m regulation through the dielectric properties of the protein environment, including the electric charges of other cofactors. Values of $+1.1$ to $+1.3$ V were obtained for the four Chls of (RC-PC) while those of $Chlz_{D1}$ and $Chlz_{D2}$ were calculated to be much lower (about 0.9 V) and not far from the E_m of monomeric Chl a in solution [64]. The calculations also reveal that the essential contributions to the drastic upshift of E_m in RC-PC originate from the D1/D2 protein matrix (about 80% of the total effect) and only to a minor extent from the other subunits. The E_ms obtained for P_{D1}, P_{D2}, Chl_{D1} and Chl_{D2} are different when using structures reported with a resolution of 3.5 and 3.2 Å. Furthermore, the calculated values for the E_m difference between P_{D1} and Chl_{D1} data predict that the hole of $P680^{+\cdot}$ should reside predominantly on Chl_{D1} at room temperature, and completely at low temperatures. This conclusion would give rise to questions on the pathway of ET from Y_Z to $P680^{+\cdot}$, in particular with respect to the experimentally observed formation of Y_Z^{OX} at 7 K in about 50% of the PS II core complexes from *T. elongatus* [65]. P_{D1} presumably could not be involved in this reaction. Clearly, more information is required on the details of the structure around the RC to resolve this conundrum.

In summary, the nature of the dielectric properties of the protein matrix is, clearly, the key factor for the unusual redox properties of P680. Furthermore, the spin distribution of the electron within RC-PC of the radical ion state $P680^{+\cdot}$ depends on the details of the microenvironment [39]. For functional reasons, the spin density should be high at P_{D1} to achieve a directed hole transfer to Y_Z. Likewise, the distance from the Chls of RC-PC to other redox active groups, including the peripheral $Chlz_{D1}$ and $Chlz_{D2}$, must be large enough to avoid undesired dissipative and destructive side reactions.

16.2.4.5 Is P680 Always a Chl a Complex?
For many years, Chl a seemed to be unique among the chlorophyll species in constituting the photochemically active species P680 of PS II and P700 of PS I, whereas the special pair in the RCs of anoxygenic bacteria was shown to contain various BChl derivatives, ranging from BChl a in *Rhodobacter* (Rb.) *sphaeroides* to BChl b in *Blastochloris viridis* and BChl g in heliobacteria (Chapters 3 and 12 for the structure of BChls and the types of anoxygenic bacteria, respectively). With the discovery of the Chl d-containing, oxygen-evolving cyanobacterium *Acaryochloris marina* [66] this unique role of Chl a for P680 became a matter of debate. It was shown that the Chl a-Chl a' heterodimer of P700 (Section 16.2.4.1) is replaced by Chl d–Chl d' in the PS I (P740) while the primary acceptor still remains a Chl a as in "conventional" Chl a containing organisms [67]. Acoordingly, questions arise about the nature of

P680 in *A. marina*. An unambiguous answer is complicated by the finding that all thylakoid preparations from this species contain a small amount of Chl *a* [66]. Analyses of oscillation patterns of flash induced oxygen evolution led to the conclusion that kinetics and energetics of oxidative water splitting are virtually the same as in "conventional" Chl *a* containing organisms [68], including the kinetics of Y_z oxidation as also reported in [69]. These data, however, do not permit a straightforward pigment assignment to (RC-PC). It was argued that Chl *a* is required for establishing a strongly oxidizing P680$^{+\cdot}$ [67]. This idea, however, is not convincing because energetics (E_m values) and kinetics are entirely tuned by the protein matrix and the chemical nature of the pigment is of minor relevance at most (Section 16.2.4.4). In fact, new electrochemical studies reveal that in solution the E_m of Chl *d*/Chl *d*$^{+\cdot}$ (+0.88 V in acetonitril) is even slightly higher than that of Chl *a*/Chl *a*$^{+\cdot}$ (+0.81 V in acetonitril) [70]. At present three different types of models are discussed, with P_{D1}-P_{D2} and Chl_{D1} assigned either to Chl *d*-Chl *d* and Chl *a*, respectively, ([71], see also Chapter 6), or Chl *a*-Chl *d* and Chl *d*, respectively [70] or Chl *a*-Chl *a* and Chl *d* [72], respectively but neither of these proposals is fully convincing. A more simple idea would be a (RC-PC) consisting of Chl *d* but in this case questions arise on the location and functional role of Chl *a* in PS II of *A. marina*.

The extent of tolerance to the chemical nature of the chlorin molecules in establishing a functionally competent RC-PC is nicely illustrated by constructing mutants through genetic engineering of *Synechocystis* sp. PCC 6803 where Chl *a* and Pheo *a* were partly replaced by Chl *b*/Pheo *b* in the PS II core [73]. The properties of these mutants indicate that Chl *a* and Pheo *a* are not necessarily the only chlorins that can constitute a functionally competent PS II with intact WOC activity.

16.2.5 Properties of Pheophytin (Pheo)

Figure 2 shows that RC-PC contains two Pheo *a* molecules ($Pheo_{D1}$ and $Pheo_{D2}$) that are structurally homologous to the two BPheo molecules in PBRCs. The most striking feature of PBRCs is the "unidirectionality" of the charge separation process despite the almost symmetric cofactor array [74–76]. Only the BPheo in the "active" branch ($BPheo_A$) is involved in the photochemical reaction; the other one ($BPheo_B$), located in the "inactive" branch, participates in a charge separation only under special conditions (e.g., in PBRCs from specifically "engineered" mutants, see [77,78]). The functional differences between the BPheos are reflected by distinct spectral properties. In the visible/near-infrared (Vis/NIR) region of the spectrum, the Q_Y transition of the "active" $BPheo_A$ at 760 nm is redshifted by almost 10 nm relative to that of "inactive" $BPheo_B$ [79]. This phenomenon is ascribed to differences in hydrogen bonding of ring V keto group ([74], see Chapter 11). Likewise, the energy of the Q_X-transitions differs, with peaks at 530 and 540 nm of $BPheo_B$ and $BPheo_A$, respectively.

In analogy to the "sideness" of the light-induced electron transfer (ET) reactions in PBRCs the same peculiarity is assumed to prevail in PS II. In this case the feature of "unidirectionality" is even more pronounced because it not only consists of the light-induced charge separation and PQH_2 formation (Section 16.4) but also extends to the donor-side reactions involving Y_Z and the WOC (Section 16.3).

Although the spectral assignment of the pigments in RC-PC of PS II is difficult (Section 16.2.4) and contradictory results are reported in the literature [80–83], two important conclusions can be gathered from the data: (i) the Q_Y peak of the "active" $Pheo_{D1}$ exhibits a redshift relative to that of the "inactive" $Pheo_{D2}$ (similar to the shifts observed in PBRCs), and (ii) in the Q_X-region the difference spectra of $Pheo_{D1}$ formation are slightly redshifted by 2–3 nm in plant material (peak around 544 nm) compared with samples from mesophilic cyanobacteria [84].

In marked contrast to the drastic upshift of the reduction potential of P680 (Section 16.2.4.4.), the modulation of the redox properties of $Pheo/Pheo^{-\bullet}$ is less pronounced. The E_m of -610 mV determined for PS II [53] is almost the same as that of Pheo a in solution [61]. However, when taking into account electrostatic effects due to the presence of $Q_A^{-\bullet}$ during the redox titration, the actual "working potential" of $Pheo_{D1}/Pheo_{D1}^-$ is expected to be shifted towards less negative values. An experimental study revealed that this effect is about 85 mV [85]. Therefore, a value of -525 mV seems to be more realistic for the reduction potential of $Pheo_{D1}^-$ in competent functional PS II complexes with oxidized Q_A.

A characteristic feature of both $BPheo_A$ in PBRCs [58,86] and $Pheo_{D1}$ in PS II is the hydrogen bonding of its ring V keto group. In PBRCs the H-bond partner of $BPheo_A$ is the Glu 104 residue of subunit L [58,86], and the $Pheo_{D1}$ of PS II is connected with Glu 130 of polypeptide D1 [87–89]. The conserved hydrogen bond raises questions on its possible functional importance. Replacement of Glu 104 by site-directed mutagenesis has only minor effects on the kinetics of the ET steps leading to $P^+{}^{\bullet}Q_A^{-\bullet}$ formation in PBRCs [74]. Analogous experiments performed with D1/D2/Cyt b559 preparations of PS II indicate that the kinetics of $P680^+{}^{\bullet}Pheo_{D1}^-$ formation are not changed in *Synechocystis* sp. PCC 6803 mutants where Glu 130 is replaced by Leu [84]. Studies on the kinetics of $Pheo_{D1}^-$ reoxidation by Q_A cannot be performed with these samples because of the loss of Q_A. In contrast to the virtual invariance of the kinetics, however, the reduction potential of $Pheo_{D1}$ is affected by hydrogen bonds. Replacing Glu 130 by Gln increases the E_m by about 30 mV whereas Leu decreases the E_m by about 75 mV.

Although these changes are comparatively small, they affect the pathways of $P680^+{}^{\bullet}Q_A^{-\bullet}$ recombination and, as a consequence, the yield of $^3P680$ formation (Section 16.3.3).

In contrast to the controversial proposals for the assignment of the chlorophyll a and d molecules in RC-PC of *A. marina* (Section 16.2.4.5), at present consensus exists that the primary acceptor of PS II is a Pheo a as in conventional Chl a containing cyanobacteria [69–72].

16.2.6 Properties of Q_A

In PBRCs the component Q_A is either an ubiquinone (UQ) (e.g., *Rhodobacter sphaeroides*) or a menaquinone (MQ) (*Blastochloris viridis*) (Chapter 12), whereas Q_A is exclusively plastoquinone-9 (PQ-9) in all PS II complexes analyzed so far. The PQ-9 molecule is noncovalently attached to the binding site in the D2 polypeptide. In contrast to PBRCs, where UQ can be removed and replaced by a great variety of quinone derivatives [90], the Q_A binding site of PS II is much more selective. Reconstitution experiments indicate that it tolerates UQ, but even in this case the capacity for stable charge separation is markedly reduced [91].

One striking feature of Q_A in both PBRCs and PS II is its functioning as a one-electron redox component under normal conditions, i.e., the UQ (MQ) and PQ-9 attain only the redox states of the quinone and semiquinone forms. A double reduction to the quinol form requires nonphysiological conditions such as continuous illumination in the presence of $Na_2S_2O_4$ [92]. This behavior differs markedly from that of p-benzo- and p-naphthoquinones in solution, including ubi-(mena-)quinone and PQ-9. UQ and PQ-9 also are reduced to the quinol form at the Q_B-site (Section 16.4). Numerous redox titration experiments have been performed over the last three decades to determine the E_m of Q_A/Q_A^-. A collection of data gathered from these measurements shows a clustering of the values around $-300, -100, 0$ and $+50\,mV$ (for illustration, see Figure 1 of [93]). A value of around $-100\,mV$ seems to be a reasonable assumption for the reduction potential of Q_A in intact PS II complexes.

The redox properties of Q_A are modulated by the protein matrix, as is illustrated by the upshift of E_m by about $150\,mV$ in samples that lack an intact WOC [93]. This effect is probably of physiological relevance because it diminishes the yield of $^3P680$ formation by favoring the pathway of direct $P680^{+\cdot}Q_A^{-\cdot}$ recombination via tunneling (Section 16.3.3).

The structure of the Q_A pocket has been unraveled by X-ray structure analysis of PS II core complexes from *T. elongatus* at $3.5\,\text{Å}$ [18] and $3.0\,\text{Å}$ [20] resolution. It is formed by residues Ile-213, His 214, Thr 217, Tyr 244, Met 246, Ala 249, Asn 250, Trp 253, Ala 260, Pheo 261 and Leu 267 of polypeptide D2.

The head group of Q_A is sandwiched between Phe 261 (and Leu 267) on one side and Trp 253 (and Threo 217) on the other side of the quinone ring plane. The π–π stacking between Trp-253 and the quinone ring is not maximal because the ring planes of the two molecules are not parallel [18,20], in contrast to the PBRC from *Blastochloris viridis* where a parallel arrangement exists with Trp 250 of subunit M [94]. However, PBRCs tolerate a replacement of this Trp residue of the M subunit by some other residues while Trp-253 of D2 is required not only for Q_A binding but also for the assembly of stable PS II [95].

The possible hydrogen bonding of Q_A has been analyzed by EPR and ENDOR spectroscopy. For these studies samples were used that were deprived of the paramagnetic high-spin NHFe (located between Q_A and the Q_B binding pocket, see Figure 2) by a special extraction treatment [96,97]. The results obtained reveal that $Q_A^{-\cdot}$ forms asymmetric hydrogen bonds with the protein matrix [98]. FTIR measurements confirm that the mode of $Q_A^{-\cdot}$ interaction with the environment in the iron-depleted PS II membrane fragments closely resembles that of the native state [99]. ESEEM studies suggest hydrogen

FUNCTIONAL PATTERN OF PHOTOSYSTEM II 255

bonding to nitrogens of His and the backbone [100]. These conclusions are confirmed by the new structure model at 3.0 Å resolution where the keto oxygens of Q_A are hydrogen bonded to His214Nε and the backbone amide nitrogen of Phe261 of polypeptide D2 ([20] and Chapter 15).

16.2.7 Mechanism and Kinetics of Charge Separation

The light-induced charge separation in PS II via the overall reaction sequence of Eqn. (4) comprises basically two steps: (i) formation of the radical ion pair $P680^{+\cdot}Pheo^{-\cdot}$ by electron transfer from the electronically excited singlet state $^1P680^*$ to Pheo acting as primary acceptor and (ii) stabilization of the primary charge separation by rapid electron transfer from $Pheo^-_{D1}$ to Q_A.

16.2.7.1 Mechanism and Kinetics of $P680^{+\cdot}Pheo^{-\cdot}$ Formation
Since P680 acts as a shallow trap for electronic excitation energy from the antenna and since the excitation energy of $^1P680^*$ is distributed over several different molecules (Section 16.2.4.1) the kinetics of $P680^{+\cdot}Pheo^{-\cdot}$ formation reflect a series of equilibration steps. Depending on the rate of the individual EET and ET steps the overall reaction can be kinetically limited either by the EET from the antenna to the trap (a diffusion- or transfer-to-the-trap limited process) or by the ET at the trap (a trapping-limited process).

The overall EET kinetics to P680 depend on the structure of the antenna system. Basically, two building blocks can be distinguished: (i) the PS II core (PS II CC) containing RC-PC, $Chlz_{Z1}$, $Chlz_{Z2}$ and CP43/CP47 and (ii) the proximal and peripheral antennas. Equilibration within $^1(RC-PC)^*$ is extremely fast and accomplished within a few hundreds of femtoseconds [30,101,102]. Calculations based on the PS II structure reveal that the EET from CP43 and CP47 occurs directly to RC-PC, i.e., $Chlz_{D1}$ and $Chlz_{D2}$ contribute only marginally to this process [103]. The overall kinetics of charge separation within PS II CC was found to be trapping-limited [104]. A more complicated situation arises for the connection with the proximal/peripheral antenna. This system has changed drastically during evolution. Pigment–protein complexes of quite different structures and pigment content were developed in cyanobacteria, red algae and higher plants (Chapters 6–8). Accordingly, a straightforward and general conclusion cannot be achieved on the mode of limitation.

Experimental evidence supports the idea that in many cases the overall reaction is trapping-limited. The rate of trapping of the excited singlet state by $P680^{+\cdot}Pheo^{-\cdot}$ formation, gathered from fluorescence life time measurements, depends on the antenna size [105–110]. This finding can be consistently described within the framework of the "exciton-radical pair equilibrium" model [105–107]. In this model the measured rate constant for photochemical $P680^{+\cdot}Pheo^{-\cdot}$ formation, k_{PC}^{trap}, is expressed as the product of the intrinsic rate constant, k_{PC}^{inst}, and a constant K_{eq}^* that summarizes all equilibration steps of the excited singlet state between the antenna and P680. The "equilibrium" constant K_{eq}^* is the probability of an excited singlet state in PS II to populate the state

^{1}P680*. The rate constant k_{PC}^{trap} is assumed to be proportional to the "spectrally weighted" antenna size [109] provided that the EET processes are sufficiently fast to assure excitation energy equilibration. It is a matter of current debate as to what extent this equilibration is really achieved [40,110–112].

The primary charge separation step takes place within RC-PC. A study using photon echo spectroscopy revealed that at 1.3 K the charge separation in D1/D2/Cyt b559 preparations starts from the excited state of Chl$_{D1}$ [113]. This finding is supported by theoretical calculations [30]. After formation of the primary radical pair Chl$_{D1}^{+\cdot}$ Pheo$_{D1}^{-\cdot}$ the electron hole is rapidly transferred to P$_{D1}$. The reaction pattern of P680$^{+\cdot}$Pheo$_{D1}^{-\cdot}$ formation can be described by the scheme depicted in Figure 4.

In this scheme ^{1}(RC-PC)* represents the initial state of electronic excitation of RC-PC via direct light absorption or EET from the antenna system and ^{1}(RC-PC)$^*_{equil}$ symbolizes the excited state population after very rapid equilibration (100–500 fs) (vide supra), k_T, k_{-T}, k_t, k_{-t} are rate constants for forward and back-EET between the antenna (including CP43 and CP47), symbolized by Ant, and RC-PC and inside ^{1}(RC-PC)*, respectively. The rate constants $k_{PC,1}^{int}$ and $k_{PC,2}^{int}$ are the intrinsic rate constants of ET in the forward direction, and k_{-1} and k_{-2} are the same for the back direction. An evaluation of the data

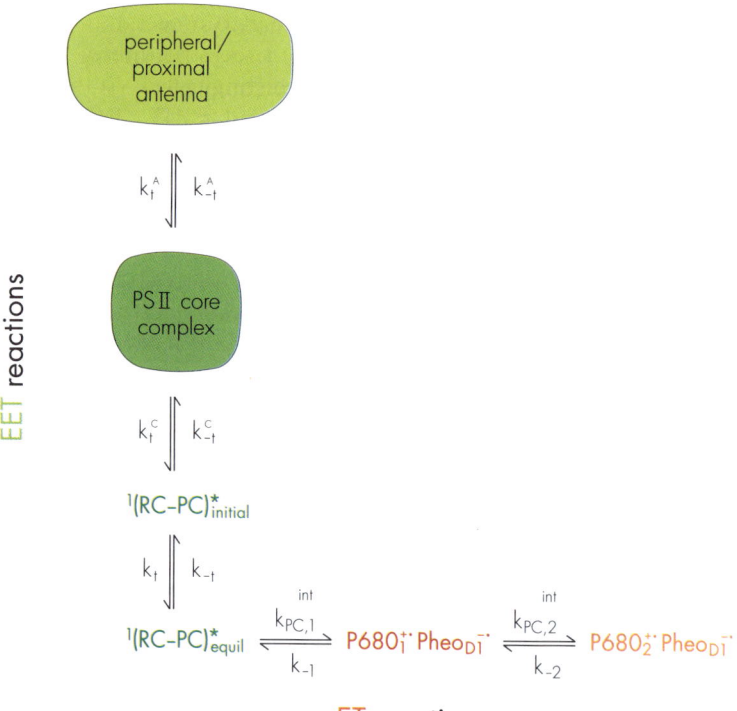

Figure 4. Reaction scheme of light-induced charge separation in PS II. See text for details.

gathered from photon echo spectroscopy leads to values of $(1.5\,\text{ps})^{-1}$ and $(25\,\text{ps})^{-1}$ for $k_{PC,1}^{int}$ and $k_{PC,21}^{int}$, respectively, for D1/D2/Cyt b559 preparations at 1.3 K [113]. The general scheme of Figure 4 is supported by analyses of flash induced absorption changes monitored at room temperature on suspensions of both D1/D2/Cytb559 preparations [114,115] and PS II core complexes which are fully active in oxygen evolution [115].

As a consequence of the complexity of the system, the experimentally observed rate constants for photochemical trapping in PS II, k_{PC}^{obs}, are highly dispersive even for D1/D2/Cyt b559 preparations [113–116] with a minimum content of Chl molecules (for further discussion, see [40]).

Regardless of this complexity, the mechanisms of photochemical charge separation are strikingly different in PBRCs and PS II. In PBRCs, the lower exciton state of the special pair P acts both as the trap for excitation energy and as primary donor for ET to the monomeric $BChl_A$, i.e., the reaction sequence is $^1P^*BChl_A\,BPheo_A \to P^{+\cdot}\,BChl_A^{-\cdot}\,BPheo_A \to P^{+\cdot}BChl_A\,BPheo_A^{-\cdot}$. In marked contrast, the Chl_{D1} at a similar spatial position in the D1D2 heterodimer as the $BChl_A$ in the L/M protein matrix is the lowest excited state in $^1(RC\text{-}PC)^*$ of PS II and the primary electron donor to $Pheo_{D1}$. Interestingly, the monomeric Chl a of PS I has also been inferred recently to be the primary donor rather than P700 ([32] and Chapter 13). If this is really the case, then a remarkable difference exists in the mechanisms of primary charge separation in the RCs of anoxygenic bacteria (type I and II) and the Photosystem I and II of oxygen evolving photosynthetic organisms. This would lead to interesting implications on the functional relevance of this evolutionary change.

16.2.7.2 Kinetics of $P680^{+\cdot}Q_A^{-\cdot}$ Formation

The radical ion pair $P680^{+\cdot}Pheo^{-\cdot}$ has to be "stabilized" by rapid electron transfer from $Pheo_{D1}^{-}$ to Q_A (Figure 1) to minimize the probability for loss reaction(s) via dissipative recombination of $P680^{+\cdot}Pheo^{-\cdot}$ (Section 16.3.3). The kinetics of the "stabilization" reaction have been resolved by measurements of flash-induced absorption changes that are characteristic for transient populations of $Pheo^{-\cdot}$ and $Q_A^{-\cdot}$ (Figure 1). $Pheo^{-\cdot}$ reoxidation [117] and $Q_A^{-\cdot}$ formation [118,119] exhibit virtually the same kinetics. Lifetimes of $(300\pm100)\,\text{ps}$ were reported for PS II membrane fragments and PS II CC from spinach [119]. Complementary analyses of fluorescence decay kinetics within the framework of the "exciton-radical pair equilibrium" model [107,109,120,121] and curve fitting of photovoltage measurements [122] led to comparable values of 300–500 ps, while the data gathered from the measurement reported in [114,115] are as about $(200\,\text{ps})^{-1}$. Interestingly, a rate constant of $(200-300\,\text{ps})^{-1}$ closely resembles the corresponding value of about $(200\,\text{ps})^{-1}$ for the electron transfer from $BPheo_A^{-\cdot}$ to Q_A in PBRCs [76,123,124]. This is another reflection of the close similarity of the acceptor side of PS II and PBRCs. The two types of reaction centers differ, however, in the effects of removal of the nonheme iron center (NHFe) (Figure 2) and in a kinetic H/D isotope effect that is more pronounced in PBRCs [125] than in PS II membrane fragments [121]. A gentle extraction of the NHFe center from PS II membrane fragments [96,97] is virtually without effect on the rate of Pheo$^-\cdot$ reoxidation by Q_A [119] and the properties of $Q_A^-\cdot$ [99], whereas the same depletion retards the ET step from BPheo$_A^-\cdot$ to Q_A in PBRCs by a factor of about 20 [126]. In contrast, the kinetics remain unaffected when NHFe-depleted PBRCs are additionally deprived of the H-subunit [126]. PS II does not contain a protein analogous to the H subunit of PBRCs. This illustrates both the differences between PS II and PBRCs and the possible regulatory role of protein subunits that do not contain cofactors.

Another important difference between PBRCs and PS II is the mode of axial coordination of the NHFe. In addition to the four His ligands in the two types of organisms, the NHFe of PBRCs is coordinated by a Glu residue [94], while in PS II the equivalent site is occupied by bicarbonate [18,20]. As a consequence, electron transfer in PS II is characterized by a striking bicarbonate effect that is missing in PBRCs [127].

The formation of the radical pair $P680^{+\cdot}Q_A^{-\cdot}$ is indispensable for a sufficiently stable charge separation that provides the driving force for the reaction sequences summarized by eqns. (2) and (3). Therefore, only PS II complexes containing Q_A in their oxidized form are functionally competent for efficient trapping of electronically excited states in the form of a useful electrochemical potential difference. PS II complexes in state P680Pheo Q_A are referred to as "open" reaction centers, while PS II is "closed" when lacking Q_A or containing reduced PQ-9 in the form of the semiquinone $Q_A^-\cdot$ or the double reduced quinol Q_AH_2. As a consequence, Q_A acts as photochemical quencher of chlorophyll a fluorescence [128]. This property is the basis of widely used fluorimetric methods for noninvasive monitoring of the functional state of the photosynthetic apparatus (for reviews, see Chapters in [129]).

16.2.8 Energetics of $P680^{+\cdot}Q_A^{-\cdot}$ Formation

In terms of thermodynamics, biological systems are generally open systems that require entropy fluxes for their development and sustenance. The energetics of these systems are described by the principles of irreversible thermodynamics (for a review, see [130]). Accordingly, a thorough analysis of the efficiency of energy transformation of photosynthetic organisms as converters of light (characterized by photon wavelength, polarization, flux rate *etc.*) into Gibbs free energy must be performed within the framework of irreversible thermodynamics. This challenging task is beyond the scope of this chapter (for a review, see [131]). Therefore, the following description is restricted to the energetics of the intermediary states of charge separation in PS II.

16.2.8.1 Energy Levels of the "Initial" ($^1P680^*$) and "Final" ($P680^{+\cdot}Q_A^{-\cdot}$) State

The overall energetics of each process is determined by the levels of the "initial" and the "final" states. The initial state of charge separation in PS II is the lowest electronically excited singlet state formed at P680 after photon absorption and subsequent rapid vibrational relaxation. A Q_Y transition of 680–684 nm corresponds to an energy of 1.83–1.82 eV. The rapid distribution of the electronically excited singlet state between the energetic levels available by a bed of pigments with nearly isoenergetic Q_Y-transitions (at room temperature the energy differences among the Chl a molecules are comparable to kT) gives rise to an entropy term $-k_B \ln W$, where k_B and W are the Boltzmann constant and the thermodynamic probability, respectively. In the simplest case of an array of identical pigment molecules with negligibly small exciton splitting but connected via rapid incoherent Förster-type EET, the value of W corresponds to the number of pigments N_{Chl}. In reality, however, levels are not isoenergetic in the PS II antenna and W is smaller than N_{Chl}. Effects owing to different site energies can be expressed to a first approximation by using an "effective pigment number" [109]. The decrease of the Gibbs energy emerging from excited-state equilibration in PS II with normal antenna size is estimated to be about -120 meV [85]. However, as discussed by Krishtalik, the configurational rather than the Gibbs energy is the key parameter for the energetics of the reactions [132]. The configurational energy of $^1P680^*/P680$ is 1.82–1.83 eV. If one takes into account very fast relaxations in the environment this value could be lower by some tens of meVs [125].

The energy level of the "final" state of stable charge separation, $P680^{+\cdot}Q_A^{-\cdot}$, is difficult to assess. In principle, redox and reduction potentials are thermodynamic parameters that are defined for equilibrium states. However, the transient radical pair $P680^{+\cdot}Q_A^{-\cdot}$ with its limited lifetime does not attain a true equilibrium. Furthermore, even the values of thermodynamically well-defined redox potentials are not precisely known for both $P680/P680^{+\cdot}$ and $Q_A^{-\cdot}/Q_A$ (Sections 16.2.4.4 and 16.2.6). On the basis of an estimation of 1.2–1.3 eV for the free energy gap between $^1P680^*Q_A$ and $P680^{+\cdot}Q_A^{-\cdot}$, the efficiency of the "useful" charge separation in PS II is calculated to be about 65–70% [40]. Comparison with PBRCs reveals that the energetic efficiency of charge separation in PS II is much higher than the reported value of about 35% for the radical pair $P870^{+\cdot}Q_A^{-\cdot}$ in $Rb.$ $sphaeroides$ [133]. This marked difference between the two types of organisms is almost entirely due to the necessity of developing the strongly oxidizing species $P680^{+\cdot}$ for photosynthetic water oxidation.

16.2.8.2 Energy Levels of Intermediary States and Role of the Protein Environment (Relaxation Processes)

The cofactors involved in $P680^{+\cdot}Q_A^{-\cdot}$ formation are embedded into a tailored protein matrix. As a consequence, the formation of different redox states of the reaction sequence [eqn. (4)] gives rise to time-dependent responses of the protein environment. Any charge density redistribution within the cofactor(s) owing to population of a particular state necessarily leads to changes of the interaction with the atoms of other cofactors and the protein matrix. For a description of general principles of conformational adaptation induced by spatial shift of charges (e.g., electron and proton movement) and the implications for biological processes see [134].

Reliable calculations of the energetics require detailed information on the electronic configuration of the different states (Section 16.2.7 and Figure 5) and their interaction with the environment. An indispensable – but not sufficient – prerequisite for a straightforward analysis is the knowledge of a high-resolution structure of the whole system. At present, this condition is not satisfied for PS II, because the highest resolution currently available is limited to 3.0 Å ([20] and Chapter 15). To illustrate the complexity of the problem, information on the functionally and structurally much better characterized RCs from purple bacteria (Chapters 11 and 12) will be used for comparison.

Energetics and Relaxation Processes During the Lifetime of $^1P680^*$. In general, the dipole moment and nuclear configuration of electronically excited pigments differ from those of the ground state and, therefore, relaxation processes of the environment are induced. Furthermore, charge-transfer states can be populated in coupled pigments such as the special pair of PBRCs in state $^1P^*$ [135,136] and in the multimeric P680 complex in state $^1(RC\text{-}PC)^*$ of PS II [30,137]. The relaxation processes within the excited state $^1P^*$ of PBRCs were found to be very rapid [135,138,139]. Ultrafast excited singlet state equilibration within $^1(RC\text{-}PC)^*$ [30,101,102] is most likely followed by a response of the protein matrix, but the energetics of this rapid environmental response is not yet resolved. Values of tens of meV are reported for PBRCs [125].

Energetics and Relaxation Processes During the Lifetime of $P680^{+\bullet}Pheo^{\bullet}$. The radical ion pair $P680^{+\bullet}Pheo^{-\bullet}$ can attain different states. $P680_1^{+\bullet}Pheo_{D1}^{-\bullet}$ and $P680_2^{+\bullet}Pheo_{D1}^{-\bullet}$, where $P680_1^{+\bullet} = [Chl_1^{+\bullet}\ P_{D1}\ P_{D2}\ Chl_{D2}]$ and $P680_2^{+\bullet} = [Chl_{D1}\ P_{D1}^{+\bullet}\ P_{D2}\ Chl_{D2}]$, are distinguished by their mode of hole localization (see scheme in Figure 4). An energetic gap of about 50 meV would be sufficient to assure that the electron density moves from $Chl_{D1}^{+\bullet}$ to P_{D1} so that the spin of the cation radical is predominantly located at P_{D1} [40]. Notably, the exact spin distribution within $(RC\text{-}PC)^{+\bullet}$ is not known (Section 16.2.4.4).

The energetics of the radical pair formation and the response of the protein environment have been analyzed by theoretical calculations for $P^{+\bullet}BPheo_A^{-\bullet}$ in PBRCs. Based on the static crystallographic structure, values of about -90 meV were calculated for the energy gap between $^1P^*$ and the initially formed radical pair $P^{+\bullet}BPheo_A^{-\bullet}$ and about -200 meV for the subsequent relaxation [140]. These values have to be compared with estimates gathered from experimental results. Delayed fluorescence measurements lead to corresponding $\Delta G°$s of -170 and -80 meV [141,142], while numbers of -55 and -135 meV, respectively, are obtained from an analysis of time-resolved decay kinetics of prompt fluorescence of an antenna-free mutant strain of *Rb. capsulatus* [143]. Apart from quantitative differences due to limitations of both theoretical and experimental approaches (for a discussion, see [40]) the results clearly show the relevance of protein relaxation for the energetics of light-induced charge separation in PBRCs.

With respect to environmental effects another important point has to be discussed. According to the Marcus theory [144] an optimal electron transfer rate requires a matching of the reorganization energy with the free energy gap. The free energy loss due to nuclear rearrangement on the ultrafast time scale of the initial electron transfer step must be very small, both due to the limited nuclear relaxation rates and the low polarity environment. Thus, an ultrafast rate for the primary photosynthetic electron transfer step can be achieved only if the free energy loss is very small, i.e., $\Delta G^0_{initial}$ between the excited state and the initial unrelaxed radical pair may be rather small. This idea is supported by earlier experiments [145].

In fact; the overall relaxation was shown to consist of a ladder of states with progressively increasing free energy gaps. As a consequence, the energetics of charge separation become a time-dependent parameter. This principle is illustrated clearly in a study on time-resolved fluorescence from PBRCs. Data gathered over a wide range of temperatures (10–295 K) and from mutants where the redox potential of $P/P^{+\cdot}$ is shifted by up to 350 mV are well described by a sequence of relaxations of the radical pair $P^{+\cdot}BPheo_A^{-\cdot}$, including three different states [146].

Compared with studies on PBRCs substantially less information is available for PS II. Values of about -150 meV for $\Delta G°$ between $^1P680^*$ and $P680^{+\cdot}Pheo_{D1}^{-}$ in "open" PS II complexes were gathered from analyses of fluorescence decay kinetics (Section 16.2.7.2) [121]. Time-resolved photovoltage measurements with unstacked PS II membrane fragments and data evaluation within the framework of the exciton radical pair equilibrium model lead to a very similar value of about -160 meV [85]. In PS II centers "closed" by keeping $Q_A^{-\cdot}$ reduced, the negative charge on $Q_A^{-\cdot}$ diminished the $\Delta G°$ gap by about 85 meV whereas formation of Q_AH_2 leads to marginal effects at most [85]. The influence of the negative charge of $Q_A^{-\cdot}$ on the properties of $Pheo^{-\cdot}$ is clearly reflected by a pronounced electrochromic effect on the Q_x band of $Pheo_{D1}$ that gives rises to the "C550 signal" [147].

A study on charge-recombination fluorescence and radical pair relaxation in D1/D2/Cyt b559 preparations at low temperature revealed that five different relaxation steps can be distinguished between $^1P680^*$ and $P680^{+\cdot}Pheo_{D1}^{-}$ [148]. The difference of free energy between the excited state $^1P680^*$ and the first radical pair RP_1, $(\Delta G_1°)_{RP}$, was shown to be only -1.5 meV at 77 K and the total energy drop $(\Delta G°_{total})_{RP}$ between $^1P680^*$ and the "relaxed" radical pair was about 46 meV within the time scale of the measurement. An analogous analysis performed at room temperature by using His-tagged PS II core complexes from *Synechocystis* sp. PCC 6803 with high O_2-evolving capacity led to a sequence of relaxation steps within a ladder of radical pair states with a total $\Delta G°$ of -167 meV [149]. This value nicely fits with the -150 meV gathered from earlier data [121]. Regardless of quantitative $\Delta G°$ differences (-46 versus -167 meV) between the two reports, which are understandable because sample material and temperature were quite different, the key point of these studies is the clear demonstration of the importance of protein relaxation modes for the stabilization of the radical pair. At low temperature these relaxation processes are substantially slower due to the decreased mobility of the protein.

The above-mentioned studies show that the radical pair energetics are characterized by a sequence of relaxation steps via a series of radical pairs of the reaction centers [148,149] as is shown schematically in Figure 5. This behavior is fundamentally different from static distributions of free energy

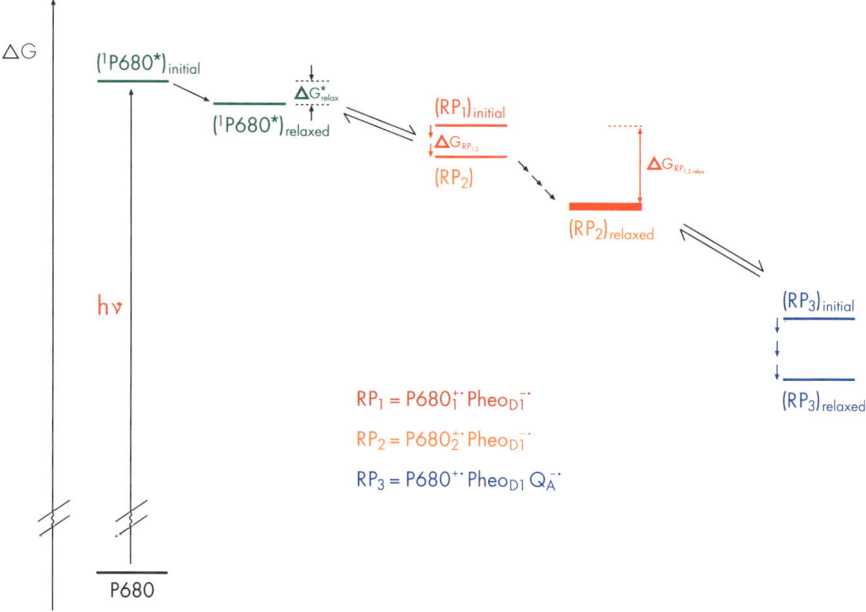

Figure 5. Simplified scheme of the energetics of $P680^{+\cdot}Q_A^{-\cdot}$ formation. See text for details.

differences that are due to sample heterogeneity and characterized by inherently different free energy gaps. It reflects the essential time-dependent role of protein conformational relaxation in stabilizing intermediate redox states. As a consequence, the protein plays an active functional role in providing rapid and efficient relaxation channels to lower the free energy gap once the radical pair is formed, which has the effect of preventing back reactions. It is attractive to hypothesize that, probably, the protein environment around the reaction center has been optimized during evolution to fulfil this task. The modulation of the energetics via protein relaxations is not restricted to the processes of light-induced charge separation but also relevant for subsequent reactions like $P680^{+\cdot}$ reduction by Y_Z ([150] and Section 16.3).

In summary, proteins play an active role in supporting charge separation by providing efficient relaxation channels that span a wide time domain from picoseconds up to nanoseconds and, perhaps, extending into the microsecond range.

16.3 Oxidative Reactions Driven by $P680^{+\cdot}$

16.3.1 $P680^{+\cdot}$ Reduction by Y_Z and Oxidative Water Splitting

$P680^{+\cdot}$ provides the driving force for a sequence of reactions that lead to oxidative water splitting into molecular oxygen and four protons. The overall scheme of this process is depicted in a simplified form in Figure 6. As shown in

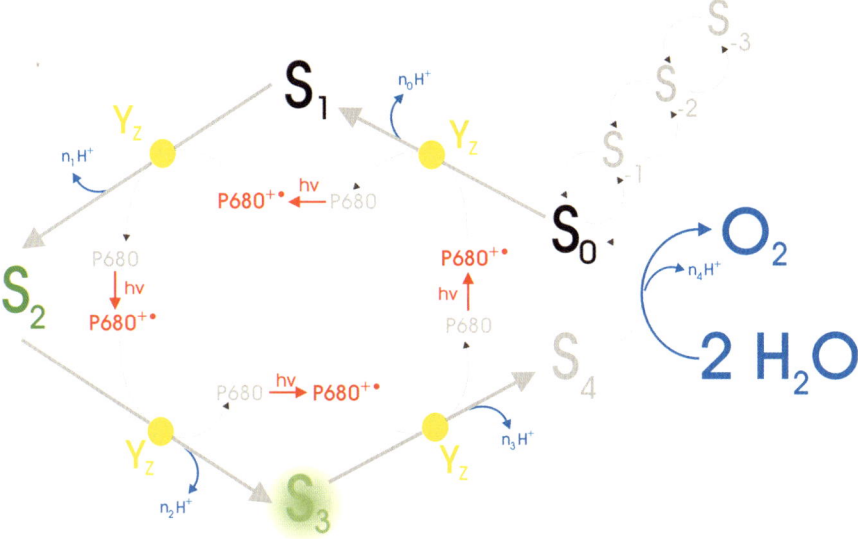

Figure 6. Simplified scheme of water oxidation with P680$^{+\cdot}$ as oxidant. See text and Chapter 17 for details.

the figure, P680$^{+\cdot}$ oxidizes a tyrosine residue Y_Z that was identified as Y161 of polypeptide D1 [151,152]. The oxidized form Y_Z^{ox} in turn extracts electrons stepwise from the water-oxidizing complex (WOC). The latter reactions are the topic of Chapter 17. Therefore, this section describes only the reduction of P680$^{+\cdot}$ by Y_Z. The oxidized form Y_Z^{ox} appears as a neutral radical in EPR studies [153]. Although P680 and Y_Z are bound to the D1/D2 heterodimeric protein matrix in a well-defined manner (Figure 2 and Chapter 15) the kinetics of P680$^{+\cdot}$ reduction by Y_Z are rather complex. The overall time course can be approximated satisfactorily by three-exponential kinetics, with "fast" ns, "slow" ns and μs components. This general feature was observed in thylakoids [154], PS II membrane fragments [155–157] and PS II core complexes from both spinach and thermophilic cyanobacteria [150,158]. Indirect lines of evidence suggest that it also pertains to intact leaves (*Arabidopsis thaliana*) [159]. The surprisingly complex kinetics, which depend on the redox state of the WOC and change drastically in systems lacking the WOC [155,156], could either reflect sample heterogeneity (e.g., an ensemble of PS II complexes with different distances between Y_Z and P680) or originate from a sequence of redox equilibria of the type [P680$^{+\cdot}$ $Y_Z \Leftrightarrow$ P680 Y_Z^{ox}]$_j$ due to relaxation processes analogous to those discussed for the radical pairs of charge separation (Section 16.2.8.2), where index *j* symbolizes one of several stages of relaxation. A critical survey of the experimental data favors the idea of a sequence of relaxation steps as outlined in [150]. Based on the approximation of a triexponential kinetics, the process of P680$^{+\cdot}$ reduction by Y_Z can be described by the scheme of Figure 7 (left-hand side) for PS II complexes with an intact WOC. The initial

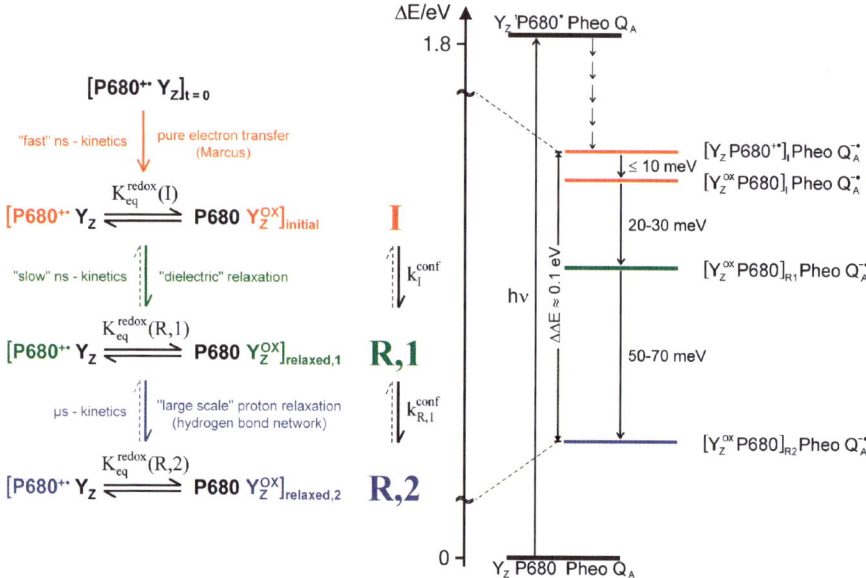

Figure 7. Reaction scheme (left-hand side) and energetics (right-hand side) of $P680^{+\cdot}$ reduction by Y_Z in PS II complexes with an intact water-oxidizing complex in redox state S_1. For simplicity, the panel on the right-hand side presents only $\Delta\Delta E$ values for the different relaxation states because the absolute energy gap between $[Y_Z{}^1 P680^* PheoQ_A]$ and $[Y_Z^{ox} P 680 PheoQ_A^{-\cdot}]$ is not exactly known (see text). Likewise, energetic relaxations around the $Q_A^{-\cdot}$ site and the Gibbs energy loss due to partial reoxidation of $Q_A^{-\cdot}$ by $Q_B(Q_B^{-\cdot})$ (Section 16.4) in the μs time domain are omitted.

step is a rapid equilibration that consists of the transfer of an electron from Y_Z to $P680^{+\cdot}$ concomitant with a proton shift within a hydrogen bond between the OH group of Y_Z and a nearby base X [156]. Several lines of evidence suggest that base X is His-190 of polypeptide D1 [18,20,160] (for a discussion on the nature of this hydrogen bond, see [161] and references therein). The rate of the equilibration within the initial state I can be described consistently by the Marcus theory of nonadiabatic electron transfer [144] with a reorganization energy of about 0.5 eV [162,163]. This reaction is characterized by rate constants of $(20-50\,\text{ns})^{-1}$ [154–159], activation energies of $10-20\,\text{kJ}\,\text{mol}^{-1}$ [150,156,164] and a vanishingly small kinetic H/D isotope effect [165]. The normalized extent of the "fast" ns kinetics to the overall $P680^{+\cdot}$ reduction by Y_Z is large in redox states S_0 and S_1 of the WOC and significantly smaller in S_2 and S_3 [155–157].

The "slow" ns-components with rate constants of $300-600\,\text{ns}^{-1}$ are assumed to originate from a local response of the nearest protein environment that does not consist of "large scale" hydrogen bond rearrangements [150]. These kinetics are invariant to replacement of exchangeable protons by deuterons [165] and the activation energy is somewhat larger (by a factor of 1.5–2) than that for the "fast" ns-kinetics [150,164]. The normalized amplitudes exhibit an opposite dependence on the redox state S_i of the WOC, i.e., higher values in S_2 and S_3 and lower values in S_0 and S_1 [155–157].

In marked contrast to the "fast" and "slow" ns-kinetics, the component with 30–35 μs kinetics exhibits a pronounced H/D exchange effect [157,166,167]. This phenomenon is ascribed to the rearrangement of a hydrogen bond network in the environment of Y_Z [157,166].

Based on the reported free energy gap, $\Delta G°$ (P680$^{+\cdot}$ Y_Z minus P680 Y_Z^{ox}), of 100 meV [152], the overall energetics of the reaction can be described by the diagram shown on the right-hand side of Figure 7 (see also [150]). It must be emphasized that these energetics depend on the S_i state of the WOC [150]. Furthermore, variations are observed among different preparations (P. Kühn and G. Renger, unpublished results).

16.3.2 P680$^{+\cdot}$ Reduction by Y_Z in PS II Complexes without Intact WOC

Newly synthesized PS II complexes lack an intact WOC [168,169]. Likewise, several stress factors such as cold or heat [170,171], drought [172], low or high pH [173,174] and UV-B irradiation [175,176] (see also Chapter 10) lead to elimination or deterioration of the WOC function. In all these cases the kinetics of P680$^{+\cdot}$ reduction by Y_Z is markedly changed: the ns-kinetics disappear in the physiological pH range and the reaction is dominated by μs-kinetics. In thylakoids or PS II membrane fragments deprived of the WOC, the kinetics with typical lifetimes of about 10 μs at pH 7.0 become retarded when the pH decreases [177,178], the activation energy is significantly larger (30–40 kJ mol^{-1}) than in samples with intact WOC [162,179,180], and the kinetics are characterized by a pronounced H/D exchange effect of about 3 [180–182]. The oxidation of Y_Z in these samples is coupled to a stoichiometric proton release into the lumen [183] and to a markedly higher reorganization energy of about 1.6 eV [162,163]. These findings indicate that the reaction coordinate is significantly altered in PS II complexes without a functional WOC, and they imply changes of the environment of Y_Z and probably also in its hydrogen bonding (for a review, see [184]). Of physiological relevance is the high susceptibility of the reaction to photoinhibition ([185–187] and Chapter 10). The quantum yield of this deleterious effect exceeds that of PS II complexes with an intact WOC by a factor of about 1000 [185]. Accordingly, newly synthesized PS II complexes without the WOC (vide supra) are especially prone to photoinhibition and need to be protected. It is assumed that cytochrome *b-559* is an important component of a protective mechanism that most likely involves a cyclic electron flow [188–190]. This integral membrane bound heme protein with its unique redox properties [188–190] is a constituent of all PS II complexes ([191] and references therein) and has no corresponding counterpart in PBRCs. A reversible transition between the high potential (HP) and intermediate/low potential (IP)/(LP) forms is assumed to be essential for the protective function of Cyt *b-559 in vivo* [192–194].

16.3.3 Recombination Reactions of $P680^{+\bullet}$ with $Q_A^{-\bullet}$ and $Pheo^{-\bullet}$; $^3P680$ Triplet Formation

The recombination reaction of $P680^{+\bullet}$ with $Q_A^{-\bullet}$ takes place in competition with $P680^{+\bullet}$ reduction by Y_Z even in open reaction centers. The lifetime of the radical pair $P680^{+\bullet}Q_A^{-\bullet}$ is limited by the tunneling rate of direct electron transfer leading to $P680Q_A$ in its ground state. According to the Marcus theory the rate constant of a nonadiabatic ET reaction depends on $\Delta G°$, the reorganization energy λ and the edge-to-edge (van der Waals) distance R_{DA} between donor (D) and acceptor (A) [144]. The distance between the spin density centers of the radicals $P680^{+\bullet}$ and $Q_A^{-\bullet}$ has been determined, by using pulsed EPR spectroscopy, as 27.4 Å [195]. Based on these findings and recent crystal structure data [18–20], a realistic distance of about 20 Å can be derived for R_{P680Q_A} (Figure 2 and Chapter 15). Within the framework of an empirical rate constant–distance relationship [196] a rate constant of the order of $(5\,\text{ms})^{-1}$ is obtained that represents the maximum value for the case of $\Delta G° + \lambda = 0$. The actual number of this maximum rate constant depends on the precise values of R_{P680Q_A} and the parameter β that describes the dependence of the matrix element of electronic coupling on the distance between both redox groups [196]. The value of about $(5\,\text{ms})^{-1}$ estimated from the rate constant–distance relationship is in good correspondence with the experimental value of $(2.5\,\text{ms})^{-1}$ [179]. In systems lacking a functionally competent WOC the re-reduction of Y_Z^{ox} is comparatively slow. If Y_Z^{ox} is kept oxidized, $P680^{+\bullet}$ recombines with $Q_A^{-\bullet}$ with a dominant time constant of 150–200 µs [197,198]. This value is not markedly affected by the redox state of Y_Z, is virtually independent of pH between 5 and 8 and is invariant to replacement of exchangeable protons by deuterons [181]. The 150–200 µs kinetics are about one order of magnitude faster than those of the direct electron transfer from $Q_A^{-\bullet}$ to $P680^{+\bullet}$ and, therefore, are indicative of an alternative pathway, which presumably involves the uphill regeneration of $P680^{+\bullet}Pheo_{D1}^-$ followed by either radiative or nonradiative charge recombination. The contribution to the overall reaction of this thermally activated route depends on the free energy gap between $P680^{+\bullet}Pheo_{D1}^-$ and $P680^{+\bullet}Q_A^{-\bullet}$. The extent of the indirect pathway via nonradiative $P680^{+\bullet}Pheo_{D1}^-$ recombination has been estimated to be almost 80% of the total recombination of $P680^{+\bullet}Q_A^{-\bullet}$ in WT cells of *Synechocystis* sp. 6803 [55] and the green alga *Chlamydomonas reinhardtii* [199]. The $P680^{+\bullet}Q_A^{-\bullet}$ recombination has two important physiological implications: (a) dissipation of oxidizing equivalents that are required for the redox advancement in the WOC, thus contributing significantly to the probability of misses of this process, and (b) a recombination comprising the intermediary $P680^{+\bullet}Pheo_{D1}^-$ formation can lead to significant population of the triplet state $^3P680$ (vide infra). As a result of the misses, the period-four oscillation pattern of flash-induced oxygen evolution (Figure 1 of Chapter 17) is damped. Based on an analysis of the H/D exchange effect on this phenomenon [200], the 150–200 µs kinetics are inferred to dominate the pathway of $P680^{+\bullet}Q_A^{-\bullet}$ recombination also in PS II complexes with an intact WOC (at least in plants).

For a comparison with anoxygenic purple bacteria, interestingly, in PBRCs marked differences exist in the recombination pathways. Despite striking overall structural homologies, the state $P^{+\cdot}Q_A^{-\cdot}$ of *Rb. sphaeroides* recombines almost entirely via the slow direct tunneling [201] while in *Blastochloris viridis* the indirect pathway via $P^{+\cdot}BPheo_A^{-\cdot}$ dominates [202].

In "closed" PS II complexes $Pheo_{D1}^{-\cdot}$ cannot be reoxidized by Q_A and instead recombines with $P680^{+\cdot}$. If the PS II complexes are "closed" by formation of $Q_A^{-\cdot}$, the recombination time of $P680^{+\cdot}Pheo_{D1}^{-\cdot}$ is of the order of a few ns [107,121,203]. The time of this reaction is slower by at least one order of magnitude in samples lacking Q_A. Time constants of about 50 ns were obtained for D1/D2/Cyt b559 preparations [36,204,205]. This $P680^{+\cdot}Q_A^{-\cdot}$ recombination is markedly slower than the 300 ps kinetics of ET from $Pheo_{D1}^{-\cdot}$ to Q_A [117–119].

In addition to the stabilization reaction leading to $P680^{+\cdot}Q_A^{-\cdot}$ formation, essentially three decay pathways of the radical ion pair $^1[P680^{+\cdot}Pheo^{-\cdot}]$ have to be taken into consideration: (i) back reaction to the electronically excited singlet state $^1P680^*$, (ii) spin dephasing under formation of the triplet radical pair $^3[P680^{+\cdot}Pheo^{-\cdot}]$ followed by recombination into the triplet state $^3P680$; and (iii) direct recombination of $^1[P680^{+\cdot}Pheo^{-\cdot}]$ into the ground state.

Among these competing pathways, only $^3P680$ formation is of physiological relevance because chlorophyll triplets give rise to generation of singlet oxygen ($^1\Delta_g O_2$) via the sensitized reaction:

$$^3Chl + {}^3\Sigma_g O_2 \rightarrow {}^1Chl + {}^1\Delta_g O_2 \tag{5}$$

The species $^1\Delta_g O_2$ is very reactive and leads to oxidative degradation reactions (for further details, see Chapter 10).

Chlorophyll triplets in the antenna are most efficiently quenched by rapid energy transfer to Car with a rate that is much faster than ^3Chl formation [206]. In the case of $^3P680$, this process is inefficient [23] and the physiologically relevant role of the two β-carotenes in the D1/D2 heterodimer is predominantly the quenching of $^1\Delta_g O_2$ generated via population of $^3P680$ and subsequent sensitized reaction with normal triplet oxygen ($^3\Sigma_g O_2$). In addition to $^1\Delta_g O_2$ suppression, the β-carotenes most likely participate in a protective cyclic electron transport pathways that involves cytochrome b_{559} (Section 16.3.2 and [188–191]) and occurs when the normal function of water splitting is disturbed [23,207]. Furthermore, the location of $^3P680^*$ on Chl_{D1} rather than P_{D1}–P_{D2} (Section 16.2.4.2) favors triplet quenching by $Q_A^{-\cdot}$ [208,209]. The implications of $^3P680$ formation for photodamage are beyond the scope of this chapter (for discussion, see [210,211] and Chapter 10).

16.4 PQH₂ Formation

16.4.1 Two-Step Reaction Sequence Induced by $Q_A^{-\cdot}$

The formation of PQH_2 takes place in a special pocket, the Q_B site of PS II, via a sequence of two one-electron redox steps with $Q_A^{-\cdot}$ as reductant [212,213]. The reaction scheme (for reviews, see [214,215] closely resembles that of the UQH_2 formation in PBRCs (Figures 12 and 7 of Chapters 11 and 12, respectively). In the first ET step from $Q_A^{-\bullet}$ to PQ-9 bound at the Q_B site, the semiquinone $Q_B^{-\bullet}$ is formed with a time constant of a few hundreds of microseconds [216,217]. The reaction is characterized by an equilibrium constant of about 20 in both spinach and *Brassica napus* thylakoids [218,219]. The second redox step occurs with somewhat slower kinetics [216–217,220] and leads to formation of PQH_2, which has a much lower affinity to the Q_B site. The very high stability of $Q_B^{-\bullet}$ in both PBRCs and PS II can be explained by electrostatic effects due to a special topology of the Q_B site that gives rise to a unique pathway for the release of the charged head group through a region with low dielectric constant [221].

The overall reaction of PQH_2 formation is coupled with the uptake of two protons from the cytoplasmic/stroma side (for reviews, see [214,215]. Analyses of the corresponding reactions in PBRCs reveal that the H^+ transfer to $Q_B^{-\bullet}$ and Q_BH^- occurs via a hydrogen-bond network in the protein environment, including carboxylic groups and bound water molecules [222–224]. A reorientation of the OH group of residue Ser-L223 (shift of hydrogen bonding with Asp-L213 to $Q_B^{-\bullet}$) is assumed to be an important step in the H^+-transfer to reduced quinone in RCs from *Rb. sphaeroides* ([225] and Chapter 11). Less information is available for the corresponding reactions in PS II. A recent FTIR study on PS II CC from *T. elongatus* [226] revealed that – in marked contrast to RCs from *Rb. sphaeroides* – the formation of $Q_B^{-\bullet}$ is not coupled with the protonation of a carboxylic amino acid residue. This finding suggests that the mechanism of protonation is different in PBRC and PS II [226]. Details of the proton transfer pathway(s) in PS II remain to be clarified.

Several lines of evidence suggest that the electron transfer step form $Q_A^{-\bullet}$ to Q_B in PBRCs requires structural flexibility of the protein matrix (Chapters 11 and 12). An X-ray crystallographic study on the structure of PBRCs from *Rb. sphaeroides* that were frozen either under light or in the dark led to the conclusion that compared with its position in the dark-adapted state, the ubiquinone head group of Q_B is displaced by about 5 Å and rotated by 180° around the isoprenoid side chain when the samples are illuminated. It was suggested that this pronounced structural change limits the rate of $Q_A^{-\bullet}$ reoxidation by Q_B [227]. However, this idea has been questioned [228] and not supported by recent FTIR measurements [229,230] and a time-resolved X-ray crystallography analysis [231]. It seems more likely that the triggering conformational change(s) consist(s) of the rearrangement of hydrogen bonds, most prominently the reorientation of Ser 223 of the L-subunit, which is required for Q_B reduction by $Q_A^{-\bullet}$ (Chapter 11). The corresponding $Q_A^{-\bullet}$ reoxidation by Q_B in PS II was also shown to depend strongly on the conformational flexibility of the protein [232–234]. The characteristic temperature of the thermal threshold for the onset of $Q_A^{-\bullet}$ reoxidation is higher for ET to Q_B than for $Q_A^{-\bullet}$ to $Q_B^{-\bullet}$ [233]. Bulk water molecules play a key role as "plasticizers" for the protein environment, as illustrated recently in PS II membrane fragments of different extent of dehydration [190,235]. In PBRCs the movement of water molecules is assumed to be coupled with the turnover of UQ at the Q_B-site (Chapter 11).

Another unresolved problem is the possible functional role of the conserved NHFe center that is localized between Q_A and Q_B in both PBRCs (Chapter 11) and PS II (Figure 2 and Chapter 15). Based on its property as transition metal center with a partially filled 3d electron shell, it appears interesting to speculate on the possibility that NHFe is involved in electronic coupling between Q_A and Q_B, thus facilitating the ET from $Q_A^{-\bullet}$ to Q_B ($Q_B^{-\bullet}$). Experiments were reported that seem to support this idea [236]. Furthermore, in PS II samples the addition of exogenous quinones (Q_{ex}) that bind to the Q_B-site were found to give rise to reductant ($Q_{ex}^{-\bullet}$)-induced oxidation of high-spin $NHFe^{2+}$ to Fe^{3+} provided that the redox properties of the semiquinone/quinol redox couple satisfy the energetic requirements of the reaction [237–239]. The midpoint potential of the $NHFe^{2+}/Fe^{3+}$ system was found to be about $+400$ mV at pH 7.0 [237,240,241]. This value seems to be unfavorable for a direct participation of the NHFe as a redox active intermediate in the ET processes leading to PQH_2 formation at the Q_B-site. In PBRCs, replacement of the NHFe center by the redox inert Zn^{2+} has little or no effect on the rate of $Q_A^{-\bullet}$ reoxidation by Q_B [242,243], thus providing clear evidence that the NHFe does not act as intermediary redox carrier but probably plays a structural or electrostatic role (Chapter 12).

Apart from the NHFe that does not function as redox mediator in native systems (vide supra) the ET from $Q_A^{-\bullet}$ was proposed to comprise another intermediate X [244] but also this possibility can be ruled out on the basis of recent FTIR measurements [245], i.e. the original concept of direct reoxidation of $Q_A^{-\bullet}$ by Q_B ($Q_B^{-\bullet}$) (for reviews, see [214,215]) is the most likely mechanism. ENDOR studies on PBRC preparations where the NHFe is replaced by Zn^{2+} revealed that $Q_A^{-\bullet}$ is characterized by a highly asymmetric hydrogen bonding which significantly affects the spin distribution in the radical. The strong bonding to M His 219 that in turn is a ligand to the NHFe (Chapter 11) was speculated to regulate the ET from $Q_B^{-\bullet}$ to Q_B ($Q_B^{-\bullet}$) [246]. However, FTIR measurements on RCs from *Rb. sphaeroides* mutants reveal that the unusually strong hydrogen bonding between M His 219 and $Q_B^{-\bullet}$ is not obligatory for an efficient ET from $Q_B^{-\bullet}$ to Q_B [247].

The electrostatics due to the NHFe affects the pK_a values of neighboring amino acid residues, as is clearly illustrated by protolytic reactions coupled with a redox turnover of the NHFe [241,248] and the pH dependence of its E_m [249]. Therefore, it seems likely that the NHFe modulates the properties of a hydrogen bond network that might be involved in proton transfer reactions that are necessary for the formation of PQH_2. Under light stress the properties of the NHFe are modulated, probably due to structural changes in its microenvironment ([250] and Chapter 10).

After stepwise electron reduction with $Q_A^{-\bullet}$ as reductant and coupled H^+ uptake the quinol is released from the Q_B-site and becomes replaced by another molecule from the PQ(UQ) pool (for a review, see [215]). A high efficiency of this process requires that the reduction potential of $Q_A^{-\bullet}$ has to be sufficiently low. An E_m of about -100 mV appears to be a reasonable value in PS II complexes with intact WOC (Section 16.2.6). However, a significant upshift of the reduction potential by about 150 mV was found for systems lacking the WOC [93]. As a consequence of this effect, the driving force for Q_B ($Q_B^{-\cdot}$) reduction by $Q_A^{-\cdot}$ is drastically diminished and a large fraction of PS II centers becomes "closed". This energetic shift is likely to be of physiological relevance for newly synthesized PS II complexes that do not contain a functionally competent WOC [168,169]. In this case, the back reaction between P680$^{+\cdot}$ and $Q_A^{-\cdot}$ could protect against the destructive action of the strongly oxidizing P680$^{+\cdot}$ radical [197]. Among the possible pathways for the back reaction one leads to population of the triplet state ^{3}P680 that acts as sensitizer for singlet oxygen formation (Section 16.3.3). A shift of the reduction potential of $Q_A^{-\cdot}$ towards a more positive value diminishes the probability of ^{3}P680 formation and therefore provides further protection against rapid photodegradation of PS II complexes without WOC ([210] and Chapter 10).

16.4.2 Structure of the Q_B Site and Quinol/Quinone Exchange Reactions

The Q_B-pocket of PS II that is formed by the D1 protein is less precisely characterized than the environment of Q_A in the structural models presented with 3.5 Å [18] and 3.2 Å [19] resolution. Significant progress has been achieved by improving the structure to a resolution of 3.0 Å [20]. Three structural elements are involved in the formation of the Q_B site: i) the C-terminal part of transmembrane helix (TMH) d (Gly207 – Val 219), ii) the surface helices de(1) and de(2) at the cytosolic side including the connecting region, and iii) TMH e (Arg 269 – Phe 274). The binding pocket includes the amino acid residues Met 214, His 215, Leu 218, Val 219, Tyr 246, His 252, Phe 255, Ser 264, Phe 265 and Leu 271 (for further details, see [20,251] and Chapter 15). The bound PQ molecule is seen to interact with D1 amino acid residues Pheo-255 and Leu-271 and is hydrogen-bonded to the Nε atom of His-215 and/or the γ O-atom of Ser-264. Of special interest is the finding of two openings from the binding cavity. The structural arrangement suggests that the environment of Q_B is flexible and lipophilic, thus facilitating the Q_B/Q_BH_2 exchange through the inner-membrane facing opening (for further structural details, see [20,251] and Chapter 15). This arrangement could facilitate the diffusion of PQH$_2$ into lipid bilayer sections of the thylakoid membrane because neutron scattering experiments on the localization of UQ in artificial lipid bilayer systems support the idea that all natural polyisoprene chains lie in the central part without any significant protrusion into the fatty acid chain region [252].

The Q_B-pocket is also the binding site for numerous herbicides that block the linear electron transport chain by suppression of $Q_A^{-\cdot}$ reoxidation by Q_B (for a review, see [253]). Accordingly, structural differences between the Q_B-sites of PBRCs and PS II are reflected by markedly different affinities to several herbicides [253,254]. More detailed information is gained from selective and elegant modifications by genetic engineering that lead to "herbicide resistant" species of both anoxygenic bacteria and PS II [255–257]. This technique has been widely used and several amino acids identified that are constituents of the Q_B-site. Mild proteolytic attack by trypsin [258] or detergent treatment required for isolation of PS II membrane fragments and core complexes also modulate the properties of the Q_B-site [259,260].

The ET reactions of PS II are markedly faster than the rate-limiting step of the linear ET chain from H_2O to $NADP^+$ (for a review, see [261]). Therefore, the quinol replacement by quinone at the Q_B-site limits the turnover of PS II under continuous illumination. There exists a pool of PQ molecules. Values ranging from 7–40 are reported for thylakoids and cyanobacterial cells [262]. As a consequence the probability of PQ occupancy at the Q_B-site depends on the redox state of the pool. The overall process leading to a steady state of the PQ/PQH_2 ratio includes the diffusion of PQH_2 to the Cyt b_6f complex, followed by reoxidation to PQ and migration back to the Q_B site. Analogous reactions take place in purple bacteria where UQH_2 becomes reoxidized at the Cyt bc complex (for details, see Chapters 18 and 20). The lateral diffusion of quinols and quinones can be responsible for a kinetic limitation of the overall linear electron transport chain, as outlined in [263]. The mobility of PQ and PQH_2 depends on the array of the complexes in the membrane because the collisional encounters with proteins decrease the effective diffusion coefficient. This effect has been clearly illustrated by several studies on both purple bacteria cells and plants ([264–268]; see also Chapter 18). Earlier experiments revealed that up to ten different PS II complexes in the thylakoid membrane are functionally coupled via a common PQ pool [269]. Similar features have been reported for PS II membrane fragments [270]. Investigations on the reconstitution of a functionally competent endogenous PQ pool in PS II membrane fragments reveal that the effect is rather specific for PQ 9 [271]. This favors the concept of PS II domains that interact with PQ molecules, as outlined in [265,266]. In addition to the ET reactions the redox state of the PQ pool also affects the regulation of the electronic excitation of PS I and PS II (for a review see [272] and Chapter 9).

16.5 Role of Lipids

The PS II complexes are embedded into the thylakoid membrane that contains specific lipids of a highly conserved composition [273]. Bulk lipids are essential constituents of the membrane in establishing a well defined "impermeable" barrier to dissipative decay of the electrochemical potential difference via "undesired" ion fluxes. Apart from this essential function of the bulk lipid phase in energy transducing membranes (for details on the coupling of directed proton transfer to ATP synthesis, see Chapter 21) lipids are also known to interact specifically with photosynthetic reaction centers thus giving rise to effects that are relevant for optimal structural and functional properties (for a review see 274). New data on the structure revealed that the dimeric PS II CC from *T. elongatus* includes 14 lipids per monomer: six monogalactosyldiacylglycerol (MGDG), four digalactosyldiacylglycerol (DGDG), three sulfoquinovosyldiacylglycerol (SQDG) molecules and one phosphatidylglycerol (PG) molecule ([20] and Chapter 15).

Several specific effects on PS II are reported for these liquids: DGDG deficiency modifies the reaction pattern, especially the probability of the back reaction between P680$^{+\bullet}$ and $Q_A^{-\bullet}$ [275] and the properties of the WOC [276], ii) SQDG is important for the structural integrity and heat tolerance of PS II [277] and iii) PG plays a role in the dimerization of PS II [278] and in maintaining the structural integrity of the Q_B binding site [279]. New data indicate that PG exerts multiple effects, in particular also on specific reactions of the WOC [280].

At present details on structure-function relationships due to the interactions between cofactors, protein and lipids are not yet clarified but recent progress in structure analysis ([20] and Chapter 15) offers a new starting point to address this important problem. Therefore interesting results on this topic are expected in future research activities.

16.6 Concluding Remarks

This chapter summarizes our knowledge on the kinetics, energetics and mechanisms of (a) light-induced charge separation leading to the "stabilized" radical ion pair P680$^{+\bullet}Q_A^{-\bullet}$, (b) reduction of P680$^{+\bullet}$ by Y_Z and (c) formation of plastoquinol with $Q_A^{-\bullet}$ as the reductant. The description outlines two striking features: there are remarkable similarities in the general structural and functional organization of reactions (a) and (c) (see Introduction) in PBRCs and PS II, but also striking differences between these units in the two types of organisms, originating from the prerequisites for oxidative water splitting. Unresolved mechanistic details are outlined that remain to be clarified in future studies. In particular, unraveling of the functional relevance of protein dynamics is a challenging task. In this respect, the classical distinction between cofactor and apoprotein must be set aside for a deeper understanding of structure–function relationships. The effect of protein relaxation on the energetics and efficiency of light-induced charge separation and the subsequent redox reactions illustrates that it is more appropriate to consider several enzyme complexes as functional and structural entities. As discussed elsewhere [161,281], these operational units, and especially PS II with its water splitting activity, should be considered as special tailored molecular machines. The enormous progress achieved through the techniques of genetic engineering and monitoring protein dynamics in combination with highly advanced theoretical approaches in the field of quantum chemistry and molecular mechanics will pave the way to a higher level of understanding of biocatalysts in general and PS II in particular.

Acknowledgements

The author would like to thank J. Kern and T. Renger for providing Figures 2 and 3, respectively, together with J. Messinger for fruitful discussions.

Likewise, many thanks to P. Kühn for providing the electronic version of Figure 1 and to S. Renger for drawing Figures 4 and 5. I am also very grateful to numerous co-workers who have contributed to many of the studies decribed in this chapters and to W.W. Parson for a critical reading of the manuscript and valuable comments. Financial support by Deutsche Forschungsgemeinschaft (Sfb 429) is gratefully acknowledged.

References

1. B. Ke, *Photosynthesis: Photobiochemistry and Photobiophysics* (2001), Kluwer, Dordrecht.
2. G. Renger, Photosystem II and water oxidation in cyanobacteria, algae and higher plants, in: *Treatise on Bioelectrochemistry*, Vol. 2: *Bioenergetics* (1997) (P. Gräber, G. Milazzo, eds.), Birkhäuser, Basel, pp. 310–358.
3. G.F. Peter, J.P. Thornber, Biochemical evidence that the higher plant photosystem II core complex is organized as a dimer. *Plant Cell Physiol.* **32** (1991) 1237–1250.
4. E.J. Boekema, B. Hankamer, D. Bald, J. Kruip, J. Nield, A.F. Boonstra, J. Barber, M. Rögner, Supramolecular structure of the photosystem II complex from green plants and cyanobacteria. *Proc. Natl. Acad. Sci. U.S.A.* **92** (1995) 175–179.
5. T.S. Bibby, J. Nield, M. Chen, A.W.D. Larkum, J. Barber, Structure of a photosystem II supercomplex isolated from Prochloron didemni retaining its chlorophyss a/b light-harvesting system. *Proc. Natl. Acad. Sci. U.S.A.* **100** (2003) 9050–9054.
6. L.X. Shi, W.P. Schröder, The low molecular mass subunit of the photosynthetic supracomplex, photosystem II. *Biochim. Biophys. Acta* **1608** (2004) 75–96.
7. G. Renger. Molecular mechanism of water oxidation, in: *Concepts in Photobiology Photosynthsis and Photomorphogenesis* (1999) (G.S Singhal, G. Renger, Govindjee, K.-D. Irrgang, S.K. Sopory, eds.), Narosa Publishing Co., New Delhi, pp. 292–329.
8. F.V. Chochran, S.P. Wu, W. Wang, V. Nanda, J.G. Saven, M.J. Therien, W.F. DeGrado, Computational de novo design and characterization of a four-helix bundle protein that selectively binds a nonbiological cofactor. *J. Am. Chem. Soc.* **127** (2005) 1346–1347.
9. M.T. Reetz, Controlling the enantioselectivity of enzymes by directed evolution: Practical and theoretical ramifications. *Proc. Natl. Acad. Sci. U.S.A.* **101** (2004) 5716–5722.
10. J. Raymond, R.E. Bankenship, The evolutionary development of the protein complement of Photosystem 2. *Biochem. Biophys. Acta* **1655** (2004) 133–139.
11. G. Döring, G. Renger, J. Vater, H.T. Witt, Properties of the photoactive chlorophyll a_{II} in photosynthesis. *Z. Naturforsch., Teil B* **24** (1969) 1139–1143.
12. V.V. Klimov, A.V. Klevanik, V.A. Shuvalov, A.A. Krasnovsky, Reduction of pheophytin in the primary light reaction of Photosystem II. *FEBS Lett.* **82** (1977) 183–186.
13. H.H. Stiehl, Untersuchungen periodisch angeregter Absorptionsänderungen im Reaktionszentrum II der Photosynthese. PhD Thesis (in German), Technische Universität Berlin (1969).
14. H.H. Stiehl, H.T. Witt, Quantitaive treatment of the function of plastoquinone in photosynthesis. *Z. Naturforsch., Teil B* **24** (1969) 1588–1598.

15. H.J. van Gorkom, Identification of the reduced primary electron acceptor of photosystem II as a bound semiquinone anion. *Biochim. Biophys. Acta* **347** (1974) 439–442.
16. A. Zouni, H.T. Witt, J. Kern, P. Fromme, N. Krauß, W. Saenger, P. Orth, Crystal structure of photosystem II from *Synechococcus elongatus* at 3.8 Å resolution. *Nature* **409** (2001) 739–743.
17. N. Kamiya, J.-R. Shen, Crystal structure of oxygen-evolving photosystem II from *Thermosynechococcus vulcanus* at 3.7-Å resolution. *Proc. Natl. Acad. Sci. U.S.A.* **100** (2003) 98–103.
18. K. Feirreira, T.M. Inverson, K. Maghlouni, J. Barber, S. Iwata, Architecture of the photosynthetic oxygen-evolving center. *Science* **303** (2004) 1831–1838.
19. J. Biesiadka, B. Loll, J. Kern, K.-D. Irrgang, A. Zouni, Crystal structure of cyanobacterial photosystem II at 3.2 Å resolution: a closer look at the Mn-cluster. *Phys. Chem. Chem. Phys.* **6** (2004) 4733–4736.
20. B. Loll, J. Kern, W. Saenger, A. Zouni, J. Biesiadka, Towards complete cofactor arrangement in the 3.0 Å resolution structure of photosystem II. *Nature* **438** (2005) 1040–1044.
21. M. Kobayashi, H. Maeda, T. Watanabe, H. Nakano, K. Satoh, Chlorophyll and β-carotene content in the D1/D2/cytochrome b559 reaction center complex from spinach. *FEBS Lett.* **260** (1990) 138–140.
22. T. Tomo, M. Mimuro, M. Iwaki, M. Kobayashi, S. Itoh, K. Satoh, Topology of pigments in the isolated Photosystem II reaction center studied by selective extraction. *Biochim. Biophys. Acta* **1321** (1997) 21–30.
23. A. Telfer, What is β-carotene doing in the Photosystem II reaction centre? *Phil. Trans. R. Soc. London* **357** (2002) 1431–1440.
24. S.V. Ruffle, J. Wang, H.G. Johnston, T.L. Gustafson, R.S. Hutchison, J. Minagawa, A. Crofts, R.T. Sayre, Photosystem II peripheral accessory chlorophyll mutants in Chlamydomonas reinhardtii. Biochemical characterization and sensitivity to photoinhibition. *Plant. Physiol.* **127** (2001) 633–644.
25. H. Johnston, S.V. Ruffle, R.T. Sayre, T.L. Gustafson, Fluorescence decay kinetics of wild type D2-H117N mutant Photosystem II reaction centers isolated from Chlamydomonas reinhardtii. *J. Phys. Chem.* **104** (2000) 4777–4781.
26. S. Vasil'ev, G.W. Brudvig, D. Bruce, Structure based kinetic modelling of excited-state transfer and trapping in histidine-tagged Photosystem II core complexes from Synechocystis. *Biochemistry* **41** (2002) 12236–12243.
27. S. Vasil'ev, J.-R. Shen, N. Kamiya, D. Bruce, The orientations of core antenna chlorophylls in Photosystem II are optimized to maximize the quantum yield of photosynthesis. *FEBS Lett.* **561** (2004) 111–116.
28. R.H. Schweitzer, A.N. Melkozernov, R.E. Blankenship, G.W. Brudvig, Time-resolved fluorescence measurements of Photosystem II: the effect of quenching by oxidized chlorophyll Z. *J. Phys. Chem.* **102B** (1998) 8320–8326.
29. M.T. Lince, W. Vermaas, Association of His 117 in the D2 protein of Photosystem II with a chlorophyll that affects excitation: energy transfer efficiency to the reaction center. *Eur. J. Biochem.* **256** (1998) 595–602.
30. G. Raszewski, W. Saenger, T. Renger, Theory of optical spectra of photosystem II reaction centrs: Location of the triplet state and the identity of the primary electron donor. *Biophys. J.* **88** (2005) 986–998.
31. J. Deisenhofer, H. Michel, Three-dimensional structure on the reaction center of Rhodopseudomonas viridis, in: *The Photosynthetic Reaction Center* (1993) (J. Deisenhofer, J.R. Norris, eds.), Academic Press, New York, Vol II, pp. 541–558.

32. A.R. Holzwarth, M.G. Müller, J. Niklas, W. Lubitz, Ultrafast transient absoption studies on photosystem I reaction centers from Chlamydomonas reinhardtii. 2. Mutations near the P700 reaction center chlorophylls provide new insight into the nature of the primary electron donor. *Biophys. J.* **90** (2006) 552–565.
33. P. Fromme, P. Jordan, N. Krauß, Structure of Photosystem I. *Biochim. Biophys. Acta* **1507** (2001) 5–31.
34. A. Warshel, W.W. Parson, Spectroscopic properties of photosynthetic reaction centers. 1. Theory. *J. Am. Chem. Soc.* **109** (1987) 6143–6152.
35. O. Nanba, K. Satoh, Isolation of a Photosystem II reaction center consisting of D1 and D2 polypeptides and cytochrome b559. *Proc. Natl. Acad. Sci. U.S.A.* **84** (1987) 109–112.
36. J. Kurreck, B. Liu, A. Napiwotzki, S. Sellin, H.-J. Eckert, H.-J. Eichler, G. Renger, Stoichiometry of pigments and radical pair formation under saturating pulse excitation in D1/D2/cytb559 preparations. *Biochim. Biophys. Acta* **1318** (1997) 307–315.
37. D.J. Chapman, K. Gounaris, J. Barber, Electron-transport properties of the isolated D1-D2-cytochrome *b*-559 Photosystem II reaction centre. *Biochim. Biophys. Acta* **933** (1989) 423–431.
38. J. Kurreck, A. Garbers, F. Parak, G. Renger, Highly purified D1/D2/Cyt b559 preparations from spinach do not contain the non heme iron center. *FEBS Lett.* **403** (1997) 283–286.
39. T. Okubo, T. Tomo, M. Sugiura, T. Noguchi, Perturbation of the structure of P680 and the charge distribution on its radical cation in isolated reaction center complexes of Photosystem II as revealed by Fourier Transform Infrared Spectroscopy. *Biochemistry* **46** (2007) 4390–4397.
40. G. Renger, A.R. Holzwarth, Primary electron transfer, in: *Photosystem II: The Water/Plastoquinone Oxido-Reductase in Photosynthesis* (2005) (T. Wydrzynski, K. Satoh, eds.), Kluwer Academic Publishers, Dordrecht, pp. 139–175.
41. L. Xiong, M. Seibert, A.V. Gusev, M.R. Wasielewski, C. Hemann, C.R. Hille, R.T. Sayre, Substitution of a chlorophyll into the inactive branch pheophytin-binding site impairs charge separation in Photosystem II. *J. Phys. Chem.* **108** (2004) 16904–16911.
42. A.J. Watson, P.K. Fyfe, D. Frolov, M.C. Wakeham, E. Nabedryk, R. van Grondelle, J. Breton, M.R. Jones, Replacement or exclusion of the B-branch bacteriopheophytin in the purple bacterial reaction centre: The H_B cofactor is not required for assembly or core function of the *Rhodobacter sphaeroides* complex. *Biochim. Biophys. Acta* **1710** (2005) 34–46.
43. T. Noguchi, T. Tomo, Y. Inoue, Fourier transform infrared study of the cation radical of P680 in the Photosystem II reaction center: evidence for charge delocalization on the chlorophyll dimer. *Biochemistry* **37** (1998) 13614–13625.
44. S.A.P. Merry, P.J. Nixon, L.M.C. Barter, M. Schilstra, G. Porter, J. Barber, J.R. Durrant, D.R. Klug, Modulation of quantum yield of primary radical pair formation in Photosystem II by site-directed mutagenesis affecting radical cations and anions. *Biochemistry* **37** (1998) 17439–17447.
45. B. Diner, E. Schlodder, P.J. Nixon, W.J. Coleman, F. Rappaport, J. Lavergne, W.F.J. Vermaas, D.A. Chisholm, Site-directed mutations at D1-His198 and D2-His197 of Photosystem II in Synechocystis PCC 6803: sites of primary charge separation and cation triplet stabilization. *Biochemistry* **40** (2001) 9265–9281.
46. B. Hillmann, Kl. Brettel, F.J.E. van Mieghem, A. Kamlowski, A.W. Rutherford, E. Schlodder, Charge recombination in Photosystem II. 2. Transient absorbance

difference spectra and their temperature dependence. *Biochemistry* **34** (1995) 4814–4827.
47. P.J. Smith, S. Peterson, V.M. Masters, T. Wydrzynski, S. Stryring, E. Krausz, R.J. Pace, Magneto-optical measurements of the pigments in fully active Photosystem II core complexes from plants. *Biochemistry* **41** (2002) 1981–1989.
48. M. Germano, C.C. Gradinaru, A.Y. Shkuropatov, I.H.M. van Stokkum, V.A. Shuvalov, J.P. Dekker, R. van Grondelle, H.J. van Gorkom, Energy and electron transfer in Photosystem II reaction centers with modified pheophytin composition. *Biophys. J.* **86** (2004) 1664–1672.
49. U. Schmid, P. Reineker, Triplet excitons in molecular pairs. *Mol. Phys.* **55** (1985) 77–95.
50. F.J.E. van Miegham, A.W. Rutherford, Comparative spectroscopy of photosystem II and purple bacterial reaction centres. *Biochem. Soc. Trans.* **21** (1993) 986–991.
51. D.M. Tiede, P.L. Dutton, Orientation of the primary quinone of bacterial photosynthetic reaction centers contained in chromatophore and reconstituted membranes. *Biochim. Biophys. Acta* **637** (1981) 278–290.
52. T. Noguchi, Y. Inoue, K. Satoh, FT-IR studies on the triplet state of P680 in the photosystem II reaction center: triplet equilibrium within a chlorophyll dimer. *Biochemistry* **32** (1993) 7186–7195.
53. V.V. Klimov, S.I. Allakhverdiev, S. Demeter, A.A. Krasnovsky, Photoreduction of pheophytin in Photosystem II of chloroplasts as a function of redox potential of the medium. *Dokl. Adad. Nauk SSSR* **249** (1979) 227–230.
54. P. Jursinic, Govindjee, Temperature dependence of delayed light emission in the 6–340 microsecond range after a single flash in chloroplasts. *Photochem. Photobiol.* **26** (1977) 617–628.
55. F. Rappaport, M. Guergova-Kuras, P.J. Nixon, B.A. Diner, J. Lavergne, Kinetics and pathways of charge recombination in Photosystem II. *Biochemistry* **41** (2002) 8518–8527.
56. A. Ivancich, K. Arltz, J.C. Williams, J.P. Allen, T.A. Mattioli, Effects of hydrogen bonds on the redox potential and electronic structure of the bacterial primary electron donor. *Biochemistry* **37** (1998) 11812–11820.
57. X. Lin, V. Murchison, V. Nagarajan, W.W. Parson, J.P. Allen, J.C. Williams, Specific alteration of the oxidation potential of the electron donor in reaction centers from Rhodobacter sphaeroides. *Proc. Natl. Acad. Sci. U.S.A.* **91** (1994) 10265–10269.
58. H. Michel, M. Deisenhofer, Relevance of the photosynthetic reaction center from purple bacteria to the structure of Photosystem II. *Biochemistry* **27** (1988) 1–7.
59. P. Fromme, P. Jordan, N. Krauß, Structure of Photosystem I. *Biochim. Biophys. Acta* **1507** (2001) 5–31.
60. A.W. Rutherford, P. Faller, The stable hydroxyl radical in Photosystem II: Why D? *Biochim. Biophys. Acta* **1655** (2004) 222–230.
61. T. Watanabe, M. Kobayashi, Electrochemistry of chlorophylls, in: *Chloropyhlls* (1991) (H. Scheer, ed.), CRC Press, Boca Raton, FL, pp. 287–315.
62. J. Fajer, Structural effects in chemistry and biology. *J. Porphyrins Phthalocyanines* **4** (2000) 382–385.
63. K. Hasegawa, T. Noguchi, Density functional theory calculations on the dielectric-constant dependence of the oxidation potential of chlorophyll: implication for the high potential of P680 in Photosystem II. *Biochemistry* **44** (2005) 8865–8872.
64. H. Ishikita, B. Loll, J. Biesiadka, W. Saenger, E.-W. Knapp, Redox potentials of chlorophylls in the Photosystem II reaction center. *Biochemistry* **44** (2005) 4118–4124.

65. C. Zhang, A. Boussac, A.W. Rutherford, Low-temperature electron transfer in Photosystem II. A tyrosyl radical and semiquinone charge pair. *Biochemistry* **43** (2004) 13787–13795.
66. M. Akiyama, H. Miyashita, H. Kise, T. Watanabe, M. Mimuro, S. Miyachi, M. Kobayashi, Quest for minor but key chlorophyll molecules in photosynthetic reaction centers-unusual pigment compositions in the reaction centers of the chlorophyll d-dominated cyanobacterium *Acaryochloris marina*. *Photosynth. Res.* **74** (2002) 97–107.
67. M. Mimuro, S. Akimoto, T. Gotoh, M. Yokono, M. Akiyama, T. Tsuchiy, H. Miyashita, M. Kobayashi, I. Yamazaki, Identification of the primary electron donor in PS II of the Chl d-dominated cyanobacterium *Acaryochloris marins*. *FEBS Lett.* **556** (2004) 95–98.
68. D. Shevela, B. Nöring, H.-J. Eckert, J. Messinger, G. Renger, Characterization of the water oxidizing complex of photosystem II of the chl d - containing cyanobacterium *Acaryochloris marina* via its reactivity towards endogenous electron donors and acceptors. *Phys. Chem. Chem. Phys.* **8** (2006) 3460–3466.
69. M.R. Razeghifard, M. Chen, J.L. Hughes, J. Freeman, E. Krausz, T. Wydrzynski, Spectroscopic studies of Photosystem II in chlorophyll *d*-containing *Acaryochloris marina*. *Biochemistry* **44** (2005) 11178–11187.
70. M. Kobayashi, S. Ohashi, K. Iwamoto, Y. Shiraiwa, Y. Kato, T. Watanabe, Redox potential of chlorophyll d *in vitro*. *Biochim. Biophys. Acta* **1767** (2007) 596–602.
71. T. Tomo, T. Okubo, Seiji Akimoto, M. Yokono, H. Miyashita, T. Tsuchiya, T. Noguchi, M. Mimuro, Identification of the special pair of photosystem II in a chlorophyll *d*-dominated cyanobacterium. *Proc. Nat. Acad. Sci. USA* **104** (2007) 7283–7288.
72. E. Schlodder, M. Çetin, H.-J. Eckert, F.-J. Schmitt, J. Barber, A. Telfer, Both chlorophylls a and d are essential for the photochemistry in photosystem II of the cyanobacteria, Acaryochloris marina. *Biochim. Biophys. Acta* **1767** (2007) 589–595.
73. D. Vavilin, H. Xu, S. Lin, W. Vermaas, Energy and electron transfer in Photosystem II of a chlorophyll b-containing Synechocystis sp. PCC 6803 mutant. *Biochemistry* **42** (2003) 1731–174.
74. E.J. Bylina, C. Kirmaier, L. McDowell, D. Holten, D.C. Youvan, Influence of an amino-acid residue on the optical properties and electron transfer dynamics of a photosynthetic reaction centre complex. *Nature* **336** (1988) 182–184.
75. M.E. Michel-Beyerle, M. Plato, J. Deisenhofer, H. Michel, M. Bixon, J. Jortner, Unidirectionality of charge separation in reaction centers of photosynthetic bacteria. *Biochim. Biophys. Acta* **932** (1988) 52–70.
76. W. Zinth, W. Kaiser, Time-resolved spectroscopy of the primary electron transfer in reaction centers of *Rhodobacter sphaeroides* and *Rhodopseudomonas viridis*, in: *The Photosynthetic Reaction Center* (1993) (J. Deisenhofer, J.R. Norris, eds.), Academic Press, San Diego, Vol. II, pp. 71–88.
77. P.D. Leible, C. Kirmaier, C.S.M. Udawatte, S.J. Hofman, D. Holten, D.K. Hanson, Quinone reduction via secondary b-branch electron transfer in mutant bacterial reaction centers. *Biochemistry* **42** (2003) 1718–1730.
78. M.C. Wakeham, M.G. Goodwin, C. McKibbin, M.R. Jones, Photo-accumulation of the $P^+Q_B^-$ radical pair state in purple bacterial reaction centres that lack the Q_A ubiquinone. *FEBS Lett.* **540** (2003) 234–240.
79. B. Robert, M. Lutz, D.M. Tiede, Selective photochemical reduction of either of the two bacteriopheophytins in reaction centers of *Rps. Sphaeroides* R-26. *FEBS Lett.* **183** (1985) 326–330.

80. M. Mimuro, T. Tomo, Y. Nishimura, T. Yamazaki, K. Satoh, Identification of a photochemically inactive pheophytin molecule in the spinach D1-D2-Cyt b559 complex. *Biochim. Biophys. Acta* **1232** (1995) 81–88.
81. L. Konermann, A.R. Holzwarth, Analysis of the absorption spectrum of Photosystem II reaction centers: temperature dependence, pigment assignment and inhomogeneous broadening. *Biochemistry* **35** (1996) 829–842.
82. A.Y. Shkuropatov, R.A. Kharypov, T.S. Volshehukova, V.A. Shkuropatova, T.G. Owens, V.A. Shuvalov, Spectral and photochemical properties of borohydride-treated D1-D2-cytochrome B-559 complex of Photosystem II. *FEBS Lett.* **420** (1997) 171–174.
83. S. Peterson-Arsköld, V.M. Masters, B.J. Prince, P.J. Smith, R.J. Pace, E. Krausz, Optical spectra of Synechocystis and spinach Photosystem II preparations at 1.7 K: identification of the D1-pheophytin energies and Stark shifts. *J. Am. Chem. Soc.* **125** (2003) 13063–13074.
84. L.B. Giorgi, P.J. Nixon, S.A.P. Merry, D.M. Joseph, J.R. Durrant, J. DeLas Rivas, J. Barber, G. Proter, D.R. Klug, Comparison of primary charge separation in the Photosystem II reaction center complex isolated from wild-type and D1–130 mutants of the cyanobacterium *Synechocystis* PCC 6803. *J. Biol. Chem.* **271** (1996) 2251–2255.
85. K. Gibasiewicz, A. Dobek, J. Breton, W. Leibl, Modulation of primary radical pair kinetics and energetics in Photosystem II by the redox state of the quinine electron acceptor Q_A. *Biophys. J.* **80** (2001) 1617–1630.
86. G. Feher, R.A. Isaacson, M.Y. Okamura, W. Lubitz, ENDOR of exchangeable protons of the reduced intermediate acceptor in reaction centers from *Rhodobacter Sphaeroides* R-26, in: *The Photosynthetic Bacterial Reaction Center: Structure and Dynamics* (1988) (J. Breton, A. Vermeglio, eds.), Plenum Press, New York, pp. 229–235.
87. W. Lubitz, R.A. Isaacson, M.Y. Okamura, E.C. Abresch, M. Plato, G. Feher, ENDOR spectroscopy, in: *Biophysical Techniques in Photosynthesis* (1996) (J. Amesz, A.J. Hoff, eds.), Kluwer Academic Publishers, Dordrecht.
88. R. Moenne-Loccoz, B. Robert, M. Lutz, A resonance Raman characterization of the primary electron acceptor in Photosystem II. *Biochemistry* **28** (1989) 3641–3645.
89. E. Nabedryk, S. Andrianambinintsoa, G. Berger, M. Leonhard, W. Mäntele, J. Breton, Characterization of bonding interactions of the intermediary electron acceptor in the reaction center of Photosystem II by FTIR spectroscopy. *Biochim. Biophys. Acta* **1016** (1990) 49–54.
90. M.R. Gunner, P.L. Dutton, Temperature and -. ΔG.degree. dependence of the electron transfer from BPh^-.- to QA in reaction center protein from *Rhodobacter sphaeroides* with different quinones as QA. *J. Am. Chem. Soc.* **111** (1989) 3400–3412.
91. B.A. Diner, C. de Vitry, J.-L. Popot, Quinone exchange in the Q_A binding site of Photosystem II reaction center core preparations isolated from *Chlamydomonas reinhardtii*. *Biochim. Biophys. Acta* **934** (1988) 47–54.
92. F. van Miegham, W. Nitschke, P. Mathis, A.W. Rutherford. The influence of the quinone-iron electron acceptor complex on the reaction centre photochemistry of photosystem II. *Biochim. Biophys. Acta* **977** (1987) 207–214.
93. A. Krieger, A.W. Rutherford, G.N. Johnson, On the determination of the redox midpoint potential of the primary quinone acceptor, Q_A in photosystem II. *Biochim. Biophys. Acta* **1229** (1995) 162–171.

94. J. Deisenhofer, O. Epp, I. Sinning, H. Michel, Crystallographic refinement at 2.3 Å resolution and refined model of the photosynthetic reaction center from *Rhodopseudomonas viridis. J. Mol. Biol.* **246** (1995) 429–457.
95. W.F.J. Vermaas, J. Charité, G. Shen, Q_A binding to D2 contributes to the functional and structural integrity of Photosystem II. *Z. Naturforsch., Teil C* **45** (1990) 359–365.
96. F. MacMillan, H. Gleiter, G. Renger, W. Lubitz, EPR/ENDOR studies of plastoquinone anion radical in Photosystem II (Q_A^{-}) and in organic solvents, in: *Current Research in Photosynthesis* (1990) (M. Baltscheffsky, ed.), Kluwer, Dordrecht, Vol. 1, pp. 849–852.
97. J. Kurreck, A. Garbers, F. Reifarth, L.-E. Andréasson, F. Parak, G. Renger, Isolation and properties of PS II membrane fragments depleted of the non heme iron center. *FEBS Lett.* **381** (1996) 53–57.
98. F. MacMillan, F. Lendzian, G. Renger, W. Lubitz, EPR and ENDOR investigation of the primary electron acceptor radical anion $Q_A^{-\cdot}$ in iron-depleted photosystem II membrane fragments. *Biochemistry* **34** (1995) 8144–8156.
99. T. Noguchi, J. Kurreck, Y. Inoue, G. Renger, Comparative FTIR analysis of the microenvironment of $Q_A^{-\cdot}$ in cyanide and high pH treated and "iron depleted" PS II membrane fragments. *Biochemistry* **38** (1999) 4846–4852.
100. F. MacMillan, J. Kurreck, N. Adir, F. Lendzian, H. Käss, F. Reifarth, G. Renger, W. Lubitz, EPR, ENDOR and ESEEM investigation of the electron acceptor radical anion $Q_A^{-\cdot}$ in photosystem II (PS II) reaction centres, in: *Photosynthesis: from Light to Biosphere* (1995) (P. Mathis ed.), Kluwer, Dordrecht, Vol. I, pp. 659–662.
101. J.R. Durrant, G. Hastings, D.M. Joseph, J. Barber, G. Porter, D.R. Klug, Subpicosecond equilibration of excitation energy in isolated photosystem II reaction centers. *Proc. Natl. Acad. Sci. U.S.A.* **89** (1992) 11632–11636.
102. M.G. Müller, M. Hucke, M. Reus, A.R. Holzwarth, Primary processes and structure of the Photosystem II reaction center: IV. Low intensity femtosecond transient absorption spectra of D1-D2 reaction centers. *J. Phys. Chem.* **100** (1996) 9527–9536.
103. S. Vasil'ev, J.-R. Shen, N. Kamiya, D. Bruce, The orientations of core antenna chlorophylls in Photosystem II are optimized to maximize the quantum yield of photosynthesis. *FEBS Lett.* **561** (2004) 111–116.
104. E.G. Andrizhiyevskaya, D. Frolov, R. van Grondelle, J.P. Dekker, On the role of the CP47 core antenna in the energy transfer and trapping dynamics of Photosystem II. *Phys. Chem. Chem. Phys.* **6** (2004) 4810–4819.
105. G.H. Schatz, H. Brock, A.R. Holzwarth, Picosecond kinetics of fluorescence and absorbance changes in Photosystem II particles excited by low photon density. *Proc. Natl. Acad. Sci. U.S.A.* **84** (1987) 8414–8418.
106. G.H. Schatz, H. Brock, A.R. Holzwarth, Kinetic and energetic model for the primary process in Photosystem II. *Biophys. J.* **54** (1988) 397–405.
107. T.A. Roelofs, A.R. Holzwarth, In search of a putative long-lived relaxed radical pair state in closed Photosystem II. Kinetic modelling of picosecond fluorescence data. *Biophys. J.* **57** (1990) 1141–1153.
108. H.W. Trissl, J. Lavergne, Fluorescence induction from Photosystem II: analytical equations for the yields of photochemistry and fluorescence derived from analysis of a model including exciton-radical pair equilibrium and restricted energy transfer between photosynthetic units. *Aust. J. Plant Physiol.* **22** (1995) 183–193.
109. G. Renger, H.-J. Eckert, A. Bergmann, J. Bernarding, B. Liu, A. Napiwotzki, F. Reifarth, H.-J. Eichler, Fluorescence and spectroscopic studies on exciton

trapping and electron transfer in Photosystem II of higher plants. *Aust. J. Plant Physiol.* **22** (1995) 167–181.
110. E.C.M. Engelmann, G. Zucchelli, F.M. Garlaschi, A.P. Casazza, R.C. Jennings, The effect of outer antenna complexes on the photochemical trapping rate in barley thyalkoid Photosystem II. *Biochim. Biophys. Acta* **1706** (2005) 276–286.
111. S. Vasil'ev, P. Orth, A. Zouni, T.G. Owens, B. Diner, Excited-state dynamics in Photosystem II: insights from the X-ray crystal structure. *Proc. Natl. Acad. Sci. U.S.A.* **98** (2001) 8602–8607.
112. H. van Amerongen, J.P. Dekker, Light-harvesting in Photosystem II, in: *Light-Harvesting Antennas in Photosynthesis* (2003) (B.R. Green, W.W. Parson, eds.), Kluwer Academic Publishers, Dordrecht, pp. 219–251.
113. V.I. Prokhorenko, A.R. Holzwarth, Primary processes and structure of the Photosystem II reaction center: a photon echo study. *J. Phys. Chem. B.* **104** (2000) 11563–11578.
114. M.L. Groot, N.P. Pawlowicz, L.J.G.W. van Wilderen, J. Breton, I.H.M. van Stokkum, R. van Grondelle, Initial electron donor and acceptor in isolated Photosystem II reaction centers identified with femtosecond mid-IR spectroscopy. *Proc. Nat. Acad. Sci. USA* **102** (2005) 13087–13092.
115. A.R. Holzwarth, M.G. Müller, M. Reus, M. Nowaczyk, J. Sander, M. Rögner, Kinetics and mechanism of electron transfer in intact photosystem II and in the isolated reaction center: pheophytin is the primary electron acceptor. *Proc. Natl. Acad. Sci. USA* **103** (2006) 6895–6900.
116. K. Riley, R. Jankowiak, M. Rätsep, G.J. Small, V. Zazubovich, Evidence for highly dispersive primary charge separation kinetics and gross heterogeneity in the isolated PS II reaction center of green plants. *J. Phys. Chem.* **108** (2004) 10346–10356.
117. A.M. Nuijs, J.J. van Gorkom, J.J. Plijter, L.N.M. Duysens, Primary-charge separation and excitation of chlorophyll a in Photosystem II particles from spinach as studied by picosecond absorbance-difference spectroscopy. *Biochim. Biophys. Acta* **848** (1986) 167–175.
118. H.J. Eckert, N. Wiese, J. Bernarding, H.-J. Eichler, G. Renger, Analysis of the electron transfer from $Pheo^-$ to Q_A in PS II membrane fragments from spinach by time resolved 325 nm absorption changes in the picosecond domain. *FEBS Lett.* **240** (1988) 153–158.
119. J. Bernarding, H.-J. Eckert, H.-J. Eichler, A. Napiwotzki, G. Renger, Kinetic studies on the stabilisation of the primary radical pair $P680^+Pheo^-$ in different Photosystem II preparations from higher plants. *Photochem. Photobiol.* **59** (1994) 566–573.
120. T.A. Roelofs, C.H. Lee, A.R. Holzwarth, Global target analysis of picosecond chlorophyll fluorescence kinetics from pea chloroplasts. *Biophys. J.* **61** (1992) 1147–1163.
121. S. Vasilèv, A. Bergmann, H. Redlin, H.-J. Eichler, G. Renger, On the role of exchangeable hydrogen bonds for the kinetics of $P_{680}^+ Q_A^-$ formation and $P_{680}^1 Pheo^-$ recombination in Photosystem II. *Biochim. Biophys. Acta* **1276** (1996) 35–44.
122. W. Leibl, J. Breton, J. Deprez, H.W. Trissl, Photoelectronic study on the kinetics of trapping and charge stabilization in oriented PS II membranes. *Photosynth. Res.* **22** (1989) 257–275.
123. M.G. Rockley, M.W. Windsor, R.J. Cogdell, W.W. Parson, Picosecond detection of an intermediate in the photochemical reaction of bacterial photosynthesis. *Proc. Natl. Acad. Sci. U.S.A.* **72** (1975) 2251–2255.

124. C. Kirmeier, D. Holten, W.W. Parson, Temperature and detection-wavelength dependence of the picosecond electron-transfer kinetics measured in *Rhodopseudomonas sphaeroides* reaction centers. Resolution of new spectral and kinetic components in the primary charge-separation process. *Biochim. Biophys. Acta* **810** (1985) 33–48.
125. V.Z. Paschenko, V.V. Gorokhov, P.P. Knox, P.M. Krasilnikov, H. Redlin, G. Renger, A.B. Rubin, Energetics and mechanisms of high efficiency of charge separation and electrons transfer processes in *Rhodobacter sphaeroides* reaction centers. *Bioelectrochemistry* **61** (2003) 73–84.
126. B. Liu, P.J.M. van Kan, A.J. Hoff, Influence of the H-subunit and Fe^{2+} on electron transport from I^- to Q_A in Fe^{2+} free and/or H-free reaction centers from *Rhodobacter sphaeroides* R-26. *FEBS Lett.* **289** (1991) 23–28.
127. J.J.S. van Rensen, C. Xu, Govindjee, Role of bicarbonate in the Photosystem II, the water-plastoquinone oxido-reductase of plant photosynthesis. *Physiol. Plant.* **105** (1999) 585–592.
128. L.M.N. Duysens, H.E. Sweers, Mechanism of two photochemical reactions in algae as studied by means of fluorocence, in: *Studies on Microalgae and Photosynthetic Bacteria* (1963) (A. Takamiya, K. Shibata, eds.), University Tokyo Press, Tokyo, pp. 353–372.
129. G.C. Papageorgiou, Govindjee (eds), *Chlorophyll a Fluorescence: A Signature of Photosynthesis* (2004), Springer, Berlin.
130. D. Walz, Nonequilibrium thermodynamics applied to energy conversion in biological systems, in: *Bioenergetics* (1997) (P. Gräber, G. Milazzo, eds.), Birkäuser Verlag, Basel, pp. 1–56.
131. L.N. Bell, N.D. Gudkov, Thermodynamics of flight energy conversion, in: *Topics in Photosynthesis, The Photosystems: Structure, Function and Molecular Biology* (1992) (J. Barber, ed.), Kluwer Academic Publishers, Dordrecht, pp. 17–43.
132. L.I. Krishtalik, Energetics of multielectron reactions. Photosynthetic oxygen evolution. *Biochim. Biophys. Acta* **849** (1995) 193–201.
133. K. Warncke, P.L. Dutton, Influence of Q_A site redox cofactor structure on equilibrium binding, in site electrochemistry and electron-transfer performance in the photosynthetic reaction center protein. *Biochemistry* **32** (1993) 4769–4779.
134. L.N. Christophorov, A.R. Holzwarth, V.N. Kharkyanen, F. van Mourik, Structure-function self-organization in nonequilibrium macromolecular systems. *Chem. Phys.* **256** (2000) 45–60.
135. G. Haran, K. Wynne, C.G. Moser, P.L. Dutton, R.M. Hochstrasser, Femtosecond infrared studies of photosynthetic reaction centers: new charge transfer bands and ultrafast energy redistribution, in: *Ultrafast Pheomena X* (1996) (P.F. Barbara, J.G. Fujimoto, W.H. Knox, Z. Zinth, eds.), Springer Verlag, Berlin, pp. 326–327.
136. D. Xu, K. Schulten, Coupling of protein motion to electron transfer in a photosynthetic reaction center: investigating the low temperature behaviour in the framework of the spin-boson model. *Chem. Phys.* **182** (1994) 91–117.
137. L.M.C. Barter, J.R. Durrant, D.R. Klug, A quantitative structure-function relationship for the Photosystem II reaction center: Supermolecular behaviour in natural photosynthesis. *Proc. Natl. Acad. Sci. U.S.A.* **100** (2003) 946–951.
138. A.M. Streltsov, A.G. Yakovlev, A.Y. Shkuropatov, V.A. Shuvalov, Dynamic hole burning within special pair absoption band of *Rhodobacter sphaeroides* (R-26) reaction cente at room temperature. *FEBS Lett.* **357** (1995).
139. V.Z. Paschenko, V.V. Gorokhov, B.N. Korvatovskii, N.P. Grishanova, O.M. Sarkisov, G. Renger, A.B. Rubin, Femtosecond dynamics of transition processes

in reaction centers of *Rhodobacter sphaeroides*. *Dokl. Biochem. Biophys.* **399** (2004) 337–340.
140. W.W. Parson, Z.-T. Chu, A. Warshel, Electrostatic control of charge separation in bacterial photosynthesis. *Biochim. Biophys. Acta* **1017** (1990) 251–272.
141. N.W. Woodbury, W.W. Parson, M.R. Gunner, R.C. Prince, P.L. Dutton, Radical-pair energetics and decay mechanisms in reaction centers containing anthraquinones, naphthoquinones or benzoquinones in place of ubiquinone. *Biochim. Biophys. Acta* **851** (1986) 6–22.
142. A. Ogrodnik, M. Volk, R. Letterer, R. Feick, M.E. Michel-Beyerle, Determination of free energies in reaction centers of *Rb. sphaeroides*. *Biochim. Biophys. Acta* **936** (1988) 361–371.
143. M.G. Müller, D. Dorra, A.R. Holzwarth, N. Gad'on, G. Drews, Time-dependent radical pair relaxation in chromatophores of an antenna-free mutant from Rhodobacter capsulatus, in: *Photosynthesis: from Light to Biosphere* (1995) (P. Mathis, ed.), Kluwer Academic Publishers, Dordrecht, pp. 595–598.
144. R.A. Marcus, N. Sutin, Electron transport in chemistry and biology. *Biochem. Biophys. Acta* **811** (1985) 265–322.
145. N.W. Woodbury, W.W. Parson, Nanosecond fluorescence from isolated photosynthetic reaction centers of *Rhodopseudomonas sphaeroides*. *Biochim. Biophys. Acta* **767** (1984) 345–361.
146. Z. Katiliene, E. Katilius, N.W. Woodbury, Energy trapping and detrapping in reaction center mutants from *Rhodobacter sphaeroides*. *Biophys. J.* **84** (2003) 3240–3251.
147. H.J. van Gorkom, Identification of the reduced primary electron acceptor of Photosystem II as a bound semiquinone anion. *Biochim. Biophys. Acta* **347** (1974) 439–442.
148. L. Konermann, G. Gatzen, A.R. Holzwarth, Analysis of the absorption spectrum of Photosystem II reaction centers: Temperature dependence, pigment assignment and inhomogeneous broadening. *Biochemistry* **35** (1996) 829–842.
149. S. Vasil'ev, P.C.-I. Lee, G.W. Brudvig, D. Bruce, Structure-based kinetic modelling of excited-state transfer and trapping in histidine-tagged Photosystem II core complexes from *Synechocystis*. *Biochemistry* **41** (2002) 12236–12243.
150. P. Kühn, H.-J. Eckert, H.-J. Eichler, G. Renger, Analysis of the $P680^{+\cdot}$ reduction pattern and its temperature dependence in oxygen evolving PS II core complexes from thermophilic cyanobacteria and higher plants. *Phys. Chem. Chem. Phys.* **6** (2004) 4838–4843.
151. R.J. Debus, B.A. Barry, G.T. Babcock, L. McIntosh, Directed mutagenesis indicates that the donor to $P680^+$ in Photosystem II is tyrosine-161 of the D1 polypeptide. *Biochemistry* **27** (1988) 9071–9074.
152. J.G. Metz, P.J. Nixon, M. Rögner, G.W. Brudvig, B.A. Diner, Directed alteration of the D1 polypeptide of Photosystem II: evidence that tyrosine 161 is the redox component, Z, connecting the oxygen-evolving complex to the primary electron donor, P680. *Biochemistry* **28** (1989) 6960–6969.
153. G.T. Babcock, B.A. Barry, R.J. Debus, C.W. Hoganson, M. Atamian, L. McIntosh, U. Sithole, C.G. Yocum, Water oxidation in Photosystem II: from radical chemistry to multielectron chemistry. *Biochemistry* **28** (1989) 327–330.
154. G. Renger, H.-J. Eckert, W. Weiss, Studies on the mechanism of photosynthetic oxygen formation, in: *The Oxygen Evolving System in Photosynthesis* (1983) (Y. Inoue, A.R. Crofts, Govindjee, N. Murata, G. Renger, K. Satoh, eds.), Academic Press, Japan, Tokyo, pp. 73–82.

155. K. Brettel, E. Schlodder, H.T. Witt, Nanosecond reduction kinetics of photooxidized chlorophyll-a$_{II}$ (P-680) in single flashes as a probe for the electron pathway, H$^+$-release and charge accumulation in the O$_2$-evolving complex. *Biochim. Biophys. Acta* **766** (1984) 403–415.
156. H.-J. Eckert, G. Renger, Temperature dependence of P680$^+$ reduction in O$_2$-evolving PS II membrane fragments at different redox states S$_i$ of the water oxidizing system. *FEBS Lett.* **236** (1988) 425–431.
157. M.J. Schilstra, F. Rappaport, J.H.A. Nugent, C. Barnett, D.R. Klug, Proton/hydrogen transfer affects the S-state-dependent microsecond phases of P680$^+$ reduction during water splitting. *Biochemistry* **37** (1998) 3974–3981.
158. M. Sugiura, F. Rappaport, K. Brettel, T. Noguchi, A.W. Rutherford, A. Boussac, Site-directed mutagenesis of *Thermosynechococcus elongatus* photosystem II: The O$_2$-evolving enzyme lacking the redox-active tyrosine D. *Biochemistry* **43** (2004) 13549–13563.
159. R. Steffen, H.-J. Eckert, A.A. Kelly, P. Dörmann, G. Renger, Investigations on the reaction pattern of photosystem II in leaves from *ArabidoPS Is thaliana* wild type plants and mutants with genetically modified lipid content: I. Basic concepts of time-resolved fluorometric analysis. *Biochemistry* **44** (2005) 3123–3133.
160. A.M.A. Hayes, I.R. Vassiliev, J.H. Golbeck, R.J. Debus, Role of D1-His 190 in proton-coupled electron transfer reactions in photosystem II: a chemical complementation study. *Biochemistry* **37** (1998) 11352–11365.
161. G. Renger, Coupling of electron and proton transfer in oxidative water splitting in photosynthesis. *Biochim. Biophys. Acta* **1655** (2004) 195–204.
162. G. Renger, G. Christen, M. Karge, H.-J. Eckert, K.-D. Irrgang, Application of the Marcus theory for analysis of the temperature dependence of the reactions leading to photosynthetic water oxidation – results and implications. *J. Bioinorg. Chem.* **3** (1998) 360–366.
163. C. Tommos, G.T. Babcock, Proton and hydrogen currents in photosynthetic water oxidation. *Biochim. Biophys. Acta* **1458** (2000) 199–299.
164. C. Jeans, J. Schilstra, D.R. Klug, The temperature dependence of P680$^+$ reduction in oxygen-evolving Photosystem II. *Biochemistry* **41** (2002) 5015–5023.
165. M. Karge, K.-D. Irrgang, S. Sellin, R. Feinäugle, B. Liu, H.-J. Eckert, H.-J. Eichler, G. Renger, Effects of hydrogen/deuterium exchange on photosynthetic water splitting in PS II core complexes from spinach. *FEBS Lett.* **378** (1996) 140–144.
166. G. Christen, F. Reifarth, G. Renger, On the origin of the "35 µs kinetics" of P680$^{+\cdot}$ reduction in Photosystem II with an intact water oxidising complex. *FEBS Lett.* **429** (1998) 40–52.
167. G. Christen, G. Renger, The role of hydrogen bonds for the multiphasic P$_{680}^{+\cdot}$ reduction by Y$_Z$ in Photosystem II with intact oxygen evolution capacity. Analysis of kinetic H/D isotope exchange effects. *Biochemistry* **38** (1999) 2068–2077.
168. G.M. Cheniae, I.F. Martin, Absence of oxygen-evolving capacity in dark-grown Chlorella: the photoactivation of oxygen-evolving centers. *Photochem. Photobiol.* **17** (1973) 441–459.
169. R.J. Strasser, C. Sironval, Induction of photosystem II activity in flashed leaves. *FEBS Lett.* **28** (1972) 56–60.
170. K. Thompson, R. Blaylock, J.M. Sturtevant, G.W. Brudvig, Molecular basis of the heat denaturation of photosystem II. *Biochemistry* **28** (1989) 6686–6695.
171. I. Enami, M. Kitamura, T. Tomo, Y. Isokawa, H. Ohta, S. Katoh, Is the primary course of thermal inactivation of oxygen evolution in spinach PS II membranes

release of the extrinsic 33 kDa protein or of Mn? *Biochim. Biophys. Acta* **1186** (1994) 52–58.
172. T. Noguchi, M. Sugiura, Flash-induced FTIR difference spectra of the water oxidizing complex in moderately hydrated Photosystem II core films: Effect of hydration extent on S-state transitions. *Biochemistry* **41** (2002) 2322–2330.
173. J.M. Briantais, C. Vernotte, J. Lavergne, C.J. Arntzen, Identification of S_2 as the sensitive state to alkaline photoinactivation of photosystem II in chloroplasts. *Biochim. Biophys. Acta* **461** (1977) 61–74.
174. G. Renger, M. Gläser, E.E. Buchwald, The control of the reduction kinetics in the dark of photooxidized chlorophyll-a^+_{II} by inner thylakoid proton concentration. *Biochim. Biophys. Acta* **461** (1977) 392–402.
175. G. Renger, M. Völker, H.J. Eckert, R. Fromme, S. Hohm-Veit, P. Gräber, On the mechanism of photosystem II deterioration by UV-B irradiation. *Photochem. Photobiol.* **49** (1989) 97–105.
176. J.F. Bornman, Target sites of UV-radiation in photosynthesis of higher plants. *J. Photochem. Photobiol. B: Biol.* **4** (1989) 145–158.
177. H. Conjeaud, P. Mathis, G. Paillotin, The effect of pH on the reduction kinetics of P680 in tris-treated chloroplasts. *Biochim. Biophys. Acta* **48** (1979) 280–291.
178. G. Renger, M. Völker, W. Weiss, Studies on the nature of the water oxidizing enzyme. I. The effect of tryPS In on the system II reaction pattern in inside-out thylakoids. *Biochim. Biophys. Acta* **766** (1984) 582–591.
179. S. Reinman, P. Mathis, Influence of temperature on photosystem II electron transfer reactions. *Biochim. Biophys. Acta* **635** (1981) 249–258.
180. R. Ahlbrink, M. Haumann, D. Cherepanov, D. Bögershausen, O. Mulkidjanian, W. Junge, Function of tyroszine Z in water oxidation by Photosystem II: electrostatical promoter instead of hydrogen abstractor. *Biochemistry* **37** (1998) 1131–1142.
181. G. Christen, M. Karge, H.-J. Eckert, G. Renger, The role of protonation steps in electron transfer reactions in Tris-treated PS II membrane fragments. *Photosynthetica* **33** (1997) 529–539.
182. B.A. Diner, D.A. Force, D.W. Randall, R.D. Britt, Hydrogen bonding, solvent exchange, and coupled proton and electron transfer in the oxidation and reduction of redox-active tyrosine Y_Z in Mn-depleted core complexes of Photosystem II. *Biochemistry* **37** (1998) 17931–17943.
183. G. Renger, M. Völker, Studies on the proton release of the donor side of system II. Correlation between oxidation and deprotonization of donor D_1 in Tris-washed inside-out thylakoids. *FEBS Lett.* **149** (1982) 203–207.
184. C. Berthomieu, R. Hienerwadel, Vibrational spectroscopy to study the properties of redox-active tyrosines in photosystem II and other proteins. *Biochim. Biophys. Acta* **1707** (2005) 51–66.
185. H.-J. Eckert, B. Geiken, J. Bernarding, A. Napiwotzki, H.J. Eichler, G. Renger, Two sites of photoinhibition of the electron transfer in oxygen evolving and Tris-treated PS II membrane fragments from spinach. *Photosynth. Res.* **27** (1991) 97–108.
186. E.E. Callahan, D.W. Beaker, G.M. Cheniae, Studies on the photoactivation of the water oxidizing enzyme. II. Characterization of weak light photoinhibition of PS II and its light-induced recovery. *Plant Physiol.* **82** (1986) 79–88.
187. S.M. Theg, L.J. Filar, R.J. Dilley, Photoinactivation of chloroplasts already inhibited on the oxidizing side of photosystem II. *Biochim. Biophys. Acta* **849** (1986) 104–111.

188. M. Poulson, S. Samson, J. Whitmarsh, Evidence that cytochrome b-559 protects Photosystem II against photoinhibition. *Biochemistry* **34** (1995) 10932–10938.
189. D.H. Stewart, G.W. Brudvig, Cytochrome b_{559} of photosystem II. *Biochim. Biophys. Acta* **1368** (1998) 63–87.
190. O. Kaminskaya, G. Renger, V.A. Shuvalov, Effect of dehydration on light induced reactions in Photosystem II: photoreactions of cytochrome b559. *Biochemistry* **42** (2003) 8119–8132.
191. O. Kaminskaya, J. Kern, V.A. Shuvalov, G. Renger, Extinction coefficients of cytochromes b559 and c550 of *Thermosynechococcus elongatus* and Cyt b559/PS II stoichiometry of higher plants. *Biochim. Biophys. Acta* **1708** (2005) 333–341.
192. J. Barber, J. De Las Rivas, A functional model for the role of cytochrome b559 in the protection against donor and acceptor side photoinhibition. *Proc. Natl. Acad. Sci. USA* **90** (1993) 10942–10946.
193. L. Nedbal, G. Samson, J. Whitmarsh, Redox state of a one-electron component controls the rate of photoinhibition of photosystem II. *Proc. Natl. Acad. Sci. USA* **89** (1992) 7929–7933.
194. R. Gadjieva, F. Mamedov, G. Renger, S. Styring, Interconversion of low and high potential forms of cytochrome b_{559} in Tris-washed photosystem II membranes under aerobic/anaerobic conditions. *Biochemistry* **38** (1999) 10578–10584.
195. S.G. Zech, J. Kurreck, H.-J. Eckert, G. Renger, W. Lubitz, R. Bittl, Pulsed EPR measurement of the distance between $P_{680}^{+\bullet}$ and $Q_A^{-\bullet}$ in Photosystem II. *FEBS Lett.* **414** (1997) 454–456.
196. C.C. Moser, P.C. Dutton, Outline of theory of protein electron transfer, in: *Protein Electron Transfer* (1996) (D.S. Bendall, ed.), BIOS Scientific Publishers, Oxford, pp. 1–21.
197. G. Renger, Ch. Wolff, The existence of a high photochemical turnover rate at the reaction centres of system II in Tris-washed chloroplasts. *Biochim. Biophys. Acta* **423** (1976) 610–614.
198. J. Haveman, P. Mathis, Flash-induced absorption changes of the primary donor of Photosystem II at 820 nm in chloroplasts inhibited by low pH or Tris-treatment. *Biochim. Biophys. Acta* **440** (1976) 346–355.
199. A. Cuni, L. Xiong, R. Sayre, F. Rappaport, J. Lavergne, Modification of the pheophytin midpoint potential in photosystem II: Modulation of the quantum yield of charge separation and of charge recombination pathways. *Chem. Phys. Phys. Chem.* **6** (2004) 4825–4831.
200. G. Christen, A. Seeliger, G. Renger, $P_{680}^{+\bullet}$ Reduction kinetics and redox transition probability of the water oxidising complex as a function of pH and H/D isotope exchange in spinach thylakoids. *Biochemistry* **38** (1999) 6082–6092.
201. N.W. Woodbury, W.W. Parson, M.R. Gunner, R.C. Prince, P.L. Dutton, Radical-pair energetics and decay mechanisms in reaction centers containing anthraquinones, naphthoquinones or benzoquinones in place of ubiquinone. *Biochim. Biophys. Acta* **851** (1986) 6–220.
202. R.J. Shopes, C.A. Wraight, The acceptor quinone complex in Rhodopseudomonas viridis. *Biochim. Biophys. Acta* **806** (1985) 348–356.
203. H.-J. Eckert, G. Renger, J. Bernarding, P. Faust, H.-J. Eichler, J. Salk, Examination of fluorescence lifetime and radical pair decay in PS II membrane fragments from spinach. *Biochim. Biophys. Acta* **893** (1987) 208–218.
204. R.V. Danielius, K. Satoh, P.J.M. van Kan, J.J. Plijter, A.M. Nuijs, H.J. van Gorkom, The primary reaction of Photosystem II in the D1-D2-cytochrome b-559 complex. *FEBS Lett.* **213** (1987) 241–244.

205. Y. Takahashi, Ö. Hansson, P. Mathis, K. Satoh, Primary radical pair in the Photosystem II reaction center. *Biochim. Biophys. Acta* **893** (1987) 49–59.
206. R. Schödel, K.-D. Irrgang, J. Voigt, G. Renger, Rate of carotenoid triplet formation in solubilized light-harvesting complex II (LHC II) from spinach. *Biophys. J.* **75** (1998) 3143–3153.
207. S. Vasil'ev, G.W. Brudvig, D. Bruce, The X-ray structure of Photosystem II reveals a novel electron transport pathway between P680, cytochrome b_{559} and the energy-quenching cation, Chl_Z^-. *FEBS Lett.* **543** (2003) 159–163.
208. F. van Miegham, K. Brettel, B. Hillmann, A. Kamlowski, A.W. Rutherford, E. Schlodder, Charge recombination reactions in photosystem II. 1-yields, recombination pathways and kinetics of the primary pair. *Biochemistry* **34** (1995) 4789–4813.
209. T. Noguchi, Dual role of triplet localization on the accessory chlorophyll in the photosystem II reaction center: photoprotection and photodamage of the D1 protein. *Plant Cell Physiol.* **43** (2002) 1112–1116.
210. A. Krieger-Liszkay, A.W. Rutherford, Influence of herbicide binding on the redox potential of the quinine acceptor in photosystem II: relevance to photodamage and phytotoxicity. *Biochemistry* **37** (1998) 17339–17344.
211. W.S. Chow, E.-M. Aro, Photoinactivation and mechanism of recovery, in: *Photosystem II: The Water/Plastoquinone Oxido-Reductase in Photosynthesis* (T. Wydrzynski, K. Satoh, eds), Springer, Dordrecht, pp. 627–648.
212. B. Bouges-Bocquet, Electron transfer between two photosystems in spinach chloroplasts. *Biochim. Biophys. Acta* **314** (1973) 250–256.
213. B.R. Velthuys, Amesz, Charge accumulation at the reducing side of photosystem II of photosynthesis. *Biochim. Biophys. Acta* **333** (1974) 85–94.
214. A.R. Crofts, C.A. Wraight, The electrochemical domain of photosynthesis. *Biochem. Biophys. Acta* **726** (1983) 149–185.
215. V. Petrouleas, A.R. Crofts, The iron-quinone acceptor complex, in: *Photosystem II: The light driven water:plastoquinone oxidoreductase. Advances in photosynthesis and respiration* (2005) (T. Wydrzynski, K. Satoh, eds) Springer, Dordrecht, pp. 177–206.
216. H.H. Robinson, A.R. Crofts, Kinetics of the oxidation-reduction reactions of the photosystem II acceptor complex and the pathway for deactivation. *FEBS Lett.* **151** (1984) 221–226.
217. W. Weiss, G. Renger, Analysis of the system II reaction by UV-absorption changes in tris-washed chloroplasts, in: *Advances in Photosynthesis Research* (1984) (C. Sybesma, ed.), Marinus Nijhoff/Dr. W. Junk Publishers, The Hague, Vol. 1, pp. 167–170.
218. J. Bowes, A.R. Crofts, C.J. Arntzen, Redox reactions on the reducing side of photosystem II in chloroplasts with altered herbicide binding properties. *Arch. Biochem. Biophys.* **200** (1980) 303–308.
219. W.C.J. Vermaas, G. Renger, G. Dohnt, The reduction of the oxygen-evolving system in chloroplasts by thylakoid components. *Biochim. Biophys. Acta* **764** (1984) 194–202.
220. R. de Wijn, H.J. van Gorkom, Kinetics of electron transfer from Q_A to Q_B in Photosystem II. *Biochemistry* **40** (2001) 11912–11922.
221. V.P. Shinkarev, Ubiquinone (coenzyme Q_{10}) binding sites: Low dielectric constant of the gate prevents the escape of the semiquinone. *FEBS Lett.* **580** (2006) 2534–2539.
222. J. Tandori, P. Sebban, H. Michel, L. Baciou, In *Rhodobacter sphaeroides* reaction centers, mutation of proline L209 to aromatic residues in the vicinity of a water

channel alters the dynamic coupling between electron and proton transfer processes. *Biochemistry* **38** (1999) 13179–13187.
223. L. Paddock, G. Feher, M.Y. Okamura, Pathway of proton transfer in bacterial reaction centers: further investigations on the role of Ser-L223 studied by site-directed mutagenesis. *Biochemistry* **34** (1995) 15742–15750.
224. R. Hienerwadel, S. Grzybek, C. Fogel, W. Kreutz, M.Y. Okamura, M.L. Paddock, J. Breton, E. Nabedryk, W. Maentele, Protonation of Glu L212 following QB-formation in the photosynthetic reaction center of *Rhodobacter sphaeroides*: evidence from time-resolved infrared spectroscopy. *Biochemistry* **34** (1995) 2832–2843.
225. E. Nabedryk, M.L. Paddock, M.Y. Okamura, J. Breton, An isotope-edited FTIR investigation of the role of Ser-L223 in binding quinone (Q_B) and semiquinone (Q_B^-) in the reaction center from *Rhodobacter sphaeroides*. *Biochemistry* **44** (2005) 14519–14527.
226. H. Suzuki, M. Nagasaka, M. Sugiura, T. Noguchi. Fourier transform infrared spectrum of the secondary quinone electron acceptor Q_B in Photosystem II. *Biochemistry* **44** (2005) 11323–11328.
227. M.H.B. Stowell, T.M. Phillips, D.C. Rees, S.M. Soltis, E. Abresch, G. Feher, Light-induced structural changes in photosynthetic reaction center: implications for mechanism of electron-proton transfer. *Science* **276** (1997) 812–816.
228. Q. Xu, L. Baciou, P. Sebban, M.R. Gunner, Exploring the energy landscape for Q_A^- to Q_B electron transfer in bacterial photosynthetic reaction centers: effect of substrate position and tail length on the conformational gating step. *Biochemistry* **41** (2002) 10021–10025.
229. A. Remy, K. Gerwert, Coupling of light-induced electron transfer to proton uptake in photosynthesis. *Nat. Struct. Biol.* **10** (2003) 637–644.
230. J. Breton, Absence of large-scale displacement of QB in bacterial photosynthetic reaction centers. *Biochemistry* **43** (2004) 3318–3326.
231. R.H.G. Baxter, N. Ponomarenko, V. Srajer, R. Pahl, K. Moffat, J.R. Norris, Time-resolved crystallographic studies of light-induced structural changes in the photosynthetic reaction center. *Proc. Natl. Acad. Sci. U.S.A.* **101** (2004) 5982–5987.
232. G. Renger, H.M. Gleiter, E. Haag, F. Reifarth, Photosystem II: thermodynamics and kinetics of electron transport from $Q_A^{-\bullet}$ to Q_B ($Q_B^{-\bullet}$) and deleterious effects of copper (II). *Z. Naturforsch., Teil C* **48** (1993) 234–240.
233. F. Reifarth, G. Renger, Indirect evidence for structural changes coupled with $Q_B^{-\bullet}$ formation in Photosystem II. *FEBS Lett.* **428** (1998) 123–126.
234. A. Garbers, J. Kurreck, F. Reifarth, G. Renger, F. Parak, Correlation between protein flexibility and electron transfer from $Q_A^{-\bullet}$ to Q_B in PS II membrane fragments from spinach. *Biochemistry* **37** (1998) 11399–11404.
235. P. Kühn, J. Pieper, O. Kaminskaya, H.-J. Eckert, R. Lechner, V. Shuvalov, G. Renger, Reaction pattern of Photosystem II: Oxidative water splitting and protein flexibility. *Photosynth. Res.* **84** (2005) 317–323.
236. A. Remy, K. Gerwert, Coupling of light-induced electron transfer to proton uptake in photosynthesis. *Nat. Struct. Biol.* **10** (2003) 637–644.
237. V. Petrouleas, B.A. Diner, Identification of Q_{400}, a high-potential electron acceptor of photosystem II, with the iron of the quinone-iron acceptor complex. *Biochim. Biophys. Acta* **849** (1986) 264–275.
238. J.-L. Zimmermann, A.W. Rutherford, Photoreductant-induced oxidation of Fe^{2+} in the electron-acceptor complex of photosystem II. *Biochim. Biophys. Acta* **851** (1986) 416–423.

239. G. Renger, B. Hanssum, H. Gleiter, H. Koike, Y. Inoue, Interaction of 1.4 benzoquinones with photosystem II in thylakoids and PS II membrane fragments from spinach. *Biochim. Biophys. Acta* **936** (1988) 435–446.
240. J.M. Bowes, A.R. Crofts, S.A. Itoh, High potential acceptor for photosystem II. *Biochim. Biophys. Acta* **547** (1979) 320–335.
241. C.A. Wraight, Modulation of herbicide-binding by the redox state of Q_{400}, an endogenous component of photosystem II. *Biochim. Biophys. Acta* **809** (1985) 320–330.
242. R.J. Debus, G. Feher, M.Y. Okamura, Iron-depleted reaction centers from *Rhodopseudomonas sphaeroides* R-26.1: characterization and reconstitution with Fe^{2+}, Mn^{2+}, Co^{2+}, Ni^{2+}, Cu^{2+}, and Zn^{2+}. *Biochemistry* **25** (1986) 2276–2287.
243. C. Kirmaier, D. Holten, R.J. Debus, G. Feher, M.Y. Okamura, Primary photochemistry of iron-depleted and zinc-reconstituted reaction centers from *Rhodopseudomonas sphaeroides*. *Proc. Natl. Acad. Sci. U.S.A.* **83** (1986) 6407–6411.
244. S. Hermes, J.M. Stachnik, D. Onidas, A. Remy, E. Hofmann, K. Gerwert, Proton uptake in the reaction center mutant L210DN from *Rhodobacter sphaeroides* via protonated water molecules. *Biochemistry* **45** (2006) 13741–13749.
245. J. Breton, Steady-state FTIR spectra of the photoreduction of Q_A and Q_B in *Rhodobacter sphaeroides* reaction centers provide evidence against the presence of a proposed transient electron acceptor X between the two quinones. *Biochemistry* **46** (2007) 4459–4465.
246. M. Flores, R. Isaacson, E. Abresch, R. Calvo, W. Lubitz, G. Feher, Protein-cofactor interactions in bacterial reaction centers from *Rhodobacter sphaeroides* R-26: II. Geometry of the hydrogen bonds to the primary quinone $Q_A^{-\cdot}$ by ^1H and ^2H ENDOR spectroscopy. *Biophys. J.* **92** (2007) 671–682.
247. J. Breton, J. Lavergne, M.C. Wakeham, E. Nabedryk, M.R. Jones, The unusually strong hydrogen bond between the carbonyl of Q_A and His M219 in the *Rhodobacter sphaeroides* reaction center is not essential for efficient electron transfer from $Q_A^{-\cdot}$ to Q_B. *Biochemistry* **46** (2007) 6468–6476.
248. G. Renger, U. Wacker, M. Völker, Studies on the protolytic reactions coupled with water splitting in photosystem II membrane fragments from spinach. *Photosynth. Res.* **13** (1987) 167–184.
249. V. Petrouleas, B.A. Diner, Light-induced oxidation of the acceptor-side Fe(II) of photosystem II by exogenous quinones acting through the Q_B binding site. I. Quinones, kinetics and pH-dependence. *Biochim. Biophys. Acta* **893** (1987) 126–137.
250. H.M. Gleiter, J.H.A. Nugent, E. Haag, G. Renger, Photoinhibition affects the non heme iron center in Photosystem II. *FEBS Lett.* **313** (1992) 75–79.
251. J. Kern, G. Renger, Photosystem II: Structure and mechanism of the water:plastoquinone oxidoreductase. *Photosynth. Res.* (2007) (in press, 10.1007/s11120-007-9201-1).
252. T. Hauß, S. Dante, H. Haines, N.A. Dencher, Localization of coenzyme Q_{10} in the center of a deuterated lipid membrane by neutron diffraction. *Biochim. Biophys. Acta* **1710** (2005) 57–62.
253. W. Oettmeier, Herbicides of photosystem II, in: *The Photosystems: Structure, Function and Molecular Biology* (1992) (J. Barber, ed.), Elsevier, Amsterdam, pp. 349–408.
254. I. Sinning, Herbicide binding in the bacterial photosynthetic reaction center. *Trends Biochem. Sci.* **17** (1992) 150–154.
255. J. Hirschberg, L. McIntosh, Molecular basis of herbicide resistance in *Amaranthus hybridus*. *Science* **222** (1983) 1346–1348.

256. S.S. Golden, R. Haselkorn, Mutation to herbicide resistance maps within the psbA gene of *Anacystis nidulans* R2. *Science* **229** (1985) 1104–1107.
257. I. Sinning, H. Michel, P. Mathis, A.W. Rutherford, Characterization of four herbicide-resistant mutants of *Rhodopseudomonas viridis* by genetic analysis, electron paramagnetic resonance and optical spectroscopy. *Biochemistry* **28** (1989) 5544–5553.
258. G. Renger, Studies on the structural and functional organization of system II of photosynthesis. The use of tryPS In as a structurally selective inhibitor at the outer surface of the thylakoid membrane. *Biochim. Biophys. Acta* **440** (1976) 287–300.
259. J. Messinger, W.P. Schröder, G. Renger, Structure–function relations in photosystem II. Effects of temperature and chaotropic agents on the period four oscillation of flash induced oxygen evolution. *Biochemistry* **32** (1993) 4444–4454.
260. H.M. Gleiter, E. Haag, Y. Inoue, G. Renger, New results on the functional properties of a Photosystem II core complex preparation from spinach. *Photosynth. Res.* **35** (1993) 41–53.
261. G. Renger, Photosynthesis, in: *Biophysics* (1983) (W. Hoppe, W. Lohmann, H. Markl, H. Ziegler, eds.), Springer, Berlin, pp. 515–542.
262. G. Hauska, E. Hurt, in: *Functions of Quinones in Energy Conserving Systems* (1982) (B. Trumpower, ed.), Academic Press, New York, pp. 87–110.
263. W. Haehnel, Photosynthetic electron transport in higher plants. *Annu. Rev. Plant Physiol.* **35** (1984) 659–693.
264. P. Joliot, A. Verméglio, A. Joliot, Photo-induced cyclic electron transfer operates in frozen cells of *Rhodobacter sphaeroides*. *Biochem. Biophys. Acta* **1318** (1997) 374–384.
265. A. Verméglio, A. Joliot, P. Joliot, Supramolecular organization of the photosynthetic chain in mutants of *Rhodobacter capsulatus* deleted in cytochrome c_2. *Biochim. Biophys. Acta* **1318** (1998) 374–338.
266. P. Joliot, J. Lavergne, D. Béal, Plastoquinone compartmentation in chloroplasts; evidence for domains with different rates of photoreduction. *Biochim. Biophys. Acta* **1101** (1992) 1–12.
267. L. Lavergne, J.P. Bouchaud, P. Joliot, Plastoquinone compartmentation in chloroplasts: 2. Theoretical aspects. *Biochim. Biophys. Acta* **1101** (1992) 13–22.
268. M. Blackwell, C. Gibas, S. Gygax, D. Roman, B. Wagner, The plastoquinone diffusion coefficient in chloroplasts and its mechanistic implications. *Biochim. Biophys. Acta* **1183** (1994) 533–543.
269. U. Siggel, G. Renger, H.H. Stiehl, B. Rumberg, -Evidence for electronic and ionic interaction between electron transport chains in chloroplasts. *Biochim. Biophys. Acta* **256** (1972) 328–335.
270. G. Renger, J. Messinger, R. Fromme, Tribromotoluquinone induced modifications of the oscillating pattern of oxygen evolution and of herbicide binding in thylakoids and PS II membrane fragments from spinach. *Z. Naturforsch.* **44** (1989) 423–430.
271. J. Kurreck, A.G. Seeliger, F. Reifarth, M. Karge, G. Renger, Reconstitution of the endogenous plastoquinone pool in Photosystem II (PS II) membrane fragments, inside-out-vesicles, and PS II core complexes from spinach. *Biochemistry* **34** (1995) 15721–15731.
272. J.F. Allen, A. Nilsson, Redox signalling and the structural basis of regulation of photosynthesis by protein phosphorylation. *Physiol. Plant.* **100** (1997) 863–868.
273. R. Douce, J. Joyard, Biochemistry and Function of the Plastid Envelope. *Annual Review of Cell Biology* **6** (1990) 173–216.

274. M.R. Jones, Lipids in photosynthetic reaction centres: Structural roles and functional holes. *Progr. Lipid Res.* **46** (2007) 56–87.
275. R. Steffen, A.A. Kelly, J. Huyer, P. Doermann, G. Renger, Investigations on the reaction pattern of photosystem II in leaves from *Arabidopsis thaliana* wild type plants and mutants with genetically modified lipid content. *Biochemistry* **44** (2005) 3134–3142.
276. F. Reifarth, G. Christen, A.G. Seeliger, P. Dörmann, C. Benning, G. Renger, Modification of the water oxidising complex in leaves of the *dgd1* mutant of *Arabidopsis thaliana* deficient in the galactolipid digalactosyldiacylglycerol. *Biochemistry* **36** (1997) 11769–11776.
277. A. Minoda, N. Sato, H. Nozaki, K. Okada, H. Takahashi, K. Sonoike, M. Tsuzuki, Role of sulfoquinovosyl diacylglycerol for the maintenance of photosystem II in *Chlamydomonas reinhardtii*. *Eur. J. Biochem.* **269** (2002) 2353–2358.
278. O. Kruse, B. Hankamer, C. Konczak, C. Gerle, Ed Morris, A. Radunz, G.H. Schmid, J. Barber, Phosphatidylglycerol is involved in the dimerization of Photosystem II. *J. Biol. Chem.* **275** (2000) 6509–6514.
279. Z. Gombos, S. Várkonyi, M. Hagio, M. Iwaki, L. Kovács, K. Masamoto, S. Itoh, H. Wada, Phosphatidylglycerol requirement for the function of electron acceptor plastoquinone Q_B in the Photosystem II reaction center. *Biochemistry* **41** (2002) 3796–3802.
280. E.-H. Kim, R. Razeghifard, J.M. Anderson, W.S. Chow, Multiple sites of retardation of electron transfer in Photosystem II after hydrolysis of phosphatidylglycerol. *Photosynth. Res.* **93** (2007) 149–158.
281. G. Renger, P. Kühn, Reaction pattern and mechanism of light induced oxidative water splitting in photosynthesis. *Biochim. Biophys. Acta.* **1767** (2007) 458–471.

Chapter 17

Photosynthetic Water Splitting

Johannes Messinger and Gernot Renger

Table of Contents

17.1 Introduction	293
17.2 Reaction Pattern of Oxidative Water Splitting	295
17.2.1 Kok Model	295
17.2.2 Lifetimes of the S_i States	297
17.2.3 Probabilities of S_i State Transitions	297
17.2.4 Mathematical Description of the Kok Model	298
17.2.5 Origin of Misses and Extensions of the Kok Model	298
17.3 Thermodynamics of Oxidative Water Splitting	300
17.4 Assembly and Structure of the WOC	302
17.4.1 Photoactivation	302
17.4.2 Structure of the WOC	304
17.4.2.1 Structure of the Mn_4O_xCa Cluster	305
17.4.2.2 Chloride and Hydrogencarbonate	311
17.4.2.3 Substrate Water Binding	312
17.4.2.4 Protein Ligands of the Mn_4O_xCa Cluster	314
17.4.2.5 Tyrosine Z and the Proton Network	315
17.5 Kinetics	316
17.5.1 Kinetics of S_i State Transitions	316
17.5.2 Activation Energies of S_i State Transitions	319
17.5.3 Kinetic Isotope Effects (KIE)	320
17.5.4 Reaction Coordinates	320
17.5.5 Nature of the Redox Reactions in the WOC	321
17.6 Mechanism of Photosynthetic Water Splitting	322
17.6.1 $S_0 \rightarrow S_1$ Transition	323
17.6.2 $S_1 \rightarrow S_2$ Transition	325
17.6.3 $S_2 \rightarrow S_3$ Transition	325
17.6.4 $S_3 \rightarrow \rightarrow S_4 \rightarrow \rightarrow S_0$ Transition	327
17.6.4.1 Previously Proposed Mechanisms for O–O Bond Formation	327

17.6.4.2 Deprotonation Reactions and $Y_Z^{OX}S_3'$ State 328
17.6.4.3 Formation of a Terminal Oxo-Group 329
17.6.4.4 Evidence for a Peroxidic Intermediate in the S_4 State 329
17.6.5 Refined Proposals for O–O Bond Formation 330
17.6.5.1 Proton-shift First Mechanisms 330
17.6.5.2 O–O Bond First Mechanism 331
17.7 Concluding Remarks and Future Perspectives 331
Acknowledgements 332
References 332

Abstract

This chapter reviews our current state of knowledge on the structure and functional pattern of the water oxidizing complex (WOC) in photosynthesis. The reactions leading to oxidative water splitting into molecular oxygen and four protons take place at a multimeric metal center, the Mn_4O_xCa cluster (x symbolizes the number of oxo-bridges). The overall process consists of a reaction sequence of four oxidation steps (Kok cycle), which is energetically driven by the strongly oxidizing cation radical $P680^{+\bullet}$ with tyrosine Y_Z acting as intermediary redox carrier. The energetics and kinetics of these reactions are described. Based on the Kok-scheme as a fingerprint for the interpretation of spectroscopic data, information is obtained on the electronic configuration and nuclear geometry of the different redox states S_i, in particular on the valence states and the distances between the metal centers. Furthermore, the exchange kinetics of substrate water in the S_i states are presented. The transitions $S_0 \to S_1$ and $S_1 \to S_2$ are shown to be metal-centered redox steps, while $S_2 \to S_3$ is favored to be a ligand-centered reaction. The redox states S_3 and/or $S_3Y_Z^{OX}$ could comprise redox isomerism and tautomerism equilibria. Finally, we attempt to cast our current knowledge about photosynthetic water splitting into a mechanism.

17.1 Introduction

Light-induced oxidative water splitting into molecular oxygen and four protons by photosynthesis is the key process of solar energy exploitation as the unique Gibbs energy source of living matter (Chapter 1). In the history of research, analysis of the overall reaction of photosynthesis in green plants had a great impact on the development of basic concepts in chemistry because it led to the discovery of molecular oxygen in the air by Priestley and at the same time to the elimination of the phlogiston theory of combustion owing to the work of Lavoisier and Scheele (for further reading, see [[1]]). However, the source of the oxygen atoms remained obscure until water was found to be the substrate for molecular oxygen produced by photosynthesis [2,3]. The key step for a deeper understanding of the underlying reaction pattern was the unraveling of the characteristic period four oscillation of the oxygen yield per flash when dark-adapted algae or chloroplasts are illuminated by a train of single turnover flashes [4]. Based on this finding and on their own data, Kok and co-workers concluded that oxidative water splitting takes place via a sequence of one-electron transfer steps that lead to a stepwise accumulation of strongly oxidizing redox equivalents at a suitable storage device until in a final cooperative reaction the formation of molecular oxygen from two substrate water molecules can occur. The basic scheme proposed by Kok and co-workers [5] is referred to as Kok cycle (Section 17.2). This reaction sequence is energetically driven by the strongly oxidizing cation radical $P680^{+\bullet}$ that is formed as the result of light-induced charge separation in photosystem II (PS II), as outlined in Chapter 16. A specific tyrosine residue, Y_Z of polypeptide D1, functionally connects the catalytic site of oxidative water splitting with $P680^{+\bullet}$ [6,7].

The Kok cycle per se provides only a formal description and immediately raises questions on the structure of the water-oxidizing complex (WOC) [alternatively the symbol OEC (oxygen-evolving complex) is used in the literature] and in particular the nature of the redox centers that directly participate in the redox reactions. Early studies had shown that the transition metal manganese is an essential constituent of the photosynthetic apparatus [8,9]. Systematic investigations performed by Cheniae and co-workers revealed that the manganese content is linearly related to the oxygen-evolution capacity [10,11]. This finding suggested that manganese is a (the) redox active component of the WOC. This idea was confirmed by different spectroscopic methods (Section 17.4.2). Quantitative determinations of the manganese content revealed that each WOC contains four Mn (for a review, see [12]).

Another component that turned out to be an essential constituent of a functionally competent WOC is the redox inert metal cation Ca^{2+} (for reviews, see [12,13]). From observed Mn–Mn distances it was furthermore inferred that the manganese atoms are bridged by μ-oxo and di-μ-oxo bridges (for reviews, see [14–16]). Based on these data and currently available information, the catalytic center of the WOC can be described as a Mn_4O_xCa cluster, which is incorporated into a functional protein matrix (Section 17.4.2).

First insight into the nature of this matrix was obtained by improvement of the biochemical techniques for isolation of PS II preparations. It was shown that PS II core complexes are samples of minimum polypeptide composition that still retain the full oxygen evolution capacity [17–20]. In contrast to the isolated and functionally fully competent reaction centers of anoxygenic purple bacteria with only 2–3 polypeptides, PS II core complexes are characterized by a rather large number of polypeptides. They contain over 18 different proteins [21], but all the cofactors that are required for light-induced charge separation are bound within a heterodimer formed by the D1 and D2 polypeptides. The enormous progress achieved during the last half decade in unraveling the PS II structure by X-ray crystallography [22–25] unambiguously shows that the Mn_4O_xCa complex is bound to the D1 protein. An additional ligation by an amino acid from CP43 (Arg-357) appears to be most likely ([24]; for details, see Chapter 15).

The stability and reactivity of the Mn_4O_xCa cluster are, however, not only determined by the first coordination shell of amino acid ligands from D1 and CP43, but also significantly affected by regulatory proteins. Among these the extrinsic PsbO protein, with an apparent MW of 33 kDa, is of special relevance for the stability of the manganese and, therefore, this polypeptide is often denoted "manganese stabilizing protein" (MSP) (for a review, see [26]; see, however, [27]). The PsbO protein binds to the integral proteins of PS II mainly through interaction with the large extrinsic loop of CP47 (see also Chapter 15 and [28,29]). It has also been proposed to play an important role for H^+ transfer from the catalytic site of the WOC into the lumen [30]. Both proteins CP43 and CP47 are characterized by unusually large loops between transmembrane helices V and VI, which protrude into the lumenal side and are essential constituents for a functionally competent

WOC [31–34]. In fact, due to the large volume of these lumenal extensions and extrinsic proteins the Mn_4O_xCa cluster of the WOC is actually located near the center of the PS II complex and is apparently well shielded from the aqueous phase. This arrangement leads to the idea that channels should exist for substrate (water) access (Section 17.4.2.4) and product (H^+, O_2) release [35–38].

Another striking feature of the WOC, which is unique for metalloproteins, was the finding that the assembly of this complex requires a light-driven process referred to as photoactivation (Section 17.4.1). In fact, the formation of an intact WOC is the last step in the ontogenetic development of the photosynthetic apparatus [39,40].

This chapter summarizes our current knowledge on assembly, structure, function and mechanisms of the WOC.

17.2 Reaction Pattern of Oxidative Water Splitting

17.2.1 Kok Model

The basis for the understanding of the mechanism of photosynthetic water oxidation was laid by Joliot and co-workers in 1969 by measurements of flash-induced oxygen evolution patterns (FIOPs) and their interpretation by Kok and colleagues in 1970 [4,5]. Illumination of dark-adapted PS II samples with short, saturating xenon flashes (FWHM of a few μs) at a frequency of 2 Hz gives rise to a period four oscillation in oxygen evolution with the following characteristics (Figure 1A): (i) the first flash does not induce any oxygen evolution (in fact, usually a small O_2 consumption is seen, which is generally assigned to O_2 reduction by PS I), (ii) only a very small oxygen yield is observed after the 2nd flash, (iii) a pronounced first maximum of O_2 evolution is generated by the 3rd flash, and (iv) the next maximum is observed after four more flashes, and this period four oscillation is damped so that eventually all flashes generate the same amount of O_2. Kok et al. [5] discovered that this characteristic oscillation, which corresponds to the four electrons that need to be extracted from two water molecules to produce $O_2 + 4H^+$, is essentially invariant to the inactivation of about 90% of the PS II centers. This finding clearly showed already, 35 years ago, without any information on the structure of PS II, that the indispensable cooperation of four oxidizing equivalents is achieved by a sequence of four one-electron oxidation steps within WOCs connected each to only one PS II reaction center. Accordingly, Kok proposed a model (Figure 1B; black symbols and arrows) where the individual WOCs cycle through five different oxidation states, denoted S_0, S_1, S_2, S_3 and S_4 [5]. The index i (0,...,4) gives the number of stored oxidizing equivalents relative to the lowest redox state that the WOC attains during the water oxidation cycle. The S_i state notation corresponds in the S_0 state formally to the catalytic site plus bound water and in the S_4 state to the catalytic site plus bound O_2, without specifying the electronic configurations or protonation state of the catalytic site and its bound substrate/product.

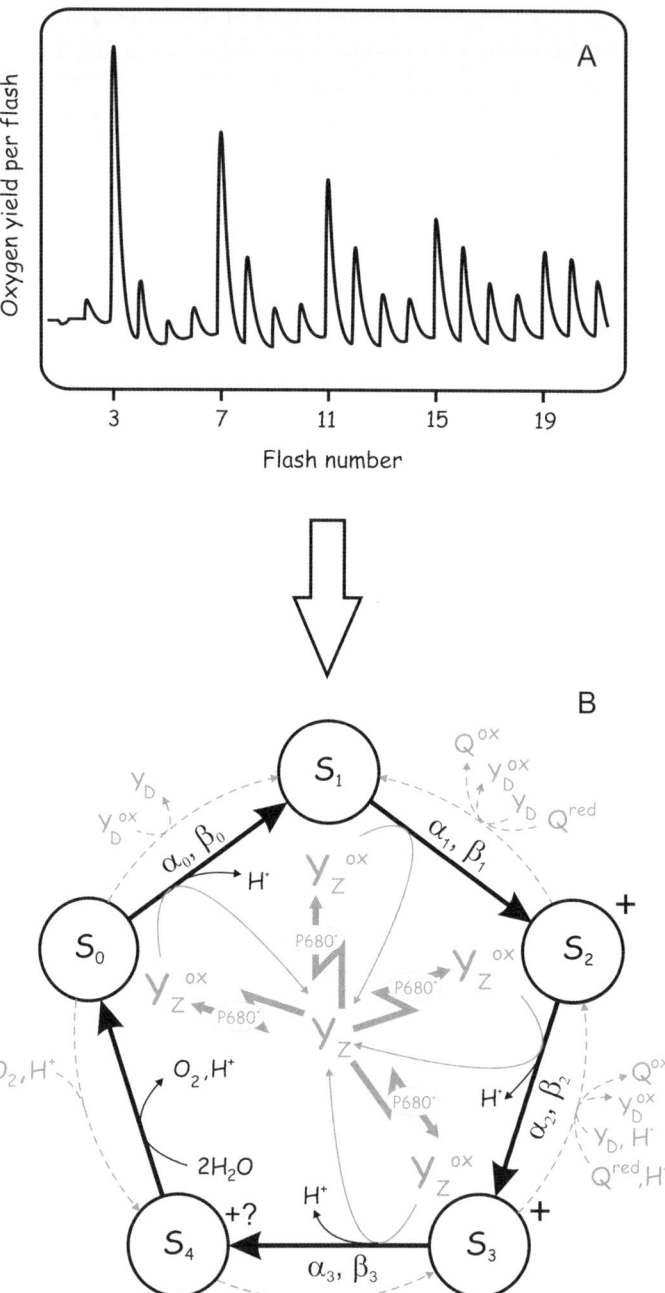

Figure 1. (A) Flash-induced oxygen evolution pattern (FIOP) of dark-adapted spinach thylakoids induced by a train of saturating xenon flashes (2 Hz frequency). This type of experiment was first reported by Joliot and co-workers [4]. (B) The extended Kok model (for the original model see [5]). All symbols are explained in the main text.

Although for some aspects Y_Z can be considered to be part of the WOC, it is a kinetically and spectroscopically well distinct entity from the Mn_4O_xCa cluster, and should therefore not be included in the S_i state terminology (for clarity one should rather write $Y_Z^{OX}S_i$).

Kok's model includes additional assumptions about the dark stabilities of the different S_i states and the S_i state transition probabilities upon excitation of PS II with saturating light flashes to explain (i) the first maximum at the 3rd flash and (ii) the damping of the oscillation [41]. These are discussed in detail below. Historically, other interpretations of Joliot's FIOPs, involving various kinds of cooperativity between PS II centers, have also been put forward (e.g., [4,42–44]). Although these proposals contain interesting suggestions, they can be excluded on the basis of today's detailed knowledge of PS II.

17.2.2 Lifetimes of the S_i States

To explain that the first maximum of oxygen evolution occurs after the 3rd flash rather than the 4th flash, the Kok model assumes that, after sufficient dark-adaptation, about 75% of the centers are in redox state S_1 and 25% in S_0. Later measurements showed that the dark-population of S_1 can actually reach almost 100% [45]. Indeed it can be shown that the S_0, S_2, and S_3 states convert during dark-adaptation into the S_1 state (Figure 1B; dashed grey arrows between S_0/S_1, S_3/S_2 and S_2/S_1). The S_0 state is oxidized to S_1 by Y_D^{OX} [46] and the S_3 and S_2 states are reduced by Y_D via a fast decay [45,47–49] or a slower decay due to electron donation from the acceptor side quinones (symbolized by Q^{red} in Figure 1B; [50–53]). The half-times of these dark-reactions vary strongly with temperature and pH, but generally range from seconds to minutes (S_2 and S_3) or occur in the tens of minutes time scale ($S_0Y_D^{OX}$) [54–57]. Because a very slow deactivation of S_2 is also observed in the presence of high levels of external electron acceptors, other not-well-characterized pathways for S_2 and S_3 deactivations may exist [58]. The S_4 state is a very reactive transient and decays rapidly in the dark into the S_0 state under the release of O_2 (Section 17.6).

17.2.3 Probabilities of S_i State Transitions

Another important feature of FIOPs is the damping of the period four oscillation. To explain this phenomenon, Kok et al. proposed probabilities for miss hits (α) and double hits (β) [5,41]. The miss probability (or "misses") reflects the percentage of WOCs that are in the same S_i state before and after flash excitation ($S_i \rightarrow S_i$). The miss event does not represent a permanent inhibition of a specific S_i state transition or a specific PS II complex, but is assumed to be statistically distributed over all PS II centers within a flash train (see below for the current molecular understanding of misses). Permanently inhibited PS II centers do not contribute to FIOPs.

The double hit probability β accounts for the small O_2 yield that occurs also in thoroughly dark-adapted samples after the 2nd flash if xenon flashes with a FWHM of a few microseconds are employed [5,41]. The double-hit probability represents the percentage of centers that undergo a double advancement ($S_i \to S_{i+2}$) in a single flash. The β probability depends on the flash profile and double hits are essentially absent if ns laser flashes are used for excitation [38,56,59].

Miss and double hit probabilities are strongly temperature and pH dependent [56,57,60–64]. In addition they are also affected by H/D exchange [65] and vary with species [60]. For spinach thylakoids, typical Kok parameters are $\alpha = 6-12\%$ and $\beta \cong 3\%$ with xenon flash illumination.

17.2.4 Mathematical Description of the Kok Model

In the original Kok model, the miss probability was assumed to be S_i state independent, although the possibility of unequal misses was considered (Section 17.2.5). Furthermore, the S_i states are treated as being stable during the dark times between flashes (usually 0.5 or 1.0 s). If also the double hit probability is assumed to be S_i state independent, the S_i state populations, $[S_i]$ with $i = 0 \ldots 3$, after the nth-flash are simply given by:

$$\begin{bmatrix} [S_0]_n \\ [S_1]_n \\ [S_2]_n \\ [S_3]_n \end{bmatrix} = \begin{bmatrix} \alpha & 0 & \beta & \gamma \\ \gamma & \alpha & 0 & \beta \\ \beta & \gamma & \alpha & 0 \\ 0 & \beta & \gamma & \alpha \end{bmatrix} * \begin{bmatrix} [S_0]_{n-1} \\ [S_1]_{n-1} \\ [S_2]_{n-1} \\ [S_3]_{n-1} \end{bmatrix} \quad (1)$$

where γ is the single-hit ($S_i \to S_{i+1}$) probability ($\gamma = 1 - \alpha - \beta$). The oxygen yield of the nth flash Y_n is obtained by the relation:

$$Y_n = (1 - \alpha) \cdot [S_3]_{n-1} + \beta \cdot [S_2]_{n-1} \quad (2)$$

In slight variance to this simple formalism, Kok and co-workers actually postulated that double hits can only occur if the centers are in the S_0 or S_1 states, because the $S_2 \to S_3$ and the $S_3 \to S_4 \to S_0$ transitions are slower then the $S_0 \to S_1$ and $S_1 \to S_2$ transitions [41] (Section 17.5.1 and Table 2). As alternative fit approaches, the sigma-analysis [66–68] and eigenvalue analysis (see [69], and references therein) were developed. These related methods first determine model-independent "sigma-coefficients", which are then interpreted in terms of the Kok model.

In practice the above formalism or extensions thereof are often used for fit programs that minimize the error between the measured O_2 amplitudes and theoretical patterns by varying α, β, and the initial S_i state populations (e.g., using spread sheet programs). Recently, an analytical solution was developed that allows direct calculation of the "Kok parameters" [70,71].

17.2.5 Origin of Misses and Extensions of the Kok Model

Redox equilibria on the donor ($S_i Y_Z P680^{+\cdot} \leftrightarrow S_i Y_Z^{OX} P680 \leftrightarrow S_{i+1} Y_Z P680$) and acceptor sides ($Q_A^- Q_B \leftrightarrow Q_A Q_B^-$) are responsible for temporary blockage of stable charge separation in PS II and, therefore, are the origin of misses [72,73], because in centers where the states Q_A^- and/or $P680^{+\cdot}$ are populated at the time of flash excitation no stable charge separation can occur. Complementary to this thermodynamic effect, competing kinetics have also been proposed to give rise to misses. In this case the rate of $P680^{+\cdot}$ reduction by Y_Z is critical, because it competes with the charge recombination between $P680^{+\cdot}$ with Q_A^-. The latter reaction prevents Y_Z oxidation by reducing $P680^{+\cdot}$, i.e., results in a miss [64,65,74,75]. Since the contribution of the µs-components to the multiphasic kinetics of $P680^{+\cdot}$ reduction by Y_Z is markedly higher during the higher S_i state transitions [76,77], an S_i state dependent miss parameter is expected with the highest miss occurring during the $S_3 \rightarrow S_4 \rightarrow S_0$ transition [64,65,74]. An additional miss can arise if Y_D is reduced and can also compete with Y_Z in the reduction of $P680^{+\cdot}$. A small difference in the miss parameter of Y_D and Y_D^{OX} thylakoids has been reported [60]. This reaction may be of even greater relevance at high pH [78]. It has also been suggested that the positive charge on Y_D^{OX} may affect the redox potential of $P680^{+\cdot}$ [79–81] and thus modulate the miss parameter [65,74]. The possible S_i state dependence of miss and double hit parameters is indicated in Figure 1(B) by α_i, β_i ($i = 1, \ldots,$ 4) at the solid black arrows, and the important role of the interaction of Y_Z with $P680^{+\cdot}$ and the S_i states for the miss parameter (and its pH dependence, see [61,65]) is indicated in the centre of the Kok cycle in grey.

When only one parameter, e.g., the O_2 yield or the amplitude of the S_2 state EPR multiline signal, is followed during a flash sequence, it is possible to fit the obtained oscillation pattern with many different combinations of S_i state-dependent miss parameters (e.g., [60]). Inspection of the different fit results revealed that compared with the equal miss fit approximation only a slight improvement could be achieved with the simplifying assumption $\alpha_0 = \alpha_1 = 0$ and $\alpha_2 = \alpha_3$. In general it is required to follow several S_i states at the same time to obtain a reliable determination of the S_i state dependence of the miss parameter. A step forward in this direction has now been achieved by following the S_2 and S_0 state EPR MLS during a flash sequence [75]. This study provides experimental support for the above model, because the S_3 state miss is reported to be only slightly greater than the miss connected with the S_2 state advancement. Consequently, these data support the idea that the extent of µs-kinetics of $P680^{+\cdot}$ reduction by Y_Z correlates with the probability of misses [64,65,74].

In addition, other factors such as addition of electron acceptors and fast deactivation of S_i states can affect the FIOPs. Therefore, advanced Kok schemes often contain extensions to describe the S_i state distributions more accurately. These may include (a) back reactions of S_2 and S_3 with Y_D during the dark-time between flashes [54,69,82,83]; (b) existence of S_i states reduced below the level of the S_0 state ($S_{-1} \ldots S_{-5}$; [69,83–86]); (c) a correction factor for a change of the number of active PS II centers during the flash train due to photoactivation, photoinhibition or a limited acceptor pool size [86–88]; (d) inactive centers that turn over only once or twice in a sequence [89–92]; (e) enhanced double hit on the first flash or on each other flash that may be caused by addition of ferricyanide or phenyl-p-benzoquinone, respectively [59,93–96]; and (f) S_i state-dependent miss parameters [60,72–75,97,98]. The effect of these corrections on the calculated S_i state populations strongly depends on the sample type, the signal followed (e.g., S_2 EPR multiline, O_2 yield, optical changes) and experimental conditions (flash frequency, temperature, pH etc.).

17.3 Thermodynamics of Oxidative Water Splitting

The thermodynamics for splitting liquid water into gaseous molecular oxygen and hydrogen is determined by the standard $\Delta G°$ of 237.13 kJ mol^{-1} [99], which corresponds to an electrochemical potential difference ΔE of –1.23 V. If one considers oxidative water splitting into O_2 and four protons, the midpoint potential becomes a pH-dependent parameter with a value of +0.82 V at pH 7. When taking the $E_{m,7}$ values for the individual one-electron oxidation steps of water in aqueous solution leading to molecular oxygen and four protons it is seen that the individual reaction steps exhibit quite different energetics (left-hand side of Figure 2).

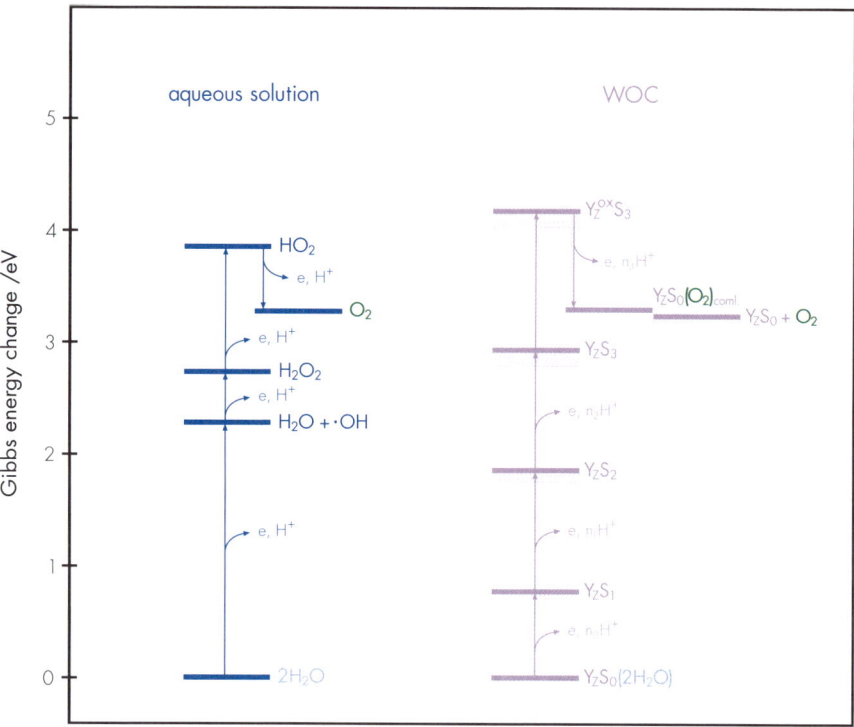

Figure 2. Energetic pattern of four-step oxidative water splitting into molecular oxygen and four protons in solution (left-hand side) and in the WOC (right-hand side). For direct comparability, the free energy levels of water molecules in bulk solutions and in the WOC are set to zero. The values for the in vitro reaction are taken from the literature [287] and those of the redox steps in the WOC are calculated according to eqn. (3) as outlined in the text.

The standard Gibbs energy differences between the redox states S_{i+1} and S_i [$\Delta G°(S_{i+1}/S_i)$] cannot be directly measured by redox titration experiments. However, indirect estimations are obtained from data reported in the literature. The $\Delta G°(S_{i+1}/S_i)$ values are given by the relation:

$$\Delta G°(S_{i+1}/S_i) = \Delta G°(P680^{+\cdot}/P680) + \Delta G°(P680Y_Z^{OX}S_i/P680^{+\cdot}Y_ZS_i) \\ + \Delta G°(Y_ZS_{i+1}/Y_Z^{OX}S_i) \quad (3)$$

where $\Delta G°(P680^{+\cdot}/P680)$, $\Delta G°(P680Y_Z^{OX}S_i/P680^{+\cdot}Y_ZS_i)$ and $\Delta G°(Y_ZS_{i+1}/Y_Z^{OX}S_i)$ are the Gibbs energy differences for the formation of the cation radical $P680^{+\cdot}$, oxidation of Y_Z by $P680^{+\cdot}$ and S_i-state transitions, respectively. The formulation of eqn. (3) tacitly implies that $\Delta G°(P680^{+\cdot}/P680)$ is virtually independent of the redox states of Y_Z and the WOC (S_i). This assumption is justified by the finding that the shift by the redox state of the nearly equidistant Y_D^{OX} is ≤ 10 meV [100]. Since the Mn_4O_xCa cluster is further apart from $P680^{+\cdot}$ the electrostatic effect is expected to be even significantly smaller than 10 meV.

The reduction potential of P680 has been recently estimated to be about +1.25 V ([101], for details see [102] and Chapter 16), corresponding to a $\Delta G°(P680^{+\cdot}/P680)$ of 1.25 eV. Values of $\Delta G°(P680Y_Z^{OX}S_i/P680^{+\cdot}Y_ZS_i)$ were reported to be −90 meV for S_0 and S_1 and −20 meV for S_2 and S_3 [76] and data on $\Delta G°(Y_ZS_{i+1}/Y_Z^{OX}S_i)$ are presented in [55,103]. On the basis of these numbers, the values of $\Delta G°(S_{i+1}/S_i)$ are calculated to be about 0.85, 1.10, 1.15 and 1.0 eV for $i = 0, 1, 2$ and 3, respectively (Figure 2, right-hand side), which exceed former estimates by about 0.15 eV. The difference originates from the revised value of $\Delta G°(P680^{+\cdot}/P680)$, which is 0.1–0.15 V higher according to recent studies (vide supra) than former estimates [104,105]. Notably, a value of 0.85 eV for the Gibbs energy gap between S_1 and S_2 is not in line with the reported redox potential of about +0.75 V for Y_D/Y_D^{OX} [106] because Y_D^{OX} is known to oxidize S_0 to S_1 in both cyanobacteria and higher plants [60] and also in Chl d-containing *Acaryochloris marina* [107]. This discrepancy indicates that further studies are required to unravel the details of the energetics of the $S_i \rightarrow S_{i+1}$ transitions.

According to the above estimates the energetics of the S_i state transitions in the WOC are all, with the exception of the $S_0 \rightarrow S_1$ transition, characterized by very similar gaps of the midpoint potentials. Consequently, the reaction pathway in the WOC must be entirely different from that in aqueous solution (for former discussion, see [108,109]).

The markedly smaller ΔE_m of the $S_0 \rightarrow S_1$ transition raises questions on its physiological relevance, because it includes an extra Gibbs energy of at least 0.2 eV that is available in the reaction sequence $P680^{+\cdot} Y_ZS_0 \rightarrow P680Y_Z^{OX}S_0 \rightarrow P680Y_ZS_1$. It has been speculated that this extra Gibbs energy could be transiently stored [110,111] but, so far, experimental evidence is lacking for this idea. Another consequence of the exceptional energetics of the $S_0 \rightarrow S_1$ transition is the virtual absence of S_0 population in dark adapted samples (vide infra).

The electronic configurations and nuclear geometries of the S_i states are affected by the protein matrix and, in particular, by the local proton activity. It was postulated that the essential O–O bound formation occurs at the level of complexed peroxide and this complexation is inferred to give rise to a significant stabilization of this peroxidic state compared with free hydrogen peroxide in aqueous solutions. Furthermore, energetic considerations also led to the idea that, thermodynamically, a state with complexed peroxide could be already reached in S_3 [108]. A later refinement of this idea postulated the existence of a redox isomerism and oxywater-complexed hydrogen peroxide tautomerism [111,112] (see Figure 8 below). The idea of a peroxidic state in S_3 is supported by reports on H_2O_2 evolution in samples with a distorted WOC [113,114]. The last step of oxidative water splitting is the product/substrate exchange, which was earlier suggested to be an exergonic process with a comparatively large Gibbs energy gap [108]. Recent studies on the back-pressure effect of molecular oxygen revealed, however, that the reaction sequence $Y_Z^{OX}S_3 \leftrightarrow Y_ZS_4[S_2(H_xO_2)] \leftrightarrow Y_ZS_0 + O_2 + nH^+$, which in addition to electron transfer also contains the product/substrate exchange, is only slightly exergonic [115]. An important consequence of this small energy gap is a low probability of the population of state $S_4[S_2(H_xO_2)]$ at atmospheric oxygen pressure (x symbolizes that the protonation state of the postulated complexed peroxide in the S_4 state is unknown; with the definition given below in Section 17.4.2.1 (Electronic structure of the WOC) this state can also be denoted as $S_4[M_2L_0W_2]$). Therefore, it was suggested that the absence of S_0 population in the dark is of physiological relevance, because it may prevent, during long dark periods, formation and release of H_2O_2 via the S_4 state [116].

The above considerations reveal that sufficient Gibbs energy is available to afford oxidative water splitting even at acidic pH values of about 5 that exist in the lumen under strong continuous illumination of tightly coupled chloroplasts [117].

Importantly, for energetic considerations on the individual reaction steps of the WOC the configurational energy rather than the Gibbs energy is the essential parameter, as outlined in detail in previous studies [118,119]. At present we do not have detailed information on the different contributions (local activity of protons, substrate water, molecular orbital energies of ligated manganese, etc.) to the $\Delta G°$ values of the S_i states, and only estimates on the redox potential gap between these states can be given. Our limited information is summarized in the scheme of the right-hand side of Figure 2 (uncertainties in the energy levels are symbolized by shadowed areas).

17.4 Assembly and Structure of the WOC

17.4.1 Photoactivation

Experiments with bean leaves grown under a special flash light/dark regime revealed that under these conditions a PS II complex is assembled that can perform the light-induced charge separation, but is lacking the capability of oxygen evolution. A subsequent illumination with continuous (CW) light was required to establish a functionally competent WOC [39]. Likewise, Cheniae and co-workers showed that if the green alga *Chlorella pyrenoidosa* is grown in the dark the oxygen-evolving capacity is absent and the formation of the WOC must be preceded by the formation of PS II complexes that are capable of stable charge separation [40]. These phenomena indicate that the formation of an intact Mn_4O_xCa cluster requires a special process, which is driven by photoreactions in the PS II reaction center. More detailed information on the mechanism of the assembly of the Mn_4O_xCa cluster was obtained by studies on manganese-deprived samples. Several treatments (incubation of thylakoids in suspensions of high pH or with solutions containing compounds like Tris or hydroxylamine at sufficiently high concentrations) lead to a release of manganese from the sample without severe destruction of the apoprotein matrix ([40]; for a review see [12]). In enzymology numerous examples are known for metalloenzymes in which the catalytic metal center can be reversibly removed from the apoprotein and reinserted or even replaced by another metal (see textbooks on metalloenzymes, e.g., [120]). In marked contrast to these systems, however, the formation of the Mn_4O_xCa cluster through ligation of manganese and Ca^{2+} into PS II is an endergonic process that can be only achieved via a light-driven reaction sequence, denoted photoactivation. The essential steps of this process are two light reactions separated by a stabilization event in the dark ([121,122] and references therein) thus leading to a complex that contains two oxidized manganese centers. Subsequent light-induced reaction(s) accomplish the reconstitution of a functionally competent WOC. Photoactivation of the WOC is absolutely specific for Mn, which cannot be replaced by any other transition metal ion. In contrast, for the redox inert Ca^{2+}, Sr^{2+} can be used as a surrogate. Under standard conditions, the O_2-evolving activity of WOCs containing a Mn_4O_xSr cluster is about 50% of that with a Mn_4O_xCa cluster [123–129].

The photoassembly of the Mn_4O_xCa cluster occurs via the oxidation of Mn(II) into Mn(III)/Mn(IV), with $P680^{+\bullet}$ acting as oxidant and Y_Z as intermediary redox carrier. A suitable ligation of the manganese requires the presence of Ca^{2+} (or Sr^{2+}). The kinetics of the reaction sequence of photoactivation have been resolved by measurements of the flash-induced oxygen yield in samples under reconstitution conditions [130,131]. Figure 3 summarizes our current knowledge on the kinetics of the photoassembly of the Mn_4O_xCa cluster in manganese deprived samples. The intermediates of the oxidation steps are not yet fully characterized.

The properties of the WOC can be specifically manipulated by several compounds. Among these agents, hydrophilic exogenous reductants give rise to the population of "super-reduced" S_i states (S_{-i} states). So far, a stable population can be achieved for states S_{-1}, S_{-2} and S_{-3} (see [86]). Indirect evidence for the possible existence of redox states S_{-4} and S_{-5} has also been presented [132]. The super-reduced states were proposed to be transients in the photoactivation process [38,133,134]. This idea is supported by the finding that the states S_{-3} to S_{-1} are populated in vivo [135,136]. As an extension of this postulate it appears attractive to assign the reduced states S_{-5} and S_{-4} to the intermediates A (one Mn^{2+} bound at the high affinity site) and B/C (one Mn^{3+} bound at the high affinity site) respectively, of the scheme in Figure 3. The low

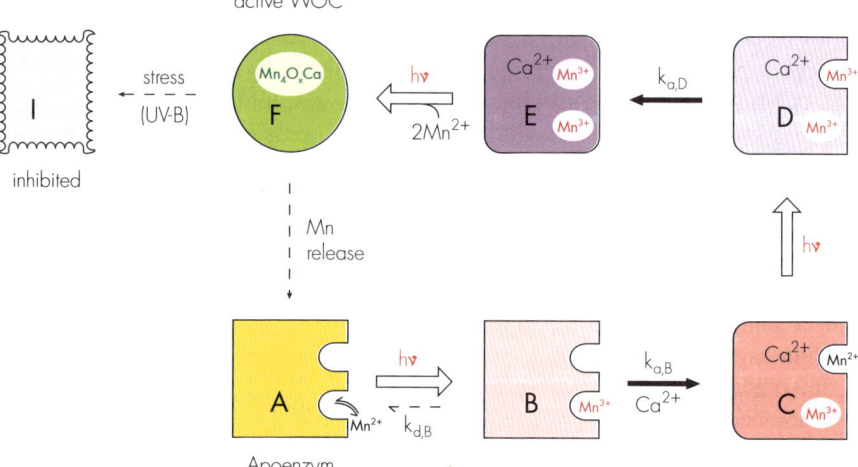

Figure 3. Scheme of photoassembly of the WOC. The states A and F represent the initial and final state of the reaction sequence, which consists of two light-driven reactions, A → B and C → D, leading each to the oxidation of one Mn^{2+} to Mn^{3+} and an intermediary Ca^{2+}-dependent dark reaction that gives rise to conformational changes as indicated by different shapes of the symbols. Formation of state D is followed by dark transition into state E and subsequent high quantum yield light reaction(s) giving rise to a fully active WOC (state F). The state I is reached after light or UV-B stress and eventually leads to repair of the PS II complex [137,138].

quantum yield of the A → B and C → D transitions would explain why the apparent population of S_{-5} and S_{-4} is rather small and hardly resolvable in the patterns of flash-induced oxygen yield detected in NH_2NH_2 treated thylakoids.

In conclusion, the photoassembly of the WOC implies that the Mn_4O_xCa cluster is a non-equilibrium state, which needs to be stabilized by the protein environment. This notion is supported by the finding that the WOC is the primary target of light- [137,138] and temperature- [139,140] induced destruction of PS II.

17.4.2 Structure of the WOC

The structure of the WOC is defined by (a) the spatial arrangement of the four manganese ions, the bridging oxygens and the Ca^{2+} ion within the Mn_4O_xCa cluster; (b) the coordination of the Mn_4O_xCa cluster by ligands; and (c) the functionally important part of the surrounding protein matrix. Among the (possible) ligands (point b) three types can be distinguished: (i) small anions like Cl^- and HCO_3^- (or less likely non-substrate H_2O, OH^-), (ii) the two substrate molecules in different protonation states (H_2O, OH^-, O^{2-}) and (iii) protein ligands. One essential function of the surrounding protein matrix (point c) appears to be the establishment of a dynamic network of hydrogen bonds and, possibly, the regulation of substrate water access and product release.

17.4.2.1 Structure of the Mn_4O_xCa Cluster

Different spectroscopic techniques can be used for structural analysis. The currently most widely used methods for unraveling the structure of the Mn_4O_xCa cluster are X-ray diffraction crystallography (XRDC) and extended X-ray absorption fine structure (EXAFS) spectroscopy.

X-Ray Diffraction Crystallography (XRDC) Data. Several crystal structures of PS II core complexes from the thermophilic cyanobacteria *T. elongatus* [22,24,25,141] and *T. vulcanus* [23] have been published in the recent past (for details see Chapter 15). In the two XRDC studies at 3.5 Å [24] and 3.0 Å [25] resolution not only the electron density of the four Mn ions is presented, but also the approximate position of Ca^{2+} has been identified by anomalous diffraction. Figure 4(a) and (b) show these XRDC-derived structures for the Mn_4O_xCa cluster together with some of the suggested ligands. Because of the limited resolution (≥ 3.0 Å), EXAFS derived information about Mn–Mn and Mn–Ca distances (see below) have also been used for the construction of these models.

For XRDC studies at these resolutions a high X-ray dose is required and, for practical reasons, the experiments are usually performed at 100 K. From EXAFS studies the Mn_4O_xCa cluster in PS II is known to be highly susceptible to photoreduction and, indeed, it was shown that the X-ray dose used for XRDC leads to the reduction of most of the Mn(III) and Mn(IV) present in intact PS II to Mn(II) during the XRDC scans. Concomitantly, all defined Mn–Mn distances and Mn–O–Mn bridges are lost [142,143]. Therefore, future XRDC studies must aim to reduce the required radiation dose. Otherwise, they can only provide an approximate picture of a damaged state of the Mn_4O_xCa cluster.

Precise Mn–Mn distances are required to obtain a detailed model that includes the oxo-bridges. Knowledge of the bridges is vital for understanding the electronic structure of the Mn_4O_xCa cluster and, thereby, for conclusions about the mechanism of oxidative water splitting.

Extended X-ray absorption fine structure (EXAFS) spectroscopy. The X-ray dose required for EXAFS experiments is about 1000-fold lower than for XRDC. In addition, EXAFS experiments are performed at 10 K, which significantly reduces the radiation damage compared with 100 K [142]. Furthermore, XANES scans allow monitoring of the absence of radiation damage.

Earlier EXAFS experiments have firmly established that the Mn_4O_xCa cluster contains two or three Mn–Mn distances of about 2.7 Å and one Mn–Mn distance of about 3.3 Å (for reviews see [16,144–146]). Using information from EXAFS and XRDC of Mn-model compounds it is possible to assign 2.7 Å Mn–Mn distances to bis-μ-oxo bridged Mn–Mn units, while a 3.3 Å Mn–Mn distance is indicative for a mono μ-oxo bridged Mn–Mn unit [15,16]. From this information ten principally different arrangements for a Mn_4 cluster were proposed and five of these were considered to be likely models [14,144,147]. EXAFS measurements on the S_0 state revealed a heterogeneity in the short Mn–Mn distances, which was best fit with a ratio of 2:1 for the 2.72 and 2.85 Å distances [148]. On the basis of this data two novel models with three 2.7 Å Mn–Mn vectors and one 3.3 Å Mn–Mn vector were proposed for the S_1 state [148].

However, in the above study [148] the distance resolution was not high enough to unambiguously prove the existence of three short Mn–Mn vectors. Standard EXAFS fluorescence detectors have an energy resolution of about 150–200 eV (FWHM), which is too low for discriminating between Fe and Mn fluorescence. Because PS II complexes isolated from cyanobacteria and higher plants contain three and two iron centers, respectively, (Chapter 15) this normally limits data collection to energies below the Fe K-edge. The obtainable distance resolution in EXAFS measurements depends on the measured energy range according to:

$$\Delta R = \frac{\pi}{2k_{max}} \quad (4)$$

where k_{max} represents the electron wave vector of the manganese photoelectron at maximal X-ray energy [144]. By employing a crystal monochromator the resolution for X-ray fluorescence detection can be improved to ~ 1 eV, which allows the collection of Mn X-ray fluorescence without interference of Fe X-ray fluorescence [149]. High-resolution (or range extended) EXAFS spectroscopy, therefore, allows one to collect EXAFS data well past the Fe-edge and to improve the resolution ΔR between two similar Mn–Mn distances from 0.14 to 0.09 Å, with a distance accuracy of 0.02 Å for a single Mn–Mn distance. With this increased resolution it is possible to unambiguously resolve a small distance heterogeneity in the short (2.7–2.8 Å) Mn–Mn distances in the S_1 state of PS II [149]. These data reveal that the Mn_4O_xCa cluster in the dark-stable S_1 state consists of three short (i.e., two ~ 2.7 Å Mn–Mn and one ~ 2.8 Å Mn–Mn) Mn–Mn distances and one long (~ 3.3 Å) Mn–Mn distance, in addition to approx. two Mn–Ca distances (see below). This information drastically limits the number of options for possible structures of the Mn_4O_xCa complex. Currently feasible Mn_4O_x motifs are displayed in Figure 4(c–f). Interestingly, prior to XRDC studies [24,25] a detailed analysis of the Mn, Ca^{2+} and Sr^{2+} K-edge EXAFS experiments clearly demonstrated that the WOC contains one Ca^{2+} in close proximity (~ 3.4 Å) to manganese [150–152] (for reviews see [14,145]).

WOC models can be further refined if the orientations of the Mn–Mn and Mn–Ca distances can be determined, i.e., if Mn–Mn and Mn–Ca vectors are known. The polarized nature of synchrotron light allows such experiments if oriented samples can be prepared. Using Sr^{2+}-substituted PS II samples that were one-dimensionally oriented on a Mylar film by a paint-dry procedure, it was revealed that the average Mn–Ca vector has an angle of 0–23° relative to the membrane normal of thylakoids [125].

Therefore, the above EXAFS data show conclusively that Ca^{2+} has to be added to models c to f in Figure 4 so that about two Mn–Ca vectors exist with an average angle of 0–23° relative to the membrane normal. This results in many different Mn_4O_xCa models. However, comparison of these models with the XRDC derived structures (Figure 4a, b) allows us to limit this number to a few options, if the relative position of Ca^{2+} above the "trimer part" towards Y_Z (i.e., within the thick end of electron density of the Mn_4 unit) is accepted.

PHOTOSYNTHETIC WATER SPLITTING

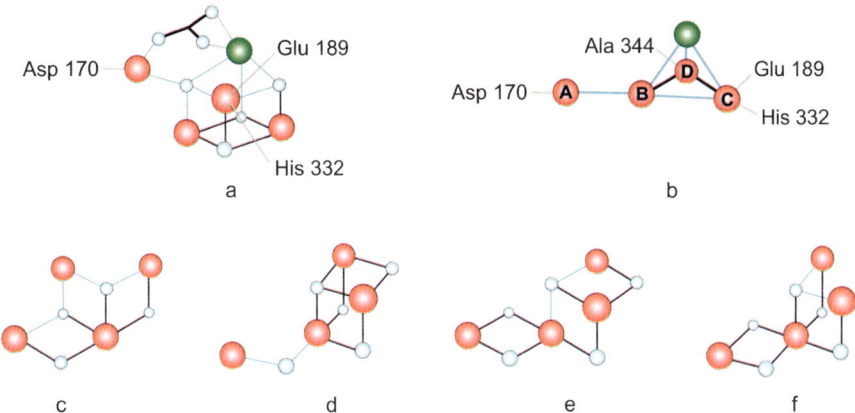

Figure 4. Proposed structures of the Mn_4O_xCa complex. The red balls represent the four Mn ions, while the green ball stands for Ca^{2+}. The small blue balls indicate bridging oxygen ions. Mn–Mn distances of ca. 2.7 Å are marked by black lines, and Mn–Mn and Mn–Ca distances of ∼3.3–3.4 Å are signified by blue lines. These lines are either drawn in a way that they directly connect the respective metal centers (model b) or the participating Mn–O bonds were colored (if a bond participates in both type of distances, the line is shown in blue). Structures a [24] and b [25] were derived from XRDC studies. Model b does not contain any suggestions for the arrangement of the μ-oxo bridges. For both models only those potential ligands are indicated, which are discussed in the text. The capital letters in model b show the labeling used in the text to identify specific Mn ions. Structures c–f are based on EXAFS studies [151]. These data do not contain Ca, since the cited study did not allow it to be placed uniquely with respect to the four Mn ions. Nevertheless, EXAFS studies show two Mn–Ca interactions with a distance of about 3.4 Å and an angle to the membrane normal of <20° [125,145].

Recently polarized EXAFS measurements on three dimensionally ordered PSII single crystals from *T. elongatus* were completed for the S_1 state [153]. Together with simulations these data allowed identifying Model e (Figure 4) as the most probable structure of the Mn_4O_5 core within the Mn_4O_xCa cluster of the intact WOC. Based on these simulations this structure can be placed in two distinct orientations into the electron density maps obtained by XRDC, with correspondingly different positions for the Ca^{2+} ion and the $μ_3$-oxo bridge [153]. This small residual ambiguity of orientation and the radiation damage to the protein environment in the XRDC studies do not allow at present to derive a unique high resolution model for the complete WOC.

S_i State Dependent Structural Changes of the Mn_4O_xCa Complex. The possible structures of the Mn_4O_xCa complex presented in Figure 4(c–f) refer to the dark-stable S_1 state. With EXAFS spectroscopy the structure of the Mn_4O_xCa cluster can also be analyzed in the other S_i states. The results show that only a minor structural change occurs during the $S_1 \rightarrow S_2$ transition. By contrast, the $S_2 \rightarrow S_3$ transition is coupled to a significant rearrangement that results in the elongation of the short (∼2.7 Å) Mn–Mn vectors to 2.82 and 2.95 Å [154] (this

finding differs greatly from the results of another report [155]). In addition, the longer Mn–Mn and Mn–Ca vectors increase by about 0.1 Å. Interestingly, this coincides with the earlier finding, that the binding affinity of Ca^{2+} is lowest in the S_3 state (compared with S_2, S_1 and S_0) [156]. Structural changes of the Mn_4O_xCa cluster during the $S_2 \to S_3$ transition were also inferred on the basis of (i) the finding that the S_3 state is much less reactive towards exogenous reductants like hydroxylamine and hydrazine than the S_2 state and even the S_0 and S_1 states [85,157] and (ii) that the reorganization energy for the $S_2 \to S_3$ transition (1.6 eV) is much higher than for $S_0 \to S_1$ (0.65 eV) and $S_1 \to S_2$ (0.63 eV) [133,158].

Bond elongation in the S_3 state is not easily reconcilable with a Mn-centered oxidation step because in this case a strengthening of Mn–Mn bond is expected. Therefore, a ligand-centered reaction appears to be more likely for the $S_2 \to S_3$ transition, e.g., a delocalized μ-oxo bridge radical (see below). In this regard, interestingly, the ~3.3–3.4 Å Mn–Mn and Mn–Ca distances are also reported to increase by about 0.04–0.2 Å during the $S_2 \to S_3$ transition [154].

In addition, the $S_3 \to S_0$ and $S_0 \to S_1$ transitions are accompanied by structural changes within the Mn_4O_xCa cluster. Compared with S_1, one of the short Mn–Mn distances is elongated in S_0 to about 2.85 Å. This finding is straightforwardly interpreted by assuming that one μ-oxo bridge is protonated in S_0 [159] and loses its proton during the $S_0 \to S_1$ transition [148,155]. In general terms, this "breathing" of the Mn_4O_xCa complex reflects its direct involvement in the water oxidation chemistry.

Electronic Structure of the WOC. A deeper understanding of the functioning of the WOC requires identification of the electronic configuration of each S_i state. For the sake of clarity in the discussion of the reactions of the WOC, it is useful to, conceptually, divide the WOC into several components: WOC = M (metal) + L (all ligands except substrate) + W (substrate "water"). With this definition, the S_i states can be specifically described as: $S_i[M_jL_kW_l]$, with $i = j + k + l$. In some cases it is convenient to neglect the distinction between (a) oxidation of M and L, and to write $S_i[(ML)_mW_l]$, with $m = j + k$ or (b) ligands and substrate, i.e., $S_i[M_j(LW)_n]$ with $n = k + l$. For example, a ligand-centered oxidation during the $S_2 \to S_3$ transition can be expressed as $S_2[M_2(LW)_0] \to S_3[M_2(LW)_1]$, while the possibility of a metal-centered oxidation during this transition is written as $S_2[M_2(LW)_0] \to S_3[M_3(LW)_0]$. The symbols j, k, l, m, n are used as integers. In general the relation between these numbers and the electron/spin density of individual atoms of M, L and W is rather complex. Quantum chemical calculations are required to establish the probabilities for the electron hole to reside on the different components of the WOC in a particular S_i state.

For metal-centered oxidations it is also important to know if mixed valence states of the manganese in the WOC are trapped or delocalized. Trapped mixed valence states exist in essentially all Mn model compounds that are relevant for the Mn_4O_xCa cluster in PS II (for a review see [160]), while in iron-sulfur clusters the states are usually delocalized [161]. Recent resonant inelastic X-ray scattering (RIXS) experiments on the S_1 and S_2 states were interpreted to show that the electron that is removed from the S_1 state originates from a delocalized orbital [162]. This raises the possibility that also in the mixed valence states S_0 and S_2 some delocalization exists. However, low temperature EPR/ENDOR data can be successfully interpreted by assuming trapped valences [163,164]. If trapped mixed valence states can be assumed to exist also at room temperature, then it is mechanistically relevant to identify the individual Mn ions that are oxidized during the different S_i state transitions.

The electronic configuration of the Mn_4O_xCa complex can best be probed by XANES, EPR and ^{55}Mn ENDOR spectroscopies. A cornerstone in analyzing this complex was the discovery that the S_2 state displays at cryogenic temperatures ($\sim$ 10 K) a $g=2$ EPR multiline signal [165]. Later it was shown that the S_0 state is also paramagnetic ($S=1/2$), displaying a different EPR multiline signal [166–168]. The origin of the multiline signals is the coupling of the spin of an unpaired electron with the nuclear spin of manganese ions ($I=5/2$). The number of lines and the spectral width prove that the S_0 and S_2 states are mixed valence states of four magnetically coupled manganese centers [163,169,170]. XANES spectroscopy studies at the Mn K-edge provide clear independent evidence that the $S_0 \to S_1$ and $S_1 \to S_2$ transitions are metal (manganese) centered (see [92] and references therein). Therefore, these reactions can be specified as $S_0[M_0(LW)_0] \to S_1[M_1(LW)_0]$ and $S_1[M_1(LW)_0] \to S_2[M_2(LW)_0]$, respectively (Figure 5). Furthermore, a comparison of the XANES spectra with those of synthetic model complexes and the ^{55}Mn ENDOR data (see below) indicate that the overall oxidation state of the manganese is $Mn_4(III,III,IV,IV)$ in the S_1 state [15,163,169].

In principle, the S_2 and S_0 EPR spectra also contain the information on the coupling of the individual Mn ions in the Mn_4O_xCa complex and, thereby, about its structure. However, due to the large number of free parameters, it has proven to be impossible to extract reliable information from fitting X-band EPR spectra without having further solid constraints. Reliable effective J couplings for the S_2 and S_0 states have only recently been determined for the S_2 [163,169] and S_0 states [169] by ^{55}Mn ENDOR spectroscopy at X- and Q-band frequencies. Detailed analysis of the Q-band S_0 ^{55}Mn ENDOR spectra excludes the presence of Mn(II) in the S_0 state ([169] and Kulik et al., unpublished results). This finding shows that the oxidation states for S_0 and S_2 are $Mn_4(III,III,III,IV)$ and $Mn_4(III,IV,IV,IV)$, respectively, in line with the above assignment of $Mn_4(III,III,IV,IV)$ to the S_1 state. Therefore, an alternative proposal of $Mn_4(III,III,III,III)$ for S_1 [171,172] can be excluded.

The electronic structure of the S_3 state is more complicated to assess. Even though agreement has been reached on the XANES spectra of the pure S_i states [92,155], it is still not clarified whether the $S_2 \to S_3$ transition is a ligand- or a Mn-centered oxidation. On the basis of several lines of evidence (reviewed in [38,92,112]) we favor the idea of a ligand-centered oxidation, i.e., $S_2[M_2(LW)_0] \to S_3[M_2(LW)_1]$ (Figure 5, path II). The key findings in support of a ligand-centered oxidation for this transition are (for a review see [173]): (i) the smaller shift of the XANES edges (on the basis of second derivatives)

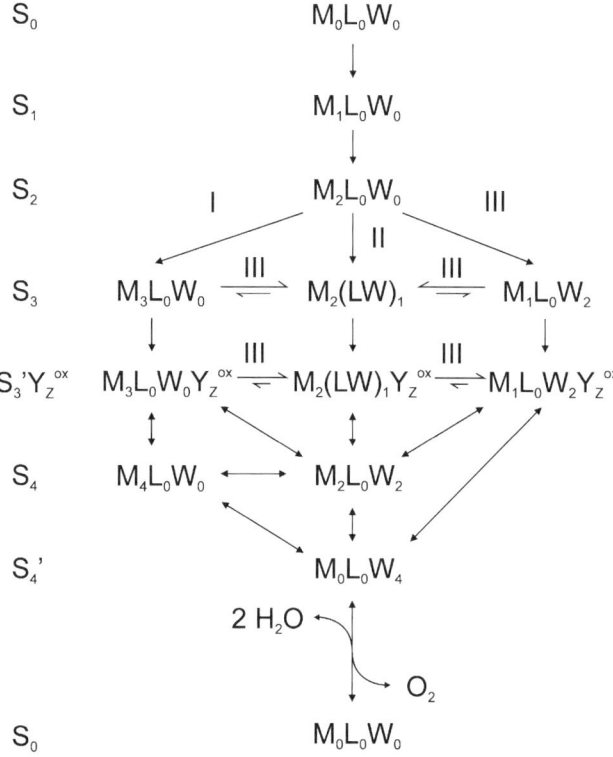

Figure 5. Formal representation of the nature of S_i state transitions. Metal (M)-centered oxidations occur during the $S_0 \rightarrow S_1$ and $S_1 \rightarrow S_2$ transitions. This is indicated by an incremental increase of the corresponding index. For simplicity fully metal-centered oxidations are assumed. For the subsequent transitions several different proposals have been put forward in the literature, which may also involve ligand (L) or substrate water (W) oxidation. For details see the text.

during the $S_2 \rightarrow S_3$ transition [92], (ii) the smaller shift in Kβ XES (X-ray emission spectroscopy) experiments for the $S_2 \rightarrow S_3$ transition compared with $S_1 \rightarrow S_2$ transition [92], (iii) the above (Section 17.4.2.1; S_i state dependent structural changes of the Mn_4O_xCa complex) discussed elongation of all Mn–Mn and Mn–Ca distances during this transition [154] and (iv) the higher reactivity of the S_3 state with NO· compared with that of the S_2 state [174], which contrasts the order of reactivity found with NH_2OH and NH_2NH_2 [85] (see also previous section). A specific suggestion is the interpretation of the ligand-centered reaction as a μ-oxo bridge oxidation [92]. Such an oxidation would lead to a weakening of the bridge and thereby to its elongation. Recent DFT calculations support this idea and show that, indeed, more than one bond may be elongated by one μ-oxo bridge radical, due to trans effects. However, a more substantial structural rearrangement also appears possible, and such a rearrangement may also include the preformation of the O–O bond in part of the centers (Figure 5, path III). In this type of mechanism the S_3 state is viewed as a multi-state system (Section 17.6.3; [112,175]). The often discussed possibility that also the $S_2 \rightarrow S_3$ state transition consists of a Mn-centered oxidation is illustrated in path I of Figure 5. However, based on our current state of knowledge this pathway appears to be a less likely option (for a discussion, see [176]). The subsequent reactions leading to the O–O bond formation are discussed in Section 17.6. Evidently, from Figure 5, full knowledge of the electronic and geometric structure of the S_3 state is a prerequisite for understanding photosynthetic water splitting.

17.4.2.2 Chloride and Hydrogencarbonate
Chloride (Cl^-) and hydrogencarbonate (also referred to as bicarbonate, HCO_3^-) have been discussed as ligands of the WOC and/or as cofactors during water splitting. Several biochemical studies show that Cl^- is of functional relevance, especially for the $S_2 \rightarrow S_3$ and $S_3 \rightarrow S_0$ transitions. Furthermore, the binding affinity is known to be at least $10\times$ lower in the S_2 and S_3 states than that in the S_1 state (for a review see [13]). Chloride can be functionally replaced by other anions with an order of efficiency of $Br^- (= Cl^-) >> NO_3^- > NO_2^- > I^-$. The fact that the easily oxidizable I^- can replace Cl^- has been used to argue against a direct binding to Mn [177,178]. Nevertheless, substitution of Cl^- by other anions usually slows the S_i state turnover and/or the Y_Z^{OX} reduction kinetics [179–181]. These results are suggestive of Cl^- binding within the WOC. Recently, EPR based evidence for a Cl^-/Br^- binding side at or near the nonheme iron was also reported [181].

Analysis of the role of hydrogencarbonate is even more complicated. Detailed studies revealed that this anion affects the reactions of the acceptor side [182] by binding at the nonheme iron. This acceptor side effect complicates the search for specific effects on the Mn_4O_xCa cluster. Nevertheless, detailed studies suggest that hydrogencarbonate also affects the donor side reactions (for a review see [183]).

At present, firm experimental evidence for direct binding at the Mn_4O_xCa complex exists neither for Cl^- nor for HCO_3^-. Experiments with radioactively labeled Cl^- demonstrate the specific binding of one Cl^- per PS II [184]. In addition, a possible signature for Cl^- has been reported on the basis of EXAFS measurements on oriented S_3 state samples [14]. However, FTIR data suggest that Cl^- is not a direct ligand to manganese [185]. This idea is supported by X-ray spectroscopy measurements on bromine reconstituted Cl^- depleted PSII membrane fragments [186]. Hydrogencarbonate was modeled to bind at the Mn_4O_xCa cluster in the XRDC structure of Ferreira with 3.5 Å resolution [24]. This assignment has not been confirmed in the later 3.0 Å XRDC structure [25]. Because of the remaining uncertainties both Cl^- and HCO_3^- will not be explicitly considered in the mechanism for oxidative water splitting in Section 17.6.

Possible functions that are discussed for Cl^- include: (i) participation in proton shuttling from the WOC to the lumen (as part of a proton relay network) [178], (ii) charge balancing of the Mn_4O_xCa cluster by only binding in certain S_i states [187–191], (iii) tuning the redox potential of the Mn_4O_xCa cluster [192], (iv) preventing the binding of harder ligands such as OH^- to the Mn_4O_xCa cluster [13] and (v) supporting functionally relevant structural changes in the protein backbone during S_i state transitions [193]. Similar suggestions have also been made for the role of hydrogencarbonate [183]. Furthermore, there is a long standing discussion on the possibility of HCO_3^- being the direct electron donor to the Mn_4O_xCa cluster instead of water. In such proposals oxidative hydrogencarbonate splitting leads to CO_2 formation and hydrogencarbonate is restored by rehydration of CO_2 through the carbonic anhydrase activity that was found to exist in PS II (reviewed in [194]). Notably, in this model water is still the ultimate source of photosynthetic oxygen but is not the direct substrate of the WOC. Recent results unambiguously show, however, that water is the sole and direct substrate for photosynthetic oxygen evolution [195,196].

17.4.2.3 Substrate Water Binding
The most direct information on binding/exchange of substrate water molecules to the WOC was gathered from mass spectrometric detection of oxygen evolution after rapid replacement of $H_2^{16}O$ by $H_2^{18}O$ in the sample (for a review, see [38]). To study, for example, water binding in the S_3 state the PS II samples suspended in normal $H_2^{16}O$ containing buffer are illuminated with two single turnover flashes, so that any substrate water-binding site present in the WOC will be occupied with $H_2^{16}O$ (or $H^{16}O^-$ or $^{16}O^{2-}$). The exchangeability of the substrate water is then probed by rapid injection and mixing (ms time scale) of $H_2^{18}O$ at various exchange times (t_{ex}) before excitation with the third flash, which leads to O_2 evolution (left-hand side of Figure 6). The key point of this method is the rapid mixing to achieve the shortest possible times for t_{ex}. Original attempts [197,198] failed due to the much too long t_{ex} values, and only the achievement of Messinger et al. [199] paved the way to resolving the kinetics of substrate water in the WOC at different redox states S_i. The flash-induced evolution of molecular oxygen is detected online by membrane inlet mass spectrometry, which allows monitoring of O_2 evolution at all three different mass peaks of ^{18}O-enriched molecular oxygen [38,199,200]. The time course of

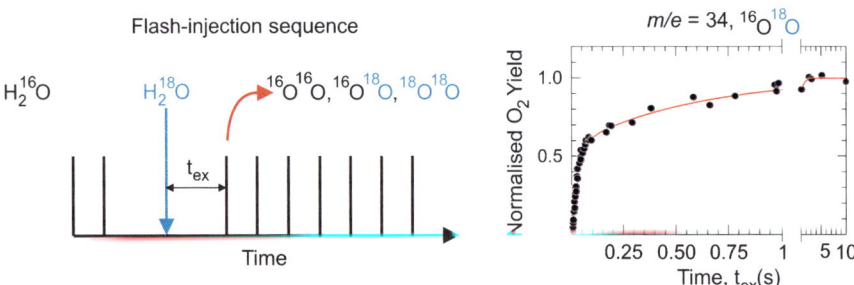

Figure 6. Left: Flash-$H_2^{18}O$-injection sequence used to determine substrate water exchange kinetics in the S_3 state of PS II. Right: Example of an experimental result for the S_3 state where the exchange was monitored at m/z 34 (singly labeled O_2). The red curve represents a bi-exponential fit to the sequentially recorded data points (each data point is obtained by a separate "pump-probe" experiment). For details see text and [288].

Table 1. $H_2^{18}O$ Exchange rates from thylakoid membranes at 10 °C

Phase of exchange	S_0 state	S_1 state	S_2 state	S_3 state
Fast, k_f (s^{-1})	–	–	118.8 ± 3.6	37.5 ± 1.6
Slow, k_s (s^{-1})	13.6 ± 1.4	0.022 ± 0.001	1.96 ± 0.12	2.02 ± 0.06

Data from Hillier and Wydrzynski [289].

$^{16}O^{18}O$ (m/z 34) evolution reveals two distinct kinetic phases (right-hand panel of Figure 6), which reflect the exchange rates of the two substrate water molecules and show that the two binding sites are different (for a review, see [38]). Similar measurements on the S_0, S_1, and S_2 states reveal that the exchange rates of the two substrate molecules vary independently with the S_i state (Table 1). This finding further supports the idea that two separate binding sites exist for the two substrate molecules. Based on a normalization to the rate of the slowly exchanging substrate water molecule (W_s) in the S_1 state, the other S_i states exhibit, in spinach thylakoids, relative exchange rates of 600:1:100:100 ($S_0:S_1:S_2:S_3$), while the relative values for the fast exchanging substrate molecules (W_f) are 5000 and 2000 in S_2 and S_3, respectively. So far, binding of the fast exchanging substrate molecule could not be detected in the S_0 and S_1 states, possibly due to kinetic limitations of the set up. Similar experiments on Sr^{2+} substituted PS II samples indicate the involvement of Ca^{2+} in the binding of the slow substrate molecule [124].

Under the assumption that the substrate water exchange rates are not limited by diffusion, they contain information about the binding mode of the substrate molecules. For the slower exchanging substrate this assumption is evidently correct (unless there is a separate, less-permeable diffusion path for W_s). If one also accepts that the permeability of a diffusion path should be independent of the S_i state, it appears also unlikely that the exchange rates of W_f is diffusion controlled.

On the basis of (i) the clear S_i state dependence and (ii) the strong influence of replacing Ca^{2+} by Sr^{2+} (vide supra), the substrate water exchange experiments suggest substrate binding at the Mn_4O_xCa cluster. However, strictly speaking they only prove binding within the WOC. The protonation state and the mode of binding (terminal or bridging) of the substrate molecules and the binding to a specific Mn and/or Ca^{2+} site cannot be directly determined on the basis of this approach. Other techniques such as EPR, ENDOR, NMR, FTIR and XANES are required to address these points. Results obtained with these techniques have recently been reviewed in great detail [38,201]. Therefore, only the most pertinent results are mentioned here.

One fairly solid conclusion is the absence of terminal oxo moieties such as, for example, Mn(IV)=O or Mn(V)=O in all states from S_0 up to S_3. This conclusion is based on a comparison of XANES pre-edge features of Mn model compounds [202] with those measured in PS II samples [92,155,203]. Time-resolved EXAFS experiments suggest [204] that a terminal oxo group is also absent in the S_4 state (Section 17.6). These results do not exclude binding of the substrate in form of an oxo bridge between either two manganese or Mn and Ca^{2+}. Recent time-resolved electro spray mass spectrometry experiments [205,206] indicate that conventional Mn-O-Mn bridges exchange slower in model systems than observed for the slow phase of the water exchange in PSII (Table 1). However, firm conclusions are not possible at present for the following reasons: 1) only a very small number of synthetic complexes were studied so far and 2) the experiments are obtained for clusters that are embedded in a quite different environment (acetonitrile with only a few percent water) compared with that of the protein, where specific H-bonds, or additional terminally bound water ligands may facilitate the exchange reactions. The idea that at least one of the substrate molecules is partially protonated up to the S_3 state and bound to Mn is supported by H/D exchange ESEEM and ENDOR measurements (for a review see [38,201]) as well as by NMR PRE (proton relaxation enhancement) experiments [207]. Direct binding of the substrate to Mn is also supported by a recent ^{17}O ESEEM experiment [208]. Specific suggestions about the mode of substrate binding to the Mn_4O_xCa complex are discussed in Section 17.6.

17.4.2.4 Protein Ligands of the Mn_4O_xCa Cluster
In addition to the metal centers and their connecting oxo bridges, the protein ligands are critical components of the WOC. They tune the redox potential of the Mn_4O_xCa cluster and allow structural changes of the cluster during the Kok cycle. Additional functions of the ligands and of the protein matrix in general are the control of both the access of water to the catalytic site and the release of the products O_2 and H^+ away from the WOC. The XRDC study of Loll et al. [25] has identified D1Asp170, D1Glu189, D1His332, D1Glu333, D1Asp342, the C-terminus of D1 protein D1Ala344 and CP43Glu354 as ligands to the Mn_4O_xCa cluster (see also Chapter 15). The Ca^{2+} is shown to be ligated by D1Glu189 and D1Ala344. Both residues are assumed to be bidentate ligands, bridging Ca^{2+} with Mn [25]. Many of these assignments are consistent with previous mutagenesis experiments; however, some critical discrepancies exist (for details, see [209]). As illustrative examples, D1His337 was proposed to be a Mn ligand on the basis of mutagenesis studies, but according to recent XRDC studies it is too far from the cluster [25]. Furthermore, the assignment of the C-terminal carboxylate of Ala-344 as a ligand to Ca^{2+} according to XDRC [25] is hardly reconcilable with FTIR data gathered from Sr^{2+}/Ca^{2+} substituted samples [126].

Likewise, mutagenesis results are best explained by assuming that D1Glu189 is an important part in the H-bonding network of PS II [210,211] rather than a Mn ligand as suggested by XRDC [24,25]. However, a recent FTIR study provides evidence for the ligation of D1Glu189 to a Mn ion that is affected by the $S_1 \to S_2$ transition [212]. Some of these discrepancies may be due to structural changes of the Mn_4O_xCa complex and of its ligand environment caused by radiation damage during XRDC [142]. On the other hand, mutagenesis studies can also be misleading due to unexpected compensatory structural changes or allosteric effects, as illustrated in bacterial reaction centers (Chapter 11).

Despite the described discrepancies in the experimental data, which result in uncertainties about the exact coordination sphere of the Mn_4O_xCa cluster, the combination of site-directed mutagenesis and FTIR spectroscopy has become a powerful tool for studying the mechanism of water splitting in PS II. For the following discussion of the ligand sphere of the Mn_4O_xCa cluster we refer to the XRDC structure of Loll et al. [25] and number the Mn ions A, B, C, D (Figure 4b). Recent FTIR studies show that (i) D1Asp170 is ligated to a Mn (MnA) that does not change its oxidation state up to the S_3 state [213], (ii) the C-terminus D1Ala344 is ligated to a Mn (MnD) that is oxidized during the $S_1 \rightarrow S_2$ transition and rereduced in the transition from S_3 to S_0 [214,215] (iii) D1His332 is ligated to a Mn (MnC) that is sensitive to structural changes of the Mn_4O_xCa complex during the S_i state transitions, but is not oxidized up to the S_3 state [216] and (iv) Asp 342 does not ligate a manganese that undergoes redox changes from S_0 up to S_3 [217]. As mentioned above, D1Glu189 was also assigned recently to bind to a Mn that is affected during the $S_1 \rightarrow S_2$ transition [212]. Since the XRDC studies indicate ligation of this residue to MnC [25], this results appears to be in conflict with points (ii) and (iii). Further studies are required to untangle the complex vibrational, structural and electronic coupling within the WOC. It cannot be ruled out that more than one Mn and its ligands are affected by a specific S_i state transition.

17.4.2.5 Tyrosine Z and the Proton Network
In addition to the amino acids in the first coordination sphere of the Mn_4O_xCa cluster, Y_Z and its environment can also be considered to be part of the WOC. A direct participation of Y_Z in water splitting via H-atom abstraction [218] is unlikely because of the long $Mn-Y_Z$ distance (~ 8 Å), but H-atom abstraction via an intervening group such as a water molecule remains an option for certain S_i state transitions [112,219].

The relevance of the coupling between proton and electron transfer in the WOC and for the proton relay network is shown by recent EPR data on so-called split signals. These EPR signals originate from the magnetic coupling of Y_Z^{OX} with the Mn_4O_xCa cluster. Accordingly they can be observed under conditions where the reduction of Y_Z^{OX} by the Mn_4O_xCa cluster and/or by Q_A^- is not possible or slowed down. The $S_2Y_Z^{OX}$ signal was first reported in Ca^{2+} depleted PS II [220,221]. However, more informative are data obtained with intact samples, in which split signals can be generated in various S_i states by visible and/or IR illumination at ~ 10 K [222–225]. A recent scheme rationalizing the generation of these "low temperature split signals" ([226], see also [227,228]) considers the presence of two bases in addition to the Mn_4O_xCa cluster, Y_Z and Q_A. One base is postulated to accept a proton from the substrate during the $S_1 \rightarrow S_2$ transition, thereby explaining the positive net charge reported for the S_2 and S_3 states [76,229–232], and the other base is thought to change its pK in response to the positive net charge of the WOC and to form an H-bond with the OH group of Y_Z (see also [77]). The central idea of this scheme is that the positive net charge is required to allow reprotonation and reduction of Y_Z^{OX} during the $S_2 \rightarrow S_3$ transition. With the assumption that alkaline pH conditions lead to a loss of the positive net charge in the WOC and considering that the added artificial electron acceptors oxidizes Q_A^- at room temperature to Q_A, this scheme can be extended to also explain the long room temperature life time (2.2 min) of the $S_2Y_Z^{OX}$ split signal that can be generated from the S_3 state by incubation at pH 8.0 [227]. Regardless of whether all details of this scheme and the discussed experiments are correct, the currently available information clearly shows that the complex water oxidation machinery of PSII critically depends on local proton gradients. The function of the WOC can already be stalled if a single proton is not in its proper place.

17.5 Kinetics

The Kok cycle in the WOC is energetically driven by $P680^{+\bullet}$ with Y_Z acting as intermediary redox component. Accordingly, the overall kinetics of oxidative water splitting consist of (i) the redox reactions, which lead to the formation of Y_Z^{OX} by $P680^{+\bullet}$ and to the subsequent S_i state transitions driven by Y_Z^{OX}, and (ii) the pathways of substrate/product exchange. The surprisingly complex kinetics of $P680^{+\bullet}$ reduction by Y_Z and the underlying mechanism of different types of rate limitation have been described in Chapter 16 in detail. Likewise, the substrate exchange is discussed in Section 17.4.2.3. Therefore, this section focuses on the kinetic properties of the S_i state transitions.

17.5.1 Kinetics of S_i State Transitions

Information on the kinetics of Y_Z^{OX} reduction and the concomitant oxidative S_i state transitions have been obtained by using different types of transient spectroscopy. In all cases the Kok cycle (Section 17.2) provides the fingerprint for the assignment of the experimentally detected time courses to the kinetics of an individual reaction.

A most suitable tool for monitoring the turnover of Y_Z^{OX} reduction is time-resolved EPR spectroscopy, because the radical state of the oxidized species gives rise to a characteristic signal [233–235]. First kinetic information using this method was obtained by Babcock et al. (1976) [236]. Despite restricted time resolution, three important conclusions could be gathered from these original data: (i) the time constants of the S_i state transitions in the Kok cycle cover a range of $\leq 100\,\mu s$ to 1 ms, (ii) the rate constant depends on the redox state S_i and (iii) the time constant of Y_Z^{OX} reduction by the WOC in redox state S_3 virtually coincides with the time for the formation of molecular oxygen that was earlier determined by amperometric measurements [237,238]. The latter finding (iii) was one of the cornerstones for the later development of the "hydrogen atom abstractor" hypothesis by Babcock and co-workers [191,218]. It took almost 20 years before significant progress could be achieved in sufficient improvement of the time resolution to monitor the kinetics of Y_Z^{OX} reduction with satisfying precision [239]. Table 2 summarizes the results obtained.

Table 2. Half life times (µs) of the reactions $Y_Z^{OX}S_i \rightarrow Y_ZS_{i+1-4\delta_{i3}} + \delta_{i3}O_2 + n_iH$ ($\delta_{i3} = 1$ for $i = 3$, otherwise zero) in thylakoids, PS II membrane fragments (m.f.) and PS II core complexes

Reaction	Y_Z^{OX} reduction		S_i state oxidation		
Species	Spinach		Spinach		T. vulcanus
Preparation	Thylakoids	PS II m.f.	PS II m.f.	PS II core	PS II core
Temperature (°C)	8–10	8–10	20	20	25
Reference	[239]	[239]	[158]	[250]	[249]
i = 0	40–60	70	50	Not determined	Not determined
i = 1	85	110	100	75	70
i = 2	140	180	220	225	120–150
i = 3	750	1400	1300	4100	1300

The same method cannot be used to monitor the kinetics of the S_i state transitions because characteristic EPR signals are observed only at cryogenic temperatures (Section 17.4.2.1) where the reactions of the WOC are blocked [58,240]. However, the turnover of the WOC at physiological temperatures gives rise to absorption changes in the near-UV [241,242]. A resolution of difference spectra and assignment to individual S_i state transitions is rather difficult due to interference by effects emerging from the rapid loss of synchronized S_i state transitions, as it is reflected by the damping of the characteristic period four oscillation of flash-induced oxygen evolution in dark-adapted samples (vide supra), and owing to overlapping absorption changes that reflect the turnover of $Q_A(Q_B)$ [243]. Therefore, unsurprisingly, the difference spectra gathered from high quality experimental data exhibit marked differences [244,245]. Furthermore, the rather broad and structureless bands of these spectra do not provide much information on the electronic structure of the S_i states [36]. In contrast, the time course of the flash-induced absorption changes in the range 350–360 nm offer a most suitable tool to monitor the individual S_i state transitions because at these wavelengths $\Delta\varepsilon(Y_Z^{OX}/Y_Z)$ is negligibly small. The results obtained by different groups are very similar [244,246,247]. The oxidation steps $S_i \rightarrow S_{i+1}$ can be described by monoexponential kinetics. Typical values of the time constants (half-lives) are compiled in Table 2. Similar data were also obtained recently by time-resolved XANES experiments at room temperature [204]. Inspection of Table 2 readily reveals a striking coincidence between the kinetics of Y_Z^{OX} reduction and S_i state oxidation steps up to $S_2 \rightarrow S_3$. This result indicates that Y_Z^{OX} is the direct oxidant of the Mn_4O_xCa cluster.

A remarkably different and less clear picture emerges for the kinetics of the reaction $Y_Z^{OX} S_3 \rightarrow \rightarrow Y_ZS_0 + O_2 + nH^+$. Firstly, inspection of Table 2 reveals that the kinetics of the $Y_Z^{OX}S_i \rightarrow Y_ZS_{i+1}$ reactions are similar for $i = 0, 1, 2$ (variation by factors of 2–4), but the reaction of $Y_Z^{OX}S_3$ is slower by factors of 5–20 than the former reactions. Secondly, the $Y_Z^{OX}S_3$ decay kinetics are particularly sensitive to structural changes induced by different sample modifications. Compared with spinach thylakoids with a half-life of $Y_Z^{OX}S_3$ of about 0.75–1.0 ms [236,239,241,242,247], PS II membrane fragments exhibit a retardation to 1.3–1.5 ms [158,244,246,248]. A similar value was found for PS II preparations from the thermophilic cyanobacterium *T. vulcanus* [249]. In PS II core complexes from spinach, which are deprived of the extrinsic regulatory subunits PsbP and PsbQ, the $t_{1/2}$ increases to 4–5 ms at room temperature [250,251]. The high susceptibility of this reaction to kinetic retardation is nicely illustrated for a *Synechocystis* PCC 6803 mutant, where replacement of Asp-61 in polypeptide D1 either by Ala or Asn, leads to retardation factors of 8 and 10, respectively, while an exchange to Gln is virtually without effect [252]. In contrast, the kinetics of the other S_i state transitions are much less affected. Likewise treatment of *Arabidopsis thaliana* thylakoids with phospholipase A_2 drastically (factor 9) retards Y_Z^{OX} reduction by the WOC in redox state S_3, while much less pronounced effects (factor 3) are observed for the other S_i states [253]. These findings reflect special properties of the reactions that take place after $Y_Z^{OX}S_3$ formation (Section 17.6).

Replacement of Ca^{2+} by Sr^{2+} gives rise to a retardation of all S_i state transitions by factors of 3–5 [123,254]. This finding is indicative for the existence of kinetic modulation by structural changes, which might be related to changes in the hydrogen bond network involved in the redox reactions [123] and fine tuning of the redox properties [254]. It was also taken as evidence for a strong coupling of electron and proton transfer reaction [123]. According to recent X-ray structure data [25] Y_Z is very close to Ca^{2+} and may, therefore, be H-bonded with a water ligated to Ca^{2+}. Such an arrangement may explain the global kinetic effects on Y_Z^{OX} reduction in all S_i state transitions caused by the replacement of Ca^{2+} by Sr^{2+}. Interestingly, the kinetics of $P680^{+\cdot}$ reduction by Y_Z also depend on the presence of Ca^{2+}/Sr^{2+} in oxygen-evolving PS II membrane fragments [255]. Thirdly, the Y_Z^{OX} reduction by S_3 seems to be characterized by a sigmoidal kinetics in PS II membrane fragments from spinach [244,246,247] and PS II preparations from *T. vulcanus* [249] and *Synechocystis* [251]. The lag phase of these kinetics, however, might be an artifact due to the scrambling of different S_i state transitions in the 3rd flash [250]. Therefore, the existence and extent of a "true" lag phase are not yet clarified. A comparative study of Y_Z^{OX} reduction (monitored via time-resolved EPR spectroscopy) and O_2 release (detected by time-resolved EPR with a spin label) revealed that in intact thylakoids the kinetics of both reactions are virtually the same and a lag phase can be no longer than 50 µs. Longer lag phases for O_2 evolution of up to 200 µs were observed with thylakoids under non-physiological conditions [256]. Based on room-temperature XANES measurements a lag phase of 250 µs was reported recently [204]. Presently, it appears possible that this comparatively long lag time might be an artifact, caused, for example, by the partial drying of the samples [98] (for a discussion, see [176]).

Rappaport et al. [244] reported a lag phase of about 30 µs as being indicative for a proton release preceding an electron transfer step during the $S_3 \rightarrow S_4$ transition, which eventually leads to O_2 formation (Section 17.6). This interpretation raises questions as to the nature of this protolytic reaction. One possibility is that a proton shift takes place within the protein environment comprising a tautomerism equilibrium (see Figure 8 in Section 17.6.4.1, reaction III) [112,175]. Importantly, a proton shift does not lead to a redox change in the Mn_4O_xCa cluster (in contrast to H-atom transfer). Therefore, such a possible intermediate state should not be considered to be a S_4 state, but should instead be denoted as S_3'.

17.5.2 Activation Energies of S_i State Transitions

The activation energies of the reactions $Y_Z^{OX}S_i \rightarrow Y_ZS_{i+1-4\delta_{i3}} + \delta_{i3}O_2 + n_iH^+$ ($i=0,\ldots 3$) were determined by measuring the temperature dependence of the time course of UV absorption changes, which are induced by a train of single turnover flashes in dark-adapted samples. The measurements were restricted to the physiological temperature range where oxygen evolution takes place. This range is rather narrow, because the upper limit is given by the thermal degradation of the WOC, which depends on the sample material, and the lower limit is determined by "freezing" of the WOC turnover. The results obtained for different sample types are compiled in Table 3, which additionally presents the threshold temperatures for 50% blockage of S_i state turnovers by freezing. Inspection of these data reveals: (i) the activation energy of S_i state transitions increases with redox state S_i of the WOC, (ii) the activation energies are very similar in PS II preparations from thermophilic cyanobacteria (*T. vulcanus*) and higher plants (spinach), (iii) the activation energies are virtually independent of the presence of the regulatory subunits PsbP and PsbQ (spinach PS II core complexes are, in contrast to PS II membrane fragments, deprived of these two extrinsic proteins, while cores from *T. vulcanus* contain subunits PsbV and PsbU instead of PsbP and PsbQ).

In *T. vulcanus* a striking break point was observed in the Arrhenius plot of the reaction $Y_Z^{OX}S_3 \rightarrow Y_ZS_0 + O_2 + nH^+$ [249]. This feature was also detected in PS II preparations from spinach, but it was less pronounced [158], and could not be found in another study [251]. Possibly, the break point in samples from mesophilic organisms is shifted towards lower temperatures and/or is less pronounced so that it often escapes detection. Therefore, the existence and extent of the break point as a general phenomenon remain to be clarified.

Table 3. Activation energies (E_A, kJ mol^{-1}) and temperature threshold for 50% blockage ($\vartheta_{1/2}$, °C) by freezing of the reactions: $Y_Z^{OX}S_i \rightarrow Y_ZS_{i+1-4\delta_{i3}} + \delta_{i3}O_2 + n_iH^+$ ($\delta_{i3}=1$ for $i=3$, otherwise zero)

	T. vulcanus PS II core		Spinach PS II membrane fragments		PS II core	
i	E_A (kJ mol^{-1}) [249]	$\vartheta_{1/2}$ (°C) [240]	E_A (kJ mol^{-1}) [158]	$\vartheta_{1/2}$ (°C) [58,278,290]	E_A (kJ mol^{-1}) [250]	$\vartheta_{1/2}$ (°C) [20]
0	N.d.[a]	N.d.	5	~−50	N.d.	N.d.
1	9.6	~−90	12.0	~−135	14.8	~−100
2	26.8	~−16	36.0	~−45	35.0	~−50
3	15.5/59.4[b]	~−10	20/46.0[b]	~−40	21/67.0[b]	N.d.

[a]Not determined.
[b]The two values for $i=3$ are gathered from the Arrhenius plots with breakpoints (above/below). Values of reports without break point phenomenon are about 30 kJ mol^{-1} (see [251]).

The activation energies of the forward reactions are rather small compared with the values obtained for reductive decay reactions of S_2 and S_3, which are 3–4 orders of magnitude slower than the oxidation steps of the WOC. These reactions exhibit activation energies in the range 45–70 kJ mol^{-1} for the "fast" reduction (a few seconds at 20 °C) of S_2 and S_3 by Y_D, and 60–100 kJ mol^{-1} for the "slow" reaction (order of a few minutes at 20 °C) with the acceptor side. The values depend on the sample material [54,56,60]. The "very slow" dark oxidation of S_0 by Y_D^{OX} (about 10 min at 20 °C) is characterized by an activation energy of 30 kJ mol^{-1} in thylakoids from both *T. elongatus* and spinach [56,60].

17.5.3 Kinetic Isotope Effects (KIE)

Kinetic isotope effects (KIE) due to replacement of exchangeable protons by deuterons were measured in different sample material and generally found to be rather small. In PS II membrane fragments from spinach the $k_i(H)/k_i(D)$ values obtained are in the range 1.3–1.4 [250,257,258] for $i = 1$, 2 and 3. Slightly larger values of 1.5–2.5 were found for PS II core complexes [250,259]. A kinetic retardation owing to H/D isotope exchange can originate from different effects (for reviews, see [260]). A primary isotope effect would consist of breaking of an X–H bond as rate-limiting step. In this case the ratio $k_i(H)/k_i(D)$ depends on the difference of the zero-point energies, i.e., the strength of this bond, and isotope effects of the order of 10 are expected. The values observed for the S_i state transitions are in the range 1.1–2.5 and, therefore, are too small for a primary isotope effect. This indicates that the rate constants may be limited by the rearrangement of few hydrogen bonds rather than by the breakage of a covalent –OH or –NH bond [250]. Of mechanistic relevance is the close similarity of the KIEs of the $Y_Z^{OX}S_3 \to \to \to Y_ZS_0 + O_2 + mH^+$ reaction and the release of molecular oxygen [261], because this finding indicates that this transition is not limited in rate by the breakage of a covalent O–H bond.

With respect to small KIEs of the WOC reactions, interestingly, very similar values of 1.4 have been observed for electron transfer steps in cytochrome *c* oxidase, which catalyzes the reverse reaction, i.e., O_2 reduction to water (for a review, see [262]). These effects were interpreted to reflect the interaction between redox intermediates and protons of a basic group (BH) of the protein [263]. Therefore – despite the unresolved underlying mechanism(s) of the KIEs in the WOC – it appears to be most likely that the small values of the S_i state transitions reflect substrate/intermediate linkage to the protein matrix via hydrogen bonds, which are rearranged during S_i state transitions.

17.5.4 Reaction Coordinates

The reaction coordinate of oxidative water splitting in the WOC is given by the sequence of redox states and the energetics and activation energies of the transitions between these states. With these data and the activation energies compiled in Table 3 the reaction coordinate can be constructed (see [250]).

17.5.5 Nature of the Redox Reactions in the WOC

Redox reactions within a protein matrix give rise to changes of pK values of amino acid residues and, as a consequence, to proton uptake or release with non-stoichiometric ratios [109]. The oxidation steps $S_0 \rightarrow S_1$ and $S_1 \rightarrow S_2$ are metal-centered reactions (Section 17.4.2.1) coupled with a pH-dependent non-integer stoichiometry of proton release [264]. In marked contrast, the transition $S_2 \rightarrow S_3$ is coupled with the release of one proton over the whole range of physiological pH values [264]. These properties suggest the possibility of different reaction pathways. The internal proton release pattern is often approximated by 1:0:1:2 for the $S_0 \rightarrow S_1 \rightarrow S_2 \rightarrow S_3 \rightarrow S_0$ transitions (for review, see [38]). The lack of a proton release observed for the $S_1 \rightarrow S_2$ transition for a wide pH range leads to the accumulation of a positive charge in the WOC that has been detected on the basis of electrochromic changes [265,266]. This finding is denoted in Figure 1(B) by plus signs at the respective S_i states.

The nature of the coupling of electron and proton transfer of redox reactions in enzymes is a fundamental problem and the subject of numerous studies [267–269]. With the WOC, straightforward analyses are prevented by the present lack of sufficiently precise structural details of atomic resolution on the Mn_4O_xCa cluster and its protein environment (Sections 17.4.2.1 and 17.4.2.4).

Some information on the redox steps can be gathered from an analysis of the reaction coordinates within the framework of the Marcus theory of non-adiabatic electron transfer [270]. The rate constant of k_{ET} of the reaction is given by the eqn. (5):

$$k_{fi}^{ET} = \frac{2\pi}{\hbar}|V_{fi}(R_{DA})|^2(4\pi\lambda_{fi}k_BT)^{-\frac{1}{2}}\exp\left[-\frac{(\Delta G_{fi}^0 + \lambda_{fi})^2}{4\lambda_{fi}k_BT}\right] \quad (5)$$

where $V_{fi}(R_{DA})$ is the quantum mechanical matrix element coupling reactant (state i = initial) and product (state f = final) electronic wave function at distance R_{DA} of the interacting redox groups, λ_{fi} is the reorganization and ΔG_{fi}^0 = change of the Gibbs-energy, k_B = Boltzmann constant and $\hbar = h/2\pi$ with h = Planck constant (for details on Marcus theory, see Chapter 2).

Rearrangement of eqn. (5) and insertion of the values for $E_A(S_{i+1}/S_i)$ and $\Delta G°(S_{i+1}/S_i)$ leads to reorganization energies of 0.65–0.75 eV for the $S_0 \rightarrow S_1$ and $S_1 \rightarrow S_2$ transitions and a much larger value of 1.6 eV for $S_2 \rightarrow S_3$ [133]. For the $Y_Z^{OX}S_3$ reaction different energies are obtained, depending on the existence of the breakpoint phenomenon; values of 1.2–1.4 eV appear to be realistic. The mechanistically most interesting feature is the difference between $\lambda(S_3/S_2)$ and $\lambda(S_2/S_1)$, $\lambda(S_1/S_0)$. This finding was interpreted as an indication of significant structural changes that take place during the $S_2 \rightarrow S_3$ transition [111]. This agrees with the EXAFS data discussed above (Section 17.4.2.1, subsection on EXAFS).

Another important conclusion can be gathered from an analysis of the data within the framework of a rate constant–distance relationship that is based on the dependence on distance R_{DA} of the matrix element of electronic coupling:

$$|V_{fi}(R_{DA})|^2 = |V_{fi}(R_{DA} = 0)|^2 \exp(-\beta \times R_{DA}) \qquad (6)$$

where R_{DA} is the edge to edge distance of the two reacting redox groups.

The magnitude of β in biological systems and in particular its possible dependence on secondary structure elements of proteins (α-helix, β-sheet, random coil) is a matter of controversial discussion [271–274]. Analyses of numerous biological electron transfer reactions revealed that $\beta = 1.4 \text{ Å}^{-1}$ is a suitable value for reliable estimates [274]. Based on this value the empirical rate constant–distance relationship:

$$\log k_{fi}^{ET} = 15 - 0.6 R_{DA} - 3.1 (\Delta G + \lambda_{fi})^2 / \lambda_{fi} \qquad (7)$$

was derived [275], where k_{fi}^{ET}, R_{DA} and ΔG_{fi}° are to be used in units of s^{-1}, Å and eV, respectively.

Application of this empirical relationship to calculate values for the edge-to-edge distance between Y_Z and the catalytic site(s) of the Mn_4O_xCa cluster led to values of $R_{DA} \geq 15$ Å [276], which are significantly larger (factor of two or more) than those known from recent X-ray crystallographic structure analyses (Chapter 15) [24,25]. This discrepancy is interpreted as an indication that the S_i state transitions are not limited by pure electron transfer, but are triggered reactions, most likely by coupling with protolytic reactions within a hydrogen bond network [112,175,176].

Basically, two different mechanisms can be discussed for the coupling of electron (ET) and proton transfer (PT): (i) separate pathways of ET and PT and (ii) concerted ET and PT corresponding to net hydrogen atom transfer (hydrogen atom abstractor model, see [191,218]). It is assumed that, probably, both mechanisms exist in the WOC, depending on redox state S_i. In S_0 and S_1 separate pathways seem to be used, while $Y_Z^{OX}S_3$ reactions and, possibly, $S_2 \rightarrow S_3$ comprise a stronger coupling of ET and PT [112,277]. This proposal is based on experimental data (Section 17.4.2.1; Electronic structure of the WOC) that suggest metal-centered oxidations during the $S_0 \rightarrow S_1$ and $S_1 \rightarrow S_2$ transitions and ligand-centered oxidations for the $S_2 \rightarrow S_3$ and $S_3 \rightarrow S_4$ transitions. The surplus charge accumulated on the OEC during the $S_1 \rightarrow S_2$ transition may be the trigger for this mechanistically important switch in reactivity in the WOC.

17.6 Mechanism of Photosynthetic Water Splitting

This section describes an attempt to propose reaction sequences that are in line with the experimental results presented in this chapter and may, therefore, occur during oxidative water splitting to molecular oxygen and four protons in PS II. In Section 17.4.2.1 (Electronic structure of the WOC) it was outlined that the electronic configuration of the WOC can be formally denoted for the different S_i states as $S_0[M_0L_0W_0]$, $S_1[M_1L_0W_0]$, $S_2[M_2L_0W_0]$, and $S_3[M_2(LW)_1]$. It is also possible that the S_3 state is better represented by a multi-state system

$S_3[(MLW)_3]$ consisting of $S_3[M_3L_0W_0]$, $S_3[M_2L_1W_0]$ and $S_3[M_1L_0W_2]$. In that case L_1 may represent a µ-oxo bridge radical and W_2 a complexed peroxide (Figure 5). Currently, three formal S_4 states are discussed: $[M_4L_0W_0]$, $[M_2L_0W_2]$ and $[M_0L_0W_4]$, where W_0 = coordinated substrate (water, hydroxo, oxo), W_2 = complexed peroxide and W_4 = bound O_2. In addition the possibility of a kinetic intermediate (lag phase) has been described for the $S_3 \to S_4$ transition, which is denoted in Figure 5 as $S_3'Y_Z^{OX}$ to indicate a possible protolytic reaction of the S_3 state during this reaction.

For clarity, it is assumed that metal-centered oxidations (M_0, M_1, M_2) can be assigned in a reasonable approximation to oxidation state changes of individual manganese ions within the WOC. Since the precise structure of the Mn_4O_xCa cluster is unknown (see Figure 4 for possible structures), we use in Figures 7 and 9 minimal structural elements for each S_i state transition that illustrate observed/proposed changes in structure and oxidation state (first line) and substrate binding (second line). Notably, the Mn ions (white, pink and red balls, depending on oxidation state) of the first and second lines do not necessarily correspond to each other. A possible assignment within the general arrangement of the Mn ions in the Mn_4O_xCa cluster is given by using the letter code defined in Figure 4(b). We hope that, once the complete structure is revealed, these elements can be cast together to solve the puzzle of photosynthetic water oxidation.

17.6.1 $S_0 \to S_1$ Transition

Based on the evidence reported in Section 17.4.2.1 (Electronic structure of the WOC) the $S_0[M_0L_0W_0]$ state is assumed to have oxidation states Mn(III,III,III,IV)L_0W_0 and those of $S_1[M_1L_0W_0]$ are consequently Mn(III,III, IV,IV)L_0W_0. Figure 7 shows in element E1 a µ-oxo-µ-hydroxo bridged Mn_2 pair that is proposed to be part of the Mn_4O_xCa cluster in the S_0 state. One manganese is in oxidation state III (pink), while the oxidation state of the other one is not specified (white), i.e., it could either be III or IV (Section 17.4.2.1; Electronic structure of the WOC). The observed reduction of one Mn–Mn distance from ~ 2.85 to ~ 2.7 Å (Section 17.4.2.1; S_i state dependent structural changes of the Mn_4O_xCa complexes) is explained by oxidation of Mn(III) to Mn(IV) (red), which is proposed to be coupled to the deprotonation of the µ-hydroxo bridge. Such a deprotonation is also consistent with the high threshold temperature for half-inhibition of this transition, which in spinach PS II membrane fragments has a value of about 220 K [58].

The slowly exchanging substrate molecule (W_s) is postulated to be fully deprotonated and to bind as a µ-oxo bridge between a manganese ion in oxidation state III and Ca^{2+} (Figure 7, E2). Such a bridge is not directly observed by EXAFS measurements, but appears to be consistent with the reported distance of ~ 3.4 Å. Furthermore, this arrangement is consistent with substrate water exchange data obtained on Sr^{2+} substituted PS II samples [124]. These data indicate the involvement of Ca^{2+}/Sr^{2+} in the binding of W_s (Section 17.4.2.3). The 600× slower exchange of W_s in S_1 compared with S_0 can be

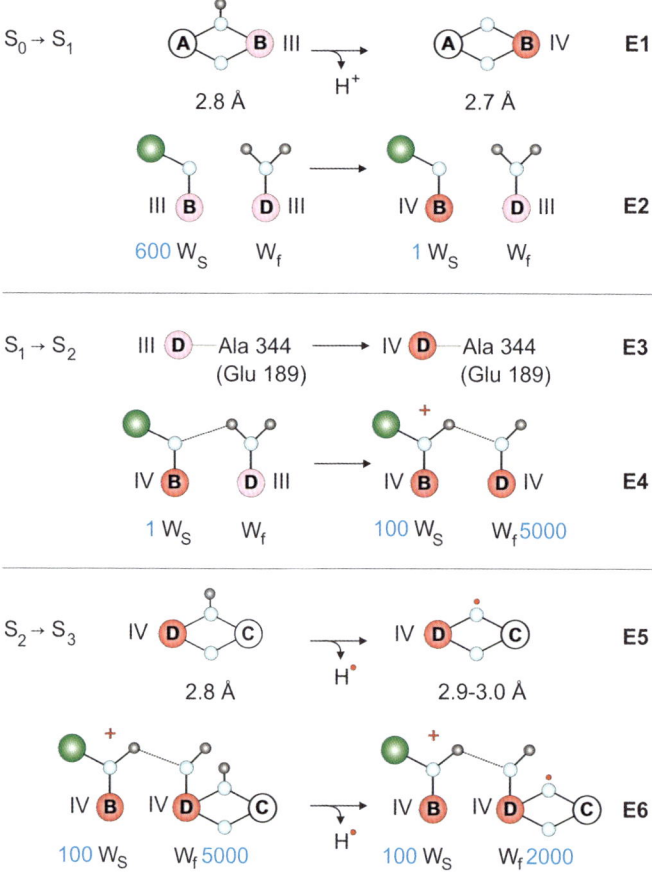

Figure 7. Minimal elements (E1–E6) of a proposal for the redox steps from S_0 up to S_3 in the WOC. The same color code as in Figure 4 is used. Elements E1, E3 and E5 describe changes in redox state and structure, while E2, E4 and E6 are attempts to assign the binding of the substrate water molecules, W_s and W_f, where the index stands for the slow and fast exchange. The blue numbers next to these symbols give the normalized (to slow exchange in S_1) substrate water exchange rates. The capital letters in the Mn ions refer to the labeling shown in Figure 4 (model b). They represent only one possible assignment, which is indicated for the clarity of presentation. Positive signs indicate a surplus charge of a given S_i state and red dots next to oxygens or hydrogens symbolize radicals. MnA and MnC are assumed to be redox inert and are symbolized by white balls.

understood if one assumes that W_s is bound to the Mn (MnB) that is oxidized during this transition (see E1).

There is as yet no experimental evidence for the binding of the fast exchanging substrate (W_f) in the S_0 and S_1 states. Nevertheless, we assume that W_f binds in S_0 as a fully protonated water molecule to Mn(III), which should result in rapid exchange kinetics, especially if a Jahn–Teller axis is involved. We do

PHOTOSYNTHETIC WATER SPLITTING 325

not specify a bridging motif between these two substrate binding Mn ions, but a 3.3 Å Mn–Mn distance (mono μ-oxobridge) appears to give a good geometry for O–O bond formation [145].

17.6.2 $S_1 \to S_2$ Transition

There is consensus that the $S_1 \to S_2$ transition involves a Mn oxidation: $S_1[M_1L_0W_0] \to S_2[M_2L_0W_0]$, and based on the above assignment of oxidation states this results in an electronic configuration for S_2 of $Mn(III,IV,IV,IV)L_0W_0$. Consequently, Figure 7 shows in element E3 the oxidation of one of the two remaining Mn(III) ions to Mn(IV). Based on FTIR data, this manganese ion is probably ligated by Ala-344 (or Glu-189) and may, therefore, be assigned to be MnD (Section 17.4.2.4 and Figure 4).

This redox transition is characterized by a markedly lower half-inhibition temperature of 130–170 K (depending on sample type; [20,58,249,278]), which could be explained if the reaction is assumed to involve proton movement only within an H-bond or to a base in the immediate vicinity of the proton donor (Figure 7, element E4; Section 17.4.2.5). This leads to a positive surplus charge in the S_2 state that has been measured by electrochromic shifts [265,266] and is likely to be of functional relevance for the subsequent S_i state transitions. The extra positive charge, denoted by a plus sign in Figure 7, E4, is likely also to be the reason why Y_Z cannot be oxidized by visible light at 10 K in the S_2 and S_3 states [226]. The water exchange experiments show that the exchange of W_f is slowed during the $S_1 \to S_2$ transition to an extent that its exchange rate becomes detectable (relative rate of 5000; Table 1), while, on the other hand, that of W_s is 100× faster in S_2 compared with S_1. This effect can be explained by the assumption that the $S_1 \to S_2$ transition involves a proton transfer from W_f to W_s, which is triggered by the oxidation of the Mn that is the binding site of W_f (Figure 7, E3).

17.6.3 $S_2 \to S_3$ Transition

The $S_2 \to S_3$ transition is more complex than the other two transitions and is strictly coupled to stoichiometric release of one proton [264]. A possible reason for this strict coupling is the positive surplus charge present in the S_2 state. The reaction requires a high protein flexibility, as reflected by both a significantly higher half-inhibition temperature of 220–255 K (depending on sample type; [20,58,249,278]) and by the severe blockage upon dehydration [98].

This transition is also coupled to significant structural changes of the Mn_4O_xCa cluster. On the basis of EXAFS and XANES experiments of the Berkeley group (e.g., [14,92,154,279]) it is assumed that a μ-oxo bridge oxidation takes place, i.e., $S_3 = Mn(III,IV,IV,IV)L_1W_0$ or $S_3 = Mn(III,IV,IV,IV)L_0W_1$. In this case we suggest that an oxo-bridge radical is formed (Figure 7, E5), which can explain the observed increase in Mn–Mn distances (Section 17.4.2.1, subsection on EXAFS).

The stoichiometric proton release can be explained in various ways: (i) H-atom abstraction from a bound substrate molecule by Y_Z^{OX}; (ii) PCET (proton coupled electron transfer), in which the substrate proton may either end up at the same place (Y_Z) as the electron, or may take another path and is possibly released into the lumen; (iii) PCET in which the electron transfer is coupled to the deprotonation of a nearby amino acid; and (iv) H-atom abstraction or PCET that involves a μ-hydroxo bridge. At this point all these options appear viable, and further research is needed to decide between them. To our knowledge the latter option has not been previously advanced, because, usually, all μ-oxo bridges are assumed to be deprotonated at the level of the S_1 and S_2 states. However, the recent high-resolution EXAFS measurements [149] indicate that also in the S_1 (and S_2) states there is one ~2.8 Å Mn–Mn left. This feature may originate for several reasons, but one possibility is that one bridge is still protonated. In that case, μ-oxo bridge radical formation and the compulsory proton release may be elegantly explained by PCET or H-atom transfer involving this bridge. This option is illustrated in Figure 7, E5.

A μ-oxo bridge oxidation has not been described yet for model complexes, but DFT calculations suggest that the reaction is energetically feasible and would increase, in agreement with experimental observations, via trans effects several Mn–Mn distances [280]. However, also, a more substantial structural change of the Mn_4O_xCa cluster can currently not be fully excluded for the $S_2 \to S_3$ transition.

It is remarkable that, despite the described structural changes in the WOC, the $H_2^{18}O/H_2^{16}O$ substrate exchange rates remain practically constant during the $S_2 \to S_3$ transition within factors of ≤ 2.5 (Table 1). This finding indicates that the binding sites and modes of the two substrate molecules (W_s and W_f) remain virtually unchanged during the $S_2 \to S_3$ transition. The slight slowing of the exchange of W_f may be explained by a structural arrangement (Figure 7, E6) where the μ-oxo radical is proposed to be formed in proximity to W_f. This may slow the exchange rate of W_f by the observed factor.

As a consequence, the above proposal for the S_3 state implies that two Mn ions do not formally change their oxidation state during the S_i state cycle up to S_3: one remains in oxidation state III and the other in oxidation state IV. On the basis of FTIR and XRDC these Mn ions may be identified with MnA and MnC (shown in white in Figure 7; see also Section 17.4.2.4). The other two manganese (possibly MnB and MnD in Figure 4; see Section 17.4.2.4) are redox active and are oxidized from a formal oxidation state III to IV (indicated in Figure 7 by a color change from pink to red). A functional heterogeneity of manganese in the WOC is a widely discussed phenomenon (e.g., [36,82]). The heterogeneity of the redox properties of the four manganese ions is understandable in case of an asymmetric protein environment [109].

Models of a metal-centered reaction where MnC(III) is oxidized to MnC(IV), i.e., $S_3[M_3L_0W_0]$ cannot be fully excluded, but appear unlikely to us at present (Section 17.4.2). An alternative to the $S_3[M_2(LW)_1]$ model is, however, the idea of a multi-state S_3 model with rapid redox isomerism $S_3 = [M_3(LW)_0] \leftrightarrow$

PHOTOSYNTHETIC WATER SPLITTING

$[M_2(LW)_1] \leftrightarrow [M_1L_0W_2]$ (for details see [112,175]), in which the population probabilities of these states depend on their mutual energy differences.

17.6.4 $S_3 \to \to S_4 \to \to S_0$ Transition

The $S_3 \to \to S_4 \to \to S_0$ transition also involves, in addition to electron and proton transfer, product release and the binding of new substrate water molecules. Therefore, this reaction sequence involves several intermediates. Recently, experimental evidence for two of these intermediate states was reported. To avoid semantic confusion we apply the following notation for intermediates:

$Y_ZS_3 \to Y_Z^{OX}S_3 \to \to Y_ZS_4 \to \to Y_ZS_0 + O_2$ where $S_i = [M_kL_lW_m]$ with $i = k + l + m$ (Section 17.4.2.1, Electronic structure of the WOC) and double-arrows indicate possible intermediary steps, which are not shown here. Accordingly, in this definition $Y_Z^{OX}S_3$ and possible deprotonated forms thereof are not S_4 states and will be denoted as $Y_Z^{OX}S_3'$, $Y_Z^{OX}S_3''$ etc. (see also Figure 5). Preliminary evidence for such intermediates comes from the observation of a lag phase in Y_Z^{OX} reduction (Section 17.5.1). Furthermore, experiments by Clausen and Junge have provided evidence for a peroxidic intermediate in the S_4 state [115]. Our fragmentary knowledge about this most important transition is summarized below in several subsections.

17.6.4.1 Previously Proposed Mechanisms for O–O Bond Formation

Figure 8 summarizes previously proposed mechanisms for O–O bond formation. In general, they can be divided into three groups (for a more detailed summary, see [38,176,281]): (i) *Nucleophilic attack* of a free or loosely bound (fast exchanging; W_f) substrate water molecule onto a highly electrophilic terminal oxo group (slowly exchanging "water"; W_s) bound to Mn(IV) or Mn(V) (Figure 8, I); (ii) a radical mechanism (Figure 8, II); and (iii) coupling of two oxo or hydroxo groups (Figure 8, III). The first proposal is currently very popular [199,219,277,282,283], but recent experimental findings (Section

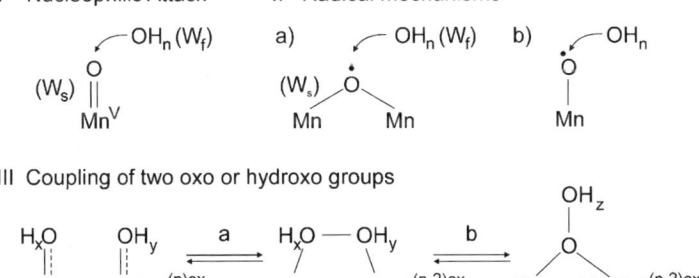

Figure 8. Summary of currently discussed proposals for O–O bond formation. Only the most essential elements are shown. For details see text.

17.6.4.3) and theoretical calculations [284] appear to argue against the formation of a terminal Mn=O bond. In addition, the substrate exchange kinetics of W_f and W_s differ only by a factor of about 20 in the S_3 state, which appears to disfavor two very different binding sites for the two substrate molecules. The *radical mechanism* is based on the idea that one μ-oxo bridge is oxidized during the $S_2 \to S_3$ transition (for discussion see Section 17.4.2.1, Electronic structure of the WOC). The O–O bond formation can occur in different ways: (a) if the oxo-bridge radical is assumed to represent the slowly exchanging substrate (Ws) the O–O bond has been proposed to be formed by the attack of a free (or weakly bound) substrate molecule (W_f) [154] or by reaction with a second bridging radical formed in the $S_3 \to S_4$ transition [16]. However, the practically identical exchange rates of W_s in the S_2 and S_3 states are difficult to reconcile with $W_s\cdot$ formation in S_3. (b) It has been proposed that the bridge radical can migrate to a nearby terminal oxo group in the S_4 state and form the O–O bond by reaction with the second substrate molecule [173,280], see also [285]. This option is further explored below. With respect to the third mechanism, two alternatives have also been discussed: (a) The *coupling of two oxo* groups that are already present in the S_3 state [218,286] is highly unlikely (Section 17.6.4.3); (b) however, the coupling of two hydroxo groups [133] appears feasible. Here both substrate molecules may be bound to Mn, or one to Mn and the other to Ca (or bridged between Ca and Mn). Such an arrangement can lead to a redox isomerism between the high-valent Mn-ions and the substrate molecules (Figure 8, IIIa) and furthermore to a peroxy-oxy water tautomerism (Figure 8, IIIb) [133].

17.6.4.2 Deprotonation Reactions and $Y_Z^{OX}S_3'$ State
The positive surplus charge created in the $S_1 \to S_2$ transition is maintained in the WOC up to the S_3 state. Therefore, in analogy to the discussion for the $S_2 \to S_3$ transition (Section 17.6.3), the $S_3 \to S_4$ transition has to be strongly coupled to a deprotonation reaction (PCET) from the WOC or may even involve a H-atom abstraction to avoid the energetic penalty due to accumulation of a second surplus charge near the Mn_4O_xCa cluster. Likewise, it must be pointed out that, due to the lack of proton release during the $S_1 \to S_2$ transition, two protons need to be released during the $S_3 \to \to S_4 \to \to S_0$ transition. Therefore, if the reported lag phase of about 30 μs between Y_Z^{OX} formation and WOC oxidation (Section 17.5.1), which has been interpreted as a proton release [244], is a real property of native samples, the following two alternative reaction sequences have to be considered, depending on the mode of coupling between Y_Z^{OX} formation and proton release: (i) Y_Z^{OX} formation is not coupled to a proton release into the lumen. In this case for a short period of time a state $(S_3Y_Z^{OX})$ would exist that consists of two positive charges in close vicinity: one near/at the Mn_4O_xCa cluster and one near Y_Z^{OX} (probably at D1-His190). This situation resembles that for the $S_2 \to S_3$ transition, because in all cases the formation of Y_Z^{OX} is approximately 1000× faster than its reduction through the WOC. In the $S_2 \to S_3$ transition e^- and H^+ transfer appear to occur essentially simultaneously, but according to

model (i) the proton transfer precedes electron transfer during the $S_3 \to S_4$ transition. The second proton is then released during the $S_4 \to \to S_0$ transition. (ii) If, however, one proton is released from the S_3 state concomitantly with $S_3Y_Z^{OX}$ formation, a second proton release could follow that gives rise to the lag phase. Depending on the origin of this second proton, either a negative surcharge would be located near/at the Mn_4O_xCa cluster (in addition to the positive charge near Y_Z^{OX}), or a fully neutral donor site be created, where also the positive charge near Y_Z^{OX} has vanished. At this point it is unclear whether either of these scenarios is required for electron transfer from the Mn_4O_xCa cluster to Y_Z^{OX} during the $S_3 \to S_4$ transition.

17.6.4.3 Formation of a Terminal Oxo-Group

It is widely assumed that the O–O bond formation does not occur until the redox state S_4 is reached. For $[M_4L_0W_0]$ a Mn(v) formation is required and a Mn(v)=O configuration has been discussed as binding motif for W_s (nucleophilic attack mechanism; Figure 8). This idea is not supported by recent XANES measurements. Studies on well-characterized Mn(v) model complexes containing a terminal oxo group display a very characteristic pre-edge feature [202]. Such a feature is not observed for the S_0–S_3 states [92,155,203], which makes the presence of a terminal Mn=O group highly unlikely up to the S_3 state. The formation of Mn(iv/v)=O in the transient S_4 state can presently not be fully excluded. However, recent time-resolved XANES measurements did not reveal any evidence for the formation of this species during the $S_3 \to \to S_4 \to \to S_0$ transition, nor for Mn oxidation or structural changes [204]. Furthermore, theoretical calculations are not in line with the formation of Mn(v)=O [284]. Therefore, it seems unlikely that the S_4 state has the electronic configuration $[Mn_4L_0W_0]$.

The lack of evidence for Mn valence and/or structural changes of the Mn_4O_xCa cluster after Y_Z oxidation supports the hypothesis that already in the S_3 state the nuclear geometry is reached that is required for O–O bond formation [108,112,133]. This idea, originally based on thermodynamic considerations [108], is supported by the finding that the kinetics of O_2 release and Y_Z^{OX} reduction are very similar, implying that the electron transfer from the WOC to Y_Z^{OX} is rate limiting for the overall transition leading from $Y_Z^{OX}S_3$ to Y_ZS_0 and the release of O_2 and protons [236].

17.6.4.4 Evidence for a Peroxidic Intermediate in the S_4 State

Clausen and Junge [115] reported that inhibition by the product O_2, at moderate pressures of 10–20 bar, leads to a blockage of the $S_3 \to \to S_4 \to \to S_0$ transition, probably at the level of the S_4 state. This result implies that the final step of O_2 formation is coupled with a surprisingly small free energy drop. Furthermore, the O_2 pressure dependence of this effect indicates the presence of an intermediate state between $S_3^{(')}Y_Z^{OX}$ and S_0Y_Z. This state was tentatively assigned by to a peroxidic intermediate, i.e., $S_4[M_2L_0W_2]$.

17.6.5 Refined Proposals for O–O Bond Formation

Starting from the S_3 state configuration depicted in Figure 7, E6, and on the basis of the above summarized results concerning the $S_3 \to \to S_4 \to \to S_0$ transition, two alternative mechanisms for O–O bond formation can be considered. They may be described as "proton-shift first mechanisms" and as "O–O bond formation first mechanism".

17.6.5.1 Proton-shift First Mechanisms

This mechanism, shown in Figure 9, top, adopts the view that, because of the surplus charge in the S_3 state, deprotonation of the WOC has to precede the electron transfer to Y_Z^{OX}. In that case it appears likely that a deprotonation of W_s occurs during $S_3'Y_Z^{OX}$ formation. Subsequently, the O–O bond is formed under Y_Z^{OX} reduction, leading to the formation of the $S_4[M_2L_0W_2]$ state (complexed peroxide). This process, which in our suggestion leads to the reduction of the μ-oxo bridge radical, may either involve (i) the formation of a second radical with subsequent coupling of the two radicals or (ii) more likely the O–O bond is formed at the level of the S_3 state in a rate-limiting step, which is a pre-requisite for the subsequent rapid electron transfer to Y_Z^{OX} (see also the next subsection). Formation of the $S_4'[M_0L_0W_4]$ (complexed O_2) involves

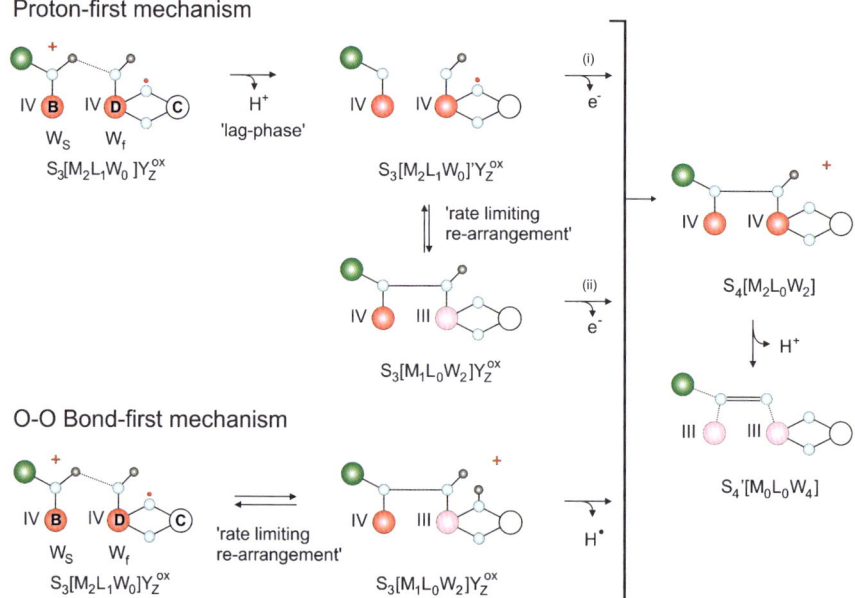

Figure 9. Two alternative proposals for O–O bond formation during water splitting in PS II. Symbols are as in Figures 4 and 7. For explanations see text.

proton release from the complexed peroxide. The S_0 state is then formed by product/substrate exchange and reprotonation of two μ-oxo bridges.

17.6.5.2 O–O Bond First Mechanism

For this mechanism we assume that PCET or H-atom abstraction can only occur in the S_3 state once the O–O bond is already formed [112,133,175]. It may, therefore, be suggested that the proposed redox isomerism equilibrium between the different possible forms of the S_3 state (Figure 5) is originally largely in favor of the $S_3[M_2(LW)_1]$ state. Formation of Y_Z^{OX} then leads to a higher population of the peroxidic $S_3[M_1L_0W_2]Y_Z^{OX}$ state. The shift of this equilibrium is shown in Figure 9 (lower part) to involve an H-atom transfer (or PCET) from the substrate to the μ-oxo bridge radical, and this reaction is assumed to be rate limiting for the subsequent reduction of Y_Z^{OX}, which is strongly coupled to a proton transfer (PCET or H-atom transfer). Under ambient O_2 pressure the formed $S_4[M_2L_0W_2]$ state rapidly decays under proton release into the $S_4'[M_0L_0W_4]$ state, while under elevated O_2 pressure the $S_4[M_2L_0W_2]$ state may be stabilized [115]. This mechanism is also consistent with the data in [204], because under normal conditions the intermediate states $S_3[M_1L_0W_2]$ and $S_4[M_2L_0W_2]$ are populated at levels of about 10%, which are below the detection limit of the XAS method. The S_0 state is formed by O_2 release and the concomitant binding of water under reprotonation of two μ-oxo bridges (Sections 17.6.1 and 17.6.2).

The S_3 multistate model also offers a straightforward explanation for the striking variations of the kinetics of Y_Z^{OX} reduction by the WOC in redox state S_3 (Section 17.5.1) because the overall rate depends on the "equilibrium" population of the peroxidic state in S_3. This population probability is prone to effects by different parameters.

17.7 Concluding Remarks and Future Perspectives

This chapter has summarized the functional and structural organization of oxidative water splitting in photosynthesis, describing our current knowledge on the structure of the WOC and the Mn_4O_xCa unit.

The two mechanisms proposed for O–O bond formation are based on the information available from different spectroscopic techniques and the simplifying assumption that the redox processes of the reaction sequence can be satisfactorily described by integer valence changes of either manganese or an attached ligand/substrate.

Despite significant progress in unraveling the structure of the Mn_4O_xCa cluster and its Mn valences in the different S_i states, several key questions are still not yet satisfactorily answered – in particular the exact mechanism of O–O bond formation is not known. A challenging problem of general relevance is a deeper understanding of the role of protein dynamics and hydrogen bond network(s). In this respect it appears necessary to consider the whole WOC as an entity [175,176]. As a consequence, the former apoprotein–cofactor concept is of limited value at most. The application of modern sensitive spectroscopic methods and further advancement in monitoring dynamic structural changes coupled with the S_i state transitions of the WOC, together with advanced quantum chemical and molecular mechanics methods, will provide new insight into the fascinating process of oxidative photosynthetic water splitting.

Acknowledgements

The authors are grateful to Warwick Hillier, Leonid Kulik, Jan Kern, Junko Yano and Vittal Yachandra for continuous insightful discussions on the structure and function of the WOC. We also acknowledge discussions with S. Styring and V. Petrouleas about EPR split signals, and critical reading of the manuscript by Ji-Hu Su. We thank Susanne Renger for drawing the electronic version of Figures 2 and 3. Financial supported was provided to J.M. by the DFG (Me1629/2–4) and the Max Planck Gesellschaft, and to G.R. by the DFG (Sfb 429, TPA1).

References

1. D.L. Gilbert, *Oxygen and Living Processes: An Interdisciplinary Approach* (1981), Springer, New York.
2. S. Ruben, M. Randall, M. Kamen, J.L. Hyde, Heavy oxygen (O^{18}) as a tracer in the study of photosynthesis. *J. Am. Chem. Soc.* **63** (1941) 877–879.
3. H. Budzikiewicz, H. Eckau, H.H. Inhoffen, Photosynthesis in green plants. I. Experiments with $H_2^{18}O$ and $K_2C^{18}O_3$ on *chlorella pyrenoidosa chick*. *Z. Naturforsch., Teil B* **24** (1969) 1147–1152.
4. P. Joliot, G. Barbieri, R. Chabaud, Un nouveau modele des centres photochimiques du systeme II. *Photochem. Photobiol.* **10** (1969) 309–329.
5. B. Kok, B. Forbush, M. McGloin, Cooperation of charges in photosynthetic O_2 evolution. *Photochem. Photobiol.* **11** (1970) 457–476.
6. R.J. Debus, B.A. Barry, I. Sithole, G.T. Babcock, L. McIntosh, Directed mutagenesis indicates that the donor to $P680^+$ in photosystem II is tyrosine-161 of the D1 polypeptide. *Biochemistry* **27** (1988) 9071–9074.
7. J.G. Metz, P.J. Nixon, M. Rögner, G.W. Brudvig, B.A. Diner, Directed alteration of the D1 polypeptide of photosystem II: evidence that tyrosine-161 is the redox component, Z, connecting the oxygen evolving complex to the primary electron donor, P680. *Biochemistry* **28** (1989) 6960–6969.
8. E. Kessler, On the role of manganese in the oxygen-evolving system of photosynthesis. *Arch. Biochem. Biophys.* **59** (1955) 527–529.
9. E. Kessler, Stoffwechselphysiologische Untersuchungen an Hydrogenase Enthaltenden Grünalgen. 1. Über die Rolle des Mangans bei Photoreduktion und Photosynthese. *Planta* **49** (1957) 435–454 (in German).
10. G.M. Cheniae, I.F. Martin, Photoreactivation of manganese catalyst in photosynthetic oxygen evolution. *Plant Physiol.* **44** (1969) 351–360.
11. G.M. Cheniae, I.F. Martin, Sites of function of manganese within photosystem II - roles in O_2 evolution and system II. *Biochim. Biophys. Acta* **197** (1970) 219–239.
12. R.J. Debus, The manganese and calcium ions of photosynthetic oxygen evolution. *Biochim. Biophys. Acta* **1102** (1992) 269–352.

13. H.J. van Gorkom, C.F. Yocum, The calcium and chloride cofactors, in: *Photosystem II. The Light-Driven Water: Plastoquinone Oxidoreductase* (2005) (T. Wydrzynski, K. Satoh, eds.), Springer, Dordrecht, pp. 307–328.
14. V.K. Yachandra, The catalytic manganese cluster: organisation of the metal ions, in: *Photosystem II. The Light-Driven Water: Plastoquinone Oxidoreductase* (2005) (T. Wydrzynski, K. Satoh, eds.), Springer, Dordrecht, pp. 235–260.
15. V.K. Yachandra, V.J. DeRose, M.J. Latimer, I. Mukerji, K. Sauer, M.P. Klein, Where plants make oxygen: a structural model for the photosynthetic oxygen evolving manganese cluster. *Science* **260** (1993) 675–679.
16. V.K. Yachandra, K. Sauer, M.P. Klein, Manganese cluster in photosynthesis: where plants oxidize water to dioxygen. *Chem. Rev.* **96** (1996) 2927–2950.
17. M. Ikeuchi, M. Yuasa, Y. Inoue, Simple and discrete isolation of an O_2-evolving PS II reaction center complex retaining Mn and the extrinsic 33 kDa protein. *FEBS Lett.* **185** (1985) 316–322.
18. L.G. Franzen, S. Styring, A.L. Etienne, O. Hansson, C. Vernotte, Spectroscopic and functional characterization of a highly oxygen evolving photosystem II reaction center complex from spinach. *Photobiochem. Photobiophys* **13** (1986) 15–28.
19. E. Haag, K.D. Irrgang, E.J. Boekema, G. Renger, Functional and structural analysis of photosystem II core complexes from spinach with high oxygen evolution capacity. *Eur. J. Biochem.* **189** (1990) 47–53.
20. H.M. Gleiter, E. Haag, Y. Inoue, G. Renger, Functional characterization of a purified homogeneous photosystem II core complex with high oxygen evolution capacity from spinach. *Photosynth. Res.* **35** (1993) 41–53.
21. L.X. Shi, W.P. Schröder, The low molecular mass subunits of the photosynthetic supracomplex, photosystem II. *Biochim. Biophys. Acta* **1608** (2004) 75–96.
22. A. Zouni, H.T. Witt, J. Kern, P. Fromme, N. Krauß, W. Saenger, P. Orth, Crystal structure of photosystem II from *Synechococcus elongatus* at 3.8 Å resolution. *Nature* **409** (2001) 739–743.
23. N. Kamiya, J.-R. Shen, Crystal structure of oxygen-evolving photosystem II from *Thermosynechococcus vulcanus* at 3.7 Å resolution. *Proc. Natl. Acad. Sci. U.S.A.* **100** (2003) 98–103.
24. K.N. Ferreira, T.M. Iverson, K. Maghlaoui, J. Barber, S. Iwata, Architecture of the photosynthetic oxygen-evolving center. *Science* **303** (2004) 1831–1838.
25. B. Loll, J. Kern, W. Saenger, A. Zouni, J. Biesiadka, Towards complete cofactor arrangement in the 3.0 Å resolution structure of photosystem II. *Nature* **438** (2005) 1040–1044.
26. A. Seidler, The extrinsic polypeptides of photosystem II. *Biochim. Biophys. Acta* **1277** (1996) 35–60.
27. H. Yu, Y. Xu, R.D. Britt, The 33 kDa protein can be removed without affecting the association of the 23 and 17 kDa proteins with the luminal side of PS II of spinach. *Biochemistry* **45** (2006) 3404–3411.
28. J.J. Eaton-Rye, N. Murata, Evidence that the amino-terminus of the 33 kDa extrinsic is required for binding to the photosystem II complex. *Biochim. Biophys. Acta* **977** (1989) 219–226.
29. W.R. Odom, T.M. Bricker, Interaction of CPa-1 with the manganese-stabilizing protein of photosystem II: identification of domains cross-linked by 1-ethyl-3-[3-(dimethylamino)propyl]carbodiimide. *Biochemistry* **31** (1992) 5616–5620.
30. T. Shutova, K.D. Irrgang, V. Shubin, V.V. Klimov, G. Renger, Analysis of pH-induced structural changes of the isolated extrinsic 33 kilodalton protein of photosystem II. *Biochemistry* **36** (1997) 6350–6358.

31. W. Vermaas, Molecular-biological approaches to analyze photosystem II structure and function. *Annu. Rev. Plant Physiol. Plant Mol. Biol.* **44** (1993) 457–481.
32. R.T. Sayre, E.A. Wrobel-Boerner, Molecular topology of the photosystem II chlorophyll *a* binding protein, CP43: topology of a thylakoid membrane protein. *Photosynth. Res.* **40** (1994) 11–19.
33. H.M. Gleiter, E. Haag, J.-R. Shen, J.J. Eaton-Rye, A.G. Seeliger, Y. Inoue, W.F.J. Vermaas, G. Renger, Involvement of the CP47 protein in stabilization and photoactivation of a functional water oxidizing complex in the cyanobacterium *Synechocystis sp* PCC 6803. *Biochemistry* **34** (1995) 6847–6856.
34. T.M. Bricker, L.K. Frankel, The structure and function of CP47 and CP43 in Photosystem II. *Photosynth. Res.* **72** (2002) 131–146.
35. T. Wydrzynski, W. Hillier, J. Messinger, On the functional significance of substrate accessibility in the photosynthetic water oxidation mechanism. *Physiol. Plant.* **96** (1996) 342–350.
36. G. Renger, Mechanism of photosynthetic water cleavage, in: *Concepts in Photobiology: Photosynthesis and Photomorphogenesis* (1999) (G.S. Singhal, G. Renger, S.K. Sopory, K.-D. Irrgang, Govindjee, eds.), Narosa Publishing House, New Delhi, India, pp. 292-329.
37. J.M. Anderson, Does functional photosystem II complex have an oxygen channel? *FEBS Lett.* **488** (2001) 1–4.
38. W. Hillier, J. Messinger, Mechanism of photosynthetic oxygen production, in: *Photosystem II. The Light-Driven Water: Plastoquinone Oxidoredutase* (2005) (T. Wydrzynski, K. Satoh, eds.), Springer, Dordrecht, pp. 567–608.
39. R.J. Strasser, C. Sironval, Induction of photosystem 2. Activity in flashed leaves. *FEBS Lett.* **28** (1972) 56–60.
40. G.M. Cheniae, I.F. Martin, Absence of oxygen-evolving capacity in dark-grown *Chlorella* - photoactivation of oxygen-evolving centers. *Photochem. Photobiol.* **17** (1973) 441–459.
41. B. Forbush, B. Kok, M.P. McGloin, Cooperation of charges in photosynthetic oxygen evolution. II. Damping of flash yield oscillation, deactivation. *Photochem. Photobiol.* **14** (1971) 307–321.
42. G. Renger, The watersplitting system of photosynthesis, I. A postulated model. *Z. Naturforsch., Teil B* **25** (1970) 966–971.
43. T. Mar, Govindjee Kinetic models of oxygen evolution in photosynthesis. *J. Theor. Biol.* **36** (1972) 427–336.
44. B. Diner, Cooperativety between photosystem II centers at the level of primary electron transfer. *Biochim. Biophys. Acta* **368** (1974) 371–385.
45. W.E.J. Vermaas, G. Renger, G. Dohnt, The reduction of the oxygen evolving system in chloroplasts by thylakoid components. *Biochim. Biophys. Acta* **764** (1984) 194–202.
46. S. Styring, A.W. Rutherford, In the oxygen evolving complex of photosystem II the S_0 state is oxidized to the S_1 State by Y_D^+ (Signal II$_{slow}$). *Biochemistry* **26** (1987) 2401–2405.
47. J.H.A. Nugent, C. Demetriou, C.J. Lockett, Electron donation in photosystem II. *Biochim. Biophys. Acta* **894** (1987) 534–542.
48. A.W. Rutherford, S. Styring, EPR signal II in photosystem II: redox and paramagnetic interactions with the molecular oxygen evolving enzyme. *Cytochrome Syst.: Mol. Biol. Bioenerg., [Proc. UNESCO Int. Symp.]* (1987) 541–547.
49. W.F.J. Vermaas, A.W. Rutherford, Ö. Hansson, Site directed mutagenesis in photosystem II of the cyanobacterium *Synechocystis sp.* PCC 6803: donor D is

a tyrosine residue in the D2 protein. *Proc. Natl. Acad. Sci. U.S.A.* **85** (1988) 8477–8481.
50. B.A. Diner, Dependence of deactivation reactions of photosystem II on redox state of plastoquinone pool-A varied under anaerobic conditions. Equilibria on the acceptor side of photosystem II. *Biochim. Biophys. Acta* **460** (1977) 247–258.
51. A.W. Rutherford, A.R. Crofts, Y. Inoue, Thermoluminescence as a probe of photosystem II photochemistry. The origin of the flash-induced glow peaks. *Biochim. Biophys. Acta* **682** (1982) 457–465.
52. H.H. Robinson, A.R. Crofts, Kinetics of the oxidation reduction reactions of the photosystem II quinone acceptor complex, and the pathway for deactivation. *FEBS Lett.* **153** (1983) 221–226.
53. A.W. Rutherford, Y. Inoue, Oscillation of delayed luminescence from PS II: recombination of $S_2Q_B^-$ and $S_3Q_B^-$. *FEBS Lett.* **165** (1984) 163–170.
54. I. Vass, Z. Deak, E. Hideg, Charge equilibrium between the water oxidizing complex and the electron donor tyrosine D in photosystem II. *Biochim. Biophys. Acta* **1017** (1990) 63–69.
55. I. Vass, S. Styring, pH dependent charge equilibria between tyrosine-D and the S-states in photosystem II. Estimation of relative midpoint potentials. *Biochemistry* **30** (1991) 830–839.
56. J. Messinger, W.P. Schröder, G. Renger, Structure-function relations in photosystem II. Effects of temperature and chaotropic agents on the period four oscillation of flash induced oxygen evolution. *Biochemistry* **32** (1993) 7658–7668.
57. J. Messinger, G. Renger, Analysis of pH-induced modifications of the period four oscillation of the flash induced oxygen evolution reveal distinct structural changes of the photosystem II donor side at characteristic pH values. *Biochemistry* **33** (1994) 10896–10905.
58. S. Styring, A.W. Rutherford, Deactivation kinetics and temperature dependence of the S-state transitions in the oxygen evolving system of photosystem II measured by EPR spectroscopy. *Biochim. Biophys. Acta* **933** (1988) 378–387.
59. P. Jursinic, Investigation of double turnovers in photosystem II charge separation and oxygen evolution with excitation flashes of different duration. *Biochim. Biophys. Acta* **635** (1981) 38–52.
60. S. Isgandarova, G. Renger, J. Messinger, Functional differences of photosystem II from *Synechococcus elongatus* and spinach characterized by flash-induced oxygen evolution patterns. *Biochemistry* **42** (2003) 8929–8938.
61. G. Bernat, F. Morvaridi, Y. Feyziyev, S. Styring, pH dependence of the four individual transitions in the catalytic S-cycle during photosynthetic oxygen evolution. *Biochemistry* **41** (2002) 5830–5843.
62. Y. Feyziyev, B.J. van Rotterdam, G. Bernat, S. Styring, Electron transfer from cytochrome b_{559} and tyrosine$_D$ to the S_2 and S_3 states of the water oxidizing complex in photosystem II. *Chem. Phys.* **294** (2003) 415–431.
63. K.G.V. Sigfridsson, G. Bernat, F. Mamedov, S. Styring, Molecular interference of Cd^{2+} with Photosystem II. *Biochim. Biophys. Acta* **1659** (2004) 19–31.
64. G. Christen, G. Renger, The role of hydrogen bonds for the multiphasic $P680^{+\bullet}$ reduction by Y_Z in photosystem II with intact oxygen evolution capacity. Analysis of kinetic H/D isotope exchange effects. *Biochemistry* **38** (1999) 2068–2077.
65. G. Christen, A. Seeliger, G. Renger, $P680^{+\bullet}$ reduction kinetics and redox transition probability of the water oxidizing complex as a function of pH and H/D isotope exchange in spinach thylakoids. *Biochemistry* **38** (1999) 6082–6092.

66. M.J. Delrieu, Simple explanation of the misses in the cooperation of charges in photosynthetic O_2 evolution. *Photochem. Photobiol.* **20** (1974) 441–454.
67. J. Lavorel, Matrix analysis of the oxygen evolving system of photosynthesis. *J. Theor. Biol.* **57** (1976) 171–185.
68. T. Thibault, A new attempt to study the oxygen evolving system of photosynthesis: determination of transition probabilities of a state i. *J. Theor. Biol.* **73** (1978) 271–284.
69. P.C. Meunier, R.L. Burnap, L.A. Sherman, Improved 5-step modeling of the photosystem II S-state mechanism in cyanobacteria. *Photosynth. Res.* **47** (1996) 61–76.
70. V.P. Shinkarev, Oxygen evolution in photosynthesis: Simple analytical solution for the Kok model. *Biophys. J.* **85** (2003) 435–441.
71. V.P. Shinkarev, Flash-induced oxygen evolution in photosynthesis: simple solution for the extended S-state model that includes misses, double-hits, inactivation, and backward-transitions. *Biophys. J.* **88** (2005) 412–421.
72. G. Renger, B. Hanssum, Studies on the deconvolution of flash induced absorption changes into the difference spectra of individual redox steps within the water oxidizing enzyme system. *Photosynth. Res.* **16** (1988) 243–259.
73. V. Shinkarev, C.A. Wraight, Oxygen evolution in photosynthesis: from unicycle to bicycle. *Proc. Natl. Acad. Sci. U.S.A.* **90** (1993) 1834–1838.
74. R. de Wijn, H.J. van Gorkom, S-state dependence of the miss probability in photosystem II. *Photosynth. Res.* **72** (2002) 217–222.
75. F. Morvaridi, The Oxygen Evolving Cycle in Photosystem II studied with EPR Spectroscopy at different pH and Temperature (2005), Ph.D. Thesis, Lund University, Lund.
76. K. Brettel, E. Schlodder, H.T. Witt, Nanosecond reduction kinetics of photooxidised chlorophyll a_{II} (P680) in single flashes as a probe for the electron pathway, H^+ release and charge accumulation in the O_2 evolving complex. *Biochim. Biophys. Acta* **766** (1984) 403–415.
77. H.-J. Eckert, G. Renger, Temperature dependence of $P680^+$ reduction in O_2 evolving PSII membrane fragments at different redox states S_i of the water oxidizing system. *FEBS Lett.* **236** (1988) 425–431.
78. P. Faller, A.W. Rutherford, R.J. Debus, Tyrosine D oxidation at cryogenic temperature in photosystem II. *Biochemistry* **41** (2002) 12914–12920.
79. B.A. Diner, F. Rappaport, Structure, dynamics, and energetics of the primary photochemistry of photosystem II of oxygenic photosynthesis. *Annu. Rev. Plant Biol.* **53** (2002) 551–580.
80. R.J. Boerner, K.A. Bixby, A.P. Nguyen, G.H. Noren, R.J. Debus, B.A. Barry, Removal of stable tyrosine radical D^+ affects the structure or redox properties of tyrosine Z in manganese-depleted photosystem II particles from *Synechocystis* 6803. *J. Biol. Chem.* **268** (1993) 1817–1823.
81. P. Faller, R.J. Debus, K. Brettel, M. Sugiura, A.W. Rutherford, A. Boussac, Rapid formation of the stable tyrosyl radical in photosystem II. *Proc. Natl. Acad. Sci. U.S.A.* **98** (2001) 14368–14373.
82. J. Messinger, G. Renger, Generation, oxidation by the oxidized form of the tyrosine of polypeptide D2, and possible electronic configuration of the redox states S_0, S_{-1} and S_{-2} of the water oxidase in isolated spinach thylakoids. *Biochemistry* **32** (1993) 9379–9386.
83. J. Sarrou, S. Isgandarova, J. Kern, A. Zouni, G. Renger, W. Lubitz, J. Messinger, Nitric oxide induced formation of the S_{-2} state in the oxygen evolving

complex of photosystem II from *Synechococcus elongatus*. *Biochemistry* **42** (2003) 1016–1023.
84. K.P. Bader, P. Thibault, G.H. Schmid, A study on oxygen evolution and on the S-state distribution in thylakoid preparations of the filamentous blue-green alga *Oscillatoria chalybea*. *Z. Naturforsch., Teil C* **38** (1983) 778–792.
85. J. Messinger, U. Wacker, G. Renger, Unusual low reactivity of the water oxidase in the redox state S_3 toward exogenous reductants. Analysis of the NH_2OH and NH_2NH_2 induced modifications of flash induced oxygen evolution in isolated spinach thylakoids. *Biochemistry* **30** (1991) 7852–7862.
86. J. Messinger, G. Seaton, T. Wydrzynski, U. Wacker, G. Renger, S_{-3} state of the water oxidase in photosystem II. *Biochemistry* **36** (1997) 6862–6873.
87. M.J. Delrieu, F. Rosengard, Fundamental differences between period-4 oscillations of the oxygen and fluorescence yield induced by flash excitation in inside-out thylakoids. *Biochim. Biophys. Acta* **892** (1987) 163–171.
88. P.C. Meunier, R. Popovic, Improvement of 4 sigma-analysis for the investigation of oxygen evolution by photosystem II. *Photosynth. Res.* **29** (1991) 113–115.
89. R.A. Chylla, G. Garab, J. Whitmarsh, Evidence for slow turnover in a fraction of photosystem II complexes in thylakoid membranes. *Biochim. Biophys. Acta* **894** (1987) 562–571.
90. R.A. Chylla, J. Whitmarsh, Inactive photosystem II complexes in leaves. Turnover rate and quantitation. *Plant Physiol.* **90** (1989) 765–772.
91. J. Lavergne, E. Leci, Properties of inactive photosystem II centers. *Photosynth. Res.* **35** (1993) 323–343.
92. J. Messinger, J.H. Robblee, U. Bergmann, C. Fernandez, P. Glatzel, H. Visser, R.M. Cinco, K.L. McFarlane, E. Bellacchio, S.A. Pizarro, S.P. Cramer, K. Sauer, M.P. Klein, V.K. Yachandra, Absence of Mn centered oxidation in the S_2 to S_3 transition: implications for the mechanism of photosynthetic water oxidation. *J. Am. Chem. Soc.* **123** (2001) 7804–7820.
93. J.L. Zimmermann, A.W. Rutherford, Photoreductant-induced oxidation of Fe^{2+} in the electron acceptor complex of photosystem II. *Biochim. Biophys. Acta* **851** (1986) 416–423.
94. V. Petrouleas, B.A. Diner, Identification of Q_{400}, a high potential electron acceptor of photosystem II, with the iron of the quinone-iron acceptor complex. *Biochim. Biophys. Acta* **849** (1986) 264–275.
95. V. Petrouleas, B.A. Diner, Light-induced oxidation of the acceptor side Fe^{II} of photosystem II by exogenous quinones acting through the Q_B binding site. 1. Quinones, kinetics and pH-dependence. *Biochim. Biophys. Acta* **893** (1987) 126–137.
96. G. Renger, U. Wacker, M. Völker, Studies on the protolytic reactions coupled with water cleavage in photosystem II membrane fragments from spinach. *Photosynth Res.* **13** (1987) 167–184.
97. M.J. Delrieu, Evidence for unequal misses in oxygen flash yield sequence in photosynthesis, *Z. Naturforsch., Teil C* **38** (1983) 247–258.
98. T. Noguchi, M. Sugiura, Flash-induced FTIR difference spectra of the water oxidizing complex in moderately hydrated photosystem II core films: effect of hydration extent on S-state transitions. *Biochemistry* **41** (2002) 2322–2330.
99. P.W. Atkins, *Physical Chemistry*, 6th edn., Oxford University Press, Oxford.
100. B.A. Diner, J.A. Bautista, P.J. Nixon, C. Berthomieu, R. Hienerwadel, R.D. Britt, W.F.J. Vermaas, D.A. Chisholm, Coordination of proton and electron transfer from the redox-active tyrosine, Y_Z, of Photosystem II and examination of the

electrostatic influence of oxidized tyrosine, $Y_D^{\cdot}(H^+)$. *Phys. Chem. Chem. Phys.* **6** (2004) 4844–4850.

101. F. Rappaport, M. Guergova-Kuras, P.J. Nixon, B.A. Diner, J. Lavergne, Kinetics and pathways of charge recombination in photosystem II. *Biochemistry* **41** (2002) 8518–8527.
102. G. Renger, A.R. Holzwarth, Primary electron transfer, in: *Photosystem II. The Light-Driven Water: Plastoquinone Oxidoreductase* (2005) (T.J. Wydrzynski, K. Satoh, eds.), Springer, Dordrecht, pp. 139-175.
103. M.H. Vos, H.J. Van Gorkom, P.J. Van Leeuwen, An electroluminescence study of stabilization reactions in the oxygen-evolving complex of photosystem II. *Biochim. Biophys. Acta* **1056** (1991) 27–39.
104. P. Jursinic, Govindjee, Temperature dependence of delayed light emission in the 6 to 340 microsecond range after a single flash in chloroplasts. *Photochem. Photobiol.* **26** (1977) 617–628.
105. V.V. Klimov, S.I. Allakhverdiev, S. Demeter, A.A. Krasnovskii, Photo-reduction of pheophytin in the photosystem 2 of chloroplasts depending on the oxidation-reduction potential of the medium. *Dokl. Akad. Nauk SSSR* **249** (1979) 227–230.
106. A. Boussac, A.L. Etienne, Midpoint potential of signal II (slow) in Tris-washed photosystem II particles. *Biochim. Biophys. Acta* **766** (1984) 576–581.
107. D. Shevela, B. Nöring, H.J. Eckert, J. Messinger, G. Renger, Characterization of the water oxidizing complex of photosystem II of the Chl d-containing cyanobacterium Acaryochloris marina via its reactivity towards endogenous electron donors and acceptors. *Phys. Chem. Chem. Phys.* **8** (2006) 3460–3466.
108. G. Renger, Theoretical studies about the functional and structural organization of the photosynthetic oxygen evolution, in: *Photosynthetic Oxygen Evolution* (1978) (H. Metzner, ed.), Academic Press, London, pp. 229–248.
109. G. Renger, Mechanistic aspects of photosynthetic water cleavage. *Photosynthetica* **21** (1987) 203–224.
110. G. Renger, J. Messinger, B. Hanssum, Thermodynamic, kinetic and mechanistic aspects of photosynthetic water oxidation, in: *Current Research in Photosynthesis* (1990) (M. Baltscheffsky, ed.), Kluwer Academic Publishers, Dordrecht, pp. 845–848.
111. G. Renger, Water Cleavage by Solar-Radiation - an Inspiring Challenge of Photosynthesis Research. *Photosynth. Res.* **38** (1993) 229–247.
112. G. Renger, Photosynthetic water oxidation to molecular oxygen: apparatus and mechanism. *Biochim. Biophys. Acta* **1503** (2001) 210–228.
113. V. Klimov, G. Ananyev, O. Zastryzhnaya, T. Wydrzynski, G. Renger, Photoproduction of hydrogen-peroxide in photosystem II membrane-fragments - a comparison of 4 signals. *Photosynth. Res.* **38** (1993) 409–416.
114. T. Wydrzynski, J. Ångstrom, T. Vanngard, H_2O_2 formation by photosystem II. *Biochim. Biophys. Acta* **973** (1989) 23–28.
115. J. Clausen, W. Junge, Detection of an intermediate of photosynthetic water oxidation. *Nature* **430** (2004) 480–483.
116. P. Kühn, J. Pieper, O. Kaminskaya, H.J. Eckert, R.E. Lechner, V. Shuvalov, G. Renger, Reaction pattern of photosystem II: oxidative water cleavage and protein flexibility. *Photosynth. Res.* **84** (2005) 317–323.
117. U. Siggel, The control of electron transport by two pH-sensitive sites, in: *Proceedings of the Third International Congress on Photosynthesis* (1975) (M. Avron, ed.), Elsevier, Amsterdam, pp. 645–654.
118. L.I. Krishtalik, Energetics of multielectron reactions. Photosynthetic oxygen evolution. *Biochim. Biophys. Acta* **849** (1986) 162–171.

119. L.I. Krishtalik, Activation energy of photosynthetic oxygen evolution: an attempt at theoretical analysis. *Bioelectrochem. Bioenerg.* **23** (1990) 249–263.
120. W. Kaim, B. Schwederski, *Bioinorganic Chemistry: Inorganic Elements in the Chemistry of Life, An Introduction and Guide* (1994) Inorganic Chemistry: A Textbook Series, John Wiley & Sons, 1994.
121. N. Tamura, G. Cheniae, Photoactivation of the water-oxidizing complex in Photosystem II membranes depleted of Mn and extrinsic proteins. I. Biochemical and kinetic characterization. *Biochim. Biophys. Acta* **890** (1987) 179–194.
122. N. Tamura, Y. Inoue, G.M. Cheniae, Photoactivation of the water oxidizing complex in photosystem II membranes depleted of Mn, Ca and extrinsic proteins. II. Studies on the functions of Ca^{2+}. *Biochim. Biophys. Acta* **976** (1989) 173–181.
123. K.L. Westphal, N. Lydakis-Simantiris, R.I. Cukier, G.T. Babcock, Effects of Sr^{2+} substitution on the reduction rates of $Y_Z^\cdot$ in PSII membranes: evidence for concerted hydrogen atom transfer in oxygen evolution. *Biochemistry* **39** (2000) 16220–16229.
124. G. Hendry, T. Wydrzynski, ^{18}O isotope exchange measurements reveal that calcium is involved in the binding of one substrate-water molecule to the oxygen-evolving complex in photosystem II. *Biochemistry* **42** (2003) 6209–6217.
125. R.M. Cinco, J.H. Robblee, J. Messinger, C. Fernandez, K.L.M. Holman, K. Sauer, V.K. Yachandra, Orientation of calcium in the Mn_4Ca cluster of the oxygen-evolving complex determined using polarized strontium EXAFS of photosystem II membranes. *Biochemistry* **43** (2004) 13271–13282.
126. M.A. Strickler, L.M. Walker, W. Hillier, R.J. Debus, Evidence from biosynthetically incorporated strontium and FTIR difference spectroscopy that the C-terminus of the D1 polypeptide of photosystem II does not ligate calcium. *Biochemistry* **44** (2005) 8571–8577.
127. A. Boussac, F. Rappaport, P. Carrier, J.M. Verbavatz, R. Gobin, D. Kirilovsky, A.W. Rutherford, M. Sugiura, Biosynthetic Ca^{2+}/Sr^{2+} exchange in the photosystem II oxygen-evolving enzyme of *Thermosynechococcus elongatus*. *J. Biol. Chem.* **279** (2004) 22809–22819.
128. A. Boussac, A.W. Rutherford, Nature of the inhibition of the oxygen-evolving enzyme of photosystem II induced by NaCl washing and reversed by the addition of Ca^{2+} or Sr^{2+}. *Biochemistry* **27** (1988) 3476–3483.
129. D.F. Ghanotakis, G.T. Babcock, C.F. Yocum, Calcium reconstitutes high rates of oxygen evolution in polypeptide depleted Photosystem II preparations. *FEBS Lett.* **167** (1984) 127–130.
130. G.M. Ananyev, G.C. Dismukes, High-resolution kinetics studies of the reassembly of the tetra-manganese cluster of photosynthetic water oxidation: proton equilibrium, cations, and electrostatic. *Biochemistry* **35** (1996) 14608–14617.
131. G.M. Ananyev, G.C. Dismukes, Assembly of the tetra-Mn site of photosynthetic water oxidation by photoactivation: Mn stoichiometry and detection of a new intermediate. *Biochemistry* **35** (1996) 4102–4109.
132. J. Messinger, J. Robblee, U. Bergmann, C. Fernandez, P. Glatzel, S. Isgandarova, B. Hanssum, G. Renger, S. Cramer, K. Sauer, V. Yachandra, Manganese oxidation states in photosystem II, in: *Proceedings of the 12th International Congress on Photosynthesis* (2001) CSIRO Publishing, Collingwood, Australia, pp. S10–019.
133. G. Renger, Mechanistic and structural aspects of photosynthetic water oxidation. *Physiol. Plant.* **100** (1997) 828–841.
134. T.-A. Ono, Metallo-radical hypothesis for photoassembly of Mn_4 cluster of photosynthetic oxygen evolving complex. *Biochim. Biophys. Acta* **1503** (2001) 40–51.

135. M. Higuchi, T. Noguchi, K. Sonoike, Over-reduced states of the Mn-cluster in cucumber leaves induced by dark-chilling treatment. *Biochim. Biophys. Acta* **1604** (2003) 151–158.
136. A. Quigg, J. Beardall, T. Wydrzynski, Photoacclimation involves modulation of the photosynthetic oxygen-evolving reactions in Dunaliella tertiolecta and Phaeodactylum tricornutum. *Funct. Plant Biol.* **30** (2003) 301–308.
137. G. Renger, M. Völker, H.J. Eckert, R. Fromme, S. Hohm-Veit, P. Gräber, On the mechanism of photosystem II deterioration by UV-B irradiation. *Photochem. Photobiol.* **49** (1989) 97–105.
138. N. Ohnishi, S.I. Allakhverdiev, S. Takahashi, S. Higashi, M. Watanabe, Y. Nishiyama, N. Murata, Two-step mechanism of photodamage to photosystem II: Step 1 occurs at the oxygen-evolving complex and step 2 occurs at the photochemical reaction center. *Biochemistry* **44** (2005) 8494–8499.
139. L.K. Thompson, R. Blaylock, J.M. Sturtevant, G.W. Brudvig, Molecular basis of the heat denaturation of photosystem II. *Biochemistry* **28** (1989) 6686–6695.
140. I. Enami, M. Kitamura, T. Tomo, Y. Isokawa, H. Ohta, S. Katoh, Is the primary cause of thermal inactivation of oxygen evolution in spinach PS II membranes release of the extrinsic 33 kDa protein or of Mn. *Biochim. Biophys. Acta* **1186** (1994) 52–58.
141. J. Biesiadka, B. Loll, J. Kern, K.-D. Irrgang, A. Zouni, Crystal structure of cyanobacterial photosystem II at 3.2 Å resolution: a closer look at the Mn-cluster. *Phys. Chem. Chem. Phys.* **6** (2004) 4733–4736.
142. J. Yano, J. Kern, K.D. Irrgang, M.J. Latimer, U. Bergmann, P. Glatzel, Y. Pushkar, J. Biesiadka, B. Loll, K. Sauer, J. Messinger, A. Zouni, V.K. Yachandra, X-ray damage to the Mn_4Ca complex in single crystals of photosystem II: a case study for metalloprotein crystallography. *Proc. Natl. Acad. Sci. U.S.A.* **102** (2005) 12047–12052.
143. M. Grabolle, M. Haumann, C. Müller, P. Liebisch, H. Dau, Rapid loss of structural motifs in the manganese complex of oxygenic photosynthesis by x-ray irradiation at 10–300 K. *J. Biol. Chem.* **281** (2006) 4580–4588.
144. J.H. Robblee, R.M. Cinco, V.K. Yachandra, X-ray spectroscopy based structure of the Mn cluster and mechanism of photosynthetic oxygen evolution. *Biochim. Biophys. Acta* **1503** (2001) 7–23.
145. J. Messinger, Evaluation of different mechanistic proposals for water oxidation in photosynthesis on the basis of Mn_4O_xCa structures for the catalytic site and spectroscopic data. *Phys. Chem. Chem. Phys.* **6** (2004) 4764–4771.
146. H. Dau, P. Liebisch, M. Haumann, The structure of the manganese complex of Photosystem II in its dark-stable S_1-state - EXAFS results in relation to recent crystallographic data. *Phys. Chem. Chem. Phys.* **6** (2004) 4781–4792.
147. V.J. DeRose, I. Mukerji, M.J. Latimer, V.K. Yachandra, K. Sauer, M.P. Klein, Comparison of the manganese oxygen-evolving complex in photosystem II of spinach and *Synechococcus* sp. with multinuclear manganese model compounds by X-ray absorption spectroscopy. *J. Am. Chem. Soc.* **116** (1994) 5239–5249.
148. J.H. Robblee, J. Messinger, R.M. Cinco, K.L. McFarlane, C. Fernandez, S.A. Pizarro, K. Sauer, V.K. Yachandra, The Mn cluster in the S_0 state of the oxygen evolving complex of photosystem II studied by EXAFS spectroscopy: are there three di-µ-oxo-bridged Mn_2 moieties in the tetranuclear Mn complex? *J. Am. Chem. Soc.* **124** (2002) 7459–7471.
149. J. Yano, Y. Pushkar, P. Glatzel, A. Lewis, K. Sauer, J. Messinger, U. Bergmann, V.K. Yachandra, High-resolution Mn EXAFS of the oxygen-evolving complex in

photosystem II: structural implications for the Mn$_4$Ca cluster. *J. Am. Chem. Soc.* **127** (2005) 14974–14975.
150. R.M. Cinco, K.L. McFarlane Holman, J.H. Robblee, J. Yano, S.A. Pizarro, E. Bellacchio, K. Sauer, V.K. Yachandra, Calcium EXAFS establishes the Mn–Ca cluster in the oxygen evolving complex of photosystem II. *Biochemistry* **41** (2002) 12928–12933.
151. M.J. Latimer, V.J. DeRose, V.K. Yachandra, K. Sauer, M.P. Klein, Structural effects of calcium depletion on the manganese cluster of photosystem II: determination by X-ray absorption spectroscopy. *J. Phys. Chem. B* **102** (1998) 8257–8265.
152. R.M. Cinco, J.H. Robblee, A. Rompel, C. Fernandez, V.K. Yachandra, K. Sauer, M.P. Klein, Strontium EXAFS reveals the proximity of calcium to the manganese cluster of oxygen evolving photosystem II. *J. Phys. Chem. B* **102** (1998) 8248–8256.
153. J. Yano, J. Kern, K. Sauer, M.J. Latimer, Y. Pushkar, J. Biesiadka, B. Loll, W. Saenger, J. Messinger, A. Zouni, V.K. Yachandra, Where water is oxidized to dioxygen: Structure of the photosynthetic Mn$_4$Ca cluster. *Science* **314** (2006) 821–825.
154. W. Liang, T.A. Roelofs, R.M. Cinco, A. Rompel, M.J. Latimer, W.O. Yu, K. Sauer, M.P. Klein, V.K. Yachandra, Structural change of the Mn cluster during the S$_2$ to S$_3$ state transition of the oxygen evolving complex of photosystem II. Does it reflect the onset of water/substrate oxidation? Determination by Mn x-ray absorption spectroscopy. *J. Am. Chem. Soc.* **122** (2000) 3399–3412.
155. M. Haumann, C. Müller, P. Liebisch, L. Iuzzolino, J. Dittmer, M. Grabolle, T. Neisius, W. Meyer-Klaucke, H. Dau, Structural and oxidation state changes of the photosystem II manganese complex in four transitions of the water oxidation cycle (S$_0 \rightarrow$ S$_1$, S$_1 \rightarrow$ S$_2$, S$_2 \rightarrow$ S$_3$, and S$_3$,S$_4 \rightarrow$ S$_0$) characterized by X-ray absorption spectroscopy at 20 K and room temperature. *Biochemistry* **44** (2005) 1894–1908.
156. A. Boussac, A.W. Rutherford, Ca^{2+} binding to the oxygen evolving enzyme varies with the redox state of the Mn cluster. *FEBS Lett.* **236** (1988) 432–436.
157. J. Messinger, G. Renger, The reactivity of hydrazine with PS II strongly depends on the redox state of the water oxidizing system. *FEBS Lett.* **277** (1990) 141–146.
158. G. Renger, B. Hanssum, Studies on the reaction coordinates of the water oxidase in PSII membrane-fragments from spinach. *FEBS Lett.* **299** (1992) 28–32.
159. M.J. Baldwin, T.L. Stemmler, P.J. Riggs-Gelasco, M.L. Kirk, J.E. Penner-Hahn, V.L. Pecoraro, Structural and magnetic effects of successive protonations of oxo bridges in high-valent manganese dimers. *J. Am. Chem. Soc.* **116** (1994) 11349–11356.
160. S. Mukhopadhyay, S.K. Mandal, S. Bhaduri, W.H. Armstrong, Manganese clusters with relevance to photosystem II. *Chem. Rev.* **104** (2004) 3981–4026.
161. H. Beinert, R.H. Holm, E. Munck, Iron-sulfur clusters: Nature's modular, multipurpose structures. *Science* **277** (1997) 653–659.
162. P. Glatzel, U. Bergmann, J. Yano, H. Visser, J.H. Robblee, W.W. Gu, F.M.F. de Groot, G. Christou, V.L. Pecoraro, S.P. Cramer, V.K. Yachandra, The electronic structure of Mn in oxides, coordination complexes, and the oxygen-evolving complex of photosystem II studied by resonant inelastic X-ray scattering. *J. Am. Chem. Soc.* **126** (2004) 9946–9959.
163. J.M. Peloquin, K.A. Campbell, D.W. Randall, M.A. Evanchik, V.L. Pecoraro, W.H. Armstrong, R.D. Britt, ^{55}Mn ENDOR of the S$_2$-state multiline EPR signal of photosystem II: implications on the structure of the tetranuclear Mn cluster. *J. Am. Chem. Soc.* **122** (2000) 10926–10942.

164. M.F. Charlot, A. Boussac, G. Blondin, Towards a spin coupling model for the Mn_4 cluster in photosystem II. *Biochim. Biophys. Acta* **1708** (2005) 120–132.
165. G.C. Dismukes, Y. Siderer, Intermediates of a polynuclear manganese cluster involved in photosynthetic oxidation of water. *Proc. Natl. Acad. Sci. U.S.A.* **78** (1981) 274–278.
166. J. Messinger, J.H.A. Nugent, M.C.W. Evans, Detection of an EPR multiline signal for the S_0^* state in photosystem II. *Biochemistry* **36** (1997) 11055–11060.
167. J. Messinger, J.H. Robblee, W.O. Yu, K. Sauer, V.K. Yachandra, M.P. Klein, The S_0 state of the oxygen evolving complex in photosystem II is paramagnetic: detection of an EPR multiline signal. *J. Am. Chem. Soc.* **119** (1997) 11349–11350.
168. K.A. Åhrling, S. Peterson, S. Styring, An oscillating manganese electron paramagnetic resonance signal from the S_0 state of the oxygen evolving complex in photosystem II. *Biochemistry* **36** (1997) 13148–13152.
169. L.V. Kulik, B. Epel, W. Lubitz, J. Messinger, ^{55}Mn pulse ENDOR at 34 GHz of the S_0 and S_2 states of the oxygen-evolving complex in photosystem II. *J. Am. Chem. Soc.* **127** (2005) 2392–2393.
170. L.V. Kulik, W. Lubitz, J. Messinger, Electron spin-lattice relaxation of the S_0 state of the oxygen-evolving complex in photosystem II and of dinuclear manganese model complexes. *Biochemistry* **44** (2005) 9368–9374.
171. T.G. Carell, A.M. Tyryshkin, G.C. Dismukes, An evaluation of structural models for the photosynthetic water oxidizing complex derived from spectroscopic and X-ray diffraction signatures. *J. Biol. Inorg. Chem.* **7** (2002) 2–22.
172. D. Kuzek, R.J. Pace, Probing the Mn oxidation states in the OEC. Insights from spectroscopic, computational and kinetic data. *Biochim. Biophys. Acta* **1503** (2001) 123–137.
173. J. Messinger, Towards understanding the chemistry of photosynthetic oxygen evolution: dynamic structural changes, redox states and substrate water binding of the Mn cluster in photosystem II. *Biochim. Biophys. Acta* **1459** (2000) 481–488.
174. N. Ioannidis, G. Schansker, V.V. Barynin, V. Petrouleas, Interaction of nitric oxide with the oxygen evolving complex of photosystem II and Mn catalase. A comparative study. *J. Biol. Inorg. Chem.* **5** (2000) 354–363.
175. G. Renger, Coupling of electron and proton transfer in oxidative water cleavage in photosynthesis. *Biochim. Biophys. Acta* **1655** (2004) 195–204.
176. G. Renger, Oxidative photosynthetic water splitting: energetics, kinetics and mechanism. *Photosynth. Res.* **92** (2007) 407–425.
177. A. Rashid, P.H. Homann, Properties of iodide activated photosynthetic water oxidizing complexes. *Biochim. Biophys. Acta* **1101** (1992) 303–310.
178. K. Olesen, L.-E. Andréasson, The function of the chloride ion in photosynthetic oxygen evolution. *Biochemistry* **42** (2003) 2025–2035.
179. H. Wincencjusz, C.F. Yocum, H.J. van Gorkom, Activating anions that replace Cl^- in the O_2 evolving complex of photosystem II slow the kinetics of the terminal step in water oxidation and destabilize the S_2 and S_3 states. *Biochemistry* **38** (1999) 3719–3725.
180. A. Jajoo, S. Bharti, A. Kawamori, Decay kinetics of tyrosine radical (Y_Z) in chloride anion-depleted photosystem 2 studied by time-resolved EPR. *Photosynthetica* **42** (2004) 59–64.
181. A. Jajoo, S. Bharti, A. Kawamori, Interactions of chloride and formate at the donor and the acceptor side of photosystem II. *J. Bioenerg. Biomembr.* **37** (2005) 49–54.

182. J.J.S. van Rensen, C. Xu, Govindjee, Role of bicarbonate in photosystem II, the water-plastoquinone oxido-reductase of plant photosynthesis. *Physiol. Plant.* **105** (1999) 585–592.
183. J.J.S. van Rensen, V.V. Klimov, Bicarbonate interactions, in: *Photosystem II. The Light-Driven Water: Plastoquinone Oxidoreductase* (2005) (T. Wydrzynski, K. Satoh, eds.), Springer, Dordrecht, pp. 329–346.
184. K. Lindberg, T. Wydrzynski, T. Vänngård, L.-E. Andréasson, Slow release of chloride from ^{36}Cl-labeled photosystem II membranes. *FEBS Lett.* **264** (1990) 153–155.
185. K. Hasegawa, Y. Kimura, T. Ono, Oxidation of the Mn cluster induces structural changes of NO_3^- functionally bound to the Cl^- site in the oxygen-evolving complex of Photosystem II. *Biophys. J* **86** (2004) 1042–1050.
186. M. Haumann, M. Barra, P. Loja, S. Loscher, R. Krivanek, A. Grundmeier, L.-E. Andreasson, H. Dau, Bromide does not bind to the Mn_4Ca complex in its S_1 state in Cl^--depleted and Br^--reconstituted oxygen-evolving Photosystem II: Evidence from X-ray absorption spectroscopy at the Br K-edge. *Biochemistry* **45** (2006) 13101–13107.
187. T. Wydrzynski, K. Sauer, Periodic changes in the oxidation state of manganese in photosynthetic oxygen evolution upon illumination with flashes. *Biochim. Biophys. Acta* **589** (1980) 56–70.
188. C. Critchley, A.M. Sargeson, A manganese-chloride cluster as the functional centre of the oxygen-evolving enzyme in photosynthetic systems. *FEBS Lett.* **177** (1984) 2–5.
189. P.O. Sandusky, C.F. Yocum, The chloride requirement for photosynthetic oxygen evolution: factors affecting nucleophilic displacement of chloride from the oxygen evolving complex. *Biochim. Biophys. Acta* **849** (1986) 85–93.
190. R. Damoder, V.V. Klimov, G.C. Dismukes, The effect of Cl^- depletion and X^- reconstitution on the oxygen evolution rate, the yield of the multiline manganese EPR signal and EPR signal II in the isolated photosystem II complex. *Biochim. Biophys. Acta* **848** (1986) 378–391.
191. C. Tommos, G.T. Babcock, Oxygen production in nature: a light-driven metalloradical enzyme process. *Acc. Chem. Res.* **31** (1998) 18–25.
192. P.O. Sandusky, C.F. Yocum, The chloride requirement for photosynthetic oxygen evolution: analysis of the effects of chloride and other anions on amine inhibition of the oxygen evolving complex. *Biochim. Biophys. Acta* **766** (1984) 603–611.
193. Y. Kimura, K. Hasegawa, T. Yamanari, T. Ono, Studies on photosynthetic oxygen-evolving complex by means of Fourier transform infrared spectroscopy: calcium and chloride cofactors. *Photosynth. Res.* **84** (2005) 245–250.
194. A.J. Stemler, The bicarbonate effect, oxygen evolution, and the shadow of Otto Warburg. *Photosynth. Res.* **73** (2002) 177–183.
195. J. Clausen, K. Beckmann, W. Junge, J. Messinger, Evidence that bicarbonate is not the substrate in photosynthetic oxygen evolution. *Plant Physiol.* **139** (2005) 1444–1450.
196. W. Hillier, I. McConnell, M.R. Badger, A. Boussac, V.V. Klimov, G.C. Dismukes, T. Wydrzynski, Quantitative assessment of intrinsic carbonic anhydrase activity and the capacity for bicarbonate oxidation in photosystem II. *Biochemistry* **45** (2006) 2094–2102.
197. R. Radmer, O. Ollinger, Do the higher oxidation states of the photosynthetic O_2 evolving system contain bound water? *FEBS Lett.* **195** (1986) 285–289.
198. K.P. Bader, G. Renger, G.H. Schmid, A mass-spectrometric analysis of the water splitting reaction. *Photosynth. Res.* **38** (1993) 355–361.

199. J. Messinger, M. Badger, T. Wydrzynski, Detection of *one* slowly exchanging substrate water molecule in the S_3 state of photosystem II. *Proc. Natl. Acad. Sci. U.S.A.* **92** (1995) 3209–3213.
200. L. Konermann, J. Messinger, W. Hillier, Mass spectrometry based methods for studying kinetics and dynamics in biological systems, in: *Biophysical Techniques in Photosynthesis (Volume II)* (2008) (T.J. Aartsma, J. Matysik, eds.), Series Advances in Photosynthesis and Respiration, Vol. 26, Springer, Dordrecht, pp. 167–190.
201. R.D. Britt, K.A. Campbell, J.M. Peloquin, M.L. Gilchrist, C.P. Aznar, M.M. Dicus, J. Robblee, J. Messinger, Recent pulsed EPR studies of the Photosystem II oxygen-evolving complex: implications as to water oxidation mechanisms. *Biochim. Biophys. Acta* **1655** (2004) 158–171.
202. T.C. Weng, W.Y. Hsieh, E.S. Uffelman, S.W. Gordon-Wylie, T.J. Collins, V.L. Pecoraro, J.E. Penner-Hahn, XANES evidence against a manganyl species in the S_3 state of the oxygen-evolving complex. *J. Am. Chem. Soc.* **126** (2004) 8070–8071.
203. T.A. Roelofs, W. Liang, M.J. Latimer, R.M. Cinco, A. Rompel, J.C. Andrews, K. Sauer, V.K. Yachandra, M.P. Klein, Oxidation states of the manganese cluster during the flash-induced S-state cycle of the photosynthetic oxygen evolving complex. *Proc. Natl. Acad. Sci. U.S.A.* **93** (1996) 3335–3340.
204. M. Haumann, P. Liebisch, C. Müller, M. Barra, M. Grabolle, H. Dau, Photosynthetic O_2 formation tracked by time-resolved X-ray experiments. *Science* **310** (2005) 1019–1021.
205. R. Tagore, H.Y. Chen, R.H. Crabtree, G.W. Brudvig, Determination of μ-oxo exchange rates in di-μ-oxo dimanganese complexes by electrospray ionization mass spectrometry. *J. Am. Chem. Soc.* **128** (2006) 9457–9465.
206. R. Tagore, R.H. Crabtree, G.W. Brudvig, Distinct mechanisms of bridging-oxo exchange in di-μ-O dimanganese complexes with and without water-binding sites: Implications for water binding in the O_2-evolving complex of photosystem II. *Inorg. Chem.* **46** (2007) 2193–2203.
207. P.R. Sharp, Proton NMR relaxation due to photosynthetic oxygen evolving center, in: *Manganese Redox Enzymes* (1992) (V.L. Pecoraro, ed.), VCH Publishers, New York, pp. 177–196.
208. M.C.W. Evans, J.H.A. Nugent, R.J. Ball, I. Muhiuddin, R.J. Pace, Evidence for a direct manganese-oxygen ligand in water binding to the S_2 state of the photosynthetic water oxidation complex. *Biochemistry* **43** (2004) 989–994.
209. R. Debus, The catalytic manganese cluster: protein ligation, in: *Photosystem II. The Light Driven Water:Plastiquinone Oxidoreductase* (2005) (T. Wydrzynski, K. Satoh, eds.), Springer, Dordrecht, pp. 261–284.
210. J. Clausen, S. Winkler, A.M.A. Hays, M. Hundelt, R.J. Debus, W. Junge, Photosynthetic water oxidation in Synechocystis sp PCC6803: mutations D1-E189K, R and Q are without influence on electron transfer at the donor side of photosystem II. *Biochim. Biophys. Acta* **1506** (2001) 224–235.
211. R.J. Debus, K.A. Campbell, D.P. Pham, A.-M.A. Hays, R.D. Britt, Glutamate 189 of the D1 polypeptide modulates the magnetic and redox properties of the manganese cluster and tyrosine Y_Z in photosystem II. *Biochemistry* **39** (2000) 6275–6287.
212. Y. Kimura, N. Mizusawa, A. Ishii, S. Nakazawa, T. Ono, Changes in structural and functional properties of oxygen-evolving complex induced by replacement of D1-glutamate 189 with glutamine in photosystem II - Ligation of glutamate 189 carboxylate to the manganese cluster. *J. Biol. Chem.* **280** (2005) 37895–37900.

213. R.J. Debus, M.A. Strickler, L.M. Walker, W. Hillier, No evidence from FTIR difference spectroscopy that aspartate-170 of the D1 polypeptide ligates a manganese ion that undergoes oxidation during the S_0 to S_1, S_1 to S_2, or S_2 to S_3 transitions in photosystem II. *Biochemistry* **44** (2005) 1367–1374.
214. H.A. Chu, W. Hillier, R.J. Debus, Evidence that the C-terminus of the D1 polypeptide of photosystem II is ligated to the manganese ion that undergoes oxidation during the S_1 to S_2 transition: an isotope-edited FTIR study. *Biochemistry* **43** (2004) 3152–3166.
215. Y. Kimura, N. Mizusawa, T. Yamanari, A. Ishii, T. Ono, Structural changes of D1 C-terminal alpha-carboxylate during S-state cycling in photosynthetic oxygen evolution. *J. Biol. Chem.* **280** (2005) 2078–2083.
216. Y. Kimura, N. Mizusawa, A. Ishii, T. Ono, FTIR detection of structural changes in a histidine ligand during S-state cycling of photosynthetic oxygen-evolving complex. *Biochemistry* **44** (2005) 16072–16078.
217. M.A. Strickler, L.M. Walker, W. Hillier, R.D. Britt, R.J. Debus, No evidence from FTIR difference spectroscopy that aspartate-342 of the D1 polypeptide ligates a Mn ion that undergoes oxidation during the S_0 to S_1, S_1 to S_2, or S_2 to S_3 transitions in photosystem II. *Biochemistry* **46** (2007) 3151–3160.
218. C.W. Hoganson, G.T. Babcock, A metalloradical mechanism for the generation of oxygen from water in photosynthesis. *Science* **277** (1997) 1953–1956.
219. J.P. McEvoy, G.W. Brudvig, Structure-based mechanism of photosynthetic water oxidation. *Phys. Chem. Chem. Phys.* **6** (2004) 4754–4763.
220. M. Sivaraja, J. Tso, G.C. Dismukes, A calcium-specific site influences the structure and activity of the manganese cluster responsible for photosynthetic water oxidation. *Biochemistry* **28** (1989) 9459–9464.
221. P. Dorlet, A. Boussac, A.W. Rutherford, S. Un, Multifrequency high-field EPR study of the interaction between the tyrosyl Z radical and the manganese cluster in plant photosystem II. *J. Phys. Chem. B* **103** (1999) 10945–10954.
222. J.H.A. Nugent, I.P. Muhiuddin, M.C.W. Evans, Electron transfer from the water oxidizing complex at cryogenic temperatures: The S_1 to S_2 step. *Biochemistry* **41** (2002) 4117–4126.
223. N. Ioannidis, J.H.A. Nugent, V. Petrouleas, Intermediates of the S_3 state of the oxygen evolving complex of photosystem II. *Biochemistry* **41** (2002) 9589–9600.
224. C.X. Zhang, S. Styring, Formation of split electron paramagnetic resonance signals in photosystem II suggests that tyrosine$_Z$ can be photooxidized at 5 K in the S_0 and S_1 states of the oxygen-evolving complex. *Biochemistry* **42** (2003) 8066–8076.
225. C.X. Zhang, A. Boussac, A.W. Rutherford, Low-temperature electron transfer in photosystem II: A tyrosyl radical and semiquinone charge pair. *Biochemistry* **43** (2004) 13787–13795.
226. V. Petrouleas, D. Koulougliotis, N. Ioannidis, Trapping of metalloradical intermediates of the S-states at liquid helium temperatures. Overview of the phenomenology and mechanistic implications. *Biochemistry* **44** (2005) 6723–6728.
227. P. Geijer, F. Morvaridi, S. Styring, The S_3 state of the oxygen evolving complex in photosystem II is converted to the $S_2Y_Z^{\cdot}$ state at alkaline pH. *Biochemistry* **40** (2001) 10881–10891.
228. N. Ioannidis, G. Zahariou, V. Petrouleas, Trapping of the S_2 to S_3 state intermediate of the oxygen-evolving complex of photosystem II. *Biochemistry* **45** (2006) 6252–6259.

229. F. Rappaport, J. Lavergne, Proton release during successive oxidation steps of the photosynthetic water oxidation process - stoichiometries and pH-dependence. *Biochemistry* **30** (1991) 10004–10012.
230. H. Kretschmann, E. Schlodder, H.T. Witt, Net charge oscillation and proton release during water oxidation in photosynthesis. An electrochromic band shift study at pH 5.5–7.0. *Biochim. Biophys. Acta* **1274** (1996) 1–8.
231. E. Schlodder, H.T. Witt, Stoichiometry of proton release from the catalytic center in photosynthetic water oxidation. *J. Biol. Chem.* **274** (1999) 30387–30392.
232. F. Rappaport, J. Lavergne, Coupling of electron and proton transfer in the photosynthetic water oxidase. *Biochim. Biophys. Acta* **1503** (2001) 246–259.
233. G.T. Babcock, K. Sauer, Electron paramagnetic resonance signal II in spinach chloroplasts. 1. Kinetic-analysis for untreated chloroplasts. *Biochim. Biophys. Acta* **325** (1973) 483–503.
234. G.T. Babcock, K. Sauer, Electron paramagnetic resonance signal II in spinach chloroplasts. 2. Alternative spectral forms and inhibitor effects on kinetics of signal II in flashing light. *Biochim. Biophys. Acta* **325** (1973) 504–519.
235. M. Boska, K. Sauer, W. Buttner, G.T. Babcock, Similarity of electron-paramagnetic-res signal-II_f rise and $P680^+$ decay kinetics in Tris-washed chloroplast photosystem II preparations as a function of pH. *Biochim. Biophys. Acta* **722** (1983) 327–330.
236. G.T. Babcock, R.E. Blankenship, K. Sauer, Reaction kinetics for positive charge accumulation on the water side of chloroplast photosystem II. *FEBS Lett.* **61** (1976) 286–289.
237. P. Joliot, M. Hofnung, R. Chabaud, Etude de lemission doxygene par des algues soumises a un eclairement module sinusoidalement. *J. Chim. Phys.* **63** (1966) 1423–1441.
238. B. Bouges-Bocquet, Limiting steps in photosystem II and water decomposition in *Chlorella* and spinach chloroplasts. *Biochim. Biophys. Acta* **292** (1973) 772–785.
239. M.R. Razeghifard, R.J. Pace, Electron paramagnetic resonance kinetic studies of the S states in spinach PSII membranes. *Biochim. Biophys. Acta* **1322** (1997) 141–150.
240. H. Koike, Y. Inoue, Temperature dependence of the S-state transitions in a thermophilic cyanobacterium measured by thermoluminescence, in: *Progress in Photosynthesis Research* (1987) (J. Biggins, ed.), Nijhoff, Dordrecht, pp. 645–648.
241. B.R. Velthuys, Spectroscopic studies of the S state transitions of photosystem II and the interactions of its charged donor chain with lipid-soluble anions, in: *Proceedings of the Vth International Congress on Photosynthesis*, Akoyunoglou, (ed.), Balaban, Rehevot, (1981), pp. 75–85.
242. G. Renger, W. Weiss, The detection of intrinsic 320 nm absorption changes reflecting the turnover of the water-splitting enzyme system Y which leads to oxygen formation in trypsinized chloroplasts. *FEBS Lett.* **137** (1982) 217–221.
243. G.H. Schatz, H.J. Van Gorkom, Absorbency difference spectra upon charge-transfer to secondary donors and acceptors in photosystem II. *Biochim. Biophys. Acta* **810** (1985) 283–294.
244. F. Rappaport, M. Blanchard-Desce, J. Lavergne, Kinetics of electron transfer and electrochromic change during the redox transitions of the photosynthetic oxygen evolving complex. *Biochim. Biophys. Acta* **1184** (1994) 178–192.
245. P.J. van Leeuwen, C. Heimann, P. Gast, J.P. Dekker, H.J. van Gorkom, Flash-induced redox changes in oxygen-evolving spinach photosystem II core particles. *Photosynth. Res.* **38** (1993) 169–176.

246. J.P. Dekker, J.J. Plijter, L. Ouwehand, H.J. van Gorkom, Kinetics of manganese redox transitions in the oxygen-evolving apparatus of photosynthesis. *Biochim. Biophys. Acta* **767** (1984) 176–179.
247. G. Renger, W. Weiss, Functional and structural aspects of photosynthetic water oxidation, *Biochem. Soc. Trans.* **14** (1986) 17–20.
248. G. Renger, W. Weiss, Spectral characterization in the ultraviolet region of the precursor of photosynthetically evolved oxygen in isolated trypsinized chloroplasts. *Biochim. Biophys. Acta* **722** (1983) 1–11.
249. H. Koike, B. Hanssum, Y. Inoue, G. Renger, Temperature dependence of the S-state transitions in a thermophilic cyanobacterium, *Synechococcus vulcanus* Copeland measured by absorption changes in the ultraviolet region. *Biochim. Biophys. Acta* **893** (1987) 524–533.
250. M. Karge, K.-D. Irrgang, G. Renger, Analysis of the reaction coordinate of photosynthetic water oxidation by kinetic measurements of 355 nm absorption changes at different temperatures in photosystem II preparations suspended in either H_2O or D_2O. *Biochemistry* **36** (1997) 8904–8913.
251. J. Clausen, R.J. Debus, W. Junge, Time-resolved oxygen production by PSII: chasing chemical intermediates. *Biochim. Biophys. Acta* **1655** (2004) 184–194.
252. M. Hundelt, A.-M.A. Hays, R.J. Debus, W. Junge, Oxygenic photosystem II: the mutation D1-D61N in *Synechocystis sp.* PCC 6803 retards S-state transitions without affecting electron transfer from Y_Z to $P680^+$. *Biochemistry* **37** (1998) 14450–14456.
253. E.-H. Kim, R. Razeghifard, J.M. Anderson, W.S. Chow, Multiple sites of retardation of electron transfer in Photosystem II after hydrolysis of phosphatidylglycerol. *Photosynth. Res.* **93** (2007) 149–158.
254. A. Boussac, F. Rappaport, P. Carrier, J.-M. Verbavatz, R. Gobin, D. Kirilovsky, A.W. Rutherford, M. Sugiura, Biosynthetic Ca^{2+}/Sr^{2+} exchange in the Photosystem II oxygen-evolving enzyme of *Thermosynechococcus elongates*. *J. Biol. Chem.* **279** (2004) 22809–22819.
255. M. Völker, H.-J. Eckert, G. Renger, Effects of trypsin and bivalent cations on $P680^+$ reduction, fluorescence induction and oxygen evolution in photosystem II membrane fragments from spinach. *Biochim. Biophys. Acta* **890** (1987) 66–76.
256. M.R. Razeghifard, R.J. Pace, EPR kinetic studies of oxygen release in thylakoids in PSII membranes: a kinetic intermediate in the S_3 to S_0 transition. *Biochemistry* **38** (1999) 1252–1257.
257. G. Renger, T. Bittner, J. Messinger, Structure-function relationships in photosynthetic water oxidation, *Biochem. Soc. Trans.* **22** (1994) 318–322.
258. N. Lydakis-Simantiris, D.F. Ghanotakis, G.T. Babcock, Kinetic isotope effects on the reduction of the Y_Z radical in oxygen evolving and Tris washed photosystem II membranes by time resolved EPR. *Biochim. Biophys. Acta* **1322** (1997) 129–140.
259. O. Bögershausen, M. Haumann, W. Junge, Photosynthetic oxygen evolution: H/D isotope effects and the coupling between electron and proton transfer during transitions S_2 to S_3 and S_3 to S_4 to S_0. *Ber. Bunsen.-Ges. Chem. Phys. Phys. Chem.* **100** (1996) 1987–1992.
260. K.B. Schowen, R.L. Schowen, Solvent isotope effects on enzyme systems. *Methods Enzymol.* **87** (1982) 551–606.
261. J. Sinclair, T. Arnason, Studies on a thermal reaction associated with photosynthetic oxygen evolution. *Biochim. Biophys. Acta* **368** (1974) 393–400.
262. G.T. Babcock, M. Wikstrom, Oxygen activation and the conservation of energy in cell respiration. *Nature* **356** (1992) 301–309.

263. S. Hallen, T. Nilsson, Proton transfer during the reaction between fully reduced cytochrome c oxidase and dioxygen - pH and deuterium isotope effects. *Biochemistry* **31** (1992) 11853–11859.
264. J. Lavergne, W. Junge, Proton release during the redox cycle of the water oxidase. *Photosynth. Res.* **38** (1993) 279–296.
265. O. Saygin, H.T. Witt, Evidence for the electrochromic identification of the change of charges in the 4 oxidation steps of the photoinduced water cleavage in photosynthesis. *FEBS Lett.* **187** (1985) 224–226.
266. J. Lavergne, Improved UV-visible spectra of S-state transitions in the photosynthetic oxygen evolving system. *Biochim. Biophys. Acta* **1060** (1991) 175–188.
267. R.I. Cukier, Theory and simulation of proton-coupled electron transfer, hydrogen-atom transfer, and proton translocation in proteins. *Biochim. Biophys. Acta* **1655** (2004) 37–44.
268. S. Hammes-Schiffer, Hydrogen tunneling and protein motion in enzyme reactions. *Acc. Chem. Res.* **39** (2006) 93–100.
269. T.J. Meyer, M. Hang, V. Huynh, H.H. Thorp, The Role of Proton Coupled Electron Transfer (PCET) in Water Oxidation by Photosystem II. Wiring for Protons. *Angew. Chem. Int. Ed.* **46** (2007) 5284–5304.
270. R.A. Marcus, N. Sutin, Electron transfers in chemistry and biology. *Biochim. Biophys. Acta* **811** (1985) 265–322.
271. A. Ponce, H.B. Gray, J.R. Winkler, Electron tunneling through water: Oxidative quenching of electronically excited $Ru(tpy)_2^{2+}$ (tpy = 2,2':6,2''-terpyridine) by ferric ions in aqueous glasses at 77 K. *J. Am. Chem. Soc.* **122** (2000) 8187–8191.
272. J.M. Nocek, J.S. Zhou, S. DeForest, S. Priyadarshy, D.N. Beratan, J.N. Onuchic, B.M. Hoffman, Theory and practice of electron transfer within protein-protein complexes: Application to the multidomain binding of cytochrome c by cytochrome c peroxidase. *Chem. Rev.* **96** (1996) 2459–2489.
273. M.L. Jones, I.V. Kurnikov, D.N. Beratan, The nature of tunneling pathway and average packing density models for protein-mediated electron transfer. *J. Phys. Chem. A* **106** (2002) 2002–2006.
274. C.C. Moser, C.C. Page, X. Chen, P.L. Dutton, Biological electron tunneling through native protein media. *J. Biol. Inorg. Chem.* **2** (1997) 393–398.
275. C.C. Page, C.C. Moser, X.X. Chen, P.L. Dutton, Natural engineering principles of electron tunnelling in biological oxidation-reduction. *Nature* **402** (1999) 47–52.
276. G. Renger, G. Christen, M. Karge, H.-J. Eckert, K.-D. Irrgang, Application of the Marcus theory for analysis of the temperature dependence of the reactions leading to photosynthetic water oxidation: results and implications. *J. Biol. Inorg. Chem.* **3** (1998) 360–366.
277. J.S. Vrettos, J. Limburg, G.W. Brudvig, Mechanism of photosynthetic water oxidation: combining biophysical studies of photosystem II with inorganic model chemistry. *Biochim. Biophys. Acta* **1503** (2001) 229–245.
278. T. Noguchi, T.A. Ono, Y. Inoue, Temperature-dependence of the $S_1 \rightarrow S_2$ transition in the oxygen-evolving complex of photosystem II studied by FT-IR spectroscopy. *Biochim. Biophys. Acta* **1143** (1993) 333–336.
279. K. Sauer, J. Yano, V.K. Yachandra, X-ray spectroscopy of the Mn_4Ca cluster in the water-oxidation complex of Photosystem II. *Photosynth. Res.* **85** (2005) 73–86.
280. P.E.M. Siegbahn, Theoretical models for the oxygen radical mechanism of water oxidation and the water oxidizing complex of photosystem II. *Inorg. Chem.* **39** (2000) 2923–2935.

281. J.P. McEvoy, G.W. Brudvig, Water-splitting chemistry of photosystem II. *Chem. Rev.* **106** (2006) 4455–4483.
282. V.L. Pecoraro, M.J. Baldwin, M.T. Caudle, W.-Y. Hsieh, N.A. Law, A proposal for water oxidation in photosystem II. *Pure Appl. Chem Eur. J.* **70** (1998) 925–929.
283. H. Dau, L. Iuzzolino, J. Dittmer, The tetra-manganese complex of photosystem II during its redox cycle: X-ray absorption results and mechanistic implications. *Biochim. Biophys. Acta* **1503** (2001) 24–39.
284. P.E.M. Siegbahn, O—O Bond Formation in the S_4 State of the Oxygen-Evolving Complex in Photosystem. *Chem. Eur. J.* **12** (2006) 9217–9227.
285. M. Haumann, W. Junge, Photosynthetic water oxidation: a simplex scheme of its partial reactions. *Biochim. Biophys. Acta* **1411** (1999) 86–91.
286. H.T. Witt, Primary reactions of oxygenic photosynthesis. *Ber. Bunsenges. Phys. Chem.* **100** (1996) 1923–1942.
287. A.B. Anderson, T.V. Albu, Ab initio determination of reversible potentials and activation energies for outer-sphere oxygen reduction to water and the reverse oxidation reaction. *J. Am. Chem. Soc.* **121** (1999) 11855–11863.
288. W. Hillier, J. Messinger, T. Wydrzynski, Kinetic determination of the fast exchanging substrate water molecule in the S_3 state of photosystem II. *Biochemistry* **37** (1998) 16908–16914.
289. W. Hillier, T. Wydrzynski, Aspects of substrate water interactions within the photosystem II oxygen evolving complex. *Phys. Chem. Chem. Phys.* **6** (2004) 4882–4889.
290. J.C. dePaula, J.B. Innes, G.W. Brudvig, Electron transfer in photosystem II at cryogenic temperatures. *Biochemistry* **24** (1985) 8114–8120.

VII. Electron Transport Chains and Phosphorylation

Chapter 18

Anoxygenic Bacteria

André Verméglio

Table of Contents

18.1 Introduction	355
18.2 The Photosynthetic Electron Transfer Chain	357
18.2.1 Various Direct Electron Donors to the RC	359
18.3 Light-Induced Cyclic Electron Transfer	359
18.3.1 Tetraheme RC Species	360
18.3.2 Triheme RC Species	363
18.3.3 Cytochrome C_2 and Cytochrome C_y RC Species	365
18.4 The Special Case of Aerobic Photosynthetic Bacteria	368
18.5 Supramolecular Organization of the Photosynthetic Apparatus	369
18.6 Concluding Remarks and Future Perspectives	373
Acknowledgements	374
References	374

Abstract

Anoxygenic photosynthetic bacteria transform light energy into chemical free energy according to a light-induced cyclic electron transfer. This fast cyclic electron transfer is coupled to the translocation of protons and to the formation of an electrochemical potential across the inner membrane, ultimately used for ATP synthesis. This chapter presents a comprehensive overview of our present knowledge of this process with special emphasis on non-sulfur photosynthetic bacteria. Thanks to a multidisciplinary approach combining biophysics, biochemistry and molecular biology, a nearly complete picture of the thermodynamics and kinetic properties, structures and interactions of the different protein complexes involved in this process is now available. Three multimeric transmembrane protein complexes compose the photosynthetic apparatus: the light-harvesting complexes, the photochemical reaction center and the cytochrome bc_1 complex. These two last complexes are connected via electron carrier proteins in the periplasmic space and quinone molecules in the membrane. One important peculiarity of species of photosynthetic bacteria is the diversity of the biochemical nature of the immediate electron donor to the reaction center and of the shuttling electron carrier with the cytochrome bc_1 complex. The secondary electron donor to the reaction center could be either a tetra-, tri-, or mono-heme cytochrome c tightly bound to the reaction center or a soluble periplasmic monoheme cytochrome c. Different soluble electron carriers (cyt c_2, cyt c_8, HiPIP) connect the reaction center and the cytochrome bc_1 complex, depending upon the considered species. The rates of electron transfer between these different partners have been determined by flash spectroscopy. Site-directed mutagenesis experiments, based on the 3D structure of the various components of the photosynthetic apparatus, have underlined the importance of both nonpolar and electrostatic interactions in the docking process of these different partners. In some cases, a higher level of interaction between the complexes of the photosynthetic apparatus has been determined by electron and atomic force microscopy techniques, highlighting their supramolecular organization in native membranes.

18.1 Introduction

Anoxygenic phototrophic bacteria have the ability to transform light energy into biochemically amenable free energy for their growth and development. Unlike cyanobacteria, they are unable to use water as electron donor and thus cannot evolve oxygen. Various electron donors of lower potential than oxygen such as H_2, H_2S or small organic molecules are used by anaerobic phototrophs. In general, their photosynthetic activity is only efficient under anaerobic or semi-aerobic conditions since the synthesis of the photosynthetic apparatus is switched on at low oxygen tension level [1]. However, one exception is found for the "aerobic anoxygenic phototrophs", which require the presence of oxygen to perform photosynthesis [2].

On the basis of phylogenic analysis, anoxygenic photosynthetic bacteria are divided into four groups: the green sulfur bacteria (*Chlorobiaceae*), the green non-sulfur bacteria (*Chloroflexus* genus and relatives), the purple bacteria (*Proteobacteria*) and the *Heliobacteriaceae* [3]. The last group belongs to the Gram-positive bacteria. For the *Proteobacteria*, three subclasses have been defined: the α-subclass [includes most of the purple non-sulfur bacteria (Rhodospirillaceae) and the "aerobic anoxygenic phototrophs"]; the β-subclass (contains the remaining purple non-sulfur bacteria like *Rhodocyclus* and *Rubrivivax* genera) and the γ-subclass (the purple sulfur bacteria Chromatiaceae and Ectothiorhodospiraceae).

These various groups of photosynthetic bacteria present significant differences in their growth capacity. The purple non-sulfur and the green non-sulfur bacteria can develop under either dark aerobic or light anaerobic conditions. Purple non-sulfur bacteria can also use various electron acceptors during anaerobic respiration [4]. They are denoted as facultative photosynthetic bacteria. With few exceptions, the purple sulfur and the green sulfur bacteria are rather strict anaerobes, and light is required for their development. The collection of light and its transformation into chemical free energy are mediated by the so-called photosynthetic apparatus. This complex system is composed of three multimeric transmembrane protein complexes: the light harvesting complexes (LH), the photochemical reaction center (RC), and the cytochrome bc_1 complex (cyt bc_1) located in the intracytoplasmic membrane. Following light absorption by the LH complexes, a charge separation occurs at the level of the RC after excitonic transfer of the energy (Chapter 12). This initiates a cyclic electron transfer between the RC and the cyt bc_1, which are connected via electron carrier proteins in the periplasmic space and quinone molecules in the membrane [5]. In terms of molecular evolution, Proteobacteria, Chloroflexaceae and "aerobic anoxygenic photosynthetic" bacteria possess a RC, which shows close resemblance to the Photosystem II of green plants and algae. In contrast, the photochemical RC of Chlorobiaceae and Heliobacteriaceae is homologous to the Photosystem I. Accordingly, these RCs are referred to as type II and type I, respectively (Chapter 12).

The combination of biophysical, biochemical and genetic approaches has provided a detailed description of the functions of the different protein complexes involved in the transformation of light energy by photosynthetic bacteria. One decisive factor has been the ability of facultative purple non-sulfur photosynthetic bacteria to develop under both dark aerobic and photosynthetic conditions. This has made possible the study of mutants deleted in essential elements of the photosynthetic apparatus. Flash-induced, time-resolved spectroscopy coupled to molecular biology has allowed the description in fine details of the cascade of molecular events that are triggered by light excitation. A major advance in the elucidation of the molecular events of bacterial photosynthesis was the resolution of the structure of the essential components of the photosynthetic apparatus (RC, LH, cyt bc_1 complex, *etc.*) (Chapters 5 and 11) thanks to the pioneering work of H. Michel and co-workers on *Blastochloris viridis* RC [6]. More recently, electron and atomic force microscopy techniques have shed light on the supramolecular organization of the photosynthetic components in the native membrane.

In the present chapter, our state of knowledge on the light-induced cyclic electron transfer and on the supramolecular organization of the electron carriers is outlined for different species of the facultative purple non-sulfur photosynthetic bacteria. Emphasis is placed on experiments performed with intact cells.

18.2 The Photosynthetic Electron Transfer Chain

After absorption of a photon by the LH complexes (Chapter 5), the excitation reaches the RC in less than 100 ps. At the level of the RC, a charge separation occurs, in a few picoseconds, between the excited primary electron donor P (a bacteriochlorophyll dimer) and a molecule of bacteriopheophytin. In the following 200 ps, the electron reaches a quinone molecule, the so-called primary acceptor Q_A (for more details, see Chapter 12). This results in a transmembrane electron transfer between the periplasmic and the cytoplasmic side of the photosynthetic membrane. Subsequent electron transfers, in the microsecond range, stabilize the separated charges. On the donor side, the photo-oxidized primary electron donor ($P^{+\cdot}$) is re-reduced by a secondary donor. On the acceptor side, the electron is transferred from the primary quinone in its reduced semiquinone form $Q_A^{-\cdot}$ to a secondary quinone (Q_B), forming a RC-bound semiquinone ($Q_B^{-\cdot}$). Following a second turnover of the RC, a doubly reduced Q_BH_2, formed after uptake of two protons from the cytoplasmic space, is released from the RC as a quinol in the membrane [7]. The light-induced cyclic electron transfer is completed by the oxidation of the quinol at the level of the cyt bc_1 complex and leads to the re-reduction of the oxidized secondary donors, redox proteins localized in the periplasm. According to the Q-cycle process (Chapter 20), electron transfer within the cyt bc_1 complex is triggered by the oxidation of the cytochrome c_1 by the positive charge formed at the donor side of RC. In anaerobic conditions, most of the quinone pool is reduced and the low potential (LP) cytochrome b_L (cyt b_L) and high potential (HP) cytochrome b_H (cyt b_H) of the cyt bc_1 complex are in their oxidized (cyt b_L^+) and reduced (cyt b_H) forms, respectively. At the Q_o site of the cyt bc_1 complex, a reduced quinone of the pool (QH_2) reduces, during a concerted process, the cyt c_1^+ and the cyt b_L^+, leading to the formation of oxidized quinone Q and the transfer of two H^+ in the periplasm (reaction 1). At the Q_i site of the cyt bc_1 complex the reduction of Q by the two cyts b is coupled to the uptake of two H^+ from the cytoplasm to form QH_2. This electron transfer process leads the cyts b in the forms cyt b_H^+ and cyt b_L^+ (reaction 2). During a second turnover induced by the oxidation of the cyt c_1 by the photo-oxidized RC, a similar concerted process leads to the formation of a second oxidized Q at site Q_o, and reduction of cyt c_1 and cyt b_H and restores the initial state of the cyt bc_1 complex. These different electron transfer steps are summarized below.

Global reaction:

$$QH_2 + 2\text{cyt } c_1^+ \rightarrow Q + 2\text{cyt } c_1 + 2H^+$$

First turnover:

$$QH_2 + \text{cyt } c_1^+ + \text{cyt } b_L^+ + \text{cyt } b_H \rightarrow Q + \text{cyt } c_1 + \text{cyt } b_L + \text{cyt } b_H + 2H^+ \text{ (in the periplasm)} \quad (1)$$

$$Q + \text{cyt } c_1 + \text{cyt } b_L + \text{cyt } b_H + 2H^+ \text{ (from cytoplasm)} \rightarrow QH_2 + \text{cyt } c_1$$
$$+ \text{cyt } b_L^+ + \text{cyt } b_H^+$$
(2)

Second turnover:
$$QH_2 + \text{cyt } c_1^+ + \text{cyt } b_L^+ + \text{cyt } b_H^+ \rightarrow Q + \text{cyt } c_1 + \text{cyt } b_L^+ + \text{cyt } b_H$$
$$+ 2H^+ \text{ (in the periplasm)}$$

The final result of this light-induced cyclic electron transfer is the translocation of protons from the cytoplasm to the periplasm (ΔpH) and the formation of transmembrane potential difference that ultimately drives ATP synthesis ([5], see Chapter 21).

Figure 1 presents a schematic representation of this light-induced electron transfer in anoxygenic photosynthetic bacteria. Although this general scheme applies to various species of facultative purple photosynthetic bacteria, it is important to note that significant differences exist between them. Firstly, photosynthetic bacterial species differ by the number and the type of their LH complexes. Some species, like *Rhodospirillum rubrum* or *Blastochloris viridis*, contain only the LH1-type complex, while up to five different LH2 complexes can be found in *Rhodopseudomonas palustris* in addition to the LH1. Secondly, the biochemical nature of the secondary electron donor to the primary donor P and that of the periplasmic electron carrier depends upon the considered species. As described in more detail below, the immediate electron donor to the RC can be either a soluble monoheme cyt c or a mono-, tri- or tetraheme membrane-bound cyt c. Although the cyt bc_1

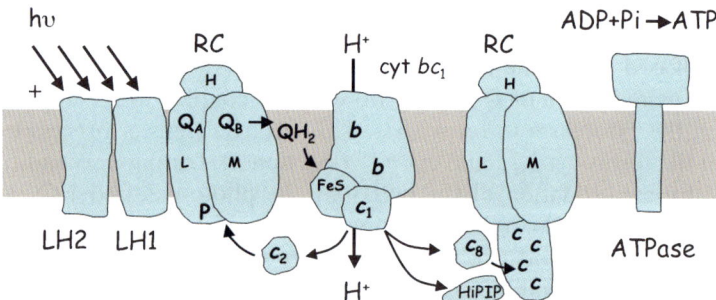

Figure 1. Schematic representation of the light-induced cyclic electron transfer in the photosynthetic membrane of purple photosynthetic bacteria. The pathway of electron transfer is represented for the two types of RC (with or without bound cytochrome). Triheme RCs are not represented. Both HiPIP and cytochrome c are efficient electron donors to the RC-bound tetraheme cytochrome. Only cytochrome c can act as secondary electron donor to the RC with no bound cytochrome. The light induces a charge separation at the level of the RCs. This charge separation is followed by a cyclic electron transfer involving quinone molecules and the cyt bc_1 complex in the membrane and various secondary electron donors in the periplasmic space. See text for further explanations.

complexes do not present significant differences for all facultative purple photosynthetic bacteria studied so far, a difference exists for the stoichiometric ratio between the RC and the cyt bc_1 complex. This ratio varies, between species, for example, for *Rhodobacter sphaeroides* and *Blastochloris viridis* from 2 to 10, respectively, and within species, depending on whether they are grown under photosynthetic or dark aerobic conditions.

18.2.1 Various Direct Electron Donors to the RC

Three types of RCs can be distinguished by the nature of their direct electron donor to the primary electron donor P. In most photosynthetic bacteria, this secondary electron donor is a tetraheme cyt c bound to the RC that protrudes into the periplasmic side of the membrane [8]. This forms the first type of RC, denoted as tetraheme RC. Masuda et al. [9] and Tsukatani et al. [10] discovered that, in species of the *Rhodovulum* genus, the binding motif for the most distal heme of the RC-bound cyt was lost. This new RC type thus possesses only three hemes instead of four, but this cyt is still competent for cyclic electron transfer.

Several species, such as *Rhodobacter sphaeroides*, *Rhodobacter capsulatus*, *Rhodopseudomonas palustris* or *Rhodospirillum rubrum*, do not possess these RC-bound cyt subunits, and the photo-oxidized primary donor accepts an electron from a periplasmic monoheme cyt [11]. This monoheme cyt is, for most species, a water-soluble cyt of the cyt c_2 family, homologous to the mitochondrial cyt c. One exception is found in *Rhodobacter capsulatus*. This species contains, in addition to the cyt c_2, a cyt denoted as c_y, anchored to the membrane by an α-helix, which can act as an efficient electron donor to the RC.

Such diversity in the nature of the secondary electron donor to $P^{+\cdot}$ has important consequences for the biochemical nature of the electron carriers, which connect the RC to the cyt bc_1 complex, and for the supramolecular organization of the photosynthetic apparatus. This will be described in detail below for several selected bacterial species.

18.3 Light-Induced Cyclic Electron Transfer

Much information on the cascade of electron transfers after light absorption and the biochemical nature of components involved in this process has been obtained by flash-induced, time-resolved spectroscopy. This technique can be applied at different levels of integration: purified complexes, isolated membranes or intact cells. The use of isolated membranes is, however, limited to species, like *Rhodobacter sphaeroides* and *Rhodobacter capsulatus*, that make closed vesicles (chromatophores) upon breakage of the cells. These closed vesicles retain most of the electron carriers necessary for an efficient photo-induced electron transfer. For those species that contain few or no invaginations, like *Rubrivivax gelatinosus* or *Blastochloris viridis*, experiments must be performed with intact cells since most of the periplasmic soluble carriers are lost during breakage of the cells.

18.3.1 Tetraheme RC Species

The four hemes of the RC-bound cyt are arranged in a roughly linear manner, extending beyond the RC and protruding into the periplasmic side of the membrane. Their spatial arrangement has been revealed with the 3D high-resolution structures of the RC of *Blastochloris viridis* [6] and *Thermochromatium tepidum* [12] (for details, see Chapter 11). They are labeled, starting from P, heme 1(III), heme 2(IV), heme 3(II) and heme 4(I). Roman numerals are used to denote the position of the heme binding motifs in the amino acid sequence, starting from the N-terminus, and Arabic numerals indicate the distance ranking from the primary electron donor of the RC. These four hemes are differentiated by their redox properties: two hemes possess a high mid-point potential (HP) and the two others a low mid-point potential (LP). In *Blastochloris viridis*, the four hemes are arranged linearly in a high-low-high-low sequence in terms of redox potential [13–15]. Despite the involvement of uphill steps in terms of redox potentials, this sequence does not impair the efficiency of inter-heme electron transfer [16–19].

All four hemes can readily reduce the photo-oxidized primary electron donor radical $P^{+\cdot}$. The rate of $P^{+\cdot}$ reduction by the tetraheme varies from hundreds of nanoseconds to a few microseconds, depending upon the considered heme. For example in *Blastochloris viridis*, when only HP hemes 1 and 3 are reduced, heme 1 equilibrates with $P^{+\cdot}$ within 200 ns. The complete re-reduction of $P^{+\cdot}$ is then limited by the interheme electron transfer between heme 3 and heme 1 (2 µs half-time) [20]. When LP hemes 2 and 4 are also reduced, the re-reduction of $P^{+\cdot}$ by heme 2, via heme 1, decreases to 115 ns and equilibration with heme 4 occurs in 2 µs [21,22]. This difference in the rate of $P^{+\cdot}$ reduction, as a function of the redox state of the hemes, is explained by electrostatic effects. In addition, a systematic discrepancy is observed for the equilibrium constant between $P^{+\cdot}$ and heme 1 when estimated either from kinetics data on intact cells or from dark-equilibrium redox titrations. Baymann and Rappaport [23] hypothesized that two different electrostatic effects could account for these results. The first effect concerns the interaction between P and the closest heme (heme 1). In dark-equilibrium redox titration, $P^{+\cdot}/P$ is titrated in the presence of oxidized heme 1 whereas in electron transfer experiments, both P and heme 1 are reduced before the flash excitation. Consequently, the operating redox potential of $P^{+\cdot}/P$ should be lower than that titrated at thermodynamic equilibrium. The second effect is linked to the presence of a transmembrane potential difference. This membrane potential can be due to either the respiratory activity, the ATPase activity or linked to the light-induced charge separation. As heme 1 is closer to the solvent interface than P, this membrane potential also decreases the equilibrium constant between P and this heme, as observed in kinetics experiments performed on intact cells [23].

When intact cells of various species of photosynthetic bacteria are placed under anaerobic dark conditions, their four hemes are usually in the reduced state. Due to their LP redox potential, the LP hemes are then photo-oxidized in preference to the HP hemes. Therefore, the two first flashes of a series photo-oxidize the LP hemes, which are slowly re-reduced in the dark (half-times from few hundred milliseconds to several seconds depending upon the considered species). Indeed the midpoint potentials of these hemes are much lower than that of the cyt c_1 of the cyt bc_1 complex; therefore, the LP hemes cannot participate in an efficient light-induced cyclic electron transfer. The exact role of the LP hemes has not yet been well established. They may be involved in the oxidation of low potential substrates in a linear photo-induced electron transfer. Subsequent flashes induce the photo-oxidation of the HP hemes, which are rapidly re-reduced by the periplasmic redox proteins. In turn, these periplasmic electron carriers are re-reduced by the cyt bc_1 complex to complete the light-induced cyclic electron transfer. This is clearly demonstrated by the correlation between the kinetics of the re-reduction of these carriers and those of the slow phase of the carotenoid bandshift (indicative of the transmembrane potential increment due to the Q-cycle at the level of the cyt bc_1 complex) and the inhibition of this reduction process by specific inhibitors of the cyt bc_1 complex. An example of these various absorbance changes following a series of saturating flashes is given in Figure 2 for intact cells of *Rubrivivax gelatinosus*. Under moderate aerobic conditions, only the HP potential hemes are reduced before illumination and the light-induced changes linked to the photo-oxidation and re-reduction of the HP hemes are already observed within the first excitation flashes.

According to the considered species, the connection between the tetraheme RC and the cyt bc_1 complex is mediated by two different types of electron carriers. One is a water-soluble c-type cyt. The other type is an iron-sulfur protein [24–26] containing a [4Fe-4S] cluster. Owing to its high redox midpoint potential compared with regular ferredoxins, this electron carrier was designated as "high-potential" iron-sulfur protein or HiPIP. In species like *Blastochloris viridis*, *Roseobacter denitrificans*, and *Rhodoblastus acidophilus*, only c-type cyts are found, e.g., either cyt c_2 or cyt c_8. Cyts c_8 are smaller than cyts c_2, which possess several extra loops [27]. Another characteristic of cyt c_8 is the presence of two to four proline residues around the sixth ligand methionine and a conserved tryptophan residue near the C-terminus [28]. Species such as *Rubrivivax gelatinosus*, *Ectothiorhodospira shaposhnikovi*, *Rhodoferax fermentans*, *Rhodocyclus tenuis*, *Allochromatium vinosum*, and *Marichromatium purpuratum* possess both types of electron carriers [29].

Electron transfer between soluble carriers, either cyt c or HiPIP, and the HP hemes is generally completed in less than 1 ms. In most cases, the cyt bc_1 complex re-reduces in turn these oxidized soluble electron carriers in a few tens of milliseconds. This rather low rate is due to the multi-turnover process of the cyt bc_1 complex in species containing a large amount of RCs per cyt bc_1 complex (see Figure 2 as an example).

For the species that contain both HiPIP and cyt acting as secondary electron donor to the tetraheme cyt, the nature of the operative electron donor depends upon several parameters. For *Rubrivivax gelatinosus* cells, it depends upon growth conditions. For cells grown under anaerobic conditions in the light, the HiPIP is the major electron donor to the RC [30,31]. Conversely, the HP cyt c_8 becomes dominant when cells have been grown under dark aerobic conditions

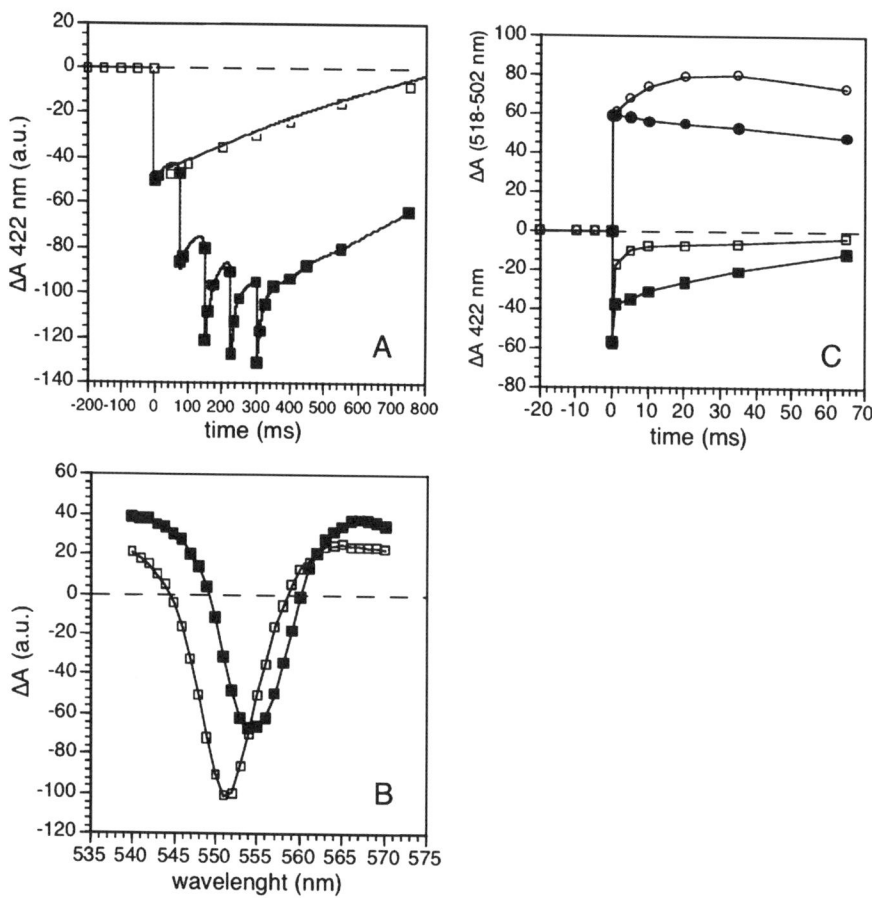

Figure 2. Light-induced absorbance changes observed for intact cells of *Rubrivivax gelatinosus*. The cells were placed under anaerobic conditions. (A) Light-induced absorption changes linked to the photo-oxidation of the RC-bound cytochrome detected at 422 nm following a single actinic flash (□) or five actinic flashes separated by 75 ms (■). The two first flashes induce the photo-oxidation of the LP hemes, as shown by the wavelength position of the light-induced difference spectrum recorded in the cytochromes α-band (B, □). On flash number 3, the HP hemes are photo-oxidized, as shown by the light-induced difference spectrum (B, ■). (C) Light-induced absorption changes linked to the formation of the carotenoid bandshift measured at 518–502 nm in the absence (○) or presence of myxothiazol (●), an inhibitor of the cyt bc_1 complex. The light-induced absorbance changes linked to the photo-oxidation of the RC-bound cytochrome in the absence (□) or the presence of myxothiazol (■) are also presented. [Adapted from [30].]

[32]. In the case of *Rhodocyclus tenuis*, both cyt c_8 and HiPIP participate in the light-induced cyclic electron transfer for cells grown under photosynthetic conditions. The cyt c_8 acts as the physiological donor at a redox poise above 350 mV or under a strong continuous illumination. At a lower ambient

ANOXYGENIC BACTERIA

potential, the link between the RC and the cyt bc_1 complex is ensured by the HiPIP [33]. In *Allochromatium vinosum*, the HiPIP is the electron donor when cells are grown photo-autotrophically in the presence of Na_2S and $Na_2S_2O_3$ with inorganic carbon as a carbon source [34]. In the absence of these sulfur compounds but in the presence of organic compounds as carbon source (photoheterotrophic growth), cells appear to use the soluble cyt c_8 as the only electron donor to the RC [34]. These various observations demonstrate the plasticity and adaptability of the bioenergetic processes to environmental conditions.

To connect the RC and the cyt bc_1 complex, HiPIP and cyt c must have the capability to reversibly dock to these complexes. Studies on in vitro electron transfer to the bound cyts modified by site-directed mutagenesis in *Rubrivivax gelatinosus* have suggested that different amino acids of the RC-bound cyt are implicated in specific binding for the c-type cyt or HiPIP [35–37]. The binding sites, partially overlapping, are located on the subunit surface close to the most distant heme, the LP heme 4(I) [38]. The interaction between the tetraheme cyt subunit and the HiPIP is predominated by the nonpolar interaction through their solvent-exposed hydrophobic regions, as shown by the critical role of Val-65 and Leu-94 [36,37]. A recent study on *Allochromatium vinosum* has identified a residue of HiPIP, Phe-48, critical for electron transfer to the cyt subunit [39]. This residue corresponds to Leu-43 in the *Rubrivivax gelatinosus* counterpart. Cyt c_8 and the tetraheme interact via salt bridges (Figure 3). Indeed, site-directed mutagenesis has revealed that two residues, Glu-77 and Glu-91 of the cyt subunit, have a critical influence on the magnitude of the second-order rate constant of the electron transfer between the tetraheme and the cyt c_8 [35]. These residues interact with Lys-21 and Lys-8/Lys-9 of cyt c_8, respectively. A putative model for the binding between the *Rubrivivax gelatinosus* RC-bound cyt and HiPIP is shown in Figure 3 [40]. No information is available so far for the docking site between HiPIP and the cyt bc_1 complex.

18.3.2 Triheme RC Species

Masuda and co-workers [9] have reported that the marine purple photosynthetic bacterium *Rhodovulum sulfidophilum* contains a new type of RC-bound cyt. Indeed, this cyt presents two unusual characteristics with respect to the well-characterized tetraheme cyts. It contains only three hemes since the binding motif CXXCH of heme 4(I) is absent. In addition, the sixth axial ligand of heme 3(II), usually a methionine, is a cysteine (C148)[†]. These unusual characteristics are found for all species of the genus *Rhodovulum* studied so far [10]. This unusual triheme cyt of *Rhodovulum sulfidophilum* has been characterized recently [41]. The midpoint potentials of the two "conserved" hemes, heme 1(III) and heme 2(IV), are +265 and +30 mV, respectively. These values are in the range of those determined for typical tetrahemic cyts. However, due to the presence of a cysteine as ligand of heme 3(II), this heme possesses a very

---

[†] For comparison with typical tetraheme subunits, the same numbering of hemes is used; heme 4(I) does not exist in the triheme cyt of *Rhodovulum sulfidophilum*.

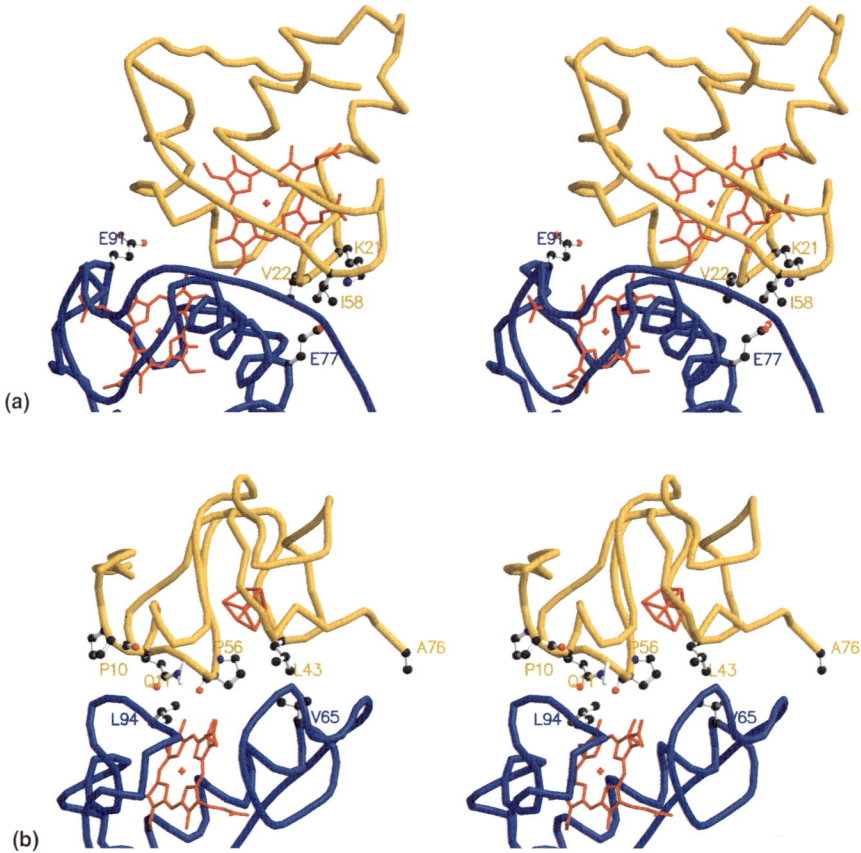

Figure 3. (a) Stereo 3D representation of the molecular docking between *Rubrivivax gelatinosus* RC-bound cytochrome (in blue) and *Rubrivivax gelatinosus* cytochrome c_8 (in yellow). The [4Fe-4S] cluster is drawn as red sticks. The residues involved in direct contact between the two electron-transfer components are highlighted. (b) Same as (a) but for *Rubrivivax gelatinosus* HiPIP. The heme is colored in red. [Adapted from [40].]

low midpoint potential ($E_{m7} = -160 \pm 10$ mV). The redox arrangement of the hemes is therefore high-low-ultralow, which is at variance with the accepted high-low-high-low sequence in the tetraheme cyts.

Heme 1(III) has been demonstrated to be involved in a light-induced cyclic electron transfer under moderate redox conditions. The reduction of the photo-oxidized primary donor by this heme is essentially monophasic, with 90% of $P^{+\cdot}$ being reduced with a halftime of 1.6 μs [41]. The photo-oxidized heme is re-reduced in turn in 1–2 ms. This reduction phase is concomitant with a rising phase of the carotenoid bandshift (indicative of the membrane potential) that is sensitive to specific inhibitors of the cyt bc_1 complex [42]. The electron carrier, which connects in vivo the RC and the cyt bc_1 complex, has not been yet identified. Although a soluble cyt c_{549} can reduce the triheme in reconstitution experiments in vitro, no light-induced absorption changes associated with its photo-oxidation can be detected in vivo [43]. Moreover, deletion of this cyt c_2 does impair photosynthetic growth. Nagashima and co-workers (personal communication) recently found a membrane-bound monoheme cyt c of 100 kDa, which acts as an efficient electron donor to the RC in reconstitution experiments. Its definite participation in the light-induced cyclic electron transfer awaits characterization of a deletion mutant. The unusual nature of this putative electron donor to the triheme cyt may be related to the loss of the main amino acids involved in the docking of soluble electron donors in their tetraheme counterparts. The concomitance of the loss of heme 4(I), together with the docking site near this heme, argues for the existence of another pathway of $P^{+\cdot}$ reduction by soluble periplasmic redox proteins.

Considering their midpoint potentials, the two LP hemes of the triheme cyt cannot be involved in a light-induced cyclic electron transfer. Their function remains elusive, as with the LP hemes of the tetraheme RC-bound cyt. Heme 3(II) may be involved in an alternative electron transfer not involving the cyt bc_1 complex. So far, light-induced experiments have been carried out at mildly reducing ambient potentials. *Rhodovulum sulfidophilum*, however, is able to grow under various rather "non-standard" environmental conditions, e.g., at the expense of reducing equivalents from thiosulfate or dimethyl sulfide (DMS). DMS dehydrogenase, for example, has been shown to deliver electrons into the photosynthetic electron transfer chain in *Rhodovulum sulfidophilum* [44].

18.3.3 Cytochrome C_2 and Cytochrome C_y RC Species

Among the species that do not possess a RC-bound cyt, *Rhodobacter sphaeroides* and *Rhodobacter capsulatus* have been the most studied. The role of cyt c_2 as a mobile electron carrier between the photo-oxidized primary electron donor $P^{+\cdot}$ and the cyt bc_1 complex has been demonstrated by biophysical, biochemical and genetic methods. For *Rhodobacter sphaeroides*, a definitive demonstration has been obtained by the characterization of a cyt c_2 deleted mutant. This mutant is unable to grow under photosynthetic conditions. The light-induced electron transfer reactions between cyt c_2 and $P^{+\cdot}$ have been extensively studied with isolated components, chromatophores and intact cells [45]. In the case of in vitro experiments with purified complexes, two phases of $P^{+\cdot}$ reduction are observed after its flash oxidation: a fast first-order phase with a rate constant of $1 \times 10^6 \, s^{-1}$ that is assigned to reaction of the cyt bound on the surface of the RC and a slow second-order phase due to the reaction with free cyt. The amplitude of the fast phase depends on the concentration of cyt, but its rate constant is independent of concentration. The rate of the slow phase depends on cyt concentration according to a second-order rate constant close to the diffusion limit [46]. Biphasic kinetic is also observed in isolated chromatophores and intact cells [47]. This behavior has been interpreted in terms of two binding states for the cyt c_2: a "close" and a "distal" state corresponding to the fast and slow re-reduction phases of $P^{+\cdot}$, respectively. An alternative explanation, discussed in more detail in Section 18.5, has been proposed in the case of intact cells [48,49].

In this model, the two phases of re-reduction are supposed to be due to the interaction of a single cyt c_2 with two RCs.

The docking between the cyt c_2 and the RC must satisfy optimal orientation and distance between the two partners for an efficient electron transfer. The interaction between the cyt c_2 and the RC takes place between positively charged residues clustered around the solvent-exposed edge of the cyt heme and complementary negatively charged residues on the periplasmic surface of the RC [50,51]. Chemical modification [52], site-directed mutagenesis experiments [53], chemical crosslinking experiments and X-ray crystal structure analysis [50,54,55] have highlighted the importance of a short-range binding domain with hydrophobic interactions and a long-range electrostatic binding domain with complementary charged residues on cyt c_2 and the RC. Figure 4 shows the interaction between the cyt c_2 and RC of *Rhodobacter sphaeroides*.

The next step in the electron transfer pathway is the reduction of the oxidized cyt c_2 by the cyt bc_1 complex. The rate of this reaction is highly dependent upon the redox state of the quinone pool. The fastest rate (1 ms half time at room temperature) is measured for chromatophores or intact cells for which the quinone pool is reduced. No structural information is yet available for the docking between the cyt c_2 and the bacterial cyt bc_1 complex. However, these components present a high homology with their counterparts of the mitochondria respiratory chain. A high similitude for the mode of docking

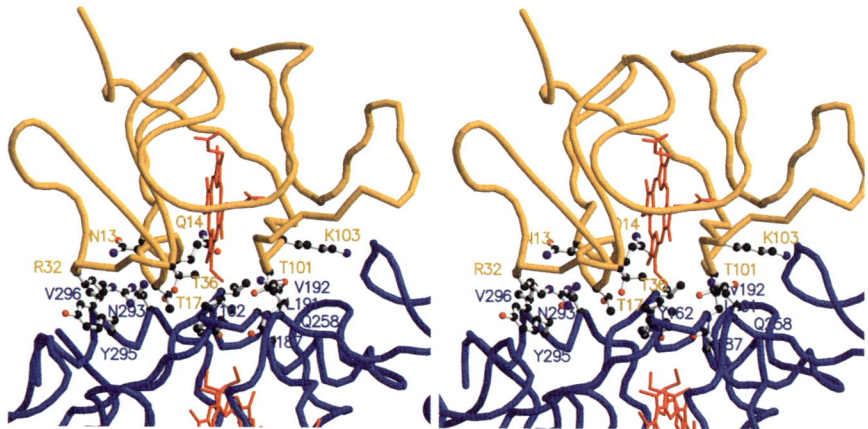

Figure 4. Stereo 3D representation of the molecular docking between *Rhodobacter sphaeroides* RC (in blue) and *Rhodobacter sphaeroides* cytochrome c_2 (in yellow). The heme is colored in red. The solvent-exposed Tyr-162 of the subunit L, at the surface of the RC, is located directly above the bacteriochlorophyll dimer. This Tyr-162 has been proposed to be the docking surface for the heme edge by analogy with the structure of the *Blastochloris viridis* RC. The residues in van der Waals contact between the two partners ([Tyr-162, Thr-36], [Leu-191, Thr-17], [Leu-191, Gln-14], [Val-192, Gln-14], [Asn-293, Asn-13], [Val-296, Asn-13]), in interprotein hydrogen bonding ([Gln-258, T-101], [Asn-187, Thr-101]) and in cation–π interaction [Tyr-295, Arg-32] are highlighted. [Adapted from [50].]

ANOXYGENIC BACTERIA

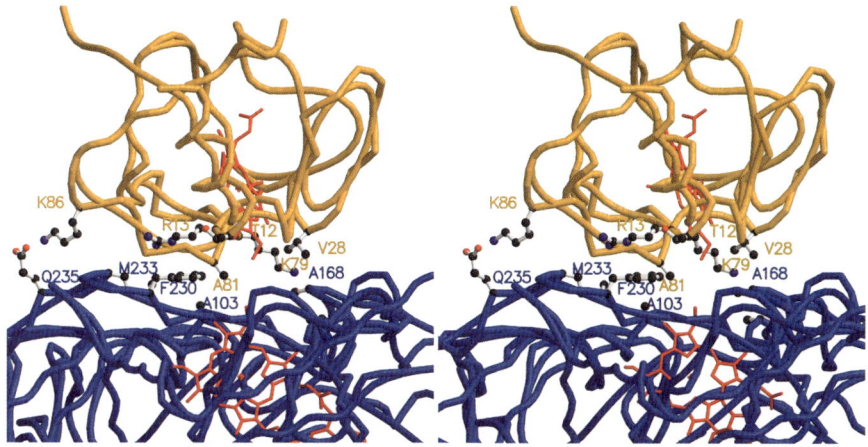

Figure 5. Stereo 3D representation of the molecular docking between yeast cytochrome bc_1 complex (in blue) and cytochrome c (in yellow). The hemes (cyt c_1 of the complex and cyt c) are in red. Residues implicated in nonpolar ([Phe-230, Arg-13], [Phe-230, Thr-12], [Met-233, Arg-13], [Ala-168, Val-28], [Ala-103, Ala-81]) or polar interactions ([Glu-235, Lys-86], [Ala-64, Lys-79]) are indicated. [Adapted from [57].]

between these components is therefore expected. In addition to mutagenesis studies, the analysis of co-crystals of mitochondrial cyt c and cyt bc_1 complex has allowed the mode of interactions between these two electron carriers to be unraveled [56,57]. These interactions are essentially mediated by nonpolar forces. In particular, Arg-13 of cyt c and Phe-230 of the cyt c_1 of the cyt bc_1 complex form a stable planar stacking interaction (Figure 5). The binding results in short distance between the two hemes, which are facing each other with their solvent exposed edges. This configuration allows a direct electron transfer between the cyt c_1 and cyt c.

The photosynthetic chain of *Rhodobacter capsulatus*, although long considered essentially equivalent to that of *Rhodobacter sphaeroides*, appears to be more complex in terms of secondary electron donors to the RC. Indeed, a series of genetic, biochemical and biophysical studies by Daldal and co-workers [58,59] clearly demonstrated that two distinct electron carriers in *Rhodobacter capsulatus* are efficient electron donors to the RC. Similar to the photosynthetic chain of *Rhodobacter sphaeroides*, the first pathway involves the diffusible cyt c_2. In the wild type, about 70% of the RCs are involved in this pathway. The remaining fraction (30%) of RCs are connected to the membrane-bound cyt c_y. The cyt c_y is anchored to the membrane by its amino terminal signal sequence, which is unprocessed [60]. Electron donation between the cyt c_y and $P^{+\cdot}$ is as fast as for cyt c_2. In contrast, the re-reduction of cyt c_y by the cyt bc_1 complex is about 8× faster than for cyt c_2 when the quinone pool is reduced. This cyt c_y is also involved in the respiratory pathway, where it shuttles electrons between the cbb_3 oxidase and the cyt bc_1 complex [61]. Owing to the membrane attachment of the cyt c_y, its movements must be highly restricted. The very efficient light-induced cyclic electron transfer and the involvement of cyt c_y in respiratory activity imply a very small distance between the RC, the cyt c_y and the cyt bc_1 complex, on the one hand, and the cbb_3 oxidase, the cyt c_y and the cyt bc_1 complex on the other hand. This supramolecular organization of the electron transfer chains is discussed in Section 18.5.

Although a cyt homologous to the cyt c_y has been found in *Rhodobacter sphaeroides* [62], this cyt is not involved in the photosynthetic electron transfer but only in the respiratory activity [63]. The membrane anchor of *Rhodobacter sphaeroides* cyt c_y is shorter than that of *Rhodobacter capsulatus*. This may explain its incompetence in the light-induced cyclic electron transfer. Notably, a monoheme membrane-bound cyt c also acts as an efficient electron donor to the RC of the green sulfur bacterium *Chlorobium tepidum* [64].

18.4 The Special Case of Aerobic Photosynthetic Bacteria

Aerobic photosynthetic bacteria were discovered in 1978 [65,66]. These bacteria are distributed in a wide variety of aerobic marine and fresh water environments. They differ from anoxygenic photosynthetic bacteria by their requirement for oxygen for bacteriochlorophyll synthesis and photosynthetic activity. Aerobic photosynthetic bacteria contain few invaginated membranes and low amounts of photosynthetic reaction centers. Nevertheless, RCs have been isolated and characterized from various strains [67–69]. The RCs have the expected 2-to-1 ratio of bacteriochlorophyll *a* to bacteriopheophytin *a*. Some of them possess a bound tetrahemic cyt while others interact with a soluble cyt as a secondary electron donor. In this respect they do not differ from RCs present in anaerobic photosynthetic bacteria.

The energetic contribution of the photosynthetic activity in these bacteria appears to be small, and light is used only as a complementary source of energy during dark–light cycles [70]. Nevertheless, their capacity to perform photosynthesis has been demonstrated by the light stimulation of ATP synthesis and the increase of the biomass under aerobic conditions [71,72]. In addition, reversible photo-oxidation of cyts has been observed in various species of aerobic photosynthetic bacteria for oxygenated samples. Specific inhibitors of the cyt bc_1 complex, such as myxothiazol, slow down re-reduction of the c-cyts, which is consistent with the operation of a light-induced cyclic electron flow involving such a complex. In contrast, no light-induced spectral changes or ATP formation are observed when the cells are placed under anaerobic conditions.

Altogether, these observations are consistent with the functioning of a light-induced cyclic electron transfer similar to that found in anaerobic photosynthetic bacteria [73–75] but only when cells are placed under aerobic conditions.

The oxygen requirement for photosynthetic electron transport and for bacteriochlorophyll synthesis has not yet been elucidated. In facultative anaerobic photosynthetic bacteria, like *Rhodobacter sphaeroides*, *Rhodovulum sulfidophilum* or *Rubrivivax gelatinosus*, two different mechanisms accomplish the cyclization of Mg-protoporphyrin monomethylester [76–79]. A hydratase is active under anaerobiosis or low oxygen tension while an oxygenase performs this cyclization under high oxygen tension. In the aerobic photosynthetic bacterium *Roseobacter denitrificans*, however, the cyclization derives only from molecular oxygen via the oxygenase. Although it has not been demonstrated, this species probably lacks the hydratase and this may explain its requirement for oxygen for the bacteriochlorophyll synthesis. This hypothesis may apply to all aerobic photosynthetic bacteria.

As already mentioned, aerobic photosynthetic bacteria lose the ability to perform light-induced electron transfer and phosphorylation under anaerobic conditions even if they contain functional RCs. This loss is due to the reduction of the primary acceptor Q_A in the dark when the cells become anaerobic, as clearly demonstrated by fluorescence yield measurements [80]. It had been suggested that this reduction of the primary electron acceptor in the dark was due to an unusually high midpoint redox potential, E_m [68,69]. However, in subsequent measurements, Schwarze et al. [75] reported that the midpoint potential of Q_A of *Roseobacter denitrificans* was not different from those determined for typical anaerobic photosynthetic bacteria. In agreement with this determination, the residues forming the Q_A pocket are perfectly conserved between anaerobic and aerobic photosynthetic bacteria, suggesting that their midpoint potentials do not differ significantly. Why the primary electron acceptor Q_A and the quinone pool become fully reduced under anaerobiosis in aerobic photosynthetic bacteria remains a mystery. This may be linked to the small amount of invaginations of the cytoplasmic membrane, which may favor a fast thermodynamic equilibrium between the respiratory and photosynthetic chains. Another non-exclusive possibility is that aerobic photosynthetic bacteria possess an unusual complex I. In anaerobic photosynthetic bacteria, the complex I transfers electrons from NADH to the quinone pool. This electron transfer is reversed, from reduced quinone to NAD^+, in the presence of a light-induced membrane potential. We have observed (P. Joliot, A. Joliot, A. Verméglio, unpublished results) that over 80% of the RCs have their primary electron acceptor reduced when intact cells of *Rhodobacter sphaeroides* are placed under anaerobiosis in growth medium of low redox potential. However, a continuous illumination of a few tens of seconds completely restores the photochemistry of all the RCs. This reoxidation of the primary electron acceptor (and of the quinone pool) is due to the reverse electron flow occurring at the level of the complex I linked to the photochemical activity and the ensuing light-induced membrane potential of the few active RCs. Therefore, one possibility is that the aerobic photosynthetic bacteria might possess a much less efficient reverse electron flow at the level of the complex I, preventing an efficient light-induced reoxidation of the acceptor pool when cells are under anaerobic conditions.

18.5 Supramolecular Organization of the Photosynthetic Apparatus

Complete understanding of the transformation of light into chemical Gibbs energy requires not only the determination of the structure and functioning of each component but also their mode of interaction and their supramolecular organization within the membrane. The structure of all membranous components (LH2, RC-LH1, RC and cyt bc_1 complex) and some of the soluble carriers (HiPIP, cyt c_2) has been determined by X-ray crystallography [56, 81–87] (for details on LH2, RC-LH1 and RCs, see Chapters 5 and 11, respectively). In addition, the mode of interaction between some of these complexes has also been determined by analysis of co-crystals, modeling or site-directed mutagenesis, as described above [40,50,54,55,57,88]. Early information on the supraorganization of the photosynthetic membrane was obtained from functional analysis (energy transfer, kinetics of electron transfer) and investigation by electron microscopy of naturally occurring crystalline membranes. More recently, further information on this supramolecular organization has been obtained by cryo-microscopy and atomic force microscopy.

The concept of energy transfer within a photosynthetic unit, developed in the early 1930s [89,90], already implies a highly ordered arrangement of the photosynthetic apparatus (Chapter 1). Indeed, the high efficiency of excited state energy transfer from the LH complexes to the RCs, which takes 35–45 ps [91], requires a very short distance between them. The first picture of the structure of the bacterial photosynthetic unit was provided by Miller [92]. Fourier image analysis of the negatively stained highly ordered membranes of *Blastochloris viridis* revealed that each RC is surrounded by a circle of LHI complexes. This organization of the photosynthetic complexes has been observed for native membranes or 2D crystals of RC-LH1 complexes of several other species of photosynthetic bacteria [93–96]. For *Blastochloris viridis*, a refined picture has been reported recently by Scheuring et al. [97] using AFM, a unique tool to obtain structural information on the arrangement of proteins in native membranes. The 16 LH1 subunits surrounding a single RC appear to adopt an elliptical shape rather than a circle. This induces a close association of the RC and the LH1 subunits positioned on the short ellipsis axis. The elliptical shape of the LH1 ring at the cytoplasmic and periplasmic sides of the membrane, in both the presence and absence of the RC, has also been observed for 2D crystals of RC-LH1 complexes of *Rhodospirillum rubrum* [98]. This closeness between LH1 complexes and RCs favors a tight coupling between the LH bacteriochlorophylls and the RC special pair and an efficient excitation transfer. However, the packed organization of the LH1 complexes around the RC raises the question of how the quinone-quinol transfer occurs between the RC acceptor site and the cyt bc_1 complex during the light-induced cyclic electron transfer. It has been proposed that the LH1 ring possesses some flexibility, which might allow its transient opening and quinone diffusion [98,99]. In the case of *Rhodobacter sphaeroides* and *Rhodobacter capsulatus*, the accepted view is that a small membrane protein, denoted PufX, is essential for an efficient exchange of quinone between the RC and the cyt bc_1 complex under anaerobic condition [100–104]. The PufX protein is also necessary for the isolation of dimeric RC-LH1 complexes after detergent solubilization of membranes of *Rhodobacter sphaeroides* [105]. This dimeric association of RCs has been visualized by electron microscopy [106–109] and more recently by AFM

[110,111] in native membranes of *Rhodobacter sphaeroides* lacking LH2 complexes, naturally or as a consequence of deletion. These dimers are composed of two open rings of LH1 surrounding the RCs. In the absence of LH2, dimeric RC-LH1-PufX complexes form a highly ordered array in tubular membranes [112]. The absence of PufX induces the formation of a complete ring of LH1 around the RC [96] and the disappearance of the tubular membranes [112,113]. Although it is well accepted that the PufX polypeptide is an essential element of the open ring of LH1, its exact location in this open ring is still a matter a debate [110,111].

Notably, PufX is only required for an efficient cyclic photo-induced electron transfer when the quinone pool is totally reduced. Partial oxidation of the quinone pool restores an efficient photo-induced cyclic electron transfer and photosynthetic growth [104,113]. This implies that quinone can diffuse through the LH1 ring in the absence of PufX at a significant rate. So far, PufX has only been found in *Rhodobacter* species [9]. In other photosynthetic bacteria, an efficient export of quinol formed at the RC level through the LH1 ring may be related to the combination of flexibility of the LH1 ring and partial oxidation of the quinone pool. Recently, a PufX-like polypeptide has been shown to be part of the LH1 ring of *Rhodopseudomonas palustris* RC-LH1 complexes [87]. Future work may reveal similar small polypeptides in LH1 rings of various species of photosynthetic bacteria.

In addition to the above demonstrations for the organization of RC-LH1-PufX complexes in dimers, arguments in favor of a tight association of such a dimer with one cyt bc_1 complex in *Rhodobacter sphaeroides* came from a series of functional measurements [48]. The first type of argument is the presence of two distinct functional pools of cyt c_t (cyt c_2+cyt c_1) out of thermodynamic equilibrium for cells grown under dark semi-aerobic conditions or in the presence of nitrate [114,115]. A first pool of cyt c_t is rapidly photo-oxidized during continuous illumination; during this fast photo-oxidation phase, one cyt c_2 and one cyt c_1 are photo-oxidized for two RCs. A second pool is only slowly photo-oxidized. This phase corresponds to a small amount of RCs connected to a large number of cyt c_2 (one RC for seven cyt c_2 in the case of cells grown under dark semi-aerobic condition). These two pools of cyt c_t are out of thermodynamic equilibrium. When *Rhodobacter sphaeroides* cells are grown under anaerobic conditions in the light, they contain only one pool of cyt c_t connected to the photosynthetic chains. This pool is rapidly photo-oxidized under illumination and its rate of photo-oxidation is independent of the medium viscosity. In addition, the different photosynthetic chains are not in rapid thermodynamic equilibrium. This has been demonstrated by measuring the apparent equilibrium constant between the cyt c_t, the cyt bc_1 complex and the RCs under low intensity illumination. This apparent equilibrium constant is much lower than expected from the measured mid-point potential of these electron carriers [48]. Modeling of this behavior led to the proposal that the photosynthetic electron transfer chain of *Rhodobacter sphaeroides* is organized in a supercomplex that includes a dimer of RCs, one cyt bc_1 complex and one cyt c_2 molecule, in agreement with the overall stoichiometry of these components in the chromatophore. The thermodynamic equilibrium between the primary donor of the RC and the high-potential carriers of cyt bc_1 is mediated in less than 1 ms by the cyt c_2 trapped in the supercomplex [48]. In contrast, thermodynamic equilibration between different supercomplexes is a much longer process. The organization in supercomplexes also explains the occurrence of a light-induced cyclic electron transfer at temperature as low as −20 °C, where a fast long-range diffusion of cyt c_2 is prevented [116]. Crofts and co-workers have challenged these views of the supramolecular organization of the photosynthetic chain in *Rhodobacter sphaeroides* [117–119]. They proposed that the low apparent equilibrium constant between the primary electron donor P and the secondary electron donors observed in chromatophores is due to the heterogeneous stoichiometric distribution of cyt c_2 versus RCs among these small vesicles, rather than to the confinement of cyt c_2 in association with the RCs dimer and the cyt bc_1 complex [119]. Although there is a consensus on a restricted diffusion of cyt c_2, at least in intact cells [117], the molecular implication has been a matter of debate [117,120]. The tubular membranes have been proposed to contain all the photosynthetic machinery organized in supercomplexes composed of a dimeric RC-LH1-PufX complex associated with a cyt bc_1 complex [109]. A more careful analysis of the proteins content of the tubular membranes has, however, clearly demonstrated that they do not contain cyt bc_1 complexes [110]. Therefore, the notion of supercomplexes between RCs and cyt bc_1 complexes in *Rhodobacter sphaeroides* is at the moment inferred solely from analysis of electron transfer kinetics. Previous proposals of supercomplexes were based on the stoichiometry of the components (two RCs, one cyt c_2 and one cyt bc_1 complex) [48,49,113] and the fact that tubular membranes of *Rhodobacter sphaeroides*, believed to contain cyt bc_1 complexes, could accommodate only monomeric cyt bc_1 complexes in interaction with dimeric RC-LH1-PufX complexes. Since it is demonstrated that the tubular membranes do not contain cyt bc_1 complexes [110], the constraint for a monomeric cyt bc_1 complex is now released. Figure 6 presents the simplest model for the supramolecular organization of the photosynthetic electron chain in *Rhodobacter sphaeroides*. In this model, two dimers of RC-LH1-PufX complexes must be associated with one dimer of cyt bc_1 complex, which satisfies the stoichiometry of two RCs per cyt bc_1 complex and the dimeric form of the cyt bc_1 complex observed in the crystallographic structures [56,86].

Views on the organization of the photosynthetic chains in *Rhodobacter capsulatus* are less controversial. In a mutant deleted in cyt c_2, fast cyclic electron transfer occurs between RCs, cyt c_y and cyt bc_1 complexes in few milliseconds upon flash excitation. Since the cyt c_y is tightly bound to the membrane, its movements are highly restricted and its interaction with a large number of partners impeded. The fast cyclic electron transfer observed clearly implies a supramolecular association between RCs, cyts c_y and cyt bc_1 complexes. This corresponds to about 30% of the RCs. Once re-reduced after a flash-induced cyclic electron transfer, the cyt c_y cannot efficiently transfer electrons to the remaining 70% photo-oxidized RCs not connected, even in the second time range. Since the two types of RCs, connected or not connected to a cyt c_y, are

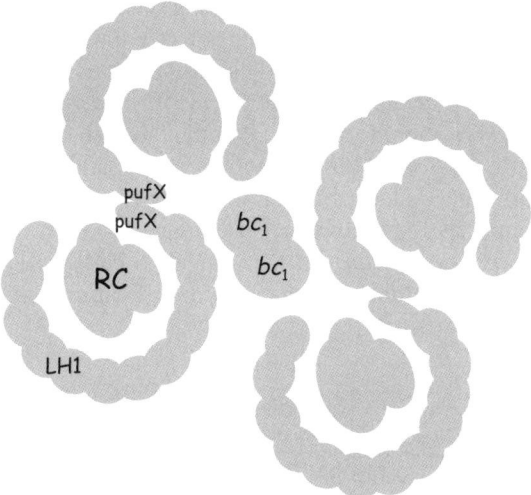

Figure 6. Putative representation of the supramolecular organization in the membrane plane of the photosynthetic chain of *Rhodobacter sphaeroides* (abbreviations: LH1: light harvesting complexes 1, RC: reaction center, pufX: polypeptide X, bc_1: cytochrome bc_1 complex).

localized in the same region of the intracytoplasmic membrane, as demonstrated by energy transfer experiments [121,122], this lack of thermodynamic equilibrium between the different photosynthetic chains is a consequence of their supramolecular organization, as proposed for *Rhodobacter sphaeroides* [123]. Structural evidence for this supramolecular association is not yet available.

18.6 Concluding Remarks and Future Perspectives

This chapter summarizes our present knowledge of the mechanisms of photoinduced electron transfer in purple non-sulfur photosynthetic bacteria. This current view is the result of the combination of biophysical, biochemical and genetic approaches during the last thirty years. During this period, unsuspected new features have been revealed by the isolation and characterization of novel photosynthetic bacteria species. This is, for example, the case with the discovery of strict aerobic photosynthetic bacteria, which require oxygen for use of light energy [65,66]. The molecular basis for such a requirement is still an open question. The discovery of photosynthetic bacteria possessing triheme cyt bound to the RC was also an unexpected [9,10]. Understanding the "raison d'être" of the biochemical diversity of the electron donor to the RC (soluble monoheme, membrane-bound tetra-, tri-, and mono-heme) and of electron carriers connecting the RC and the cyt bc_1 complex (cyt c_2, cyt c_8, HiPIP) is a challenge for future research. The role of the LP heme hemes of the RC-bound tetraheme, which is a long-standing enigma, has also to be elucidated.

Although the structure of the various components of the photosynthetic apparatus is known at nearly atomic resolution (Chapters 5 and 11), resolution of the supramolecular organization of these components for various species of photosynthetic bacteria remains a challenge for future studies. Determination of interactions between membranes and soluble electron carriers of the photosynthetic unit is the next area for researchers in the field. One may hope that biochemical approaches, such as those that have been successful in demonstrating supercomplexes for the respiratory chains of yeast, bovine mitochondria and *Paracoccus denitrificans* [124], coupled to electron and atomic force microscopy techniques, will help in elucidating this captivating area of biological energy transduction.

Acknowledgements

I thank J. Lavergne, J. Alric and S. Driever for helpful discussions and a careful reading of the manuscript. I wish to thank D. Pignol for drawing the 3D pictures. I would also to thank P. and A. Joliot (IBPC, Paris) and K.V.P. Nagashima (University of Tokyo, Japan) for our long standing and fruitful collaborations. This work was supported by the Commissariat à l'Énergie Atomique.

References

1. G. Drews, J.R. Golecki, Structure, molecular organization, and biosynthesis of membranes of purple bacteria, in: *Anoxygenic Photosynthetic Bacteria* (1995) (R.E. Blankenship, M.T. Madigan, C.E. Bauer, eds.), Kluwer Academic, Dordrecht, pp. 725–745.
2. V.V. Yurkov, J.T. Beatty, Aerobic anoxygenic phototrophic bacteria. *Microbiol. Mol. Biol. Rev.* **62** (1998) 695–724.
3. E. Stackebrandt, R.G.E. Murray, H.G. Trüper, Proteobacteria classis nov., a name for the phylogenetic taxon that includes the "purple bacteria and their relatives". *Int. J. Sys. Bacteriol.* **38** (1988) 321–325.
4. D. Zannoni, Aerobic and anaerobic electron transport chains in anoxygenic phototrophic bacteria, in: *Anoxygenic Photosynthetic Bacteria* (1995) (R.E. Blankenship, M.T. Madigan, C.E. Bauer, eds.), Kluwer Academic, Dordrecht, pp. 949–971.
5. R.C. Prince, Bacterial photosynthesis: from photons to Δp, in: *Bacterial Energetics of the Bacteria* (1990) (T.A. Kulwich, ed.), Academic Press, New York, pp. 111–150.
6. J. Deisenhofer, O. Epp, K. Miki, R. Huber, H. Michel, X-ray structure analysis at 3 Å resolution of a membrane protein complex: folding of the protein subunits in the photosynthetic reaction centre from *Rhodopseudomonas viridis*. *Nature* **318** (1985) 618–624.
7. C.A. Wraight, Proton and electron transfer in the acceptor quinone complex of photosynthetic reaction center from *Rhodobacter sphaeroides*. *Fron. Biosci.* **9** (2004) 309–337.
8. W. Nitschke, S.M. Dracheva, Reaction center associated cytochromes, in: *Anoxygenic Photosynthetic Bacteria* (1995) (R.E. Blankenship, M.T. Madigan, C.E. Bauer, eds.), Kluwer Academic, Dordrecht, pp. 775–805.

9. S. Masuda, M. Yoshida, K.V.P. Nagashima, K. Shimada, K. Matsuura, A new cytochrome subunit bound to the photosynthetic reaction center in the purple bacterium. *Rhodovulum sulfidophilum. J. Biol. Chem.* **274** (1999) 10795–10801.
10. Y. Tsukatani, K. Matsuura, S. Masuda, K. Shimada, A. Hiraishi, K.V.P. Nagashima, Phylogenetic distribution of unusual triheme to tetraheme cytochrome subunit in the reaction center complex of purple photosynthetic bacteria. *Photosynth. Res.* **79** (2004) 83–91.
11. T.E. Meyer, T.J. Donohue, Cytochromes, iron-sulfur and copper proteins mediating electron transfer from the cyt bc_1 complex to photosynthetic reaction center complexes, in: *Anoxygenic Photosynthetic Bacteria* (1995) (R.E. Blankenship, M.T. Madigan, C.E. Bauer eds.), Kluwer Academic, Dordrecht, pp. 725–745.
12. T. Nogi, I. Fathir, M. Kobayashi, T. Nozawa, K. Miki, Crystal structures of photosynthetic reaction center and high-potential iron-sulfur protein from *Thermochromatium tepidum:* thermostability and electron transfer. *Proc. Natl. Acad. Sci. U.S.A.* **97** (2000) 13561–13566.
13. W. Nitschke, A.W. Rutherford, Tetrahem cytochrome *c* subunit of *Rhodopseudomonas viridis* characterized by EPR. *Biochemistry* **28** (1989) 3161–3168.
14. A. Verméglio, P. Richaud, J. Breton, Orientation and assignment of the four cytochrome hemes in *Rhodopseudomonas viridis* reaction centers. *FEBS Lett.* **243** (1989) 259–263.
15. G. Alegria, P.L. Dutton, Langmuir-Blodgett monolayer films of the *Rhodopseudomonas viridis* reaction center: determination of the order of the hemes in the cytochrome *c* subunit. *Biochim. Biophys. Acta* **1057** (1991) 258–272.
16. C.C. Moser, J.M. Keske, K. Warncke, R.S. Farid, P.L. Dutton, Nature of biological electron transfer. *Nature* **355** (1992) 796–802.
17. C.C. Moser, C.C. Page, X. Chen, P.L. Dutton, Electron transfer in natural proteins theory and design. *Subcell. Biochem.* **35** (2000) 1–28.
18. C.C. Page, C.C. Moser, X. Chen, P.L. Dutton, Natural engineering principles of electron tunneling in biological oxidation-reduction. *Nature* **402** (1999) 47–52.
19. I.P. Chen, P., Mathis, J. Koepke, H. Michel, Uphill electron transfer in the tetraheme cytochrome subunit of the *Rhodopseudomonas viridis* photosynthetic reaction center: evidence from site-directed mutagenesis. *Biochemistry* **39** (2000) 3592–3602.
20. J.M. Ortega, P. Mathis, Electron transfer from the tetraheme cytochrome to the special pair in isolated reaction centers of *Rhodopseudomonas viridis. Biochemistry* **32** (1993) 1141–1151.
21. S.M. Dracheva, L.A. Drachev, S.M. Zaberezhnaya, A.A. Konstantinov, A.Y. Semenov, V.P. Skulachev, Spectral, redox and kinetic characteristics of high-potential cytochrome *c* hemes in *Rhodopseudomonas viridis* reaction center. *FEBS Lett.* **205** (1986) 41–46.
22. S.M. Dracheva, L.A. Drachev, A.A. Konstantinov, A.Y. Semenov, V.P. Skulachev, A.M. Arutjunjan, V.A. Shuvalov, S.M. Zaberezhnaya, Electrogenic steps in the redox reactions catalyzed by photosynthetic reaction-centre complex from *Rhodopseudomonas viridis. Eur. J. Biochem.* **171** (1988) 253–264.
23. F. Baymann, F. Rappaport, Electrostatic interactions at the donor side of the photosynthetic reaction center of *Rhodopseudomonas viridis. Biochemistry* **37** (1998) 15320–15326.
24. L. Menin, J. Gaillard, P. Parot, B. Schoepp, W. Nitschke, A. Verméglio, Role of HiPIP as electron donor to the RC-bound cytochrome in photosynthetic purple bacteria. *Photosynth. Res.* **55** (1998) 343–348.

25. A. Hochkoeppler, S. Ciurli, G. Venturoli, D. Zannoni, The high potential iron-sulfur protein (HiPIP) from *Rhodoferax fermentans* is competent in photosynthetic electron transfer. *FEBS Lett.* **357** (1995) 70–74.
26. A. Hochkoeppler, D. Zannoni, S. Ciurli, T.E. Meyer, M.A. Cusanovich, G. Tollin, Kinetics of photo-induced electron transfer from high-potential iron-sulfur protein to the photosynthetic reaction center of the purple phototroph *Rhodoferax fermentans*. *Proc. Natl. Acad. Sci. U.S.A.* **93** (1996) 6998–7002.
27. R.P. Ambler, M. Daniel, J. Hermoso, T.E. Meyer, R.G. Bartsch, M.D. Kamen, Cytochrome c_2 sequence variation among the recognized species of purple non-sulphur photosynthetic bacteria. *Nature* **278** (1979) 659–660.
28. R.P. Ambler, Sequence variability in bacterial cytochrome *c*. *Biochim. Biophys. Acta* **1058** (1991) 42–47.
29. R.G. Bartsch, The distribution of soluble metallo-redox proteins in purple photo-trophic bacteria. *Biochim. Biophys. Acta* **1058** (1991) 28–30.
30. B. Schoepp, P. Parot, L. Menin, J. Gaillard, P. Richaud, A. Verméglio, In vivo participation of a high-potential iron-sulfur protein as electron donor to the photochemical reaction center of *Rubrivivax gelatinosus*. *Biochemistry* **34** (1995) 11736–11742.
31. K.V.P. Nagashima, K. Matsuura, K. Shimada, A. Verméglio, High-potential iron-sulfur protein (HiPIP) is the major electron donor to the reaction center complex in photosynthetically growing cells of the purple bacterium *Rubrivivax gelatinosus*. *Biochemistry* **41** (2002) 14028–14032.
32. L. Menin, M. Yoshida, M. Jaquinod, K.V.P. Nagashima, K. Matsuura, P. Parot, A. Verméglio, Dark aerobic growth conditions induce the synthesis of a high midpoint potential cytochrome c_8 in the photosynthetic bacterium *Rubrivivax gelatinosus*. *Biochemistry* **38** (1999) 15238–15244.
33. L. Menin, B. Schoepp, P. Parot, A. Verméglio, The photoinduced cyclic electron transfer in *Rhodocyclus tenuis* cells: participation of HiPIP or cyt c_8 depending on the ambient redox potential. *Biochemistry* **36** (1997) 12183–12188.
34. A. Verméglio, J. Li, B. Schoepp-Cothenet, N. Pratt, D.B. Knaff, The role of high-potential iron protein and cytochrome c_8 as alternative electron donors to the reaction center of *Chromatium vinosum*. *Biochemistry* **41** (2002) 8868–8875.
35. A. Osyczka, K.V.P. Nagashima, S. Sogabe, K. Miki, M. Yoshida, K. Shimada, K. Matsuura, Interaction site for soluble cytochromes on the tetraheme cytochrome subunit bound to the bacterial photosynthetic reaction center mapped by site-directed mutagenesis. *Biochemistry* **37** (1998) 11732–11744.
36. A. Osyczka, K.V.P. Nagashima, S. Sogabe, K. Miki, K. Shimada, K. Matsuura, Comparison of the binding sites for high-potential iron-sulfur protein and cytochrome *c* on the tetraheme cytochrome subunit bound to the bacterial photosynthetic reaction center. *Biochemistry* **38** (1999) 15779–15790.
37. A. Osyczka, K.V. Nagashima, K. Shimada, K. Matsuura, Interaction site for high-potential iron-sulfur protein on the tetraheme cytochrome subunit bound to the photosynthetic reaction center of *Rubrivivax gelatinosus*. *Biochemistry* **38** (1999) 2861–2865.
38. D. Knaff, A. Willie, J. Long, A. Kriauciunas, B. Durham, F. Millett, Reaction of cytochrome c_2 with photosynthetic reaction centers from *Rhodopseudomonas viridis*. *Biochemistry* **30** (1991) 1303–1310.
39. G. Venturoli, M.D. Mamedov, S. Mansy, F. Musiani, M. Strocchi, F. Francia, A.Y. Semenov, J.A. Cowan, S. Ciurli, Electron transfer from HiPIP to the photooxidized tetraheme cytochrome subunit of *Allochromatium vinosum* reaction

center: new insights from site-directed mutagenesis and computational studies. *Biochemistry* **43** (2004) 437–445.
40. J. Alric, M. Yoshida, K.V.P. Nagashima, R. Hienerwadel, P. Parot, A. Verméglio, S.W. Chen, J-L. Pellequer, Two distinct binding sites for HiPIP and cytochrome c on the reaction center-bound cytochrome of *Rubrivivax gelatinous*. *J. Biol. Chem.* **279** (2004) 32545–32553.
41. J. Alric, Y. Tsukatani, M. Yoshida, K. Matsuura, K. Shimada, R. Hienerwadel, B. Schoepp-Cothenet, W. Nitschke, K.V.P. Nagashima, A. Verméglio, Structural and functional characterization of the unusual triheme cytochrome bound to the reaction center of *Rhodovulum sulfidophilum*. *J. Biol. Chem.* **279** (2004) 26090–26097.
42. M. Yoshida, S. Masuda, K.V. Nagashima, A. Verméglio, K. Shimada, K. Matsuura, In vitro and in vivo electron transfer to the triheme cytochrome subunit bound to the photosynthetic reaction center complex in the purple bacterium *Rhodovulum sulfidophilum*. *Biochim. Biophys. Acta* **1506** (2001) 23–30.
43. S. Masuda, Y. Tsukatani, Y. Kimura, K.V.P. Nagashima, K. Shimada, K. Matsuura, Mutational analyses of the photosynthetic reaction center-bound triheme cytochrome subunit and cytochrome c_2 in the purple bacterium *Rhodovulum sulfidophilum*. *Biochemistry* **37** (2002) 11211–11217.
44. C.A. McDevitt, P. Hugenholtz, G.R. Hanson, A.G. McEwan, Molecular analysis of dimethyl sulphide dehydrogenase from *Rhodovulum sulfidophilum*: its place in the dimethyl sulphoxide reductase family of microbial molybdopterin-containing enzyme. *Mol. Microbiol.* **44** (2002) 1575–1587.
45. D. Tiede, P.L. Dutton, in: *The Photosynthetic Reaction Center* (1993) (J. Deisenhofer, J. Norris, eds.), Academic Press, San Diego, pp. 258–288.
46. P.L. Dutton, R.C. Prince, Reaction-center-driven cytochrome interactions in electron and proton translocation and energy coupling, in: *The Photosynthetic Bacteria* (1978) (R.K. Clayton, W.R. Sistrom, eds.), Plenum Press, New York, pp. 525–570.
47. R.E. Overfield, C.A. Wraight, D. Devault, Microsecond photooxidation kinetics of cytochrome c_2 from *Rhodopseudomonas sphaeroides*: in vivo and solution studies. *FEBS Lett.* **105** (1979) 137–142.
48. P. Joliot, A. Verméglio, A. Joliot, Evidence for supercomplexes between reaction centers, cytochrome c_2 and cytochrome bc_1 complex in *Rhodobacter sphaeroides* whole cells. *Biochim. Biophys. Acta* **975** (1989) 336–345.
49. A. Verméglio, P. Joliot, The photosynthetic apparatus of *Rhodobacter sphaeroides*. *Trends Microbiol.* **7** (1999) 435–440.
50. H.L. Axelrod, E.C. Albresch, M.Y. Okamura, A.P. Yeh, D.C. Rees, G. Feher, X-ray structure determination of the cytochrome c_2: reaction center electron transfer complex from *Rhodobacter sphaeroides*. *J. Mol. Biol.* **319** (2002) 501–515.
51. D.M. Tiede, A.C. Vashishta, M.R. Gunner, Electron-transfer kinetics and electrostatic properties of the *Rhodobacter sphaeroides* reaction center and soluble c-cytochromes. *Biochemistry* **32** (1993) 4515–4531.
52. J.E. Long, B. Durham, M.Y. Okamura, F. Millett, Role of specific lysine residues in binding cytochrome c_2 to the *Rhodobacter sphaeroides* reaction center in optimal orientation for rapid electron transfer. *Biochemistry* **28** (1989) 6970–6974.
53. M.S. Caffrey, R.G. Bartsch, M.A. Cusanovich, Study of the cytochrome c_2-reaction center interaction by site-directed mutagenesis. *J. Biol. Chem.* **267** (1992) 6317–6321.
54. D. Rosen, M.Y. Okamura, E.C. Abresch, G.E. Valkris, G. Feher, Interaction of cytochrome c with reaction centers of *Rhodopseudomonas sphaeroides* R-26:

localization of the binding site by chemical cross-linking and immunochemical studies. *Biochemistry* **22** (1983) 335–341.
55. F. Drepper, P. Dorlet, P. Mathis, Crosslinked electron transfer complex between cytochrome c_2 and the photosynthetic reaction center of *Rhodobacter sphaeroides*. *Biochemistry* **36** (1997) 1418–1427.
56. D. Xia, C.A. Yu, H. Kim, J.Z. Xia, A.M. Zachurin, L. Zhang, L. Yu, J. Deisenhofer, Crystal structure of the cytochrome bc_1 complex from bovine heart mitochondria. *Science* **277** (1997) 60–66.
57. C. Lange, C. Hunte, Crystal structure of the yeast cytochrome bc_1 complex with its bound substrate cytochrome *c*. *Proc. Natl. Acad. Sci. U.S.A.* **99** (2002) 2800–2805.
58. F.E. Jenney, F. Daldal, A novel membrane-bound *c*-type cytochrome, cyt c_y can mediate the photosynthetic growth of *Rhodobacter capsulatus* and *Rhodobacter sphaeroide*. *EMBO J.* **12** (1993) 1283–1292.
59. F.E. Jenney, R.C. Prince, F. Daldal, Roles of the soluble cytochrome c_2 and membrane-associated cytochrome c_y of *Rhodobacter capsulatus* in photosynthetic electron transfer. *Biochemistry* **33** (1994) 2496–2502.
60. H. Myllykallio, F.E. Jenney, C.R. Moomaw, C.A. Slaughter, F. Daldal, Cytochrome c_y of *Rhodobacter capsulatus* is attached to the cytoplasmic membrane by an uncleaved signal sequence like anchor. *J. Bacteriol* **179** (1997) 2623–2631.
61. A. Hochkoeppler, F.E. Jenney, D. Zannoni, F. Daldal, Membrane-associated cytochrome c_y of *Rhodobacter capsulatus* is an electron carrier from the cytochrome bc_1 complex to the cytochrome *c* oxidase during respiration. *J. Bacteriol.* **177** (1995) 608–613.
62. J. Zeilstra-Ryalls, S. Kaplan, Aerobic and anaerobic regulation in *Rhodobacter sphaeroides* 2-4-1: the role of the *fnrL* gene. *J. Bacteriol.* **177** (1995) 6422–6431.
63. H. Myllykallio, D. Zannoni, F. Daldal, *Rhodobacter sphaeroides* cyt c_y is a membrane-attached electron carrier that is deficient in photosynthesis but proficient in respiration. *Proc. Natl. Acad. Sci. U.S.A.* **96** (1999) 4348–4353.
64. H. Oh-oka, M. Iwaki, S. Itoh, Membrane-bound cytochrome c_Z couples quinol oxidoreductase to the P840 reaction center complex in isolated membranes of the green sulfur bacterium *Chlorobium tepidum*. *Biochemistry* **37** (1998) 12293–12300.
65. K. Harashima, T. Shiba, N. Murata, *Aerobic Photosynthetic Bacteria* (1989), Japan Scientific Societies Press and Springer Verlag, Tokyo.
66. K. Shimada, Aerobic anoxygenic phototrophs, in: *Anoxygenic Photosynthetic Bacteria* (1995) (R.E. Blankenship, M.T. Madigan, C.E. Bauer eds.), Kluwer Academic, Dordrecht, pp. 105–122.
67. K. Shimada, H. Hayashi, M. Tasumi, Bacteriochlorophyll-protein complexes of aerobic bacteria, *Erythrobacter longus* and *Erythrobacter* sp. OCh 114. *Arch. Microbiol.* **143** (1985) 244–247.
68. K. Takamiya, K. Iba, K. Okamura, Reaction center complex from an aerobic photosynthetic bacterium. *Biochim. Biophys. Acta* **890** (1987) 127–133.
69. V.V. Yurkov, L. Menin, B. Schoepp, A. Verméglio, Purification and characterization of reaction centers of the obligately aerobic anoxygenic phototrophic bacteria *Erythrobacter litoralis*, *Erythromicrobium ursincola* and *Erythromicrobium sibiricum*. *Photosynth. Res.* **57** (1998) 129–138.
70. V.V. Yurkov, H. van Gemerden, Impact of light/dark regime on growth rate, biomass formation and bacteriochlorophyll synthesis in *Erythromicrobium hydrolyticum*. *Arch. Microbiol.* **159** (1993) 84–89.
71. K.F. Okamura, O. Mitsuori, K. Ito, K. Takamiya, M. Nishimura, Photophosphorylation and oxidative phosphorylation in intact cells and chromatophores

of an aerobic photosynthetic bacterium, *Erythrobacter* sp. strain OCh114. *J. Bacteriol.* **168** (1986) 142–1146.
72. K. Takamiya, K. Okamura, Photochemical activities and photosynthetic ATP formation in membrane preparation from a facultative methylotroph, *Protaminobacter ruber* strain NR-1. *Arch. Microbiol.* **140** (1984) 21–26.
73. D. Garcia, P. Richaud, J. Breton, A. Verméglio, Structure and function of the tetraheme cytochrome associated to the reaction centers of *Roseobacter denitrificans*. *Biochimie* **76** (1994) 666–673.
74. V.V. Yurkov, B. Schoepp, A. Verméglio, Photoinduced electron transfer and cytochrome content in obligate aerobic phototrophic bacteria from genera *Erythromicrobium, Sandaracinobacter, Erythromonas, Roseococcus* and *Erythrobacter*. *Photosynth. Res.* **57** (1998) 117–128.
75. C. Schwarze, A.V. Carluccio, G. Venturoli, A. Labahn, Photo-induced cyclic electron transfer involving cytochrome bc_1 complex and reaction center in the obligate aerobic phototroph *Roseobacter denitrificans*. *Eur. J. Biochem.* **267** (2000) 422–433.
76. R.J. Porra, W. Schäfer, N. Gad'on, I. Katheder, G. Drews, H. Scheer, Origin of the two carbonyl oxygens of bacteriochlorophyll *a:* Demonstration of two different pathways for the formation of ring E in *Rhodobacter sphaeroides* and *Roseobacter denitrificans*, and a common hydratase pathway for 3-acetyl group formation. *Eur. J. Biochem.* **239** (1996) 85–92.
77. R.J. Porra, M. Urzinger, J. Winkler, C. Bubenzer, H. Scheer, Biosynthesis of the 3-acetyl and 131-oxo groups of bacteriochlorophyll *a* in the facultative aerobic bacterium, *Rhodovulum sulfidophilum*: the presence of both oxygenase and hydratase pathways for isocyclic ring formation. *Eur. J. Biochem.* **257** (1998) 185–191.
78. R.J. Porra, W. Schäfer, N. Gad'on, I. Katheder, H. Scheer, The derivation of the oxygen atoms of the 131-oxo and 3-acetyl groups of bacteriochlorophyll *a* from water in *Rhodobacter sphaeroides* cells adapting from respiratory to photosynthetic conditions: evidence for an anaerobic pathway for the formation of isocyclic ring E. *FEBS Lett.* **371** (1995) 21–24.
79. S. Ouchane, A.-S. Steunou, M. Picaud, C. Astier, Aerobic and anaerobic Mg-protoporphyrin monomethyl ester cyclases in purple bacteria, a strategy adopted to bypass the repressive oxygen control system. *J. Biol. Chem.* **279** (2004) 6385–6394.
80. D.M. Kramer, A. Kanazawa, D. Fleischman, Oxygen dependence of photosynthetic electron transport in a bacteriochlorophyll-containing rhizobium. *FEBS Lett.* **417** (1997) 275–278.
81. G. McDermott, S.M. Prince, A.A. Freer, A.M. Hawthornthwaite-Lawlee, M.Z. Papiz, R.J. Cogdell, N.W. Isaacs, Crystal structure of an integral membrane light-harvesting complex from photosynthetic bacteria. *Nature* **374** (1995) 517–525.
82. J. Koepke, X. Hu, C. Muenke, K. Schulten, H. Michel, The crystal structure of the light-harvesting complex II (B800–850) from *Rhodospirillum molischianum*. *Structure* **4** (1996) 581–597.
83. J.P. Allen, G. Feher, T.O. Yeates, H. Komya, D.C. Rees, Structure of the reaction centre from *Rhodobacter sphaeroides* R-26: the cofactors. *Proc. Natl. Acad. Sci. U.S.A.* **84** (1987) 5730–5734.
84. H.L. Axelrod, G. Feher, J.P. Allen, A. Chirino, M.W. Day, B.T. Hsu, D.C. Rees, Crystallization and X-ray structure determination of cytochrome c_2 from *Rhodobacter sphaeroides* in three crystals forms. *Acta Crystallog., Sect. D* **50** (1994) 596–602.
85. D.R. Breiter, T.E. Meyer, I. Rayment, M. Holden, The molecular structure of the high potential iron-sulfur protein isolated from *Ectothiorhodospira halophila* determined at 2.5Å resolution. *J. Biol. Chem.* **266** (1991) 18660–18667.

86. Z. Zhang, L. Huang, V.M. Shulmeister, Y.-I. Chi, K.K. Kim, L.-W. Hung, A.R. Crofts, E.R. Berry, S.-H. Kim, Electron transfer by domain movement in cytochrome bc_1. Nature 392 (1998) 677–684.
87. A.W. Roszak, T.D. Howard, J. Southall, A.T. Gardiner, C.J. Law, N.W. Isaacs, R.J. Cogdell, Crystal structure of the RC-LH1 core complex from Rhodopseudomonas palustris. Science 302 (2003) 1969–1972.
88. N. Adir, H.L. Axelrod, P. Beroza, R.A. Isaacson, S.H. Rongey, M.Y. Okamura, G. Feher, Co-crystallization and characterization of the photosynthetic reaction center–cytochrome c_2 complex from Rhodobacter sphaeroides. Biochemistry 35 (1996) 2535–2547.
89. H. Gaffron, K. Wohl, Naturwissenschaften 24 (1936) 81–103.
90. R. Emerson, W. Arnold, J. Gen. Physiol. 16 (1932) 191–205.
91. K.J. Visscher, H. Bergström, V. Sundström, C.N. Hunter, R. van Grondelle, Temperature dependence of energy transfer from the longwavelength antenna Bch1896 to the reaction center in Rhodospirillum rubrum, Rhodobacter sphaeroides (wt and M21 mutant) from 77 to 177K, studied by picosecond absorption spectroscopy. Photosynth. Res. 22 (1989) 211–217.
92. K.R. Miller, Three-dimensional structure of a photosynthetic membrane. Nature 300 (1982) 53–55.
93. H. Engelhardt, A. Engel, W. Baumeister, Stoichiometric model of the photosynthetic unit of Ectothiorhodospira halochloris. Proc. Natl. Acad. Sci. U.S.A. 83 (1986) 8972–8976.
94. A.F. Boonstra, L. Germeroth, E.J. Boekema, Structure of the light-harvesting antenna from Rhodospirillum molischianum studied by electron microsopy. Biochim. Biophys. Acta 1184 (1994) 227–234.
95. T. Walz, R. Ghosh, Two-dimensionnal crystallization of the light-harvesting I-reaction center photounit from Rhodospirillum rubrum. J. Mol. Biol. 265 (1997) 107–111.
96. T. Walz, S.J. Jamieson, C.M. Bowers, P.A. Bullough, C.N. Hunter, Projection structures of three photosynthetic complexes from Rhodobacter sphaeroides. J. Mol. Biol. 282 (1998) 833–845.
97. S. Scheuring, J. Seguin, S. Marco, D. Levy, B. Robert, J.-L. Rigaud, Nanodissection and high-resolution imaging of the Rhodopseudomonas viridis photosynthetic core complex in native membrane by AFM. Proc. Natl. Acad. Sci. U.S.A. 100 (2003) 1690–1693.
98. D. Fotiadis, P. Qian, A. Philippsen, P.A. Bullough, A. Engel, C.N. Hunter, Structural analysis of the RC-LH1 photosynthetic core complex of Rhodospirillum rubrum using atomic force microscopy. J. Biol. Chem. 279 (2004) 2063–2068.
99. S. Karrasch, P.A. Bullough, R. Ghosh, The 8.5 Å projection map of the light-harvesting complex I from Rhodospirillum rubrum reveals a ring composed of 16 subunits. EMBO J. 14 (1995) 631–638.
100. J.W. Farchaus, H. Grünberg, D. Oesterhelt, Complementation of a reaction centre-deficient Rhodobacter sphaeroides pufLMX deletion strain in trans with pufBALM does not restore the photosynthetic positive phenotype. J. Bacteriol. 172 (1990) 977–985.
101. T.G. Liburn, C.E. Haith, R.C. Prince, J.T. Beatty, Pleiotropic effects of pufX gene deletion on the structure and function of the photosynthetic apparatus of Rhodobacter capsulatus. Biochim. Biophys. Acta 1100 (1992) 160–170.

102. J.W. Farchaus, W.P. Barz, H. Grünberg, D. Oesterhelt, Studies on the expression of the pufX polypeptide and its requirement for photoheterotrophic growth in *Rhodobacter sphaeroides*. *EMBO J.* **11** (1992) 2779–2788.
103. W.P. Barz, F. Francia, G. Venturoli, B.A. Melandri, A. Verméglio, D. Oesterhelt, Role of PufX protein in photosynthetic growth of *Rhodobacter sphaeroides*. 1. PufX is required for efficient light driven electron transfer and photophosphorylation under anaerobic conditions. *Biochemistry* **34** (1995) 15235–15247.
104. W.P. Barz, A. Verméglio, F. Francia, G. Venturoli, B.A. Melandri, D. Oesterhelt, Role of PufX protein in photosynthetic growth of *Rhodobacter sphaeroides*. 2. PufX is required for efficient ubiquinone/ubiquinol exchange between the reaction centre Q_B site and the cytochrome bc_1 complex. *Biochemistry* **34** (1995) 15248–15258.
105. F. Francia, J. Wang, G. Venturoli, B.A. Melandri, W.P. Barz, D. Oesterhelt, The reaction center-LH1 antenna complex of *Rhodobacter sphaeroides* contains one PufX molecule which is involved in dimerization of this complex. *Biochemistry* **38** (1999) 6834–6845.
106. C.N. Hunter, J.D. Pennoyer, J.N. Sturgis, D. Farrelly, R.A. Niederman, Oligomerization states and associations of light-harvesting pigment protein complexes of *Rhodobacter sphaeroides* as analyzed by lithium dodecyl-sulfate polyacrylamide-gel electrophoresis. *Biochemistry* **27** (1988) 3459–3467.
107. J.R. Golecki, S. Ventura, J. Oelze, The architecture of unusual membrane tubes in the B800–850 light-harvesting bacteriochlorophyll-deficient mutant 19 of *Rhodobacter sphaeroides*. *FEMS Lett.* **77** (1991) 335–340.
108. M. Sabaty, J. Jappé, J. Olive, A. Verméglio, Organization of the electron-transfer components in *Rhodobacter sphaeroides* forma sp. *denitrificans* whole cells. *Biochim. Biophys. Acta* **1187** (1994) 313–323.
109. C. Jungas, J.L. Ranck, J.L. Rigaud, P. Joliot, A. Verméglio, Supramolecular organization of the photosynthetic apparatus of *Rhodobacter sphaeroides*. *EMBO J.* **18** (1999) 534–542.
110. C.A. Siebert, P. Qian, D. Fotiadis, A. Engel, C.N. Hunter, P.A. Bullough, Molecular architecture of photosynthetic membranes in *Rhodobacter sphaeroides*: the role of PufX. *EMBO J.* **23** (2004) 690–700.
111. S. Scheuring, F. Francia, J. Busselez, B.A. Melandri, J.-L. Rigaud, D. Lévy, Structural role of PufX in the dimerization of the photosynthetic core complex of *Rhodobacter sphaeroides*. *J. Biol. Chem.* **279** (2004) 3620–3626.
112. R.N. Freese, J.D. Olsen, R. Branvall, W.H. Westerhuis, C.N. Hunter, R. van Grondelle, The long-range supraorganization of the bacterial photosynthetic unit: a key role for PufX. *Proc. Natl. Acad. Sci. U.S.A.* **97** (2000) 5197–5202.
113. A. Verméglio, P. Joliot, Supramolecular organization of the photosynthetic chain in anoxygenic bacteria. *Biochim. Biophys. Acta* **1555** (2002) 60–64.
114. K. Matsuura, M. Mori, T. Satoh, Heterogeneous pools of cytochrome c_2 in photodenitrifying cells of *Rhodobacter sphaeroides* forma sp. *denitrificans*. *J. Biochem.* **104** (1988) 1016–1020.
115. A. Verméglio, P. Joliot, A. Joliot, The rate of cytochrome c_2 photooxidation reflects the subcellular distribution of reaction centers in *Rhodobacter sphaeroides*. *Biochim. Biophys. Acta* **1183** (1993) 352–360.
116. P. Joliot, A. Verméglio, A. Joliot, Photo-induced cyclic electron transfer operates in frozen cells of *Rhodobacter sphaeroides*. *Biochim. Biophys. Acta* **1318** (1997) 374–384.

117. A.R. Crofts, Photosynthesis in *Rhodobacter sphaeroides*. *Trends Microbiol.* **8** (2000) 105–106.
118. J. Fernàndez-Velasco, A.R. Crofts, Complex or supercomplexes: inhibitor titrations show that electron transfer in chromatophores from *Rhodobacter sphaeroides* involves a dimeric UQH_2: cytochrome c_2 oxidase, and is delocalized. *Biochem. Soc. Trans.* **19** (1991) 588–593.
119. A.R. Crofts, M. Guergova-Kuras, S. Hong, Chromatophores heterogeneity explains phenomena seen in *Rhodobacter sphaeroides* previously attributed to supercomplexes. *Photosynth. Res.* **55** (1998) 357–362.
120. A. Verméglio, P. Joliot, Response from Verméglio and Joliot. *Trends Microbiol.* **8** (2000) 106–107.
121. H. Myllykallio, F. Drepper, P. Mathis, F. Daldal, Membrane-anchored cytochrome c_y mediated microsecond time electron transfer from the cytochrome bc_1 complex to the reaction center in *Rhodobacter capsulatus*. *Biochemistry* **37** (1998) 5501–5510.
122. A. Verméglio, A. Joliot, P. Joliot, Supramolecular organization of the photosynthetic chain in mutants of *Rhodobacter capsulatus* deleted in cytochrome c_2. *Photosynth. Res.* **56** (1998) 329–337.
123. H. Myllykallio, F. Drepper, P. Mathis, F. Daldal, Electron transfer super-complexes in photosynthesis and respiration. *Trends Microbiol.* **8** (2000) 493–494.
124. H. Schägger, Respiratory chain supercomplexes of mitochondria and bacteria. *Biochim. Biophys. Acta* **1555** (2002) 154–159.

Chapter 19

Electron Transport Chains in Oxygenic Cyanobacteria

Günter A. Peschek

Table of Contents

19.1 Introduction...385
19.2 Thermodynamic Considerations 386
19.3 Evolutionary Considerations...............................387
19.4 Electron Transport Pathways in Cyanobacteria 394
    19.4.1 Comparison of the Photosynthetic Apparatus in
           Cyanobacteria and Higher Plants......................396
    19.4.2 Membrane Systems in Cyanobacteria...................396
    19.4.3 Photosynthetic and Respiratory Activities 397
    19.4.4 Mesophilic and Thermophilic Cyanobacteria 398
    19.4.5 Crystal Structure Analysis with Samples from Thermophilic
           Cyanobacteria 398
           19.4.5.1 Structure of PS I and PS II...................399
           19.4.5.2 Structure and Function of the Cytochrome b_6f
                  Complex 399
    19.4.6 Electron Transport Chains in Photosynthesis and
           Respiration and their Mutual Interaction................400
19.5 Concluding Remarks and Future Perspectives 405
Acknowledgements 405
References..406

Abstract

Cyanobacteria (blue-green algae) are introduced here and discussed as *the* paradigmatic organisms of oxygenic (plant-type) photosynthesis *and* aerobic (mitochondrial-type) respiration in both bioenergetic, evolutionary and ecological respects. As the most important energy-conserving biological mechanisms, both photosynthesis and respiration crucially depend on the membrane-bound chemiosmotic electron transport principle. Within the framework of a generalized endosymbiont hypothesis, therefore, the term free-living protochloromitochondria seems to be most suitable for these *prokaryotic plants*, which are also rightly named the *bioenergetic nonplus-ultra*. Being ideal laboratory organisms for (biochemical and biophysical) photosynthesis research some thermophilic species among them have recently been used for detailed X-ray structural analysis of no less than three of the most important energy-converting electron transfer complexes of plant-type photosynthesis, viz., Photosystems II and I and the cytochrome $b_6 f$ complex.

19.1 Introduction

It seems more than appropriate that the blue-green algae (cyanobacteria) find a legitimate place in a book on the primary processes of photosynthesis since these oxygenic phototrophic organisms, most of which are in addition also capable of N_2 fixation [1–3], rightly deserve the predicate of being the bioenergetic "nonplus-ultra" among living beings: At the expense of sunlight, water, atmospheric air, and a few ubiquitous minerals they cover all their needs for growth and proliferation. Also for photosynthesis research, the cyanobacteria are truly paradigmatic, in particular the thermophilic species, which provide the most suitable material for the modern field of biocrystallography (Chapters 13, 15 and 20). However, since – on average – 50% of all the time available is clearly darkness, not even cyanobacteria can survive without chemoheterotrophic energy conversion (respiration and/or fermentation), be it only for short-term maintenance. Therefore, not only the photosynthetic reactions of cyanobacteria but also the chemoheterotrophic modes of biological energy conversion are briefly touched in this chapter. Though structurally and functionally very much similar to a chloroplast, in marked contrast to this semiautonomous organelle of a eukaryotic photosynthesizing cell a cyanobacterium combines both oxygenic photosynthesis and aerobic (mitochondrial-like) respiration (and, frequently, also nitrogenase) together in a prokaryotic cell structure. The latter, of course, is quite similar to that of a conventional chloroplast. Very pertinently, therefore, we should view a cyanobacterium as a free-living *(proto)chloromitochondrion* (Chapter 22) [4,5]. This chapter focuses on the peculiarities of the electron transport chains in cyanobacteria because their "invention" during evolution marks the cornerstone in the development of all higher forms of living matter, including mankind.

19.2 Thermodynamic Considerations

Biological electron transport must be conceived of in analogy to the flow of electrons in a wire from cathode (−) to anode (+), atomistically speaking. In biology the electron-conducting medium is the cascade of redox carriers ("enzymes") located in the membrane. The thermodynamic driving force is the electrical potential difference (ΔE) between an electron donor (more negative redox potential, "cathode") and an electron acceptor (more positive redox potential, "anode"). The Gibbs energy stored by n electrons moving downhill (exergonically) along an electric potential gradient ("electronmotive force" ΔE) is $\Delta G = -nF\Delta E$, where F is the electrocaloric equivalent or Faraday constant ($F = 96.5\,\text{kJ}\,\text{mol}^{-1}\,\text{V}^{-1}$). In oxygenic photosynthetic electron transport, four electrons resulting from the oxidative cleavage of $2H_2O$ to molecular O_2 and four protons, are "photoexcited" in PS II up to a redox potential of around −0.1 V at $Q_A^{-\bullet}$ (the "high energy" electrons at reduced pheophytin with $E_m = -0.5\,\text{V}$ are not sufficiently stabilized, see Chapter 1), followed by exergonic movement along the electrochemical potential gradient of the inter-system electron transport chain down to oxidized $P700^+$ in PS I (about +0.5 V), i.e., bridging a potential difference of about 0.6 V, which will store $4 \times 96.5 \times 0.6 = 231.6\,\text{kJ}$ of Gibbs energy. Assuming the known "free energy content" ($\Delta G^{o\prime}$ of 1-mol ATP from ADP plus $P_i = +28.5\,\text{kJ}$ per ATP under standard conditions) and further assuming the usual thermodynamic maximum efficiency of chemiosmotic energy conversion of around 30–40% [6], this would be (energetically, not *mechanistically!*) equivalent to the synthesis of 2.4–3.2 ATP/$4e^-$ moving, during the photosynthetic "dark" electron transport, from photoreduced $Q_A^{-\bullet}$ in PS II to oxidized $P700^+$ in PS I (Chapter 1), i.e., per mol O_2 from the photooxidation of water. Herewith compare mitochondrial respiration: The (empiric) P/O value of 3 (ATP synthesized per $2e^-$ moving through the mitochondrial respiratory chain from NADH to oxygen) means the conservation of 85.5 kJ of Gibbs energy vs. 220 kJ available per two electrons (0.5 O_2) between NADH and O_2. See the scheme below in Figure 3; also see eqn. (1).

With respect to the "photosynthetic" electron transport and conforming to the conversion hypothesis that assumes a monophyletic origin of all biological electron transport systems ([7–9]; see also Chapter 22), solar radiation as the inevitable ultimate Gibbs energy source for photosynthetic ATP formation would thus find its "mechanistic motivation" or necessity only for promoting or "activating" electrons up to a high-diving board or parachute practice tower from which they could "freely" (= exergonically) return, in a work-performing fashion, to the lower level from which they had started. This process occurs along a more or less universal ("canonical") membrane-bound biological electron transport chain of surprisingly similar redox catalysts for all, irrespective of whether prokaryotes or eukaryotes, photosynthesis or respiration, anaerobic or aerobic types of electron transport processes [7].

19.3 Evolutionary Considerations

As it is not very feasible to perform experiments on the evolution of living beings on a compatible time scale all corresponding hypotheses must necessarily result in an educated guess. However, there are a few scientific "evolutionary landmarks" that are difficult to deny. One of these is the geological history of our blue planet, which owes its "blue color" simply to the unique occurrence of the likewise uniquely paramagnetic diatomic gas oxygen [10–12]. The geological history of our earth is fairly well established and almost unequivocally documented by results from several independent sciences such as astrophysics, astronomy, geology, geochemistry, paleontology, comparative biochemistry, etc. (cf. Table 1, Figure 1 and Chapter 22). A second scientific landmark on this path would be given by Charles R. Darwin (1809–1882), whose elaborately formulated descendence theory (1859) nowadays, basically, can hardly be denied any more, though there are admittedly still problems with the available time scale and cultural-humanitarian considerations have called for a slight revision of typically Darwinian terms like "struggle for existence" and "survival of the fittest" [13].

A combination of all the above-named "exact natural sciences" is fully capable of descriptively reconstructing a reasonable estimate of the time course of evolutionary highlights that we meet on the way from the (astrophysical) "Big Bang" up to *Homo sapiens sapiens* who, however, in the sense of

Table 1. Summary of the crucial steps in the evolution of the universe, of our earth, and of life on this earth. The Wilkinson Microwave Anisotropy Satellite launched by NASA 2003/4 has determined the age of the universe T_o (astrophysical "Big Bang") as $13.7 \pm 1\%(!)$ billion years. Yet, in the absence of any other more convincing proof from astrophysics, the right-hand side gives the original Hebrew sentence (Mose 1,1: "In the beginning God made heaven and earth…") introducing the creation myth in the "Holy Bible"…

Origin or appearance of:	Gy (gigayears) before now:	
	According to NASA WMWAP*2004*:	or according to *Mose 1,1*:
Universe	13.7	בְּרֵאשִׁית
Sun (=planetary system)	10.0	בָּרָא אֱלֹהִים
Earth (solid crust)	4.6	אֵת הַשָּׁמַיִם
Life (prokaryotes)	3.5	וְאֵת הָאָרֶץ:
CYANOBACTERIA (O_2!)	3.2	וְהָאָרֶץ הָיְתָה
O_2 in the atmosphere	2.0	תֹהוּ וָבֹהוּ
Eukaryotes	1.6	וְחֹשֶׁךְ עַל־פְּנֵי
Terrestrial life (ozone shield !)	0.4	תְהוֹם
Proconsul (pro-hominide)	0.010 (miocene)	וְרוּחַ אֱלֹהִים
Homo erectus (*Pithecanthropus*)	0.002 (pleistocene)	מְרַחֶפֶת
Homo sapiens[2] (*destruens fundulosus*)	0.000 010	עַל־פְּנֵי הַמָּיִם:

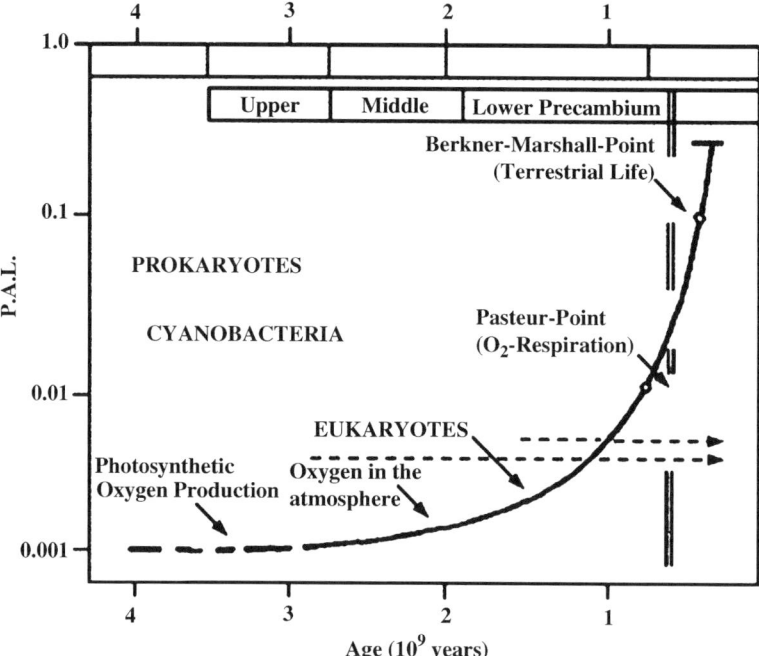

Figure 1. Oxygen content of the earth's biosphere and atmosphere during the previous 4 billion years. P.A.L., present atmospheric level, i.e., fractions of 21% (v/v). (Compare this with the present 0.03% (v/v) CO_2 in the contemporary terrestrial atmosphere! Also see eqn. (1) The Pasteur point marks the time when the global efficiency of respiration (in terms of ATP production), because of increasing availability of O_2, exceeded that of fermentation (substrate-level phosphorylation). The Berkner-Marshall point marks the time when the ozone layer in the upper atmosphere, a result of the photochemical reactions of O_2, started to prevent deleterious ionizing radiation from outer space reaching the surface of the earth. The transient overshoot of O_2 concentrations peaking at 35% (v/v) during the carboniferous period about 300 million years ago (Chapter 22) was due to the massive development of terrestrial (in particular: fern) plants under the shielding ozone layer in the upper atmosphere. It is the time to which all our (diminishing!) present fossil fuel deposits date back, and the overshooting O_2 at first could not be compensated for by a likewise rapid development of animals. The figure is compiled from data in [7,10,11,14–16].

pessimism already expressed by ancient Homer might rather deserve epithets such as "destructive" and "cul-de-sac of evolution" (Table 1).

Table 1 shows this "long march of mankind" in the form of an evolutionary list while Figure 1 illustrates, for the evolution of life, the same way in the form of the evolution of the earth's oxygen budget. It must be borne in mind that it was the molecular oxygen, first set free in bulk amounts by the blue-green algae (Figure 1), that had not only rendered our earth to what it still is, viz., the blue planet, but which also represents by far the most decisive turning point in the evolution of life (Table 1; also see Chapter 1).

In the course of many million years of biological evolution (Chapter 22), energy conversion through membrane-bound electron transfer/transport (i.e., the chemiosmotic principle of Peter Mitchell [17]; see Chapters 1 and 21) finally has, by far, won the race, and in our present-day biosphere the most important, widespread and efficient bioenergetic processes are (aerobic) respiration and (oxygenic) photosynthesis [eqn. (1)], the ecological interplay of which not only closes the terrestrial hydrogen and oxygen cycles but also sustains the fundamental steady-state of our aerobic biosphere and atmosphere, which is absolutely indispensable for human and most other life [10–12]. Hereby, please, note the unique and unprecedented role of blue-green algae (cyanobacteria), as briefly summarized in the context of eqn. (1):

$$6CO_2 + 12H_2O \rightarrow C_6H_{12}O_6 + 6O_2 + 6H_2O$$
$$\Delta G^{\circ\prime} = \pm 2821.5 \, kJ \, mol^{-1} \, (hexose)$$
(1)

Equation (1) combines the reactions of oxygenic photosynthesis [endergonic, (+), from left to right] and of aerobic respiration [exergonic, (−), from right to left]. It also reflects, at the same time, the present terrestrial steady-state of our atmosphere and biosphere established by the concurrent and (in toto) equally efficient actions of oxygenic, plant-type photosynthesis and aerobic respiration, ensuring the 21% (v/v) O_2 in the atmosphere that we all critically depend on. The equation is based on the famous Van Niel equation for autotrophic CO_2 fixation [eqn. (2)]. In the endergonic direction (+2821.5 kJ mol^{-1}), exemplifying the photosynthetic primary production of biomass (start of terrestrial food chains), the process is energetically driven by light. *Chemo*synthetic primary production as found associated with so-called *black smokers* [18] is without any significant quantitative ecological impact. An estimated 10^{11} tons of carbon (in the form of CO_2) per year is converted into biomass by plant-type photosynthesis and the equivalent amount of O_2 (the "poop oxygen" of Babcock, see [19,20]) is thereby released from water according to eqn. (1). Interestingly, there are striking mechanistic similarities in the enzymatic redox conversions (formation and cleavage of the O–O bond) between water and oxygen [20–24], see also Chapter 17.

Recent estimates assign between 20% and 30% of this worldwide primary productivity to *cyanobacteria*, in particular to small unicellular marine *Synechococcus* species [25] and to likewise unicellular planktonic Prochlorophytes [26] that, though not especially concentrated anywhere in the euphotic zone of terrestrial water-bodies, are nevertheless extremely widespread in *all* oceans etc., finally almost equaling the overall share provided by the diminishing tropical rain forests (at present!).

A further remarkable evolutionary note on cyanobacteria stems from the observation of molecular vestiges of oxygenic photosynthetic organelles ("thylakosomes") in several (chemoheterotrophic!) protists such as *Psalteriomonas lanterna* and some representatives of the parasitic genus *Apicomplexa* [27]. The latter findings seem to go well with the assumption of a so-called generalized (unifying) endosymbiont hypothesis [4,5]. This hypothesis, though perhaps not yet sufficiently corroborated by "genomic proofs", starts from the admittedly extraordinary unlikelihood of a stable endosymbiont event in evolution. Since the early work of Mereschkowsky [28], this scenario has always been convergently discussed only with respect to a possible origin of chloroplasts from endosymbiotic cyanobacteria [29]. The generalized endosymbiont hypothesis, viewing the cyanobacteria as kind of free-living "(proto)chloromitochondria", would instead suggest that the only and unique primary endosymbiont was a unicellular cyanobacterium (for discussion also see Chapter 22). From such *intra*cellular protochloromitochondrion, over many millions of years all other "living" (= metabolizing protoplasmatic) membranous intracellular inclusions might have evolved. These "inclusions" – within and up to that point necessarily also prokaryotic or extinct "proto-eukaryotic" [30–32] host cell – would have consisted of, for example, truly endosymbiotic cyanobacteria as in *Cyanophora paradoxa* [33], Golgi apparatus, peroxisomes, glyoxysomes, etc., but above all the most important bioenergetic organelles chloroplast *and* mitochondrion. For the latter, commonly *Paracoccus denitrificans* or another respiring α-proteobacterium is assumed as an independent free-living precursor. The hypothesis would have the advantage of avoiding the assumption of an extremely improbable accumulation of several independent (stable!) endosymbiont events.

It must be recalled that in photosynthesis, as well as in respiration, the basic *mechanism* of energy conversion (ATP synthesis) is chemiosmotic electron transport phosphorylation ("photophosphorylation", see Chapter 21). Very distinctly, to follow the words of the late Gerald T. Babcock, the photobiological tapping of the colossal reservoir of terrestrial water, this ideal thermodynamic electron sink, by the primordial cyanobacteria for the simultaneous production of most potent electron donors (metabolic hydrogen) *and* acceptors (= O_2, the "Promethean fire" of evolution) may also be called the "evolutionary Big Bang" as opposed to the astrophysical "Big Bang" in Table 1.

As extensively discussed elsewhere [8–9,34,35], the quintessence of chemiosmosis, the transmembrane electrochemical proton [17] or sodium [36,37] potential difference or protonmotive/sodium-motive force ($\Delta\mu_{H}^{+}/_{Na}^{+}$), could initially have been created simply by vectorial transmembrane *electron* transfer from a H^{+}-releasing dehydrogenase (on the outside of the membrane) to a H^{+}-consuming reductase on the inside. In such primitive "pre-respiratory disguise" [8,35] the well-known contemporary (anaerobic) fumarate respiration [38–40] (Table 2) might first have emerged on earth under conditions when external oxidants of sufficiently positive redox potential (including also the often hypothesized precursors of "nitrate respiration"; for discussion see [7,10,12]) were still absent from the O_2-free biosphere.

All of the "energy-yielding" biological mechanisms of Tables 2 and 3 use the chemiosmotic membrane principle for ATP synthesis, as also do all contemporary forms of photosynthesis (see Chapters 1 and 21). Concerning the *energy content of light* note the following numerical correlations: 1 mol (einstein) of green/red (500/700 nm) light corresponds to 240/171.5 kJ.

ELECTRON TRANSPORT CHAINS

Table 2. Comprehensive bioenergetic schemes of usually aerobic types of chemolitho(auto)trophic forms of energy conversion (O_2 with $E_0' = 820$ mV taken as the standard acceptor throughout)

Electron donor	E_0' (mV)	Chemical reaction	$\Delta G_0'$ (kJ)	Bacteria
CO/CO_2	−513	$CO + 0.5O_2 = CO_2$	−257.2	Carboxydo-
$H_2/2H^+$	−420	$H_2 + 0.5O_2 = H_2O$	−239.3	Knallgas-
CH_4/CO_2	−244	$CH_4 + 2O_2 = CO_2 + 2H_2O$	−818.0	Methylotrophs
H_2S/SO_4''	−223	$H_2S + 2O_2 = H_2SO_4$	−805.3	Thiobacilli
S^0/SO_4''	−205	$S + 1.5O_2 + H_2O = H_2SO_4$	−593.6	Thiobacilli
NH_4^+/NO_2'	+334	$NH_3 + 1.5O_2 = HNO_2 + H_2O$	−281.5	Nitroso-
NO_2'/NO_3'	+425	$NO_2' + 0.5O_2 = NO_3'$	−76.1	Nitro-
Fe^{2+}/Fe^{3+}	+762	$Fe^{2+} + 0.25O_2 + H^+ = Fe^{3+} + 0.5H_2O$	−4.35 (−44.3 at pH 0)	Thio-(ferro-)
$(N_2/NO_3'$	+752	$N_2 + 2.5O_2 + H_2O = 2NO_3' + 2H^+$	−65.6	*hypothetic*)

For calculations: $\Delta G = -n.F.\Delta E$, Δ = acc.−don., (+)−(−), anod.−cath. n = number of electrons transferred; F (Faraday constant) = 96.5 kJ. mol^{-1}. V^{-1}

Table 3. Comprehensive bioenergetic schemes of anaerobic types of several types of respiration (aerobic and anaerobic) (H_2 with $E_0' = -420$ mV taken as the standard donor throughout)

Electron acceptor	E_0' (mV)	Chemical reaction	$\Delta G_0'$	Bacteria
O_2/H_2O	+820	$O_2 + 2H_2 = 2H_2O$	−478.6	Knallgas
NO_3'/N_2	+740	$NO_3' + 2.5H_2 + H^+ = 0.5N_2 + 3H_2O$	−560.0	Nitrate resp.
NO_3'/NO_2'	+425	$NO_3' + H_2 = NO_2' + H_2O$	−163.2	Denitrification
Fumarate/Succinate	+33	fum. + H_2 = succ.	−87.4	Fumarate resp.
SO_4''/H_2S	−223	$SO_4'' + 4H_2 = S'' + 4H_2O$	−152.2	Sulphate resp.
S^0/H_2S	−271	$S^0 + H2 = H_2S$	−28.8	Sulphur resp.
CO_2/CH_4	−244	$CO_2 + 4H_2 = CH_4 + 2H_2O$	−135.0	Carbonate resp.
CO_2/Acetate	−285	$CO_2 + 2H_2 = 0.5AcOH + H_2O$	−52.3	*Clostridium aceticum*
$(N_2/NH_4^+$	−284	$N_2 + 3H_2 + 2H^+ = 2NH_4^+$	−78.7	hypothetic. N_2-resp.)

For calculations: $\Delta G = -n.F.\Delta E$, Δ = acc.-don., (+)-(−), anode-cath. n = number of electrons transferred; F (Faraday constant) = 96.5 kJ. mol^{-1}. V^{-1}

The outstanding evolutionary success of chemiosmotic energy conversion is due to:

First, and *mechanistically* speaking, a fairly "handy" and uniform membrane-bound electron transfer device, e.g., a dehydrogenase-quinol-cytochrome sequence coupled to the trans-membrane "movement" of protons or sodium ions, thereby giving rise to a protonmotive (p.m.f.) or sodium-motive force (s.m.f.), respectively, is the "simple missing link" between electromotive force (redox potential difference ΔE between the electron transport components in the membrane) and ATP/ΔG_P [6]. This p.m.f.-generating "hard core of biological electron transport" could easily be attached to a versatile dehydrogenating device on the low-potential ("negative") side and to a likewise more versatile oxidase system on the high-potential ("positive") side. Such a versatile membrane-bound electron transport assembly could have freed, in the words of J.B. Hall [41], the organisms "from the slavish dependence on particular phosphorylatable substrates" as are inevitably necessary for substrate-level phosphorylation (fermentation). Moreover, the roles of "reducing" and "oxidizing ends" of electron transport chains (see before) might also be taken over by PS II and PS I, respectively, but the coupling of the exergonic, membrane-bound, H^+/Na^+-translocating "longitudinal" electron transport to an anisotropic, reversible membrane-bound F_oF_1 ATPase (ATP synthase) of proper orientation (Figure 3 below) could have remained essentially the same throughout billions of years. Note, however, the obligatory necessity of a *membrane* for chemiosmotic energy conversion.

The thermodynamic reversibility of the chemiosmotic energy-converting reactions (electronmotive force → proton (or sodium) translocation → ATP synthesis), all operating close to the thermodynamic equilibrium [6], underlies Howard Gest's ingenious concept of "reverse electron transport" [42], originally discovered in "artificially energized" mitochondria by Chance and Klingenberg in the late 1960s. Without reverse electron transport most chemo- as well as photo-lithoautotrophic bacteria would never be able to pursue an autotrophic life style since the (standard) redox potentials of the specific photo- or chemolithotrophic electron donors (H_2S, S^o, thiosulfate, sulfate, NH_3, NO_2, etc.) are not nearly sufficiently negative to reduce ferredoxin ($E_o' = -420$ mV) or $NADP^+$ ($E_o' = -320$ mV), the *chemical* reductants for CO_2 in the respective CO_2-fixing pathways.

It was Cornelis Bernardus Van Niel (1897–1985) who presented, in a systematic and unifying formalistic way, a generally valid unitary concept of both photo- and chemoauto-trophic CO_2 fixation [43,44]:

$$2H_2D + CO_2 \rightarrow \tfrac{1}{6}C_6H_{12}O_6 + H_2O + 2D \qquad (2)$$

where H_2D is a (litho- or organotrophic) electron donor such as H_2, H_2S, H_2O, $C_3H_8O_3$ (*i*-propanol), etc., and D is the oxidized donor (H^+, elemental sulfur, dioxygen, acetone, etc.).

The *second*, and perhaps even more compelling, reason for the "evolutionary victory" of chemiosmosis, i.e., electron transport phosphorylation (ETP) over substrate-level phosphorylation (SLP) [41,45,46], is *energetic efficiency* as the ultimate driving force. Chemotrophically, the numerical net yield of ATP per mol of glucose in SLP (fermentation in a purely soluble cytosolic system) is 2 while in ETP (aerobic respiration = complete biological oxidation = "combustion" of glucose with the aid of membrane-bound electron flow) it is 36 or 38. Needless to say, therefore, the chemiosmotic membrane principle has been most widely exploited by all prokaryotic organisms (bacteria), either in the light (*phototrophs*) or in the dark (*chemotrophs*). The latter might have found it difficult to get a suitable external oxidant (electron acceptor) of sufficiently positive redox potential in a biosphere still devoid of molecular oxygen, the most potent, yet at the same time also ambivalent and hazardous [47], biological oxidant in our present world [10–12]. Photosynthesizers, using *photo*oxidation, would of course have avoided those problems. Tables 2 and 3 show the various modes of anaerobic respirations, and of litho(auto)trophic life styles, all exploiting the chemiosmotic membrane-electron transport principle for ATP synthesis in the absence and presence of O_2, respectively.

At any rate, free molecular oxygen (O_2) – physicochemically speaking a highly reactive, yet kinetically hampered [12] bi*radical* – even nowadays is a deadly cell poison to strict anaerobes [48–50]. Surprisingly, research performed at UCB in California in the groups of Bruce Ames and J. F. Kasting has clearly shown that the mechanisms of *radiation* damage and *oxygen* damage can be rationalized by strikingly similar concepts [51,52]. Thus it became obvious that *oxidative stress* on earth must have been around long before the advent of free molecular oxygen. It is particularly interesting in this respect that substantial amounts of (the relatively mild ROS) H_2O_2 seem to have been produced on the anaerobic earth [53] due to the following photochemical reaction (formally a reversible and dehydrogenating catalase reaction with intermediate steps represented by hydroxyl or superoxyl radicals) with UV-A/B radiation as the driving force:

$$H_2O + H_2O + \mathbf{UV} \rightarrow H_2O_2 + [H_2] \qquad (3)$$

In the still essentially anaerobic Precambrian era (approx. 3.5 billion years ago) the concentration of (abiogenic) O_2 owing to the UV-C induced photochemical reaction:

$$H_2O + H_2O + \mathbf{UV} \rightarrow O_2 + 2[H_2] \qquad (4)$$

was less than 0.1 P.A.L. (Figure 1; also see [11]). However, at the same time H_2O_2, photochemically formed by UV radiation according to eqn. (3) and washed out of the atmosphere by rainwater [54], arrived at a rate of about 100 billion molecules per s and cm^2 on the surface of the earth. This resulted in localized puddles with nano- to micromolar H_2O_2 concentrations, which might well have given rise to the (adaptive and protective) formation of a detoxifying enzyme, e.g., manganese catalase, in one of the strict anaerobes of those days (Figure 2). Yet, even more striking, in this way, by progressive adaptation to more and more positive redox potentials in the primordial environment, the path was paved for the evolution of a full-fledged WOC from the ancient Mn-catalase, attached to the likewise newly arising high-potential PS II (Chapters 1, 17 and 22). This view of an evolution of the PS II-WOC from a primordial Mn-catalase gains support from a molecular comparison of the structures and redox mechanisms of the two enzymes [55–60]. For structural details of the WOC see Chapters 15 and 17.

Finally, inspection of Table 1 and Figure 1 leaves little doubt about the pivotal role blue-green algae (cyanobacteria) played in the evolution of life on

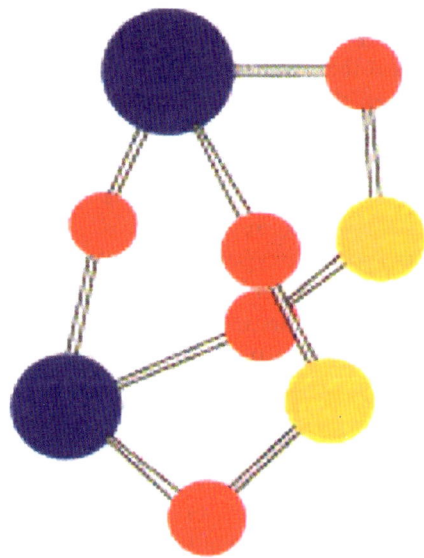

Figure 2. Structure of the active centre of the di-manganese catalase from *Thermus thermophilus* [57], to be compared with presently available WOC structures as discussed in Chapters 15 and 17 (also see [55–60]). The di-Mn-catalase could have been a starting point for the evolution of the tetranuclear Mn_4O_xCa cluster of the WOC from the former by gene-doubling and incorporation of the catalytic Ca^{2+}. The three ball sizes represent: Mn (blue), O (red), and C (yellow).

earth from primitive prokaryotes up to *Homo sapiens* and for the most decisive turning point that they represent within this evolution simply due to the release of free molecular oxygen into a hitherto practically anaerobic biosphere and atmosphere. This event dates back about 3.2 billion years if the microfossil record remains correct [61–63] (Chapter 22).

19.4 Electron Transport Pathways in Cyanobacteria

Regarding the wealth of comments to be found in numerous reviews on plant photosynthetic electron transport components and the striking relatedness to their cyanobacterial counterparts, the synoptic sketch of the membrane functions in a model cyanobacterium (Figure 3) should be able to clearly show the comprehensive capabilities of these intriguing obligately aerobic (oxygenic) phototrophic bacteria.

Usually, the characteristic photosynthetic pigment of cyanobacteria (plants), chlorophyll *a*, is only found in the ICM. Therefore, clearly, a full-fledged photosynthetic electron transport chain is absent from the chlorophyll-free CM. (Note *Gloeobacter* as the only exception; see below.) However, based on the dual function of the photosynthetic-respiratory assembly in the ICM [78–81],

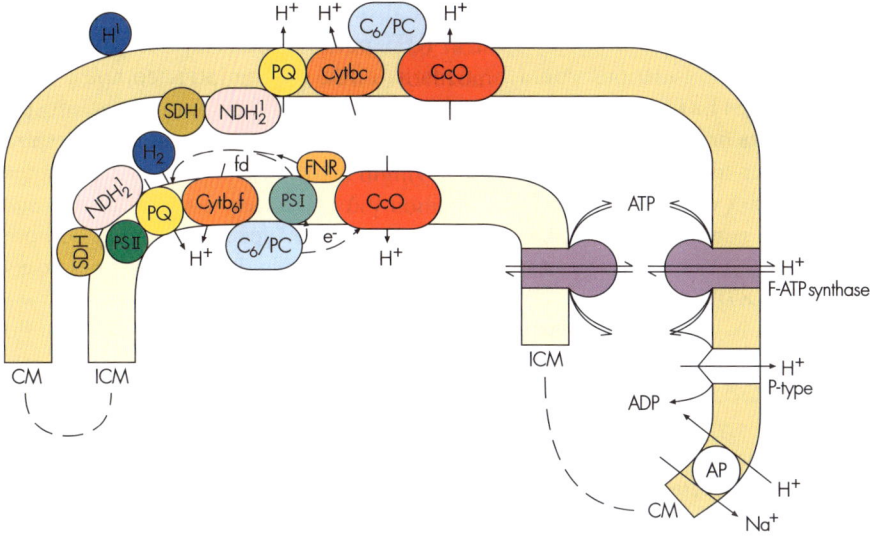

Figure 3. General structural and functional organization of electron transport carriers and ATP synthase in the membrane systems of a model cyanobacterium. Abbreviations: CM, cytoplasmic (plasma) membrane(s); ICM, intracytoplasmic (thylakoid) membrane(s); PS II and PS I, Photosystems II and I; fd, ferredoxin; PQ, plastoquinone; PC, plastocyanin; C_6, cytochrome c_6; FNR, ferredoxin-NADP$^+$ reductase; H^1, "bidirectional" or respiratory hydrogenase; H$_2$, "unidirectional", uptake, or photosynthetic hydrogenase [64–66]; NDH^1, (mitochondrial-like) NDH-1 enzyme [67–69] and NDH$_2$, (nonproton-pumping) NDH-2 enzyme [70]; SDH, succinate dehydrogenase [38–40, 71]. Proton-pumping P-type ATPase (ATP hydrolase [72]) and F-type ATPase (ATP synthase [73,74]) and the Na$^+$/H$^+$ antiporter (AP; [75]) are also shown. Note that neither in cyanobacteria [76] nor in mature chloroplasts [77] has a plain structural continuity between CM and ICM been discovered so far.

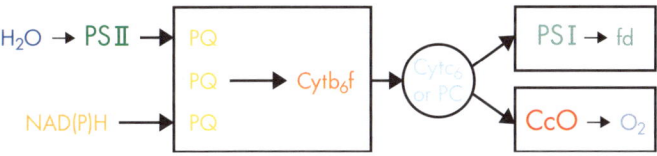

Figure 4. Scheme of the dual-function photosynthetic-respiratory electron transport chain in cyanobacterial ICM. Note that, contrary to previous claims [88], a water-soluble mobile carrier {either cytochrome c_6 (or c_M [155]) or PC} is indispensable for ensuring integral electron transport from the low-potential side (left) to the high-potential electron sink, viz. PS I in the light and CcO in the dark, respectively (right), see [78–80,89–96].

this membrane system is endowed with both respiratory and photosynthetic functions, as was speculated a long time ago [82]. Photosynthetic and respiratory electron transport (PET and RET) share a series of common components, most prominently the NAD(P)H/PQ/cyt bc/cyt c/PC electron transport sequence [83–85], see also Figures 3 and 4. Only the terminal respiratory oxidase (TRO) or cyt-*c* oxidase (CcO) [12] and perhaps also the NAD(P)H dehydrogenase(s) appear to qualify as uniquely specific RET components, since as yet no truly photosynthetic functions could be demonstrated for the latter complex either (see [67,68,81]). Therefore, evidently, the ICM electron transport system must be regarded as *branched*, being partitioned between a photosynthetic and a respiratory branch as is illustrated in Figure 4. However, the assumption of a separately "branched cyanobacterial RET" [86] continues to rely solely on the *nonfunctional* genomic witness, i.e., on circumstantial evidence. For more comprehensive reviews on cyanobacterial RET and the terminal respiratory oxidase(s) see [12,81,87].

Based on the close similarity of photosynthetic electron transport components in cyanobacteria and chloroplasts the following short and specifically cyanobacterial prefatory notes appear to be appropriate.

19.4.1 Comparison of the Photosynthetic Apparatus in Cyanobacteria and Higher Plants

As a whole, the photosynthetic apparatus in cyanobacteria is almost identical to that in higher plant chloroplasts in both functional and structural respects. This extreme similarity is best reflected by the (classical) endosymbiont hypothesis [29]. As discussed in Section 19.3, a more generalized (unifying) endosymbiont hypothesis would suggest the evolutionary origin of all intracytoplasmic eukaryotic protoplasmatic "inclusions" (including chloroplasts *and* mitochondria) from a primordially and singularly engulfed unicellular cyanobacterium. It is noteworthy in this respect that a thorough mathematical analysis of completely sequenced genomes of (eukaryotic) mitochondria, chloroplasts, and corresponding nuclei on the basis of a genome signature-based comparison clearly pointed to a common cyanobacterial ancestry of both chloroplasts and mitochondria (R. Sasikumar, J. Joseph and G.A. Peschek, in preparation). This hypothesis also alleviates the problem of an extremely, almost inconceivably, improbable primary establishment of multiple *stable* endosymbioses between prokaryotes and other prokaryotes (or Woese's elusive proto-eukaryotes; see [30–32]).

19.4.2 Membrane Systems in Cyanobacteria

With a single exception (see below) all cyanobacteria contain two bioenergetically competent but physically separated (Figure 3) intracellular membrane systems, the (yellow) chlorophyll-free cytoplasmic or plasma membrane (CM) and the green chlorophyll-containing thylakoid or intracytoplasmic membrane (ICM). Either of the two encloses an osmotically autonomous compartment, the cytosol (surrounded by the CM) and the intrathylakoid or lumenal space (surrounded by the ICM). The first successful preparative ("necrochemical") separation of fully functional CM and ICM from cell-free extracts of cyanobacteria was achieved in my research group in the mid-1980s [97–100], see also [101]. As a surprising result it was firmly established that both membrane types,

CM *and* ICM, are endowed with a canonical, mitochondrial-like respiratory chain (see [81] for review), while only the (chlorophyll-containing) ICM is photosynthetically competent, too. In this case (viz. in ICM) photosynthetic and respiratory electron transport chains share common components, as had already been suspected decades before ([82]; see Figure 4) and was later confirmed by results with isolated membranes [83,84]. Only in *Gloeobacter violaceus*, which does not at all form a thylakoid membrane [102], does the CM also contain chlorophyll *a* and all the other photosynthetic components. Being, nevertheless, an obligate phototroph [103] *Gloeobacter* is correspondingly tedious and difficult to grow. Yet, importantly, also in a "normal" cyanobacterium, in terms of protein, the CM accounts for barely more than 1% (w/w) of ICM [81].

19.4.3 Photosynthetic and Respiratory Activities

Most cyanobacteria are obligate photo (auto)trophs, being restricted to the utilization of light as the sole energy source and of CO_2 as the sole (major) carbon source even if, biochemically speaking, respiration is fully functional in these cells [104]. Although lactic acid fermentation was documented, in part, in some cyanobacteria [105,106] it is clear that substrate-level phosphorylation is a much less efficient way of energy conversion from the very beginning, even when ecologically none of these potential bioenergetic dark processes (respiration and fermentation) is to be regarded as "useless". Yet, even for respiration the maximum rates of endogenous (= "exogenous") O_2 uptake are usually between 1% and at most 10% of the maximum photosynthetic rates of saturating O_2 evolution in all species tested so far, and in laboratory cultures, at least up to now, not a single cyanobacterium could successfully be grown in the absence of both light and oxygen.

Facultatively anoxygenic (sulfide-supported) photosynthesis was first discovered in *Oscillatoria limnetica* and *Aphanothece halophytica* [107], but also in purely artificial laboratory conditions in the well-known *Anacystis nidulans* (*Synechococcus* PCC6301) [108]. Ecologically speaking, this activity seems to be an adaptive short-term emergency valve rather than a stable long-term alternative to the usual oxygenic photosynthesis. The reported "light-activated heterotrophic growth" of *Synechocystis* PCC 6803 [109] has to be considered with even greater reservation. Moreover, even those few species capable of true chemoheterotrophic dark growth are restricted to the utilization of a few types of carbohydrates as respiratory substrates, and the chemoheterotrophic doubling times are extremely long compared with oxygenic phototrophic growth or even (artificial) photoorganoheterotrophic growth [103]. Indeed, there can be no doubt that cyanobacteria "are born to live as prokaryotic plants", as it were, and still there is undisputed reason to maintain the term "nonplus-ultra of bioenergetics" for (particularly the many N_2-fixing representatives among) them being uniquely capable of sustaining all their life processes at the expense of light, water, atmospheric air, and a few ubiquitous minerals. Nevertheless, as was briefly mentioned before, a few photoheterotrophic cyanobacteria (such as the "completely sequenced" *Synechocystis* sp. PCC 6803) do exist that need light as an energy source but can utilize (instead of CO_2), glucose or fructose as a carbon source. The potential of such species as model systems for genetic engineering of the oxygenic photosynthetic apparatus is considerable.

19.4.4 Mesophilic and Thermophilic Cyanobacteria

According to a well-known microbiological rule-of-thumb definition thermophilic microorganisms display growth optima between 55 and 75 °C, mesophilic species between 30 and 45 °C, and psychrophilic ones between 15 and 18 °C. The hyperthermophilic "archaea" may grow, under elevated pressure, at temperatures up to 110 °C, and the pH of the medium may be <2, hence the name "extremophiles". Extremophilic "archaea" need not necessarily reflect an extremely ancient origin but may equally mirror a later adaptation to extreme growth conditions in *extant* environments, though the conditions near deep-sea vents ("black smokers" [18]) are commonly often identified with conditions on the early earth [110]. For cyanobacteria the highest optimum growth temperatures were observed on *Mastigocladus* sp. (62 °C) and *Synechococcus lividus* (*Synechococcus* sp. PCC strains 27149, 27179 and 27180 [103] at around 53 °C), i.e., a temperature range still far from what a microbiologist would name "thermophilic". Interestingly, biochemical reasons for the capability of living cells to endure high and very high temperatures (known for chemotrophic *pro*karyotes exclusively!) are still completely unclear but seem to have to do with rates of protein turnover rather than the static stability of proteins (and other vital biomolecules).

Normally, on an average-level, the rate of protein turnover in mesophilic living cells is around one per day (but ATP in bacteria turns over at a rate of $3\ s^{-1}$!) and in thermophiles it must be still higher, corresponding to the naturally higher denaturation and degradation rate of proteins etc. at higher temperatures, but the phenomenon is only poorly investigated. Nevertheless, as a matter of fact, proteins (and other biomolecules) isolated from thermophilic sources generally prove to be more stable than the same molecules isolated from mesophilic counterparts. Unsurprisingly, therefore, the three crystallized photosynthetic electron transport complexes (see Chapters 13, 15 and 20) were isolated from the (moderately) thermophilic cyanobacteria *Mastigocladus laminosus* (b_6f-complex) and *Thermosynechococcus* (*T.*) *elongatus* (Photosystems I and II), respectively (see next section). Again, it is emphasized that, so far, not a single truly thermophilic *phototrophic* (archae)bacterium nor whatever *eukaryote* has become known.

19.4.5 Crystal Structure Analysis with Samples from Thermophilic Cyanobacteria

Doubtless the most significant contribution of (thermophilic) cyanobacteria to photosynthesis research is the high-resolution X-ray structure analysis of the three most important energy-transducing electron transport complexes of oxygenic photosynthesis, PS I, PS II, and the cyt b_6f complex, as mentioned at the beginning of this chapter (for details see Chapters 13, 15, and 20).

19.4.5.1 Structure of PS I and PS II

After many years of intensive research by the famous Berlin photosynthesis research groups, H.T. Witt, Petra Fromme, A. Zouni and co-workers in cooperation with N. Krauß, W. Saenger and co-workers were able to present the first complete and detailed high-resolution X-ray structures, both from the (thermophilic) unicellular cyanobacterium *T. elongatus*, of Photosystem I [111] (for details see Chapter 13) and Photosystem II [59,60,112] (for details see Chapter 15). Complementary structures were reported by other research groups for the PS II core complex from *T. oulcanus* [113] and *T. elongatus* [58]. In marked contrast, less detailed information is currently available on the structure of PS I and PS II in ("true") plants (see [114]).

19.4.5.2 Structure and Function of the Cytochrome b_6f Complex

In a similarly momentous achievement Bill Cramer and associates [115] were able to resolve the high-resolution structure of the cytochrome b_6f complex from the thermophilic cyanobacterium *Mastigocladus laminosus* (possibly synonymous with *Fischerella* Gomont 1895, PCC 7414 or 7521, see [103]). At almost the same time the same type of complex was isolated and structurally resolved in detail from *Chlamydomonas reinhardtii* chloroplasts [116]. In connection with this oxyphototrophic b_6f-complex the surprising discovery of a novel "supernumerary" semi-*c*-type cytochrome, termed cytochrome *x* or c_n (Chapter 20), deserves special attention: The heme group of this odd cytochrome c_n is covalently attached, through only one thioether linkage, to cystein-35 of the apoprotein. The fifth and sixth coordination sites of its Fe are H_2O-only and free, respectively. Cyt c_n in the complex resides between heme b_n and PQ on the cytosolic or "stromal" (−) side of the membrane in close vicinity to a conspicuous positively charged amino acid region of the b_6f-complex. Cyt c_n is a highly plausible candidate for the long-sought-for fd:PQ oxidoreductase necessary for cyclic endogenous photosynthetic electron transport around PS I [115]; also see Chapter 20.

Conceivably, it might be directly (and non-enzymatically?) reduced not only by fd but also by NAD(P)H freely dissolved in the cytosol. In this case the cyt c_n of the oxyphototrophic b_6f-complex could mimic the function of the much-discussed cyanobacterial (CN-sensitive, respiratory!) NAD(P)H oxidase (NDH-1 enzyme, see [81]). The mitochondrial-like complex I of cyanobacteria [67,68] has always been a mystery since, on the one hand, the oxidation (dehydrogenation) of NADH, NADPH, and deamino-NADH was repeatedly demonstrated with isolated and purified cyanobacterial membrane (both CM and ICM) preparations (see [81]) while, on the other hand, any, even genetic, evidence (lack of genes *ndh*- or *nuo*-L,M,N) device or NADH dehydrogenase module [67–69] on this enzyme is still missing for an electron-input. Yet, this idea seems to shed new light on older studies on membrane preparations from hydrogenase-induced

A. nidulans whose PQ was inactivated or extracted. Interestingly, rates of NAD(P)H:ferricytochrome-*c* reduction in quinone extracted membranes decreased (unspecifically) no more than the PQ-independent (aerobic) ferrocytochrome-*c* oxidase reaction, while the (O_2-independent) H_2:ferricytochrome-*c* reduction and other PQ-dependent electron transport reactions [117–119] decreased to a much larger extent [120,121] (also see Figure 3). On the other hand, it remains to be seen whether or not the newly discovered cyanobacterial FDPs [122] or A-type flavoproteins [123], which, in the form of three different condensed "modules", fuse a whole "electron transport chain" from NAD(P)H to O_2/H_2O (?) together in a single *soluble* polypeptide, might be able to physiologically replace membrane-bound O_2-reductases in light [124] or darkness. Similar non-energy-transducing "electron transport chains" from NADPH via cyt P450 to $0.5O_2/H_2O$ are present in endoplasmatic reticulum-(ER)-derived mammalian liver "microsomes" but this cascade of FeS-containing hydroxylases (monooxygenases) only serves the purpose of detoxification of xenobiotics. Clearly, all such "soluble electron transport chains" will work only when cell energy is abundant, a situation that is certainly never obtained in cyanobacteria in darkness. Note that the so-called "plant-type alternative oxidase" also contains a binuclear di-iron centre similar to the FDPs [122,123] but was proven to be absent from cyanobacteria in an extended series of immunological experiments (Wastyn, Trnka, Molitor, Peschek, unpublished results).

19.4.6 Electron Transport Chains in Photosynthesis and Respiration and their Mutual Interaction

As briefly mentioned above, the electron transport assembly in cyanobacterial ICM, but also in ICM of anoxyphototrophs [125], is designed for functioning in both photosynthesis and respiration (Figure 4).

A pure-bred respiratory chain terminating in an aa_3-type CcO was discovered in purified and fully functional CM isolated from *Anacystis nidulans* (*Synechococcus* PCC6301) and 33 other cyanobacterial strains and species from 1980 onward [97–100,126–130], a finding that initially surprised most researchers in the field [131,132] but was later reconciled with new results on the effect of growth conditions (in particular: light limitation, ionic strength, etc.) on the expression of respiratory properties in cyanobacteria [97,133–136]. It is outside the scope of this chapter to recapitulate the rather tricky story of cyanobacterial respiratory electron transport and terminal oxidase(s) [12,78,80,81,87] but brief reference may be made to pertinent reviews of the dual photosynthetic–respiratory function of the cyanobacterial ICM electron transport system [78–80,85,137].

In this context, briefly, continuing the specification of the (photosynthetic) electron transport components in a cyanobacterium we get the following sequence (Figure 3):

Photosystem II; canonical electron transport chain between approx. -0.1 V (reduced $Q_A^{-\bullet}$ in PS II, see Chapter 16) and about $+0.5$ V (oxidized $P700^{+\bullet}$ in PS I, see Chapter 14) which consists of the following invariable and accessory (*) steps: *Hydrogenases [64–66]; *NAD(P)H dehydrogenases (see [81] for discussion); plastoquinone-9 (lipophilic mobile carrier, "electron pool"); the transmembrane cyt bc-complex (cyt b_6f in all oxyphototrophs but cyt bc_1 in anoxyphototrophs, see Chapter 20), including "bound" PQ and the Rieske FeS protein ([138–142]; cyt c_6 or c_M [155] and/or PC as mutually exchangeable [91–96]), yet absolutely indispensable [89,90] membrane-peripheral water-soluble mobile carriers. Photosystem I; plant-ferredoxin; FNR; $NADP^+$ (in all oxyphototrophs but NAD^+ in anoxyphototrophs and chemoautotrophic bacteria).

Regarding cyanobacterial hydrogenases ($E^{o\prime} = -420$ mV), the reader is referred to more specialized reviews [64–66]. In cyanobacteria, the photosynthetic [108,117] or "uptake" hydrogenase ("H_2" in Figure 3), encoded by the *hup* genes [66], seems to couple with photosynthetic electron transport in ICM, while the respiratory [118,119] or "bidirectional" hydrogenase ("H^1" in Figure 3), encoded by the *hox* genes, may feed electrons from H_2 into the CM-bound RET. Many cyanobacteria (including the non-nitrogen-fixing and obligately photoautotrophic *A. nidulans*) actually contain both types of hydrogenases [119] but a few others contain the uptake hydrogenase only [66]. Notably, *all* prokaryotes capable of N_2-fixation, contain for economic reasons (recycling of the H_2 inevitably released by nitrogenase), an uptake hydrogenase, too. For a microbiologist, the so-called hydrogen relief valve, active in anaerobes [42], may deserve special attention (for review see [3,64–66,81]).

The major entrance gate to oxygenic photosynthesis is the water-splitting apparatus (WOC or OEC) attached to Photosystem II, which is doubtless an invention of the primordial cyanobacteria and at the same time by far the most decisive turning point in the evolution of life on earth altogether (Table 1 and Figure 1; see also Chapters 1 and 22). The four-electron transfer reactions catalyzed by the photosynthetic water-splitting apparatus ([21,23,24]; see also Chapter 17) and by the respiratory $O_2 \rightarrow H_2O$ reductase enzymes [20,143–146], both enzyme types being biophysically addressed as "capacitor enzymes", are of unprecedented ecological importance for closing the terrestrial O_2 cycle [eqn. (1)]. Both reactions have strikingly similar traits in common [20–24] so that it seems legitimate to speculate about a common origin or at least a common progenitor, as implicated by the generalized endosymbiont hypothesis (see before).

Despite insights into the *structure* of the PS II complex [58–60,112–113] several *mechanistic* details on light-induced charge separation (Chapter 16) and in particular on the subsequent reaction sequence of oxidative water cleavage (Chapter 17) and on the conformational triggering of plastoquinol formation (Chapter 16) are not yet conclusively resolved [147]. The crystallization and high-resolution X-ray structure of Photosystem I (again from *Synechococcus elongatus* [111,148], as well as from "true" plants [114]) were also introduced (see above). Petra Fromme and coworkers [148] first pointed out homologies between PS II and PS I in the context of a unique and singular importance of photosynthesis for the evolution of life on earth (see also [148–153]). As both photosystems were initially "taken" from a *cyanobacterium* it is surprising that the question was not addressed as to if there might be any deeper molecular relationship between cyanobacterial PS I and the (dark) respiratory terminal oxidase in this (or another) cyanobacterium, notably as *both* PS I *and* the TRO (CcO) represent different electron sinks only for practically one and the same membrane-bound electron transport system. Moreover, it is known, particularly through the group of De la Rosa in Seville, that identical soluble electron transport proteins, viz. plastocyanin and/or cytochrome c_6 are physiological electron donors to *both* P700 *and* the CcO [89–96,154–158].

The PQ-9 in oxygenic photosynthesis is functionally equivalent to ubiquinone-10 in (mitochondrial) respiration. Both are *p*-benzoquinones with closely similar redox potentials between +0.1 and 0 V. By contrast, the redox potentials of naphthoquinones (such as menaquinones, phylloquinone, *Sulfolobus* quinone, *Caldariella* quinone, *Thermoplasma* quinone, etc.), which are often encountered in electron transport chains of (facultatively) anaerobic bacteria, are significantly more negative (down to -0.1 V). In cyanobacteria, which are devoid of any other major quinone species [120,121], PQ-9 is both a photosynthetic and a respiratory quinone (Figures 3 and 4), a unique situation in a living cell [12,81]. Owing to their lipophilic polyprenyl side-chains biological electron transport quinones are soluble in the lipid core of the membrane where their concentration usually exceeds that of one-electron carriers (e.g., photosynthetic RCs, cytochromes, etc.) by factors of up to twenty. This surplus of storage capacity for redox equivalents enables the quinones to perform their well-known *pool function*, accepting and gathering electrons from various dehydrogenating branches of the electron transport chain, temporarily storing them as the corresponding hydroquinones ("quinols"), then delivering them further on to the high-potential side of the chain. The ubiquitous canonical electron transport quinones are absent only from a few "archaea" such as methanogens, where they are replaced by (functionally equivalent, yet structurally divergent) redox compounds such as coenzymes F_{420} or F_{430} [159–161]. Quinones best signify the coupling of electron transport with proton translocation, the cornerstone of the chemiosmotic hypothesis ([6] and Chapters 1 and 21). In addition to their "pool function", the quinones also play an important role as "fixed" electron transfer components, most clearly seen from the so-called protonmotive quinone cycle [162]. Electron transport quinones give rise to a dismutation of biological electron transport between the $2e^-$ from hydroquinone and the $2 \times 1e^-$ transport onward into different directions, thereby energetically recycling one of the two electrons, thus doubling the H^+/e^- stoichiometry of electron transport in the respective sequence [6]. This ingenious protonmotive Q cycle, proposed by Peter Mitchell, is indispensable for both photosynthesis (in cyanobacteria and chloroplasts) and respiration (in mitochondria) as well as in other bacterial electron transport systems [162] (for further reading, see Chapter 20).

The electrons abstracted from plasto- (or ubi-)quinol enter the membrane-bound cyt *bc* ($b_6 f$) complex (complex III in mitochondria). Much has been written about the similarities and differences between $b_6 f$ and bc_1 complexes ([139–142]; as far as it concerns the cyanobacteria specifically, see [81], also see Section 19.4.5.2). Undoubtedly, both complexes must share a common evolutionary origin. In cyanobacteria, immunologically cross-reactive and redox competent b- and c-type cytochromes as well as the Rieske FeS complex (indispensable for the protonmotive Q cycle) were detected in both chlorophyll-free CM and in ICM [138]. Notably, the "chimerical" b_6f-complex in cyanobacterial membranes shares immunological as well as inhibition characteristics with the mitochondrial bc_1-complex (see [12,81] and Chapter 20). Note that "cyt f" (a purely historical name, "f" from *folium*, the Latin word for *leaf*) is nothing but a membrane-bound c-type cyt exhibiting the typical covalent thioether bonds between protoporphyrin IX (heme B) and two cysteines of the apoprotein. Discovery of its function *between* the two photosystems had initiated the concept of the "Z-scheme" [163,164]. Interestingly, the rather positive redox potential of the Rieske FeS protein (a component common to both photosynthesis and respiration with an $E^{o\prime}$ of around +230 mV) obviously results from the fact that its Fe_2S_2 cluster, contrary to that of the low-potential ordinary (soluble) ferredoxin ($E^{o\prime} = -420$ mV), is attached not only to cysteine-sulfur but also to (more electronegative) histidine-nitrogen.

The next electron transfer step occurs via a more or less membrane-peripheral, water-soluble, mobile electron carrier, viz. plastocyanin (a redox active blue copper protein) and/or cytochrome c_6 (analogous to the mitochondrial "horse heart" cytochrome c). Among cyanobacteria there are species that are constitutively unable to synthesize PC (e.g., *Synechococcus*, devoid of the Pet E gene) and others (e.g., *Synechocystis* or *Anabaena*) possessing both pet E and pet J (PC *and* cyt c_6) genes whose expression may be regulated by the availability of Cu in the growth medium [91]. The isoelectric points (IEPs) of those water-soluble redox proteins, usually alkaline in filamentous species and (slightly) acidic in unicellular species, control the initial diffusion step of electron transfer to the usually negatively charged ("acidic") surface of the membrane or membrane-embedded acceptor proteins [165–167]. A characteristic feature in *all* cyanobacteria is the interchangeability of (reduced) PC and cyt c_6 as electron donors to both $P700^{+\cdot}$ in photosynthesis and the CcO in respiration [12,81,91–96,168,169]. Another alternative for electron donation to $P700^{+\cdot}$ and/or the CcO in cyanobacteria could be the poorly investigated cyt M or c_M [155] whose molecular properties are significantly different from the "ordinary" cyt c_6 and which may thus replace the former, e.g., under stress conditions. Recent (immunological) experiments in our laboratory have unequivocally shown that in *Anacystis* and *Synechocystis* the synthesis of cyt c_M is definitely enhanced under (salt) stress conditions, and that the cyt is attached to both CM and ICM through a membrane anchor (M. Bernroitner, C. Obinger and G.A. Peschek, in preparation). However, contrary to cyt c_6 and PC, the IEPs of cyt c_M (alkaline or acidic) are *not* correlated with filamentous or unicellular cell shapes of the cyanobacteria. After all, and omitting the additional alternative of a (membrane-bound) quinol as the electron donor to the terminal respiratory oxidase (which, in this case, would be a not-yet-found quinol instead of a cyt-c oxidase, see [12,87]), it has now been sufficiently proven that biological electron transport in general *needs* the membrane-extrinsic detour between the (membranous) cyt b_6f/bc_1-complex and P700 or the CcO [89,90] though it is not yet plainly evident why electron transport should not have entirely stayed *within* the membrane [88].

The detailed structure of Photosystem I, the photosynthetic "electron sink" for electrons arriving from Photosystem II (Figure 3; see also Chapter 1), is known since the high-resolution X-ray structure was published [111] (see also [114] and Chapter 13) and, as suggested, the structure fits to a derivative of the homodimeric FeS reaction centre still present, in "isolated" form, in green sulfur bacteria and heliobacteria (Chapter 12). Photosystem I may also be regarded the "low-potential RC" since only in chloroplasts and cyanobacteria is there no doubt that electrons excited by the light absorption event up to a potential of as low as almost -1.3 V for $^1P700^*/P700^{+\cdot}$ (Chapter 14) are easily capable of directly reducing a soluble electron acceptor such as ("plant") ferredoxin ($E^{o\prime} = -420$ mV), while it is still doubtful if the same (direct) photoreduction can also be achieved in green sulfur and heliobacteria. Most researchers still prefer the idea of a reverse electron transport for the eventual autotrophic CO_2 fixation in *all* anoxyphototrophs with whatever electron donor, including H_2 [42]; also see Section 19.3. Regarding the interesting hypothesis of an evolution of RCs from primordial UV-protecting pigments [170], see also Chapter 22.

The photoreduced ferredoxin then reduces "soluble" FNR [171], a low-potential flavoprotein that, in turn, reduces $NADP^+$ to NADPH, the biochemical reductant of 3-phosphoglycerate (to glyceraldehyde phosphate, the first carbohydrate – a triose phosphate – in the Calvin cycle; see textbooks on biochemistry). FNR had formerly been made responsible for respiratory NADPH oxidation in cyanobacteria [172] but results from immunochemical experiments are incompatible with this idea (for a review see [81]). The key enzyme of CO_2 reduction in the Calvin cycle is GAP dehydrogenase (GAP-DH) and this enzyme is specific for NADPH in oxyphototrophs (cyanobacteria and chloroplasts). In most other prokaryotes, however, GAP-DH is specific for NADH; this is one of the very few exceptions to the so-called Kaplan rule, which postulates that, in biochemistry, NADPH is the preferred electron donor in anabolic (biosynthetic) reactions while NAD^+ is the preferred electron acceptor in catabolic (bioenergetic) reactions (cf., for example, gluconeogenesis with glycolysis, or fatty acid synthesis with the β-oxidation of fatty acids, etc.).

With NADPH in the cyanobacteria's Calvin cycle [for CO_2 fixation, i.e., biomass primary production, see above, for example, eqn. (1)], and taking into account that the cyanobacterial NDH-1 enzyme (mitochondrial-type NADH dehydrogenase or complex I) or its substitute in cyanobacteria (Section 19.4.5.2. and Figure 3) can also accept NADPH as an electron donor (see [81] for discussion; also see [173]), the ecological hydrogen cycle is thereby closed: "Hydrogen" (= reducing equivalents) is oxidatively extracted from water with solar energy as the driving force (O_2 is thereby produced) and this hydrogen ends up in biomass (= reduced organic matter), which finally reduces O_2 in the RET back to H_2O. Thus, the closing of the hydrogen cycle (on the "reductive end") is equivalent to the closing of the terrestrial oxygen cycle [on the "oxidative end"; see eqn. (1)] and "the wheel" is driven by our sun. Sometimes this wheel is also called the "water–water cycle" [174]. Yet, for cyanobacteria in their "uncompartmentalized" prokaryotic cells, it might be a problem to avoid a futile cycling of NADPH being produced photosynthetically (for biosynthesis) but being potentially oxidized, at the same time in the same prokaryotic system, through respiration. However, the electrons in photosynthesis and in respiration have to pass the same membrane-bound steps as a "bottleneck" (Figures 3 and 4). In addition, since in cyanobacteria the inherent turnover rate of photosynthesis is known to be higher by factors of up to 100 compared with respiration (the common denominator being the membrane-associated p.m.f.), in illuminated cell respiration slows further down. Thus, futile respiratory oxidation of photoreduced NADPH is avoided in the light. Despite the quantitatively modest share of CM in total membrane-supported bioenergetics (see above) the dehydrogenations catalyzed by CM-bound reduced pyridine nucleotide and succinate dehydrogenases (Figure 3) could prime the overall through-put of electrons in a cyanobacterium. This is also reflected by the observation that illumination inhibits respiration under (e.g., salt-stress) conditions, which increase RET in CM much more than in ICM [97,128], to a much lesser degree than in "normal" conditions or in species that, constitutively, accommodate more RET in ICM than in CM ([133,175,176]; also Ardelean and Peschek, unpublished). At any rate, taken per se, the rates of NAD(P)H dehydrogenation catalyzed by NDH-1 *and* NDH-2 enzymes, *and* the rate of succinate dehydrogenation in cyanobacterial CM *and* ICM, all adding up to electron transport rates that are perfectly compatible with O_2 uptake rates by intact cells in the dark (130–150 nmol O_2 per hour per mg-d.w.), are much too significant to be explained by a simple "regulatory function" [177].

19.5 Concluding Remarks and Future Perspectives

Discussion of the properties of cyanobacteria clearly shows that these unique prokaryotic oxyphototrophs, "the tamers of molecular O_2" [12], have most successfully combined in evolution the O_2-dependent membrane-supported electron transport activities of plant-type photosynthesis *and* mitochondrial-type respiration in a single prokaryotic cell as a kind of "*free-living chloromitochondria*". Thus, they not only render themselves as true pace-makers of evolution for our earth as a whole, and for life on this earth up to "*Homo sapiens sapiens*", but have always been and will continue to be paradigmatic model organisms and highlight the elucidation of fundamental biochemical and bioenergetic processes in a living cell.

Acknowledgements

Research in the author's laboratory has been generously supported for several decades by numerous projects from the Fonds zur Förderung der wissenschaftlichen Forschung in Österreich (FWF) (no. P17928 at present), the

Österreichische Forschungsgemeinschaft, the Österreichische Nationalbank, and the Kulturamt der Stadt Wien. Devoted and invaluable technical assistance has always been provided by Mr Otto Kuntner. The help of Mrs Susanne Renger in preparing the color figures is gratefully acknowledged. Last but not least, I owe many thanks to Gernot Renger for most helpful discussions and for his patience.

References

1. D.A. Bryant (ed.), *Advances in Photosynthesis, Volume 1: The Molecular Biology of Cyanobacteria*, (1994), Kluwer Academic Publishers, Dordrecht-Boston-London, pp. 1–881.
2. G.A. Peschek, W. Löffelhardt, G. Schmetterer (eds.), *The Phototrophic Prokaryotes*, (1999), Kluwer Academic/Plenum Publishers, New York, pp. 1–836.
3. J.R. Gallon, Reconciling the incompatible: N_2 fixation and O_2. *New Phytol.* **122** (1992) 571–609.
4. G.A. Peschek, Cyanobacteria viewed as free-living chloromitochondria, in: *Photosynthesis: Fundamental Aspects to Global Perspectives* (2005) (A. van der Est, D. Bruce, eds.), The International Society of Photosynthesis, Toronto, pp. 746–749.
5. G.A. Peschek, Cyanobacteria viewed as free-living chloromitochondria: the endosymbiont hypothesis revisited. *Plant Physiol. Biochem.* **38** (2000) 266.
6. D.B. Nicholls, S.J. Ferguson, *Bioenergetics* 2nd edn. (1992), Academic Press Limited, London, pp. 1–255.
7. E. Broda, *The Evolution of the Bioenergetic Processes*, (1975), Pergamon Press, Oxford, pp. 1–211.
8. E. Broda, G.A. Peschek, Did respiration or photosynthesis come first? *J. Theor. Biol.* **81** (1979) 201–212.
9. G.A. Peschek, Phylogeny of potosynthesis and the evolution of electron transport: the bioenergetic backbone. *Photosynthetica* **15** (1981) 543–554.
10. D.L. Gilbert, Significance of oxygen on earth, in: *Oxygen and Living Processes. An Interdisciplinary Approach* (1981) (D.L. Gilbert, ed.), Springer Verlag, New York, pp. 73–101.
11. N. Lane, *Oxygen-The Molecule that made the World* (2002), Oxford University Press, Oxford, pp. 1–374.
12. M. Paumann, G. Regelsberger, C. Obinger, G.A. Peschek, The bioenergetic role of dioxygen and the terminal oxidase(s) in cyanobacteria. *Biochim. Biophys. Acta* **1707** (2005) 231–253.
13. R. Tarnas, *The Passion of Western Mind* (1991), Random House, Inc., New York, pp. 1–671.
14. G.M. Rutten, Geologic data on atmospheric history. *Palaeogeogr. Palaeoclimatol. Palaeoecol.* **2** (1966) 47–57.
15. D.C. Rhoads, J.W. Morse, Evolutionary and geological significance of oxygen deficient marine basins. *Lethaia* **4** (1970) 413–428.
16. M. Schidlowski, Probleme der atmosphärischen Evolution im Präkambrium. *Geol. Rundsch.* **60** (1971) 1351–1384 (in German).

17. P. Mitchell, Coupling of phosphorylation to electron and hydrogen transfer by a chemi-osmotic type of mechanism. *Nature* **191** (1961) 144–148.
18. R.H. Crabtree, Where smokers rule. *Science* **276** (1997) 222.
19. J. Barber, Water, water everywhere, and its remarkable chemistry. *Biochim. Biophys. Acta.* **1655** (2004) 123–132.
20. G.T. Babcock, M. Wikström, Oxygen activation and the conservation of energy in cell respiration. *Nature* **356** (1992) 301–309.
21. P. Joliot, B. Kok, Oxygen evolution in photosynthesis, in: *Bioenergetics of Photosynthesis* (1975) (Govindjee, ed.), Academic Press Limited, London, pp. 387–412.
22. C.W. Hoganson, M.A. Pressier, D.A. Proshlyakov, G.T. Babcock, From water to oxygen and back again: mechanistic similarities in the enzymatic redox conversions between water and dioxygen. *Biochim. Biophys. Acta* **1365** (1998) 170–174.
23. G. Renger, Photosynthetic water oxidation to molecular oxygen: apparatus and mechanism. *Biochim. Biophys. Acta* **1503** (2001) 210–228.
24. G. Renger, Coupling of electron and proton transfer in oxidative water cleavage in photosynthesis. *Biochim. Biophys. Acta* **1655** (2004) 195–204.
25. J.B. Waterbury, S.W. Watson, R.R.L. Guillard, L.E. Brand, Widespread occurrence of a unicellular, marine, planktonic cyanobacterium. *Nature* **277** (1979) 293–294.
26. S.W. Chisholm, R.J. Olson, E.R. Zettler, R. Goericke, J.B. Waterbury, N.A. Welschmeyer, A novel, free living Prochlorophyte abundant in the oceanic euphotic zone. *Nature* **340** (1988) 340–343.
27. J.H.P. Hackstein, H. Schubert, J. Rosenberg, U. Mackenstedt, M. van den Berg, S. Brul, J. Derksen, H.C.P. Matthijs, Plastid-like organelles in anaerobic mastigotes and parasitic Apicomplexans, in: *Eukaryotism and Symbiosis, Intertaxonic Combination versus Symbiotic Adaptation* (1997) (H.E.A. Schenk, R.G. Herrmann, K.W. Jeon, N.E. Müller, W. Schwemmler, eds), Springer Verlag, Berlin, pp. 49–55.
28. C. Mereschkowsky, Über Natur und Ursprung der Chromatophoren im Pflanzenreiche. *Biol. Zentralbl.* **25** (1905) 593–604 (in German).
29. M.W. Gray, W.F. Doolittle, Has the endosymbiont hypothesis been proven? *Microbiol. Rev.* **46** (1982) 1–42.
30. C.R. Woese, Bacterial evolution. *Microbiol. Rev.* **51** (1987) 221–231.
31. C.R. Woese, O. Kandler, M.L. Wheelis, Towards a natural system of organisms: proposal for the domains archaea, bacteria, and eucarya. *Proc. Natl. Acad. Sci. U.S.A.* **87** (1990) 4576–4579.
32. C.R. Woese, The universal ancestor. *Proc. Natl. Acad. Sci. U.S.A.* **95** (1998) 6854–6859.
33. W. Löffelhardt, H.J. Bohnert, The cyanelle (muroplast) of Cyanophora paradoxa: A paradigm for endosymbiotic organelle evolution, in: *Symbiosis* (2001) (J. Seckbach, ed.), Springer Verlag, Berlin, pp. 111–130.
34. J.A. Raven, F.A. Smith, The evolution of chemiosmotic energy coupling. *J. Theor. Biol.* **57** (1976) 301–312.
35. G.A. Peschek, E. Broda, Fermentation-prerespiration-photosynthesis-respiration: a bioenergetic succession revisited, in: *An Interdisciplinary Study of the Origin and Evolution of Earth's Earliest Biosphere* (1980) (J.W. Schopf, ed.), UCLA, Los Angeles, p. 23.
36. P. Dimroth, Sodium ion transport decarboxylases and other aspects of sodium ion cycling in bacteria. *Microbiol. Rev.* **51** (1987) 320–340.
37. V.P. Skulachev, Chemiosmotic systems and the basic principles of cell energetics, in: *Molecular Mechanisms in Bioenergetics* (1992) (L. Ernster, ed.), Elsevier, Amsterdam, pp. 37–73.

38. C. Hägerhäll, Succinate: quinone oxidoreductases – variations on a conserved theme. *Biochim. Biophys. Acta* **1320** (1997) 107–141.
39. C.R.D. Lancaster, *Wolinella succinogenes* quinol:fumarate reductase – 2.2-Å resolution crystal structure and the E-pathway hypothesis of coupled transmembrane proton and electron transfer. *Biochim. Biophys. Acta* **1565** (2002) 215–231.
40. C.R.D. Lancaster, *Wolinella succinogenes* quinol:fumarate reductase and its comparison to *E. coli* succinate:quinone reductase. *FEBS Lett.* **555** (2003) 21–28.
41. J.B. Hall, Substrate-level phosphorylation *versus* electron transport phosphorylation. *J. Theor. Biol.* **30** (1971) 429–436.
42. H. Gest, Bioenergetic and metabolic process patterns in anoxyphototrophs, in: *The Phototrophic Prokaryotes* (1999) (G.A. Peschek, W. Löffelhardt, G. Schmetterer, eds.), Kluwer Academic-Plenum Publishers, New York, pp. 11–19.
43. R.Y. Stanier, Photosynthetic mechanisms in bacteria and plants: development of a unitary concept. *Bacteriol. Rev.* **25** (1961) 1–17.
44. R.Y. Stanier, C.B. Van Niel, The concept of a bacterium. *Arch. Mikrobiol.* **42** (1962) 17–35.
45. H. Baltscheffsky, M. Baltscheffsky, Electron transport phosphorylation. *Annu. Rev. Biochem.* **43** (1974) 871–897.
46. R.K. Thauer, K. Jungermann, K. Decker, Energy conservation in chemotrophic anaerobic bacteria. *Bacteriol. Rev.* **41** (1977) 100–160.
47. V.P. Skulachev, Role of uncoupled and non-coupled oxidations in maintenance of safely low levels of oxygen and its one-electron reductants. *Q. Rev. Biophys.* **29** (1996) 169–202.
48. J.G. Morris, The physiology of obligate anaerobiosis. *Adv. Microb. Physiol.* **12** (1975) 169–202.
49. J.A. Cole, Microbial gas metabolism. *Adv. Microb. Physiol.* **14** (1976) 1–84.
50. E. Cadenas, Biochemistry of oxygen toxicity. *Annu. Rev. Biochem.* **58** (1989) 79–110.
51. R. Gerschman, D.L. Gilbert, S.W. Nye, P. Dwyer, W.O. Fenn, Oxygen poisoning and X-irradiation: a mechanism in common. *Science* **119** (1954) 623–626.
52. J.F. Kasting, Earth's early atmosphere. *Science* **259** (1993) 920–926.
53. C.P. McKay, H. Hartman, Hydrogen peroxide and the evolution of oxygenic photosynthesis. *Origins Life Evolution Biosphere* **21** (1991) 157–163.
54. J.F. Kasting, H.D. Holland, J.D. Pinto, Oxidant abundances in rainwater and the evolution of atmospheric oxygen. *J. Geophys. Res.* **90** (1985) 10497–10510.
55. R.E. Blankenship, H. Hartman, The origin and evolution of oxygenic photosynthesis. *Trends Biochem. Sci.* **23** (1998) 94–97.
56. N. Ioannidis, G. Schanker, V.V. Barynin, V. Petrouleas, Interaction of nitric oxide with the oxygen evolving complex of Photosystem II and manganese catalase: a comparative study. *J. Bioinorg. Chem.* **5** (2000) 354–363.
57. (*a*) V.V. Barynin, M.M. Whittaker, S.V. Antonyuk, V.S. Lamzin, P.M. Harrison, P.J. Artymiuk, J.W. Whittaker, Crystal structure of manganese catalase from *Lactobacillus plantarum*. *Structure* **9** (2001) 725–738; (*b*) A. Kono, I. Fridovich, Isolation and characterization of the pseudocatalase from *Lactobacillus plantarum*. *J. Biol. Chem.* **258** (1983) 6015–6019.
58. K.N. Ferreira, T.M. Iverson, K. Maghlaoui, J. Barber, S. Iwata, Architecture of the photosynthetic oxygen-evolving center. *Science* **303** (2004) 1831–1838.
59. J. Biesiadka, B. Loll, J. Kern, K.-D. Irrgang, A. Zouni, Crystal structure of cyanobacterial Photosystem II at 3.2 Å resolution: a closer look at the Mn cluster. *Phys. Chem. Chem. Phys.* **6** (2004) 4733–4736.

60. B. Loll, J. Kern, W. Saenger, A. Zouni, J. Biesiadka, Towards complete cofactor arrangement in the 3.0 Å resolution structure of Photosystem II. *Nature* **438** (2005) 1040–1044.
61. E.S. Barghoorn, J.W. Schopf, Microorganisms from the late precambrian of Central Australia. *Science* **150** (1965) 337–339.
62. E.S. Barghoorn, J.W. Schopf, Microorganisms three billion years old from the precambrian of South Africa. *Science* **152** (1966) 758–763.
63. J.W. Schopf, Precambrian microorganisms and evolutionary events prior to the origin of vascular plants. *Biol. Rev.* **45** (1970) 319–352.
64. P. Houchins, The physiology and biochemistry of hydrogen metabolism in cyanobacteria. *Biochim. Biophys. Acta* **768** (1984) 227–255.
65. H. Bothe, G. Boison, O. Schmitz, Hydrogenases in cyanonobacteria, in: *The Phototrophic Prokaryotes* (1999) (G.A. Peschek, W. Löffelhardt, G. Schmetterer, eds.), Kluwer Academic/Plenum Publishers, New York, pp. 589–601.
66. P. Tamagnini, R. Axelsson, P. Lindberg, F. Oxelfelt, R. Wünschiers, P. Lindblad, Hydrogenases and hydrogen metabolism in cyanobacteria. *Microbiol. Mol. Biol. Rev.* **66** (2002) 1–20.
67. S. Berger, U. Ellersiek, K. Steinmüller, Cyanobacteria contain a mitochondrial complex I-homologous NADH-dehydrogenase. *FEBS Lett.* **286** (1991) 129–132.
68. T. Friedrich, K. Steinmüller, H. Weiss, The proton-pumping respiratory complex I of bacteria and mitochondria and its homologue in chloroplasts. *FEBS Lett.* **367** (1995) 107–111.
69. H. Leif, V.D. Sled, T. Ohnishi, H. Weiss, T. Friedrich, Isolation and characterization of the proton-translocating NADH:ubiquinone oxidoreductase from *Escherichia coli*. *Eur. J. Biochem.* **230** (1995) 538–548.
70. A.M.P. Melo, T.M. Bandeiras, M. Teixeira, New insights into type II NAD(P)H:quinone oxidoreductases. *Microbiol. Mol. Biol. Rev.* **68** (2004) 603–616.
71. J.W. Cooley, C.A. Howitt, W.F.J. Vermaas, Succinate:quinol oxidoreductases in the cyanobacterium *Synechocystis* sp. strain PCC 6803: presence and function in metabolism and electron transport. *J. Bacteriol.* **182** (2000) 714–722.
72. M. Geisler, J. Richter, J. Schumann, Molecular cloning of a P-type ATPase gene from the cyanobacterium *Synechocystis* sp. PCC 6803. *J. Mol. Biol.* **234** (1993) 1284–1289.
73. P.L. Pedersen, M. Amzel, ATP synthases-structure, reaction center, mechanism, and regulation of one of nature's most unique machines. *J. Biol. Chem.* **268** (1993) 9937–9940.
74. J.P. Abrahams, A.G.W. Leslie, R. Lutter, E.J. Walker, Structure at 2.8 Å resolution of F_1-ATPase from bovine heart mitochondria. *Nature* **370** (1994) 621–628.
75. E. Padan, S. Schuldiner, Bacterial Na^+/H^+ antiporters-molecular biology, biochemistry and physiology, in: *Handbook of Biological Physics* (1996) (W.N. Konings, H.R. Kaback, J.S. Lolkema, eds.), Elsevier, Amsterdam, Vol. 2, pp. 501–531.
76. S.A. Nierzwicki-Bauer, D.L. Balkwill, S.E. Stevens Jr, Three-dimensional ultrastructure of a unicellular cyanobacterium. *J. Cell. Biol.* **97** (1983) 713–722.
77. R. Douce, M.A. Block, A.-J. Dorne, J. Joyard, The plastid envelope membranes: their structure, composition, and role in chloroplast biogenesis. *Subcell. Biochem.* **10** (1984) 1–84.
78. G.A. Peschek, Cytochrome oxidase and the *cta* operon of cyanobacteria. *Biochim. Biophys. Acta* **1275** (1996) 27–32.

79. G.A. Peschek, Structure-function relationships in the dual-function photosynthetic-respiratory electron transport assembly of cyanobacteria (blue-green algae). *Biochem. Soc. Trans.* **24** (1996) 729–733.
80. G.A. Peschek, Photosynthesis and respiration in cyanobacteria: bioenergetic significance and molecular interactions, in: *The Phototrophic Prokaryotes* (1999) (G.A. Peschek, W. Löffelhardt, G. Schmetterer, eds.), Kluwer Academic/Plenum Publishers, New York, pp. 201–209.
81. G.A. Peschek, C. Obinger, M. Paumann, The respiratory chain of blue-green algae (cyanobacteria). *Physiol. Plant* **120** (2004) 358–369.
82. L.W. Jones, J. Myers, A common link between photosynthesis and respiration in a blue-green alga. *Nature* **199** (1963) 670–672.
83. G.A. Peschek, G. Schmetterer, Evidence for plastoquinol-cytochrome f/b-563 reductase as a common electron donor to P700 and cytochrome oxidase in cyanobacteria. *Biochem. Biophys. Res. Commun.* **108** (1982) 1188–1195.
84. G.A. Peschek, The cytochrome f/b electron transport complex: a common link between photosynthesis and respiration in the cyanobacterium *Anacystis nidulans*. *Biochem. J.* **210** (1983) 269–272.
85. S. Scherer, Do photosynthetic and respiratory electron transport chains share redox proteins? *Trends Biochem. Sci.* **15** (1990) 458–462.
86. D. Pils, G. Schmetterer, Characterization of three bioenergetically active respiratory terminal oxidases in the cyanobacterium *Synechocystis* sp. strain PCC 6803. *FEMS Microbiol. Lett.* **203** (2001) 217–222.
87. S.E. Hart, B.G. Schlarb-Ridley, D.S. Bendall, C.J. Howe, Terminal oxidases of cyanobacteria. *Biochem. Soc. Trans.* **33** (2005) 833–835.
88. L. Zhang, H.B. Pakrasi, J. Whitmarsh, Photoautotrophic growth of the cyanobacterium *Synechocystis* sp. PCC 6803 in the absence of cytochrome c and plastocyanin. *J. Biol. Chem.* **269** (1994) 5036–5042.
89. D. Moser, P. Nicholls, M. Wastyn, G.A. Peschek, Acidic cytochrome c of unicellular cyanobacteria is an indispensable and kinetically competent electron donor to cytochrome oxidase in plasma and thylakoid membranes. *Biochem. Int.* **24** (1991) 757–768.
90. V. Duran, M.A. Hervas, M.A. De la Rosa, J.A. Navarro, The efficient functioning of photosynthesis and respiration in *Synechocystis* sp. PCC 6803 strictly requires the presence of either cytochrome c_6 or plastocyanin. *J. Biol. Chem.* **279** (2004) 7229–7233.
91. G. Sandmann, P. Böger, Copper-induced exchange of plastocyanin and cytochrome c-553 in cultures of *Anabaena variabilis* and *Plectonema boryanum*. *Plant Sci. Lett.* **17** (1980) 417–424.
92. W. Lockau, Evidence for a dual role of cytochrome c-553 and plastocyanin in photosynthesis and respiration of the cyanobacterium *Anabaena variabilis*. *Arch. Microbiol.* **128** (1981) 336–340.
93. M. Paumann, B. Lubura, G. Regelsberger, M. Feichtinger, G. Köllensberger, C. Jakopitsch, P.G. Furtmüller, C. Obinger, G.A. Peschek, Soluble Cu_A domain of cyanobacterial cytochrome c oxidase. *J. Biol. Chem.* **27** (2004) 10293–10303.
94. M. Paumann, M. Feichtinger, M. Bernroitner, J. Goldfuhs, C. Jakopitsch, P.G. Furtmüller, G. Regelsberger, G.A. Peschek, C. Obinger, Kinetics of interprotein electron transfer between cytochrome c_6 and the soluble Cu_A domain of cyanobacterial cytochrome c oxidase. *FEBS Lett.* **576** (2004) 101–106.
95. M. Paumann, M. Bernroitner, B. Lubura, M. Peer, C. Jakopitsch, P.G. Furtmüller, G.A. Peschek, C. Obinger, Kinetics of electron transfer between plastocyanin and

the soluble Cu_A domain of cyanobacterial cytochrome c oxidase. *FEMS Microbiol. Lett.* **239** (2004) 301–307.
96. J.A. Navarro, R.V. Duran, M.A. De la Rosa, M. Hervas, Respiratory cytochrome c oxidase can be efficiently reduced by the photosynthetic redox proteins cytochrome c_6 and plastocyanin. *FEBS Lett.* **579** (2005) 3565–3568.
97. G.A. Peschek, V. Molitor, M. Trnka, M. Wastyn, W. Erber, Characterization of cytochrome-c oxidase in isolated and purified plasma and thylakoid membranes from cyanobacteria. *Methods Enzymol.* **167** (1988) 437–449.
98. G.A. Peschek, M. Wastyn, M. Trnka, V. Molitor, I.V. Fry, L. Packer, Characterization of the cytochrome-c oxidase in isolated and purified plasma membranes from the cyanobacterium *Anacystis nidulans*. *Biochemistry* **28** (1989) 3057–3063.
99. G.A. Peschek, B. Hinterstoisser, M. Wastyn, O. Kuntner, B. Pineau, A. Missbichler, J. Lang, Chlorophyll precursors in the plasma membrane of a cyanobacterium, *Anacystis nidulans*. *J. Biol. Chem.* **264** (1989) 11827–11832.
100. G.A. Peschek, M. Wastyn, V. Molitor, Kraushaar, C. Obinger, H.C.P. Matthijs, Self-contained or accessory respiration in the phototrophic cyanobacteria (blue-green algae)?, in: *Highlights of Modern Biochemistry* (1989) (A. Kotyk, J. Skoda, V. Paces, V. Kostas, eds.), VSP International Scientific Publishers, Zeist, The Netherlands, pp. 893–902.
101. N. Murata, T. Omata, Isolation of cyanobacterial plasma membranes. *Methods Enzymol.* **167** (1988) 245–251.
102. R. Rippka, J. Waterbury, G. Cohen-Bazire, A cyanobacterium which lacks thylakoids. *Arch. Mikrobiol.* **100** (1974) 419–436.
103. R. Rippka, J. Deruelles, J.B. Waterbury, M. Herdman, R.Y. Stanier, Generic assignments, strain histories and properties of pure cultures of cyanobacteria. *J. Gen. Microbiol.* **31** (1979) 225–274.
104. G.A. Peschek, Respiratory electron transport, in: *The Cyanobacteria* (1987) (P. Fay, C. Van Baalen, eds.), Elsevier, Amsterdam, pp. 119–161.
105. G.A. Peschek, E. Broda, Utilization of fructose by a unicellular blue-green alga, *Anacystis nidulans*. *Naturwissenschaften* **60** (1973) 479–480.
106. L.J. Stal, R. Moezelaar, Fermentation in cyanobacteria. *FEMS Microbiol. Rev.* **21** (1997) 179–211.
107. E. Padan, Facultative anoxygenic photosynthesis in cyanobacteria. *Annu. Rev. Plant Physiol.* **30** (1979) 27–40.
108. G.A. Peschek, Reduced sulfur and nitrogen compounds and molecular hydrogen as electron donors for anaerobic CO_2 photoreduction in *Anacystis nidulans*. *Arch. Microbiol.* **119** (1978) 13–22.
109. S. Anderson, L. McIntosh, Light-activated heterotrophic growth of the cyanobacterium *Synechocystis* sp PCC 6803: a blue light requiring process? *J. Bacteriol.* **173** (1991) 2761–2767.
110. M.J. Danson, D.W. Hough, G.G. Lunt (eds.), *The Archaebacteria: Biochemistry and Biotechnology* (1992), Portland Press, London, pp. 1–212.
111. T. Jordan, P. Fromme, H.T. Witt, O. Klukas, W. Saenger, N. Krauß, Three-dimensional structure of cyanobacterial Photosystem I at 2.4 Å resolution. *Nature* **411** (2001) 909–917.
112. A. Zouni, H.T. Witt, J. Kern, P. Fromme, N. Krauß, W. Saenger, P. Orth, Crystal structure of Photosystem II from *Synechococcus elongatus* at 3.8 Å resolution. *Nature* **409** (2001) 739–743.

113. N. Kamiya, J.R. Shen, Crystal structure of oxygen-evolving Photosystem II from *Thermosynechococcus vulcanus* at 3.7 Å resolution. *Proc. Natl. Acad. Sci. U.S.A.* **100** (2003) 98–192.
114. A. Ben-Shem, F. Frolow, N. Nelson, Crystal structure of plant Photosystem I. *Nature* **426** (2003) 630–635.
115. G. Kurisu, H. Zhang, J.L. Smith, W.A. Cramer, Structure of the cytochrome b_6f complex of oxygenic photosynthesis: tuning the cavity. *Science* **302** (2003) 1009–1014.
116. D. Stroebel, Y. Choquet, J.-L. Popot, D. Picot, An atypical haem in the cytochrome b_6f complex. *Nature* **246** (2003) 413–418.
117. G.A. Peschek, Anaerobic hydrogenase activity in *Anacystis nidulans*: H_2-dependent photoreduction and related reactions. *Biochim. Biophys. Acta* **548** (1979) 187–202.
118. G.A. Peschek, Aerobic hydrogenase activity in *Anacystis nidulans:* the oxyhydrogen reaction. *Biochim. Biophys. Acta* **548** (1979) 203–215.
119. G.A. Peschek, Evidence for two functionally distinct hydrogenases in *Anacystis nidulans*. *Arch. Microbiol.* **123** (1979) 81–92.
120. G.A. Peschek, Restoration of respiratory electron transport in quinone-depleted particle preparations of *Anacystis nidulans. Biochem. J.* **186** (1980) 515–523.
121. G.A. Peschek, O. Kuntner, Differential effects of plastoquinone and phylloquinone in photosynthetic and respiratory electron transfer reactions of *n*-pentane-extracted membrane preparations from cyanobacteria. *Photobiochem. Photobiophys.* (Suppl.) (1987) 157–166.
122. L.M. Saraiva, J.B. Vicente, M. Teixeira, The role of the flavodiiron proteins in microbial nitric oxide detoxification. *Adv. Microb. Physiol.* **49** (2004) 77–129.
123. J.B. Vicente, C.M. Gomes, A. Wasserfallen, M. Teixeira, Module fusion in an A-type flavoprotein from the cyanobacterium *Synechocystis* condenses a multiple-component pathway in a single polypeptide chain. *Biochem. Biophys. Res. Commun.* **294** (2002) 82–87.
124. Y. Helman, D. Tchernov, L. Reinhold, M. Shibata, T. Ogawa, R. Schwarz, I. Ohad, A. Kaplan, Genes encoding A-type flavoproteins are essential for photoreduction of O_2 in cyanobacteria. *Curr. Biol.* **13** (2003) 230–235.
125. J. Oelze, G. Drews, Membranes of photosynthetic bacteria. *Biochim. Biophys. Acta.* **265** (1972) 209–239.
126. G.A. Peschek, Spectral properties of a cyanobacterial cytochrome oxidase: evidence for cytochrome aa_3. *Biochem. Biophys. Res. Commun.* **98** (1981) 72–79.
127. G.A. Peschek, Occurrence of cytochrome aa_3 in *Anacystis nidulans*. *Biochim. Biophys. Acta* **635** (1981) 470–475.
128. V. Molitor, W. Erber, G.A. Peschek, Increased levels of cytochrome oxidase and sodium-proton antiporter in the plasma membrane of *Anacystis nidulans* after growth in sodium-enriched media. *FEBS Lett.* **204** (1986) 251–256.
129. G.A. Peschek, G. Schmetterer, G. Lauritsch, R. Muchl, P.F. Kienzl, W.H. Nitschmann, Do cyanobacteria contain "mammalian-type" cytochrome oxidase? *Arch. Microbiol.* **131** (1982) 261–265.
130. V. Molitor, M. Trnka, G.A. Peschek, Isolated and purified plasma and thylakoid membranes of the cyanobacterium *Anacystis nidulans* contain immunologically cross-reactive aa_3-type cytochrome oxidase. *Curr. Microbiol.* **14** (1987) 263–268.
131. T. Omata, N. Murata, Cytochromes and prenylquinones in preparations of cytoplasmic and thylakoid membranes from the cyanobacterium (blue-green alga) *Anacystis nidulans*. *Biochim. Biophys. Acta* **766** (1984) 395–402.

132. T. Omata, N. Murata, Electron transport reactions in cytoplasmic and thylakoid membranes prepared from the cyanobacteria (blue-green algae) *Anacystis nidulans* and *Synechocystis* PCC 6714. *Biochim. Biophys. Acta* **810** (1985) 354–361.
133. M. Wastyn, A. Achatz, M. Trnka, G.A. Peschek, Immunological and spectral characterization of partly purified cytochrome oxidase from the cyanobacterium *Synechocystis* 6714. *Biochem. Biophys. Res. Commun.* **149** (1987) 102–111.
134. M. Wastyn, A. Achatz, V. Molitor, G.A. Peschek, Respiratory activities and aa_3-type cytochrome oxidase in plasma and thylakoid membranes from vegetative cells and heterocysts of the cyanobacterium *Anabaena* ATCC 29413. *Biochim. Biophys. Acta* **935** (1988) 217–224.
135. S. Scherer, H. Almon, P. Böger, Interaction of photosynthesis, respiration and nitrogen fixation in cyanobacteria. *Photosynth. Res.* **15** (1988) 95–114.
136. G.A. Peschek, R. Zoder, Temperature stress and basic bioenergetic strategies for stress defence, in: *Algal Adaptation to Environmental Stresses. Physiological, Biochemical and Molecular Mechanisms* (2001) (L.C. Rai, J.P. Gaur, eds.), Springer Verlag, Berlin-Heidelberg-New York, pp. 203–258.
137. G.A. Peschek, Structure and function of respiratory membranes in cyanobacteria (blue-green algae). *Subcell. Biochem.* **10** (1984) 85–191.
138. H. Kraushaar, S. Hager, M. Wastyn, G.A. Peschek, Immunologically cross-reactive and redox-competent cytochrome b_6f-complexes in the chlorophyll-free plasma membrane of cyanobacteria. *FEBS Lett.* **273** (1990) 227–231.
139. G. Hauska, E. Hurt, N. Gabellini, W. Lockau, Comparative aspects of quinol-cytochrome c/plastocyanin oxidoreductases. *Biochim. Biophys. Acta* **726** (1983) 97–133.
140. R. Malkin, Cytochrome bc_1 and b_6f complexes of photosynthetic membranes. *Photosynth. Res.* **33** (1992) 121–136.
141. E.A. Berry, M. Guergova-Kuras, L. Huang, A.R. Crofts, Structure and function of cytochrome *bc* complexes. *Annu. Rev. Biochem.* **69** (2000) 1005–1075.
142. B.L. Trumpower, Cytochrome bc_1 complexes of microorganisms. *Microbiol. Rev.* **54** (1990) 101–129.
143. J.A. Garcia-Horsman, B. Barquera, J. Rumbley, J. Ma, R.B. Gennis, The superfamily of heme-copper respiratory oxidases. *J. Bacteriol.* **176** (1994) 5587–5600.
144. S. Ferguson-Miller, G.T. Babcock, Heme/copper terminal oxidases. *Chem. Rev.* **96** (1996) 2889–2907.
145. M.M. Pereira, M. Santana, M. Teixeira, A novel scenario for the evolution of haem-copper oxygen reductases. *Biochim. Biophys. Acta* **1505** (2001) 185–208.
146. M.M. Pereira, C.M. Gomes, M. Teixeira, Plasticity of proton pathways in haem-copper oxygen reductases. *FEBS Lett.* **522** (2002) 14–18.
147. G. Renger, A.R. Holzwarth, Primary electron transfer, in: *Photosystem II. The Light-driven Water:Plastoquinone Oxidoreductase in Photosynthesis* (2005) (T. Wydrzynski, K. Satoh, Eds), Springer Verlag, Dordrecht, pp. 139–175.
148. W.-D. Schubert, O. Klukas, W. Saenger, H.T. Witt, P. Fromme, Norbert Krauß, A common ancestor for oxygenic and anoxygenic photosynthetic systems. A comparison based on the structural model of photosystem I. *J. Mol. Biol.* **280** (1998) 297–314.
149. W. Nitschke, A.W. Rutherford, Photosynthetic reaction centers: variations on a common structural theme? *Trends Biochem. Sci.* **16** (1991) 241–245.
150. R.E. Blankenship, Origin and early evolution of photosynthesis. *Photosynth. Res.* **33** (1992) 91–111.

151. H. Hartman, Photosynthesis and the origin of life. *Origins Life Evolution Biosphere* **28** (1998) 515–521.
152. J. Xiong, W.M. Fischer, K. Inoue, M. Nakahara C.E. Bauer, Molecular evidence for the early evolution of photosynthesis. *Science* **289** (2000) 1724–1730.
153. D.J. Des Marais, When did photosynthesis emerge on earth? *Science* **289** (2000) 1703–1705.
154. J.A. Navarro, M. Hervas, C. Gutierrez-Merino, M.A. De la Rosa, Comparative kinetic analysis of the flavin-photosensitized oxidation and reduction of plastocyanin and cytochrome c_6 from different organisms. *Photochem. Photobiol.* **63** (1996) 86–91.
155. F.P. Molina-Heredia, A. Balme, M. Hervas, J.A. Navarro, M.A. De la Rosa, A comparative structural and functional analysis of cytochrome c_M, cytochrome c_6 and plastocyanin from the cyanobacterium *Synechocystis* sp PCC 6803. *FEBS Lett.* **517** (2002) 50–54.
156. F.P. Molina-Heredia, J. Wastl, J.A. Navarro, D.S. Bendall, M. Hervas, C.J. Howe, M.A. De la Rosa, A new function for an old cytochrome? *Nature* **424** (2003) 33–34.
157. P. Nicholls, C. Obinger, H. Niederhauser, G.A. Peschek, Cytochrome c and c-554 oxidation by membraneous *Anacystis nidulans* cytochrome oxidase. *Biochem. Soc. Trans.* **19** (1991) 252S.
158. P. Nicholls, C. Obinger, H. Niederhauser, G.A. Peschek, Cytochrome oxidase in *Anacystis nidulans*: stoichiometries and possible functions in cytoplasmic and thylakoid membranes. *Biochim. Biophys. Acta* **1098** (1992) 184–190.
159. M. Lübben, J. Morand, Novel prenylated hemes as cofactors of cytochrome oxidases. *J. Biol. Chem.* **269** (1994) 21473–21479.
160. M. Lübben, Cytochromes of archaeal electron transfer chains. *Biochim. Biophys. Acta* **1229** (1994) 1–22.
161. G. Schäfer, M. Engelhard, V. Müller, Bioenergetics of the archaea. *Microbiol. Mol. Biol. Rev.* **63** (1999) 570–620.
162. B.L. Trumpower, The protonmotive Q cycle. *J. Biol. Chem.* **265** (1990) 11409–11412.
163. R. Hill, Oxygen evolved by isolated chloroplasts. *Nature* **139** (1937) 281–282.
164. R. Hill, F. Bendall, Function of the two cytochrome components in chloroplasts: a working hypothesis. *Nature* **186** (1960) 136–137.
165. B.G. Schlarb-Ridley, D.S. Bendall, C.J. Howe, Role of electrostatics in the interaction between cytochrome *f* and plastocyanin of the cyanobacterium *Phormidium laminosum*. *Biochemistry* **41** (2002) 3279–3285.
166. B.G. Schlarb-Ridley, D.S. Bendall, C.J. Howe, Relation between interface properties and kinetics of electron transfer in the interaction of cytochrome *f* and plastocyanin from plants and the cyanobacterium *Phormidium laminosum*. *Biochemistry* **42** (2003) 4057–4063.
167. B.G. Schlarb-Ridley, J.A. Navarro, M. Spencer, D.S. Bendall, M. Hervas, C.J. Howe, M.A. De la Rosa, Role of electrostatics in the interaction between plastocyanin and Photosystem I of the cyanobacterium *Phormidium laminosum*. *Eur. J. Biochem.* **269** (2002) 5893–5902.
168. M. Hervas, J.M. Ortega, J.A. Navarro, M.A. De la Rosa, H. Bottin, Laser flash kinetic analysis of *Synechocystis* PCC 6803 cytochrome c_6 and plastocyanin oxidation by Photosystem I. *Biochim. Biophys. Acta* **1184** (1994) 235–241.
169. M. Hervas, J.A. Navarro, A. Diaz, M.A. De la Rosa, A comparative thermodynamic analysis by laser-flash absorption spectroscopy of Photosystem I reduction by plastocyanin and cytochrome c_6 in *Anabaena* PCC 7119, *Synechocystis* PCC 6803, and spinach. *Biochemistry* **35** (1996) 2693–2698.

170. A.Y. Mulkidjanian, W. Junge, Primordial UV-protectors as ancestors of the photosythetic pigment-proteins, in: *The Phototrophic Prokaryotes* (1999) (G.A. Peschek, W. Löffelhardt, G. Schmetterer, eds.), Kluwer Academic/Plenum Publishers, New York, pp. 805–815.
171. P.A. Karplus, M.J. Daniels, J.R. Herriott, Atomic structure of ferredoxin-$NADP^+$ reductase: prototype for a structurally novel flavoprotein family. *Science* **251** (1991) 60–66.
172. S. Scherer, I. Alpes, H. Sadowski, P. Böger, Ferredoxin-$NADP^+$ oxido-reductase is the respiratory NADPH dehydrogenase of the cyanobacterium *Anabaena variabilis*. *Arch. Biochem. Biophys.* **267** (1988) 228–235.
173. J. Biggins, Respiration in blue-green algae. *J. Bacteriol.* **99** (1969) 570–575.
174. K. Asada, The water-water cycle in chloroplasts: scavanging of active oxygens and dissipation of excess photons. *Annu. Rev. Plant Physiol. Plant Mol. Biol.* **50** (1999) 601–639.
175. G.A. Peschek, C. Obinger, S. Fromwald, B. Bergman, Correlation between immuno-gold labels and activities of the cytochrome-*c* oxidase (aa_3-type) in membranes of salt-stressed cyanobacteria. *FEMS Microbiol. Lett.* **124** (1994) 431–438.
176. I. Ardelean, S. Tunaru, M.L. Flonta, G. Teodosiu, M. Enache, L. Dumitru, G. Zarnea, Increased respiratory activity in light in salt-stressed Synechocystis PCC 6803, in: *The Phototrophic Prokaryotes* (1999) (G.A. Peschek, W. Löffelhardt, G. Schmetterer, eds.), Kluwer Academic/Plenum Publishers, New York, pp. 403–409.
177. C.A. Howitt, P.K. Udall, W.F. Vermaas, Type 2 NADH dehydrogenases in the cyanobacterium *Synechocystis* sp. strain PCC 6803 are involved in regulation rather than respiration. *J. Bacteriol.* **181** (1999) 3994–4003.

Chapter 20

Structure–Function of the Cytochrome b_6f Complex: A Design that has Worked for Three Billion Years

William A. Cramer, Huamin Zhang, Jiusheng Yan, Genji Kurisu, Eiki Yamashita, Naranbaatar Dashdorj, Hanyoup Kim and Sergei Savikhin

Table of Contents

20.1 Functions of the Cytochrome b_6f Complex in Photosynthetic
  Electron Transport.. 419
  20.1.1 Three-Electron Transport Complexes.................. 419
  20.1.2 Coupled Electron/Proton Transfer..................... 421
  20.1.3 PS I Cyclic Pathway.................................... 422
  20.1.4 Trans-Membrane Signaling............................ 422
20.2 Preparation and Crystallization of the b_6f Complex............ 422
  20.2.1 Three-Dimensional Structure (Recent Reviews [9,10,32–34]) . 424
  20.2.2 Organization of the Structure; Prosthetic Groups......... 425
  20.2.3 Comparison with the Cytochrome bc_1 Complex [10]....... 427
  20.2.4 Organization of TMH; Domain-Swapped ISP TM Helix.... 427
  20.2.5 Small Subunits; the Hydrophobic "Picket Fence"......... 427
  20.2.6 The b_6f Complex from Higher Plants; the Ferredoxin: NADP$^+$
      Reductase 428
20.3 Function of the Dimer: Quinone Exchange Cavity; Intermonomer
  "Cross-Talk"... 428
  20.3.1 Prosthetic Groups in the Quinone Exchange Cavity; "The
      Entry Portal to the p-Side Quinone Binding Niche"....... 429
  20.3.2 Q-Space.. 429
20.4 Electron Transport and Proton Translocation Pathways........... 430
  20.4.1 Conversion from Two-Electron to One-Electron Transfer in
      Cytochrome bc Complexes 430
  20.4.2 Caveats to Q-Cycle Operation in the b_6f Complex........ 430

    20.4.3 Application of the Q-cycle Model to the $b_6 f$ Complex. 432
    20.4.4 Motion of the Rieske Protein 433
    20.4.5 Cyclic Electron Transport; Heme c_n. 434
20.5 Two Other Novel Prosthetic Groups in the Structure of the $b_6 f$
    Complex: Chlorophyll a, and β-Carotene. 436
    20.5.1 Monomeric Chl a in the Complex 436
    20.5.2 Short Lifetime of the Chl a Singlet Excited State 437
    20.5.3 Long Distance Triplet–Triplet Energy Transfer. 439
Acknowledgements 439
References. 440

Abstract

The 3.0–3.1 Å X-ray structures of the cytochrome b_6f complex from the thermophilic cyanobacterium *Mastigocladus laminosus* and from the green alga *Chlamydomonas reinhardtii* are very similar. Eight natural prosthetic groups, four hemes, one [2Fe-2S] cluster, one Chl, one β-carotene, and one n-side plastoquinone are embedded in the eight polypeptide subunits of the complex, four large (18–33 kDa) and four small (~4 kDa). The complex is organized as a dimer with a molecular weight of 217 kDa in *M. laminosus*. Other subunits such as ferredoxin: $NADP^+$ reductase may bind transiently and more weakly to the n-side of the complex. Major features of the structure are: (i) a large inter-monomer lipophilic "quinone exchange cavity" that exchanges plastoquinone/quinol with the quinone pool in the lipid bilayer membrane; (ii) a labyrinthine pathway of plastoquinone movement between n- and p-electron exchange sites through the 11×12 Å portal at the roof of the cavity; (iii) three prosthetic groups with unknown function, a novel high-spin heme (c_n) close to heme b_n, a chlorophyll *a*, and a β-carotene; (iv) a proposed function of heme c_n is in PS I-linked cyclic electron transport, although the presumed binding site of a "sometime" inhibitor of cyclic ET, antimycin A, is occluded by heme c_n; (v) the single Chl *a* molecule in the monomer is characterized by a short (200 ps) fluorescence lifetime and large anisotropy of fluorescence; and (vi) transfer of energy from the Chl triplet state to the β-carotene occurs despite the 14 Å separation of the pigments – it is proposed that this transfer operates through an intraprotein, interpigment O_2 channel.

20.1 Functions of the Cytochrome b_6f Complex in Photosynthetic Electron Transport

20.1.1 Three-Electron Transport Complexes

The cytochrome b_6f complex, whose three-dimensional structure has been solved recently [1,2], provides the electronic connection and a proton translocation apparatus between the Photosystem II [3] and Photosystem I [4] reaction centers of oxygenic photosynthesis (Chapters 14 and 16). X-ray structures have been obtained from the thermophilic cyanobacterium *Thermosynechococcus elongatus* for PS I at 2.5 Å [4] (Chapter 13), and PS II, for which the most recent and highest resolution (3.0 Å) published structure is that of Zouni et al. [5] (Chapter 15). Photooxidation of the PS II reaction center complex is responsible for the generation of a strong oxidant ($E_m \approx +1.25$ V) [6]. Four such oxidative events can then poise a four Mn cluster to oxidize water to molecular oxygen in a four proton–four electron reaction ($2H_2O \rightarrow O_2 + 4H^+ + 4e^-$), and to deposit one H^+/e^- into the aqueous phase on the electropositive (p) side of the PS II complex. PS I generates a strong reductant ($E_m \approx -0.5$–0.6 V) of the F_A-F_B 4Fe-4S clusters in the PsaC subunit on the electronegative (n-) side of the PS I complex ([4]; see Chapter 14), which reduces ferredoxin, FNR, and then $NADP^+$ to the NADPH (Figure 1A) needed for carbon fixation.

A

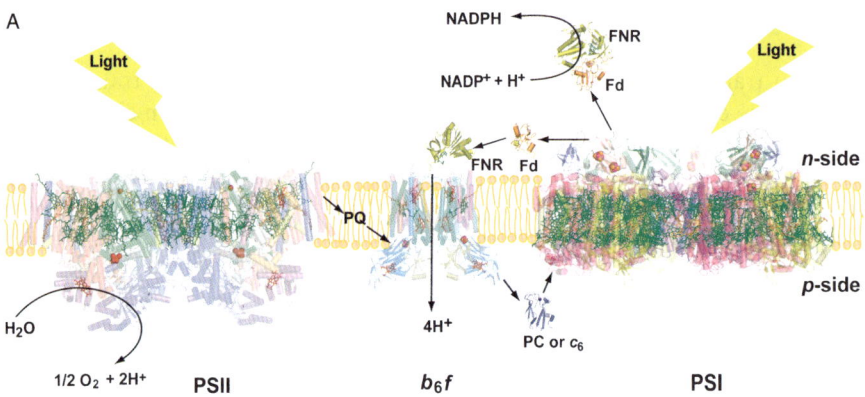

B

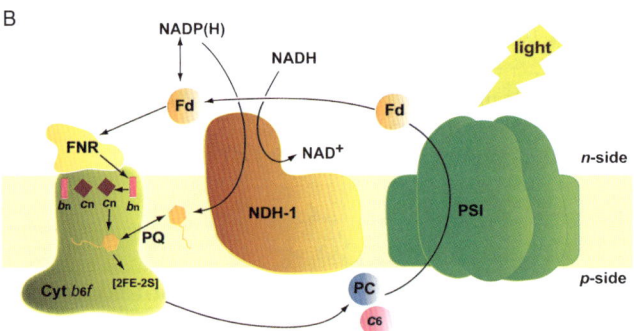

Figure 1. (A) Structures viewed parallel to the plane of the membrane of the three integral membrane protein complexes, PS II and PS I reaction center and $b_6 f$ complex in oxygenic photosynthesis that are responsible for "linear" electron transport from water, the electron donor to the PS II reaction center, to $NADP^+$, and the electron acceptor of the PS I RC. Proton translocation to the p- or lumen side of the membrane is coupled to the oxidation of water in the Photosystem II reaction center, and electron transfer through the $b_6 f$ complex. Proton transfer ($4H^+/2$ electrons transferred) is shown across the $b_6 f$ complex. (B) PS I-linked "cyclic" electron transfer. Proposed pathway from PS I to the $b_6 f$ complex involving electron transfer from the reducing side of PS I to ferredoxin (Fd), possibly through FNR, to cytochrome b_n–heme c_n, and plastoquinone (PQ), which is then oxidized by the [2Fe-2S] cluster (not shown). The sequence b_n to c_n derives from the midpoint potentials determined by [71]. ET from c_n through PQ to its immediate oxidant, the [2Fe-2S] cluster, is shown for only one monomer. Cytochrome f is not shown. An alternative cyclic pathway involving reduction of the intra-membrane plastoquinone pool by NADH dehydrogenase (NDH-1) is described. Panels (A) and (B) are modified, respectively, from [48] and [34].

20.1.2 Coupled Electron/Proton Transfer

Electron transfer through the $b_6 f$ complex is coupled to proton translocation through the complex and formation of a trans-membrane proton electrochemical potential, $\Delta\tilde{\mu}_H^+$ [7–11], that is utilized for the synthesis of the high energy $[\Delta G_o' (+Mg^{2+}) = +7.7$ kcal mol$^{-1}]$ chemical intermediate adenosine 5′-triphosphate (ATP) (Chapter 21). The $b_6 f$ complex mediates electron and proton transfer by oxidizing lipophilic plastoquinol, a quinone with a 45-carbon chain (Figure 2a) on the p-side of the complex [reactions (1) and (2) in Section 20.4.3 below], thereby reducing the soluble one-electron carriers, plastocyanin or cytochrome c_6 and the trap, P700, in the PS I reaction center for transferred excitation light energy. The existence of long distance (10–20 Å) electron transfer in proteins that can occur in timescales on the order of ns–ms [12,13] is relevant to the consideration of possible ET pathways. Mechanisms of proton transfer have been reviewed recently in another volume of this series [14].

The superoxide radical, $O_2^{\cdot-}$, a reactive oxygen species, is also formed on the p-side of the complex in low yield, $\sim 1\%$, as inferred from studies on the

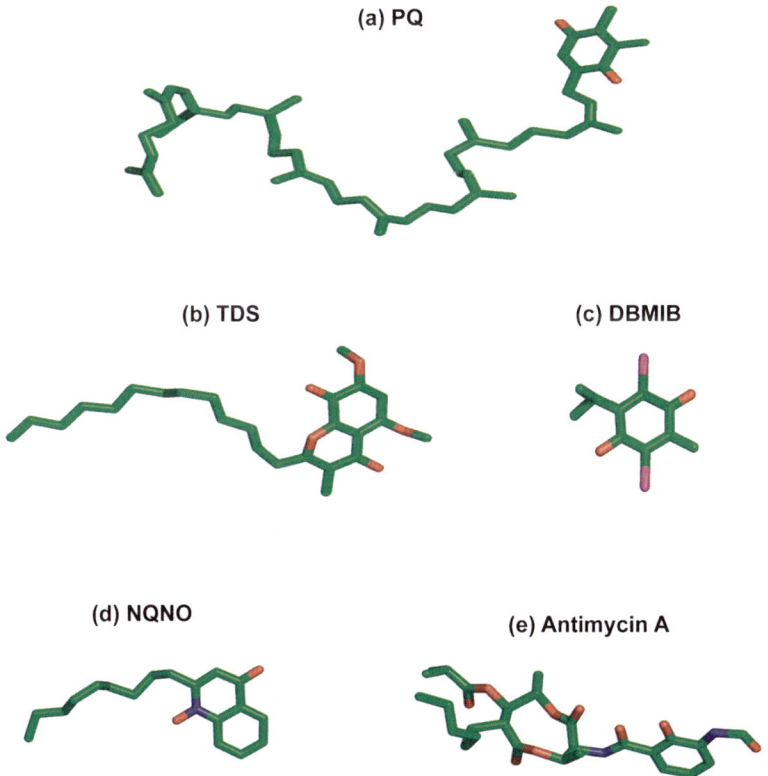

Figure 2. Chemical structures of (a) plastoquinone (PQ), and the quinone analogue inhibitors, (b) tridecyl-stigmatellin, (c) DBMIB, (d) NQNO, and (e) antimycin A.

cytochrome bc_1 complex [15], presumably through reduction of O_2 by the semiquinone formed in the one-electron oxidation of plastoquinol [reaction (3a), Section 20.4.3] [16].

Although the role of the $b_6 f$ complex in the electron transport pathway from H_2O to $NADP^+$ is described as "linear" in its net transfer properties, the detailed ET pathway within the $b_6 f$ complex is complicated. Most workers in the field believe it to consist of a "Q cycle" based partly on analogy with the mechanism established in the bc_1 complex (however, see Sections 20.4.2, 20.4.3).

20.1.3 PS I Cyclic Pathway

In addition to the overall linear pathway, the $b_6 f$ complex may also function in a "cyclic" PS I-linked pathway [17–21]. In the PS I-cyclic pathway, PS I does not reduce $NADP^+$ but, via ferredoxin, returns the electrons to the lipophilic plastoquinone pool through one or more ET complexes in the main ET chain (Figure 1B). These ET complexes include the $b_6 f$ complex and NADH dehydrogenase [22]. In any case, the $b_6 f$ complex is used to oxidize the quinol and to complete a PS I-linked ET cycle by donating electrons to the PS I complex through plastocyanin or cytochrome c_6 (Figure 1B; see Section 20.4.2).

20.1.4 Trans-Membrane Signaling

In higher plants and green algae, the $b_6 f$ complex has been proposed to function in trans-membrane signaling from the quinol binding site on the p-side of the complex to the light-harvesting chlorophyll protein kinase on its n-side surface [23]. It has also been proposed that the bound chlorophyll *a* in the complex may be involved in the signaling [2]. The function of the kinase is to phosphorylate the LHCP and thus modulate the distribution of antenna pigment-proteins associated with the two photosystems [24]. In plants and green algae, the phosphorylated LHCP tends to move by diffusion to a region of the membrane that is enriched in PS I when the quinone is over-reduced, thus regulating the distribution of light energy absorption.

20.2 Preparation and Crystallization of the $b_6 f$ Complex

The $b_6 f$ complex was first purified from a higher plant source, and contained a heme b:f heme ratio of 2:1, a molecular weight of 103 000 per heme f, and an $E_m = -100$ mV for the cytochrome b [25]. Highly active dimeric $b_6 f$ complex from the cyanobacterium *M. laminosus* was obtained by a methodology that has its origins in the previous purification studies of [26,27]. The major changes in the purification of the spinach complex were to avoid $(NH_4)_2SO_4$ precipitation and, instead of Triton-X-100, to exchange the extracted complex into a "mild" non-ionic maltoside detergent, which, originally, was not available.

$(NH_4)_2SO_4$ precipitation of the complex [26] was replaced by hydrophobic chromatography, using propyl agarose [27]. The complex purified by [26] showed the presence of five subunits, four large subunits that are bound in a 1:1 stoichiometry and found in all known purified $b_6 f$ complexes (Table 1), and FNR that is present only in the complex from higher plants [19]. The complex seemed to contain three hemes and one iron-sulfur cluster in a monomeric unit [26]. It was subsequently found through biochemical purification studies that the active complex is dimeric [28], and that it contains one Chl a [28] and one β-carotene molecule [29]. *M. laminosus* is the only cyanobacterium from which it has been possible to purify an active dimeric $b_6 f$ complex. Unfortunately, this organism is not genetically transformable at present. Cytochrome $b_6 f$ complex isolated from the more commonly used transformable cyanobacteria, such as *Synechocystis* sp. PCC 6803 or *Synechococcus* sp. PCC 7002, has thus far been found to be inactive, presumably because of the monomerization that accompanies its isolation and that renders the complex inactive, structurally altered, and non-crystallizable. The inactivation may be a consequence of delipidation and/or proteolysis of the complex. After many unsuccessful crystallization trials with the *M. laminosus* complex, it was realized that it was delipidated and contained <1 lipid molecule per monomer. Proteolysis of the initially active intact complex, which could not be prevented by the common protease inhibitors, was also observed in *M. laminosus* after a week's incubation of the complex at room temperature. This resulted in cleavage of the ISP in the flexible hinge region between two hydrophobic residues at positions 40–41, and thereby a shortening of the ISP from 179 to 139 residues, a cleavage that can readily be observed on SDS-PAGE. The modification in crystallization strategy that allowed the *M. laminosus* complex to form diffraction quality crystals was stoichiometric addition of the synthetic lipid DOPC (dioleoyl-phosphatidylcholine) to the complex (lipid:monomer = 10:1) immediately after the last sucrose gradient step in the purification and during crystallization. This resulted in rapid (1–2 days) formation of reasonably sized (~ 0.2 mm) hexagonal crystals

Table 1. Subunit masses of the spinach and *M. laminosus* cytochrome $b_6 f$ complex determined by electrospray-ionization spectrometry [35]

Protein	Measured mass (Da)	
	M. laminosus	Spinach
Large subunits		
FNR	Not applicable	35314
Cyt f	32273	31940
Cyt b_6	24712	24884
ISP	19295	18938
SuIV	17528	17313
Small subunits		
PetG	4058	4198
PetL	3841	3973
PetM	3530	3478
PetN	3304	3198

Figure 3. Crystal of the $b_6 f$ complex from *M. laminosus*. Crystals were grown in the presence of the synthetic lipid DOPC [30].

(Figure 3) that diffracted to ~ 3.4 Å [30,31] and to 3.0 Å in the presence of the quinone analogue inhibitor TDS, using re-crystallized complex [1] and in the presence of the divalent cation, Cd^{2+} [119].

20.2.1 Three-Dimensional Structure (Recent Reviews [9,10,32–34])

Determination of the crystal structure of the cytochrome $b_6 f$ complex at a resolution of 3.0–3.1 Å [1,2] from the filamentous thermophilic cyanobacterium *Mastigocladus laminosus* and the green alga *Chlamydomonas reinhardtii* completed the description of the protein architecture responsible for charge-coupled energy transduction (electron transport, proton translocation, formation of the proton electrochemical potential gradient) in oxygenic photosynthesis. With the exception of the $b_6 f$ complex, the structures of the three complexes that define the photosynthetic electron transport chain are derived from thermophilic cyanobacteria. It was, therefore, important that a structure of the $b_6 f$ complex from the eukaryotic green alga *C. reinhardtii* was solved [2]. The extensive similarity of the 3.1 and 3.0 Å structures from *C. reinhardtii* (pdb id: stigmatellin complex, 1Q90) and *M. laminosus* (pdb id: native, NQNO, and stigmatellin complexes, 2E74, 2E75 and 2E76) in highly active native preparations (turnover number, 150–250 electrons per cytochrome *f* per s) provides proof that the structures from the thermophilic cyanobacteria are representative of those in green algae and plants. Despite the $\sim 10^9$ year difference in the appearance of cyanobacteria and green algae on the Earth, the stable cytochrome $b_6 f$ complex isolated from these two sources is very similar, with the same number, eight, and arrangement of stoichiometrically and stably bound subunits, four "large" and four "small" (Table 1, defined by electrospray mass spectroscopy [35]). The protein moiety of the eight-subunit dimeric complex in

M. laminosus has a molecular weight of 217 kDa. Additional subunits such as the LHCP kinase [24,36] may bind more weakly to the complex, and FNR may bind more weakly or transiently to the complex in higher plants such as spinach [19]. It can be seen (Table 1) that the second largest subunit in the complex, the 215 residue cytochrome b_6 polypeptide, displayed a large (~ 500 mass units) mass excess relative to the prediction from genomic analysis. The structure ultimately revealed this discrepancy to be caused by covalent attachment of a heme (heme c_n, see below) that had previously been almost unrecognized. One additional subunit, FNR, was found with high but not complete occupancy in the complex isolated from spinach (Table 1), as mentioned above, and is discussed below (Section 20.2.5). It has also been possible to solve structures of the "native" complex from *M. laminosus* in the absence of inhibitors to a diffraction spacing of 3.4 Å, and in the presence of the quinone analogue inhibitor, DBMIB (Figure 2c), to 3.8 Å (pdb id: 2D2B) [37]. A diffraction-quality preparation of the $b_6 f$ complex from the green alga *C. reinhardtii* has been solved in a more rational manner because of its transformability, using $b_6 f$ complex in which the cytochrome *f* was His-tagged, allowing more rapid purification. In this structure, obtained in the presence of TDS, the extrinsic domain of cytochrome *f* and extrinsic large domain of the ISP were disordered and built from the structures of the isolated cytochrome *f* [38] and ISP [39].

20.2.2 Organization of the Structure; Prosthetic Groups

The dimeric complex contains 26 trans-membrane helices (TMH), 13 per eight-subunit monomer (view parallel to membrane plane; Figure 4A), with the following distribution of TMH: cytochrome b_6 (four), subunit IV (three), and cytochrome *f*, ISP, and the Pet G, M, L, and N subunits (one each). The dimeric complex contains 7–8 natural prosthetic groups per monomer (5–6 redox groups and two pigment molecules) in the eight ("large"+"small") subunits. The four "large" (MW = 17.5–32 kDa) core polypeptide subunits (Table 1, *M. laminosus*), which bind the redox prosthetic groups (four hemes, one [2Fe-2S] cluster, and a plastoquinone in *M. laminosus*) and directly participate in electron and proton transfer reactions are: (i, ii) cytochromes *f* and b_6 (the *pet*A and B gene products), (iii) the [2Fe-2S] Rieske protein (*pet*C), and (iv) subunit IV (*pet*D). Subunit IV also provides the binding environment for the two additional prosthetic groups in each monomer, the chlorophyll *a* and β-carotene. Crystal structures of the p-side extrinsic components of cytochrome *f* and the ISP were previously obtained to a resolution of 1.9 Å for the C-terminal 250 residue fragment of cytochrome *f* from a higher plant (turnip) [40,41], cyanobacterium [42] and green alga [38], and to 1.83 Å for the N-terminal 139 residue soluble domain of the ISP [39].

Figure 4(C) shows a pathway for electron transfer, following the concept of the Q-cycle. Some of the distances between the redox prosthetic groups are shown in this figure, and intra-monomer distances between all prosthetic groups are summarized in Table 2, along with the inter-monomer heme b_p–b_p and b_n–b_n distances.

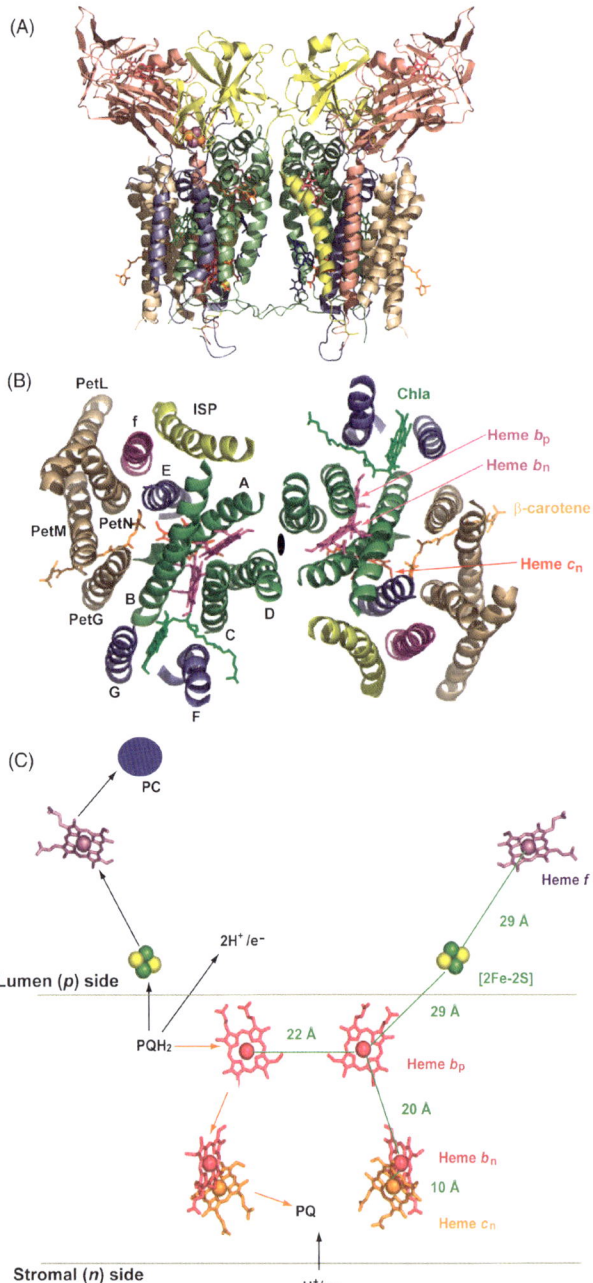

Figure 4. Views of the cytochrome b_6f complex parallel (A) and perpendicular (B) to the membrane plane [117]; assignment of single TMH (trans-membrane helices) for the small subunits [2]. Color code for (A): cyt f (pink), ISP (yellow); cyt b_6 (green), subunit IV (blue), Pet G, L, M, and N (brown). (C) Outline of quinone-mediated pathway for electron and proton transfer in a Q-cycle format, with concerted reduction of the [2Fe-2S] cluster and heme b_p proposed in [80]. Center to center distances are shown.

20.2.3 Comparison with the Cytochrome bc_1 Complex [10]

The seven TMH associated with cytochrome b_6 (helices labeled A–D)-subunit IV (helices E–G) subunits form the hydrophobic core of the complex that is seen, through the distribution of hydrophobic segments in the comparison of the amino acid sequences, to be highly conserved between the b_6f complex and animal and plant cytochrome bc_1 complexes that function in respiration [43] and purple bacterial photosynthesis. However, away from this core, in directions both parallel (Figure 4A) and perpendicular to the membrane plane (Figure 4B), there is major dissimilarity between the b_6f and bc_1 complexes [10]. The ten β-strand motif of the ISP shows significant similarity between the b_6f and bc_1 complexes [39]. However, the membrane-bound c-type cytochromes f and c_1, respectively, of the b_6f and bc_1 complexes are completely unrelated [40].

20.2.4 Organization of TMH; Domain-Swapped ISP TM Helix

In the view perpendicular to the membrane plane (Figure 4B), the single TM helix of cytochrome f is the only one that spans the complex and the membrane in the "classical Kyte and Doolittle (K & D) fashion" [44], with 20 hydrophobic residues in a TMH arranged orthogonally to the membrane plane and punctuated at each end with a charged residue(s). The 25–27 residue TM helix of the ISP is longer than the classical K & D trans-membrane helix and is seen to cross over from the soluble domain in one monomer to the hydrophobic TM domain of the other (Figure 4A). This domain-swapped arrangement of the TM helix of the iron-sulfur protein, together with interactions of hydrophobic aromatic residues at the monomer–monomer interface (not shown), are responsible for stabilization of the dimer.

20.2.5 Small Subunits; the Hydrophobic "Picket Fence"

The four small ($M_r = 3-4$ kDa) subunits, in order of ascending molecular weight (3.3–4.1 kDa), are designated PetN, M, L, and G (Table 1). The set of small subunits, each of which spans the complex and the membrane once, can be considered to be "hydrophobic sticks," with 1–2 C-terminal charged residues on the n- or stromal side of the complex. The orientation of each of these subunits obeys the cis-positive rule (*i.e.*, more Lys and Arg residues on the side of insertion) for the topology of proteins inserted into a membrane bilayer [45,46]. The four small subunits, PetG, M, L, N, have a "picket fence" arrangement at the lateral periphery of each monomer (Figure 4A and B), and thereby, presumably, provide structural support. The orientation of all four hydrophobic sticks with positively charged C-terminal domain on the n- or stromal side of the membrane suggests that the insertion of the components of this fence, either individually or collectively, occurs according to thermodynamic rules. A more accurate initial identification of the small hydrophobic subunits was achieved in *C. reinhardtii* because PetG and Pet N contain a Cys residue that could be labeled with Hg. Improved refinement of the *M. laminosus* structure has now yielded a change of the assignment in the original model [47], with subunit G now changed to N, N to L, L to G, and M subunit unchanged, as in the *C. reinhardtii* structure [2]. The β-carotene is inserted into the complex between the helices of the M and G subunits like a "toothpick", making van der Waals contact with helices B and E, respectively, of cytochrome b_6 and subunit IV, suggesting that the toothpick could function as a scaffold or guide in the assembly of the complex [48]. Deletion of the gene coding for the M-subunit [49], but not G [50], disrupts the structure.

20.2.6 The b_6f Complex from Higher Plants; the Ferredoxin: $NADP^+$ Reductase

The same eight subunits found in the b_6f complex from *M. laminosus* and *C. reinhardtii* are also found, with very similar masses determined by electrospray mass spectroscopy, in the complex isolated from spinach (*Spinacea oleracea*) thylakoid membranes (Table 1, spinach). This supports the conclusion that the eight subunit core b_6f complex has not changed significantly in evolution since its "birth" in the cyanobacteria. However, a ninth subunit was found in the complex from spinach which, at 35.3 kDa, is the largest in the set. This ninth and largest subunit in the complex was identified to be ferredoxin:$NADP^+$ reductase (FNR). The occupancy of FNR in the complex, where it was first identified in biochemical studies [19,51], was estimated to be less than complete, approximately 70–90% [19]. The lack of complete occupancy implies that, during the evolution of the b_6f complex, it developed a relatively weak affinity for transient binding of peripheral proteins, such as FNR that is proposed to function in PS I-mediated cyclic electron transport, with which it can be coupled for function.

20.3 Function of the Dimer: Quinone Exchange Cavity; Intermonomer "Cross-Talk"

The two monomers of the b_6f complex enclose a large cavity, the "quinone exchange cavity" [47], which extends 30 Å along the symmetry axis of the dimer, and 25 × 15 Å in the membrane plane (Figure 4A). This cavity, first observed in the mitochondrial cytochrome bc_1 complex [52], exchanges the lipophilic quinone-quinol with the bulk phase lipid of the membrane. The lipophilic nature of the cavity was defined by the observation that two of the ten lipid molecules per monomer added to the complex reside [1] and, presumably, stabilize, this cavity. Identification of the cavity as serving the function of Q/QH$_2$ exchange seemed initially obvious, but was further strengthened by the finding of a sulfolipid and plastoquinone molecule, respectively, near the n-side of the cavity in *M. laminosus* and *C. reinhardtii*. Thus, one function of the dimer is to define the boundaries of this cavity. A second function, which has been considered in the bc_1 [53,54], but not the b_6f complex, is inter-monomer crosstalk, in which electrons are shared between the two hemes b_p. Comparison of

Table 2. Intra- and inter-monomer distances between prosthetic groups in the
M. laminosus b_6f complex

Prosthetic group	Intra-monomer distance (Å)	
	Fe to Fe	Edge to edge
[2Fe-2S]–cyt f	28	26
[2Fe-2S]–heme b_p	28	24
Heme b_p–heme b_n	20	7
Heme b_n–heme c_n	9.6	4 (b_n propionate to c_n Fe)
Chl a–heme b_p	–	12
Chl a–heme b_n	–	5.5
Chl a–β-carotene	–	14
	Inter-monomer distance (Å)	
Heme b_p–heme b_p	13	11
Heme b_n–heme b_n	35	29

the heme–heme distances (Table 2) [55] indicates that the rate of the inter-monomer transfer should be competitive with intra-monomer electron transfer between hemes b_p and b_n (Section 20.4.3).

20.3.1 Prosthetic Groups in the Quinone Exchange Cavity; "The Entry Portal to the p-Side Quinone Binding Niche"

The prosthetic groups observed to insert into the Q/QH$_2$ exchange cavity are (i) the n-side heme c_n (Section 20.4.3); (ii) the phytyl chain of the bound Chl a molecule that extends around the G helix of subunit IV into the cavity through the 11 × 12 Å portal from the quinone-binding niche on the p-side of the cavity; (iii) because of extra electron density outside the portal that initially seemed to be correlated with the presence of the quinone-analogue inhibitor, TDS (Figure 2C) it was believed that TDS is inserted through the portal in opposite orientations, "ring-out" vs. "ring-in" in *M. laminosus* vs. *C. reinhardtii*. However, when TDS was added to the complex before lipid, the TDS ring was seen to be proximal to the [2Fe-2S] cluster, [119], as observed in the *C. reinhardtii* complex [2], and for stigmatellin in the respiratory bc_1 complex [56]. The sensitivity of *M. laminosus* to TDS and stigmatellin inhibition is 10–100 times smaller than *C. reinhardtii*. Entry of TDS, and presumably PQ as well, through the portal is controlled by residue 81 in helix G of subunit IV, which protrudes into the portal entrance in helix G of subunit IV [57]. A more hydrophobic Phe residue in *C. reinhardtii* compared to Leu in *M. laminosus*, increases the response to TDS/stigmatellin by the factor of 10–100 fold and thus appears to facilitate entry of the TDS through the portal entrance [57].

20.3.2 Q-Space

The p-side binding of TDS is one of three sites in the b_6f complex in which the occupancy by PQ or quinone analogue has been detected in the X-ray structures: (i) TDS inserted through the portal into the p-side quinone-binding niche, its O-4 within hydrogen-binding distance of the His155 ligand of the [2Fe-2S] cluster [2,119]; (ii) the high affinity binding site of the quinone analogue inhibitor DBMIB is peripheral to the major quinone binding space defined in studies of the bc_1 complex [58]. It is located in a peripheral position near the p-side interfacial niche bounded by cytochrome f, cytochrome b_6, and subunit IV, 19 Å from the [2Fe-2S] cluster [37]; (iii) the high-affinity binding site of the quinone analogue inhibitor DBMIB is peripheral to the major quinone binding space defined in structure studies of the bc_1 complex [58]; it is located in a peripheral position near the p-side interfacial niche bounded by cytochrome f, cytochrome b_6, and subunit IV, 19 Å from the [2Fe-2S] cluster [37]; (iv) electron density resembling PQ is seen close to heme c_n near the n-side of the quinone-exchange cavity. These sites define a labyrinthine pathway for the movement of the quinone through the intraprotein crevices and caverns of the complex [34].

20.4 Electron Transport and Proton Translocation Pathways

20.4.1 Conversion from Two-Electron to One-Electron Transfer in Cytochrome bc Complexes

The lipophilic quinol that serves as an electron and proton donor to b_6f/bc_1 complexes is a two-electron carrier. The mechanism by which it accomplishes electron transfer to the one electron metalloprotein carriers in the complex, the [2Fe-2S] cluster, hemes b and f, is a fundamental question. For the bc_1 complex, a Q-cycle mechanism was proposed by P. Mitchell [59,60], in which oxidation of the two electron quinol system occurs via a bifurcated pathway in which one electron is transferred to a high potential ($E_{m7} \geq 0.3$ V), and one to a low potential ($E_{m7} \leq -0.05$ V), chain [11,61–66]. The paradigm-changing experiment that underlay Mitchell's proposal was the oxidant-induced reduction of b heme [67]. Subsequently, the amplitude and kinetics of the redox events involving the b- and c-hemes could be measured, and a specific quinone analogue inhibitor, antimycin A, for the n-side of the complex, and several for the p-side, could be employed to define the sequence of the reactions.

20.4.2 Caveats to Q-Cycle Operation in the b_6f Complex

Application of the Q-cycle model to the b_6f complex is based to a significant extent on analogy with the bc_1 complex. Three properties of the b_6f complex make the application of the Q cycle more difficult to analyze: (i) the alpha-band maxima of the two b hemes are almost indistinguishable; (ii) no specific n-side inhibitor analogous to antimycin A in the bc_1 complex is known for the b_6f complex. Regarding the latter point, it was thought that the increase in the flash-induced amplitude of cytochrome b (believed to be heme b_n) implied that the analogue NQNO acted in the b_6f complex [68] as antimycin A does in the

STRUCTURE–FUNCTION OF THE CYTOCHROME

bc_1 complex. However, with the re-discovery of heme c_n and its placement in the structures of the $b_6 f$ complex [2,47], together with the previous [69,70] and recent spectrophotometric analysis [71], it is now realized that the binding site of heme c_n occludes the site that would be filled by antimycin in the bc_1 complex (Figure 5). The mechanism of inhibition by NQNO seems likely to result [119] from its effecting a large decrease in the E_m of heme c_n [71]. The hypothesis that heme c_n is associated with the pathway of PS I cyclic electron transport [1,2], if correct, would imply that electron traffic through heme b_n must be shared between a Q-cycle and the cyclic pathway (Section 20.4.4). The operation of a Q-cycle using the n-side of the $b_6 f$ complex would then seem to require a time-sharing mechanism. A way around this problem could be spatial separation of the two pathways, with cyclic and linear ET separated spatially in the non-appressed and appressed membrane domains, respectively [72,73].

(iii) A third *caveat* to the operation of the Q cycle is the small amplitude of heme b reduction seen (a) in many single flash experiments in the absence of NQNO (~ 0.2–0.3 hemes per cyt f, compared with a maximum value of 1.0) [74,75], and (b) in chemical reduction by NADPH (~ 0.8 per cyt f, compared with an expected value of 2) [75]. An answer or *counter-caveat* to the former point is that the proximity (~ 4 Å) of heme b_n and c_n implies that a net reduction of heme b_n will never be seen unless electron flow through heme c_n is inhibited.

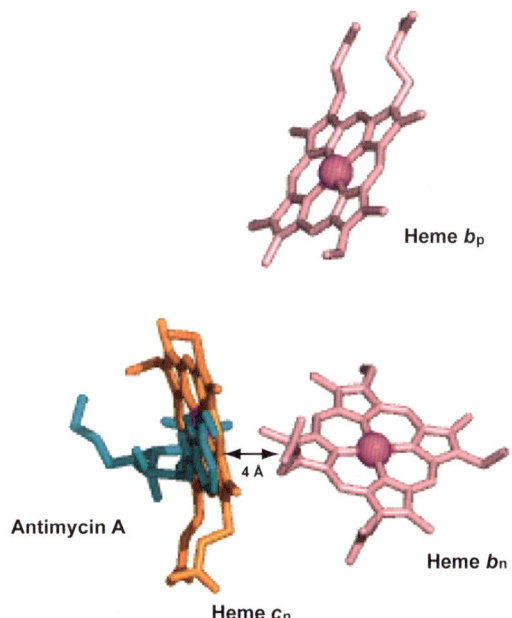

Figure 5. *n*-side binding environment of heme c_n showing its overlap with the binding site of antimycin A determined in the structure of the bovine bc_1 complex [118]. Distance between propionate of heme b_n and heme-Fe of heme c_n is 4 Å.

The difference in structure of bc complexes outside of the central core, and the difference in structure on the p-side (cyt f vs. cyt c_1) and structure–function on the n-side (presence and absence of heme c_n) might lead to an expectation of a difference in overall mechanism. For these reasons and because of some shortage of independent data for the b_6f complex, it is not obvious that the b_6f and bc_1 complexes can simply be exchanged in the framework of a Q-cycle model. However, the latter is presently the consensus model for trans-complex and trans-membrane electron and proton transfer, and is presented below.

20.4.3 Application of the Q-cycle Model to the b_6f Complex

One-electron oxidation of doubly reduced dihydroplastoquinone, PQH_2, by the initial acceptor, the [2Fe-2S] protein ($E_{m7} \cong +0.3$ V) in the p-side high-potential chain, is accompanied by release of two H^+ (formulae 1–2 below) to the p-side aqueous or lumen phase ($H^+/e = 2$). A mechanism of proton-coupled electron transfer from quinol to the [2Fe-2S] cluster at this site has been discussed, and it has been proposed that this reaction constitutes the rate-limiting step in the turnover of the complex [76]. Transfer of the second proton appears to involve transfer to and through a glutamate (Glu78 in *C. reinhardtii*) residue in the conserved PEWY sequence [43] near heme b_p [62,77,78]. Transfer of the second electron from the quinol to heme b_p, which may occur via the semiquinone [79] (formula 3 below) or directly to the heme [80], accounts for "oxidant-induced reduction." The second electron from PQH_2 is transferred across the complex consecutively through the two b hemes, b_p and b_n (formula 4), or as anionic plastosemiquinone [81–83]. The resulting proton uptake from the electronegative (n-side) of the membrane (formulae 5) completes the "Q cycle" mechanism for charge transfer and describes the contribution to the trans-membrane $\Delta\tilde{\mu}_H^+$ by the complex.

$$PQH_2 + [2Fe - 2S\,(ox)] \rightarrow PQ^{\bullet-} + [2Fe - 2S\,(red)] + 2H^+ \qquad (1)$$
[p-side aqueous phase]

$$FeS\,(red) + cyt f\,(ox) \rightarrow FeS\,(ox) + cyt f\,(red) \qquad (2)$$
[*high potential chain; n. b., structure indicates* ~ 28 Å *for center-center distance of transfer; subsequent steps in the HP chain are* cyt $f \rightarrow$ PC *or* cyt $c_6 \rightarrow$ P700]

$$PQ^{\bullet-} + \text{heme } b_p\,(ox) \rightarrow PQ + \text{heme } b_p\,(red) \qquad (3)$$
[*low potential chain*]

$$PQ^{\bullet-} + O_2 \rightarrow PQ + O^{\bullet-} \qquad (3a)$$
[*side path reaction forming potentially toxic superoxide*]

2 heme b_p (r) + hemes b_n (o)/c_n(o) → $2b_p$(o) + b_n(r)/c_r (4)

[*two turnovers of p-side PQH_2 oxidation; trans-membrane electron transfer to $b_n c_n$ complex*]

b_n(r)/c_n(r) + 2H$^+$ + PQ → b_n (o) + c_n(o) + PQH_2 (5)

[*n-side 2e- reduction of PQ, using the heme $b_n c_n$ 2 electron gate*]

The above reactions are written in the context of a monomer. Intra-monomer distances between the redox prosthetic groups are summarized in Table 2. The distances allow all of these reactions to occur in a time faster than the rate-limiting step(s) for electron transfer in the complex, which proceed in times on the order of a millisecond. It is not understood how the labyrinthine nature of the inside of the $b_6 f$ complex would be conducive to the required quinone movement on this time scale. In addition to the ET pathway through the monomer, the 13 Å edge-edge inter-monomer distance between the two hemes b_p (Table 2) implies the possibility of p-side electron sharing between the two monomers 55].

20.4.4 Motion of the Rieske Protein

Completion of reaction (1) in the above set describing the Q cycle faces the problem of the large distance, ~29 Å, between the [2Fe-2S] cluster and the cytochrome heme iron. This implies that the time required for electron transfer through the high potential chain (2, above) would be a thousand times greater than the rate-limiting step, 1–5 ms, of the linear electron transfer chain from H_2O to NADP$^+$. Thus, during the electron transfer cycle, either the soluble (extrinsic) domain of the ISP or of cytochrome *f* must move relative to the other partner to shorten the intraprotein electron transfer distance to the 15 Å that would be compatible with a ms electron transfer time. Such movement of the ISP should be facilitated by the glycine-enriched hinge region that connects the TM α-helix of the ISP and its soluble domain, although mutagenesis of the hinge region did not indicate that the requirement for the Gly residues was crucial [84]. For the bc_1 complex, structures obtained from different crystal forms have implied that the [2Fe-2S] cluster can be translated by approximately 17 Å, through a 60° rotation-translation of the ISP soluble domain, from its membrane-proximal position close to the p-side ubiquinol binding site to a site proximal to cytochrome c_1 [85–87]. Motion of the soluble (extrinsic) domain of the ISP that would bring the cluster close to the cytochrome *f* heme has also been proposed, but has not yet been documented by a structure determination. Because of the distant position of the cytochrome *f* heme that is on the side of the protein exposed to the aqueous phase (Figure 4A), the motion of the Rieske iron-sulfur protein extrinsic domain required to shorten the ET distance must be different in the $b_6 f$ complex [1]. A positional change of the ISP that would allow a competent rate of [2Fe-2S] → cyt *f* electron transfer would be a smaller amplitude rotation that would bring the cluster in contact with cytochrome f and allow intraprotein electron transfer through cytochrome f over a distance of ~ 15 Å to the axial histidine ligand of the heme [1].

20.4.5 Cyclic Electron Transport; Heme c_n

The structures of the cytochrome $b_6 f$ complex showed the presence of a unique heme facing the inter-monomer quinone exchange cavity on the n-side of the complex that is covalently linked by a single thioether bond to a Cys residue (Cys35) on the n-side of the first (A) TMH of cytochrome b_6. The only axial ligand associated with this heme is an H_2O that is H-bonded to the propionate of the stromal side heme b_n (Figure 5), showing that heme c_n is penta-coordinate and close (~ 4 Å) to the heme b_n, allowing rapid inter-heme electron transfer. For purposes of teaching and inter-disciplinary communication, this heme, which was tentatively called heme x and heme c_i, respectively, in the structure from *M. laminosus* and *C. reinhardtii*, is more appropriately denoted as heme c_n [34]. The latter nomenclature incorporates the facts that the heme is covalently bound, and thereby c-type, as expressed in the notation originally used in the *C. reinhardtii* structure [2], and that it is located on the electrochemically negative (n-) side of the membrane. Before the determination of the X-ray structures, a heme of unknown location, now identified as heme c_n, was defined in two spectrophotometric low noise kinetic studies, in which it was called "G" [69,70] and was shown to have a somewhat more positive E_m than heme b_n. This covalently-bound heme in the $b_6 f$ complex was also observed in SDS-PAGE [26,71,88,89]. The midpoint potential of heme c_n is pH-dependent in the physiological range, with an $E_{m7} \cong +100$ mV, approximately 150 mV more positive than the E_{m7} of heme b_n. The heme c_n E_{m7} is shifted by approximately -225 mV by the quinone analogue inhibitor NQNO [71], thus providing a mechanism for the action of NQNO distinct from that of antimycin A in the bc_1 complex. Heme c_n is characterized by an absorbance band at approximately 425 nm in the Soret region in redox difference visible spectra [71], or in CO- or butyl isocyanide-difference spectra [89].

The pyridine hemochromogen redox difference spectrum for heme x covalently bound to the cytochrome b polypeptide isolated from SDS-PAGE displays a broad spectrum with a small extinction coefficient and a peak at 553 nm, similar to that of other hemes with a single thioether linkage. The binding of CO or the hydrophobic cyanide analogue, butyl isocyanide (BIC), to dithionite-reduced $b_6 f$ complex shifts the redox difference spectrum. Together with EPR spectra displaying "g" values of the oxidized complex at 6.7 and 7.4, heme c_n was defined as ferric high spin [90]. More recently the use of parallel field EPR and low magnetic fields have shown the hemes b_n and c_n are spin-coupled [120]. The absence of this heme in the cytochrome bc_1

complex implies that a plausible function of heme c_n is in cyclic electron transport.

Considering heme c_n, it is proposed that the n-side of the $b_6 f$ complex participates in the cyclic electron transport pathway. The ATP provided by such a pathway, coupled to formation of $\Delta\tilde{\mu}_H^+$, is a metabolic requirement to establish a proper balance of NADPH and ATP for the fixation of CO_2 [32]. The extent of the contribution of this cyclic pathway to the $\Delta\tilde{\mu}_H^+$ and ATP synthesis is not known, nor are the regulatory mechanisms that may apply under different light intensities and conditions of plant stress. The requirement of the cyclic pathway and the minimum extent of its contribution can be estimated as follows: (i) The maximum $H^+/2e^-$ ratio is 6 for a two-electron reduction of $NADP^+$ via linear electron transport from water, assuming that a "Q cycle" is completely obligatory and continuously engaged [91]; in this mechanism, 2/3 of the protons that form the $\Delta\tilde{\mu}_H^+$ result from electron transfer through the $b_6 f$ complex; (ii) for C_3 carbon fixation, three ATP, two NADPH and, therefore, 12 H^+ are needed, which yields an H^+/ATP stoichiometry of 4; (iii) three ATP are synthesized in one complete rotation of the chloroplast extrinsic CF_1 sector of the ATPase [92] (for further details, see Chapter 21); (iv) the F_o sector of the ATPase contains 14 c-subunits [93], so that the required H^+/ATP stoichiometry $=4.7$. Thus, H^+ production by the linear electron transfer pathway, even with a completely engaged Q cycle, falls short of what is necessary to generate sufficient ATP for carbon fixation. ATP production by the linear pathway is known to be less than fully efficient [94,95], implying that it is necessary for the plant to produce even more ATP by a cyclic pathway. In fact, the turnover rate of cyclic ET, measured in dark-adapted *Arabidopsis* leaves, is ~ 130 s^{-1} [96], which is comparable to the rate-limiting step of the linear pathway.

Noting that the ΔE_m of hemes b_n and c_n is approximately 150 mV, downhill to heme c_n, which would favor a sequence of electron transfer, $b_n \to c_n$, that the E_m of heme c_n is pH-dependent [71], and considering studies on the involvement of ferredoxin [17,18,75] and FNR [19,51] in the pathway, the n-side of the $b_6 f$ complex could be utilized in a PS I- linked ferredoxin (Fd) cyclic pathway, as follows:

$$2Fd\,(red) + FNR\,(ox) \to 2Fd\,(ox) + FNR\,(red) \qquad (6)$$

$$FNR\,(red) + heme\,b_n\,(ox)/c_n\,(ox) \to FNR\,(ox) + heme\,b_n\,(red)/c_n\,(red) \qquad (7)$$

$$b_n\,(red)/c_n\,(red) + 2H^+ + PQ \to b_n\,(ox)/c_n\,(ox) + PQH_2 \qquad (8)$$

The reduced plastoquinol, PQH_2, would then traverse the quinone exchange cavity of the $b_6 f$ complex (Figure 1), enter the p-side Q/QH_2 niche through the portal in the roof of the quinone-exchange cavity (Section 20.3 above), and serve as an electron and proton donor to the [2Fe-2S] cluster [Section 20.4.3, reaction (1)]. Heme c_n could also then work in tandem with heme b_p to cooperatively reduce PQ near the center of the complex [75].

20.5 Two Other Novel Prosthetic Groups in the Structure of the b_6f Complex: Chlorophyll a, and β-Carotene

20.5.1 Monomeric Chl a in the Complex

The function of the single monomeric Chl a molecule originally seen in both structures of the cytochrome b_6f complex is a mystery [97]. The function of the cytochrome b_6f complex does not require light harvesting, and the Chl a molecule is not part of the electron-transfer chain, which are the usual functions of chlorophyll molecules in photosynthetic complexes. Moreover, the functionally similar cytochrome bc_1 complex of the respiratory chain does not contain a Chl a molecule [52,62,85,86,98]. It has been proposed that the Chl a may serve as a lipid-like space-filler [1], or that it may act as a sensor in interactions with Photosystem I [2].

Regardless of the role of the Chl a in the cytochrome b_6f complex, the introduction of a chlorophyll molecule into the protein structure poses a threat to the stability of the complex [29,99]. The triplet excited state of the Chl a molecule (^{3}Chl*) is known to form efficiently under illumination [100], and to transfer its energy with almost 100% yield to molecular oxygen, generating singlet oxygen ($^1O_2^*$) [101] that is toxic to the pigment–protein complex [102]. To prevent singlet oxygen formation in chlorophyll-containing proteins, a carotenoid (Car) is typically positioned close (~4Å) to the Chl a molecule, effectively quenching the triplet excited state of the Chl a due to rapid triplet–triplet energy transfer to carotenoid [103]. It was expected that a similar protection mechanism would exist in the cytochrome b_6f complex, because, along with the Chl a molecule, a β-carotene was found to be stoichiometrically bound in the cytochrome b_6f complex [29]. These expectations were shattered by the high-resolution X-ray structures of the complex, showing the β-carotene to be positioned no closer than 14 Å from the Chl a [1,2] (Figure 6). This distance is too large for direct triplet–triplet energy transfer from ^{3}Chl* to Car, as the latter occurs via a Dexter-type exchange mechanism and requires the interacting cofactors to form a collision complex [104,105]. Using the theory of Dexter [106], the characteristic time for triplet energy transfer from the ^{3}Chl* to Car in the cytochrome b_6f complex was estimated to be ~0.3 ms, far too slow to compete with the triplet energy transfer to oxygen that takes place on a (sub)microsecond time scale [107]. Despite being seemingly unprotected, the Chl a in the cytochrome b_6f complex was shown to be 130–140 times more stable under light illumination than molecular Chl a in solution [99]. To account for the observed high stability of the Chl a in the cytochrome b_6f complex, two novel singlet oxygen protection mechanisms have been proposed: (i) a decrease of the Chl a triplet state formation due to the unusually short

STRUCTURE–FUNCTION OF THE CYTOCHROME

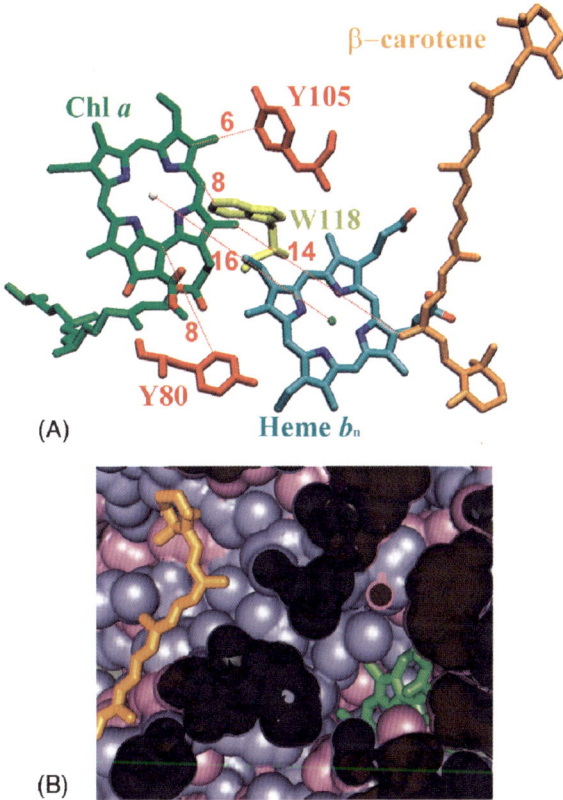

Figure 6. (A) Environment of the single chlorophyll *a* molecule in *M. laminosus*, showing the immediate environment of aromatic amino acids that can function as part of the protection mechanism against formation of singlet oxygen [99]. The Chl ring is inserted between the F and G helices of subunit IV of the $b_6 f$ complex, whose phytyl chain is wrapped around the G helix and inserted through the portal into the quinone exchange cavity [47]. (B) Putative channel for singlet oxygen, lined by hydrophobic residues in PetB (cytochrome b_6), Leu95, Met96, Leu99, and in PetG, Phe7, Val110, Phe11, Leu14, which bridge the 14 Å gap between the Chl *a* and β-carotene [107]. These residues are drawn in blue.

lifetime (~200 ps) of the Chl *a* singlet excited state; (ii) long distance triplet–triplet energy transfer from ^{3}Chl* to Car mediated by a third molecule [99,107].

20.5.2 Short Lifetime of the Chl a Singlet Excited State

The fluorescence lifetime of the single Chl *a* in the $b_6 f$ complex isolated from the cyanobacterium *Synechocystis* PCC sp. 6803 was found to be 250 ± 20 ps [108], compared with the 5–6 ns lifetime reported for monomeric Chl *a* in solution [109]. Although the complex from *Synechocystis* is known to be monomeric and functionally inactive, this lifetime is similar to the lifetime of

~200 ps found for the singlet excited state of the Chl *a* from transient absorption measurements in the enzymatically active dimeric $b_6 f$ complex of *Mastigocladus laminosus* and spinach, as well as inactive monomeric complexes from *Synechococcus* PCC 7002 [99]. Thus, the local environment of the Chl *a* is similar in the dimeric and monomeric forms of the $b_6 f$ complex. A consequence of the decrease of the Chl* lifetime from 5–6 ns to 200 ps is a 25–30-fold decrease in the quantum yield of the ^{3}Chl* state formation, thereby significantly reducing the rate of singlet oxygen production. It was proposed that the mechanism responsible for the quenching of the Chl *a* singlet excited state involves electron transfer exchange with a nearby aromatic amino acid residue. In this scenario, absorption of a photon promotes the Chl *a* into its singlet excited state, thereby generating a strong oxidant with an oxidation–reduction potential changed from approximately −0.88 to +0.97 V (Figure 7, wavy arrow). Quenching then results from electron donation to the Chl* from a nearby aromatic residue (arrow 1), oxidizing the residue and transforming Chl* into an unexcited but reduced Chl⁻ state with an electron donating potential = −0.88 V. In the second electron transfer step (arrow 2), the Chl⁻ donates an electron to the oxidized residue, resulting in neutralization of the Chl and the aromatic residue and completing the quenching process. Based on structural data and the available amino acid residue redox potentials, Dashdorj et al. [99] proposed Tyr105 from several aromatic amino acid residues surrounding the

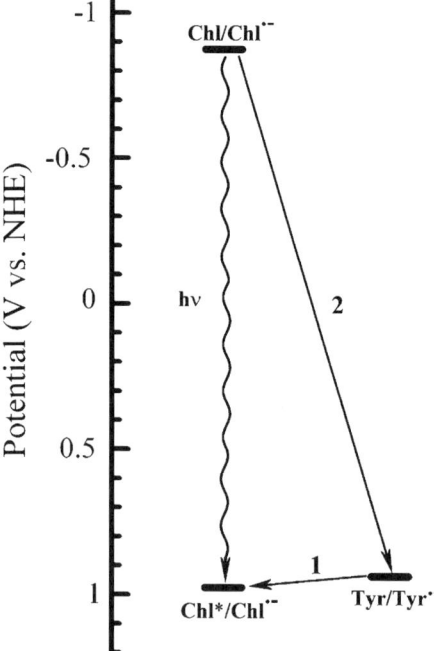

Figure 7. Energy level diagram of chlorophyll *a* and adjacent Tyr105, a putative electron acceptor of the Chl [99].

Chl *a* (Figure 6A) as the most likely candidate responsible for the described electron-transfer mediated quenching of the Chl *a* excited state. A similar electron-transfer exchange mechanism has previously been proposed for fluorescence quenching of a protein-bound flavin chromophore [110,111]. This quenching mechanism for the Chl *a* singlet excited state would account for only ~25-fold protection (the ratio of the Chl* lifetime in organic solvent and in the complex) against singlet oxygen formation, implying that one or more additional unconventional protection mechanism(s) exist in the cytochrome b_6f complex.

20.5.3 Long Distance Triplet–Triplet Energy Transfer

Despite the long distance between the Chl *a* and the β-carotene, rapid triplet energy transfer from the Chl *a* to the β-carotene was observed in the cytochrome b_6f complex from *M. laminosus* [107]. To avoid possible signal contamination by adventitious Chl *a*, the samples were refined to an ultra-pure state by dissolving diffraction-quality crystals with a stoichiometry of Chl *a* 1.0:1 relative to cytochrome *f* defined by crystallization and the crystal structure. The time-resolved optical experiments demonstrated that, upon excitation into the Chl *a* band, the triplet state of β-carotene (^{3}Car) in these samples was formed within <8 ns, which is ~5 orders of magnitude faster than the direct triplet–triplet energy transfer expected through the Dexter mechanism for the pair of these molecules separated by 14 Å. It was proposed that oxygen can mediate triplet energy transfer between the Chl *a* and β-carotene. Singlet oxygen in solvents can be effectively quenched by a carotenoid, promoting the latter into the triplet excited state [103,112]. The putative intraprotein channel for singlet oxygen would be lined by hydrophobic residues in PetB (cytochrome b_6), Leu95, Met96, Leu99, and in PetG, Phe7, Va110, Phe11, Leu14, which bridge the 14 Å gap between the Chl *a* and β-carotene (Figure 6B) [107]. Because the rate of the $^1O_2$ quenching by β-carotene (~1.3×10^{10} M^{-1} s^{-1}) is over two orders of magnitude greater than the reactivity of $^1O_2$ toward surrounding hydrophobic amino acids [113], this mechanism for triplet energy transfer to β-carotene would allow it to serve a protective function. The reason for distant placement of the necessary protective β-carotene relative to the Chl *a* implies that the carotene has another function, presumably related to the structure or assembly of the complex [48]. An oxygen, but not singlet oxygen, channel has been described in the bovine cytochrome oxidase [114], and oxygen binding reactions consistent with the likelihood of an intraprotein O_2 channel have been documented in the metalloproteins, copper amine oxidase [115] and lipoxygenase [116].

Acknowledgements

We thank J.L. Smith for important contributions to the structure studies, A. Szczepaniak for early crystallization studies on the b_6f system, and

Mr X. Shi for recent efforts to improve the diffraction resolution. The research studies underlying this chapter were supported by grant GM-38323 from the NIH (WAC) and NSF grant MCB-0516939 (S.S.). X-ray diffraction analysis was carried out on beam line SBC-19ID at the Advanced Photon Source, Argonne, IL, supported by U. S. DOE grant W31–109-ENG-389, and at Spring-8 BL44XU (Hyogo, Japan).

References

1. G. Kurisu, H. Zhang, J.L. Smith, W.A. Cramer, Structure of the cytochrome $b_6 f$ complex of oxygenic photosynthesis: tuning the cavity. *Science* **302** (2003) 1009–1014.
2. D. Stroebel, Y. Choquet, J.-L. Popot, D. Picot, An atypical heam in the cytochrome $b_6 f$ complex. *Nature* **426** (2003) 413–418.
3. A. Zouni, H. Witt, J. Kern, P. Fromme, N. Krauss, W. Saenger, P. Orth, Crystal structure of Photosystem II from *Synechococcus elongatus* at 3.8 Å resolution. *Nature* **409** (2001) 739–743.
4. P. Jordan, P. Fromme, H. Witt, O. Klukas, W. Saenger, N. Krauss, Three-dimensional structure of cyanobacterial Photosystem I at 2.5 Å resolution. *Nature* **411** (2001) 909–917.
5. B. Loll, J. Kern, W. Saenger, A. Zouni, J. Biesiadka, Towards complete cofactor arrangement in the 3.0 Å resolution structure of Photosystem II. *Nature* **438** (2005) 1040–1044.
6. G. Renger, A.-R. Holzwarth, Photosystem II: The water/plastoquinone oxidoreductase, in: *Photosystem II: The Water/Plastoquinone Oxido-Reductase in Photosynthesis* (2005) (T. Wydrzynski, K. Satoh, eds.), Kluwer Academic Publishers, Dordrecht, pp. 139–175.
7. T. Kallas, The cytochrome $b_6 f$ complex, in: *The Molecular Biology of Cyanobacteria* (1994) (D.A. Bryant, ed.), Kluwer Academic Publishers, Dordrecht, pp. 259–317.
8. W.A. Cramer, G.M. Soriano, M. Ponomarev, D. Huang, H. Zhang, S.E. Martinez, J.L. Smith, Some new structural aspects and old controversies concerning the cytochrome $b_6 f$ complex of oxygenic photosynthesis. *Annu. Rev. Plant Physiol. Plant Mol. Biol.* **47** (1996) 477–508.
9. W.A. Cramer, H. Zhang, J. Yan, G. Kurisu, J.L. Smith, Evolution of photosynthesis: time-independent structure of the cytochrome $b_6 f$ complex. *Biochemistry* **43** (2004) 5921–5929.
10. J.L. Smith, H. Zhang, J. Yan, G. Kurisu, W.A. Cramer, Cytochrome *bc* complexes: a common core of structure and function surrounded by diversity in the outlying provinces. *Curr. Opin. Struct. Biol.* **14** (2004) 432–439.
11. J.L. Cape, M.K. Bowman, D.M. Kramer, Understanding the cytochrome *bc* complexes by what they don't do. The Q-cycle at 30. *Trends Plant Sci.* **11** (2006) 46–55.
12. C.C. Page, C.C. Moser, X. Chen, P.L. Dutton, Natural engineering principles of electron tunnelling in biological oxidation-reduction. *Nature* **402** (1999) 47–52.
13. H.B. Gray, J.R. Winkler, Long-range electron transfer. *Proc. Natl. Acad. Sci. U.S.A.* **102** (2005) 3534–3539.

14. C.A. Wraight, Intraprotein proton transfer-concepts and realities from the bacterial photosynthetic reaction center in: *Book*, (M., Wikstrom, ed.), Royal Society of Chemistry, Cambridge, pp. 273–311.
15. F. Muller, A.R. Crofts, D.M. Kramer, Multiple Q-cycle bypass reactions at the Qo site of the cytochrome bc1 complex. *Biochemistry* **41** (2002) 7866–7874.
16. P. Brantmier, D. Horn, T. Kallas, in: *Annual Midwest Photosynthesis Meeting* (2005) (K. Redding, S. Savikhin, eds.), Turkey Run State Park, Marshall, IN, Vol. 31, pp. 14.
17. D.I. Arnon, H.Y. Tsujimoto, B.D. McSwain, Ferredoxin and photosynthetic phosphorylation. *Nature* **214** (1967) 562–566.
18. D.S. Bendall, R. Manasse, Cyclic photophosphorylation and electron transport. *Biochim. Biophys. Acta* **1229** (1995) 23–38.
19. H. Zhang, J.P. Whitelegge, W.A. Cramer, Ferredoxin:$NADP^+$ oxidoreductase is a subunit of the chloroplast cytochrome b_6f complex. *J. Biol. Chem.* **276** (2001) 38159–38165.
20. Y. Munekage, M. Hashimoto, C. Miyake, K. Tomizawa, T. Endo, M. Tasaka, T. Shikanai, Cyclic electron flow around Photosystem I is essential for photosynthesis. *Nature* **429** (2004) 579–582.
21. G.N. Johnson, Cyclic electron transport in C3 plants: fact or artefact? *J. Exp. Bot.* **56** (2005) 407–416.
22. N. Battchikova, P. Zhang, S. Rudd, T. Ogawa, E.M. Aro, Identification of NdhL and Ss11690 (NdhO) in NDH-1L and NDH-1M complexes of *Synechocystis* sp. PCC 6803. *J. Biol. Chem.* **280** (2005) 2587–2596.
23. A. Vener, P.J. van Kan, P.R. Rich, I.I. Ohad, B. Andersson, Plastoquinol at the quinol oxidation site of reduced cytochrome bf mediates signal transduction between light and protein phosphorylation: thylakoid protein kinase deactivation by a single-turnover flash. *Proc. Natl. Acad. Sci. U.S.A.* **94** (1997) 1585–1590.
24. J.F. Allen, Protein phosphorylation in regulation of photosynthesis. *Biochim. Biophys. Acta* **1098** (1992) 275–335.
25. N. Nelson, J. Neumann, Isolation of a cytochrome b_6f particle from chloroplasts. *J. Biol. Chem.* **247** (1972) 1817–1824.
26. E.C. Hurt, G. Hauska, A cytochrome f/b_6 complex of five polypeptides with plastoquinol-plastocyanin-oxidoreductase activity from spinach chloroplasts. *Eur. J. Biochem.* **117** (1981) 591–599.
27. C. Schmidt, R. Malkin, Low molecular weight subunits associated with the cytochrome b_6f complexes from spinach and *Chlamydomonas reinhardtii*. *Photosynth. Res.* **38** (1993) 73–81.
28. D. Huang, R.M. Everly, R.H. Cheng, J.B. Heymann, H. Schägger, V. Sled, T. Ohnishi, T.S. Baker, W.A. Cramer, Characterization of the chloroplast cytochrome b_6f complex as a structural and functional dimmer. *Biochemistry* **33** (1994) 4401–4409.
29. H. Zhang, D. Huang, W.A. Cramer, Stoichiometrically bound beta-carotene in the cytochrome b_6f complex of oxygenic photosynthesis protects against oxygen damage. *J. Biol. Chem.* **274** (1999) 1581–1587.
30. H. Zhang, G. Kurisu, J.L. Smith, W.A. Cramer, A defined protein-detergent-lipid complex for crystallization of integral membrane proteins: The cytochrome b_6f complex of oxygenic photosynthesis. *Proc. Natl. Acad. Sci. U.S.A.* **100** (2003) 5160–5163.
31. H. Zhang, W.A. Cramer, Purification and crystallization of the cytochrome b_6f complex in oxygenic photosynthesis, in: *Methods in Molecular Biology, Vol. 274*,

Photosynthesis Research Protocols (2004) (R. Carpentier, ed.), Humana Press, Totowa NJ, pp. 67–78.
32. J.F. Allen, Cytochrome b6f: structure for signaling and vectorial metabolism. *Trends Plant Sci.* **9** (2004) 130–137.
33. G. Kurisu, H. Zhang, J.L. Smith, W.A. Cramer, Structure and function of the cytochrome b6f complex of oxygenic photosynthesis. *Proteins, Nucleic Acids, Enzymes* **49** (2004) 1265–1273.
34. W.A. Cramer, H. Zhang, J. Yan, G. Kurisu, J.L. Smith, Transmembrane traffic in the cytochrome b_6f complex. *Annu. Rev. Biochem.* **75** (2006) 769–790.
35. J.P. Whitelegge, H. Zhang, R. Taylor, W.A. Cramer, Full subunit coverage liquid chromatography electrospray-ionization mass spectrometry (LCMS+) of an oligomeric membrane protein complex: the cytochrome b_6f complex from spinach and the cyanobacterium. *M. laminosus. Mol. Cel. Proteomics* **1** (2002) 816–827.
36. S. Bellafiore, F. Barneche, G. Peltier, J.D. Rochaix, State transitions and light adaptation require chloroplast thylakoid protein kinase STN7. *Nature* **433** (2005) 892–895.
37. J. Yan, G. Kurisu, W.A. Cramer, Structure of the cytochrome b_6f complex: Binding site and intraprotein transfer of the quinone analogue inhibitor 2, 5-dibromo-3-methyl-6-isopropyl-*p*-benzoquinone. *Proc. Nat. Acad. Sci. U.S.A.* **103** (2006) 67–74.
38. G. Sainz, C.J. Carrell, M.V. Ponamarev, G.M. Soriano, W.A. Cramer, J.L. Smith, Interruption of the internal water chain of cytochrome *f* impairs photosynthetic function. *Biochemistry* **39** (2000) 9164–9173.
39. C.J. Carrell, H. Zhang, W.A. Cramer, J.L. Smith, Biological identity and diversity in photosynthesis and respiration: structure of the lumen-side domain of the chloroplast Rieske protein. *Structure* **5** (1997) 1613–1625.
40. S.E. Martinez, D. Huang, A. Szczepaniak, W.A. Cramer, J.L. Smith, Crystal structure of the chloroplast cytochrome *f* reveals a novel cytochrome fold and unexpected heme ligation. *Structure* **2** (1994) 95–105.
41. S. Martinez, D. Huang, M. Ponamarev, W.A. Cramer, J.L. Smith, The heme redox center of chloroplast cytochrome *f* is linked to a buried five-water chain. *Protein Sci.* **5** (1996) 1081–1092.
42. C.J. Carrell, B.G. Schlarb, D.S. Bendall, C.J. Howe, W.A. Cramer, J.L. Smith, Structure of the soluble domain of cytochrome f from the cyanobacterium. *Phormidium laminosum, Biochemistry* **38** (1999) 9590–9599.
43. W.R. Widger, W.A. Cramer, R.G. Herrmann, A. Trebst, Sequence homology and structural similarity between the *b* cytochrome of mitochondrial complex III and the chloroplast b_6f complex: position of the cytochrome *b* hemes in the membrane. *Proc. Natl. Acad. Sci. U.S.A.* **81** (1984) 674–678.
44. J. Kyte, R.F. Doolittle, A simple method for displaying the hydropathic character of a protein. *J. Mol. Biol.* **157** (1982) 105–132.
45. Y. Gavel, J. Steppuhn, R. Herrmann, G. von Heijne, The 'positive-inside rule' applies to thylakoid membrane proteins. *FEBS Lett.* **282** (1991) 41–46.
46. L.I. Krishtalik, W.A. Cramer, On the physical basis for the cis-positive rule describing protein orientation in biological membranes. *FEBS Lett.* **369** (1995) 140–143.
47. G. Kurisu, S.D. Zakharov, M.V. Zhalnina, S. Bano, V.Y. Eroukova, T.I. Rokitskaya, Y.N. Antonenko, M.C. Wiener, W.A. Cramer, The structure of BtuB with bound colicin E3 R-domain implies a translocon. *Nat. Struct. Biol.* **10** (2003) 948–954.

48. W.A. Cramer, J. Yan, H. Zhang, G. Kurisu, J.L. Smith, Structure of the cytochrome b6f complex: new prosthetic groups, Q-space, and the 'hors d'oeuvres hypothesis' for assembly of the complex. *Photosynth. Res.* **85** (2005) 133–143.

49. D. Schneider, S. Berry, P. Rich, A. Seidler, M. Rogner, A regulatory role of the PetM subunit in a cyanobacterial cytochrome b6f complex. *J. Biol. Chem.* **276** (2001) 16780–16785.

50. D. Berthold, C.L. Schmidt, R. Malkin, The deletion of petG in *Chlamydomonas reinhardtii* disrupts the cyt *bf* complex. *J. Biol. Chem.* **270** (1995) 29293–29298.

51. R.D. Clark, M.J. Hawkesford, S.J. Coughlan, G. Hind, Association of ferredoxin-NADP$^+$ oxidoreductase with the chloroplast cytochrome *b-f* complex. *FEBS Lett.* **174** (1984) 137–142.

52. D. Xia, C.-A. Yu, H. Kim, J.-Z. Xia, A.M. Kachurin, L. Yu, J. Deisenhofer, Crystal structure of the cytochrome bc_1 complex from bovine heart mitochondria. *Science* **277** (1997) 60–66.

53. R. Covian, E.B. Gutierrez-Cirlos, B.L. Trumpower, Anti-cooperative oxidation of ubiquinol by the yeast cytochrome bc1 complex. *J. Biol. Chem.* **279** (2004) 15040–15049.

54. R. Covian, B.L. Trumpower, Rapid electron transfer between monomers when the cytochrome bc1 complex dimer is reduced through center N. *J. Biol. Chem.* **280** (2005) 22732–22740.

55. G.M. Soriano, M.V. Ponamarev, C.J. Carrell, D. Xia, J.L. Smith, W.A. Cramer, Comparison of the cytochrome bc(1) complex with the anticipated structure of the cytochrome b(6)f complex: De plus ca change de plus c'est la meme chose. *J. Bioenerg. Biomembr.* **31** (1999) 201–213.

56. C. Lange, C. Hunte, Crystal structure of the yeast cytochrome bc_1 complex with its bound substrate cytochrome *c*. *Proc. Nat. Acad. Sci. U.S.A.* **99** (2002) 2800–2805.

57. J. Yan, W.A. Cramer, Molecular control of a bimodal distribution of quinone-analogue inhibitor binding sites in the cytochrome b(6)f complex. *J. Mol. Biol.* **344** (2004) 481–93.

58. L. Esser, B. Quinn, Y.F. Li, M. Zhang, M. Elberry, L. Yu, C.A. Yu, D. Xia, Crystallographic studies of quinol oxidation site inhibitors: a modified classification of inhibitors for the cytochrome bc(1) complex. *J. Mol. Biol.* **341** (2004) 281–302.

59. P. Mitchell, The protonmotive Q cycle: a general formulation. *FEBS Lett.* **59** (1975) 137–139.

60. P. Mitchell, Possible molecular mechanisms of the protonmotive function of cytochrome systems. *J. Theor. Biol.* **62** (1976) 327–367.

61. B.L. Trumpower, R.B. Gennis, Energy transduction by cytochrome complexes in mitochondrial and bacterial respiration: the enzymology of coupling electron transfer reactions to transmembrane proton translocation. *Annu. Rev. Biochem.* **63** (1994) 675–716.

62. E.A. Berry, M. Guergova-Kuras, L.-S. Huang, A.R. Crofts, Structure and function of cytochrome *bc* complexes. *Annu. Rev. Biochem.* **69** (2000) 1005–1075.

63. E. Darrouzet, C.C. Moser, P.L. Leslie, F. Daldal, Large scale domain movement in cytochrome bc_1: a new device for electron transfer in proteins. *Trends Biochem. Sci.* **26** (2001) 445–451.

64. P.R. Rich, The quinone chemistry of *bc* complexes. *Biochim. Biophys. Acta* **1658** (2004) 165–171.

65. A.R. Crofts, The cytochrome bc_1 complex: function in the context of structure. *Annu. Rev. Psychol.* **66** (2004) 689–733.

66. A.Y. Mulkidjanian, Ubiquinol oxidation in the cytochrome bc(1) complex: reaction mechanism and prevention of short-circuiting. *Biochim. Biophys. Acta* **1709** (2005) 5–34.
67. M.K.F. Wikström, J.A. Berden, Oxidoreduction of cytochrome *b* in the presence of antimycin. *Biochim. Biophys. Acta* **283** (1972) 403–420.
68. M.A. Selak, J. Whitmarsh, Kinetics of the electrogenic step and cytochrome b_6 and *f* redox changes in chloroplasts. *FEBS Lett.* **150** (1982) 286–292.
69. J. Lavergne, Membrane potential-dependent reduction of cytochrome *b*-6 in an algal mutant lacking Photosystem I centers. *Biochim. Biophys. Acta* **725** (1983) 25–33.
70. P. Joliot, A. Joliot, The low-potential electron-transfer chain in the cytochrome *b/f* complex. *Biochim. Biophys. Acta* **933** (1988) 319–333.
71. J. Alric, Y. Pierre, D. Picot, J. Lavergne, F. Rappaport, Spectral and redox characterization of the heme ci of the cytochrome b6f complex. *Proc. Natl. Acad. Sci. U.S.A.* **102** (2005) 15860–15865.
72. P. Joliot, A. Joliot, Cyclic electron transfer in plant leaf. *Proc. Nat. Acad. Sci. U.S.A.* **99** (2002) 10209–10214.
73. P. Joliot, A. Joliot, Quantification of cyclic and linear electron flows in plants. *Proc. Nat. Acad. Sci. U.S.A.* **102** (2005) 4913–4918.
74. M.E. Girvin, W.A. Cramer, A redox study of the electron transport pathway responsible for generation of the slow electrochromic phase in chloroplasts. *Biochim. Biophys. Acta* **767** (1984) 29–38.
75. P.N. Furbacher, M.E. Girvin, W.A. Cramer, On the question of interheme electron transfer in the chloroplast cytochrome b_6 *in situ*. *Biochemistry* **28** (1989) 8990–8998.
76. A.R. Crofts, Proton-coupled electron transfer at the Q_o-site of the bc_1 complex controls the rate of ubihydroquinone oxidation. *Biochim. Biophys. Acta* **1655** (2004) 77–92.
77. A.R. Crofts, M. Guergova-Kuras, L. Huang, R. Kuras, Z. Zhang, E. Berry, Mechanisms of ubiquinol oxidation by the bc_1 complex: role of the iron sulfur protein and its mobility. *Biochemistry* **38** (1999) 15791–15806.
78. G. Finazzi, Redox-coupled proton pumping activity in cytochrome b6f, as evidenced by the pH dependence of electron transfer in whole cells of Chlamydomonas reinhardtii. *Biochemistry* **41** (2002) 7475–7482.
79. B.L. Trumpower, The protonmotive Q cycle. Energy transduction by coupling of proton translocation to electron transfer by the cytochrome bc_1 complex. *J. Biol. Chem.* **265** (1990) 11409–11412.
80. A. Osyczka, C.C. Moser, P.L. Dutton, Reversible redox energy coupling in electron transfer chains. *Nature* **427** (2004) 607–612.
81. M.E. Girvin, Ph.D. Thesis, Purdue University (1985).
82. M. Wikström, K. Krab, The semiquinone cycle. A hypothesis of electron transfer and proton translocation in cytochrome *bc*-type complexes. *J. Bioenerg. Biomembr.* **18** (1986) 181–193.
83. P. Joliot, A. Joliot, Mechanism of electron transfer in the cytochrome *b/f* complex of algae: evidence for a semiquinone cycle. *Proc. Natl. Acad. Sci. U.S.A.* **91** (1994) 1034–1038.
84. J. Yan, W.A. Cramer, Functional insensitivity of the cytochrome b_6f complex to structure changes in the hinge region of the Rieske iron-sulfur protein. *J. Biol. Chem.* **278** (2003) 20925–20933.
85. Z. Zhang, L. Huang, V.M. Shulmeister, Y.I. Chi, K.K. Kim, L.W. Hung, A.R. Crofts, E.A. Berry, S.H. Kim, Electron transfer by domain movement in cytochrome bc_1. *Nature* **392** (1998) 677–684.

86. S. Iwata, J.W. Lee, K. Okada, J.K. Lee, M. Iwata, B. Rasmussen, T.A. Link, S. Ramaswamy, B.K. Jap, Complete structure of the 11-subunit mitochondrial cytochrome bc_1 complex. *Science* **281** (1998) 64–71.
87. S. Izrailev, A.R. Crofts, E.A. Berry, K. Schulten, Steered molecular dynamics simulation of the Rieske subunit motion in the cytochrome bc(1) complex. *Biophys. J.* **77** (1999) 1753–1768.
88. C. de Vitry, A. Desbois, V. Redeker, F. Zito, F.-A. Wollman, Biochemical and spectroscopic characterization of the covalent binding of heme to cytochrome b_6. *Biochemistry* **43** (2004) 3956–3968.
89. H. Zhang, A. Primak, M.K. Bowman, D.M. Kramer, W.A. Cramer, Characterization of the high-spin heme x in the cytochrome b_6f complex of oxygenic photosynthesis. *Biochemistry* **43** (2004) 16329–16336.
90. P. Zhang, N. Battchikova, T. Jansen, J. Appel, T. Ogawa, E.M. Aro, Expression and functional roles of the two distinct NDH-1 complexes and the carbon acquisition complex NdhD3/NdhF3/CupA/SlI1735 in *Synechocystis* sp PCC 6803. *Plant Cell* **16** (2004) 3326–3340.
91. C.A. Sacksteder, A. Kanazawa, M.E. Jacoby, D.M. Kramer, The proton to electron stoichiometry of steady-state photosynthesis in living plants: a proton-pumping Q cycle is continuously engaged. *Proc. Natl. Acad. Sci. U.S.A.* **97** (2000) 14283–14288.
92. D. Stock, C. Gibbons, I. Arechaga, A.G. Leslie, J.E. Walker, The rotary mechanism of ATP synthase. *Curr. Opin. Struct. Biol.* **10** (2000) 672–679.
93. H. Seelert, A. Poetsch, N.A. Dencher, A. Engel, H. Stahlberg, D.J. Muller, Structural biology. Proton-powered turbine of a plant motor. *Nature* **405** (2000) 418–419.
94. D.R. Ort, B.A. Melandri, Mechanism of ATP synthesis, in: *Photosynthesis: Energy Conversion by Plants and Bacteria, Vol. 1*, (1982) (Govindjee, ed.), Academic Press, New York, pp. 537–587.
95. J.P. Hosler, C.F. Yocum, Evidence for two photophosphorylation reactions concurrent with ferredoxin-catalyzed non-cyclic electron transport. *Biochim. Biophys. Acta* **808** (1985) 21–31.
96. P. Joliot, D. Beal, A. Joliot, Cyclic electron flow under saturating excitation of dark-adapted Arapidopsis leaves. *Biochim. Biophys. Acta* **1656** (2004) 166–176.
97. W. Kuhlbrandt, Structural biology: dual approach to a light problem. *Nature* **426** (2003) 399–400.
98. C. Hunte, J. Koepke, C. Lange, T. Rossmanith, H. Michel, Structure at 2.3 Å resolution of the cytochrome bc_1 complex from the yeast *Saccharomyces cerevisiae* with an antibody Fv fragment. *Struct. Fold Des.* **8** (2000) 669–684.
99. N. Dashdorj, H. Zhang, H. Kim, J. Yan, W.A. Cramer, S. Savikhin, The single chlorophyll a molecule in the cytochrome b6f complex: unusual optical properties protect the complex against singlet oxygen. *Biophys. J.* **88** (2005) 4178–4187.
100. P. Bowers, G. Porter, Quantum yields of triplet formation in solutions of chlorophyll. *Proc. Royal Soc. A* **296** (1967) 435–441.
101. E. Fujimori, R. Livingston, Interactions of chlorophyll in its triplet state with oxygen, carotene, etc. *Nature* **180** (1957) 1036–1038.
102. N. Krinsky, Carotenoid protection against oxidation. *Pure Appl. Chem.* **51** (1979) 649–660.
103. C. Foote, Photosensitized oxidation and singlet oxygen: consequences in biological systems, in: *Free Radicals in Biology* (1976) (W. Pryor, ed.), Academic Press, New York, pp. 85–133.

104. G. Renger, Energy transfer and trapping in Photosystem II, in: *Topics in Photosynthesis: the Photosystems, Structure, Function and Molecular Biology* (1992) (J. Barber, ed.), Elsevier, Amsterdam, pp. 45–99.
105. R. van Grondelle, J.P. Dekker, T. Gillbro, V. Sundstrom, Energy trapping and trapping in photosynthesis. *Biochim. Biophys. Acta* **1187** (1994) 1–65.
106. D. Dexter, A theory of sensitized luminescence in solids. *J. Chem. Phys.* **21** (1953) 836–850.
107. H. Kim, N. Dashdorj, H. Zhang, J. Yan, W.A. Cramer, S. Savikhin, An anomalous distance dependence of intra-protein chlorophyll-carotenoid triplet energy transfer. *Biophys. J.* **89** (2005) 28–30.
108. E. Peterman, S. Wenk, T. Pullerits, L.O. Pallsson, R. van Grondelle, J. Dekker, M. Rogner, H. van Amerongen, Fluorescence and absorption spectrocopy of the weakly fluorescent chlorophyll a in cytochrome b6f of Synechocystis PCC 6803. *Biophys. J.* **75** (1998) 389–398.
109. G. Seely, J.S. Connolly, Fluorescence of photosynthetic pigments in vitro, in: *Light Emission by Plants and Bacteria* (1986) (Govindjee, D.C. Fork, eds.), Academic Press, New York, pp. 99–103.
110. D. Zhong, A.H. Zewail, Femtosecond dynamics of flavoproteins: charge separation and recombination in riboflavine (vitamin B12)- binding protein and in glucose oxidase enzyme. *Proc. Nat. Acad. Sci. U.S.A.* **98** (2001) 11867–11872.
111. N. Mataga, H. Chosrowjan, Y. Shibata, F. Tanaka, Y. Nishina, K. Shiga, Dynamics and mechanisms of ultrafast fluorescence quenching reactions of flavin chromophores in protein nanospace. *J. Phys. Chem. B* **104** (2000) 10667–10677.
112. D. Siefermann-Harms, The light-harvesting and protective functions of carotenoids. *Physiol. Plant.* **69** (1987) 561–568.
113. A. Michaeli, J. Feitelson, Reactivity of singlet oxygen toward amino acids and peptides. *Photochem. Photobiol.* **59** (1994) 284–289.
114. T. Tsukihara, H. Aoyama, E. Yamashita, T. Tomizaki, H. Yamaguchi, K. Shinzawa-Itono, R. Nakashima, R. Yaono, S. Yoshikawa, The whole structure of the 13-subunit oxidized cytochrome c oxidase at 2.8 A. *Science* **272** (1996) 1136–1144.
115. J.L. DuBois, J.P. Klinman, The nature of O2 reactivity leading to topa quinone in the copper amine oxidase from Hansenula polymorpha and its relationship to catalytic turnover. *Biochemistry* **44** (2005) 11381–11388.
116. M.J. Knapp, J.P. Klinman, Kinetic studies of oxygen reactivity in soybean lipoxygenase-1. *Biochemistry* **42** (2003) 11466–11475.
117. G. Kurisu, M. Kusonoki, E. Katoh, T. Yamazaki, K. Teshima, Y. Onda, KImata-Ariga, T. Hase, et al., Structure of the electron transfer complex between ferredoxin and ferredoxin-NADP+ reductase. *Nat. Struct. Biol.* **8** (2001) 117–121.
118. L.S. Huang, D. Cobessi, E.Y. Tung, E.A. Berry, Binding of the respiratory chain inhibitor antimycin to the mitochondrial bc1 complex: a new crystal structure reveals an altered intramolecular hydrogen-bonding pattern. *J. Mol. Biol.* **351** (2005) 573–597.
119. E. Yamashita, H. Zhang, W. A. Cramer, Structure of the cytochrome b_6f complex: quinone analogue inhibitors as ligands of heme c_n. *J. Mol. Biol.* **370** (2007) 39–52.
120. A. I. Zatsman, H. Zhang, W. A. Gunderson, W. A. Cramer, M. P. Hendrich, Heme-heme interactions in the cytochrome b_6f complex EPR spectroscopy and correlation with structure. *J. Am. Chem. Soc.* **128** (2006) 14246–14247.

Chapter 21

Photophosphorylation

Wolfgang Junge

Table of Contents

- 21.1 Introduction.. 449
- 21.2 Chemiosmotic Energy Coupling 452
  - 21.2.1 Energetics 452
  - 21.2.2 Photosynthetic Membranes 454
  - 21.2.3 Proton Pumps and Pathways...................... 455
  - 21.2.4 H^+/ATP Stoichiometric Ratio...................... 458
  - 21.2.5 Regulation 459
- 21.3 ATP Synthase (F_0F_1-ATPase)............................. 461
  - 21.3.1 Structure 461
  - 21.3.2 F1, the Rotary Catalyst............................ 464
    - 21.3.2.1 Nucleotide Binding Sites and Cooperativity........ 464
    - 21.3.2.2 Rotations 465
    - 21.3.2.3 Torque and Thermodynamic Efficiency 468
  - 21.3.3 F_0, the Rotary Electromotor 473
    - 21.3.3.1 Concept of Rotary Proton Transport 473
    - 21.3.3.2 Proton Conductance of F_0 475
  - 21.3.4 F_0F_1, the Rotary Twin-Engine..................... 476
    - 21.3.4.1 Fine-Tuning Versus Robustness 476
    - 21.3.4.2 Elastic Power Transmission 478
    - 21.3.4.3 Kinetic Efficiency........................... 478
- 21.4 Outlook.. 480
- References.. 481

Abstract

Adenosine triphosphate (ATP), the general fuel of the cell, is the primary product of photosynthesis in most bacteria, and it is one major product, accounting for about 20% of the captured light energy, in oxygenic photosynthesis by cyanobacteria and plants. The proton driven ATP synthase is a paradigmatic enzyme that has it all, an electrical rotary motor being coupled to a rotary chemical generator by a mechanical power transmission. The simplicity and robustness of its construction is just splendid. This chapter describes the interplay of proton pumps and the ATP synthase in photosynthetic organisms and the structure and function of this remarkable enzyme in bacteria and eukarya.

21.1 Introduction

Nature uses adenosine triphosphate (ATP, see Figure 1) as the common fuel to drive chemical syntheses, transport, information processing and other activities of the cell. The (pseudo-)standard molar free energy of ATP hydrolysis is $\Delta G°_{ATP \to ADP} = -30 \,\text{kJ}\,\text{mol}^{-1}$. Its single-molecule mechanical equivalent, $-50\,\text{pN}\,\text{nm}$, which equals $-12 k_B T$, expresses the fact that ATP hydrolysis provides the necessary driving force to win over chaotic thermal impact, whose energy input is related to the product of the Boltzmann factor (k_B) and the temperature (T/K).

ATP is regenerated from adenosine diphosphate (ADP) and (inorganic) phosphate (P_i) by photosynthesis (photophosphorylation) and respiration (oxidative phosphorylation). Although the total content of ATP and ADP in an organism is small, the daily turnover can be large. Some ten grams contained in the human body are cycled around to the daily equivalent of the bodyweight.

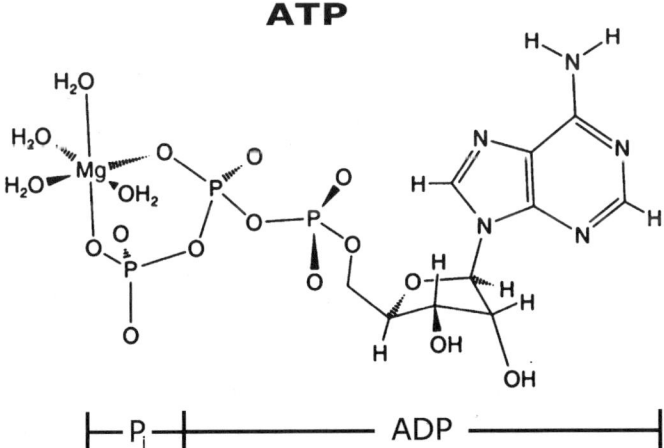

Figure 1. Magnesium adenosine 5′-triphosphate, Mg-ATP.

In purple bacteria ATP-formation accounts for 100% of the useful work recovered from sunlight and in green plants still 20%.

Fritz Lipmann had already emphasized the universal role of ATP in cellular metabolism in 1941. In 1954 Dan Arnon discovered the production of ATP upon illumination of broken chloroplasts [1]. At that time it was assumed that photosynthetic or oxidative electron transport generated a phosphorylated chemical intermediate followed by phosphoryl-transfer to ADP [2], a mechanism coined substrate level phosphorylation. During the ongoing but futile search for the supposed phosphorylated intermediate Peter Mitchell stirred up the research community when he claimed, in 1961, that ATP might be formed without such an intermediate. Instead, he envisaged the direct coupling of ATP synthesis to proton flow as driven by the transmembrane difference of the electrochemical potential, which he coined protonmotive force [3,4]. He named this hypothesis "chemiosmotic". It became evident that chloroplasts can use an artificially induced pH difference to produce ATP [5], and/or a light induced voltage difference [6]. The bacteriorhodopsin-driven proton pump from *H. halobium* was co-reconstituted in liposomes with the mitochondrial ATP synthase, and they were shown to be functionally coupled by protonmotive force [7]. Ion-driven ATP synthesis and its reversal, ion-pumping under ATP hydrolysis, are now well established in archaea, bacteria and in chloroplasts and mitochondria of eukarya.

The molecular details of the coupling mechanism were not touched upon by Mitchell's hypothesis. The discovery in 1960 of an ATP synthase in mitochondria and the isolation of its soluble portion, the "coupling *factor*" (F_1), acting on a membrane-embedded portion (now known as F_0) by Ephraim Racker and his co-workers [8] started the search for a molecular mechanism. Three decades after Mitchell's first proposal, the joint attack by protein chemistry, molecular biology, structural biology and biophysics has disclosed the astounding fact that proton flow across the enzyme is *mechanically* coupled to ATP synthesis.

Around 1990 it was established that ATP hydrolysis occurred in alternation between at least two equivalent reaction sites on F_1 by what Paul Boyer coined the "binding change mechanism" [9]. A rotary mechanism, involving three catalytic sites, was considered as a possibility [10] (see [11] for review). The crystal structure of bovine mitochondrial F_1, elucidated by John Walker and his colleagues [12], suggested that rotation, and not alternation, was nature's choice (see [13] for a review). The structure revealed six nucleotide binding sites falling into two classes that are now understood as catalytic and non-catalytic – their position alternates in the hexagon of $(\alpha\beta)_3$. In the crystal structure the former three were differently filled, being empty, containing ADP, and AMP-PNP (as ATP analogue). This was interpreted as a still picture of three, in principle, equivalent catalytic sites that, when driven by the rotation of the central stalk, change their role, one binding ADP and P, the next processing it into ATP and third releasing ATP and so on, cyclically. A rotary mechanism is supported by a biochemical assay using cleavable crosslinks [14]. It was time resolved by polarized laser-photometry [15], and spectacularly proven by

PHOTOPHOSPHORYLATION

Hiruyuki Noji in the laboratories of Masasuke Yoshida and Kazuhiko Kinosita, who applied a fluorescent actin-filament to the rotor portion of the immobilized enzyme and videographed the rotation [16].

The present view of the ATP synthase is that of a molecular twin machine. The catalytic function is contained in the soluble portion (F_1) and the ion-transporting function in the membrane-intrinsic portion (F_0), each being a rotary motor/generator. They are coupled by a central rotary shaft and held together by an eccentric stalk (Figure 2B). Figure 2(B) also accounts for the fact that there are crystal structures on certain portions of the enzyme and less detailed information on others.

This chapter starts with an up-to-date view of the tenets of the chemiosmotic theory, covers proton pumps and pathways, the proton-to-ATP stoichiometry and the enzyme regulation in a physiological context. Up to this point it is focused on photosynthetic organisms. The subsequent description of ATP synthase as a rotary electro-mechano-chemical transducer merges knowledge obtained with this enzyme from different kingdoms of life. This accounts for the fact that the enzyme emerged before the separation of archaea and eubacteria, and that it has been conserved to an astounding similarity over the former and in chloroplasts and mitochondria of eukarya.

Usually, the terms F-ATPase, F_0F_1-ATPase, and ATP synthase are used synonymously. The proton driven, membrane-intrinsic portion is termed F_0 (for historical reasons the suffix reads capital O, not zero) and the peripheral portion that performs ATP synthesis/hydrolysis is termed F_1. Where species specific properties are discussed, the letters C for *c*hloroplast, M for *m*itochondrion, B for purple *b*acterium, E for *E. coli*, T for the *t*hermophilic *Bacillus PS3*, P for the Na^+-translocating *P. modestum*, and A for *a*rchaeon are annexed to the F. Thus, CF_0F_1 denotes the ATP synthase of chloroplasts.

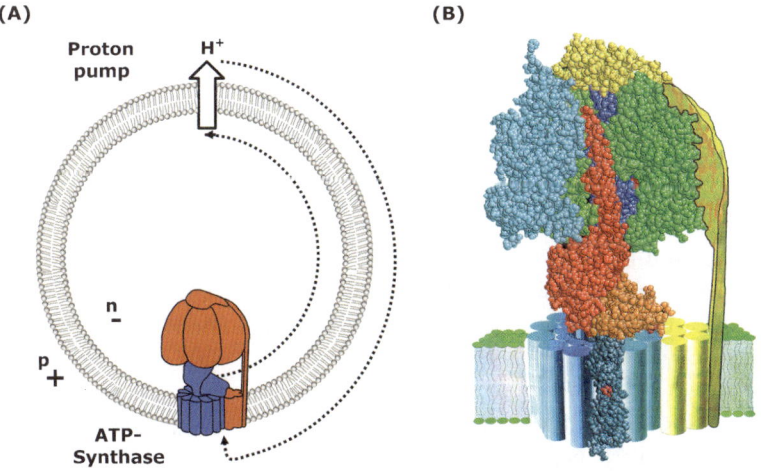

Figure 2. (A) Chemiosmotic mechanism of ATP synthesis. (B) ATP synthase.

21.2 Chemiosmotic Energy Coupling

The synthesis/hydrolysis of ATP proceeds according to the following reaction scheme (written for aqueous medium at pH 8, for stability constants see [17]):

$$ADP^{3-} + P_i^{2-} + H^+ \leftrightarrow ATP^{4-} + H_2O \tag{1}$$

Before 1960 it was assumed that photosynthetic or respiratory electron transfer was directly linked to ATP synthesis. Bob Williams introduced a new twist by emphasizing a role for the proton [18,19]. He thought of electron transport generating an extreme acidic milieu "inside the membrane" to shift the equilibrium [eqn. (1)] towards ATP. Taken at face value (ADP, P_i and ATP had to be moved into and out of the membrane!) this view had obvious flaws right from the beginning, but in milder form "membrane localized" protons have remained around for quite a while. At the same time Peter Mitchell also emphasized the role of protons, but he took the membrane simply as a permeability barrier between two aqueous phases and postulated two now well-established properties of the membrane: (i) zig-zagging vectorial electron/hydrogen transfer, generating a difference of the electrochemical potential of the proton between the aqueous phases, and (ii) the ATP synthase utilizing the "protonmotive force" by transporting protons from the acid and electropositive side to the alkaline and negative one [3,4]. It implied adding of m "vectorial protons" to the one "scalar proton" in eqn. (1).

$$ADP_n^{3-} + Pi_n^{2-} + H_n^+ + mH_p^+ \leftrightarrow ATP_n^{4-} + H_2O + mH_n^+ \tag{2}$$

Herein m denotes the number of protons that are transported from the positive (p) side to the negative (n) side of the membrane for every ATP molecule that is formed at the n-side. The scalar proton (H^+_n) accounts for electroneutrality if the ionization states of the nucleotides and of phosphate are as given in eqn. (1) (written for pH 8). Broadly speaking, Mitchell's concept, as simplified in Figure 2(A) has been validated, except for refinements, as given in Section 21.2.3.

21.2.1 Energetics

The basic tenets of the chemiosmotic hypothesis are proton pumps, which generate a difference of the electrochemical potential across the coupling membrane, and the ATP synthase, which couples the backflow of protons to ATP synthesis (Figure 2A). The electrochemical potential difference of the proton, in Mitchell's term the "protonmotive force" (p.m.f.), is given by:

p.m.f. $= \Delta\mu^0 - 2.3\,RT\Delta\text{pH} + F\Delta\varphi$

If the aqueous phases have the same properties (their standard potentials being equal, $\Delta\mu^0 = 0$) it reduces to:

$$\text{p.m.f.} = -2.3\,RT\Delta\text{pH} + F\Delta\varphi \tag{3}$$

wherein ΔpH and $\Delta\varphi$ denote the transmembrane pH difference (pH$_n$–pH$_p$) and the electric potential difference (ϕ_n–φ_p in volt), T is the temperature (in Kelvin), R is the universal gas-constant and F the Faraday constant. Under isothermal and isobaric conditions the p.m.f. describes the maximum useful work that can be derived from the translocation across the membrane of one mol proton. It is equivalent to the molar Gibbs Free Energy difference, $\overline{\Delta G_{H^+}}$. The often used term "proton gradient", a lab slang, should be avoided, neither has the proton any gradient nor does the local first derivative matter in this context. The equivalence of the electrical and the chemical contribution to the p.m.f. in determining the production of ATP holds only for the thermodynamic equilibrium, i.e., for processes conducted at infinitely slow speed. Far from the equilibrium, a physiologically more relevant regime, it is probably violated [20].

At 25°C or 298.15 K the numerical factors are $2.3RT = 5.7$ kJ mol^{-1}, and $2.3RT/F = 59$ mV, so that eqn. (3) accounts for the fact that a voltage of –59 mV contributes as much to the driving force as a pH difference of +1 unit. In single-molecule terms these figures are often given in pN nm ("pico-Newton-nanometer") or in units of $k_B T$, with 5.7 kJ mol^{-1} being equivalent to 9.5 pN nm or 2.3 $k_B T_{298.15}$.

In reality, the aqueous phases at both sides of a coupling membrane differ. Not only are the membrane surfaces covered with fixed charges but the often narrow "bulk phases" are differently filled with proteins, i.e., polyelectrolytes. These complications invoke surface- and Donnan-potentials. Both are equilibrium potentials, i.e., the electrochemical potential of the proton at the surface equals that in an adjacent bulk phase (if there is any bulk), but the distribution of energy between the electric ($\Delta\varphi$) and the chemical component (ΔpH) differs.

Peter Mitchell postulated that the strict coupling of ATP synthesis with the transfer of m protons gives rise to the net reaction in eqn. (2). A cell synthesizing ATP at higher velocity than it is consumed will eventually reach the "static head" where the forward and the backward reaction compensate each other. If the consumers of ATP in the cytoplasm and those of p.m.f. in the membrane are slow enough this state approximates the equilibrium, such that the p.m.f. is balanced by the molar free energy of ATP hydrolysis:

$$m \times \text{p.m.f.} = \Delta G^0_{\text{ATP}\rightarrow\text{ADP}} + 2.3RT \log\frac{[\text{ADP}][\text{P}_i][\text{H}^+]}{[\text{ATP}]} \quad (4)$$

wherein m denotes the proton-over-ATP stoichiometry (not necessarily an integer, see below), [X] is the dimensionless activity of the respective species X, and RT is as usual. All activities are dimensionless and normalized to 1 M, except for the one of the proton, where normalization is to 10^{-7} M (pH 7). $\Delta G°_{\text{ATP}\rightarrow\text{ADP}}$, the pseudo-standard free energy of ATP hydrolysis is – 30 kJ mol^{-1} at pH 7, 1 mM Mg^{2+}, and an ionic strength of 0.2 M. For the dependence of $\Delta G°_{\text{ATP}\rightarrow\text{ADP}}$ on these parameters see [21].

The balance between the stoichiometry-weighted p.m.f. [eqn. (4), left] and the so-called phosphate potential [eqn. (4), right] determines whether ATP is formed or hydrolyzed. In thermodynamic equilibrium they are equal. For illuminated chloroplasts the following stroma concentrations have been reported: ATP (2.5 mM), ADP (0.5 mM), P_i (5 mM), pH 8. The calculated phosphate potential [eqn. (4), right] is $53\,kJ\,mol^{-1}$. If the H^+/ATP-stoichiometry was 4, which is debatable (Section 21.2.4), the p.m.f. sustaining this phosphate potential should amount to 2.3 pH units or 136 mV.

21.2.2 Photosynthetic Membranes

Photosynthesis is of prokaryotic origin and so is ATP synthesis. Figure 3(A, C) illustrates the outer and inner membrane of a purple bacterium, e.g., *Rhodobacter capsulatus*, whose plasma membrane forms invaginations carrying the whole complement for photosynthesis, named chromatophores (see also Chapters 1 and 18). In prokarya, proton pumping is outward directed; the backflow into the cytoplasm drives the synthesis of ATP, which is released into the cytoplasm. The compartment into which protons are pumped is termed p-side (positive side) and the opposite one n-side. If chromatophores are isolated by sonication of bacteria they reseal as inside-out vesicles, so that protons are pumped into their small lumen, and ATP is released into the suspending medium. In the chloroplasts of green plants (Figure 3B and D) these former invaginations are sealed off from the envelope. They form an interlaced

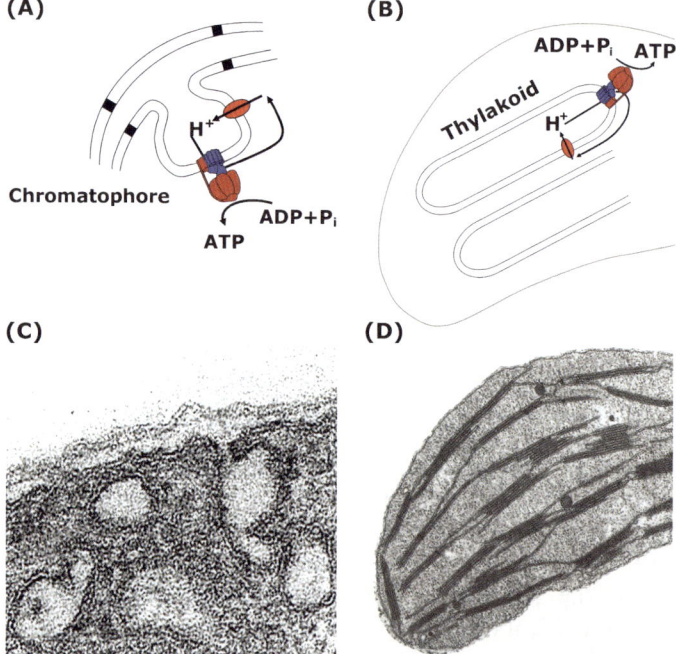

Figure 3. Photosynthetic membranes (schematic): (A, C) Purple bacterium with c chromatophore [120], (B, D) Chloroplast with thylakoids. [Courtesy of Andrew Staehelin.]

network of thylakoid membranes. Protons are pumped into the lumen and ATP is released into the chloroplast stroma. If thylakoids were fused into the outer membrane of chloroplasts the lumen formed part of the peri- or exoplasma of the chloroplast. Thylakoids form a tightly apposed system of disk-shaped membranes (these stacks appearing as "grana" in the light microscope) with a repeat distance of only 20 nm and about 5 nm thin spacing in the outer partitions and in the lumen. The grana are interconnected by "stroma lamellae" (Figure 3C, see also Chapter 1).

The volume of the lumen of one disk is so small that one wonders whether the pH is well defined in such a small compartment. Taking the typical diameter of one disk as 400 nm and a thickness of 5 nm, one calculates a volume of only 6×10^{-22} m^3. At pH 7, a proton concentration of 10^{-4} mol m^{-3}, the number of hydrated ("free") protons in this volume is less than 0.05. Contrary to the first impression, the smallness of the volume does not imply that the pH is ill-defined so that it varies greatly from one disk to the other. Instead, protons dissociate from and associate with thousands of buffering groups on proteins and lipids at the lumenal surface of the membrane, each with a typical rate (at pH 7) of 10^4 s^{-1}. This implies that the standard deviation from the average proton concentration is very small indeed, such that the mean pH is well defined in the time average at the millisecond time scale where ATP synthesis occurs.

Notably, the complicated web of grana and interconnecting stroma lamellae in one chloroplast forms a very large contiguous sheet. Contiguity has been evident from both structural and functional studies. The osmotic swelling of broken thylakoids produces large blebs of up to 20 μm diameter [22] and EM-pictures have suggested the interlacing of grana [23]. Studies on the electric discharge rate in thylakoids have revealed that a single dimer of the potent ionophore gramicidin accelerates the electric discharge across the membrane patch containing at least 5×10^7 chlorophyll molecules, which is close to the estimated number of 2×10^8 total per chloroplast [24]. This implies that almost all electrogenic pumps can be (at least electrically) coupled with all ATP synthases by one contiguous membrane. The tightly apposed grana lamellae and the exposed stroma lamellae have different lipid and protein composition. Photosystem II (PS II) is enriched in the stacked domains whereas Photosystem I (PSI) and the F_0F_1-ATPase are located in the stroma-exposed regions of the thylakoid membrane (see also Chapter 1). Their segregation by several 100 nm does not bear much on the efficiency of coupling – it is only slightly lower for PS II-driven photophosphorylation than for PSI-driven one.

21.2.3 Proton Pumps and Pathways

Absorption of a quantum of light induces a very rapid charge separation in photosynthetic reaction centers. The vectorial electron transfer from the p- to the n-side electrically charges the coupling membrane in less than one nanosecond (10^{-9} s). The high speed of voltage generation has been resolved spectrophotometrically by using the molecular voltmeters that are intrinsic to many photosynthetic membranes, namely the electrochromic response of carotenoids and chlorophylls [25–29]. The magnitude of the rapid voltage jump induced, e.g., by a laser flash of nanosecond duration, ranges from 30 to 50 mV in thylakoids to 70 mV in chromatophores [29,30]. These figures are broadly compatible with structural data on photosynthetic membranes. In plant thylakoids the membrane area per chlorophyll molecule has been estimated to be 2 nm^2; there are about 600 chlorophyll molecules per two photosystems, and the specific electric capacitance of biomembranes is usually 10^{-2} F m^{-2}.

Vectorial electron transfer causes net proton translocation by alternating with vectorial hydrogen transfer. When Photosystem II of cyanobacteria and plants or the related reaction centre of purple bacteria (BRC) reduce their respective quinone, one proton per electron is taken up at the n-side of the membrane. When PS II extracts electrons from water to produce dioxygen it ejects one proton per electron at the p-side. Thereby, PS II is both electrogenic (by primary electron transfer) and (net) proton pumping, the latter as the result of one vectorial and two scalar reactions. The quinol that is formed at the n-side of PS II, and likewise of BRC, acts as a hydrogen carrier when diffusing over to the p-side to reduce cytochrome b_6f in green plants, and cytochrome bc_1 in bacteria (Chapter 20). Upon oxidation of the respective quinol at the p-side one proton per electron is released. The two electrons from the quinol proceed along different pathways. Whereas the first is transferred to plastocyanin (in plants), cytochrome c_6 (in cyanobacteria) and cytochrome c_1 (in purple bacteria), respectively, the second is transported back across the membrane within the protein to eventually reduce quinone at the n-side. This Q-cycle (in P. Mitchell's terms [31]) is again both electrogenic and proton pumping, being linked to proton uptake at the n-side and proton release at the p-side (for details see Chapter 20). Plastocyanin and cytochrome c_6 eventually reduce PSI (in plants and cyanobacteria, respectively), and cytochrome bc_1 reduces BRC (in purple bacteria), and when another quantum of light drives the next rapid charge separation it is again linked to proton uptake at the n-side. In oxygenic photosynthesis the stoichiometry of protons pumped/voltage units generated/ electrons transferred is 2:2:1 for the linear electron transport chain from water to NADP$^+$ and further on, and it is 3:3:1 including the cyclic operation and extra proton pumping round of the cytochrome bc_1 (b_6f)-complex.

P. Mitchell's concept that all proton pumps are electrochemically coupled with all ATP synthase molecules by the same bulk-to-bulk protonmotive force has been frequently challenged over the years and detailed models for localized coupling were put forward, favoring, for example, neighbor-to-neighbor coupling, or intra-membrane proton conducting domains, or enhanced proton diffusion at the membrane surface (see [32–35] for reviews). The interest in these models has since faded, except when dealing with alkaliphilic bacteria. These organisms live at pH 10, and they reportedly sustain a bulk-to-bulk p.m.f. close to zero. It has been difficult to understand how they can produce ATP by a F_0F_1-type enzyme, if not by a non-Mitchellian mechanism [36]. The dogma of bulk-to-bulk coupling has recently been reevaluated by standard theory of proton diffusion and assuming an "infinite sink" for protons in the p-phase, as encountered by alkaliphilic bacteria at pH 10 [37,38].

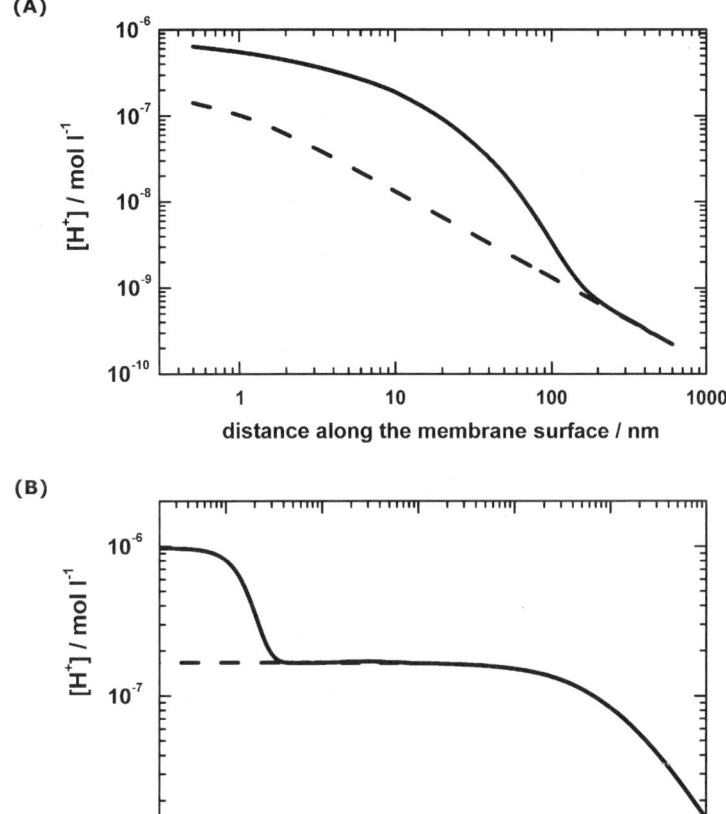

Figure 4. Steady-state pH-profiles at the surface of a proton-ejecting membrane [37]. (A) Proton distribution along a planar membrane containing only one proton pump. The cylindrical axis z is perpendicular to the membrane plane, and the axis r is directed along the membrane. The protons ejected by the pump are spread initially along the membrane surface and then escape through the interfacial barrier (no proton sinks in the membrane were considered). The turnover rate of the pump was $5 \times 10^2 \, \text{s}^{-1}$, the height of the potential barrier was 0.12 eV, the surface potential was −0.06 V, the bulk diffusion coefficient of protons was $10^{-4} \, \text{cm}^2 \, \text{s}^{-1}$; other details of the model are described in the text. (B) Steady-state pH profile at the surface of sealed membrane vesicles with a radius of 1 mm and surface pump density of $2.3 \times 10^{11} \, \text{cm}^{-2}$. The potential barrier as calculated for the ionic strength of 0.1 M (solid line) was used in modeling. The dashed line shows the proton concentration as calculated without potential barrier.

Modeling under reasonable assumptions on turnover rates, the mutual distance between proton pumps and ATP synthase molecules, and on the curvature of the membrane revealed that the protonmotive force is greater in the vicinity of a pump than farther away (Figure 4). This result was obtained without invoking either of the following special mechanisms: (a) enhanced proton diffusion at the membrane surface and (b) a diffusion barrier for protons between the surface and the bulk phase. It holds for steady turnover of pumps and ATP synthase [37,38]. The proton concentration away from one continuously active singular pump and along the membrane surface facing an infinitely alkaline medium is illustrated in Figure 4(A). The one away from the surface of a pump-covered vesicle into the medium is given in Figure 4(B). The effects are more pronounced if there is a diffusion barrier at the membrane surface (solid lines in Figure 4), for which there is some evidence [38]. In conclusion, the delocalized coupling concept of P. Mitchell is basically correct, but it needs modification in as much as the surface-to-surface p.m.f. that drives the ATP synthase may be greater than the bulk-to-bulk one. This effect is particularly pronounced in alkaliphilic bacteria because they pump protons into an alkaline medium (the "infinite sink") and it is much less so in thylakoids, which pump protons into a finite volume, as has been discussed elsewhere (see [37] and references therein).

21.2.4 H^+/ATP Stoichiometric Ratio

The stoichiometric ratio between proton translocation and ATP synthesis has been extensively studied in photosynthetic membranes using both non-invasive generation of p.m.f. by illumination and an artificial one by mixing techniques (pH-jump, salt-jump). The stoichiometric ratio of H^+/ATP in thylakoid membranes and in proteoliposomes was determined by two different approaches, (i) thermodynamical by recording the equilibrium between the protonmotive force and the phosphate potential [eqn. (4)] and (ii) kinetical, disturbing the equilibrium and recording the ratio of transient proton flow over transient ATP synthesis/hydrolysis. Over the decades, published stoichiometric ratios went up from 2 mol H^+ per mol-ATP to over 3.3 to, eventually, 4, the latter figure being the résumé of extensive work by three groups, H. Strotmann's, B. Rumberg's and H. van Walraven's (see [39] and the references therein). P. Gräber's group determined the same figure, namely 4 ± 0.3, for the reconstituted spinach enzyme in liposomes [40]. This agreed figure has resulted from repeated, very careful studies by both the thermodynamic and the kinetic approach, with the enzyme from spinach and cyanobacteria, and by applying several independent techniques to control the magnitude of the protonmotive force and the amount of ATP synthesized/hydrolyzed. Nevertheless the figure of 4 is not compatible with the structural symmetry of the chloroplast enzyme. The rotary electromotor, F_0, of the chloroplast enzyme shows C_{14}-symmetry, and the chemical reactor, CF_1, C_3-pseudosymmetry. The former was determined by atomic force microscopy of the isolated c-ring of CF_0 [41] and the latter by X-ray crystal structure analysis [42].

With 14 proton binding groups in CF_0 and three chemical reaction sites in CF_1 one expects a H^+/ATP-stoichiometry of 4.67 rather than 4. Imperfect coupling of the enzyme (e.g., proton slip in the enzyme or leakiness of the membrane) and a possible underestimation of the protonmotive force (e.g., because the surface-to-surface p.m.f. is greater than the determined bulk-to-bulk p.m.f.) were both expected to rather overestimate the stoichiometric ratio. Thus, the discrepancy between the structurally expected figure of 4.7 and the thermodynamically and kinetically determined figure of 4 has remained without a convincing rationale.

21.2.5 Regulation

Enzyme molecules are reversible catalysts. An enzyme is denoted as irreversible to indicate that the proportion of active over inactive enzymes in an ensemble is regulated, e.g., by product inhibition. The ATP synthase is regulated by different techniques and in different extent in different organisms. In *E. coli* the enzyme runs reversibly forward or backward depending on the needs of the cell. If the p.m.f. is high, as under aerobic conditions, the enzyme synthesizes ATP, or, should the respiratory proton pumps run low, as under anaerobic conditions, it operates in the reverse direction, hydrolyzing the ATP provided by glycolysis to generate p.m.f. If the chloroplast ATP synthase had the same reversibility, at night, when the light-driven proton pumps of chloroplasts do not work, it would hydrolyze the ATP generated by mitochondria. This is avoided by both p.m.f.- and thiol-regulation of the chloroplast enzyme. CF_0F_1 is down-regulated (i) if the p.m.f. drops below a certain threshold and (ii) if the electron-transport chain fails to sustain a sufficiently reducing milieu.

Figure 5 illustrates the behavior of the reduced (solid curve) and the oxidized enzyme (broken curve) as a function of the p.m.f. The reduced enzyme synthesizes ATP with a turnover number ranging up to $300 \, s^{-1}$ if the proton-motive force exceeds 3.5 pH-units. If the p.m.f. is lowered from say 3.5 pH-units to about 2.8 the rate of ATP hydrolysis equals the one of synthesis, i.e., net ATP production is zero. It marks the compensation point where eqn. (4) is expected to hold. If the p.m.f. is lowered further, net ATP hydrolysis dominates until at even lower p.m.f. the enzyme activity is shut off although its driving force prevails. The oxidized enzyme, on the other hand, stops operation before reaching the thermodynamic compensation point, because its p.m.f. threshold for deactivation is augmented by more than a pH unit.

Thiol-regulation relates the activity of F-ATPase to the reducing power of the linear electron transport chain. It is conferred to the enzyme via ferredoxin/thioredoxin, and involves two closely spaced cysteine residues on subunit γ. These are present in the enzyme from green algae and higher plants, but absent in those of bacteria and mitochondria. If these cysteines are engineered into γ of the cyanobacterium *Synechocystis* they confer redox modulation to the mutant enzyme – so far, however, without any detectable benefit for the cell (see [43] and references therein).

The F-ATPase from all sources is regulated by protonmotive force. At least with CF_0F_1 both components, the transmembrane voltage and the pH difference, can activate the enzyme and they do so in equivalent proportion [eqn. (3)]. Activation might require the binding of more than one proton to the enzyme, it is linked to the release of tightly bound ADP from F_1 (see [44] and references

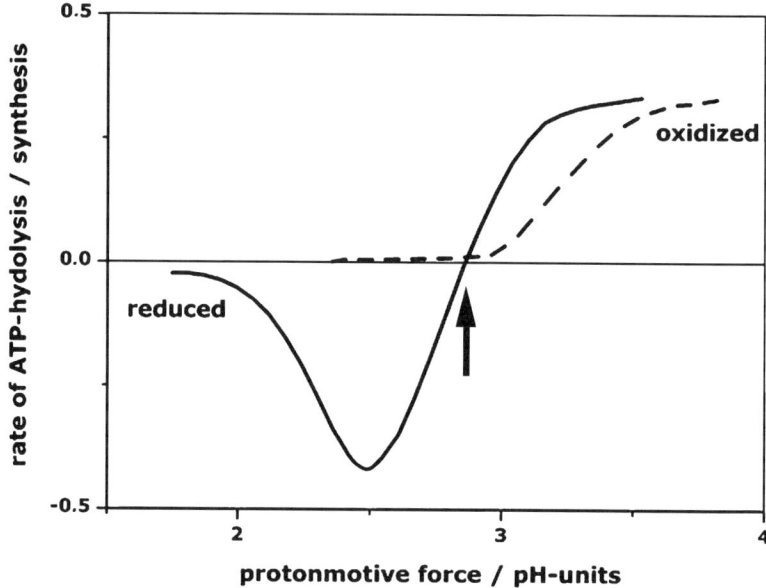

Figure 5. Schematic representation of the p.m.f.- and thiol-regulation of CF_0CF_1 (redrawn after [121]). The rate of net ATP synthesis (positive branch) and hydrolysis (negative branch) as function of the protonmotive force (in pH units), both under oxidizing and reducing conditions. The arrow denotes the thermodynamic compensation point where the phosphate potential is expected to match the protonmotive force according to eqn. (4). The calculated phosphate potential was about $57\,kJ\,mol^{-1}$ (room temperature) (Figure 2 in [121]). That the calculated compensation point in the respective experiments implies a proton-over-ATP stoichiometry of 3.5 and not 4, as eventually agreed on by several laboratories, or 4.67, as suggested by the enzyme structure (see above), illustrates the difficulties in correctly assessing the p.m.f.

therein), and it involves conformational changes of the ε-subunit. The molecular detail of p.m.f. regulation, with emphasis on the role of subunit ε, is the subject of active research (see [45] and references therein).

A low p.m.f. shuts down both the catalytic activity of F_1 and the coupled proton conductance of F_0 (not the one of exposed F_0, see Section 21.3.3.2). A leak conductance of F_0F_1 is, however, induced at low ADP concentration (<100 nM) and this "proton slip" has been interpreted as a safety valve, protecting the membrane against over-voltage or over-pH-difference. That this is not the case has been demonstrated in chloroplasts where proton slip is blocked by as low as 200 nM of ADP (with mM P_i present) or with 2 μM ATP, conditions that are always met in chloroplasts (see [46] and references therein). Thus, proton slip does probably not function as a safety valve. A similar behavior has been reported for a purple bacterium [47]. Viewed from today, proton slip appears as a consequence of a loose grip of $(\alpha\beta)_3$ on subunit γ if only one out of the three catalytic nucleotide binding sites is occupied. This allows "free" rotation of the rotary proton carrier F_0 (see below).

21.3 ATP Synthase (F_0F_1-ATPase)

21.3.1 Structure

Figure 6(A) illustrates the gross structure of ATP synthase. Its hydrophilic and peripheral portion, F_1, is mounted on the hydrophobic and membrane intrinsic portion, F_0. F_1 and F_0 are held together by a peripheral stalk and a central shaft. The total mass of EF_0F_1 is about 530 kDa and the total height about 20 nm. Soluble F_1 functions as an ATPase, and membrane embedded F_0 without attached F_1 as a proton-conductor. ATP hydrolysis/synthesis by F_1 and proton translocation by F_0 are mechanically coupled. The "rotor" (blue in Figure 6A) rotates against the "stator" portion of the enzyme (brown). The terms stator and rotor are arbitrary, what matters is their relative rotation against each other. The functional rotational turnover time (milliseconds) is longer than the rotational correlation time by diffusion of F_0F_1 (200 µs) [48].

The enzyme's partial functions are attributable to certain subunits. For historical reasons the subunit nomenclature differs between organisms – the one for *E. coli* is mostly used in the following. In *E. coli* the composition of the rotor is $\gamma\varepsilon c_{10}$ (molecular masses: 31.4, 14.9 and 8.3 kDa) and the one of the stator $ab_2\delta(\alpha\beta)_3$ (molecular masses: 30.3, 17.2, 19.6, 55.3 and 50.2 kDa). In chloroplasts and in purple bacteria a heterodimer, bb', substitutes for the homodimer, b_2 [chloroplast nomenclature IV/I/II/$\delta(\alpha\beta)_3$], and in mitochondria there are three subunits in the role of bb', named b, d and F_6. In *E. coli* all subunits are arranged on a single operon (unc). In chloroplasts the genes are distributed between the plastome and the nuclear genome. The latter codes for three subunits, namely γ, δ and b' (alias II), and the former for the rest. The hexagon of $(\alpha\beta)_3$ incorporates a total of six nucleotide binding sites. Only three are catalytically active, they are considered in the following. These sites are mainly formed by subunit β at the interface with subunit α.

Four key structural features of F_1 are indicated in Figure 6(B), namely (i) one out of a total of three catalytic nucleotide binding sites on subunit β (in red), (ii) the central curved shaft, subunit γ (in yellow), (iii) the hydrophobic bearing at the N-terminal collar of $(\alpha\beta)_3$ anchoring the C-terminal end of γ, and (iv) the lever on subunit β that is moved back and forth by the rotating "crank"-shaft. These assignments were already made in 1994 when John Walker and collaborators described the first asymmetric crystal-structure of MF_1 [2]. Their function is illustrated in Movie 1[†]. Asymmetric nucleotide occupancy in the three catalytic subunits was apparently required to fix the position of the central shaft in the hexagon of $(\alpha\beta)_3$. Crystal-structures with symmetric occupancy of the nucleotide binding sites have produced lower resolution and, in particular, blurred electron densities in the region of γ [42,49,50]. In the asymmetric crystal structure the convex side of the curved shaft faces the lever on the particular β-subunit with an empty nucleotide binding site. One major feature discriminating between a catalytic site filled with ADP and another one with an ATP-analogue is the redirection of an arginine on subunit α from pointing away from ADP to leaning over to contact the γ-phosphate position of

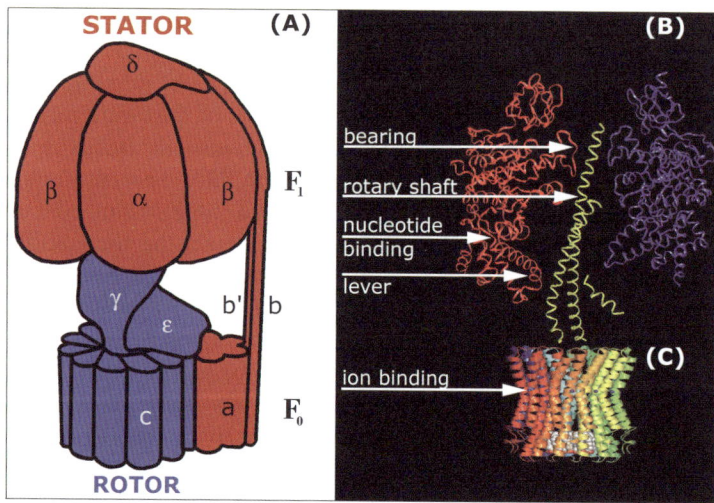

Figure 6. (A) Schematic representation of the ATP synthase from photosynthetic organisms, its subunits, their association with the membrane embedded F_0 and the peripheral F_1, and the bipartite functional units, stator (red) and rotor (blue). (B) A central slab of the F_1 structure [12] (see the interpolative Movie 1†) with the mechanical elements of rotary F_1 indicated. (C) Crystal structure of the c-ring of F_0 of the sodium translocating bacterium *Iliobacter tartaricus* [60].

ATP, possibly a fixed but flexible counter-ion to lower the energy penalty of the negatively charged γ-phosphate in the protein.

John Walker and his colleges obtained several different asymmetric crystal structures of MF_1 down to a resolution of 0.2 nm [51]: some with aluminum and beryllium fluorides as planar transition state analogues in the phosphate binding position [51–53], with bound inhibitors [54,55], and a symmetrical structure of $(\alpha\beta)_3$ without nucleotides [56]. Most of the crystal structures published so far showing $(\alpha\beta)_3$ and γ have at least one empty nucleotide binding site, none of them has bound ATP in any site, and the ones with the best resolution have either ADPPNP, ADP·AlF$_3$ or ADP·(AlF$_4$)$_2$ as ATP analogues bound in one or two sites. It appears as if crystallization selects stable but not necessarily active conformations.

One key element of the rotary electromotor is a ring of identical subunits, subunit c. This subunit, a small hairpin of only 8.3 kDa molecular mass, has been coined "proteolipid" because of its hydrophobicity. Its hairpin folding with an essential acid residue (cArg61 in *E. coli*) located in the middle of the membrane was first revealed by in situ photoaffinity labeling [57], and the homo-oligomeric ring structure by cysteine mapping [58]. Solution NMR of the

---

†Animation of ATP-hydrolysis by F_1 (energy minimized interpolation of the crystal structure) (2001, D. Cherepanov). The movie can be viewed at www.biologie.uni-osnabrueck.de/biophysik/junge, with permission of Prof. Wolfgang Junge.

isolated c-subunit in a mixed solvent provided a closer look at the structure of the monomer (see [58,59] and references therein), and atomic force microscopy corroborated the ring and led to an assessment of the number of subunits involved (see below). Recently, the crystal structure of the c-ring was elucidated at 0.24 nm resolution. It was obtained from *Ilyobacter tartaricus*, a bacterium with a sodium transporting F_0F_1-ATP synthase [60]. The ring is hour-glass shaped, and composed of eleven identical and hairpin-shaped subunits c (Figure 6C). Each carries one sodium cation, right in the middle of the membrane, that is coordinated by residues from the two legs of one c-subunit plus one residue of a neighboring hairpin. In contrast with the C_{11}-symmetry in *I. tartaricus* the c-ring of the proton translocating yeast enzyme has C_{10}-symmetry (obtained by X-ray crystallography [61]), the one of chloroplasts C_{14}-symmetry (obtained by atomic force microscopy (AFM) [41]), the ring of *Spirolina platensis* C_{15}-symmetry (again by AFM) [122], and the ones of *E. coli* and of thermophilic *Bacillus* PS3 C_{10}-symmetry (by crosslinking and function-tests [62,63]). The c-ring of the electromotor of the ATP synthase is, therefore, composed of 10, 11, 14 or 15 identical subunits, depending on the organism. This has the following consequences: (i) The rotary holoenzyme, F_0F_1, copes with symmetry mismatch between F_1 (pseudo-C_3) and F_0 ($C_{10,11,14}$), but it must not (C_{15}). (ii) Different organisms run at a different gear between the electrochemical and the chemical motor/generator. (iii) The stoichiometric ratio of H^+/ATP is not necessarily an integer number, in chloroplasts it is expected to be 4.67 rather than 4, as has emerged from functional studies (Section 21.2.4). (iv) At equal p.m.f. different organisms can sustain higher or lower ATP/ADP ratios, depending on the respective gear.

In the holoenzyme the c-ring is firmly bound to the rotor elements of F_1, namely the "foot" of subunit γ and subunit ε. This has been evident from the fact that some crosslinks between γ and ε [64], and between ε and c [65], do not inhibit the activity, so that it is reasonable to conceive subunits γ and ε as sitting on the c-wheel like a firmly attached spoke (see [66]).

The subunit **a** of F_0 is likely a transmembrane five-helix bundle [67] with an essential arginine (aArg210 in *E. coli*) located on helix 4, one turn above the middle of the membrane dielectric. The other subunits of F_0, namely bb' or b_2 in *E. coli*, are largely α-helical proteins, the two helices of b_2 or bb' probably form a coiled-coil that stretches out from the membrane, over to and tightly binding to one αβ-cleft and farther up to and again firmly binding to subunit δ (see [68] and references therein). The binding of subunits δ at the very top of $(αβ)_3$ is very strong, with a dissociation constant of less than 1 nM [69], and b binds with a dissociation constant of 150 nM to one αβ-cleft [70]. The complex of three different subunits, named b, δ, and F_6, which make up the peripheral stalk in MF_0F_1, has recently been crystallized and found to form an extended and supposedly rather rigid double strand of parallel and anti-parallel helices [71]. It is agreed that the peripheral stalk is firmly attached to $(αβ)_3$ on one side and probably also to subunit a on the other. Whether this linkage is elastically stiff, soft, or even floppy is a matter of debate, but see below.

21.3.2 F1, the Rotary Catalyst

21.3.2.1 Nucleotide Binding Sites and Cooperativity

Paul Boyer developed the concept of an alternating function of at least two catalytic sites on the F_1-ATPase, the binding change mechanism [72]. A rotating mechanism involving three catalytic sites became evident by the X-ray structure [12]. The hexagon of $(\alpha\beta)_3$ incorporates a total of six nucleotide binding sites, three of which are catalytically active. If the affinity of the other three is greatly reduced by mutation, these sites are unoccupied but the enzyme remains functional (see [73] and references therein). The three catalytic sites bind Mg-ATP with negative cooperativity. In a mutant F_1 from *E. coli* with engineered tryptophan residues as reporters of the nucleotide occupancy, the respective dissociation constants are ≤ 1 nM for the first, some 100 nM for the second (with the first one occupied), and some 10–100 μM for the third site (see [74]; for TF_1 see [75]). The "negative binding cooperativity" contrasts with "positive catalytic cooperativity" between these sites; the catalytic constant of uni-site and bi-site catalysis (at very low ATP concentration) is much smaller than the one of tri-site catalysis, which is considered as obligatory by A. Senior and J. Weber [76]. Whether the structural coupling behind those cooperativities is mainly attributable to contacts between subunits α-β-α or rather to the position of subunit γ in α-γ-β contacts is not settled.

Movie 2[§] is a rather free animation of a concerted operation of three catalytic sites in the synthesis direction powered by the proton-driven rotation of the central shaft. These sites are supposed to be equivalent in the time average. During forced turnover each of them cycles over three steps: (i) binding of substrates, Mg-ADP and P_i, (ii) anhydride bond formation to yield bound Mg-ATP, and (iii) release of the product, Mg-ATP.

Biochemical studies have led to the postulate of a reaction sequence where one nucleotide site is always unoccupied ("bi-site mechanism") *o*pen, *l*ow affinity and a *t*ight site (O-, L-, T-site) [72,77]. They were later coined β*E*, β*DP* and β*TP* because the crystal structure [12] showed one site *e*mpty, one filled with A*DP*, and the third filled with AMPPNP (thought to mimic A*TP*). Thus the crystal structure seemingly supports bi-site functioning. Whether or not there is a real discrepancy between structural and biochemical data is not quite clear. The crystals have been grown in the presence of the bactericide azide, which promotes ADP-inhibition, and, therefore, they are built from the ADP-inhibited and not from the working enzyme. However, mutant enzymes with engineered tryptophans as fluorescent reporters of nucleotide occupancy may have altered affinities for nucleotides. This matter has remained open.

Figure 7 illustrates a tri-site version of the binding change mechanism. It involves three filled sites that change their states of affinity between *l*ow,

---

[§]Animation of the proton driven F_0F_1 ATP synthase (2005 by iAS, courtesy of IWF.de). The movie can be viewed at www.biologie.uni-osnabrueck.de/biophysik/junge, with permission of Prof. Wolfgang Junge.

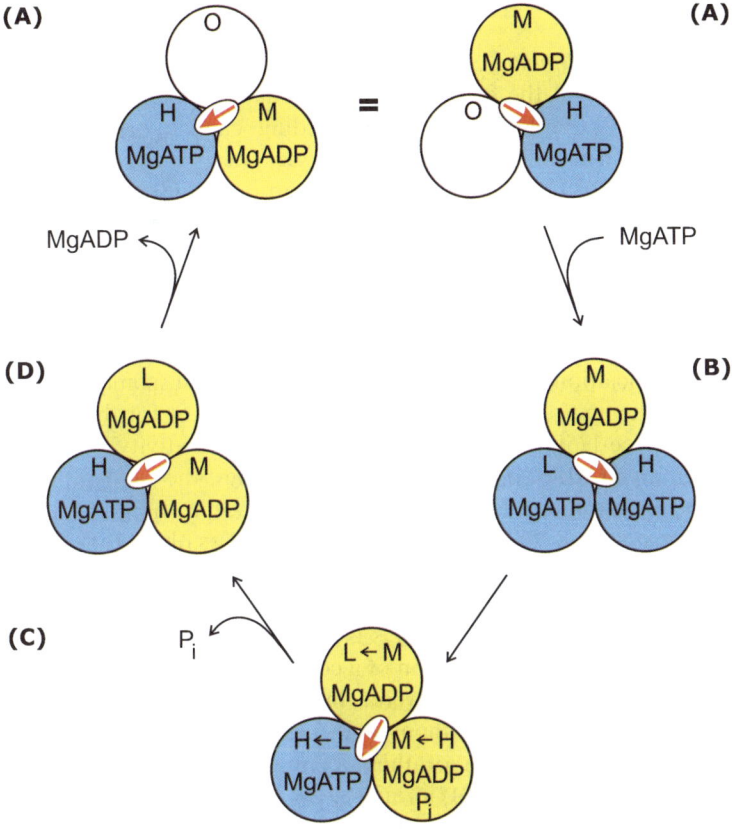

Figure 7. Schematic representation of the rotary binding change mechanism in ATP hydrolysis, after [78] (see text).

*m*edium and *h*igh (L-, M-, H-site) [78]. Hydrolysis of ATP rotates the central shaft (red arrow) over 120°, which is divided into two rotary sub-steps, the first one initiated by the hydrolysis of bound ATP and the second one, claimed in this model, by the release of phosphate (see Section 21.3.2.2 for biophysical evidence on which step generates torque). The very steps that generate torque in F_1 (in the model shown in Figure 7, the cleavage of bound ATP and the release of phosphate) are the ones that drive proton pumping by F_0F_1 (see below).

21.3.2.2 Rotations
A rotary mechanism of ATP hydrolysis by F_1 was plausible as soon as the first asymmetric crystal structure revealed the still picture of a molecular Wankel engine. The first to catch the enzyme "in flight" was Richard Cross' group [14].

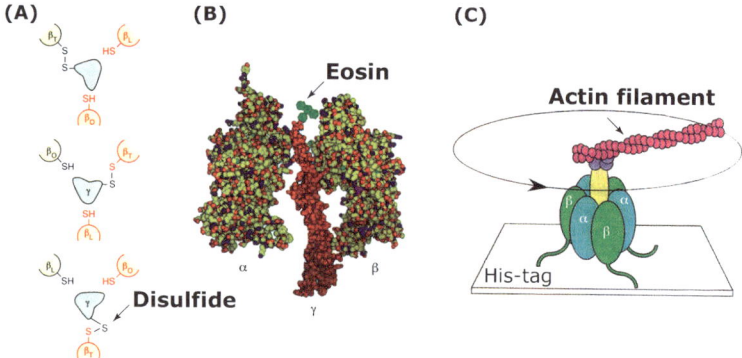

Figure 8. Three techniques to detect inter-subunit rotation in F_1 [66] (see text).

They relied on crosslinking two engineered cysteines in subunits β and γ (Figure 8A). Assembling EF_1 from a disulfite linked βγ-pair (black-black in Figure 8) plus two "hot" copies of subunit β (red), they found that the cleavage and the subsequent reformation of the SS-bridge produced new βγ-pairs (red-black) if the enzyme hydrolyzed ATP, but the same pair if it was inactive. Their conclusion was that the cysteine on subunit γ could be linked to its partner cysteines on all three copies of β. They found a similar result for the reassembled EF_0F_1 under ATP synthesis [79].

The author's group embarked on time resolving the rotation by a spectroscopic probe attached to the penultimate amino acid in subunit γ, a cysteine, of chloroplast CF_1 (Figure 8B). The enzyme was immobilized on an ion-exchange gel and the rotation of the dye eosin recorded by polarized laser photo-bleaching and recovery [15,80]. Three phases of rotation were detected: (i) A very rapid and range-limited librational motion of the long axis of the chromophore in nano-seconds (librational diffusion around the single bond of the dye's attachment, with the range limited by protein contacts), (ii) further rotational relaxation in about 30 μs (again libration around the single bond, with the range widened by protein conformational changes in some ten μs), and (iii) a slow phase (of about 100 ms duration) that was only observed if the enzyme was hydrolyzing ATP. The rotational relaxation time conformed with the enzymatic turnover time under the given conditions [82,83]. The monotonic decay of the polarization anisotropy implied that the rotation was stepping with two or three but not more steps [80].

Whereas the first approach lacked time resolution and both the first and second lacked information on the direction of rotation. The third approach by the groups of Masasuke Yoshida and Kazuhiko Kinosita had it all (Figure 8C). An engineered TF_1 was fixed by His-tags to a Ni-coated solid support, a fluorophore-labeled actin-filament was attached to the C-terminal end of subunit γ, and the position of the filament recorded by video-microscopy. Under conditions of ATP hydrolysis they observed the counter-clockwise rotation, viewing from the membrane side of F_1 [16]. It conformed with the expected sequence of events based on the asymmetric crystal structure, namely that the convex side of subunit γ progresses from facing βE via βDP to βTP [2]. A filament of typical length 2 μm is over 100× longer than the diameter of the enzyme (≈ 10 nm), its motion is overdamped by viscous drag such that substeps are not detectable, and the enzyme turnover is slowed down from milliseconds to seconds. To overcome the rate limitation by viscous drag the same laboratories used 40 nm gold beads on subunit γ as reporter and recorded the rotational speed at high speed (8000 video-frames per second) [81]. The large size of the diffraction limited spot of the bead (width ≈ 300 nm) was not deleterious because its centroid position was more sharply defined owing to the eccentric mounting on the enzyme via BSA.

Figure 9 illustrates the experimental set-up and documents the stepping of the eccentric spots. The stepping length was 120°, as expected, with two substeps of 90° and 30°. The 90° step was at least triggered if not driven by the binding of ATP, the 30° step was independent of ATP. Both steps were rapid, taken together they were completed in less than 250 μs (at saturating ATP). That the "interim dwell", 2 ms, was shorter than the apparent turnover time of 7.7 ms in solution (turnover number $130 \, s^{-1}$) was attributed to the difference between single molecule experiments (detecting the behavior of active enzyme

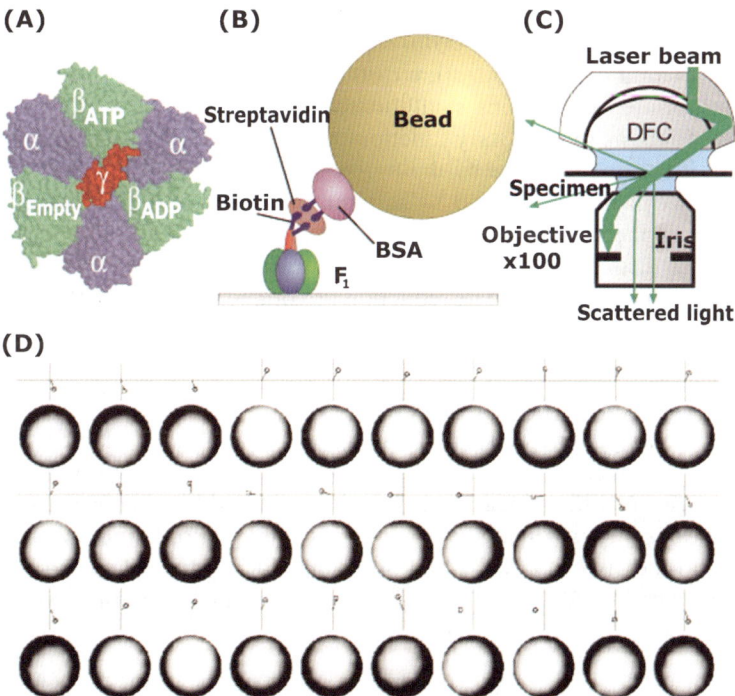

Figure 9. Recording of the rotary dynamics of rotary F_1-ATPase using 30 nm gold beads in dark-field microscopy and a high-speed video-camera [81] (see text).

molecules) and ensemble experiments (detecting the mean behavior of active and inactive ones) [81]. The same laboratories later revised the width of the substeps into 80° and 40° intervals and assigned one of the "interim dwells" to the cleavage of ATP [82] and to product release [83], respectively. The latter study with fluorescent nucleotide analogues supported a tri-site (Figure 7) over a bi-site mechanism.

Spectroscopic rotation assays have been refined as well. Polarized confocal microscopy applied to immobilized single molecules yielded the first evidence for three stepped rotary progression of subunit γ [84]. The first to prove rotation in the membrane bound enzyme, were Peter Dimroth and his colleagues. They used PF_0F_1-proteoliposomes, fixed by the enzyme on a solid support, and recorded the rotating polarization of a dye molecule that was covalently linked to subunit c. It revealed the rotation of the c-ring not only in the direction of ATP hydrolysis but also for Na^+-driven synthesis [85]. Peter Gräber's group used fluorescence resonance energy transfer (FRET) to monitor the distance between two chromophores, one attached to the rotor and the other one to the stator of EF_0F_1. Reconstituted in proteoliposomes, they monitored transients of the resonance energy transfer during the rather long passage time of the liposome through the femto-liter focal spot of a confocal microscope, and observed the stepped rotation in either direction – synthesis and hydrolysis of ATP [86,87]. Confocal single-molecule FRET is hampered, like other single-molecule fluorescence techniques, by a poor signal-to-noise ratio. This is because organic fluorophores bleach after absorption of less than 10^6 quanta of light. Quantum dots do not, but their size, some 10 nm, is not appropriate for sampling small distances within a protein.

If any doubt as to the rotary function of F_1 both in hydrolysis and synthesis was left, it became obsolete by the following experiment: Hiroyasu Itoh et al. [88] attached a magnetic bead to subunit γ of immobilized TF_1, rotated an externally applied magnetic field and detected ATP production by chemiluminescence of luciferin-luciferase. Straightforward as it sounds, this experiment was a tough piece of work. The reduction of volume to minimize the dilution of ATP and background photons were major challenges.

21.3.2.3 Torque and Thermodynamic Efficiency
The average angular velocity of a rotating fluorescent actin-filament was used to estimate the average torque produced by F_1 during ATP hydrolysis. In doing so it was assumed that the angular velocity is limited by viscous drag, that the filament can be approximated as a straight cylindrical rod, and that this rod is exposed to the viscosity of the bulk medium. The torque (M) is then given by eqn. (5), wherein ω denotes the angular velocity and Γ the drag coefficient:

$$M = \Gamma \omega \qquad (5)$$

Consider a thin, long cylinder (length L, radius r) rotating in an unbound fluid (viscosity η). If the rotation is perpendicular to the long axis of the cylinder and fixed to one end the drag coefficient is approximately (see [89,90]):

$$\Gamma \cong \frac{4\pi}{3} \cdot \frac{\eta \cdot L^3}{\ln\left(\frac{L}{r}\right) - 0.447} \tag{6}$$

In their pioneering paper, H. Noji et al. [16] arrived at the conclusion that the torque amounts up to 40 pN nm. When sustained over an angle of $120° = 2\pi/3$, the progression per ATP molecule hydrolyzed, this torque implies a molar mechanical work of 50 kJ mol^{-1}, which is less than the calculated free energy of ATP hydrolysis under their conditions (72–87 kJ mol^{-1}, see [91]). Still, it was taken to indicate nearly 100% efficiency of F_1-ATPase [92,93]. H. Noji et al. [16] were aware of a possible underestimation of the torque. An actin filament (e.g., 2 μm long, 5 nm thick) anchored to a rotating shaft sticking out at a height of about 10 nm over a surface does not "feel" the viscosity of the unbounded bulk solution but a greater one, because of flow coupling to the surface, not to mention surface friction and obstacles. The single molecule observation of rotation by filaments, though spectacular, is actually restricted to a very small fraction, 0.1–1%, of typically 100 filaments in the microscope field. ATP-driven rotation is often obstructed, not only by ADP-inhibition of the enzyme but also by surface contacts. Rotary trajectories with a constant slope (used to calculate the torque) are highly selected examples.

Figure 10 illustrates an alternative way to determine the torque. It avoids the above complications. The actin-filament is used as a spring-balance and the torque is gauged by its elastic deformation [94–96]. The bending of filaments at given torque depends very little on whether the counter-torque is due to viscous drag, surface friction or blockade of the filament by an obstacle [96]. This technique was applied to monitor the torque profile generated by ATP hydrolysis in EF_0F_1 with the filament specifically attached to the c-ring of F_0 (Figure 10C) [95]. The first row (Figure 10A) of video frames (40 ms exposure each) shows a rotating filament 3.2 μm long (see Movie 3¶ for an original record). The filaments curvature is obvious. The second row (Figure 10B) shows the same filament, now stalled. That it is still curved implies torque generation by the enzyme despite stalling, probably by hitting an obstacle. The torque can be calculated from the curvature once the flexural rigidity of the filament is known. It follows from the variance of thermal fluctuations of the filament tip (see [11]). A figure of 10^{-25} Nm^2 was the typical rigidity [95]. Figure 11 shows the resulting profile of the torque as a function of the angle. The mean was 50 ± 6 pN nm. In the same set of experiments the torque calculated from the angular velocity of rotation [eqn. (5)] was much smaller, only 20 pN nm, revealing the inadequacy of torque determination from the rate of rotation.

Torque (M) times the angular displacement per ATP molecule ($\delta\Phi = 2\pi/3$) gives the mechanical work (ΔW) done on the filament. The molar mechanical

---

¶Original video of rotating filament of 3.2 mm length attached to the c-ring of immobilized F_0F_1 as illustrated in Figure 10(C) (95). The movie can be viewed at www.biologie.uni-osnabrueck.de/biophysik/junge, with permission of Prof. Wolfgang Junge.

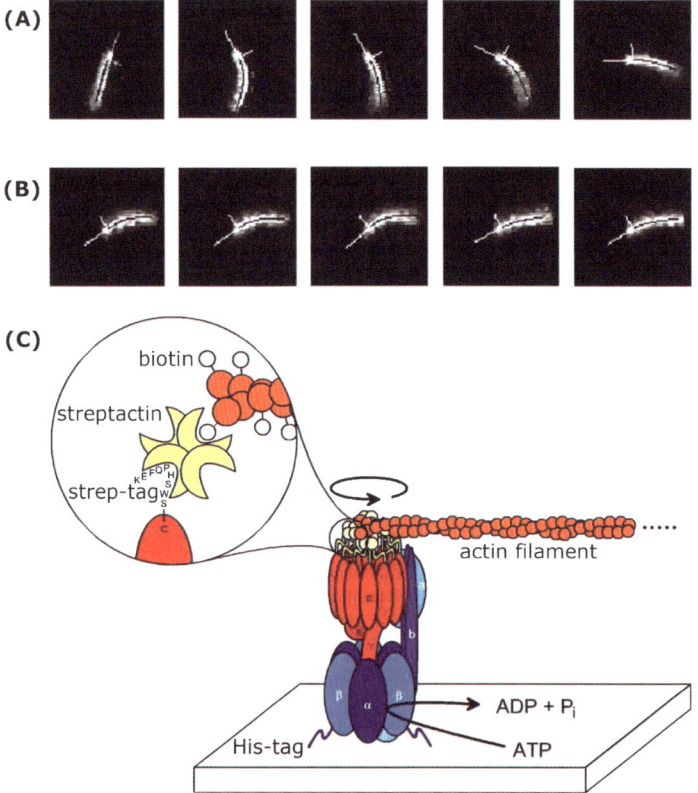

Figure 10. Rotary F_0F_1-ATPase with attached actin filament (length 3.2 μm). Enzyme turnover is several orders of magnitude slower than without filament, which is curved by the enzyme torque. The curvature of the filament has been used as a rotary spring balance to gauge the torque independent of the magnitude of viscous drag and of the interference of surface obstacles [94–96]. (A) Rotating enzyme with attached filament bent by viscous drag. (B) Stalled enzyme by blocked filament contacting an obstacle on the surface, the enzyme torque still bending the filament. (C) Specific attachment of actin filament to the c-ring of detergent solubilized and immobilized EF_0F_1 [108].

work is:

$$\Delta W = M \cdot \frac{2\pi}{3} \cdot N_A \tag{7a}$$

where N_A denotes the Avogadro number.

A mean torque of 50 pN nm implies a molar work of 63 kJ mol^{-1}. This figure matches the calculated free energy of ATP hydrolysis in these experiments:

$$\Delta W = M \cdot \frac{2\pi}{3} \cdot N_A = -\Delta G_P = -\Delta G_P^\circ - RT \ln \frac{[\text{ADP}] \cdot [\text{P}] \cdot [\text{H}^+]}{[\text{ATP}]} \tag{7b}$$

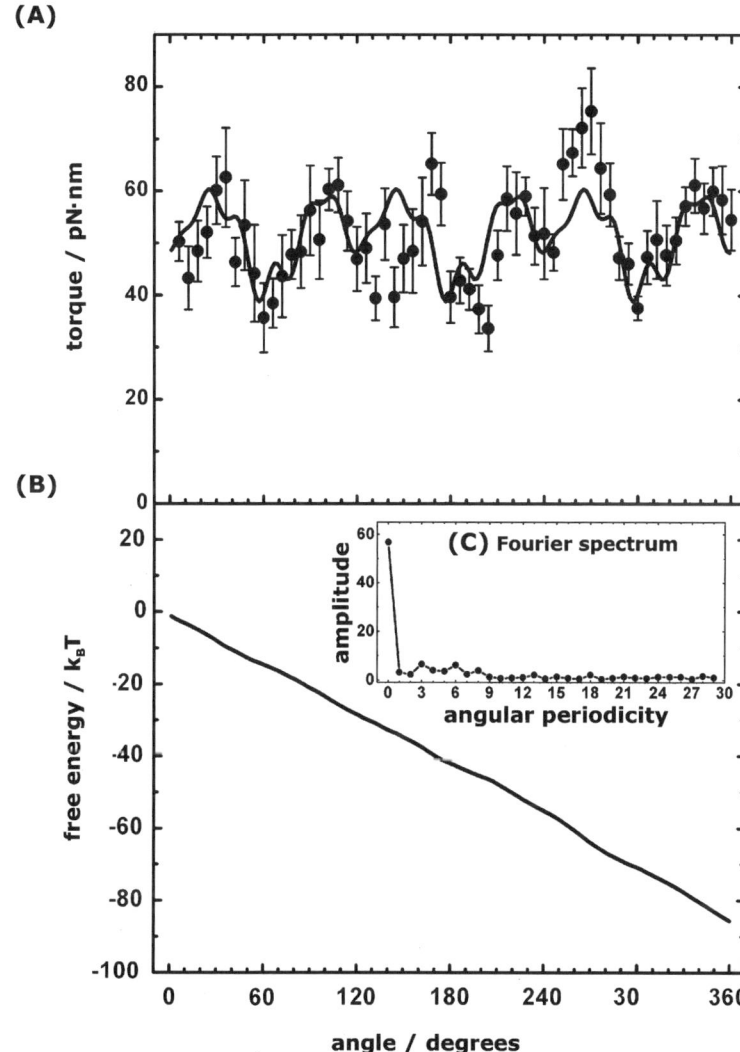

Figure 11. Torque and free-energy profile of EF_0F_1 determined by the curvature of a long actin filament attached to the c-ring of EF_0 [95].

It implies that the enzyme indeed operates at 100% efficiency [94,95]. The 100% efficiency under these conditions has been considered as a particular achievement, which it is not really. A filament 3 μm long reduces the rate of ATP hydrolysis from $>100\,s^{-1}$ in the free enzyme to less than $1\,s^{-1}$. The rotating enzyme thus operates slowly and close to equilibrium, as documented in Figure 10(A), if not truly in thermodynamic equilibrium when stalled by an obstacle (Figure 10B). Because the internal friction is negligible, the thermodynamic efficiency between filament deformation and enzyme chemistry is, trivially, expected to be 100%. A better way to appreciate this efficiency is to say, "there is no slip in the power transmission between the chemical reaction site and the proton translocating c-ring".

The above considerations [eqn. (7b)] give the thermodynamic view of the chemo-mechanical transducer F_1. It is approximated if the enzyme turns over much more slowly under a heavy load than it would if free. In eqn. (7b) the right-hand term is the entropic contribution to the free energy; it contributes to the torque only if the on/off-rates of educts and products are higher than the enzyme rotates, so that educts and products are in equilibrium. What about the torque produced under kinetic limitation, far away from the equilibrium? K. Kinosita and colleagues have investigated this situation. They recorded the rotation rate as function of the ATP-concentration ranging from nano- to milli-molar, using objects of different sizes to vary the load on the enzyme [97]. The results were discussed in terms of Michaelis–Menten's description, which relates the reaction velocity (v) to the substrate concentration (here [ATP]) by two parameters, the Michaelis-constant (K_m) and the maximum velocity (v_m):

$$v = v_m \cdot \frac{[\text{ATP}]}{([\text{ATP}] + K_m)} \text{ and at limiting } [\text{ATP}] \ll K_m \qquad (8a)$$

$$v \cong \frac{v_m}{K_m} \cdot [\text{ATP}] = k_{\text{on}}^{\text{app}} \cdot [\text{ATP}] \qquad (8b)$$

At saturating ATP concentration they found v_m determined by the magnitude of the torque and the viscous drag as expected [eqns. (5–7)]. However, K_m varied accordingly so that the apparent rate constant of ATP binding, $k_{\text{on}}^{\text{app}}$, of $\approx 2 \times 10^7 \,\text{M}^{-1}\,\text{s}^{-1}$ remained almost constant among enzymes with different load and in the wide concentration range 1 nM to 100 μM ATP [97]. The latter was not quite expected in view of the site-site-cooperativity. But, above 1 nM concentration, there was no indication for switching from one mechanism of rotation to another, from uni- via bi- to tri-site catalysis. As an obvious consequence the possible functioning by a tri-site mechanism calls for a dissociation constant below 1 nM for the first two binding sites. There is a clear discrepancy between this figure [97] and the dissociation constants determined by tryptophans as engineered reporter group in the binding pockets [75].

At nanomolar ATP-concentration the rotion is stepped. During occasional 120°-jumps the same angular velocity, i.e., the same torque, was observed at 2 nM ATP as in the average under saturating 2 mM ATP [97]. Let us consider an enzyme waiting some ten seconds for the next ATP molecule to bind (the rate being $4 \times 10^{-2}\,\text{s}^{-1}$ at 2 nM ATP). In the very moment when an ATP molecule happens to jump (diffusion controlled) into the receptive binding site the enzyme is certainly not in equilibrium with the nucleotides in the solution. The torque produced during the sudden jump into the next angular position that follows cannot depend on the entropic term on the right-hand side of eqn. (7b). Pulsed torque under ATP-limitation is not expected to be the same as the one detectable in thermodynamic equilibrium. Why it seems to be of equal magnitude, whether by chance or not, has remained an open question.

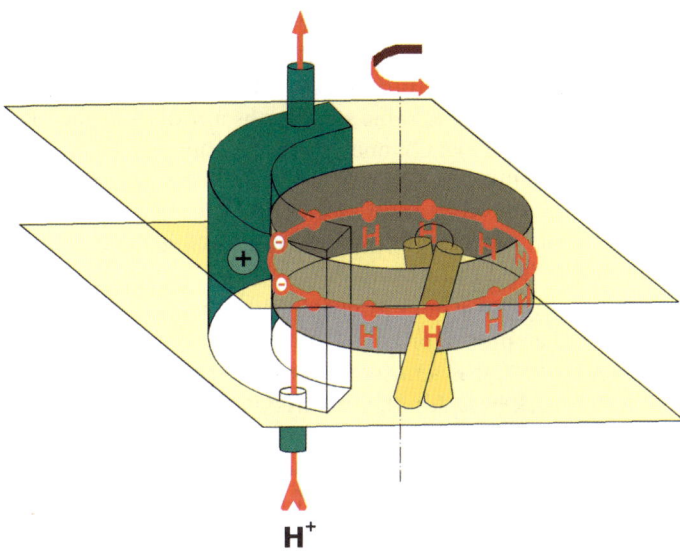

Figure 12. Schematic representation of the rotary electromotor, F_0 [66].

21.3.3 F_0, the Rotary Electromotor

21.3.3.1 Concept of Rotary Proton Transport

Figure 12 illustrates a model for how proton transport may be coupled to torque generation. It incorporates both essential elements, the homo-oligomeric ring of c-subunits, each hairpin shaped and with an acid residue in the middle of the membrane, and the a-subunit with the essential positive arginine. This model has several fathers. Conceived by the author in 1992 and discussed at several conferences since 1993 (see [66]), it was independently conceived by Steve Vik [98] and has been theoretically treated by statistical mechanics by George Oster and colleagues [99,100] and Dmitri Cherepanov in the author's laboratory [30].

The following simple principles of operation are agreed on: (1) The c-ring carries out rotational diffusion relative to the a-subunit. (2) This stochastic librational motion is restricted by two electrostatic constraints, namely that the essential acid residue must be (a) deprotonated when facing the positive arginine residue on subunit a and (b) protonated when facing the lipid core. (3) There are two non-collinear access channels for protons from either aqueous phase leading to acid residues on the c-ring. The electrostatic constraint related to the arginine in subunit a prevents short-circuiting of proton flow and, together with the two non-collinear channels, it conveys chirality to the electromotor. Movie 4‖ illustrates the back and forth fluctuation of the c-ring

---

‖ Animation of the rotary electromotor, F_0 (2001, M. Sauer and W. Junge). The movie can be viewed at www.biologie.uni-osnabrueck.de/biophysik/junge, with permission of Prof. Wolfgang Junge.

relative to subunit a, which is constrained by electrostatic penalty until a proton coming from the lower phase binds to a negatively charged residue and relieves the constraint. This allows the progression of the ring by one step in the counter-clockwise direction. The same step brings a proton at the other end of the ring in contact with the exit channel, so that it leaves into the upper phase. In this view the rotary drive counts and compares the probability of proton entry from either side – it is an entropic ratchet. This simple model describes equally well torque generation by proton transfer and proton pumping by applied torque.

The model belongs to Brownian ratchets, which have been amply discussed in the context of other motor proteins. As discussed in Richard Feynman's textbook on physics [101], it is a misconception that they are Maxwell demons that perform useful work based on thermal fluctuations. Figure 13 illustrates an archetypal ratchet. A particle diffuses asymmetrically in a saw-tooth potential but it is essentially kept in place while the potential is on. When the potential is off this constraint is relieved, and the diffusion is symmetrical. When the potential is switched on again the particle drifts. The drift is asymmetrical because of the saw-tooth shape of the potential, and it causes directed transport. The energy input for transport is supplied by gearing up the potential but not by Brownian motion. Compared with this classical ratchet with periodical energy input, the above model for the electromotor of F-ATPase is an entropic ratchet, where different probabilities of proton entry from the lower and the

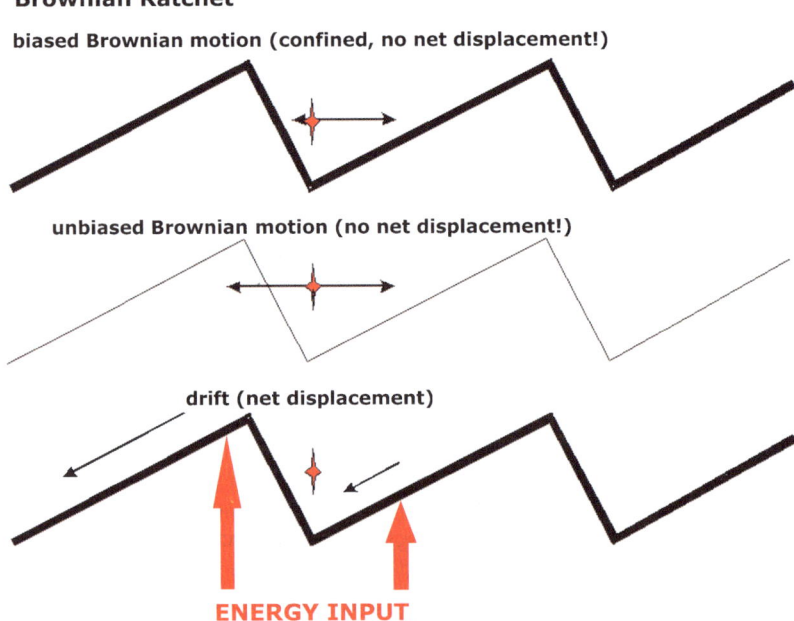

Figure 13. Brownian ratchet mechanism (see text).

upper phase, respectively, determine the direction of rotation and produce work. The model for F_0 is basically conceived to sample the entropic term ($RT\ln[H^+]$) of the free energy of the proton.

How does the transmembrane voltage come into play? One concept has been based on the assumption that the two access channels are monospecific for protons [66]. Obviously, a voltage difference of 120 mV between the two phases will decrease the pH at the central acid residue by one unit when viewed towards the plus side and increase it by the same amount viewing towards the negative side. Then we are back to the entropic ratchet.

Two modifications to the above simple mechanisms of rotary ion transport have been discussed in the literature (see [102] and references therein). (i) Bob Fillingame – based on seemingly conflicting structural data obtained by solution NMR of the c-monomer, on the one hand, and by cysteine-mapping of the c-ring, on the other – proposed a model where the c-ring was not rotating as a stiff entity but with obligatory swiveling of the hairpin-helices when in contact with subunit a [103]. The recent crystal structure of the c-ring of *I. tartaricus* [60], however, deviates from the one inferred from solution NMR of *E. coli* subunit c. Because the arrangement of helices is now compatible with the one from cysteine-mapping, a swiveling mechanism no longer needs to be invoked. (ii) An asymmetric position in the membrane of the acid residues on the c-ring was claimed, based on several lines of circumstantial evidence, and it led Peter Dimroth to postulate a "one-channel model" [104] as opposed to the "two-channel model" shown in Figure 12. Again this topology is not supported by the crystal structure [60].

The question of whether or not the c-ring rotates together with subunits γ and ε relative to the stator subunits has been positively answered by cross-linking subunit c with subunit ε without loss of function in EF_0F_1 [65,105] and by video-micrographic rotation assay [106–108].

21.3.3.2 Proton Conductance of F_0

The magnitude of the proton conductance of F_0 has been under debate for mainly two reasons, (i) inadequate resolution of the pH-detector (e.g., glass electrodes) and (ii) uncertainty about the number of active F_0 in the assay chamber. This has led to both under- and overestimation of the conductance by orders of magnitude. Another factor is that a rotary proton carrier like F_0 is expected to show a conductance of femto- rather than pico-Siemens ($10^{-12}\,A\,V^{-1}$) at physiological pH. This has prevented the application of the patch-clamp technique (resolution of pS) to the proton conduction of single copies of F_0.

A solution was found by spectroscopic techniques using the inbuilt "molecular voltmeters" of photosynthetic membranes (see pioneering study in [109]). Chromatophore vesicles of a purple bacterium were prepared to such small size (diameter 30 nm) that they contained only about 0.3 copies of F_0 on the average (F_1 removed). This allowed the determination of the unitary conductance in the subset of vesicles containing a single copy of F_0 [30]. These mini-chromatophores contained the full complement for the primary processes of photosynthesis, i.e., about 10 copies of the bacterial reaction centre and the cytochrome bc_1-complex. A sudden jump of the transmembrane voltage (magnitude about 70 mV) was generated by flashing the chromatophores with a 2 ns laser, and the decay of the voltage was monitored spectrophotometrically by electrochromic absorption changes of intrinsic pigments, serving as a molecular voltmeter with high time resolution [25–27]. The relaxation time of the voltage was about 2.2 ms in vesicles with F_0 and was several orders of magnitude longer after the proton conduction by F_0 was specifically blocked. The calculated unitary proton conductance of BF_0 is 10 fS, which, at a voltage of 100 mV, implies 6240 protons transported per second. The conductance is ohmic, and the proton specificity is extremely high. At pH 8 and against a background of 100 mM of K^+ or Na^+ the rejection factor is 10^7. Despite the very high specificity the pH-dependence is rather low, in the wide pH range 6.5–10 it varies only by a factor of two [30]. This behavior was simulated by statistical mechanics in terms of the rotary transport model of Figure 12. The simulation required only three free parameters, including two different pK-values in the access channels (6.1 and 10, respectively). The least that can be said is that the rotary model is compatible with the observed conductance of F_0 [30]. How does the conductance of F_0 compare with the conductance of gramicidin A? It has been determined in the pH-range 0–4 units [110]. Extrapolated to pH 8 the expected proton conductance of gramicidin A is only 1 fS; this is tenfold lower than that of F_0, which is astounding in the light of the required rotation in the latter.

How does the conductance of F_0 compare with the conductance of the coupled enzyme, F_0F_1? The typical rate of ATP synthesis under high proton-motive force (say at 200 mV) is $300\,s^{-1}$ or 100 rps. With a C_{10}-symmetrical c-ring the rate of proton transport is $1000\,s^{-1}$, which is by one order of magnitude less than the expected rate of proton transport by free F_0 ($> 10000\,s^{-1}$ at 200 mV). Thus, F_0 operates as a low-impedance motor for the chemical generator, F_1.

21.3.4 F_0F_1, the Rotary Twin-Engine

21.3.4.1 Fine-Tuning Versus Robustness
The ATP synthase, F_0F_1, is a paradigmatic enzyme that has it all, a rotary electro-motor, a mechanical power transmission and a rotary chemical generator. How do they work together? Is one particular reaction step in one component, e.g., the passage of one proton through F_0, fine-tuned to a corresponding step in the other portion, e.g., the breaking of one particular hydrogen bond in F_1? The evidence clearly favors a robust over a finely tuned operation of this enzyme (see [94]).

Both its motor/generators are steppers. Their symmetries, C_3 and $C_{10,11,14}$, respectively, do not match in some organisms, but they do, C_3 versus C_{15}, in at least one. Sequence alignments between related subunits from different species show high similarity for a few key domains, e.g., the nucleotide binding pockets between αβ and the ion-binding domain on c, but very low similarity between

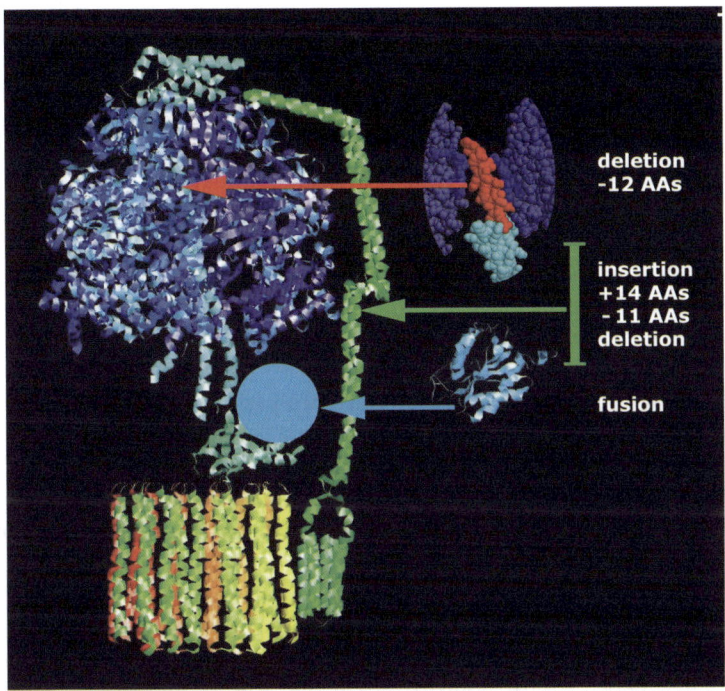

Figure 14. Robustness of the F_0F_1-ATP synthase; gross structural modifications without that EF_0F_1 loses its function. (i) Deletion of twelve C-terminal amino acids (marked in red) that normally anchor subunit γ in the "hydrophobic bearing" (dark blue) of $(\alpha\beta)_3$ [69]. (ii) Insertion of 14 or deletion of eleven residues from subunit b (the total length difference marked in green) [96]. (iii) Genetic fusion of flavodoxin light blue into subunit ε [14].

those portions and subunits involved in the mechanical action (e.g., only 13% sequence identity for δ between spinach chloroplasts and *E. coli* [111]). Figure 14 illustrates three types of severe structural alterations of the *E. coli* enzyme that do not inactivate the enzyme. (i) The deletion of 3–12 residues at the C-terminus of subunit γ neither impairs ATP hydrolysis by solubilized F_1 nor the ability of the fixed enzyme to generate torque and to drive an actin filament around [112]. This stretch on γ – shown in red in Figure 14 – supposedly holds the rotating shaft in its hydrophobic bearing (shown in dark blue). (ii) Insertion of 14 residues or deletion of 11 in subunit b – the length-difference of 25 given as a green bar in Figure 14 – does not impair the ability to perform proton-coupled ATP hydrolysis and synthesis [113,114]. (iii) The fusion of flavodoxin – shown in light blue – to subunit ε left EF_0F_1 functional as well [115]. Another wild construct, the chimeric enzyme, PF_0EF_1, gene-fused from α, β, γ, and ε of *E. coli* and subunits a, b, c, and δ of *P. modestum* is fully functional and displays the Na^+-translocation of its PF_0 portion [116]. The fusion of two, three [117] or five and ten copies of subunit c [63] in the rotor ring of bacterial enzymes is likewise tolerated. From the above, clearly, the two motor/generators of ATP synthase have not been coupled into a "finely tuned machine" as suggested by some. The question is what makes this enzyme so tolerant against gross structural modifications and change of gear in different organisms?

21.3.4.2 Elastic Power Transmission
The robustness of the function has fostered speculation on an elastic power transmission between and within F_0 and F_1 [118,119]. Kinetic modeling of proton transport and ATP synthesis seemed to support this view [66,93]. Conceivably, the rotor, with subunits γ, ε and the c-ring as a torsion spring, stores elastic energy provided by proton transport though F_0, and the peripheral stalk acts as an elastic counter-bearing. What is the evidence?

Figure 10(C) shows the experimental set-up to address this question. The enzyme is fixed on a solid support and hydrolyses ATP in a stepwise progression by 120°. Stepping implies discrete peaks of the torque (in loose terms power strokes). An actin filament is specifically bound to the c-ring by engineered step-tags [108]. It is exposed to the discrete torque pulses but its motion is overdamped, so that the free end does not immediately follow the jumps of the driving motor. It rotates quasi-continuously, and the stepping of the driving motor is blurred (see [96] for the theory). Because of the slow motion under heavy load (approximating thermodynamic equilibrium, as discussed above) the momentary torque is reflected by the filament's curvature. Curvature analysis revealed the rather flat torque-profile shown in Figure 11(A) [95], a minor period of 3 over 360°-rotation, was evident from Fourier analysis (see insert in Figure 11B). Integration of torque over the angle yielded the work output at the c-ring (Fig 11B), a rather straight line here calibrated in units of $k_B T$. Over 360° it covers $83kT$, i.e., $28k_B T$ per ATP-molecule ($67\,\text{kJ}\,\text{mol}^{-1}$). Why does the stepper motor F_1, which by itself has a strongly undulated energy profile (activation energy of 40–$50\,\text{kJ}\,\text{mol}^{-1}$), deliver an almost linear work profile, i.e., almost constant torque, to its partner motor, F_0? This situation has been analyzed by solving the Fokker–Planck equation for a stepper motor that is elastically coupled to a heavy load [95,96], and the result is illustrated in Figure 15.

The solid line in Figure 15(A) describes the free energy profile of free F_1 over 240°. The free energy difference between two minima reflects the useful work from the hydrolysis of ATP. When the enzyme runs downhill to the right it produces torque and delivers heat to the bath. When it runs uphill further to the right, it borrows energy from the heat bath to cross the barrier. If the enzyme is elastically coupled to the load, the elastic element stores the otherwise dissipated energy and flattens the profile, as shown by the broken lines in Figure 15(A). The smaller the torsional rigidity of the power transmission, the straighter the energy profile. [The torsional rigidity (C) relates the torque (M) to the deformation angle (Φ) of a spring (length L) such that: $M = (C/L)\Phi$.]

21.3.4.3 Kinetic Efficiency
The elastic power transmission has important consequences for the performance of rotary engines under load. Figure 15(B) describes the calculated

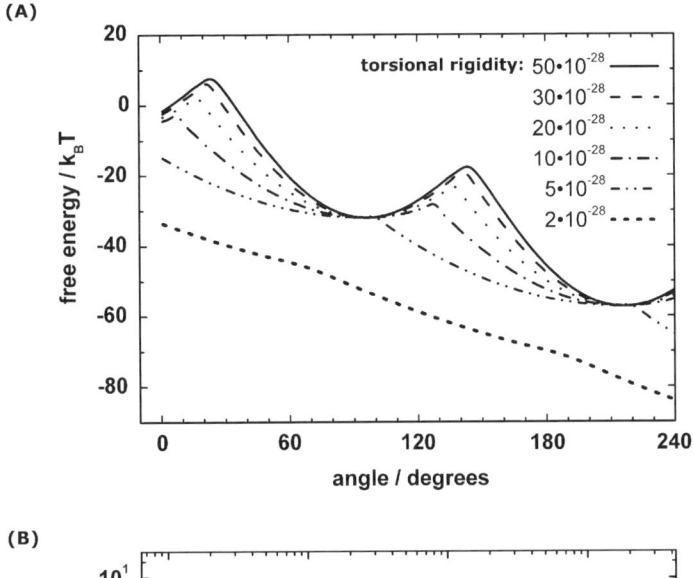

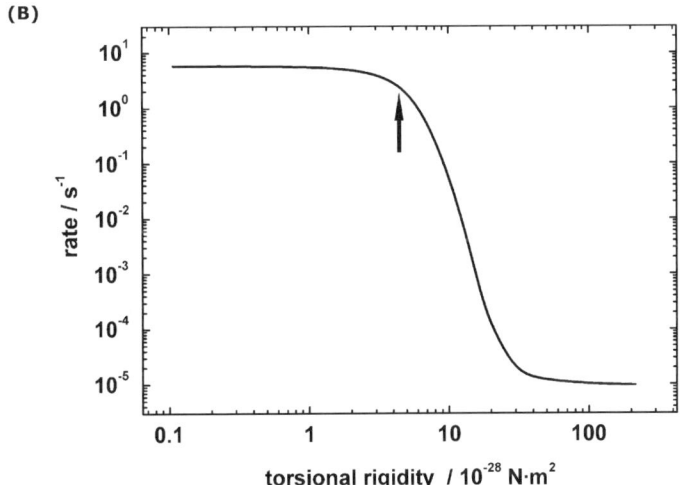

Figure 15. The free energy profile (A) and the turnover rate (B) of a rotary stepper motor as a function of the torsional rigidity of the elastic power transmission to a heavy load [95] (for a detailed description, see text).

rotation rate of the stepper motor F_1 as a function of the torsional rigidity of the elastic power transmission. A high rate requires a soft elastic transmission, whereas a rigid one reduces the rate by orders of magnitude (see [95] for details).

This invokes another efficiency of the enzyme, namely the kinetic efficiency (η_{kin}), as defined by the ratio of the reaction flux (J) over the maximum possible flux (J_{max}):

$$\eta_{kin} = \frac{J}{J_{max}} \tag{9a}$$

as opposed to the thermodynamic efficiency (η_{therm}):

$$\eta_{\text{therm}} = \frac{\Delta W}{-\Delta G} \tag{9b}$$

wherein δW denotes the work done and ΔG the free energy difference of the driving motor.

The thermodynamic efficiency is maximum if the enzyme is stalled, $\eta_{\text{therm}} = 1$, by definition of ΔG. For any realistic turnover rate of the enzyme the thermodynamic efficiency drops. The kinetic efficiency, on the other hand, can be influenced by engineering. An elastic power transmission straightens the free energy profile to achieve constant torque and high turnover rate. Thus, the elastic coupling is essential for the performance of ATP synthase under physiological conditions. Take, for example, E. coli, where the enzyme uses p.m.f. to produce ATP, and, vice versa, uses ATP to restore p.m.f. should it fall low. At the compensation point each of the two motors runs against the heavy load presented by the other one. Whether ATP production or consumption wins is determined by the consumers of ATP and p.m.f. in the cell. This is where an elastic power transmission provides a high turnover rate (Figure 15B). It appears almost as a side effect of the elastic transmission that it guarantees the robustness of function with different gears, using 4.7 protons per ATP in one organism and 3.3 in another. Which physiological conditions call for different gears is not yet clear. Elasticity also accounts for the functioning in structurally modified constructs. ATP synthase is surely not the finely tuned twin-motor as admired by some, it is rather its simplicity and versatility that is beautiful.

The molecular basis of the elastic power transmission between F_0 and F_1 is the subject of present research. The torsional and flexural compliance of α-helices, the bending or the sequential breaking of hydrogen bonds, and the proportion of elastic energy storage in the central shaft versus the peripheral stalk are interesting questions to follow.

21.4 Outlook

ATP synthase is a paradigmatic enzyme that has it all, an electrical rotary motor, a mechanical power transmission and a rotary chemical generator. ATP synthase is surely not the finely tuned twin-motor as often imagined. Its construction is rather distinguished by simplicity, robustness and versatility – that is its beauty. ATP synthase is among the smallest, surely the most versatile and perhaps the best understood, of nature's nano-engines. With the clear separation of its electrochemical, mechanical and chemical functions, their association with distinct subunits, and with the conservation of these properties over the kingdoms of life the F_0F_1-ATPase has been an ideal target for an integrated attack by molecular genetics (best EF_0F_1), structural biology (best MF_1 and PF_0), rotation assay (best TF_1), and kinetic techniques (best CF_0F_1 and BF_0F_1). It has also been a unique feature that its dynamic behavior over the major reaction coordinate can almost be followed "by eye". Thus ATP synthase presents itself as the appropriate subject for elucidating principles of the electro-mechano-chemical couplings in enzymes. Although it is "done" for undergraduate textbooks, it is not for deeper understanding, which is why it will remain a subject of active research over the next decade, in the same way that the bacterial reaction centre, bacteriorhodopsin and even myoglobin have, long after the first principles of their operation were evident.

References

1. D.I. Arnon, M.B. Allen, F.R. Whatley, Photosynthesis by isolated chloroplasts. *Nature* **174** (1954) 394–396.
2. E.C. Slater, Mechanism of phosphorylation in the respiratory chain. *Nature* **172** (1953) 975–978.
3. P. Mitchell, Coupling of photophosphorylation to electron and hydrogen transfer by a chemiosmotic type of mechanism. *Nature* **191** (1961) 144–148.
4. P. Mitchell, Chemiosmotic coupling in oxidative and photosynthetic phosphorylation. *Physiol. Rev.* **41** (1966) 445–502.
5. A.T. Jagendorf, E. Uribe, ATP formation caused by acid-base transition of spinach chloroplast. *Proc. Natl. Acad. Sci. U.S.A.* **55** (1966) 170–177.
6. W. Junge, B. Rumberg, H. Schroeder, Necessity of an electric potential difference and its use for photophosphorylation in short flash groups. *Eur. J. Biochem.* **14** (1970) 575–581.
7. E. Racker, W. Stoeckenius, Reconstitution of purple membrane vesicles catalyzing light-driven proton uptake and adenosine triphosphate formation. *J. Biol. Chem.* **25** (1974) 662–663.
8. H.S. Penefsky, M.E. Pullman, A. Datta, E. Racker, Partial resolution of the enzymes catalyzing oxidative phosphorylation. II. Participation of a soluble adenosine triphosphatase in oxidative phosphorylation. *J. Biol. Chem.* **235** (1960) 3330–3336.
9. P.D. Boyer, The binding-change mechanism of ATP synthesis, in: *Membrane Bioenergetics* (1979) (C.P. Lee, G. Schatz, L. Ernster, eds.), Addison-Wesley, Reading, Mass, pp. 476–479.
10. P.D. Boyer, W.E. Kohlbrenner, The present status of the binding-change mechanism and its relation to ATP formation by chloroplasts, in: *Energy coupling in Photosynthesis* (1981) (B.R. Selman, S. Selman-Reimer, eds.), Elsevier, Amsterdam, pp. 231–241.
11. P.D. Boyer, The ATP synthase – a splendid molecular machine. *Annu. Rev. Biochem.* **66** (1997) 717–749.
12. J.P. Abrahams, A.G.W. Leslie, R. Lutter, J.E. Walker, The structure of F_1-ATPase from bovine heart mitochondria determined at 2.8 Å resolution. *Nature* **370** (1994) 621–628.
13. D. Stock, C. Gibbons, I. Arechaga, A.G. Leslie, J.E. Walker, The rotary mechanism of ATP synthase. *Curr. Opin. Chem. Biol.* **10** (2000) 672–679.
14. T.M. Duncan, V.V. Bulygin, Y. Zhou, M.L. Hutcheon, R.L. Cross, Rotation of subunits during catalysis by *Escherichia coli* F_1- ATPase. *Proc. Natl. Acad. Sci. U.S.A.* **92** (1995) 10964–10968.

15. D. Sabbert, S. Engelbrecht, W. Junge, Intersubunit rotation in active F-ATPase. *Nature* **381** (1996) 623–625.
16. H. Noji, R. Yasuda, M. Yoshida, K. Kinosita, Direct observation of the rotation of F-ATPase. *Nature* **386** (1997) 299–302.
17. L.G. Sillén, A.E. Martell, *Stability Constants of Metal-Ion Complexes* (1964), The Chemical Society, London.
18. R.J.P. Williams, Possible functions of chains of catalysts. *J. Theor. Biol.* **1** (1961) 1–17.
19. R.J.P. Williams, Possible functions of chains of catalysts II. *J. Theor. Biol.* **3** (1962) 209–229.
20. J.F. Nagle, Propaedeutics of ion transport across biomembranes, in: *Ion Transport through Membranes* (1987) (K. Yagi, B. Pullmann, eds.), Academic Press, Tokyo, pp. 181–191.
21. J. Rosing, E.C. Slater, The value of ΔG for the hydrolysis of ATP. *Biochim. Biophys. Acta* **267** (1972) 275–290.
22. S.C. Hinnah, R. Wagner, Thylakoid membranes contain a high-conductance channel. *Eur. J. Biochem.* **253** (1998) 606–613.
23. L.A. Staehelin, *Encyclopedia of Plant Physiology* (1986), Springer-Verlag, Berlin.
24. G. Schönknecht, G. Althoff, W. Junge, The electric unit size of thylakoid membranes. *FEBS Lett.* **277** (1990) 65–68.
25. W. Junge, H.T. Witt, On the ion transport system of photosynthesis – Investigation on a molecular level-. *Z. Naturforsch., Teil B* **23** (1968) 244–254.
26. C. Wolff, H.T. Witt, Metastable states of carotenoids in primary events of photosynthesis. Registration by repetitive ultra-short-flash photometry. *Z. Naturforsch.* **24** (1969) 1031–1037.
27. J.B. Jackson, A.R. Crofts, High energy state in chromatophores of *Rhodopseudomonas speroides*. *FEBS Lett.* **4** (1969) 185–189.
28. H.T. Witt, Coupling of quanta, electrons, fields, ions, and phosphorylation in the functional membrane of photosynthesis. Results by pulse spectroscopic methods. *Q. Rev. Biophys.* **4** (1971) 365–477.
29. W. Junge, J.B. Jackson, The development of electrochemical potential gradients across photosynthetic membranes, in: *Photosynthesis: Energy Conversion by Plants and Bacteria* (1982) (R.A. Govindjee, ed.), Academic Press Inc., New York, pp. 589–646.
30. B.A. Feniouk, M.A. Kozlova, D.A. Knorre, D. Cherepanov, A. Mulkidjanian, W. Junge, The proton driven rotor of ATP synthase: Ohmic conductance, (10fS) and absence of voltage gating. *Biophys. J.* **86** (2004) 4094–4109.
31. P. Mitchell, Proton motive redox mechanism of the cytochrome b-c_1 complex in the respiratory chain: Proton motive ubiquinone cycle. *FEBS Lett.* **56** (1975) 1–6.
32. D.B. Kell, On the functional proton current pathway of electron transport phosphorylation. An electrodic view. *Biochim. Biophys. Acta* **549** (1979) 55–99.
33. S.J. Ferguson, Fully delocalised chemiosmotic or localised proton flow pathways in energy coupling? A scrutiny of experimental evidence. *Biochim. Biophys. Acta* **811** (1985) 47–95.
34. W.A. Cramer, D.B. Knaff, *Energy Transduction in Biological Membranes: A Textbook of Bioenergetics* (1990), Springer-Verlag, New York.
35. R.A. Dilley, Energy coupling in chloroplasts – a calcium-gated switch controls proton fluxes between localized and delocalized proton gradients. *Curr. Top. Bioenerg.* **16** (1991) 265–318.

36. T.A. Krulwich, M. Ito, R. Gilmour, D.B. Hicks, A.A. Guffanti, Energetics of alkaliphilic Bacillus species: physiology and molecules. *Adv. Microb. Physiol.* **40** (1998) 401–438.
37. D.A. Cherepanov, W. Junge, A.Y. Mulkidjanian, Proton transfer dynamics at the membrane/water interface: Dependence on fixed and mobile pH buffers, on the size and form of membrane particles, and on the interfacial potential barrier. *Biophys. J.* **86** (2004) 665–680.
38. D.A. Cherepanov, B.A. Feniouk, W. Junge, A.Y. Mulkidjanian, Low dielectric permittivity of water at the membrane interface: effect on the energy coupling mechanism in biological membranes. *Biophys. J.* **85** (2003) 1307–1316.
39. H.S. van Walraven, H. Strotmann, O. Schwarz, B. Rumberg, The H^+/ATP coupling ratio of the ATP synthase from thiol-modulated chloroplasts and two cyanobacterial strains is four. *FEBS Lett.* **379** (1996) 309–313.
40. P. Turina, D. Samoray, P. Gräber, H^+/ATP ratio of proton transport-coupled ATP synthesis and hydrolysis catalysed by CF0F1-liposomes. *EMBO J.* **22** (2003) 418–426.
41. H. Seelert, A. Poetsch, N.A. Dencher, A. Engel, H. Stahlberg, D.J. Mueller, Proton-powered turbine of a plant motor. *Nature* **405** (2000) 418–419.
42. G. Groth, E. Pohl, The structure of the chloroplast F1-ATPase at 3.2 Å resolution. *J. Biol. Chem.* **276** (2001) 1345–1352.
43. T. Hisabori, H. Konno, H. Ichimura, H. Strotmann, D. Bald, Molecular devices of chloroplast F(1)-ATP synthase for the regulation. *Biochim. Biophys. Acta* **1555** (2002) 140–146.
44. P. Gräber, The H^+-ATPase from chloroplasts: energetics of the catalytic cycle. *Biochim. Biophys. Acta* **1187** (1994) 171–176.
45. B.A. Feniouk, T. Suzuki, M. Yoshida, The role of subunit epsilon in the catalysis and regulation of F(O)F(1)-ATP synthase. *Biochim. Biophys. Acta* **1757** (2006) 326–338.
46. G. Groth, W. Junge, Proton slip of chloroplast ATPase: Its nucleotide dependence, energetic threshold and relation to an alternating site mechanism of catalysis. *Biochemistry* **32** (1993) 8103–8111.
47. B.A. Feniouk, A.Y. Mulkidjanian, W. Junge, Induction and properties of proton slip in the ATP synthase from Rhodobacter capsulatus. *Biochim. Biophys. Acta-Bioenerg.* **1658** (2004) 109.
48. D. Sabbert, S. Engelbrecht, W. Junge, Functional and idling rotatory motion within F-ATPase. *Proc. Natl. Acad. Sci. U.S.A.* **94** (1997) 4401–4405.
49. M. Bianchet, X. Ysern, J. Hullihen, P.L. Pedersen, L.M. Amzel, Mitochondrial ATP synthase – quaternary structure of the F_1 moiety at 3.6 Å determined by X-ray diffraction analysis. *J. Biol. Chem.* **266** (1991) 21197–21201.
50. G. Groth, Structure of spinach chloroplast F1-ATPase complexed with the phytopathogenic inhibitor tentoxin. *Proc. Natl. Acad. Sci. U.S.A.* **99** (2002) 3464–3468.
51. R.I. Menz, J.E. Walker, A.G. Leslie, Structure of bovine mitochondrial F(1)-ATPase with nucleotide bound to all three catalytic sites: implications for the mechanism of rotary catalysis. *Cell* **106** (2001) 331–341.
52. R. Kagawa, M.G. Montgomery, K. Braig, A.G.W. Leslie, J.E. Walker, The structure of bovine F-1-ATPase inhibited by ADP and beryllium fluoride. *EMBO J.* **23** (2004) 2734–2744.
53. K. Braig, R.I. Menz, M.G. Montgomery, A.G. Leslie, J.E. Walker, Structure of bovine mitochondrial F(1)-ATPase inhibited by Mg^{2+} ADP and aluminium fluoride. *Structure* **8** (2000) 567–573.

54. G.L. Orriss, A.G.W. Leslie, K. Braig, J.E. Walker, Bovine F_1-ATPase covalently inhibited with 4-chloro-7-nitrobenzofurazan – the structure provides further support for a rotary catalytic mechanism. *Structure* **6** (1998) 831–837.
55. J.P. Abrahams, S.K. Buchanan, M.J. van Raaij, I.M. Fearnley, A.G. Leslie, J.E. Walker, The structure of bovine F1-ATPase complexed with the peptide antibiotic efrapeptin. *Proc. Natl. Acad. Sci. U.S.A.* **93** (1996) 9420–9424.
56. Y. Shirakihara, A.G.W. Leslie, J.P. Abrahams, J.E. Walker, T. Ueda, Y. Sekimoto, M. Kambara, K. Saika, Y. Kagawa, M. Yoshida, The crystal structure of the nucleotide-free alpha-3-beta-3 subcomplex of F_1-ATPase from the thermophilic *Bacillus* PS3 is a symmetric trimer. *Structure* **5** (1997) 825–836.
57. J. Hoppe, M. Brunner, B.B. Jorgensen, Structure of the membrane-embedded F_0 part of F_1F_0 ATP synthase from *Escherichia coli* as inferred from labeling with 3-(trifluoromethyl)-3-(m-[125I]iodophenyl)diazirine. *Biochemistry* **23** (1984) 5610–5616.
58. P.C. Jones, W.P. Jiang, R.H. Fillingame, Arrangement of the multicopy H^+-translocating subunit c in the membrane sector of the *Escherichia coli* F_1F_0 ATP synthase. *J. Biol. Chem.* **273** (1998) 17178–17185.
59. M.E. Girvin, V.K. Rastogi, F. Abildgaard, J.L. Markley, R.H. Fillingame, Solution structure of the transmembrane H^+-transporting subunit c of the F_1F_0 ATP synthase. *Biochemistry* **37** (1998) 8817–8824.
60. T. Meier, P. Polzer, K. Diederichs, W. Welte, P. Dimroth, Structure of the rotor ring of F-Type Na^+-ATPase from Ilyobacter tartaricus. *Science* **308** (2005) 659–662.
61. D. Stock, A.G. Leslie, J.E. Walker, Molecular architecture of the rotary motor in ATP synthase. *Science* **286** (1999) 1700–1705.
62. W. Jiang, J. Hermolin, R.H. Fillingame, The preferred stoichiometry of c subunits in the rotary motor sector of Escherichia coli ATP synthase is 10. *Proc. Natl. Acad. Sci. U.S.A.* **98** (2001) 4966–4971.
63. N. Mitome, T. Suzuki, S. Hayashi, M. Yoshida, Thermophilic ATP synthase has a decamer c-ring: indication of noninteger 10:3 H+/ATP ratio and permissive elastic coupling. *Proc. Natl. Acad. Sci. U.S.A.* **101** (2004) 12159–12164.
64. C.L. Tang, R.A. Capaldi, Characterization of the interface between gamma and epsilon subunits of *Escherichia coli* F_1-ATPase. *J. Biol. Chem.* **271** (1996) 3018–3024.
65. B. Schulenberg, R. Aggeler, J. Murray, R.A. Capaldi, The gammaepsilon-c subunit interface in the ATP synthase of Escherichia coli. Cross-linking of the epsilon subunit to the c subunit ring does not impair enzyme function, that of gamma to c subunits leads to uncoupling. *J. Biol. Chem.* **274** (1999) 34233–34237.
66. W. Junge, H. Lill, S. Engelbrecht, ATP synthase: an electrochemical transducer with rotatory mechanics. *Trends Biochem. Sci.* **22** (1997) 420–423.
67. D. Zhang, S.B. Vik, Helix packing in subunit a of the Escherichia coli ATP synthase as determined by chemical labeling and proteolysis of the cysteine-substituted protein. *Biochemistry* **42** (2003) 331–337.
68. S.D. Dunn, D.T. McLachlin, M. Revington, The second stalk of Escherichia coli ATP synthase. *Biochim. Biophys. Acta* **1458** (2000) 356–363.
69. K. Häsler, O. Pänke, W. Junge, On the stator of rotary ATP synthase: the binding strength of subunit delta to $(\alpha\beta)_3$ as determined by fluorescence correlation spectroscopy. *Biochemistry* **38** (1999) 13759–13765.
70. J. Weber, S. Wilke-Mounts, S. Nadanaciva, A.E. Senior, Quantitative determination of direct binding of b subunit to F1 in Escherichia coli F_1F_0-ATP synthase. *J. Biol Chem.* **279** (2004) 11253–11258.

71. V.K. Dickson, J.A. Silvester, I.M. Fearnley, A.G. Leslie, J.E. Walker, On the structure of the stator of the mitochondrial ATP synthase. *EMBO J.* **25** (2006) 2911–2918.
72. P.D. Boyer, The binding change mechanism for ATP synthase – Some probabilities and possibilities. *Biochim. Biophys. Acta* **1140** (1993) 215–250.
73. J. Weber, A.E. Senior, ATP synthase: what we know about ATP hydrolysis and what we do not know about ATP synthesis. *Biochim. Biophys. Acta* **1458** (2000) 300–309.
74. J. Weber, A.E. Senior, Catalytic mechanism of F_1-ATPase. *Biochim. Biophys. Acta* **1319** (1997) 19–58.
75. H. Ren, S. Bandyopadhyay, W.S. Allison, The $\alpha_3\beta_3$(Met222Ser/Tyr345Trp) gamma subcomplex of the TF1-ATPase does not hydolyze ATP at a significant rate until the substrate binds to the catalytic site of the lowest affinity. *Biochemistry* **45** (2006) 6222–6230.
76. A.E. Senior, J. Weber, Happy motoring with ATP synthase. *Nat. Struct. Mol. Biol.* **11** (2004) 110–112.
77. R.L. Cross, The mechanism and regulation of ATP synthesis by F_1-ATPases. *Annu. Rev. Biochem.* **50** (1981) 681–714.
78. J. Weber, A.E. Senior, ATP synthesis driven by proton transport in F1F0-ATP synthase. *FEBS Lett.* **545** (2003) 61–70.
79. Y. Zhou, T.M. Duncan, R.L. Cross, Subunit rotation in *Escherichia coli* F_0F_1-ATP synthase during oxidative phosphorylation. *Proc. Natl. Acad. Sci. U.S.A.* **94** (1997) 10583–10587.
80. D. Sabbert, W. Junge, Stepped versus continuous rotatory motors at the molecular scale. *Proc. Natl. Acad. Sci. U.S.A.* **94** (1997) 2312–2317.
81. R. Yasuda, H. Noji, M. Yoshida, K. Kinosita, Jr., H. Itoh, Resolution of distinct rotational substeps by submillisecond kinetic analysis of F1-ATPase. *Nature* **410** (2001) 898–904.
82. K. Shimabukuro, R. Yasuda, E. Muneyuki, K.Y. Hara, K. Kinosita, Jr., M. Yoshida, Catalysis and rotation of F1 motor: cleavage of ATP at the catalytic site occurs in 1 ms before 40 degree substep rotation. *Proc. Natl. Acad. Sci. U.S.A.* **100** (2003) 14731–14736.
83. T. Nishizaka, K. Oiwa, H. Noji, S. Kimura, E. Muneyuki, M. Yoshida, K. Kinosita, Jr., Chemomechanical coupling in F1-ATPase revealed by simultaneous observation of nucleotide kinetics and rotation. *Nat. Struct. Mol. Biol* **11** (2004) 142–148.
84. K. Häsler, S. Engelbrecht, W. Junge, Three-stepped rotation of subunits γ and ε in single molecules of F-ATPase as revealed by polarized, confocal fluorometry. *FEBS Lett.* **426** (1998) 301–304.
85. G. Kaim, M. Prummer, B. Sick, G. Zumofen, A. Renn, U.P. Wild, P. Dimroth, Coupled rotation within single F0F1 enzyme complexes during ATP synthesis or hydrolysis. *FEBS Lett.* **525** (2002) 156–163.
86. M. Diez, B. Zimmermann, M. Borsch, M. Konig, E. Schweinberger, S. Steigmiller, R. Reuter, S. Felekyan, V. Kudryavtsev, C. A. Seidel, P. Graber, Proton-powered subunit rotation in single membrane-bound F_0F_1-ATP synthase. *Nat. Struct. Mol. Biol.* **11** (2004) 135–141.
87. B. Zimmermann, M. Diez, N. Zarrabi, P. Graber, M. Borsch, Movements of the epsilon-subunit during catalysis and activation in single membrane-bound H^+-ATP synthase. *EMBO J.* **24** (2005) 2053–2063.
88. H. Itoh, A. Takahashi, K. Adachi, H. Noji, R. Yasuda, M. Yoshida, K. Kinosita, Mechanically driven ATP synthesis by F_1-ATPase. *Nature* **427** (2004) 465–468.

89. A.J. Hunt, F. Gittes, J. Howard, The force exerted by a single kinesin molecule against a viscous load. *Biophys. J.* **67** (1994) 766–781.
90. M.M. Tirado, J. Garcia de la Torre, Rotational dynamics of rigid, symmetrical top macromolecules. Application to circular cylinders. *J. Chem. Phys.* **73** (1980) 1986–1993.
91. R. Yasuda, H. Noji, K. Kinosita, M. Yoshida, F_1-ATPase is a highly efficient molecular motor that rotates with discrete 120° steps. *Cell* **93** (1998) 1117–1124.
92. K. Kinosita, Jr., R. Yasuda, H. Noji, K. Adachi, A rotary molecular motor that can work at near 100% efficiency. *Philos. Trans. R. Soc. London B Biol. Sci.* **355** (2000) 473–489.
93. H.Y. Wang, G. Oster, Energy transduction in the F_1 motor of ATP synthase. *Nature* **396** (1998) 279–282.
94. W. Junge, O. Pänke, D. Cherepanov, K. Gumbiowski, M. Müller, S. Engelbrecht, Inter-subunit rotation and elastic power transmission in F_0F_1-ATPase. *FEBS Lett.* **504** (2001) 152–160.
95. O. Pänke, D.A. Cherepanov, K. Gumbiowski, S. Engelbrecht, W. Junge, Viscoelastic dynamics of actin filaments coupled to rotary F-ATPase: torque profile of the enzyme. *Biophys. J.* **81** (2001) 1220–1233.
96. D.A. Cherepanov, W. Junge, Viscoelastic dynamics of actin filaments coupled to rotary F-ATPase: Curvature as an indicator of the torque. *Biophys. J.* **81** (2001) 1234–1244.
97. N. Sakaki, R. Shimo-Kon, K. Adachi, H. Itoh, S. Furuike, E. Muneyuki, M. Yoshida, K. Kinosita Jr, One rotary mechanism for F_1-ATPase over ATP concentrations from millimolar down to nanomolar. *Biophys. J.* **88** (2005) 2047–2056.
98. S.B. Vik, B.J. Antonio, A mechanism of proton translocation by F_1F_0 ATP synthases suggested by double mutants of the a subunit. *J. Biol. Chem.* **269** (1994) 30364–30369.
99. P. Dimroth, H. Wang, M. Grabe, G. Oster, Energy transduction in the sodium F-ATPase of *Propionigenium modestum*. *Proc. Natl. Acad. Sci. U.S.A.* **96** (1999) 4924–4928.
100. T. Elston, H. Wang, G. Oster, Energy transduction in ATP synthase. *Nature* **391** (1998) 510–514.
101. R.P. Feynman, R.B. Leighton, M. Sands, *The Feynman Lectures on Physics* (1963) Addison-Wesley Publishing, Palo Alto, London, New York.
102. W. Junge, N. Nelson, Nature's rotary electromotors. *Science* **308** (2005) 642–644.
103. R.H. Fillingame, W. Jiang, O.Y. Dmitriev, Coupling H^+ transport to rotary catalysis in F-type ATP synthases: structure and organization of the transmembrane rotary motor. *J. Exp. Biol.* **203**(Pt 1) (2000) 9–17.
104. P. Dimroth, U. Matthey, G. Kaim, Critical evaluation of the one- versus the two-channel model for the operation of the ATP synthase's F_0 motor. *Biochim. Biophys. Acta-Bioenerg.* **1459** (2000) 506–513.
105. S.P. Tsunoda, R. Aggeler, M. Yoshida, R.A. Capaldi, Rotation of the c subunit oligomer in fully functional F_1F_0 ATP synthase. *Proc. Natl. Acad. Sci. U.S.A.* **98** (2001) 898–902.
106. Y. Sambongi, Y. Iko, M. Tanabe, H. Omote, A. Iwamoto-Kihara, I. Ueda, T. Yanagida, Y. Wada, M. Futai, Mechanical rotation of the c subunit oligomer in ATP synthase, (F_1F_0): direct observation. *Science* **286** (1999) 1722–1724.

107. S.P. Tsunoda, R. Aggeler, H. Noji, K. Kinosita, M. Yoshida, R.A. Capaldi, Observations of rotatison within the F_0F_1-ATP synthase: deciding between rotation of the F_0c subunit ring and artifact. *FEBS Lett.* **470** (2000) 244–248.
108. O. Pänke, K. Gumbiowski, W. Junge, S. Engelbrecht, F-ATPase: specific observation of the rotating c subunit oligomer of EF_0EF_1. *FEBS Lett.* **472** (2000) 34–38.
109. G. Schönknecht, W. Junge, H. Lill, S. Engelbrecht, Complete tracking of proton flow in thylakoids – the unit conductance of CF_0 is greater than 10 fS. *FEBS Lett.* **203** (1986) 289–294.
110. S. Cukierman, Proton mobilities in water and in different stereoisomers of covalently linked gramicidin A channels. *Biophys. J.* **78** (2000) 1825–1834.
111. S. Engelbrecht, W. Junge, Subunit δ of H^+-ATPases: at the interface between proton flow and ATP synthesis. *Biochim. Biophys. Acta* **1015** (1990) 379–390.
112. M. Müller, O. Pänke, W. Junge, S. Engelbrecht, F_1-ATPase: the C-terminal end of subunit γ is not required for ATP hydrolysis-driven rotation. *J. Biol. Chem.* **277** (2002) 23308–23313.
113. P.L. Sorgen, T.L. Caviston, R.C. Perry, B.D. Cain, Deletions in the second stalk of F_1F_0-ATP synthase in *Escherichia coli*. *J. Biol. Chem.* **273** (1998) 27873–27878.
114. P.L. Sorgen, M.R. Bubb, B.D. Cain, Lengthening the second stalk of F_1F_0 ATP synthase in Escherichia coli. *J. Biol. Chem.* **274** (1999) 36261–36266.
115. D.J. Cipriano, Y. Bi, S.D. Dunn, Genetic fusions of globular proteins to the epsilon subunit of the Escherichia coli ATP synthase: Implications for in vivo rotational catalysis and epsilon subunit function. *J. Biol. Chem.* **277** (2002) 16782–16790.
116. G. Kaim, P. Dimroth, Formation of a functionally active sodium-translocating hybrid F_1F_0 ATPase in *Propionigenium modestum* by homologous recombination. *Eur. J. Biochem.* **218** (1995) 937–944.
117. P.C. Jones, J. Hermolin, R.H. Fillingame, Mutations in single hairpin units of genetically fused subunit c provide support for a rotary catalytic mechanism in F_0F_1 ATP synthase. *J. Biol. Chem.* **275** (2000) 11355–11360.
118. D.A. Cherepanov, A. Mulkidjanian, W. Junge, Transient accumulation of elastic energy in proton translocating ATP synthase. *FEBS Lett.* **449** (1999) 1–6.
119. O. Pänke, B. Rumberg, Kinetic modeling of rotary CF_0F_1-ATP synthase: storage of elastic energy during energy transduction. *Biochim. Biophys. Acta* **1412** (1999) 118–128.
120. G. Drews, J.R. Golecki, Structure, molecular organization, and biosynthesis of membranes of purple bacteria; R.E. Blankenship, M.T. Madigan, C.E. Bauer, [2], in: *Advances in Photosynthesis: Anoxygenic Photosynthetic Bacteria* (1995) (Govindjee, ed), Kluwer, Dordrecht, pp. 231–257.
121. B. Rumberg, U. Becher, Multiple delta pH control of H^+-ATP synthase function in chloroplasts, in: *H^+-ATPase(ATP Synthase): Structure, Function, Biogenesis. The F_0F_1 Complex of Coupling Membranes* (1984) (S. Papa, K. Altendorf, L. Ernster, L. Packer, eds), Adriatica Editrice, Bari Italy, pp. 421–430.
122. D. Pogoryelor, J. Yu, T. Meier, J. Vonck, P. Dimroth, D.J. Müller, The C_{15}-ring of the *Spirulina platensis* F-ATP synthase: F_1/F_0 symmetry mismatch is not obligatory. *EMBO Rep.* **6**, 1040–1044.

VIII. Evolution

Chapter 22

The Evolution of Photosynthesis

Anthony W.D. Larkum

Table of Contents

- 22.1 Formation of the Earth and Early Life ....
  - 22.1.1 Introduction ....
  - 22.1.2 Formation of the Moon and the Asteroid Phase
  - 22.1.3 First Signs of Life ....
- 22.2 Respiration and Photosynthesis. ....
- 22.3 Significance of Photosynthesis for Early Life on Earth
- 22.4 First Phase of Photosynthesis: Harvesting Energy ...
- 22.5 Possible Scenarios for the Evolution of Chlorophylls/ Bacteriochlorophylls. ....
  - 22.5.1 Biosynthetic Pathway. ....
  - 22.5.2 Chlorophyll or Bacteriochlorophyll First?....
- 22.6 Reaction Centers and Light-Harvesting Antennae ..
  - 22.6.1 Reaction Centers.....................
  - 22.6.2 Light-Harvesting Complexes ....
- 22.7 Anoxygenic Bacterial Photosynthesis............
  - 22.7.1 General Description...................
  - 22.7.2 Types of Anoxygenic PS Bacteria ....
- 22.8 Evolution of Two Photosystems in One Organism .
  - 22.8.1 Fusion Hypothesis....................
  - 22.8.2 Fission Hypothesis ....
- 22.9 Evolution of Water Splitting and Release of Molecular Oxygen ....
- 22.10 Evolutionary Timing of Major Photosynthetic Events
- 22.11 The Oxygen Revolution ....
- 22.12 Light-Harvesting Proteins..................
- 22.13 The Rise of Eukaryotes and Algal Protists. .....
- 22.14 Evolution of Plants, Animals and Fungi ....
- 22.15 The Future ....
- Acknowledgements ....
- References...................................

Abstract

Photosynthesis probably began on the Earth soon after life itself, as the early sources of chemical energy (geothermal, reducing compounds, hydrogen) were exhausted [about 3.7 giga years (Ga) ago]. However, a primitive form of respiration is likely to have preceded photosynthesis, providing complexes such as cytochromes and iron-sulfur centers. Anoxygenic photosynthetic (PS) bacteria were the first organisms involved, but it should not be assumed that these were similar to those found today, and it is possible that they used both chlorophylls and bacteriochlorophylls, in simple light-driven reactions. This was followed by the evolution of complex reaction centers and light-harvesting complexes, which could cope with light and oxidative stresses. This leads to the development of reaction centre I-type (RCI-type) centers, with iron-sulfur centers as secondary electron acceptors, and RC-II-type centers, with quinones as the secondary electron acceptors. These events may have occurred in two lines of PS bacteria, with the later development of cyanobacterial-like organisms, with both types of RC, brought about by fusion (Fusion Hypothesis). However, it is also possible that the two types of RC developed in one organism and later separated (Fission hypothesis), giving rise to the present situation with anoxygenic photosynthetic bacteria with either one or the other type of RC but not both. The next big development was the ability to split water to gain hydrogen that is vital for the reduction of inorganic carbon (CO_2). This developed in the forerunners of present day cyanobacteria about 2.2–2.8 Ga. This was one of the most revolutionary events to happen on the Earth: it turned the atmosphere into an oxidizing rather than a reducing one, allowed the evolution of oxidative bacteria, allowed the evolution of mitochondriate protists, which in turn paved the way for the evolution of algae (protists with mitochondria and chloroplasts). The final step, multicellularity, led to the three multicellular domains dominant on terrestrial parts of the Earth today, the animals, plants and fungi.

22.1 Formation of the Earth and Early Life

22.1.1 Introduction

There is now good agreement amongst cosmologists that the Earth formed from a primordial cloud of dust, of earthy materials, approximately 4.5 billion years ago [1]. This same dust cloud also gave rise to all four of the innermost planets (Mercury, Venus, Earth and Mars) and a remnant of this cloud is probably still present as the belt of asteroids between Uranus and Neptune. Thus these four planets are formed of earth-like materials; notably, the remainder of the planets (Jupiter, Saturn, Uranus, Neptune with the exception of Pluto) are formed of material that is much more in the image of the Sun, with much higher amounts of the lighter elements, including hydrogen and helium [1].

It is thought that the Moon was also formed at the same time as the Earth, possibly by the Earth capturing a small planet of similar material to itself. However, three other characteristics of the Earth are now missing from the Moon. These are three of the four familiar Greek essences (attributed to

Empedocles, 490–430 BCE): air, fire and water (the fourth being earth). The small amount of atmosphere and water vapor that the Moon might have had would have been quickly lost because of its low gravitational field. A near-collision with the Earth may have robbed the moon of any metallic core that it had (its density is significantly less than that of the Earth – [1]) and in any case it did not inherit enough radioactive compounds to sustain a molten core, as has happened on the Earth and other planets. For the Moon these differences have had great significance. Thus the Moon presents to us a surface pock-marked with many craters, which show no weathering, or reshaping from volcanism, as would occur on the Earth. Some of these craters must therefore be billions of years old.

22.1.2 Formation of the Moon and the Asteroid Phase

Following the formation of the Earth another significant event is thought to have occurred. This is the bombardment of the Earth's surface with asteroids or planetesimals, the residuum of planet formation [2]. This occurred for some 500 MY. Many of these asteroids were enriched in water and organic carbon. Thus, although the situation was catastrophic at the time, causing the Earth's surface to heat up beyond the possibility of sustaining life, as soon as the process abated it left the Earth's surface 70% covered with water (about half coming from the initial dust condensation and half from the asteroids) and enriched in organic carbon compounds, a set of circumstances highly favorable to the formation of life. In addition, much of the nitrogen in the Earth's atmosphere (77%) arrived in this event [2].

It is not often appreciated that the formation of the Moon at the same time as the Earth gave rise to three important features for life on the planet Earth: (1) the present day length (the entraining of the entropies of the Earth and Moon have meant that the Earth's rotation has slowed by a factor of about two giving rise to our 24 h day, instead of a 12 h day); (2) perhaps more importantly, the Moon has dampened the wobble in the Earth's rotation, which has meant that the seasons follow each other with constancy and predictability (notwithstanding long-term variations due to the poorly understood Melankovitch cycle); and (3) perhaps most important of all, the Moon causes the twice daily tides that allow the oceans to "breathe" [1].

Abatement of asteroid bombardment occurred about 4 Ga and conditions probably became favorable for the formation of life on the Earth not long after this. The surface cooled to below 100 °C, and the out-gassing of the mantle by volcanism brought a rich supply of energy-rich compounds to the Earth's surface, where also much organic carbon had accumulated from the asteroid bombardment. At this time the Earth's atmosphere contained almost no O_2 and relatively high levels of CO_2 [3] (Figure 1).

22.1.3 First Signs of Life

There are several theories as to where life started (e.g., [4]), but for our purpose we need simply note that it did start about this time and that by about 3.7 Ga

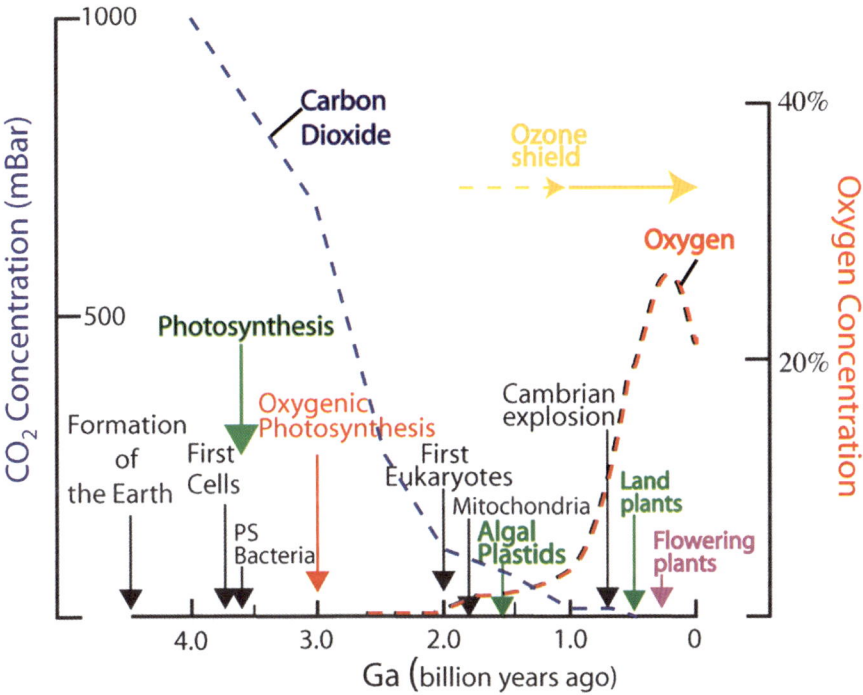

Figure 1. Important events in the evolution of photosynthesis since the formation of the Earth, starting 4.5 giga years ago (Ga).

there were, probably, cellular organisms in existence. The reducing nature of the early Earth was a powerful constraint on evolution. The cooling of the outer crust and the development of crustal plates, with subsequent mantle turnover meant that out-gassing would have been a dominant process for the first 2 billion years of Earth history: meaning that even when oxygen was formed later by oxygenic photosynthesis it would not have accumulated in the atmosphere, because of reactions with reducing compounds and elements in the Earth's crust such as hydrogen and ferrous iron. However, that is jumping ahead of our story by a long way. Perhaps the most interesting question to ask is how we can say anything about the metabolism of these early cells?

22.2 Respiration and Photosynthesis

The earliest organisms would almost certainly have gained their energy supply by simple fermentative reactions, i.e., the catabolism of the simple organic compounds in their environment (which came from the original asteroid bombardment) [5]. However, there were useful sources of energy in the environment (H_2, CH_4, H_2S) that could be harnessed, if electron transfer reactions could be tapped. Today's organisms use cytochromes [5], heme proteins, in the electron transport reactions involved in respiration and photosynthesis and it likely that these molecules were rapidly incorporated into respiratory and photosynthetic systems. We can, therefore, use the amino acid sequence of these proteins to draw comparisons of the relationship of these proteins. This approach is known as *phylogenetic tree inference* or *gene sequence analysis*. Even though we are trying to work out patterns that occurred 3 Ga ago or more, the unique patterns in gene/protein sequences can often confidently predict the sequence of events for us. Phylogenetic tree analysis has even been used to try to work out what was the last universal common ancestor (LUCA) of all life on Earth [6]. Analysis of cytochromes has established that cytochromes, involved in respiration, came first and those involved in photosynthesis came afterwards (Figure 1, [7]). Confidence limits can be set for these estimates and the probability that respiration preceded photosynthesis based on this approach is very good [7]. According to this analysis aerobic respiration preceded the split into the two types of prokaryotic cells (Archaea and Bacteria), which certainly preceded photosynthesis as we know it. While in this case the evidence is clear, going back so far in evolution can present serious problems for phylogenetic inference, as we shall see later in terms of the evolutionary pathway of plastid endosymbiosis and the origin of the eleven membrane-spanning helix which is the archetypal reaction center (Section 22.6.2).

22.3 Significance of Photosynthesis for Early Life on Earth

While life almost certainly got a head start from the accumulation of organic compounds on the surface of the early Earth and from reducing compounds (H_2, H_2S), which were out-gassing from the mantle, it is probable that these sources were becoming exhausted by about 3 Ga [8]. In any case, the supply was not great enough to generate an abundant biomass on the surface of the Earth. Thus, life was faced with a challenge of obtaining sufficient energy to supply autotrophic growth, upon which heterotrophic organisms could feed. The Sun is an obvious source of energy for autotrophic organisms. The Sun radiates a colossal amount of energy in all directions (4×10^{26} J s^{-1}). It does so by a controlled nuclear hydrogen fusion process, which has been going for 4.6 Ga and will continue for another 5. In contrast, the amount of this energy that falls on the Earth is comparatively small (1.7×10^{17} J s^{-1} or 5.4×10^{24} J a^{-1}). However, it is still vast by human standards. If all the energy falling on a relatively small area of the USA, or Europe, or Australia were to be captured it would supply all the current energy needs of human kind, from whatever source (mainly fossil fuels, at present) ($\sim 1 \times 10^{20}$ J a^{-1}). Therefore, unsurprisingly, early organisms on the surface of the Earth evolved mechanisms to take up this energy, and to use it to create organic compounds, in an early photosynthetic process, using hydrogen donors (Figure 2, [9,10]); a mechanism that was probably in place by ~ 3.5 Ga [5,11,12]. However, it is even more surprising

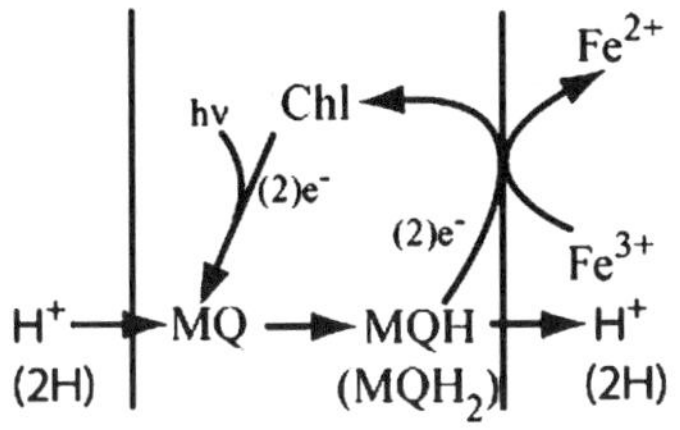

THE EVOLUTION OF PHOTOSYNTHESIS

$$H^+ \xrightarrow{} MQ \xrightarrow{h\nu, Chl, (2)e^-} MQH \xrightarrow{(2)e^-, Fe^{2+}/Fe^{3+}} H^+$$
(2H) → (MQH$_2$) → (2H)

Figure 2. Possible scheme for a primitive photosystem, which may have housed an ancestral reaction center based on chlorophyll or a similar pigment. For other schemes see [10,12].

that the next logical step was ever achieved, though, as often pointed out, given enough time any thermodynamically-feasible process will eventually evolve. This step is the splitting of water, one of the most abundant compounds on the planet, with the release of molecular oxygen. This far-from-simple reaction would have taken much longer to achieve than any early photosynthetic reactions. However, by about 3 Ga the steady progress of abundant life was threatened by the lack of reducing sources for photosynthesis (or chemosynthesis) [3,8].

Water splitting was undoubtedly the most significant achievement of life on the planet, making possible all subsequent evolution. Initially, however, this was a life-threatening challenge to other organisms, because oxygen at that time was a toxic compound. New enzyme systems had to be evolved for most organisms to survive, e.g., the evolution of superoxide dismutases, to transform highly reactive superoxide, just one of a number of reactive oxygen species (ROS), which cause wide-scale damage to proteins, fats and nucleic acids of living organisms. Nevertheless, damage control was achieved and out of it came the evolution of aerobic respiration, a more efficient form of energy transduction, first in Archaea and Bacteria, but subsequently in eukaryotic organisms.

Out of this potential disaster for heterotrophic organisms came a whole new branch of life – the eukaryotes: first protists, and then the three forms of multicellular life, animals, plants and fungi. It was largely these organisms that conquered the land. Plants evolved quickly on land and were so successful that although the land surface of the Earth forms only ~30% of the total area, the land supplies over 50% of the photosynthesis on the planet [13]. This success of plants supplied herbivorous animals with a diverse source of food, and laid the basis for successful evolution of more and more complex animals.

22.4 First Phase of Photosynthesis: Harvesting Energy

By harnessing a pigment to a redox reaction, solar (light) energy can be converted into chemical energy. The best example of this today is bacteriorhodopsin, a photopigment, which occurs in an archaebacterium,

Halobacterium salinarium and in others [14]. This membrane protein binds the visual pigment rhodopsin and uses the light energy absorbed (at 540 nm) to pump protons across the membrane. The resultant pH gradient is used to generate ATP by means of an ATP (proton-linked) synthase. It has been established that a similar reaction occurs in many eu/archaebacteria [15]. These are widespread in the sea and must gain supplemental energy from this simple phototransduction reaction.

The presence of bacteriorhodopsin-using organisms tells us nothing of the original light-driven photosynthetic reaction, which may well have been subsumed, and therefore lost, into more advanced photosynthetic organisms. Nor does it tell us when it might have evolved. The possibilities for such redox-linked pigment systems are large (Figure 2, [9,10]). However, it must be acknowledged that the mostly likely pigment is one on the biosynthetic pathway to chlorophyll, because chlorophyll, and its closely-linked bacteriochlorophyll, are the only extant photosynthetic systems. In addition, chlorophyll biosynthesis is based on porphyrin synthesis and if respiration preceded photosynthesis then porphyrin synthesis must have existed already. Assuming that some sort of cellular organisms were present between 3.8 and 3.5 Ga [5] it is very likely, as argued above, that a primitive photosynthetic reaction evolved soon after the first steps in evolving cytochrome-based respiration.

It has been argued that the earliest photosynthetic pigment was Mg-protoporphyrin monomethyl ester [16]. This pigment has a good absorption band at 419 nm (Table 1). However, Larkum [9] and Mulkidjanian and Junge [17] have argued that the photosynthetic process started as a mechanism to protect organisms against UV-B radiation damage. None of the chlorophyll precursors would suit this role, so one would have to postulate some other pigment entirely, with a switch to a chlorophyll precursor later. Nonetheless, consideration of UV-B protection is important because before the advent of significant oxygen in the atmosphere (see below and Figure 1), there would have been no ozone shield in the upper atmosphere and levels of UV-A and UV-B radiation would have been high and injurious to life as we know it today.

Table 1. Important pigments in the biosynthetic pathway to Chlorophyll *a* and their spectral properties; wavelength in nm followed in parentheses by the extinction coefficient of spectral band in acetone or ether. For further details consult [9,12]

Pigment	λ (nm) ε (mm^{-1} cm^{-1})					
Uroporphyrin-III	406 (215)	502 (16)	536 (9)	572 (7)		627 (4)
Protoporphyrin-IX	404 (158)	503 (15)	536 (12)	576 (7)	605 (2)	627 (7)
Mg protoporphyrin monomethyl ester	419 (100)	510 (1)	553 (6)	591 (6)		
Mg 2,4-divinyl pheoporphyrin a5 monomethyl ester	437 (100)		574 (0.5)			624 (1)
Protochlorophyll *a*	438 (137)	533 (137)	570 (4)	570 (7)	602 (22)	622 (182)
Chlorophyll *a*	410 (85)	430 (118)	530 (3)	578 (8)	615 (13)	663 (95)

22.5 Possible Scenarios for the Evolution of Chlorophylls/Bacteriochlorophylls

22.5.1 Biosynthetic Pathway

The evolution of the early pathway for chlorophyll biosynthesis has been discussed by Mauzerall [16,18] and Larkum [9,12], amongst others; and the biosynthesis of bacteriochlorophyll from chlorophyll by the modern biosynthetic pathway is only two further steps (Figure 3). Many of these reactions could, quite possibly, have occurred without the need for specific enzymes, although today each is linked to an enzymatic reaction: thermodynamically the reactions are feasible, except for the formation of protoporphyrin IX (whose formation is thermodynamically very unfavorable) [12,16]. It is also possible that magnesium was replaced by other metals initially [16,19]. Even today it is known that Mg can be replaced by Zn in certain PS bacteria [20].

From Mg-protoporphyrin monomethyl ester the pathway would have been to a Chl c-type pigment [9,12,16]; Mg-2,4 divinyl pheoporphyrin A5 monomethyl ester is the intermediate on the biosynthetic pathway most likely to have served the role of "chlorophyll" (but Chl c_1 and Chl c_2 are structurally similar).

From a Chl c-like pigment to Chl a is also not difficult biosynthetically [9]. From there to bacteriochlorophyll is also only a two-step pathway (Figure 3). Thus it is quite logical to postulate that Chl preceded BChl, at least in terms of biosynthetic intermediate. It is also possible to argue that Chl a preceded BChl a functionally, or at least coexisted with it. However, against this is the evidence showing that all anoxygenic photosynthetic organisms [i.e., photosynthetic (eu)bacteria which do not release oxygen, from splitting water] use BChls and not Chls, and this important point needs to be discussed.

22.5.2 Chlorophyll or Bacteriochlorophyll First?

One is therefore faced with a difficult – and possibly insoluble conundrum – concerning the first fully photosynthetic organisms: did they use BChl and, if so, how did they synthesize it? And if this was the case, how did the situation come about where BChl was replaced by Chl in later photosynthetic organisms, viz. extant Cyanobacteria, algae and higher plants.

Firstly, the absorption spectra of BChls are not as efficient in absorbing visible light as that of Chls (Figure 4). To begin with, this need not have been a disadvantage, as initially any PS system would have been highly selected for by evolution. Nevertheless, it is difficult to see how Chl would have been absent in favor of BChl, if both were easily formed. Thus, unless the biosynthetic pathway took a different course from the present one it seems probable that the earliest photosynthetic organisms formed both Chl and BChl. Blankenship and Hartman proposed, in broad terms [21], an alternative scenario for BChl biosynthesis. They noted the similarity between certain BChls and Chl c-type pigments, especially Mg-2,4-divinyl-phaeoporphyrin A5 monomethyl ester.

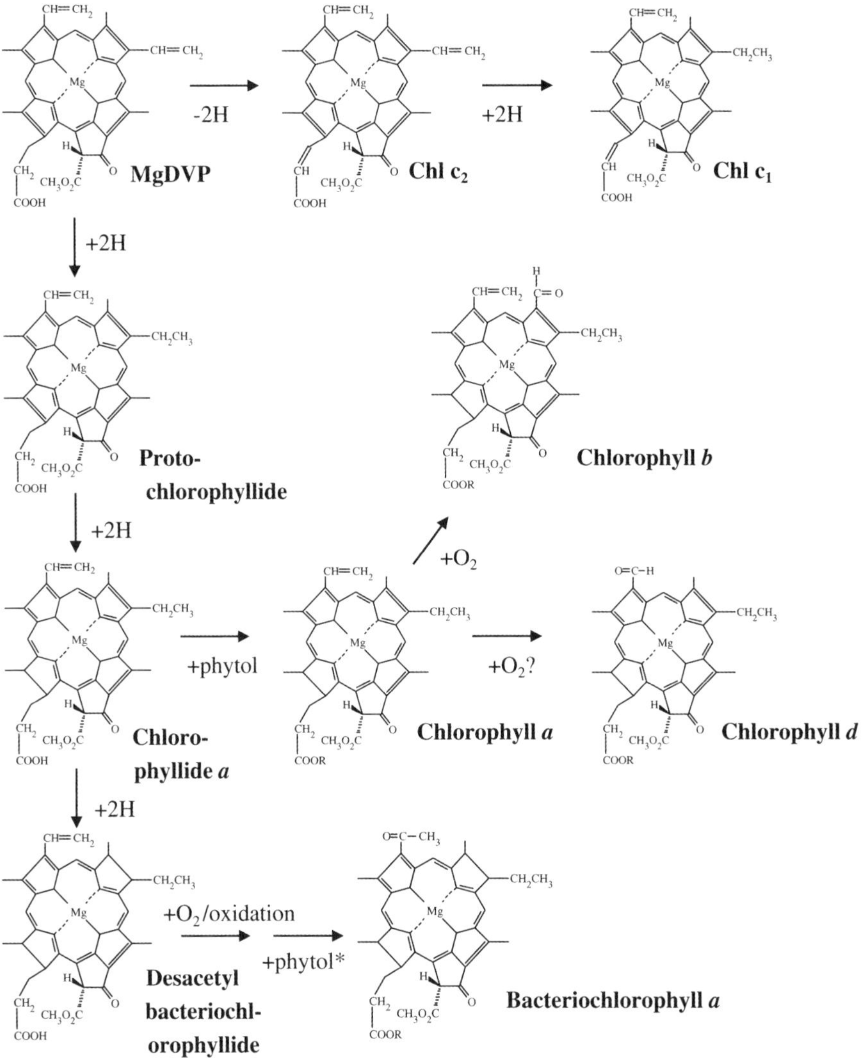

Figure 3. Biosynthetic pathways in the formation of chlorophyll a, chlorophyll b and bacteriochlorophyll a.

They suggested that an early biosynthetic pathway involved this route, although no details were proposed. A later change could then have led to the current biosynthetic pathway.

Nothing is known of these putative earlier pathways. In the case of the modern pathways, two sets of enzymes are involved in the final reduction of the tetrapyrrole ring, one for Chl synthesis and the other for BChl synthesis. Phylogenetic tree analysis is therefore possible based on these enzymes. The

THE EVOLUTION OF PHOTOSYNTHESIS

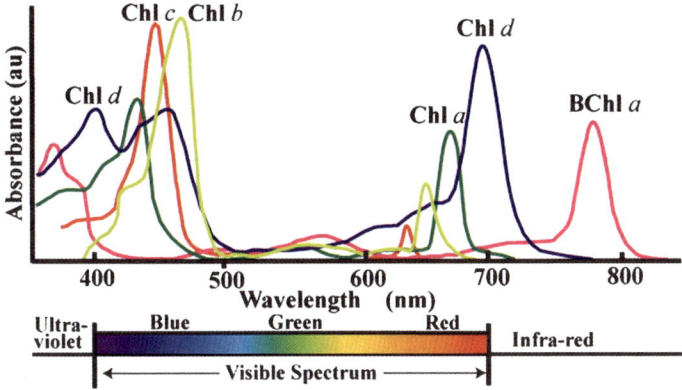

Figure 4. Absorption spectra of various pigments (in organic solvent) used in photosynthesis by various photosynthetic organisms.

enzymes are homologous to *nif*H genes, which are used to provide the reducing power needed to reduce molecular nitrogen with hydrogen (suggesting that nitrogen fixation predates photosynthesis). The first analyses of these enzymes suggested that the enzymes for BChl were older than those for Chl biosynthesis [22] and were taken to indicate an earlier origin of BChl. However, Lockhart et al. [23] showed that this earlier analysis was not robust and that it was equally likely that Chl preceded, or was coexistent with, BChl, based on these data. Once again trying to deduced events that occurred long ago, in this instance over 3 Ga, necessarily involves gene sequences in which much substitution has taken place with resulting loss of power in phylogenetic inference.

22.6 Reaction Centers and Light-Harvesting Antennae

If photosynthesis is as old as the evidence suggests, there is little chance that we can accurately predict what the first photosynthetic mechanism was like. The simplest systems, in today's anoxygenic photosynthetic bacteria, show evidence of wide scale lateral transfer of genes [24–26] and, therefore, these organisms and their photosynthetic mechanisms have undoubtedly undergone much evolutionary change.

22.6.1 Reaction Centers

From the general form of modern reaction centers we can say that, overall, the process would have consisted of the following type of reactions, linked in a cycle [9]:

1. secondary donor   D   Special Chl   A   secondary acceptor
2. secondary donor   D $hv \searrow$ A   secondary acceptor
                                    Special Chl*
3. secondary donor   D   Special Chl$^+ \Rightarrow e^-$ A$^-$ secondary acceptor
4. secondary donor   D$^+ \Rightarrow e^-$ Special Chl   A$\Rightarrow e^-$ secondary acceptor$^-$
5. secondary donor$^+ \Rightarrow e^-$ D   Special Chl   A   secondary acceptor$^-$

where D = primary donor, Special Chl = a special chlorophyll with the property of acting as a oxidoreductant under the influence of light, and A = Primary acceptor. It is most easy to envisage these assembled across a membrane as in today's photosystems (Chapter 1).

The special chlorophyll must be a chlorophyll, whose properties were modified by special ligands, presumably associated with a special protein as in today's reaction centers (Chapters 11–16) [27,28]. The ancestral RC appears to have been a protein with five membrane-spanning helices (MSHs). However, recent evidence suggests that this fused with a light-harvesting antenna protein at an early stage (Figure 5) [29]. Only later, probably, did a gene duplication

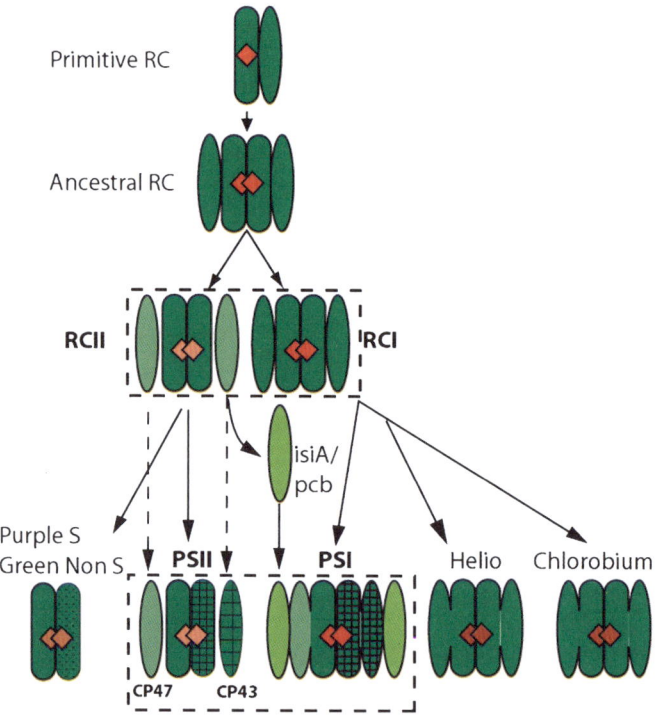

Figure 5. The likely evolution of modern reaction centers in anoxygenic photosynthetic bacteria, cyanobacteria, algae and plants, based on a starting point of an 11 membrane-spanning helix protein in the reaction center of the ancestral photosynthetic bacterium.

THE EVOLUTION OF PHOTOSYNTHESIS

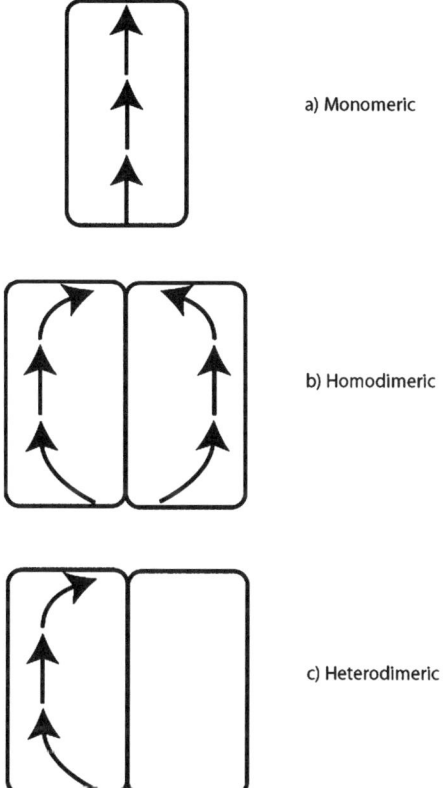

Figure 6. Stages in the evolution of reaction centers.

lead to a dimer arrangement with two (B)Chl molecules arranged in a special pair between two polypeptides (Chapter 12). However, since this arrangement of two (B)Chls is found in all extant reaction centers, it must have contributed a great benefit to the system. Initially, the dimer would have been made up of identical units (homodimeric) (Figure 6). However, in two cases (*Chlorobium* and heliobacteria), both anoxygenic photosynthetic bacteria with RCI-type, there is now a homodimer: in all other RCs a heterodimer is found, suggesting that this gives added advantages, possibly associated with the fact that electrons show a preference for one of the two pathways.

22.6.2 Light-Harvesting Complexes

Along with the reaction center came the need for light-harvesting capability to make the photosynthetic machinery efficient over a range of incident radiation (Chapters 5 and 6). This involved the evolution of special proteins, antenna proteins, which could bind chlorophylls and carotenoids. As mentioned above, it appears that a very early antenna protein with six MSHs became fused with the early RC to give a fused protein with eleven MSHs. However, it is possible that the antenna protein coexisted with the five MSH RC and the eleven MSH fused polypeptide for a long time. Thus the RCs that take after photosystem I RCI-type (*Chlorobium*, *Heliobacter*, PSI – see Chapters 11 and 12) all have eleven MSH RCs (homodimeric in *Chlorobium* and *Heliobacter*, heterodimeric in PSI), while those RCs with five MSHs have either the six MSH antenna (CP43 and CP47 in PSII, see Chapter 15) or have bacterial light-harvesting antennae, LH1 or LH2 or both (*Chlorobium*, *Rhodobacter*) (Figure 5), and in some cases also have a chlorosome (Chapter 5).

22.7 Anoxygenic Bacterial Photosynthesis

22.7.1 General Description

Anoxygenic photosynthetic bacteria (APB) today are a widespread group of Eubacteria (Chapters 5, 11, 12 and 18). In terms of phylogenetic tree analysis based on the common approach of single subunit 16S rRNA comparison, the taxa fall on divergent branches of the eubacterial tree. Most taxa lie with Gram-negative bacteria, but one group, the heliobacteria, are Gram-positive bacteria. APB divide into two groups: (i) RCI-type, those with an FeS secondary electron acceptor system (allied to Photosystem I of Cyanobacteria, algae and higher plants), and (ii) RCII-type, those with a quinone secondary electron acceptor system (allied to Photosystem II of Cyanobacteria, algae and plants). In these terms the tree analysis based on 16S rRNA indicates that APB are rather randomly scattered across the tree. More recently a wider range of proteins has become available for analysis, particularly the enzymes, mentioned above, for BChl synthesis. Trees based on these other (structural) genes have been produced [26,30]. They show that purple sulfur bacteria are basal on the trees and that Heliobacteria were derived late but before Cyanobacteria. However, in an analysis of many genes in APB, where whole genomes are available, Raymond et al. [24] showed that often the origin of genes in these organisms is a mosaic left behind by much lateral transfer. If we accept that lateral transfer of genes has taken place, i.e., the horizontal transfer of one or more genes from one organism to another, it is then possible to see why the SSU 16S rRNA tree indicates a disjoint evolution of APB. However, if a suitable gene is chosen, i.e., it has not suffered too much substitution at each site (site saturation), then it ought to be possible to reconstruct a true evolutionary tree of any particular photosynthetic gene. Whether any of the genes that have been used so far (above) fit this criterion is still a matter of debate.

22.7.2 Types of Anoxygenic PS Bacteria

The extant anoxygenic photosynthetic bacteria are briefly described as follows (for further details see Chapters 11 and 12 and [5]). Purple bacteria (e.g., *Rhodobacter sphaeroides* and *Chromatium vinosum*) have an RCII-type reaction centre; they possess BChl *a* or *b* and can use a wide variety of reductants in photosynthesis (H_2S, other sulfur compounds, organic compounds and H_2); they carry out cyclic electron transport, which is coupled to proton transport and many also carry out nitrogen fixation. Green sulfur bacteria (e.g., *Chlorobium tepidum*) have an RCI-type reaction center; they possess BChls *a*, *c*, *d* and *e*; they carry out a cyclic electron transport similar in many ways to purple bacteria, although several of their *ETC* components are different; they use mainly H_2S and have specialized antenna systems known as chlorosomes (see Chapter 5 and [5]). Green non-sulfur bacteria (e.g., *Chloroflexus aurantiacus*) have an RC-II type of reaction center and are not closely related to green sulfur bacteria although they do possess chlorosomes; they possess BChl *a* and BChl *c* (the latter in the chlorosomes); they have a unique carbon fixation pathway, the hydroxypropionate pathway; they have various nutritional modes: autotrophy, photoheterotrophy and aerobic respiration. Heliobacteria have an RCI-type of reaction center and are the only Gram-negative bacteria that are photosynthetic; they possess BChl *g* and appear not to be capable of photoautotrophic growth; in many ways they are a hybrid between green sulfur bacteria and Cyanobacteria; they carry out nitrogen fixation.

22.8 Evolution of Two Photosystems in One Organism

Anoxygenic photosynthetic bacteria (APB) must undoubtedly have been the first photosynthetic organisms to evolve, i.e., where a light-driven electron transport chain was harnessed to reducing a donor and oxidizing an acceptor. However, it is not wise to assume that these primitive organisms bore any resemblance to any of the mechanisms in modern APB. It also seems natural to suppose that either a Type I RC or a Type II RC evolved first. However, we now know that the RCs are homologous: with strong similarity in their structure in terms of position of the special pair, the primary donor, the primary acceptor and many of the remaining Chls/BChls. Consequently, the original RC may have borne little resemblance to either of the modern RC types.

Two scenarios are therefore possible for the evolution of two photosystems in one organism (in the predecessors of Cyanobacteria, which we will call Chloroxybacteria, to distinguish them from the extant clade of Cyanobacteria) [31].

22.8.1 Fusion Hypothesis

This hypothesis proposes that the two types of APB, with Type 1 RCs and Type 2 RCs, evolved separately from an ancestor that had a primitive special pair as the primary donor and quinone as primary/secondary acceptor, and H_2S (and similar reductants) as the secondary electron donor. What would have influenced a primitive RC to evolve along two separate pathways to give the characteristics of the two types of modern RC is not clear. However, it must further be proposed that one of these early-derived RCs was transferred laterally into an organism with the other type of RC. For example, Hartman [32] chose a lateral transfer from a *Chloroflexus*-type organism into a purple sulfur bacterium. This is possible since both these organisms, in contrast to *Chlorobium* and heliobacteria, have heterodimeric RCs, and this type of RC is found both in PSI and PSII of Cyanobacteria, algae and plants (Chapters 13–16).

What were the selective advantages for this lateral transfer in the first instance? This is not clear. In Cyanobacteria the photosystems are linked by the cytochrome b_6f complex, cytochrome c_6 and/or plastocyanin and a pool of plastoquinone (Chapter 20). In purple sulfur bacteria the reduced electrons are fed into a cyclic *ETC*, which is used to generate energy through a proton gradient and an ATP synthase enzyme. However, in addition to this, there are other redox reactions, which supply reduced NAD, needed to fix CO_2 [5]. In *Chlorobium* the oxidizing pool is cytochrome c and the cytochrome bc complex, and the reducing pool is ferredoxin, which is used to reduce NAD, in a non-cyclic *ETC* like PSI. Heliobacteria have a somewhat similar set of components, with the exception of ferredoxin, but carry out cyclic electron transport, as do green non-sulfur bacteria (Chapter 18).

The clear advantage, ultimately, of placing two photosystems in series is to gain enough energy to split water, forming reducing equivalents (H^+ and e^-) and molecular oxygen. The first stages of the evolutionary changes leading to water splitting must have taken place in the early chloroxybacteria some 2.5–3.0 Ga ago. It is very unlikely that this mechanism evolved rapidly and it is more likely that it evolved over 500 million years or so. For example, the asymmetric manganese cubane centre, which is crucial to this reaction (Chapters 15 and 17), is unlikely to have evolved de novo along with the lateral transfer of the RCI. Nevertheless one can imagine that some sort of primitive system with the two types of RCs in series, but without water splitting, could have evolved and been of selective advantage to the organism(s) that possessed it [33].

22.8.2 Fission Hypothesis

This hypothesis supposes that the primitive RC split into the two derived types in the same organism, presumably by a gene duplication, and then evolved into an RCI- and RCII-type. The impetus for this may have been the advantage of harnessing two photosystems in series, on an evolutionary route that would ultimately lead to oxidation of water. This hypothesis has some advantages over the fusion hypothesis, in that the small steps involved in the change can be seen to have easily occurred (e.g., [34]). In contrast, the reason for the drift apart of RCI and RCII types in the fusion hypothesis is not so easy to envisage.

In the fission hypothesis one must imagine that the second type of RC, the one that evolved alongside the first type, was transferred laterally into another bacterium, one or more times. The first type of organism could then have given rise to APB with RCI-type or RCII-type reaction centers by loss of one type of RC.

Note that we have not specified which came first, an RCI or an RCII type (but others have; see [31]), and the original RC may have had properties of both – it may have had a special pair of Chl *a* or BChl *a*, or both, as the primary donor and a quinone as the primary acceptor and some kind of electron donor, such as H_2S.

22.9 Evolution of Water Splitting and Release of Molecular Oxygen

We now come to possibly the most influential evolutionary step that has occurred on the Earth apart from the evolution of life itself. That is the splitting of water to provide electrons for an RCII reaction linked to the release of molecular oxygen as a by-product. The enzyme complex involved in this is called either the Oxygen Evolving Complex (OEC) or the Water Oxidizing Complex (WOC) (see Messinger and Renger, Chapter 17). We can see this reaction as a central requirement for of evolution on the early Earth. Life struggled to form cellular organisms, using as its energy sources fermentation reactions, which catabolized organic compounds left on the Earth by the early meteor/comet bombardment, and cytochrome-based oxidative respiratory processes fuelled by reduced compounds (H_2S, H_2, CH_4, etc.) and oxidized compounds (NO_3, HCO_3, etc) on the early Earth. These compounds were in short supply and thus selection pressure must have been great for the evolution of a photosynthetic mechanism to harvest light energy; and this was achieved by the anoxygenic photosynthetic bacteria, which competed for compounds to provide reducing equivalents. Thus, right from the start, water was a potential electron source if the difficult chemistry of water splitting could be achieved.

As mentioned above, it is highly unlikely that the pivotal reaction of water-splitting occurred in one step. Other electron donors are likely to have preceded the splitting of water. Likely donors are peroxides [21,35] formate [35], nitrate [35] and bicarbonate [33]. The case for bicarbonate is now made more likely by the support for a bicarbonate ion in the active site for water-splitting close to the asymmetric manganese cubane structure (Chapter 17, [28]). It is possible, as proposed by Dismukes et al. [33] (Figure 7), that bicarbonate was the earliest electron donor since this ion may have been present in 1000-fold higher concentrations in the seas and water bodies of the early Earth [36] (Figure 1).

It is likely that the D1 and D2 proteins, P680 (the primary donor), pheophytin (the primary acceptor) and the asymmetric tetra-manganese cubane center all co-evolved to form the extant structure. However, the evolutionary steps that were involved are not known. To provide the extended positive redox potential needed to take electrons from water the redox span of the primary donor (P680) and primary acceptor (pheophytin) had to be extended (Chapter 16). Initially, in an oxygen-poor atmosphere, this would have been a simple evolutionary step. However, with the rise of oxygen (Figure 1) this would have exposed the RC to triplet formation and the formation of harmful singlet

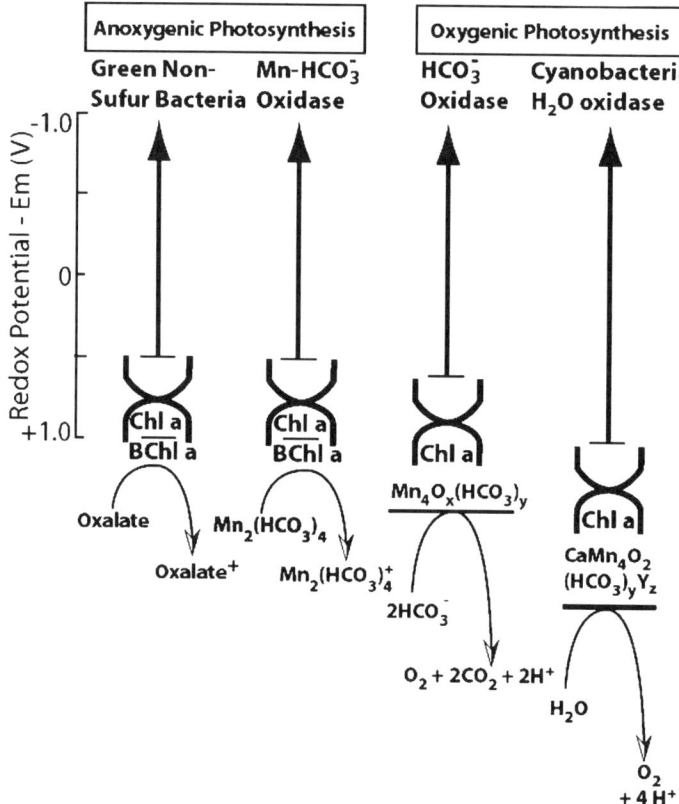

Figure 7. Possible stages in the evolution of water-splitting and release of molecular oxygen in photosystem II. [Based on the model of Dismukes et al. [33].]

oxygen radicals [5] and it would not have been possible to utilize the carotenoid triplet valve of PSI and bacterial RCs (Chapter 12) because the increased oxidizing potential would only have led to oxidized carotenoid (and no protection). Consequently, alongside the development of the central features of the RCII mechanism there must have evolved (i) the mechanism of rapid D1 replacement, whereby the damaged D1 molecules were removed and replaced by fresh D1 (Chapter 10), (ii) non-photochemical quenching, the photoprotective mechanism that is entrained under high-light conditions (Chapter 9), and (iii) a mechanism for reducing the two carotenoids closest to P680 when they occasionally got oxidized (Chapter 16); a mechanism involving reduction of the carotenoids by high potential cytochromes b_{559}. However, the chloroxybacteria, where these features evolved, almost certainly did not have a full non-photochemical quenching system, since this is even absent in extant Cyanobacteria: a full non-photochemical quenching system evolving, apparently, in (eukaryotic) algae (Chapter 9).

The release of molecular oxygen must have been a dramatic shift for the biological systems of the early Earth – because oxygen would have been toxic to most forms of life at that time (Section 22.11). In the longer term even more dramatic changes were foreshadowed by the release of oxygen in photosynthesis. Thus, the evolution was made possible of aerobic bacteria, which could carry out aerobic respiration with oxygen (not nitrate, etc.) and had a greatly enlarged set of biochemical building blocks [37], was enabled. This then eventually led to the endosymbiosis of an α-proteobacterium in a primitive eukaryotic (protistan) organism to form the proto-mitochondrion [38]. In turn, this led to the prevalent life forms on the Earth today: protists, animals, plants and fungi. However, before this came about there were many millennia of intermediate changes.

22.10 Evolutionary Timing of Major Photosynthetic Events

The timing of all these changes, following the "invention" of water-splitting, is still a matter of great debate. The first photosynthetic organisms possibly occurred as far back as 3.5 Ga (Figure 1), i.e., it is assumed that life began soon after conditions improved around 3.8 Ga (Section 22.2). The possibility of cellular fossils resembling cyanobacteria at 3.45 Ga has been advanced [39,40], although this is disputed (e.g., [41]). More recent evidence has been presented that, although these organisms were photosynthetic, they did not evolve oxygen [11]. The first evidence of organisms with affinities to the ancestors of Cyanobacteria (chloroxybacteria) comes from chemical evidence, concerning hopanes, at a date of ~2.8 Ga [42,43]. However, it is reasonable to suggest (Section 22.3) that the evolution of the mechanism for oxygen formation and water splitting took place over an extended period, perhaps as long as 500 million years. Therefore, efficient oxygen evolution may not have occurred until as recently as 2.0 Ga.

The history of oxygen evolution is made more complicated because of the complex geochemistry of the Earth up to 2.0 Ga. Whatever the timing for the release of significant amounts of oxygen into the biosphere, little appreciable accumulation of molecular oxygen would have occurred for long afterwards. Degassing of reducing elements from the Earth's mantle (H_2, S and Fe^{2+}) would have held oxygen partial pressures at very low levels. Furthermore, the oceans would have acted as a very large sink for any oxygen that was released into the atmosphere. Thus it has been suggested that there are at least three periods in terms of oxygen levels, (i) a period of extremely low molecular oxygen ($0-10^{-8}$ present atmospheric level – PAL) up to 2.8 Ga, (ii) a period of low but significant oxygen ($1 \times 10^{-7}-1 \times 10^{-2}$ PAL), possibly from 2.8 to 2.0 Ga and (iii) a period, beginning approximately 2 Ga, when oxygen levels began to rise to present atmospheric levels (or above) (Figure 1, [3]).

Local pockets of oxygen would have formed in marine and freshwater bodies [44] and these would have afforded the opportunity for the development of aerobic eubacteria. These in turn would have led to the endosymbiotic event, which led to ancestors of mitochondria within primitive aerobic eukaryotic protists. This pivotal event has been suggested as taking place about 2.2 Ga (Figure 1). Not long after this, the first endosymbiotic event to form an incipient plastid would have occurred (~ 2.0 Ga) (Figures 1 and 10). This must have occurred in a subset of the protists, which were harbouring ancestral mitochondria (Section 22.13). Fossil evidence of these organisms is of course fragmentary, and so, therefore, is knowledge on the timing. However, by 1.8 Ga one can expect that both aerobic protists and primitive algae would be present in wide areas of the Earth. The process of capture of plastids by various groups of protists appears to have been random. Several secondary captures (secondary endosymbioses; Figures 10 and 11) are known to have taken place and some of these may have occurred relatively recently (e.g., diatoms, [45]):

(i) Creating organic carbon compounds with reducing power from easily obtained hydrogen/electron sources (H_2, H_2S, S, organic compounds).
(ii) Creating organic compounds with reducing power from water (release of molecular oxygen).

22.11 The Oxygen Revolution

The invention of water-splitting and the release of oxygen into the atmosphere was one of the most profound changes undergone by the Earth during its history. It has particular importance for the evolution of life on the planet. We can trace back to this single event the evolution of (1) anaerobic eubacteria, (2) mitochondriate protists, (3) metazoans (animals), (4) algae, (5) plants, and (6) fungi. However, to accommodate this revolution it was necessary to overcome the toxic effects of oxygen.

Oxygen is a very powerful oxidizing agent and would have been toxic to all organisms, initially, even those producing it by splitting water. Furthermore, if oxygen is present in their environment, many redox-coupled reactions tend to form reactive oxygen species (ROS), such as singlet oxygen, a much more powerful oxidant than molecular oxygen. Thus, for those organisms around in this oxidizing environment, mechanisms would have been evolved first to detoxify oxygen and ROS, i.e., react with them to form oxides, etc., and secondly to evolve biochemical systems that could operate under aerobic conditions; notably, even today there are many organisms that choose to live in anaerobic environments (such as the photosynthetic bacteria, *Rhodobacter elongatus*, *Chlorobium tepidum* and *Chloroflexus aurantiacus*, and many non-photosynthetic bacteria). Many oxidation reactions are needed in cellular metabolism. Before the invention of the water splitting reaction molecular oxygen was not available to do this task and it was carried our by other means [46]. When molecular oxygen was available this was the easiest way and it appears that many new enzymes evolved to suit this purpose [46]. One good example is the oxidative decarboxylation of coproporphyrinogen III to protoporphyrinogen III, a key step in the formation of protoheme, which is essential to cytochrome formation and oxidative phosphorylation, and in (bacterio)chlorophyll formation. Today this reaction is catalyzed by the enzymic products of two different genes, *hemF* in aerobic, using molecular oxygen, and *hemN* in anaerobic organisms using oxygen from a hydration reaction. One other example in photosynthesis is the oxidative cyclase that makes the isocyclic ring in the biosynthesis of (bacterio)chlorophylls (*bchE* vs. *acsF* (see [46]). Another non-photosynthetic example is ribonucleotide reductase (*nrdG* vs. *nrdB*). Another possible example is the oxidase that changes Chl *a* into Chl *b* by oxidizing a methyl group at position C-7 to a formyl group (chl *a* oxygenase), in algae and higher plants, although the anaerobic form is unknown.

22.12 Light-Harvesting Proteins

From the earliest photosynthetic systems there must have been a need for light-harvesting proteins. This is because reaction centers alone would be an inefficient way of carrying out photosynthesis; self-shading would mean that many RCs would turn over relatively slowly. Thus all known photosynthetic organisms have some light-harvesting proteins, and usually a complex array of such proteins [47]. One might think therefore that these proteins would demonstrate a clear evolutionary progression. Unfortunately, this is not the case. The anoxygenic photosynthetic bacteria, and on the oxygenic side the Cyanobacteria, algae and plants, each have quite different families of light harvesting proteins, although in some cases there is some overlap.

Anoxygenic photosynthetic bacteria possess two related light-harvesting proteins. Light-harvesting complex 1 (LH-1) forms large rings, each of which surrounds a reaction center, with ~16 α-β subunits in each ring (Chapter 5). Light-harvesting complex 2 (LH-2) is formed of nine α-β subunits and is therefore smaller, and acts to harvest light, which is passed on to LH-1 rings and then on to the RCs. In addition to this there is the unique chlorosome light-harvesting system found in green sulfur and non-green sulfur bacteria (Chapter 5). The LH-1 and LH-2 proteins are clearly related but they are unrelated to any other light-harvesting proteins. The origin and evolution of the chlorosome proteins is largely unknown.

Cyanobacteria have two light-harvesting systems. The phycobiliproteins are extrinsic proteins and form rods, grouped together in structures called phycobilisomes, which harvest green, yellow and orange light (Chapter 6). Phycobiliproteins are, arguably, a late evolutionary development in chloroxybacteria/Cyanobacteria [9]. They are unrelated to any other light-harvesting proteins, but they share common features with the globins [48]. The other system is a family of intrinsic light-harvesting chlorophyll proteins, which bind Chl *a*, and, in the case of prochlorophytes, Chl *b* (Chapter 6 and [49]) and, in the case of *Acaryochloris marina*, Chl *d* (Chapter 6 and [49]). These proteins, which, respectively, are called iron stress-induced protein A (isiA) and prochlorophyte chlorophyll *a/b*- (or *d*-) binding protein (pcb) are in the same family as that which forms the inner antenna proteins, CP43 and CP47 of Photosystem II and the antenna 6 MSH part of Photosystem I (Chapter 6 and [49]) (Figure 5). These sequences are also homologous to the antenna part of the RCI-type reaction centers of green sulfur bacteria and heliobacteria [29]. It is, therefore, possible to ask the question as to the evolutionary relationship of all these proteins and polypeptide sequences. Recent phylogenetic work suggests that the 6 MSH antenna sequence is an ancient property of the RCI-type 11 MSH reaction center, possibly the result of a gene fusion in a line of organisms no longer in existence. This 11 MSH reaction center must have given rise to the separate antenna units of PSII (CP43 and CP47) and the isiA and pcb antennas evolved rather recently from CP43 (Figure 5, [29]). The isiA and pcb proteins form 18-mer rings around PSI, analogous to the LH1 rings of anoxygenic photosynthetic bacteria [50] and they also form supercomplexes with PSII [50]. Their evolutionary diversification ended with the Cyanobacteria, and they are not found in algae or plants.

The predominant light-harvesting system of the algae and plants is the intrinsic 3 MSH light-harvesting chlorophyll (LHC) protein (Chapter 8). In green algae, euglenoids and *Chlorarachnion* (see below) these proteins bind approx eight Chl *a* molecules and seven Chl *b* molecules (Chapters 7 and 8). In chromophyte algae containing Chl *c*, in addition to Chl *a* (see below), these proteins bind an unknown ratio of Chl *a* and Chl *c* molecules. In red algae, a small subset of these proteins occurs in PSI and binds only Chl *a* (see [51]). Although these proteins do not function as lhc proteins in Cyanobacteria it appears that a small, single-MSH protein, high-light induced protein (HLIP) is homologous (Figure 8). It is, therefore, proposed that a series of two gene duplications with the loss of one MSH gave rise evolutionarily to the LHC protein of algae and plants (Figure 8, [52]): plants contain an early light-inducible protein (ELIP) that is homologous and has two MSHs and the product of the gene, psbS, which is also homologues and contains four MSHs [51]. It, therefore, seems clear that the origins of the LHC protein is with the Cyanobacteria, which makes it all the more puzzling that the Cyanobacteria should have their own family of intrinsic light-harvesting proteins (isiA and pcb proteins) and show no trace of the LHC protein, which is so predominant in algae and plants.

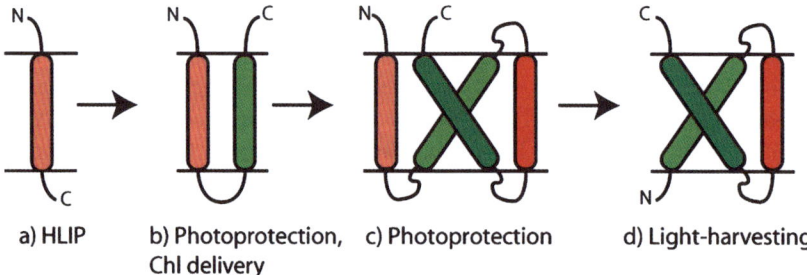

Figure 8. Evolution of the intrinsic light harvesting chlorophyll-binding (LHC) protein of algae and plants.

THE EVOLUTION OF PHOTOSYNTHESIS

Another light-harvesting protein, unrelated to any of the others, is the peridinin chlorophyll protein (PCP) found only in dinoflagellate algae [52].

While there is no homology between the various types of light-harvesting proteins mentioned above, photosynthetic organisms clearly compete for light and it is possible to postulate some sequence in evolution of light-harvesting pigments and their proteins. If Chlorophyll *a* was the first major chlorophyll, as seems likely (Chl *c* or MgDVP may have preceded it [11]), then it is likely that Chl *b* evolved later to fill in between violet and red wavelengths in which Chl *a* absorbed; and phycobiliproteins may be seen as a still later event to completely fill in the "green" window (Figure 9, [9]). Chl *d* may be seen to have evolved in certain Cyanobacteria living in niches enriched in near-infrared light [53,54]. Similarly, the anoxygenic photosynthetic bacteria may have evolved BChl pigments and pigment proteins in response to light gradients [5], although

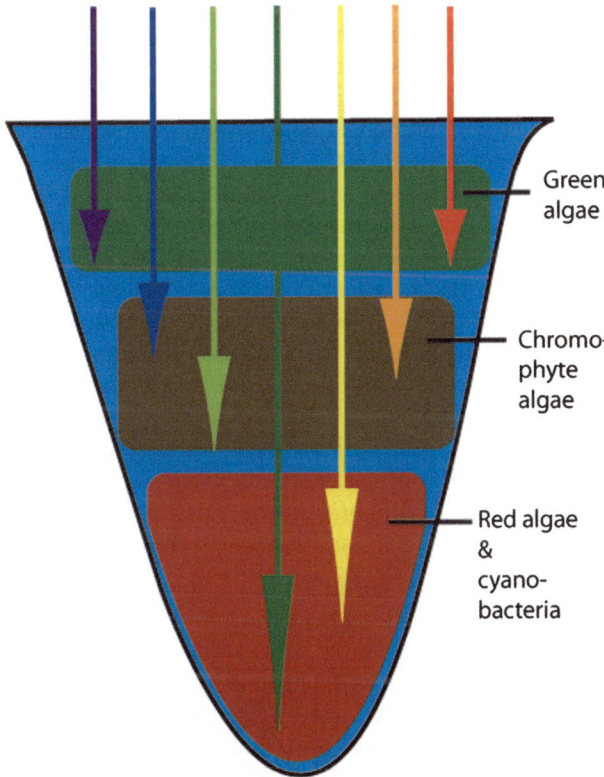

Figure 9. Cartoon showing the principle of evolution of light harvesting pigments and pigment proteins, as applied to algae in a lake. The length of each arrow corresponds to the depth penetration; the color corresponds to its approximate wavelength. Algae living at greater depth need pigments that can absorb wavelengths penetrating to those depths. Similar principles must apply to anoxygenic photosynthetic bacteria and cyanobacteria in somewhat similar situations and in benthic mats. [Adapted from [65].]

the length of time involved and lack of knowledge of early organisms probably precludes any definite conclusions in this case.

22.13 The Rise of Eukaryotes and Algal Protists

There is still much debate about how the Eukaryotes arose (e.g., [55–57]). These organisms are distinct from Bacteria and Archaebacteria in having nuclei bounded by a membrane, which is interconnected with cytoplasmic membranes that compartmentalize the cytoplasm. Protein synthesis is also distinctly different, with larger ribosomes (80S), which may be attached to the endoplasmic reticulum. Eukaryote cells are typically much larger than bacterial cells and have certain organelles, which are clearly derived from an endosymbiotic origin. Two of the latter are mitochondria and plastids. Mitochondria are the powerhouse of most eukaryotic cells, carrying out oxidative phosphorylation and providing the major source of ATP to many cells. Plastids are the photosynthetic machinery of algae and higher plants, both of which are eukaryotic.

Both mitochondria and plastids almost certainly arose by primitive, anaerobic eukaryotic (protist) cells taking in bacteria as symbionts: α-proteobacteria in the case of mitochondria and precursors of modern Cyanobacteria (chloroxybacteria, with Chl a and oxygenic photosynthesis) in the case of algae. Since all algae have mitochondria and mitochondria seem to be the result of a single event (monophyletic endosymbiosis) it seems certain that plastids evolved after the mitochondrial endosymbiosis. Furthermore, because of the diversity of algal cell types it seems certain that much evolutionary time took place during the period of plastid endosymbiosis. This would argue against a single endosymbiotic event in the case of plastid evolution, i.e., there were multiple events (polyphyletic endosymbiosis) (Figure 10). Notwithstanding this, many scientists still argue for a single event (monophyletic endosymbiosis) and subsequent diversification, e.g., see [58]. Both hypotheses have their good points and their difficulties [5]. What needs to be explained is the existence today of the following two types of plastids:

A. Those in which there has been only one endosymbiosis; the plastids of (a) green algae, possessing Chl a+Chl b, (b) red algae possessing Chl a and phycobiliproteins arranged into phycobilisomes, and (c) *Cyanophora*, possessing Chl a and phycobiliproteins arranged into phycobilisomes (but differing in several important respects from red algal plastids) [59]. The plastids in these organism are said to be derived by primary endosymbiosis (Figure 10) [59].

B. Those in which there has been two (or more) serial endosymbioses, as demonstrated by the presence of three or four plastid envelope membranes [59]), which include:

   a. chrysophytes and heterokont algae, possessing Ch a+Chl c (c_1, c_2, c_3) and the xanthophyll, fucoxanthin;

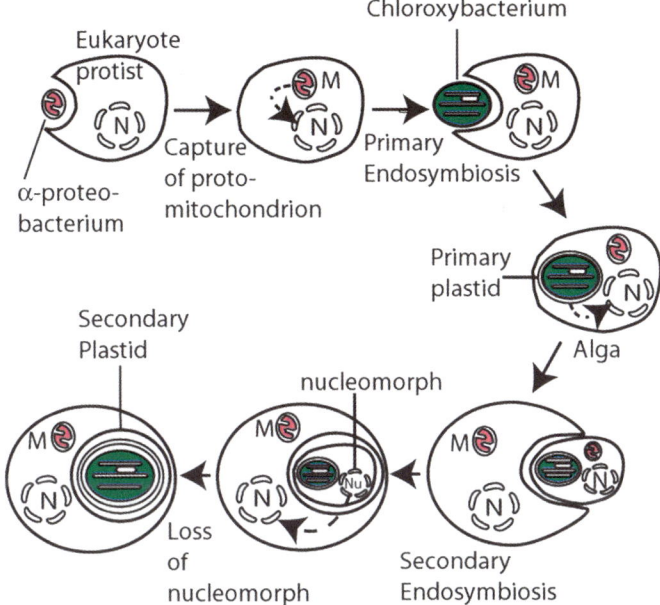

Figure 10. Generalized scheme of how primary and secondary endosymbiosis of plastids is thought to have taken place. M, mitochondrion; N, nucleus.

b. Cryptomonads, possessing Chl a+Chl c_2 and a nucleomorph, representing the degenerate nucleus of the first host;
c. dinoflagellates, possessing (in the major type) Chl a+Chlc_2, peridinin and a number of unique features, including condensed chromosomes during interphase and the special light-harvesting pigment, peridinin-chlorophyll protein.
d. euglenoids, with Chl a+Chl b, paramylon granules and three plastid envelope membranes;
e. *Chlorarachnion*, with Chl a+Chl b, and nucleomorph, representing a degenerate nucleus of the first host.

The plastids in these latter organisms are said to be derived by secondary endosymbiosis (Figure 10) [59].

The best evidence for two serial endosymbiotic events in some algae (Figures 10 and 11) is found in the nucleomorphs of *Chlorarachnion* and Cryptomonads [59]. These nucleomorphs carry three chromosomes with a limited set of genes, which can be typed phylogenetically. In *Cryptomonas* Φ the chromosomes have been fully sequenced [60]. This information indicates that the first host was a red algal-type cell, which became engulfed in a flagellate protist (in the case of *Chlorarachnion* the first host appears to have been a green alga that became engulfed by an amoeboid-type organism [59]).

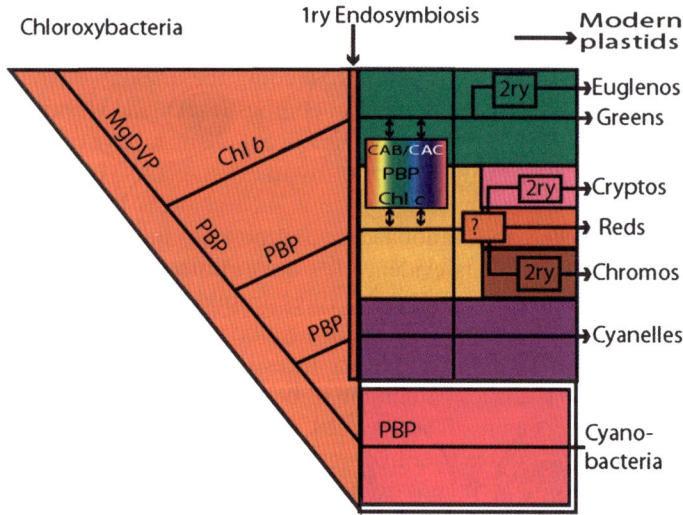

Figure 11. Possible events that took place in the formation of plastids by a polyphyletic route, in the evolution of extant algal groups. PBP, phycobiliprotein.

22.14 Evolution of Plants, Animals and Fungi

Plants arose from a specific group of green algae. The algae were, and are (with a few exceptions), aquatic organisms: terrestrial algae are much rarer. Plants, in contrast, are almost entirely terrestrial (hydrophytes and seagrasses are the exception here). Nevertheless, in their forerunners, the streptophyte algae [59] one can see various characteristics arising over a long period of time, such as wall thickenings (including lignin and sporopollenin), heterotrichous growth, complex reproductive structures and the enzyme glycolate oxidase (replacing glycolate dehydrogenase). It was the evolution of plants, which were essentially terrestrial, that gave the final crowning of the tree of life, opening up the continents to the wealth of diverse ecosystems known today. Animals (metazoans) kept pace with the evolutionary complexity of plants, giving rise to the ever-more complex animal phyla, and finally leading to the evolution of *Homo sapiens*. At the same time there arose the third great group of largely land-based multicellular organisms, the fungi, which recycle so much of the terrestrial organic remains. This is Darwin's grand view of life as expressed in the final paragraphs of the "Origin of Species" [61]. We can now see that the evolution of photosynthesis played a pivotal role at several stages of Earth history in bringing this all about.

22.15 The Future

Interestingly, in reviewing the evolution of photosynthesis in the recent past and looking to the future, one can see that there have been very few evolutionary changes in plants. The only significant advance has been the CAM and C4 strategies in arid zone plants [62,63]. The "motor" of photosynthesis, the photosystems, has remained essentially the same since the evolution of the streptophyte algae more than 0.5 Ga. Extending the analogy of the motor car engine, we can see that once the internal combustion engine was in place at the end of the nineteenth century very few significant changes have come about, and so, it seems, for the basic features of photosynthesis in plants. This does not mean that changes have not been occurring, but such changes have been occurring elsewhere, in the algae, in Cyanobacteria and possibly in anoxygenic photosynthetic bacteria. Here there is evidence for quite profound changes such as the evolution of Chl *d* and supramolecular rings around PSI in Cyanobacteria and significant changes in PSI in certain algae, including the ability to produce hydrogen [64]. Now as the new century faces the prospect of dwindling fossil fuels to run motor vehicles, attention is being turned to alternatives to the internal combustion engine. The fuel cell running off hydrogen is a very real alternative. And if we move to a hydrogen economy then renewable sources of hydrogen will be sought. It may well be that Cyanobacteria, algae and even plants will play an important role in producing hydrogen for these developments.

Acknowledgements

I thank the Australian Research Council for a discovery grant and many colleagues and friends for their help in many ways. I would like to thank in particular Professors J. Barber, R.E. Blankenship, C.J. Howe, P.J. Lockhart, J.A. Raven and H. Scheer for specific help with this manuscript, and many ideas, which they have shared with me over the years.

Note Added in Proof

Two papers have appeared since this article was written, which will be of interest to readers.

C. Goldblatt, T. M. Lenton, A. J. Watson, Bistability of atmospheric oxygen and the Great Oxidation. *Nature* **443**, (2006) 683–686.

A. Y. Mulkidjanian, E. V. Koonin, K. S. Makarova, S. L. Mekhedov, A. Sorokin, Y. I. Wolf, A. Dufresne, F. Partensky, H. Burd, D. Kaznadzey, R. Haselkorn, M. Y. Galperin, The cyanobacterial genome core and the origin of photosynthesis. *Proc. Natl. Acad. Sciences, USA* **103**, (2006) 13126–13131.

References

1. K.F. Kuhn, *Quest of the Universe* (1998), Jones and Barlett, Boston.
2. T.C. Owen, A. Bar-Nun, Contributions of icy planetisimals to the Earth's early atmosphere. *Origins Life Evol. Biosphere* **31** (2001) 435–458.

3. J.F. Kasting, J.L. Siefert, Life and the evolution of Earth's atmosphere. *Science* **296** (2002) 1066–1068.
4. A. Brack (ed.), *The Molecular Origins of Life. Assembling Pieces of the Puzzle* (1998), Cambridge University Press, Cambridge.
5. R.E. Blankenship, *Molecular Mechanisms of Photosynthesis* (2002), Blackwell Science, Oxford.
6. E. Bapteste, C. Brochier, On the conceptual difficulties in rooting the tree of life. *Trends Microbiol.* **12** (2004) 9–13.
7. J. Castresana, M. Sarastre, Evolution of energetic metabolism: The respiration-early hypothesis. *Trends Biochem. Sci.* **20** (1995) 443–448.
8. D.E. Catling, K.J. Zahnle, C.P. Mackay, Biogenic methane, hydrogen escape, and the irreversible oxidation of early Earth. *Science* **293** (2001) 839–843.
9. A.W.D. Larkum, The evolution of chlorophylls, in: *Chlorophylls* (1991) (H. Scheer, ed.), CRC Press, Boca Raton, FL, pp. 367–383.
10. J.M. Olson, Early evolution of chlorophyll-based photosynthesis. *Chemtracts–Biochem. Mol. Biol.* **12** (1999) 468–482.
11. M.M. Tice, D.R. Lowe, Photosynthetic microbial mats in the 3,416-Myr-old ocean. *Nature* **431** (2004) 549–552.
12. A.W.D. Larkum, Evolution of chlorophylls and photosynthesis, in: *Chlorophylls and Bacteriochlorophylls: Biochemistry, Biophysics, Functions and Applications* (2006) (B. Grimm, R. Porra, W. Rüdiger, H. Scheer, eds.), Vol. 25 of Advances in Photosynthesis and Respiration Series, Springer, Dordrecht pp. 261–282.
13. P.G. Falkowski, J.A. Raven, *Aquatic Photosynthesis* (1997), Blackwell Scientific Publications, Oxford.
14. A.L. Béjà, E.V. Koonin, M.T. Suzuki, A. Hadd, L.P. Nguyen, S.B. Jovanovich, C.M. Gates, R.A. Feldman, J.L. Spudich, E.N. Spudich, E.F. DeLong, Bacterial rhodopsin: evidence for a new type of phototrophy in the sea. *Science* **289** (2000) 1902–1906.
15. D. Osterhelt, J. Tittor, Two pumps, one principle: light-driven ion transport in halobacteria. *Trends Biochem. Sci.* **14** (1989) 57–61.
16. D. Mauzerall, Porphyrins, chlorophyll and photosynthesis, in: *Encylopedia of Plant Physiology* (1978) (A.A. Trebst, M. Avron, eds.), Springer, New York, Vol. V, pp. 117–124.
17. A.Y. Mulkidjanian, W. Junge, On the origin of photosynthesis as inferred from sequence analysis – a primordial UV-protector as common ancestor of reaction centers and antenna proteins. *Photosynth. Res.* **51** (1997) 27–42.
18. D. Mauzerall, Why chlorophyll? *Ann. New York Acad. Sci.* **206** (1973) 483–494.
19. A.W.D. Larkum, J. Barrett, Light-harvesting systems in algae. *Adv. Bot. Res.* **10** (1983) 1–219.
20. N. Wakao, N. Yokoi, N. Isoyama, A. Hiraishi, K. Shimada, H. Kise, M. Iwaki, S. Itoh, S. Takaichi, Y. Sakurai, Discovery of natural photosynthesis using Zn-containing bacteriochlorophyll in an aerobic bacterium *Acidophilum rubrum*. *Plant Cell Physiol.* **37** (1996) 889–893.
21. R.E. Blankenship, H. Hartman, The origin and evolution of oxygenic photosynthesis. *Trends Biochem. Sci.* **23** (1998) 94–97.
22. D.H. Burke, J.E. Hearst, A. Sidow, Early evolution of photosynthesis: clues from nitrogenase and chlorophyll iron proteins. *Proc. Natl. Acad. Sci. U.S.A.* **90** (1993) 7134–7138.
23. P.J. Lockhart, A.W.D. Larkum, M.A. Steel, P. Wardell, D. Penny, Evolution of chlorophyll and bacteriochlorophyll: the problem of invariant sites in sequence analysis. *Proc. Natl. Acad. Sci. U.S.A.* **93** (1996) 1930–1934.

24. J. Raymond, O. Zhaxybayeva, J.P. Gogarten, S.V. Gerdes, R.E. Blankenship, Whole-genome analysis of photosynthetic prokaryotes. *Science* **298** (2002) 1616–1620.
25. J. Xiong, M. Fischer, K. Inoue, M. Nakahara, C.E. Bauer, Molecular evidence for the early evolution of photosynthesis. *Science* **289** (2000) 1724–1729.
26. J. Xiong, C.E. Bauer, Complex evolution of photosynthesis. *Annu. Rev. Plant Biol.* **53** (2002) 503–521.
27. P. Jordan, P. Fromme, H.T. Witt, O. Klukas, W. Saenger, N. Krauss, Three-dimensional structure of cyanobacterial photosystem I at 2.5 ångstrom resolution. *Nature* **411** (2001) 909–917.
28. K.N. Ferreira, T.M. Iverson, K. Maghlaoui, J. Barber, S. Iwata, Architecture of the photosynthetic oxygen-evolving center. *Science* **303** (2004) 1831–1838.
29. Y. Zhang, L.S. Jermiin, A.W.D. Larkum, Phylogenetic analysis of light-harvesting antenna peptides from plants and bacteria, in: *Photosynthesis:Fundamental Aspects to Global Perspectives* (2004) (J. van der Est, D. Bruce eds.), Alliance Communication Group, Kansas, pp. 745–746.
30. L.J. Jermiin, R.E. Blankenship, P.J. Lockhart, A.W.D. Larkum, Phylogenetic reconstruction of ancient photosynthetic lineages using chlorophyll and bacteriochlorophyll biosynthetic genes, *Proceedings: 12th International Congress on Photosynthesis* (2001), CSIRO Publishing, Melbourne, Australia, (S09–12, PS2001), ISBN 0643 067 116.
31. R.E. Blankenship, Origin and early evolution of photosynthesis. *Photosynth. Res.* **33** (1992) 91–111.
32. H. Hartman, Photosynthesis and the origins of life. *Origins Life Evol. Biosphere* **28** (1998) 515–521.
33. G.C. Dismukes, V.V. Klimov, S.V. Baranov, J. Das Gupta, A. Tyryshkin, The origin of atmospheric oxygen on Earth: the innovation of oxygenic photosynthesis. *Proc. Natl. Acad. Sci. U.S.A.* **98** (2001) 2170–2175.
34. J.F. Allen, A redox switch hypothesis for the origin of two light reactions in photosynthesis. *FEBS Lett.* **579** (2005) 963–968.
35. J.M. Olson, The evolution of photosynthesis. *Science* **168** (1970) 438–446.
36. J.F. Kasting, Earth's early atmosphere. *Science* **259** (1993) 920–925.
37. J. Raymond, D. Segrè, The effect of oxygen on biochemical networks and the evolution of complex life. *Science* **311** (2006) 1764–1767.
38. C. Esser, N. Ahmadinejad, C. Wiegand, C. Rotte, F. Sebastiani, G. Gelius-Dietrich, K. Henze, E. Kretschmann, E. Richly, D. Leister, D. Bryant, M.A. Steel, P.J. Lockhart, D. Penny, W. Martin, A genome phylogeny for mitochondria among α-proteobacteria and a predominantly eubacterial ancestry of yeast nuclear genes. *Mol. Biol. Evol.* **21** (2004) 1643–1660.
39. J.W. Schopf, Microfossils of the early archean apex chert: new evidence on the antiquity of life. *Science* **260** (1993) 640–646.
40. J.W. Schopf, A.B. Kudryavtsef, D.G. Agresti, D.J. Wdoviak, A.D. Czaja, Laser-Raman imagery of Earth's earliest fossils. *Nature* **416** (2002) 73–76.
41. M.D. Brassier, O.R. Green, A.P. Jephcoat, A.K. Kleppe, M.J. van Kranendonk, J.F. Lindsay, A. Steele, N.V. Grassineau, Questioning the evidence for Earth's oldest fossils. *Nature* **416** (2002) 76–81.
42. J.J. Brocks, G.A. Logan, R. Buick, R.E. Summons, Archean molecular fossils and the early rise of eukaryotes. *Science* **285** (1999) 1033–1036.
43. R.E. Summons, L.L. Janhke, J.M. Hop, G.A. Logan, 2-Methylhopanoids as biomarkers for cyanobacterial oxygenic photosynthesis. *Nature* **400** (1999) 1554–557.

44. D.E. Canfield, A. Teske, Late Proterozoic rise in atmospheric oxygen concentration inferred from phylogenetic and sulphur-isotope studies. *Nature* **382** (1996) 127–132.
45. P.G. Falkowski, M.E. Katz, A.H. Knoll, A. Quigg, J.A. Raven, O. Schofield, F.J.R. Taylor, The evolution of modern eukaryotic phytoplankton. *Science* **16** (2004) 354–360.
46. J. Raymond, R.E. Blankenship, Biosynthetic pathways, gene replacement and the antiquity of life. *Geobiology* **2** (2004) 199–203.
47. B.R. Green, Evolution light-harvesting antennas in photosynthesis, in: *Light Harvesting Antennas*, Advances in Photosynthesis and Respiration, Vol. 13, (2004) (B.R. Green, W.W. Parsons, eds.), Kluwer Academic Publishers, Dordrecht, pp. 129–168.
48. T. Schirmer, W. Bode, R. Huber, W. Sidler, H. Zuber, X-ray crystallographic structure of the light-harvesting biliproteins of c-phycocyanin from the thermophilic cyanonacterium *Mastigocladus laminosus* and its resemblance to globin structure. *J. Mol. Biol.* **184** (1985) 257–277.
49. M. Chen, R.G. Hiller, C.J. Howe, A.W.D. Larkum, Unique origin and lateral transfer of prokaryotic chlorophyll-*b* and chlorophyll *d* light-harvesting systems. *Mol. Biol. Evol.* **22** (2005) 21–28.
50. T. Bibby, J. Nield, F. Partensky, J. Barber, Oxyphotobacteria – antenna ring around photosystem I. *Nature* **413** (2001) 590.
51. A.W.D. Larkum, M. Kühl, Chlorophyll *d*: the puzzle resolved. *Trends Plant Sci.* **10** (2005) 355–356.
52. A.W.D. Larkum, Light-harvesting systems in algae, in: *Photosynthesis in Algae*, Advances in Photosynthesis and Respiration, Vol. 14, (2003) (A.W.D Larkum, S.E. Douglas, J.A. Raven, eds.), Kluwer Academic Publishers, Dordrecht, pp. 227–304.
53. M. Kühl, M. Chen, P. Ralph, U. Schreiber, A.W.D. Larkum, Niche and photosynthesis of chlorophyll *d*-containing cyanobacteria. *Nature* **433** (2005) 820.
54. A.W.D. Larkum, M. Kühl, Chlorophyll *d*: the puzzle resolved. *Trends Plant Sci.* **10** (2005) 355–356.
55. J.B. Dacks, A. Marinets, W.F. Doolittle, T. Cavalier-Smith, J.M. Logsdon, Analyses of RNA polymerase II genes from free-living protests: phylogeny, long branch attraction, and the eukaryotic big bang. *Mol. Biol. Evol.* **19** (2002) 830–840.
56. J.J. Brocks, G.A. Logan, R. Buick, R.E. Summons, Archean molecular fossils and the early rise of eukaryotes. *Science* **285** (1999) 1033–1036.
57. T.M. Embley, W. Martin, Eukaryotic evolution, changes and challenges. *Nature* **440** (2006) 623–630.
58. J. Palmer, Molecular evolution; a single birth of all plastids. *Nature* **405** (2000) 32–33.
59. A.W.D. Larkum, M. Vesk, Algal plastids: their fine structure and properties, in: *Photosynthesis in Algae*, Advances in Photosynthesis and Respiration, Vol. 14, (2003) (A.W.D. Larkum, S.E. Douglas, J.A. Raven, eds.), Kluwer Academic Publishers, Dordrecht, pp. 11–28.
60. S. Douglas, S. Zauber, M. Fraunhotz, M. Beaton, S. Penny, L.-T. Deng, X. Wu, M. Reith, T. Cavalier-Smith, U. Maier, The highly reduced genome of an enslaved algal nucleus. *Nature* **410** (2001) 1091–1096.
61. C. Darwin, *On the Origin of Species* (1859), J. Murray, London.
62. J.A. Raven, R.A. Spicer, The evolution of crassulacean acid metabolism, in: *Crassulacean Acid Metabolism: Biochemistry and Evolution* (1995) (K. Winter, J.A.C. Smith, eds.), Springer, Berlin, pp. 360–385.

63. R.F. Sage, The evolution of C4 photosynthesis. *New Phytologist* **161** (2004) 341–370.
64. V.A. Boichenko, E. Greenbaum, M. Seibert, Hydrogen production by photosynthetic organisms, in: *Molecular to Global Photosynthesis* (2004) (M.D. Archer, J. Barber, eds.), Imperial College Press, London, pp. 397–452.
65. A.W.D. Larkum, Evolution of photosynthetic systems, in: *Research in Photosynthesis* (1992) (N. Murata, ed.), Kluwer Academic Publishers, Dordrecht, Vol III, pp. 475–482.

Subject Index

Note: Roman page numbers refer to Part 1, **bold page numbers** refer to Part 2.

α *see* alpha; miss hits
$\Delta G_{store}(hv)$ *see* stored Gibbs energy
$\alpha_2\beta_2$ complex 220
AAS *see* atom absorption spectroscopy
A-branch
  bacterial RC cofactors **18**
  chlorobial RC site-directed mutagenesis **81**
  Photosystem I
    cyanobacteria **116, 117, 119–20**
    oxygen evolving organisms **150–1, 154, 167–71**
absorption spectra
  Acaryochloris marina 267
  bacteriochlorophylls **499, 501**
  basic principles 39–89
  carotenoids of purple bacteria 159, 160, 162, 164, 167, 169
  chemically-modified chromophores 117
  chlorophylls 104, 266, 267
  CP29 355–6
  gap pigments 306–7
  Gloeobacter violaceus PCC 7421 267
  Lax and Kubo theory 58
  LHCII 339–40, 346–52
  pheophytin *a* 267
  pigment–protein complexes of purple non-sulfur bacteria 209
  pigments 111
  proteobacterial RC alternative pathways **75**
  proteobacterial RCs with BChl *a* and BPh *a* **69**
  PSILHCI 306–7
  purple non-sulfur bacterial PSU organization 217, 237
  Rhodopseudomonas acidophila LH2 211
  secondary ET in PSI of oxygen evolving organisms **164**
  Synechocystis spp. PCC 6803 267, 271
  time-scales 116
  Type II RCs directionality **74**
  see also difference absorption spectra
Acaryochloris spp.
  A. marina 16
    absorption spectra 267
    chlorophyll *d'* 268
    d-type chlorophylls 109
    light-induced ET in chlorophylls 105
    minor chlorophylls 114
    P680 in PSII **251–2**
    P740 singlet excited states **152–3**
    photosystems model 281
    phycobilisome-lacking cyanobacteria 273
  chlorophyll *d* 266, 268
  chlorophyll diversity 265
Acc₁ *see* primary quinone acceptor
Acc₂ *see* secondary quinone acceptor
'accepting mode' 163

acceptor-sided induced photodamage
  mechanisms 397–8
accessory bacteriochlorophylls **25**
accessory pigments 153–95
  see also carotenoids
acclimation, PSI antenna size 309–11
acidic conditions 113, 376, 404
Acidiphilium rubrum 113
actin filament rotation **451, 466–72, 478**
activation energies **319–21**
activation of photopigment and *puc*
  suppression (AppA) 213
active center structure **394**
adaptation mechanisms 14–15, 153,
  176–89
adenosine 5'-triphosphate (ATP)
  ATP synthase **449–81**
  cyanobacteria 372
  cytochrome b_6f complex **421**
  ET thermodynamics **386**
  function/structure **449–50**
  heme c_n cyclic electron transport **435**
  hydrolysis: Gibbs free energy **449**
  synthesis
    aerobic photosynthetic bacteria **368**
    anoxygenic photosynthetic
      bacteria **358**
    biomimetic 29
    chemiosmotic membrane-ET
      principle **393, 395**
    H$^+$/ATP stoichiometric ratio **458–9**
adjustable chromophore properties 116
ADMR studies **166**
aerobic atmosphere 10, **388–9**
aerobic chemo-litho(auto)trophic
  energy conversion **391**
aerobic growth 207, 208, **368–9**
  see also cyanobacteria
aggregates
  bacteriochlorophyll luminescence 119
  chlorophyll as structure stabilizer 106
  circular dichroism 121
  cyanobacterial PSIIcc
    characterization **200–4**
  Förster theory 76
A helix, LHCII structure 335–6

ALA *see* 5-aminolevulinic acid
alanine **40, 41**
algae
  cytochrome b_6f complex **422, 424, 425**
  light-harvesting protein evolution
    512, 513
  oxygenic photosynthetic process **195**
  photosynthetic apparatus 23–4, 25
  protists evolution **514–16**
  PsaF subunit **131**
  state transitions 374
  see also cyanobacteria
alkaliphilic bacteria **456, 458**
Allochromatium vinosum **363**
allophycocyanin (APC) 269–70, 272–3,
  274
all-trans configuration 155–7, 189–92
alpha^{APB} 279
alpha apoproteins 216, 221–3, 228–9
alpha-carotene 268
alternative proteobacterial RC
  pathways **75**
amino acid homology *see* sequence
  homology
amino acid sidechains **34–6**
amino acid substitutions *see* site-
  directed mutagenesis
5-aminolevulinic acid (ALA) 124, 126
Anabaena **175–6**, 411
  A. variabilis **132**
Anacystis nidulans see
  Thermosynechococcus PCC 6301
anaerobic Earth **393**
anaerobic growth
  purple non-sulfur bacteria 207, 208
  see also anoxygenic photosynthetic
    bacteria
anaerobic respiration schemes **391**
analytical ultracentrifugation (AUC)
  203–4
anchor proteins 279–80
angular momentum 191
angular velocity *see* torque
anharmonic PES 56–7
anhydrorhodovibrin
  fluorescence quantum yields 166

Subject Index

near-infrared sub-picosecond time-resolved absorption spectra 160
quantum efficiency of singlet energy transfer to bacteriochlorophyll 174
relaxation scheme 163
singlet excited states 158
singlet lifetimes versus double bond numbers 161
structure 159
visible sub-picosecond time-resolved absorption spectroscopy 162, 175
animal evolution **516**
anion exchange chromatography **11, 200, 201**
annihilation experiments 352
annihilation operators 55
anoxygenic photosynthetic bacteria
 antenna systems 371, 372
 bacteriochlorophylls 108, 109, 112
 C_5 pathway 124
 classification **59–60, 355–6**
 c-type bacteriochlorophylls 108, 109
 electron transfer **61, 63, 65, 67 84**
 electron transport chain **353–74**
 light-harvesting protein evolution **511**
 overview **355–6**
 photosynthesis evolution **504–5**
 reaction centers 16, 371–2
  functional patterns **57–85**
  structures **7–45**
  tetraheme species **360–3**
  triheme species **363–5**
  Type I **60–7, 77–84**
  Type II **60–77**
 species name revisions **67**
 types **504–5**
 vesicle structures 22–3
 see also individual organisms
antenna complexes
 anoxygenic bacteria 372
 assembly 106
 biomimetic 27, 28
 carotenoid natural selection 189–92

carotenoid-to-bacteriochlorophyll singlet-energy transfer 172–6
cyanobacteria **113, 133–5**, 263–4, 273–8, 283–5, 372
evolution 15
excitation quenching photoprotection 404–5
green sulfur bacteria **78**
heliobacteria without **82**
higher plants 301–22, 329–52, 369–85
iron-depleted conditions 283–5
isolation from PSI-LHCI 311–12
LHCII minor 352–6
membrane-bound 273–8
overview 371–3
P680$^+$·Pheo$^-$ radical ion pair formation **255**
photosystem stoichiometry regulation 285–6
phycobilisomes 372
PSI in higher plants 301–22
PSII 329–56
purple non-sulfur bacteria 205–390
regulatory EET 373–5
size regulation/acclimation 309–11
supramolecular organization 304–11
topology 304–7
see also light-harvesting complexes
antenna pigments (P_A) 12, 14, 103–29
antheroxanthin 343
anthracene 179
anthraquinone **155**
antimycin A **419, 421, 430, 431, 434**
anti-parallel stranded beta-sheets **126, 127**
APC see allophycocyanin
Aphanothece halophytica **397**
Apicomplexa **389**
apoproteins 216, 221–3, 228–9, 334–52
AppA (activation of photopigment and puc suppression) protein 213
Arabidopsis thaliana
 D1 protein repair cycle 408, 409
 genomic sequence 380
 Lhca1–4 proteins 313, 314, 317
 Lhcb1-Lhcb6 sequence homology 333

light-harvesting chlorophyll I
  pigment composition 312
mutant studies on PsbS protein
  symmetrical structure 377
non-triplet producing charge
  recombination 405
photoprotection in the antenna 404
protein phosphorylation in damage
  repair 411
PSI photodamage mechanism 402
TAKs antisense plants 375
time-resolved PSII fluorescence
  spectra 382
UV photoprotection 411
archaebacteria, early photosynthesis
  497–8
arginine residues **34–6, 41, 42, 473**
aromatic amino acids 217
artifacts, luminescence spectrometry 117
artificial photosynthesis 26–30
asparagine residues **44**
aspartic acid **34–6, 41**
assembly
  antenna structure stabilization 106
  building principles 41–8
  cyanobacterial PSI **121**
  photosynthetic apparatus architecture
    22–5
  PSIIcc integral lipid molecules **217**
  thylakoid membrane molecules 277–8
  see also dimeric structures;
    stabilization; trimeric complexes
asteroid phase **494**
a-subunit, ATP synthase **463**
asymmetric manganese cubane center
  506, 507
asymmetry *see* directionality
atmospheric oxygen **388**
atomic absorption spectroscopy
  (AAS) **11, 206, 223–7**
atomic force microscopy (AFM) 222–
  3, 234, **370–1**
ATP *see* adenosie 5'-triphosphate
ATP synthase ($F_O F_1$-ATPase)
  artificial complexes 29
  bacterial RC structure **8**

chemiosmotic energy coupling **452–60**
cyanobacterial **392, 395**
evolution **60**
higher plants **198**
inter-subunit rotation in F_1 **465–8**
peripheral stalk **463**
photophosphorylation **447–81**
regulation **459–60**
rotary catalyst F_1 **464–72**
rotary electromotor F_O concept **473–6**
rotary twin engine concept **476–80**
structure **451–2, 461–80**
atrazine **12, 30, 31**
A-type flavoproteins, discovery **400**
AUC *see* analytical ultracentrifugation
auracyanin **77**
axial coordination **258**
axial ligands **170, 171**

B777 FMO-complex 42–3, 67, 77–81
B800-850 complexes 210
B800 bacteriochlorophyll 42, 178,
  223–5, 240, 241
B850 bacteriochlorophyll 178, 223–4,
  238, 240, 241
B880 bacteriochlorophyll 238, 241
Bacillariophyceae 110
bacteria
  LH1 core antenna complex, B777
    complex free energy 42–3
  photosynthetic unit, purple non-
    sulfur bacteria 210–12
  reaction centers
    cofactor conformation **21–9**
    crystallization process **12–13**
    higher plant PSII comparison **44–5**
    membrane protein structure **34–9**
    modified **39–44**
    substrate binding sites **29–34**
  see also individual classes/species
    of bacteria
bacteriochlorin rings 224
bacteriochlorin-type chlorophylls
  108, 109, 112
bacteriochlorin-type cyclic
  conjugated tetrapyrroles 115

Subject Index

bacteriochlorophyll *a* (BChl *a*)
  bacterial RC structure **11–12, 18, 25**
  binding in purple non-sulfur bacterial antennas 223–4
  EM studies of core complexes 232–3
  evolution **499–501**
  mutations 117
  phytyl tails 224–5
  primary electron donor location **22, 24**
  proteobacterial RC absorption spectra **69**
  Q_x transition 209
  Rhodopseudomonas palustris RC-LH1 complex 236
bacteriochlorophyll *b* (BChl *b*) **11–12, 22, 24, 25**
bacteriochlorophyll (BChl)
  absorption spectra **499, 501**
  aggregates 119, 121
  anoxygenic photosynthetic bacterial reaction centers 12, 16
  biosynthesis 124–8
  Blastochloris viridis RC **68**
  characteristics 103
  evolution **499–501**
  FMO complexes 87–8
  luminescence spectroscopy 118–19
  photosystem processes 41–2
  purple bacterial antenna complexes 172–9, 217
  purple non-sulfur bacteria 209–10
  structures 108–9
  structures in anoxygenic bacterial RCs **61–2**
bacteriochlorophyll *c* (BChl *c*) 108, 109, 110, 112
bacteriopheophytin *a* (BPhe *a*) **69**
bacteriopheophytin (BPhe)
  bacterial RC structure **11–12, 18, 25–6**
  Blastochloris viridis RC **68**
  functional differences **252**
  light-induced ET in chlorophylls 105
  structures in anoxygenic bacterial RCs **61–2**
bacteriorhodopsin **497–8**
barley 312, 383, 402

basic principles 12–25
  electron transport chains 18–22
  light absorption 39–89
  light harvesting 14–15
  light-induced charge separation 15–17
  photosystems 41
B-band optical absorption 114, 115
B-branch
  bacterial RC cofactors **18**
  chlorobial RC site-directed mutagenesis **81–2**
  cyanobacterial PSI **116, 117, 119–20**
  primary charge separation in PSI of oxygen evolving organisms **154**
  PSI in oxygen evolving organisms **150–1, 167–71**
BChl *see* bacteriochlorophyll
Berkner-Marshall-Point **388**
beta apoproteins 216, 221–3, 228–9
beta carotene *see* carotene
beta-sheet structures **126, 127**
B helix 335–7, 342, 343
BIC *see* butyl isocyanide
bicarbonate ions **311–12**
bidirectional hydrogenase **395, 401**
'Big Bang' theory **387, 390**
bilin biosynthesis 124
binding change mechanism, ATP synthase **450**
binding pockets
  Q_A 254–5, 369
  Q_B 7, 216–18, 219, 267, 270–1
  site-directed mutagenesis 116–17
binding sites
  bacteriochlorophyll *a* in purple bacterial antennas 217, 223–4
  CP29 354
  inhibitors **29–32**
  integral membrane lipids **217**
  LHCII chlorophyll organization 338–40
  mixed Chl *a/b* occupancy in LHCII 343–4
  substrates in bacterial RCs **29–34**
  WOC substrate water binding **313**
  see also pigment binding

binding states **365**
biochemical models 375–7
biochemical properties 311–15
bioenergetic 'nonplus-ultra' *see* cyanobacteria
bioenergetic schemes **391**
biomass, primary production **389**
biomimetic systems 26–30
biosynthetic pathways
   BChl/Chl *a/b* evolution **499–500**
   carotenoids in anoxygenic purple bacteria 154, 155
   chlorophyll in cyanobacteria 286–8
   chlorophylls 124–8
biotin **467**, **470**
biphasic reoxidation kinetics **164, 168–9**
bi-site mechanism **464, 472**
'black smokers' **389**, **398**
Blastochloris viridis reaction centers
   bound water **36–7**
   characterization **11–12**
   crystallization **12–13**
   crystal structure **66–7**
   C subunit structure **23**
   c-type cytochromes **361**
   electron carriers **68**
   electron donor substrate binding **33–4**
   heme-iron site geometries **28–9**
   herbicide-resistant mutants **42**
   H subunit structure **22**
   intramembrane phospholipids **37–9**
   isolated membrane studies **359**
   LH complexes number/type **358**
   L subunit structure **18–19**
   modified reaction centers **39–42**
   M subunit structure **20–1**
   Q_B site derivatives **30**
   quantum yield in chlorophylls 105
   RC-LH1 core complexes 229–31
   stereo pairs **24, 26, 27**
   structure comparison with PSII structure **44–5**
   structure/function **8–9**
   supramolecular organization of membranous components **370**
   tetraheme species **360**
   X-ray crystal form **14, 15, 18**
   X-ray structure analysis **196**
blue color, Earth **387**
blue-green algae *see* cyanobacteria
blue-shift 217
Boltzmann distribution 54
Born–Oppenheimer approximation 49
Bose–Einstein distribution function 55
bound water **36–7**
BPhe *see* bacteriopheophytin
breakage of cells **359**
broadening of absorption bands 347–8
Brownian oscillator model 73, 74
Brownian ratchet mechanism **474**
building principles 41–8
bulk-to-bulk coupling **456**
butyl isocyanide (BIC) **434**

$C_2S_2M_2$ supercomplex 332
C_5 pathway 124, 125
C-9 acetyl group 223
C *see* torsional rigidity
C=C stretching line 170–1
cadmium **32, 33, 72**, 113
calcium **129, 294**, 354
Calothrix PCC 7601 272
Calvin–Benson cycle 9, 11, 17, **404**
canopies 320
CAO *see* chlorophyll *a* oxygenase
capacitor enzymes **401**
Capsicum annuum 405
carbon dioxide 9, 11, 17, 29–30, **392, 495**
cardiolipin **38**, 41
β-carotene
   all-trans β-carotene 13
   Chl *a* position in cytochrome b_6f complex **436–7, 439**
   chlorophyll triplets quenching in antenna **267**
   15-cis to all-trans isomerization 179–80
   cyanobacteria **220–2**, 268, 276–7
   functions 153
   mini-9-β-carotene 159
carotenoids
   absorption spectra 159, 160, 162, 164, 167, 169

Subject Index

anoxygenic purple bacteria 151–95
binding sites, LHCII in higher
  plants 343
characteristics 12, 13
cyanobacteria 268–9
  energy dissipation 283
  PsaF subunit **131**
  PSI **135, 136**
  PSIIcc **220–2**
electronic conversions 168–72
functions 103
gap pigments 306–7
LHCII in higher plants 337, 340–1,
  344–6
luminescence quenching 120
natural selection of structures 189–92
photophysical properties 151–95
photoprotective functions 105–6,
  176–89, **508**
photosystem processes 41–2
purple bacteria 151–95
purple non-sulfur bacteria 209–10,
  225–7
triplet formation 321
valve action to chlorophyll triplets 283
see also xanthophylls
carotenoid-to-bacteriochlorophyll
  singlet-energy transfer 172–6
cation radicals 105–6, **250**
cbb_3/RdxB pathway 212–14
cc see core complexes
c chromatophore **454**
CcO see cytochrome c oxidase
CD see circular dichroism
cell breakage **359**
center–center distances **250**
chain length, carotenoids 153–7, 177–9, 191
characterization, molecular **9–12, 162–3,
  200–4**
charge recombination **160, 261**, 398–9,
  405–6
charge separation
  anoxygenic photosynthetic bacteria **60**
  green non-sulfur bacteria **76**
  green sulfur bacteria RCs **80**
  light-induced 15–17

primary **152–4, 160–1**, 371–3
proteobacterial kinetics/energetics
  69–72
PSIIcc **240–62**
reaction center chlorophylls 371–3
triplet forming charge recombination
  398–9
charge transfer coupling 43–8
CHARMM program 88
C helix 335–6, 343
chemically-modified chromophores 117
chemical structure see structure
chemiosmotic mechanism
  ATP synthase **452–60**
  ATP synthesis **450, 451**
  energy conversion basic mechanism
    390
  evolutionary success **391–4**
  photo/chemoautotrophs **392**
chemoheterotrophic energy conversion
  385, 397
chemosynthetic primary production **389**
Chl see chlorophyll
Chlamydomonas
  C. reinhardtii
    $Chlz_{D1}$/$Chlz_{D2}$ chlorophylls mutant
      studies **244**
    cytochrome b_6f complex **419, 424,
      425, 427, 428, 434**
    electron transfer in PSI **120**
    Lhca sequences 318
    P700 in PSI of oxygen evolving
      organisms **165**
    $Pheo_{D2}$ mutant studies **247**
    PSI to Fd/Fld in vitro ET kinetics
      172–3
    PSI trapping mechanism **160**
    two-ET branches of PSI **168, 169–71**
  LHCII mutants 341
  state transition-deficient mutants 375
Chlide a 128
Chlorarachnion **515**
Chlorarachniophyta 110
Chlorella 12
  C. pyrenoidosa **302–3**
  C. sorokiniana **81**

chloride ions **311–12**
chlorins **244–5**, **246**, **248**, **250**
chlorin-type chlorophylls 108, 109
chlorin-type cyclic conjugated tetrapyrroles 115
2-chloro-4-ethylamino-6-isopropylamino-s-triazine *see* atrazine
Chlorobi **7–45**, 18, **59**, **63**, 110
　characteristics **505**
　chlorophylls 108, 109
　C. limicola **81**, **159**
　C. tepidum 44, 82, 87, 128, **368**
　direct photoreduction **404**
　FMO-complex local excitation energies 87
　habitat 77
　light-harvesting protein evolution **512**
　RC functional patterns **77–82**
　RC I resembles PSI **60**
　RC structure **7–45**
chlorobiumquinone **80**
Chloroflexi 16, 19, 110
　C. aurantiacus **70**, **75–7**, 106
　characteristics **505**
　classification 77
　functional patterns of RCs **75–7**
　growth conditions **356**
　RC components/thermodynamic properties **63**
　RC II resembles PSII **60**
　species **59**
　see also Chlorobi; green bacteria
Chlorophyceae 110
chlorophyll A_0 (Chl A_0)
　cyanobacterial PSI **113**
　cyanobacterial PSI structure **118–19**
　eC-B2/eC-A3 dimer **151**, **153**
　energetics modifications in oxygen evolving organisms **170**
　primary ET in PSI of oxygen evolving organisms **159–63**
　PSI ET in oxygen evolving organisms **151**, **153–4**
chlorophyll A_1 (Chl A_1) **159–63**
chlorophyll A5-B5 318

chlorophyll *a'* (Chl *a'*)
　cyanobacterial ET system 266
　P700 in cyanobacterial PSI structure **117–18**
　special pair in oxygen evolving organisms **150**
chlorophyll *a* (Chl *a*)
　A_0 chlorophyll **113**
　absorption spectra 266, 267, 268
　bacteriochlorin type 108, 112
　biosynthesis 128, **498–500**
　CP43/Cp47 protein arrangement **215**
　cyanobacterial ET chain **222–3**
　cyanobacteria photosystem I complexes 275–6
　cytochrome b_6f complex **436–9**
　eC-A2/eC-B3 dimer **151**, **153**
　eC-B2/eC-A3 dimer **151**, **153**
　evolution **499–501**
　gap pigments 306–7
　LHCII in higher plants 331, 339–40, 343–4
　occurrence 110
　oxygenic phototrophs 108, 109
　P680 in PSII **244–6**, **251–2**
　P700 in cyanobacterial PSI structure **117**
　phytyl chains **227**
　primary ET in PSI of oxygen evolving organisms **159**
　red forms 315
　special pair in oxygen evolving organisms **150**
　spectral/chemical properties 268
　structure 13, 108
chlorophyll *a* oxygenase (CAO) 344, 376, 380, 383
chlorophyll *b* (Chl *b*)
　absorption spectra 267, 268
　Arabidopsis replete/deficient mutants 380–1, 382–3
　bacteriochlorin type 108, 112
　biosynthesis 128
　evolution **499–501**
　gap pigments 306–7
　LHCII in higher plants 331, 339–40, 343–4

Subject Index

oxygenic phototrophs 108, 109
structures 108
chlorophyll *c* (Chl *c*) 107–9, **499–501**
chlorophyll (Chl) 103–29
  a/*b* ratios 335, 353
  bacteriochlorophylls comparison **61–2**
  binding sites, CP29 354
  biosynthesis 124–8, 286–8, **498**
  characteristics 12, 13
  circular dichroism 120–1
  CP43/Cp47 protein arrangement **213–15**
  cyanobacteria **113**, **133–5**, 264, 265–8
  dimer system, non-perturbative treatment 66
  diversity in cyanobacteria 265
  electrochemistry 123–4
  electron spin resonance spectroscopy 121–2
  evolution **499–501**
  excitation energy quenching 105–6
  fluorescence 376–7
  functions 104–6
  LHCII in higher plants 335, 336–40, 351
  light-induced electron transfer 105
  luminescence spectrometry 117–20
  mass spectrometry 122
  minor 113–14
  molecular structures 107–14
  NMR spectroscopy 121
  optical absorption spectroscopy 114–17
  pair P680, redox potentials 89
  photosystem processes 41–2
  porphyrin synthesis **498**
  PSIght hart harvesting chlorophyll I complex 305
  structure stabilization 106
  transmetalated 113
  triplets **267**, 283, 321
  unsaturation degree 107
  vibrational spectroscopy 122–3
  see also chlorophyll *a*; chlorophyll *b*; 'special pair'
chlorophyll *d'* (Chl *d'*) 268

chlorophyll *d* (Chl *d*)
  absorption spectra 267
  cyanobacteria 266, 268
  evolution **499–501**
  oxygenic phototrophs 108, 109
  structures 108, 112
chlorophyll eC-A3 **118–19**
chlorophyll eC-B3 **119**, **151**, **153–4**
chlorophyll *e* (Chl *e*) 108, 109, 112
chlorophyll *g* (Chl *g*) 108, 112
chlorophyllide *a* **500**
chlorophyllide *a* oxygenase 287–8
chlorophyllides *see* chlorophyll *c*
chlorophyll–protein interactions 337
chlorophyll–protein proteins 103
chloroplasts
  characteristics **454–5**
  cyanobacteria **385**, **390**, **396**
  envelope structure **197**
  FNR in supramolecular organization **174–5**
  higher plants EET/dissipation 373–5
  membrane system, energy dissipation types 374–5
  organization 334
  photosynthetic membranes **196–8**
  protein kinase state transitions 375
  structure 23–5
  thylakoid lumen acidification 376, 404
  thylakoid membrane discovery **196**
chlorosomes 76, **80**, 106, 121
$Chlz_{D1}/Chlz_{D2}$ chlorophylls **244–5**
Chromatiaceae 9
Chromatium vinosum 214–15
chromatography **11**, **201**, **202**, **206–9**, **434**
chromatophore vesicles **454**, **475–6**
chromophores
  adjustable properties 116
  binding pockets 116–17
  classes 12
  organization, higher plants 304
  red forms 317–19
chromophytes 107
chronological ordering prescription (COP) 66–7, 68
Chrysophyceae 110

circular dichroism (CD) 120–1, 226, 306, 307, 347, 349
cis-carotenoids **135, 136**, 155–7, 179–83, 189–91, 194–5
cis-positive rule **427**
15-cis to all-trans isomerization 179–80
CK2 site, CP29 354
classification
    anoxygenic photosynthetic bacteria **59–60, 355–6**
    Chloroflexi **77**
    purple non-sulfur bacteria 207, 208
    reaction centers **356**
    revised bacterial species names **67**
$C_{MKKL}(t)$ see correlation function
coal energy 11
'cofactor-apoprotein' concept **241**
cofactors
    bacterial RCs **9–10, 18, 21–9**
    Blastochloris viridis **9–10**
    chemical nature in PSII **242–3**
    cyanobacterial PSI **116–21**
    cyanobacterial PSIIcc crystallization **204–9**
    PSII water splitting process **240**
    reaction centers basic sequence 16
    redox potentials 88, **151–9**
    structural arrangement in PSII **243–5**
    see also individual cofactors
complementary chromatic adaptation 271
complex I **369**
computer-aided design (CAD) **241**
concentration quenching 119–20
Condon approximation 57
confocal single-molecule FRET **468**
conformations
    carotenoid natural selection 189–92
    carotenoids in purple bacteria 155–7
    motion **433**
    reaction center-bound T_1 spheroidene 183–9
    15-cis-spheroidene 190
conjugated chain length 153–7, 177–9, 191
connectein **174**
'connecting chlorophylls' **134**

consensus sequences 213
conserved sequences/residues see sequence homology
continuous wave (CW) excitation 177–8, **302**
cooperativity **464–5**
coordinate sets **15, 18**
COP see chronological ordering prescription
copper 113
coproporphyrinogen III **510**
core antenna proteins see CP...
core antenna systems **116, 134, 136**
core complexes (cc)
    antenna system of higher plants' photosystem I 301–22
    cyanobacterial PSII crystallographic structure **193–228**
    electron microscopy studies 229–31
    LH1 ring encircles RC 233–4
    light-harvesting chlorophyll I association 309
    purple non-sulfur bacteria 210–11
    Rhodospirillum rubrum 230–1
core units **122–3**
correlation function ($C_{MKKL}(t)$) 56, 69–70
Coulomb coupling 83, 84, 85
coupled electron/proton transfer **421**
coupling factor (F_1) **450, 464–72**
coupling of ion movements **450**
couplings, electronic 41–89
CP24 core antenna protein 331, 353
CP26 core antenna protein 331, 353–4
CP29 core antenna protein 331, 340, 344, 354, 355
CP43 core antenna protein
    carotenoid locations in cyanobacterial PSIIcc **222**
    chlorophyll arrangement **213–15**
    CP43' and Isi 277, 285
    energy flux in PSII 381
    LHCII 334
    PSIIcc in cyanobacteria **198, 199**
    SDS–urea–PAGE analysis **209**
    transmembrane α-helices **211**
    WOC function **294**

Subject Index

CP47 core antenna protein
  carotenoid locations in cyanobacterial PSIIcc 222
  chlorophyll arrangement 213–15
  LHCII 334
  PSIIcc in cyanobacteria 198, 199
  SDS–urea–PAGE analysis 209
  transmembrane α-helices 211
  WOC function 294
C-PC see cyanophyte phycocyanin
cpSecY translocon channel 409–10
cpSRP54 chloroplast signal recognition particle 409
creation operators 55
c-ring of F_O 462–3, 469–72, 473, 475
crosslinking studies 127
cross-talk 428–30
cryo-EM techniques 230–1, 370
Cryptomonads 515
Cryptophyta 110
crystallization
  bacterial RC crystal shapes 13–14
  bacterial RCs 12–13
  cyanobacterial ET complexes 398
  cyanobacterial PSIIcc 204–9
  cytochrome b_6f complex 422–8
  dimeric PSIIcc from Thermosynechococcus elongatus 205
  oxygen evolving PSIIcc crystals 200
  phycobiliproteins crystal structure 273, 274
C subunit of bacterial RC 9–11, 21, 23, 32–4
C-terminal domains
  antenna polypeptides 215–17
  cyanobacterial PsaD subunit 127
  LH2 complex from Rhodopseudomonas acidophila 221
  PsaA/PsaB in cyanobacterial PSI 122
Cyanidium caldarium 113
cyanobacteria
  antenna systems 263–4, 283–5, 372, 373
  chlorophyll 284–8

cytochrome b_6f complex 399–400, 402–3, 424
ET chains 383–405
excitation energy transfer 278–83
FNR in supramolecular organization 175
higher plant photosynthetic apparatus comparison 396
historical development timescale 387–8
hydrogenases 395, 401
light-harvesting protein evolution 511–12, 513
membrane systems 23, 273–8, 396–7
oxygen-evolving 261–88, 372, 373, 383–405
pheophytin 264
photosynthetic/respiratory activities 397–8, 400–5
photosystem stoichiometry regulation 285–6
phycobilisomes 271–3
pigments 264, 265–71
proton translocation 456
PSI 113–38
PSII 193–228, 410
reaction centers 16, 372, 373
thylakoids 23, 197, 198
transformable 423
trimeric PSI 373
water cleavage 9–10
Cyanophora paradoxa 390
Cyanophyta I/II[b] 110
cyanophyte phycocyanin (C-PC) 270, 274
cyclic conjugated tetrapyrroles 114, 115
cyclic electron transport 8–9
  alternative to linear electron transport 420, 422, 434–6
  anoxygenic photosynthetic bacteria 353–74
  antimycin A inhibition 419, 430, 431, 434
  cyanobacterial PsaE subunit 127, 128
cyclic Mg-tetrapyrroles see chlorophylls

cysteine residues **120–1, 459**
cytochrome b_6f complex 103
   cyanobacteria **399–400, 402–3, 424**
   intermonomer cross-talk **428–30**
   linear electron transport 20, 21
   photodamage sites 396
   prosthetic groups **425–6, 429, 436–9**
   proton translocation pathways **430–6**
   Q-cycle 425–6, 430–3, 435
   quinone exchange cavity **419, 426, 428–30, 435**
   structure/function **399–400, 417–39**
   three-dimensional structure **424–5**
cytochrome b-559
   D1/D2/Cyt b-559 isolation **246**
   ^{1}P680* electronic states **247–8**
   photoprotection in PSIIcc without WOC **265**
   PSIIcc structure in cyanobacteria **198–9, 212**
cytochrome bc_1 complex
   cyanobacteria **402–3**
   cyt c co-crystals X-ray crystallography **367**
   cytochrome b_6f complex comparison **427**
   cytochrome c^2 role in anoxygenic bacterial RC **365, 366**
   ET steps in anoxygenic bacterial RC **357–8**
   facultative photosynthetic bacteria **356–7**
   HiPIP/cyt c docking **363**
   pheophytin–quinone type RCs **7–8**
   species variations **359**
   tetraheme connection in anoxygenic bacterial RCs **361**
cytochrome c_2 **32–4, 66–7, 365–8, 372**
cytochrome $c6$ **113, 123, 149, 403**
cytochrome c **358, 359, 367**
cytochrome c_m **403**
cytochrome c_n **399**
cytochrome c oxidase (CcO) **403**
cytochrome c_t **371**
cytochrome f heme **433–4**

cytochromes
   green sulfur bacteria Type I RCs **82**
   organisms possessing subunit **69**
   proteobacterial secondary electron transfer **72–4**
   see also individual cytochromes
cytochrome x see cytochrome c_n
cytoplasmic membrane (CM), cyanobacteria **395, 396–7**
cytosol see stroma

D1/D2/Cyt b559 **246, 247–8, 256**
D1/D2 proteins
   cyanobacterial PSII structure **196, 198–9, 209, 212–14, 216–27**
   de novo synthesis 409–10
   evolution **507, 508**
   non-triplet producing charge recombination 405
   photoprotection 406–11
   PSII cofactors **244–5**
   RC structure comparison with PSII structure **44–5**
   repair cycle 407
   structure of D2 **63–5**
   WOC function **294**
D1-L210H mutants **247**
damage repair 393–412
   see also photodamage; photoprotection
dark-adapted bacterial reaction centers **43–4**
dark-equilibrium redox titration **360**
dark-operative protochlorophyllide oxidoreductase (DPOR) 125, 128, 287
dark processes **397**
dark stabilities **297**
Darwin, Charles R. **387**
day length **494**
DBMIB quinone analogue inhibitor **421, 430**
DCCD see dicyclohexylcarbodiimide
5-deazariboflavin **175**
DegP proteases 408
dehydrogenase-quinol-cytochrome sequences **391–2**

Subject Index

delayed luminescence 120, 281
deletion studies
  cyanobacterial PsaF subunit **131**
  cytochrome c^2 role **365–6**
  F_OF_1-ATP synthase robustness **477**
  triheme RC species **365**
delipidation **423**
delocalization *see* exciton states
delocalized mixed valence states **308–9**
de novo D1 protein synthesis 409–10
de novo membrane synthesis 208
density functional theory (DFT) **250**
density matrix theory 67–73
deprotonation reactions **328–9**
desacetyl bacteriochlorophyllide **500**
Dexter mechanism 104, 239, **436**, **439**
DGDG *see* digalactosyldiacylglycerol
D helix, LHCII structure 335–6
diabatic states 49
dicyclohexylcarbodiimide (DCCD) 378
difference absorption spectra **242–3**, 317, 339–40
diffusion, WOC substrate water **313**
diffusion coefficient D_Z **202–3**
digalactosyldiacylglycerol (DGDG) **196**, **215–18**, **271**, 341
dihydroplastoquinone (PQH$_2$) **267–71**, **432–3**
di-manganese catalase **394**
dimensionless coupling constant 52, 64
dimeric structures
  cytochrome b_6f complex **417–39**
  Lhca1/4 reconstitution 313
  PSIIcc, cyanobacterial X-ray studies **200–27**
  RC-LH1-PufX complexes, supramolecular organization **371–3**
dinoflagellates **515**
Dinophyta 110
dipole strength 349–50
direct electron donors **359**
directionality **74–5**, **81–2**, **161**, **252**
dispersed polaron model 81–2
dissipation-free dynamics 68
dissociation rates **173**
dissymmetric molecules 120–1

distance dependencies 43
distorted carotenoids 226–7
disulfide bridges **466**
divinyl PChlide a 108, 109
DLS *see* dynamic light scattering
D_M *see* Lorentzian lineshape
docking
  cyanobacterial PSI **114**
  ferredoxin in cyanobacterial PsaD/PsaE subunits **126–8**
  HiPIP/cyt c in anoxygenic bacterial RCs **363**
  PSI for Fd/Fld in oxygen evolving organisms **172**
  Rhodobacter sphaeroides cyt c_2 and RC **366**
  soluble electron donors in cyanobacterial PsaA/PsaB role **123**
  triheme RC species **365**
n-dodecyl-β-D-maltoside (β-DM) **200**
domain-swapped ISP TM helix **427**
Donnelly and Cogdell model 219
donor-side induced photodamage 398
double bonds 161
double-flash techniques **72**
double-hit probability (β) **297–8**
DPOR *see* dark-operative protchlorophyllide oxidoreductase
dual function photosynthetic-respiratory ET chain **394–5**, **400–5**
Dutton ruler 86
dyads 27
dynamical theories 41–89
dynamic light scattering (DLS) **202–3**
D_Z *see* diffusion coefficient

E122 glutamine 378–9
E122Q mutation 378–9
E226 glutamine 378–9
E226Q mutation 378–9

Earth
  early life **494–6**
  atmospheric oxygen content **388–9**
  energy release 8

formation **493–5**
geological history **387–8**
mantle out-gassing **495, 496**
eC-A3 *see* chlorophyll A$_0$
Ectothiorhodospira **9**, 229
edge to edge distance (R_{DA}) **321**
EET *see* excitation energy transfer
efficiency, ATP synthase torque **471–2**
EF$_O$F$_1$-ATPase **471**
E helix, LHCII X-ray structure 342
eigenstates 49, 350
eigenvalue analysis 65, **298**
elastic deformation **469–72**
elastic power transmission **478**
ELDOR *see* electron–electron double-resonance techniques
electrical analogy, biological ET **386**
electrical potential gradients **386**
electrochemical potential difference of the proton *see* protonmotive force
electrochemical potential gradients **386**
electrochemistry, chlorophylls 123–4
electron acceptors **63, 118–21, 218–20**
electron-acceptor substrate *see* secondary electron acceptor quinone
electron density maps **211–12, 225**
electron donors **63, 117–18, 507–8**
electron donor substrate **32–4**
electron–electron double-resonance (ELDOR) techniques 121
electron exchange (Dexter mechanism) 104, 239, **436, 439**
electronic configurations **247, 248–9, 301–2**
electronic conversions 159–64, 168–72
electronic couplings 48–89
electronic states **247–8**
electronic structure, WOC **308–11**
electron microscopy (EM) **196**, 207–8, 229–31, 332
electronmotive force **386, 391–2**
electron–nucleus double resonance technique (ENDOR) **117**, 121, **166, 309**
electron paramagnetic resonance (EPR) studies

F$_B$/F$_A$ FeS cluster **121**
heme c_n **434**
phylloquinone A$_1$ characterization **162**
secondary ET in PSI of oxygen evolving organisms **163–4**
two-ET branches of PSI in oxygen evolving organisms **167–8**
WOC electronic structure **309**
electron–photon double-resonance techniques (ODMR) 121
electron spin envelope echo modulation (ESEEM) **314**
electron spin resonance (ESR) spectroscopy 121–2
electron transfer chain (ETC) **199, 221**, 263
anoxygenic bacteria **353–74**
basic principles 18–22
cyanobacterial PSI **116–21**
light-induced processes 10–11
oxygenic cyanobacteria **383–405**
electron transfer (ET)
aerobic photosynthetic bacteria **368–9**
anoxygenic bacteria **61, 63, 65, 67–84, 359–68**
antenna/reaction center pigment coupling 12, 14
chain of PSI in oxygen evolving organisms **150–1**
coupling 85–6
cyanobacterial minor pigments 266
cyanobacterial pathways **394–405**
cytochrome b_6f complex structure/function **417–39**
directionality in Type I RCs **81–2**
dispersed polaron model 81–2
energetics in PSI of oxygen evolving organisms **151–9**
green non-sulfur bacteria **76–7**
green sulfur bacterial Type I RCs **79–82**
heliobacterial RCs **83–4**
light-induced charge separation in PSII **256**
light-induced in chlorophylls 105
out of PSI in oxygen evolving organisms **171–6**

Subject Index

photodamage sites 396
photoinhibition 393–412
pigment locations/functions/
  absorptions 111
PSI in oxygen evolving organisms
  149–76
PT coupling in WOC **322, 326**
quinol/quinone exchange reactions
  in PSIIcc **271**
reaction centers basic sequence 15
reaction regimes 61
reorganization energy 83
supramolecular organization in
  anoxygenic bacteria **369–73**
thermodynamics **386**
Type I/II reaction center schemes 61
see also Marcus theory
electron transport phosphorylation (ETP)
see chemiosmotic energy conversion
electrospray ionization mass
  spectrometry (ESI-MS) **423**
electrostatic continuum model **251**
electrostatic effects **360**
elliptical structures 235–6
EM *see* electron microscopy
E_m *see* midpoint oxidation potential
Emiliana huxleyi 108, 109
ENDOR *see* electron–nucleus double
  resonance technique
endosymbiosis **396, 510, 514–16**
  see also generalized (unifying)
  endosymbiont hypothesis
energetics
  chemiosmotic energy conversion
    efficiency **392–3**
  chemiosmotic energy coupling **452–4**
  ET in green non-sulfur bacteria **76–7**
  ET in green sulfur bacteria **79–82**
  ET in heliobacteria **83–4**
  four-step oxidative water splitting
    300–2
  initial ET in proteobacteria **69–72**
  $P680^{+\cdot}Pheo^{-\cdot}$ radical ion pair **260–2**
  $P680^{+\cdot}Q_A^{-\cdot}$ radical pair formation **258**
  PSI ET in oxygen evolving
    organisms **151–9**

type I/II reaction centers 18
energy conversion schemes **391**
energy dissipation 283, 369–85
energy gap
  dispersed polaron model 81–2
  ET reactions reorganization energy 83
  POP/COP theories 67
  singlet lifetimes in carotenoids of
    purple bacteria 161–2
energy levels
  chlorophyll *a* and Tyr105 in
    cytochrome b_6f complex **438**
  P680 states **258–62**
  single monomeric LHCII complex 348
energy radiation, Sun **496**
energy transfer
  carotenoids in purple bacteria 172–6
  cyanobacteria photosystems 280–2
  LHCII carotenoids stabilization
    role 345
  purple non-sulfur bacterial
    photosynthetic apparatus
    arrangement 237–42
energy trapping 280–2
entropic contributions **158–9**
entropic ratchets **474**
environmental conditions 309
enzyme-catalyzed chains of steps 10–11
eosin label **466**
EPR *see* electron paramagnetic
  resonance
epsilon (ATP-synthase) subunit **463**
ERPE *see* exciton/radical pair
  equilibrium model
Escherichia coli **459, 461, 464, 471**
ESEEM *see* electron spin envelope
  echo modulation
ESI-MS *see* electrospray ionization
  mass spectrometry
ESR *see* electron spin resonance
  spectroscopy
ET *see* electron transfer
ETC *see* electron transfer chain
ETP (electron transport
  phosphorylation) *see*
  chemiosmotic energy conversion

euglenoids 515
Euglenophyta 110
eukaryotes 23, **387–8**, **514–16**
Eustigmatophyceae 110
evolution
 algal protists **514–16**
 anoxygenic bacterial photosynthesis **504–5**
 antenna system regulatory mechanisms 371–3
 ATP synthase **60**
 chlorophylls/bacteriochlorophylls **499–501**
 chloroplasts **385**, **396**
 cyanobacteria 263
 Earth formation **493–5**
 ET chains **387–94**
 eukaryotes **514–16**
 Fusion hypothesis **505–6**
 Homo sapiens **387-8**
 light-harvesting proteins **511–14**
 light intensity variations 15
 mitochondria **396**
 monophyletic origin of ET chains **386**
 overview **489–517**
 oxidative water splitting **195–6**
 oxygen-evolving organisms 331
 P_{D1}/P_{D2} center–center distance in PSII **250**
 primary charge separation in PSIIcc **257**
 PsaA/PsaB in cyanobacterial PSI **122**
 PsaI subunit **129**
 PSIIcc **239**
 reaction centers **501–4**
 timing of major events **509–10**
 two photosystems **502**, **505–7**
 Type I/II RCs **67**
 water oxidizing complex **393**
 water splitting **507–9**
EXAFS *see* extended X-ray absorption fine structure
excitation energies, local 86–8
excitation energy transfer (EET)
 antenna/reaction center pigment coupling 12, 14
 biomimetic antenna systems 27
 chlorophylls 104–5
 cyanobacteria 278–83
  PsaI subunit **130**
  PsaM subunit **130**
 Förster theory 41, 46, 59–60
 LHCII 331, 346–8, 350–2
 $P680^+ \cdot Pheo^-$ radical ion pair formation in PSIIcc **255–6**
 photoactive reaction center chlorophylls 371–3
 primary ET in PSI of oxygen evolving organisms **159–60**
 regulatory in PSII of higher plants 373–5
 spectral density 42–3, 77–81
excitation quenching 105–6, 404–5
 carotenoids 153–4
 Chl *a* singlet excited state lifetime in cytochrome $b_6 f$ complex **438–9**
 chlorophylls excitation energy 105–6
 chlorophyll triplets **267**, 321
 cyanobacterial PSI carotenoids **135**
 Lhc of higher plants 331, 369–85
 luminescence 119–20
 photoprotection 404–5
excited singlet states *see* singlet excited states
excitonic coupling
 definition 43–4
 LHCII 349–50
 multi-level Redfield theory 41, 46
 parameter extraction 83
 pigment–pigment 43–8, 83
 red forms 317
 strong 62–77
excitonic degrees of freedom 68
exciton-radiational coupling 68
exciton/radical pair equilibrium (ERPE) model **257**, 352
exciton states
 LHCII EET modeling 350–1
 LHCII excitonic interactions 349–50
 peridinin-chlorophyll *a* complex 44, 47, 60
 photosystem II reaction centers 45

Prosthecochloris aestuarii FMO-complex 44, 46
purple non-sulfur bacterial PSU 240
single monomeric LHCII complex 348
strongly coupled pigments in RC-PC unit **248–9**
exciton transition dipole moments 65
exciton–vibrational coupling 64, 66, 70, 71
expression regulation 212–15
extended-dipole approximation 84
extended X-ray absorption fine structure (EXAFS) **228, 305–8, 321**
extremophiles **398**

F_1 *see* coupling factor
F680 band 381–3
F685 band 381–3
F695 band 381–4
$F_{A/B}$ iron–sulfur clusters
  cyanobacterial PSI **121**
  ET in PSI of oxygen evolving organisms **158–9**
  PSI damage mechanism 402
  PSI in oxygen evolving organisms **151**
  secondary ET in PSI of oxygen evolving organisms **163–5**
fast acceptor (W_f) **322, 326**
fast electron transfer **175–6**
fast nanosecond kinetics **264–5**
fast phase **168**
  see also B-branch
F-ATPase *see* ATP synthase
fd:PQ oxidoreductase, cytochrome c_n as candidate **399**
Fd *see* ferredoxin
feedback mechanisms 125, 369–85, 404–5
femtosecond studies 348–9
Fenna–Matthews–Olson (FMO) complexes **78**
  Chlorobium tepidum 44, 82, 87
  fluorescence line narrowing spectra 81
  Prosthecochloris aestuarii 44, 46, 87
fermentative reactions **495–6**
Fermi's Golden Rule 41, 53–4, 57

ferredoxin (Fd)
  cyanobacteria 113, 114, 126–8, **395, 404**
  ET out of PSI in oxygen evolving organisms **171–6**
  F-ATPase thiol regulation **459**
  heme c_n cyclic electron transport **435**
  isoforms **172**
  reduction by PSI in oxygen evolving organisms **172–3**
  see also Photosystem I; Type I reaction centers
ferredoxin-NADP$^+$-oxidoreductase (FNR)
  consensus sequence
    PSU genes 213
    Rhodobacter sphaeroides 213
  fast ET to Fd/Fld in oxygen evolving organisms **175–6**
  heme c_n cyclic electron pathway **435**
  membrane association in oxygen evolving organisms **174–5**
  membrane structures **420**
  NADP$^+$ reduction in oxygen evolving organisms **149**
  photoreduction in PSI of oxygen evolving organisms **173–4**
  photosynthesis interaction in ET chains **404**
  spinach cytochrome b_6f complex **425**
Fe–S *see* iron–sulfur centers; tetraheme–tetrasulfur centers
final state P680 energy levels **258–9**
fine tuning, F_OF_1 rotary twin engine **476–8**
FIOPS *see* flash-induced oxygen evolution patterns
Firmicutes *see* heliobacteria
first-order perturbation theory 165
Fission hypothesis **493**
flash-induced oxygen evolution patterns (FIOPs) **295–300**
flash photometry studies 239, **312–13, 317, 356, 359, 362**
flavodoxin (Fld) **172–3**, 284

Fld *see* flavodoxin
FLN *see* fluorescence line narrowing
fluorescence
   carotenoids in purple bacteria 166–9
   Lax and Kubo theory 58
   luminescence spectrometry 117–20
   neurosporene 167
   nonphotochemical quenching 376
   nucleotide analogues, F_1-ATPase tri-site binding mechanism **468**
   thylakoids 315
   zeaxanthin quenching 311
fluorescence line-narrowing (FLN) 77–81, 349
fluorescence resonance energy transfer (FRET) **468–72**
fluorophore-labeled actin filaments **466–7**
FMN cofactor **173**
FMO *see* Fenna–Matthews–Olson
FNR *see* ferredoxin-NADP$^+$-reductase
fnrL gene 213
F_OF_1-ATPase *see* ATP synthase
Fokker–Planck equation **478**
folding *see* protein folding
F_O rotary electromotor concept **473–6**
Förster EET mechanism
   chlorophylls 104
      LHCII absorption spectra 347–8, 356
      LHCII EET modeling 350
      pigment–pigment coupling 41, 46, 47, 48, 59–60, 75–7
      purple non-sulfur bacterial photosynthetic apparatus 239, 240
fossil fuels 11
four-electron transfer reactions **401**
four-heme cytochrome **72, 73, 74, 77**
Fourier–Laplace transform 69, 70, 71
Fourier processed images 230, 231
Fourier transform 56, 218
Fourier transform infrared (FTIR) spectroscopy **162–3, 165–7,** 311, **315–16**
four-orbital model (Gouterman) 114, 115
four oxidizing equivalents **295–300**
four proton–four electron reaction **419**

four-step oxidative water splitting **300–2**
four tilted helices model 218–19
fragmentation patterns 122–3
Franck–Condon factor/principle 62, 119, 168, 169
free energy gaps **261–2**
free energy profiles **471**
free energy surfaces 60–1, 63
Fremyella diplosiphon **UTEX 481** 270, 272
FTIR *see* Fourier transform infrared
FtsH metalloprotease complex 407, 408–9
fullerenes 28
full-width at half-maximum (FWHM) 316
functional aspects
   anoxygenic photosynthetic bacterial RCs **57–85**
   ATP 449–50
   chlorophylls 104–6
   cyanobacterial ET carriers **395**
   cytochrome b_6f complex **399–400, 417–39**
   green non-sulfur bacteria RCs **75–7**
   PSI 111–38, 147–76
   PSII 237–73
functional asymmetry *see* directionality
fungi **516**
'funneling' of excitation energy **134**
Fusion hypothesis **493, 505–6**
futile NADPH cycling **405**
FWHM *see* full-width at half-maximum
F_x iron–sulfur center
   A_1 binding site effects in PSI of oxygen evolving organisms **163**
   electron transfer in cyanobacterial PSI **120–1**
   midpoint potential in PSI of oxygen evolving organisms **156–8**
   phylloquinones in PSI of oxygen evolving organisms **155–8**
   PsaA/PsaB in cyanobacterial PSI **123**
   secondary ET in PSI of oxygen evolving organisms **163–5**

Galdieria sulphuraria see Cyanidium caldarium
gamma (ATP synthase) subunit **463, 468**
GAP-dehydrogenase (GAP-DH) **404**
gap pigments 304–7, 309, 310
gas chromatography **206**
gear ratios **463, 480**
gel permeation chromatography (GPC) **201, 202**
gene expression regulation 212–15
gene fusion studies **477**
generalized Förster theory 48, 75–7
generalized (unifying) endosymbiont hypothesis **389–90**
gene sequence analysis
 Arabidopsis 380, 408
 cyanobacterial PsaX subunit **132**
 mitochondria **396**
 phylogenetic tree inference **496**
 PsbS protein symmetrical structure 377
geological history **387–8**
Gibbs energy
 ATP hydrolysis **449**
 biomimetic systems 26–30
 converters in photoautotrophs/ heterotrophs 8–9
 ET thermodynamics **386**
 fossil fuels 11
 four-step oxidative water splitting **300–1, 302**
 solar source 8
 see also free energy...
Gilmore's three-state model 379
Glaucophyta 110
gliding ability **75, 77**
global-fitting analyses 159, 160, 162, 164, 169
Gloeobacter
 electron transfer **394**
 G. violaceus 23
  PCC 7421 267, 270, 272–3
  thylakoid membranes **397**
glutamates 374, 378–9
glutamate semialdehyde 124
glutamic acid **34–6, 41, 44**

gold 40 nm beads **467**
Gouterman's four-orbital model 114, 115
GPC see gel permeation chromatography
gramicidin **455, 476**
grana
 D1 protein repair cycle 407
 LHCI-PSI supercomplexes 332
 membrane domains, thylakoids fluorescence emission spectra 315
 stacked/unstacked **198**
 structure 24–5, **455**
grana-thylakoid **197**, 373–5
green bacteria 76, 108, 109, 207
 see also Chlorobi; Chloroflexi
'green gap' (chlorophylls) 104, 109
green glue 310
green non-sulfur bacteria see Chloroflexi
green plants see higher plants
Green's function technique 76
green sulfur bacteria see Chlorobi

H^+/ATP stoichiometric ratio **458–9, 463**
habitats **75, 77, 363, 397–8, 400**
hairpin folding **462, 463**
half-life times **317–19**
Halobacterium salinarium **60, 498**
Hamiltonian (H) 49, 51, 54, 63, 64, 65
Hamilton's classical equations of motion 52
hand-shaking interactions 225
Haptophyta 110
harmonic oscillator model
 Marcus theory 60
 modified Redfield theory 73
 pigment–protein (electron–vibrational) coupling 42
 spectral density 42–3
 weak pigment–pigment coupling 48–62
helices A/B/C/D (LHCII) 335–7
heliobacteria **59, 63**
 characteristics **505, 506**
 chlorophylls 110
 direct photoreduction **404**
 H. chlorum **82–3**, 114, **159**
 H. mobilis RCs **70, 82–3**

light-harvesting protein evolution **512**
reaction centers 16, 19, **60**, **82–3**
heme-iron site geometries **28–9**
hemes
   bacterial cytochrome subunits **69**
   bacterial RCs **10**, **11–12**
   biosynthesis 124, 126
   b_n in cyt b_6f **431**, **434**
   c_n in cyt b_6f **431–4**
   reduction rates in anoxygenic bacterial RCs **360**
   x pyridine hemochromagen redox difference spectrum **434**
heme–sulfur *see* iron–sulfur
hemF genes **511**
hemi-discoidal phycobilisomes 271, 272–3
hemi-spherical phycobilisomes 271
hemN genes **511**
Henderson–Hasselbach titration 377
herbicides **31**, **42**, **270**
heterodimeric reaction centers **503**
heterotrophs 8–9
higher plants
   antenna function regulation 369–85
   Chlide *a* 128
   chlorophylls 110
   chloroplasts EET/dissipation 373–5
   chloroplast structure **197–8**, **454–5**
   cytochrome b_6f complex transmembrane signaling **422**
   evolution **516**
   light-harvesting protein evolution **512**
   oxygenic photosynthetic process **195**
   protein phosphorylation in damage repair 410–11
   PsaF subunit **131**, **132**
   PsaK subunit interactions **133**
   PSI antenna system 301–22
   PSII comparison with bacterial RC structure **44–5**
   PSII Lhcb proteins 329–56
   reaction centers 372–3
   thylakoid membrane composition **196–8**
   see also individual plants; spinach

highest occupied molecular orbital (HOMO) 12, 14
high light induced protein (HLIP) 284–5, **512**
high-low-high-low sequences **364**
high midpoint potential (HP) **360–3**
high-potential iron–sulfur protein (HiPIP) **32–4**, **74**, **361–3**
high-resolution X-ray structure **167**, **168**
high-sensitivity emission spectroscopy 165
HiPIP *see* high-potential iron–sulfur protein
histidine kinase/phosphatase 212–14
histidine residues
   conserved in P700 in PSI of oxygen evolving organisms **165**
   conserved in PsaA/PsaB in cyanobacterial PSI **122**
   conserved in purple non-sulfur bacterial LH1/LH2 complexes 217, 219, 223
   His-tagged PSIIcc in *Synechocystis* sp. PCC 6803 **261**
   ligands: bacterial RC structure **28**
   light-induced *Rhodobacter sphaeroides* RC structural changes **43**
   modified bacterial RCs **41**, **42**
   primary electron donor location **22–3**
   RC structure comparison with PSII structure **44**
history
   ATP synthesis research **450**
   chloroplast origins **389–90**
   Earth **387–9**
   oxidative water splitting research **293**
   photoinhibition studies 395
   photosynthesis discoveries 10, 12
   PSII structure elucidation **196**
   PSI studies **150**
HLIP *see* high light induced protein
hole-burning spectroscopy 350, 355
holes *see* photochemical hole formation
hole-transfer band **166**

HOMO *see* highest occupied molecular orbital
homodimeric reaction center evolution **503**
homology *see* sequence homology
Homo sapiens evolution **387–8**
hook arrangements **224–5**
hox genes **401**
HP hemes **361**
H subunit of bacterial RC **9–11, 18, 21–2**
Huang Rhys factor (*S*) 59, 62, 72
hup genes **401**
hybrid reconstitution assays 228
hydratases **368–9**
hydrodynamic radius (R_H) **202–3**
hydrogenases **395, 401**
hydrogen atom abstractor hypothesis **316**
hydrogen bonding
  B800 bacteriochlorophyll in purple non-sulfur bacterial LH2 complex 225
  P700 special pair in two-ET branches of PSI **170**
  pheophytins ring V keto group **253**
  Q_A in PSIIcc **254–5**
  triplet state ^{3}P680 in PSII **250**
hydrogen cycle **389, 404**
hydrogen donors **496–7**
hydrogen peroxide **393**
hydrophilic exogenous reductants **303**
hydrophobic protein subunits **130–3**
hydrophobic residues **439**
'hydrophobic sticks' **427**
8-hydroxychlorophyll *a* **83–4**
hydroxyl groups coupling mechanism **328**
hydroxyl radicals 403
hydroxymethylbilane 124, 126

ICM *see* intracytoplasmic membranes
IEF *see* isoelectric focussing
IEP *see* isoelectric point
Iliobacter tartaricus **462, 463, 475**
illumination conditions *see* adaptation mechanisms; light intensity; photoprotection

inactive PSII centers 405
INDO/S method 88
infrared (IR) spectroscopy 123, **150, 162**
initial charge separation *see* primary charge separation
initial electron acceptor **118**
initial electron transfer **69–72**
initial P680 energy levels **258–9**
insertion studies **133, 477**
intact WOCs **265**
intense fluorescence 117–18
intermediary P680 states **259–62**
intermolecular energy transfer times 241
inter-monomer cross-talk **428–30, 433**
interpretation problems **211–12, 225**
inter-protein FeS clusters **120–1, 123**
intersystem crossing (ISC) 118, 119
intervening ET medium 86
intracytoplasmic membrane (ICM)
  chlorophyll *a* **394**
  cyanobacteria **395, 396–7**
  cyanobacterial ET chains in photosynthesis and respiration **400**
  purple non-sulfur bacteria 207–8, 229–30, 237–42
intramolecular energy transfer 241
intra-monomer distances **425–6, 429, 433**
intraprotein O_2 channels **439**
intrinsic time constant **159–60**
in vitro re-folding/reconstitution 338
IR *see* infrared spectroscopy
iron, nonheme **25, 27–8, 72, 257–8, 311**
iron-depleted conditions **283–5**
iron-stress-induced (Isi) protein family **131–2, 277, 284**
iron–sulfur centers
  cyanobacterial PSI **116, 120–1, 123–4**
  green sulfur bacterial Type I RCs **78**
  midpoint potential in PSI of oxygen evolving organisms **156–8**
  phylloquinones in PSI of oxygen evolving organisms **155–8**
  secondary ET in PSI of oxygen evolving organisms **163–5**
  structure in anoxygenic bacteria **62–5**

three in chlorobial RCs **80–1**
see also $F_{A/B}$ iron–sulfur clusters
iron–sulfur protein (ISP) *see* Rieske iron-sulfur protein
iron–sulfur type RCs *see* anaerobic green sulfur bacteria; heliobacteria
irradiation level adaptation 14–15
ISC *see* intersystem crossing
Isi *see* iron-stress-induced
isocyclic five-membered rings 107
isoelectric focussing (IEF) 335, 353–4
isoelectric points (IEPs) **403**
isoforms of ferredoxin **172**
isolated RC membrane studies **359**
isotropic powder spectra 186, 187
ISP *see* Rieske iron–sulfur protein

Jablonski diagrams 114, 118–19
Jacobian 51
Jang and Silbey's theory 76
J_ω *see* spectral density

Kaplan rule **404**
Karlsberg program 89
Kerr-gate fluorescence spectroscopy 169, 192
kinetic isotope effects (KIE) **320**
kinetics
  ET in green non-sulfur bacteria **76–7**
  ET in green sulfur bacteria **79–82**
  ET in heliobacteria **83–4**
  ET in PSI of oxygen evolving organisms **159–65**
  Fd/Fld reduction by PSI in oxygen evolving organisms **172–3**
  $F_O F_1$-ATP synthase **478–80**
  H^+/ATP stoichiometric ratio **458–9**
  initial ET in proteobacteria **69–72**
  oxidative water splitting **316–24**
  $P680_+ Q_A^-$ formation in PSIIcc **257–8**
  PSIIcc charge separation **255–8**
  secondary ET in proteobacteria **72–4**
  singlet–singlet ET from carotenoids to bacteriochlorophyll 176
  S_i state transitions **316–20**

substrate water exchange in PSIIcc **312–13**
WOC 303, 316–24
Kok model
  extensions **298–300**
  FIOPS measurements **295–300**
  kinetics **316–18**
  mathematics **298**
  origin of misses **298–300**
  scheme **293–4**
Kramer model 220
Kramers–Kronig relationship 71

L2 site 345
L *see* lutein
labeling notations **308**, **360**
lag phases **318**
'lake' model 237
Lambert–Beer's law 58
lamellae **197–8**
large-scale purification **200**
laser photo-bleaching **466–7**
lateral transfer of characteristics **506**
Lax and Kubo theory 41, 57–9, 67
lead (Pb) 113
length of conjugated chain 153–7, 177–9, 191
leucine residues **40**, **41**, **44**
LH *see* light harvesting
Lhca proteins 305, 307–9, 313–20
Lhcb proteins 333, 334, 353, 372–5, 380–4
Lhc superfamily 331
lifetime states **297**, 376–7
ligands **314–17**, 336, 337, 338–40
light-adapted bacterial RC structures **43–4**
light capture process 39–89, 104, **113**, 320–1
light-dependent protochlorophyllide oxidoreductase (LPOR) 287
light energy distribution 282–3
light harvesting complex I (LHCI) 311–12
  chlorophyll red forms 315–21
  evolution **511**
  LHCI-PSI supercomplexes 332

Subject Index 545

pigment composition 311–12
purple bacteria 154, 157
purple non-sulfur bacteria 207–42
light harvesting complex of
    Photosystem II (LHCII)
  carotenoids role 344–6
  cyanobacterial PsaI subunit
      interactions **129–30**
  evolution 331, **511**
  fluorescence line-narrowing spectra 81
  higher plants 329–52
  photoprotection by excitation
      quenching 404–5
  pigment binding in native 334–5
  purple bacteria 154, 155–7
  purple non-sulfur bacteria 207–42
  recombinant protein studies 338–42
  Rhodopseudomonas acidophila
      211, 220–7, 240
  spectroscopy 346–52
  steady-state spectra 346–7
  structure at 2.72 Angstrom units 342–4
  structure from 2D crystals 335–8
  thylakoid membranes **197–8**
  trimerization 342
light harvesting III (LHIII) complex 212
light harvesting (LH)
  antennae evolution **501–4**
  antennae pigments 12
  basic principles 14–15
  carotenoids in purple bacteria 157–76
  complexes: bacterial species
      variations **358**
  cyanobacteria/PSI **113, 133–5**
  early photosynthesis **497–8**
  LH1 antenna complex 42–3, 371, 372
  LH2-minus mutants 233, 234
  LHC superfamily in cyanobacteria
      284–5
  oxygenic phototrophs 109–11
  pigment locations/functions/
      absorptions 111
  pigments in heliobacteria **82**
  proteins evolution **511–14**
  regulation PSI higher plants 310–11
  singlet excited states 157–9

light intensity 14–15, 212–15
  see also photon fluxes
'light' PORA, derivation 125
limited proteolysis 218
linear dichroism (LD) 347
linear electron transport 18, 19–22,
    420, 422, 434–6
lineshape functions 58, 72
linker chlorophylls 305–6
Liouville operator 68
lipids
  cyanobacterial PSI **135–7**
  cyanobacterial PSIIcc crystallization
      204–9
  integral to cyanobacterial PSIIcc
      215–18
  LHCII thylakoid stabilization 341–2
  PSIIcc integral lipid molecules **217**
  PSIIcc role **271–2**
  PSII thylakoid membrane **196–7**
lipophilic cavities **428–9**
litho(auto)trophic life styles **391, 393**
L-,M-,H-site **464–5**
load in rotary engines **478–9**
local excitation energies 86–8
localized exciton states 64
longer chain selection 191
long-wavelength chlorophylls **134**
loop regions **128, 129**
Lorentzian lineshape (D_M) 72
lowest unoccupied molecular orbital
    (LUMO) 12, 14
low midpoint potential (LP) **360–1**
low temperature EPR **168, 309**
low temperature split signals 315
LP *see* low midpoint potential
LPOR *see* light-dependent
    protochlorophyllide
    oxidoreductase
L subunit of bacterial RC **9–11**
  bacteriopheophytins **25**
  bound water **36**
  D1 subunit comparison **213**
  primary electron donor location **21–2**
  RC structure comparison with PSII
      structure **44–5**

side-chain distributions **34–6**
structure **18–19**
lumen volume vs. pH **455**
luminescence spectrometry 114, 117–20
LUMO *see* lowest unoccupied molecular orbital
lutein (L) 340–1, 345
lycopene
  absorption spectra 160, 162, 167, 173, 175
  fluorescence quantum yields 166
  quantum efficiency of singlet energy transfer to bacteriochlorophyll 174
  relaxation scheme 163
  singlet excited states 158
  singlet lifetimes versus double bond numbers 161
  structure 159
lysine **34–6**

M *see* torque
macrocyclic pi systems 123–4
magnesium **11–12**, 113, **116**, **117**
magnesium-adenosine 5'-triphosphate (Mg-ATP) **449**, **464**
magnetic beads **468**
maize 312, 347
MALDI-TOF MS **206–11**
manganese
  bacterial PSII-type RC **68**
  content **206**
  functional heterogeneity in WOC **326**
  Mn_4O_xCa cluster formation studies **303**
  Mn_4O_x motifs: EXAFS data **306–7**
  ^{55}Mn ENDOR spectroscopy **309**
  Mn–Ca distances: EXAFS studies **306–7**
  Mn–Mn distances: EXAFS studies **305–7**
  oxidation state changes in WOC **322**
  PSII structure **65**
  UV photodamage 399–400
  WOC redox active component **294**
  see also Mn_4O_xCa clusters

manganese stabilizing protein *see* PsbO
mantle out-gassing **495**, **496**
Marcus theory of non-adiabatic electron transfer 14
  biomimetic reaction centers 28
  light absorption 44
  $P680^{+}\cdot Pheo^{-\cdot}$ radical ion pair formation **260**
  $P680^{+\cdot}$ reduction by Y_Z/oxidative water splitting **264**
  phylloquinones in PSI of oxygen evolving organisms **155**
  pigment–pigment coupling 14, 44, 48–62, **264**, **321**
Markov approximation 70, 72–3
Markovian theory 66
mass spectrometry 122, **312–13**
Mastigocladus laminosus **419**, **422–5**, **429**, **434**, **438**, **439**
  ET complex crystals **398**, **399**
matrix element 57
Maxwell demons **474**
MDGD *see* monogalactosyldiacylglycerol
MEAD program 88
mean transition energies *see* site energies
mechanical coupling **450**, **468–72**
membrane area per chlorophyll **456**
membrane-bound antenna complexes 273–8
membrane-bound ET devices **391–2**
membrane-intrinsic portion (F_O) **451**
membranes
  artificial proton pumps 28–9
  associations **174–5**
  bound monoheme cytochrome *c* **365**
  characteristics of photosynthetic membranes **454–5**
  extrinsic proteins **198**, **213–14**
  inlet mass spectrometry **312–13**
  localized protons **452**
  organization, LHCII protein mass 332, 334
  photosynthetic apparatus 22–5
  photosynthetic constructs **454–5**

photosynthetic RC incorporation 17
potential **360–1**
proteins **34–9**, **130–3**, **212**, 406–11
purple non-sulfur bacteria 207–8, 229–30, 237–42
RC components **369–73**
systems 373, **396–7**
see also intracytoplasmic membranes; organelles; transmembrane...
membrane-spanning helices *see* transmembrane helices
'memory' 66, 72
menaquinone (MK) **12**, **62–3**, **80**, **84**, 254
mercury 113
mesophilic cyanobacteria **398**
metal-centered oxidations **310**
metaloproteases 407, 408–9
methine bridges 122
Mg^{2+}–Mg^{2+} distance 223–4
Mg-2,4-divinyl-phaeoporphyrin (MgDVP) **499–500**
Mg-ATP *see* magnesium adenosine 5'-triphosphate
MGDG *see* monogalactosyldiacylglycerol
MgDVP *see* Mg-2,4-divinyl-phaeoporphyrin
Mg-protoporphyrin monomethylester **368–9**
Michaelis–Menten description **472**
microscopic simulations 83
midpoint oxidation potential (E_m)
cation radical P680$^{+\cdot}$ in PSII **251**
heme c_n **434**
oxidative water splitting thermodynamics **300**, **301**
P700 states in PSI of oxygen evolving organisms **152–3**, **161**
PhQ_A and F_A/F_B in PSI of oxygen evolving organisms **156–8**
PSI ET in oxygen evolving organisms **162**
ring puckering **250**
triheme RC species **363–4**
see also high midpoint potential; low midpoint potential

minor antenna complexes 352–6
'minor' chlorophylls 113–14
miss hits (α) **297–300**
Mitchell chemiosmotic principle **389**, **450**
Mitchell's Q-cycle mechanism **430**
mitochondria
cyanobacterial ancestry **396**
evolution **509–10**, **514–16**
respiration **366–7**, **368**, **385**, **386**
mixed binding sites 343–4, 350
mixed valence states **308–9**
MK *see* menaquinone
Mn_4O_xCa clusters
cyanobacterial PSIIcc WOC **221**, **224–8**
evolution **394**
protein ligands **314–17**
S_i state-dependent structural changes **307–8**
WOC function **294**
WOC photoactivation **303**
WOC structure **304–17**
models
anoxygenic bacterial ET chain supramolecular organization **372–3**
ATP synthase **451**, **466–7**, **470**, **473**, **477**
LHCII EET 350–2
multiphasic A_1^- reoxidation kinetics **169**
photosynthetic unit in purple non-sulfur bacteria 238–9
primary charge separation in PSI of oxygen evolving organisms **160–1**
purple non-sulfur bacteria antenna complexes 218–20, 238–9
relative midpoint potentials of $PhQ_A/PhQ_B/F_x$ iron–sulfur center **157–8**
modified properties, chromophores 116, 117
modified reaction centers **39–44**, **71**
modified Redfield theory 47–8, 73–5, 348, 350

molar Gibbs free energy difference **453**
molar weight **203–4**
molecular assembly *see* assembly
molecular characterization **9–12, 162–3, 200–4**
molecular docking *see* docking
molecular mass 122, **201, 202**
molecular mechanisms 397–403, 404–12
molecular orbital (MO) schemes **247**
molecular oxygen **312–13, 393, 507–9**
molecular structures *see* structure
monogalactosyldiacylglycerol (MGDG) **135, 137, 196, 215–18, 271**
monomer–monomer interfaces **128–30**
monomers
   antenna system higher plants' photosystem I 307–8
   chlorophyll *a* **436–7**
   cyanobacterial PSI **114–16, 121–33**
   inter-monomer cross-talk **428–30, 433**
   intra-monomer distances **425–6, 429, 433**
   LHCII in higher plants 332, 336, 338, 341–2
   LHCII minor antenna complexes 352–6
   PSIIcc cyanobacterial X-ray studies **200–4, 212, 214, 216–17**
   reaction center evolution **503**
monophyletic endosymbiosis **514–15**
Monte Carlo methods 89
Moon **493–4**
morphology 207–8
motion, conformational **433**
motion equations 52
m protons **453**
MSH *see* membrane-spanning helices
M subunit of bacterial RC **9–11**
   accessory bacteriochlorophylls **25**
   bound water **36**
   D2 subunit comparison **213**
   primary electron donor location **21–2**
   RC structure comparison with PSII structure **44–5**
   side-chain distributions **34–6**
   structure **10, 18, 20–1**

multi-level Redfield theory 41, 46, 48, 66
multiphasic A_1^- reoxidation kinetics **169**
multiple connections **133**
multiple gene sets 214–15
mu-oxo bridges
   Mn_4O_xCa cluster in cyanobacterial PSIIcc WOC **224–5, 227**
   Mn_4O_xCa clusters S_i state-dependent structural changes **308**
   $S_2 \rightarrow S_3$ transition in WOC **326**
   S_i state transitions **310**
   WOC function **294**
mutant studies
   Arabidopsis PsbS-dependent energy dissipation 380–1
   chlorophyll organization in LHCII 338–40
   chlorophyll spectrometry 116, 117
   CP29 354
   cyanobacterial PSI PG synthesis **137**
   LHCII trimerization complexes 342
   Lhc protein structure 317
   modified proteobacterial reaction centers **71**
   $Pheo_{D2}$ in Chlamydomonas reinhardtii **247**
   protein redshifted emission peak 318, 319
   regulatory EET in PSII of higher plants 375
   see also site-directed mutagenesis
myxothiazol **368**

n *see* negative side; neoxanthin
$NADP^+$ reduction **149, 173–4**
NADPH 372, **404, 405**
NADPH dehydrogenase **174**
NAD(P)H oxidase **399**
naphthoquinones **402**
native LHCII 334–5
natural selection 154–7, 189–92
   see also evolution
near-infrared (NIR) absorption spectra **70**, 160, 209–10
negative binding cooperativity **464**

Subject Index

negative (n) side **452, 454, 455, 456**
neoxanthin (N) 341, 343, 345, 346
neurosporene
   near-infrared sub-picosecond time-resolved absorption spectra 160
   quantum efficiency of singlet energy transfer to bacteriochlorophyll 174
   relaxation scheme 163
   Rhodobacter sphaeroides G1C 157
   singlet states 161, 165, 168
   species-associated fluorescence spectra 167
   structure 159
   sub-picosecond time-resolved Raman spectra 168–9, 170
   visible sub-picosecond time-resolved absorption spectroscopy 162, 173, 175
newly-identified singlet states 193–4
NHFe *see* nonheme iron centers
nickel 113
NIR *see* near-infrared
NMR *see* nuclear magnetic resonance
nomenclature *see* terminology
non-adiabatic electron transfer *see* Marcus theory...
non-collinear access channels **473**
nonheme iron **25, 27–8, 72, 257–8, 311**
nonlinear polarization spectroscopy measurements 355
non-Markovian density matrix theory 47–8, 66
nonphotochemical quenching (NPQ) evolution **508**
   LHCII monomers 332
   Lhc proteins 331
   photoprotection in the antenna 404
   PSII chlorophyll fluorescence 376
non-radiative transfer 104
non-sulfur green bacteria *see* Chloroflexi
non-sulfur purple bacteria **4–45**
   see also individual species
non-triplet producing charge recombination 405–6
2-*n*-nonyl-4-hydroxyquinolone N-oxide (NQNO) **430–1, 434**

notation *see* classification; terminology
NPQ *see* nonphotochemical quenching
NQNO *see* 2-*n*-nonyl-4-hydroxyquinolone N-oxide
N-terminal domains **122, 131, 132,** 215–17, 221
nuclear geometries **301–2**
nuclear magnetic resonance (NMR) 121, **127,** 150
nuclei, tunneling 60–3
nucleophilic attack mechanism **328**
nucleotide binding sites **450, 464–5**

ODMR *see* electron–photon double-resonance techniques
Oestreobium 105
oil resources 11
oligomerization states *see* aggregation states
oligomers 106
O-,L-,T-site **464**
one-channel model **475**
one-electron oxidation **432–3**
one-electron transfer **430**
O–O bond first mechanism **330**
O–O bond formation **326, 328, 330–1**
optical dipole transition 190
optical energy gap 80
optically-forbidden singlet states 165
optical spectra 114–17, 118–19
   fluorescence line-narrowing 77–81
   Lax and Kubo theory 57–9
   multi-level Redfield theory 41, 46
   secondary ET in PSI of oxygen evolving organisms **164**
   vibrational sidebands 48
   see also absorption spectra; spectral density
orbital angular momentum 189
organelles 23, **390, 509–10, 514–16**
   see also mitochondria; thylakoids; vesicle...
Oscillatoria limnetica **397**
oscillaxanthin 268
outer antenna Chl *a*/Chl *b*/Xan–protein complexes 331

out-gassing **495, 496**
out-of-plane waggings 182
oxidation–reduction potentials at equilibrium **8–9**
oxidation states **295–300**
oxidative reactions **262–7**
oxidative water splitting **291–331**
  evolution 195
  kinetics **252, 316–24**
  mechanism **322–331**
  $P680^{+\cdot}$ driven in PSIIcc **262–5**
  PSII process **240**
  reaction pattern **295–300**
  thermodynamics **300–2**
  WOC assembly/structure **302–17**
  see also water oxidizing complex
oxo groups **328, 329**
oxygen
  aerobic photosynthetic bacteria **368–9**
  Earth's oxidizing atmosphere **388–9, 495, 510**
  molecular **312–13, 393, 507–9**
  tension 208, 212–15
  water splitting evolution **507–9**
  see also reactive oxygen species; singlet oxygen
oxygen evolution
  chlorin type chlorophylls 108, 109
  cyanobacteria 261–88, 372, 373, **383–405**
  history 10, 331, **509**
  lag phase **318**
  linear electron transport 19–22
  period four oscillation **295–300**
  photosynthetic apparatus 22, 23–5
  process **195**
  RC and LH complexes 109–11
  steady-state terrestrial atmosphere **389**
  three-electron transport complexes **419–20**
  WOC flash-induced **312–13**
ozone layer **387–8**

$P^{+\cdot}$ see primary electron donor radical
$^3P_{680}$-producing states 397
$^1P680^*$ **247–8**

P680
  cyanobacterial PSIIcc **199, 222–3**
  electrostatic interactions 89
  nature/properties **239, 242–3, 244–52, 255–60, 262–7**
  reduction potential **301**
  spectroscopic analyses, cyanobacteria 286
$P680^{+\cdot}$ **262–5, 299**
$P680^{+\cdot}Pheo^{-\cdot}$ radical ion pair **255–7, 260–2**
$P680^{+\cdot}Q_A^{-\cdot}$ radical pair **257–8, 262**
P700
  cyanobacterial PSI structure **117–18**
  discovery **150**
  energetics in PSI of oxygen evolving organisms **152–3**
  hydrogen bonds in two-ET branches of PSI in oxygen evolving organisms **170**
  P_{D1}/P_{D2} chlorophyll a molecules comparison **246**
  primary ET in PSI of oxygen evolving organisms **159–63**
  spectroscopic analyses, cyanobacteria 286
  spectroscopy/structure in PSI of oxygen evolving organisms **165–7**
P798 83
P840 **79–81**
p see positive side; primary electron donor
P_A see absorption/antenna pigments
paramagnetic states **150**
parameter extraction
  dispersed polaron model 81–2
  electron transfer coupling 85–6
  excitonic couplings 77–89
  extended-dipole approximation 84
  local excitation energies 86–8
  point-dipole approximation 84
  redox potentials 88–9
  reorganization energy of ET 83
  spectral density 77–82
  transition density 85

Subject Index

Pariser–Parr–Pople method 85, 180
Pariser's signs 164, 165, 190
partial charges 88
partial ordering prescription (POP) 66–7, 68
Pasteur-Point **388**
PBRC *see* purple bacterial reaction center
PBS *see* phycobilisomes
PC *see* phycocyanin
PCET *see* proton coupled electron transfer
PChlide, formation 125
PCP *see* peridinin chlorophyll protein
P_{D1}/P_{D2} chlorophyll *a* **222–3, 245–6**
PE *see* phycoerythrin
pea 312
PEC *see* phycoerythrocyanin
pentads 28
peridinin chlorophyll protein (PCP) 44, 47, 60, **513**
period four oscillation **295–300**
peripheral antennae 373
peripheral stalks **463**
periplasmic redox proteins **361**
peroxidic intermediates **302, 329**
  see also hydrogen peroxide
perturbation theory 66, 74
PET *see* photosynthetic electron transport
PEWY conserved sequence **432**
PF_OEF_1 chimeric enzyme **477**
PG *see* phosphatidylglycerol
pH 378–9, **453, 455, 457–8**
  see also transmembrane pH difference
Phe *see* pheophytin
phenylalanine **40, 42**
Pheophyceae 110
pheophytin *a* (Phe *a*) **222–3, 227,** 266, 267
pheophytin (Phe) **247, 252–3,** 264, **266–7**
pheophytin–quinone type RCs **7–45**
philloquinone A_1 electron acceptor *see* chlorophyll A_1
phosphate potential **453–4**
phosphatidylglycerol (PG)
  cyanobacterial PSI **135, 136, 137**
  LHCII trimerization 341, 342
  PSIIcc role **271**
  thylakoid membrane composition **196, 215–18**
phospholipids **37–9, 120**
phosphorus **70–2, 75**
phosphorylatable DNA-binding protein component 212
phosphorylation sites 354
photoacoustic spectroscopy 118
photoactivation **295, 302–4**
photoactive pigment in RC (P_{RC}) 12, 14, **240, 242–3**
photoassembly **303–4**
photoautotrophs 8–9
photobioreactors **200–1**
photochemical hole formation **239, 260**
photodamage
  acceptor-sided induced photodamage 397–8
  donor-side induced photodamage 398
  integral lipid molecules **217**
  photoinhibition of electron transport 393–412
  photon counter behavior 401–2
  photosystem II 395, 397–403
  PSI mechanism 402
  triplet forming charge recombination 398–9
  two-step mechanism 401
  ultraviolet light **393,** 399–401, 411–12, **498**
photodynamic action 118
photo flux density 285–6
photoinhibition (qI) **135,** 376, 393–412
photoinhibitory related thermal energy dissipation 373–5
photon counter behavior 401–2
photon echo spectroscopy **256**
photon flux rates 153
photoorganoheterotrophic growth **397**
photophosphorylation **447–81**
photophysical principles 41–89, 151–95
photopigment suppression (PpsR) factor 213–14

photoprotection
  carotenoids 153, 176–89, 194–5
  Chl *a* in cytochrome b_6f complex **436–7, 439**
  cyanobacterial PSI carotenoids **135**
  de novo D1 protein synthesis 409–10
  excitation quenching 404–5
  inactive PSII centers 405
  integral lipid molecules **217**
  light harvesting protein evolution **512**
  molecular mechanisms 404–12
  non-triplet producing charge recombination 405–6
  protein repair 406–11
  PSIIcc without WOC **265**
  quenching evolution **508**
  red forms 320–1
  thermal energy dissipation 375–7
photoreduction **173–4**
photosynthetic apparatus architecture 22–5
photosynthetic electron transport (PET) **357–9, 393–412, 395**
photosynthetic hydrogenase *see* uptake hydrogenase
photosynthetic membranes *see* intracytoplasmic membranes
photosynthetic-respiratory assemblies **394–405**
photosynthetic transition reaction 9
photosynthetic units (PSUs) 12, 210–15, 237–42
photosystem gene expression 214–15
Photosystem I–light harvesting chlorophyll I (PSI–LHCI) complex 304–5, 311–12, 316
Photosystem I (PSI)
  basic principles 16–22
  building principles 41–8
  cyanobacteria **125**
    assembly 277–8
    cofactors **116–21**
    energy transfer 280–2
    membrane-bound antenna complexes 275–6
    stoichiometry regulation 285–6
  structure/function **111–38**
  X-ray crystallography studies **395, 399, 404**
  cytochrome b_6f complex **419–20, 422**
  evolution **502, 505–7**
  gap pigments 304–7
  green sulfur bacterial conserved residues **79**
  higher plants 301–22, 372–3
  light harvesting regulation 310–11
  light-induced ET in chlorophylls 105
  oxygen evolving organisms **147–76**
  photodamage mechanism 402
  photodamage sites 396
  photoinhibition 310–11
  PSII antenna characterization differences 321–2
  supramolecular organization of antenna system in vascular plants 304–11
  Type I reaction center comparison **60–7**
Photosystem II core complex (PSIIcc) **239, 401**
Photosystem II (PSII)
  artificial 30
  basic principles 16–22
  building principles 41–8
  cyanobacteria
    assembly 277–8
    cc crystallography **193–228**
    energy transfer 280–2
    membrane-bound antenna complexes 276–7
    stoichiometry regulation 285–6
    X-ray crystallography studies **395, 399, 404**
  cytochrome b_6f complex **419–20**
  D1 protein rapid turnover 406–11
  damage repair 409–10
  EET types 374–5
  evolution **502, 505–7**
  functional pattern **237–73**
  higher plants 329–56, 372–3
  Lhcb proteins 329–56
  light-induced ET in chlorophylls 105
  minor antenna complexes 352–6

Subject Index 553

oxygen evolution period four oscillation **295–300**
photodamage mechanisms 395, 397–403
photodamage sites 396
photoprotective energy dissipation biochemical models 375–7
primary electron transfer 44, 45
proton translocation **456**
PsbS protein symmetrical structure 377–80
purple bacterial RC structure comparison **44–5**
regulatory EET 373–5
stable charge separation **241–62**
trap-limited charge separation 334
Type II reaction center comparison **60–7**
photovoltage measurements **164**
PhQ *see* phylloquinones
PhQ$_A$ *see* phylloquinone A
PhQ$_B$ *see* phylloquinone B
phycobilins 12, 13, 126
phycobiliproteins
  crystal structure 273, 274
  cyanobacteria 269–71
  excitation energy transfer 104, 278–9
  molecular species 270–1
phycobilisomes (PBS)
  cyanobacteria 271–3, 372
    PsaF subunit **131**
    thylakoid structures **198**
  energy transfer to membrane proteins 279–80
  excitation energy transfer 278–9
  ferredoxin-NADP$^+$-reductase **174–5**
  state transitions 282–3
  transient excitation energy reservoirs 278–9
phycocyanin (PC) 269–70, 272–3, 274
phycocyanobilin 13
phycoerythrin (PE) 269–71, 272–3, 274
phycoerythrocyanin (PEC) 269–70, 272–3, 274
phylloquinones (PhQ) **64–5, 119–20, 153–8, 162–5, 168–9**

phyllosemiquinones **81, 171**
phylogenetic tree analysis **496, 504**
physiological roles 320–1, 385
phytol 108, 109
phytyl chains **223**, 224–5, **227**, 337, **429**
'picket fence' arrangement **427**
picoplanktons 269
picosecond studies 160–2, 165–9, 170, 173, 175, 348–9
pigment lineshape function ($D(\omega)$) 71
pigment–pigment complexes
  charge transfer coupling 43–8
  coupling types 43
  dynamical theories 41–89
  excitonic coupling 43–8
  Fermi's Golden Rule 53–4, 57
  Förster theory 41, 59–60
  Marcus theory 44, 60–2
  quantum mechanics 53–7
pigment–protein complexes
  adjustable chromophore properties 116
  anoxygenic bacterial vesicles 23
  chlorophyll as stabilizer 106
  dynamical theories 41–89
  LHCII monomeric minor 352–6
  local pigment excitation energies 86–8
  Photosystem structures 41–8
  PSII functional pattern **237–73**
  purple non-sulfur bacteria 209–10
  see also individual pigment–protein complexes
pigment–protein (electron–vibrational) coupling *see* spectral density
pigments
  Chlorella organization 12
  chlorophylls 103–29
  cyanobacteria 263–71
  light harvesting chlorophyll I composition 311–12
  location 111
  native LHCII binding 334–5
  spectral properties **498**
  see also individual pigments
Pisum sativum 304–5

plastid inclusion **509–10, 514–16**
  see also organelles
plastocyanin **123, 149**
plastoquinine-9 (PQ-9) **254**
plastoquinol formation **240**
plastoquinone-9 (PQ-9) **402**
plastoquinone (PQ)
  cytochrome b_6f complex **395, 400**
  diffusion channel in cyanobacterial PSIIcc **228**
  linear electron transport 21
  photodamage 396, 397
  PS-I/II coupling **113**
  PSII structure **64–5**
  quinol/quinone exchange reactions in PSIIcc **271**
  reduction state 311
  structure **421**
p.m.f. *see* protonmotive force
point-dipole approximation 84
polarized laser photo-bleaching and recovery **466–7**
polyene models 185–7
polypeptides **204–9, 304–8, 315–16**
polyphyletic endosymbiosis **514–15**
'poop oxygen' **389**
POP *see* partial ordering prescription
POR *see* protochlorophyllide oxidoreductases
porphobilinogen 124, 126
porphyrins
  biomimetic antenna systems 27
  chlorophylls 108–9
  chlorophyll synthesis 124, **498**
  c-type chlorophylls 107–9
porphyrin-type cyclic conjugated tetrapyrroles 115
positive catalytic cooperativity **464**
'positive inside rule' **133**
positive (p) side **452, 454, 455, 456**
potential energy surfaces (PES) 52–3, 56–7, 64, 65, 74
power transmission **476–80**
Poynting vector 57
PpsR (photopigment suppression) factor 213–14

PQ *see* plastoquinone
PQH$_2$ *see* dihydroplastoquinone
Prasinophyceae 110
P$_{RC}$ *see* photoactive pigment in RC
'PRC' barrel **21**
Precambrian era **388, 393**
pre-structural studies 215–20
primary acceptor quinone (Q$_A$)
  aerobic photosynthetic bacteria **369**
  proteobacterial secondary electron transfer reactions **72–4**
  PS II difference absorption spectra **242–3**
  PS II water splitting **240**
  RC cofactors/inhibitors **11–12**
  structure/location in bacterial RC **24–8, 31–2**
primary amino acid sequences 215–17
primary biomass production **389**
primary electron donor (P) **21–5, 117–18, 359**
  see also P700
primary electron donor radical (P$^{+\cdot}$)
  anoxygenic bacterial tetraheme RC species **360**
  bacterial RC three types **359**
  bacterial species variations **358**
  fast/slow reduction phases in anoxygenic bacterial RC **365–6**
  heme reduction rates in anoxygenic bacterial RCs **360**
primary electron transfer 44, 45, **159–63**
primary endosymbiosis **514–15**
primary quinone acceptor (Q$_A$)
  anoxygenic bacterial ET chain **357–8**
  binding pocket **254–5, 369**
  cyanobacterial PSIIcc structure **218–19, 221**
  P680$^{+\cdot}$ recombination reactions with Q$_A^{-}$/Pheo^{-} **266–7**
  PBRCs **253–4**
  PQH$_2$ formation induced by Q$_A^{-\cdot}$ **267–70**
  properties in PSII **253–5**
  PSI ET in oxygen evolving organisms **162**

PSIIcc integral lipids **217**
PSII light-induced charge separation **242**
prime-chlorophylls 120
probabilities of S_i state transitions **297**
Prochlorococcus spp. 113, 128, 265, 273
Prochloron 265, 277
Prochlorophytes 373, **389**
Prochlorothrix 265, 277
prokaryotes **387–8**, **454**
'promoting mode' 163
17-propionic acid 107
Prosthecochloris aestuarii 44, 46, **70**, 87
prosthetic groups **425–6**, **429**, **436–9**
protective mechanisms 153, 176–89, 194–5
  see also photodamage; photoprotection
protein–cofactor interactions **21–9**
protein kinase STN7 (*Arabidopsis*) 375
protein-like scaffolds 26, 27, 221–3
protein–protein interactions 307–8, 316
proteins
  cyanobacterial antenna systems 263–4
  environments 86–8, **162**, **222–3**, **259–62**
  LHCII folding 338, 341–2
  ligands, Mn$_4$O$_x$Ca cluster **314–17**
  matrix, WOC function **294**
  PSII backbone UV damage 400, 410–11
  reaction centers 263–4
  repair, photoprotection 406–11
  turnover, mesophilic cyanobacteria **398**
  vibrational degrees of freedom 42, 43, 48
protein subunits (psb)
  anoxygenic photosynthetic bacterial RCs 63
  ATP synthase **461**, **463**
  bacterial RCs **9–12**, **18–21**
  cyanobacterial PSI **121–33**
  cytochrome b_6f complex **423**
  cytochrome bc_1 complex/cytochrome b_6f complex comparison **427–8**
  green sulfur bacterial Type I RCs **78**

MALDI-TOF MS of cyanobacterial dimeric PSII cc **206–11**
PSIIcc composition in cyanobacteria **198–200**
Rhodospirillum rubrum LH1 complex formation 228
see also individual subunits
protein W 235–6
proteobacteria **68–75**
  see also purple bacteria
proteolysis 218, 406–11
Proto *see* protoporphyrin IX
protochlorophyllide **500**
protochlorophyllide *a* reductase 287
protochlorophyllide oxidoreductases (POR) 125
proton conductance **475–6**
proton coupled electron transfer (PCET) **326**, **328–9**
proton-ejecting membranes **457**
proton ENDOR spectroscopy **159**
proton-first mechanism **330**
protonmotive force (p.m.f.)
  ATP synthase regulation **459–60**
  ATP synthesis/hydrolysis **452–4**
  chemiosmotic energy conversion **391–2**
  H$^+$/ATP stoichiometric ratio **458–9**
  Mitchell's hypothesis **450**
  proton pumps **457–8**
protonmotive quinone cycle **402**
proton-over-ATP stoichiometry **453–4**
protons
  ATP synthesis/hydrolysis **452**
  pumps 28–9, **451**, **452**, **455–8**
  relay networks **315**
  release patterns **320**
  translocation pathways **430–6**
proton-shift first mechanisms **330**
proton transfer (PT) **322**, **326**, **328–9**
protoporphyrin IX (Proto) 107, 124, 125, 127
protoporphyrinogen IX 126
PrrBA system 212–14
PsaA subunit 63–5, 114–16, 121–3, 124, 150–1

PsaB subunit 63–5, 114–16, 121–3, 124, 150–1
PsaC subunit **64–5, 114–15, 123–6, 164**
PsaD subunit **114–15, 123–7**
PsaE subunit **114–15, 123–6, 127–8, 174**
PsaF subunit **114–16, 125, 130–2**
PsaI subunit **114–15, 128–30**
PsaJ subunit **114–16, 125, 130, 132**
PsaK subunit **114–16, 125, 130, 132–3**
PsaL subunit **114–15, 125, 128–9**
Psalteriomonas lanterna **389–90**
PsaM subunit **114–16, 125, 128–9, 130**
PsaX subunit **114–16, 125, 130, 132**
psb *see* protein subunits
PsbE **209**
PsbF **209**
psb genes 411
PsbO (manganese stabilizing protein) **198–9, 209, 213–14, 294**
PsbS-dependent de-excitation pathway 311
psbS gene 380
PsbS protein
  glutamate residues 374
  influence on energy flux in PSII 381–4
  photoprotection in the antenna 404
  physiological significance 384
  PSII photoprotective energy dissipation 376–7
  symmetrical structure 377–80
PsbU 213–14
PsbV 213–14
PscA homodimer **63, 78**
PscC *see* single-heme cytochrome
pseudo-twofold axis (pseudo-*C2*) **212, 220, 221**
PshA homodimer **82, 83**
PSI *see* Photosystem I
p-side quinone binding niche **429, 430**
PSII *see* Photosystem II
PSI–LHCI *see* Photosystem I–light harvesting chlorophyll I
PSUs *see* photosynthetic units
psychrophilic cyanobacteria **398**
puc operon 213–14
'puddle' model 237

PufX protein 208, 233, **370–3**
pulsed EPR spectroscopy **266**
pump–probe measurements **69–72**, 355
purification procedures **200**, 311–12, **422–8**
purple bacteria
  ATP formation **450**
  bacteriochlorophylls 108, 112
  carotenoids 151–95
  c chromatophores **454**
  chlorophylls 110
  excitation energy transfer 76
  F_O proton conductance **475–6**
  light harvesting system 207–42
  light-induced ET in chlorophylls 105
  non-sulfur
    bacterial photosynthetic unit 210–12
    growth conditions **356**
    light harvesting system 207–42
    photo-induced ET mechanisms **353–73**
    photosynthetic pigment–protein complexes 209–10
    RC cytochrome subunit with four hemes **69**
    RC-LH1 core complex structure 227–37
  P700 in PSI of oxygen evolving organisms **167**
  primary charge separation in RC I **160**
  secondary electron transfer reactions **72–4**
  species **59**
  sulfur **9, 69, 504–5, 506**
  transmetalated chlorophylls 107, 113
  Zn chlorophylls 107
  see also purple bacterial reaction centers
purple bacterial reaction center (PBRC) 16, 18, 371–2
  BPheo$_A$ hydrogen bonding **253**
  chlorines role in RC pigment core **247**
  components/thermodynamic properties **63**
  cyanobacterial PSIIcc structure comparison **209, 222–3**

ET chains **355–74**
NHFe center removal effects **257–8**
P680$^{+\cdot}$ recombination reactions with
  Q_A^-/Pheo$^-$ comparison **266–7**
PQH$_2$ formation **267–9**
primary charge separation in PSIIcc
  257
proton translocation **456**
PSII comparison **239**
PSII water splitting process
  comparison **240**
Q_A component **253–4**
radical pair relaxation processes **261**
RC II resembles PSII **60**
'special pair' P **246**
structure **7–45**
triheme RC species **363–5**
unidirectionality **252**
pyridine hemochromogen redox
  difference spectrum **434**

Q_A *see* primary quinone acceptor
Q_B *see* secondary quinone acceptor
Q-bands 114, 115
Q-cycle 357–8, 425–6, 430–3, 435, 456
qE *see* thermal energy dissipation
qI *see* photoinhibition
Q-space **429–30**
qT *see* state transitions
Q-type *see* quinone-type
quality checks **206–9**
QualWat see water quality factor
quantum mode, Huang Rhys factor 62
quantum studies 53–7, 62, 85, **162**, 174
quantum yields
  carotenoid fluorescence in purple
    bacteria 165, 166
  15-cis to all-trans isomerization in
    carotenoids of purple bacteria
    179–80
  EET in chlorophylls 104–5
  electron transfer in green non-sulfur
    bacteria 76
quenching *see* excitation quenching
quinol/quinone exchange reactions **270–1**
quinols 73–4, **402**

quinone analogue inhibitors **421**
quinone cycle **73**
quinone electron acceptors
  UV photodamage 397, 399, 400
  see also primary quinone acceptor;
    secondary quinone acceptor
quinone exchange cavity **419, 426,
  428–30, 435**
quinone-mediated pathways **426**
quinone-quinol transfer **370**
quinones
  aerobic photosynthetic bacteria **369**
  anoxygenic bacteria **357–8**, 371
  Blastochloris viridis RC **8–9, 68**
  cyanobacterial **116**, 402
  structure **62–3**
quinone-type reaction centers *see*
  Photosystem I; Type I reaction
  centers
Q_x transition 209
Q_Y peak
  bacteriochlorophylls in purple
    bacteria 178–9
  initial/final P680 states in PSIIcc **259**
  LHCII absorption spectra 346–7
  Pheo$_{D1}$ in PSII **253**
Q_Y transition **247–8**

radiation damage 225, 393
radical mechanism of O–O bond
  formation in WOC **328**
radical pair states **71, 255–7, 258**
radioactive chloride ions **311**
Raman spectra 123, 170–1, 182
Raphidophyceae 110
RC-LH1 complexes **370**
RC-LH1 core complex 210, 211, 227–37
RC-LH1-PufX complexes **371–3**
RCs *see* reaction centers
R_{DA} *see* edge to edge distance
reaction center pigments *see*
  photoactive pigment in RC
reaction centers (RCs)
  anoxygenic bacterial cyclic electron
    transfer **355–74**
  anoxygenic photosynthetic bacteria 16

bacterial structures **7–45**
biomimetic 27–8
bound spheroidene 180–9
building 263–4
chlorophylls EET 104–5
classification 16, **356**
cofactor conformation **21–9**
crystallization process **12–13**
cyanobacteria energy trapping 280–2
dark-adapted vs. light-adapted **43–4**
definition 7
evolution 67, 150, 501–7
functional patterns in bacteria **57–85**
green non-sulfur bacteria **75–7**
heliobacteria **82–4**
higher plants 372–3
LH1 in anoxygenic purple bacteria 154
membrane protein structure 17, **34–9**
modified **39–44**
overview 15, 371–3
oxygenic phototrophs 109–11
primary donors 103
protein–cofactor interactions **21–9**
PSI in oxygen evolving organisms **149–76**
purple non-sulfur bacteria 210, 227–37
substrate binding sites **29–34**
subunit composition **9–12**
three anoxygenic bacterial types **359**
Type I
  anoxygenic photosynthetic bacteria 16, **60–7**, **77–84**
  bacteriochlorophylls 103
  directionality of electron transfer **81–2**
  electron-transfer schemes **61**
  energetics 18
  green sulfur bacteria **78–82**
  heliobacteria **82–4**
  structure **63–7**
Type II
  anoxygenic photosynthetic bacteria 16, **60–77**
  bacteriochlorophylls 103
  Chloroflexus aurantiacus **76**
  directionality **74–5**
  electron-transfer schemes **61**
  energetics 18
  structure **63–7**
reaction sequences
  ATP synthase bi-site mechanism **464**
  ATP synthesis/hydrolysis **452**
  bacterial ET chain **357–8**
  deprotonation reactions in WOC **329**
  light-induced charge separation in PSII **256–7**
  oxidative water splitting **295–300**
  PSII water splitting process **240**
  WOC photoactivation **303–4**
reactive oxygen species (ROS)
  acceptor-sided induced photodamage 397
  carotenoid quenching 153, 154, 176–89
  cytochrome b_6f complex p-side formation **421**
  early photosynthesis **497**
  Earth's atmosphere **393**, **510**
  luminescence spectroscopy 118–19
  photoinhibitory conditions 402–3
  PSI damage mechanism 402
reciprocity relationships 401
recombinant Lhca4 321
recombinant proteins 313–15, 338–42
recombination reactions **266–7**
reconstitution studies **29**, 228–9, 338, 344–5
red algae 374, **513**
'red' chlorophylls **134**, 280, 282
Redfield relaxation theory 72–3, 350
red forms
  chromophores 317–19
  Lhca1-4 315–19
  Lhca5 and Lhca6 319–20
  light absorption increase 320–1
  light harvesting chlorophyll I 315–21
  photoprotection 320–1
  physiological role 320–1
  polypeptides 315–16
  properties 316–17
redox-active cofactors **220–1**
redox-active tyrosines 399
redox difference spectra **434**

redox equivalents **402**
redox gaps **155–6**
redox isomerism **302**
redox states
  cofactors of PSI ET in oxygen evolving organisms **151–9**
  parameter extraction 88–9
  pheophytins in PSII **253**
  Q_A in PSIIcc **254**
  S_i states in WOC **322**
redshift **134**, 315–16, 318, 319
reduction potentials **301**
regulatory control
  antenna function, higher plants 369–85
  ATP synthase **459–60**
  EET, PSII antenna of higher plants 373–5
  photosynthetic unit expression 212–15
  Photosystem I antenna size 309–11
relative midpoint potentials **157–8**
relaxation processes
  carotenoids in purple bacteria 163
  D1/D2/Cyt b559 preparations at low temperature **261**
  energy levels of P680 intermediate states in PSIIcc **259–62**
  P680$^+$·Pheo$^-$ radical ion pair **260–2**
reorganization effects 47, 53, 83
reoxidation **171**
reporter function 120
resolution increases **193–228**
resonance-Raman excitation profiles (RREPs) 157–8
resonance Raman spectra 182, 223
respiration
  bioenergetic schemes **391**
  cyanobacteria **385**, **394–5**, **397–8**
  dual function photosynthetic-respiratory assembly **394–5**
  earliest organisms **495–6**
  photosynthetic ET chains interaction **400–5**
  process 8–9
  steady-state terrestrial atmosphere **389**
respiratory electron transport (RET) 23, **368**, **395–6**, **405**

respiratory hydrogenase **395**, **401**
RET see respiratory electron transport
retinylidine Schiff base **60**
reverse electron transport **392**, **404**
reverse genetics 313–15
R_H see hydrodynamic radius
Rhodobacter spp.
  R. capsulatus
    cytochrome c^2 role **365–8**
    ICM synthesis 208
    isolated RC membrane studies **359**
    modified reaction centers **39–41**
    PSU gene expression 212, 213
    supramolecular organization of membranous RC components **370, 372–3**
    two distinct electron carriers **367**
  RC types **359**
  R. sphaeroides 16, 128
    C subunit structure **23**
    cyt c_t two pools **371**
    cytochrome c^2 role **365–8**
    electron donor substrate binding **33–4**
    ET chain **359**, **365–8**, **370–3**
    ET rates **32**
    FNR consensus sequence 213
    heme-iron site geometries **28**
    H subunit structure **22**
    ICM morphology 208
    intramembrane phospholipids **37–9**
    L subunit structure **19**
    membrane architecture 208
    modified reaction centers **39–44**
    M subunit structure **20–1**
    neurosporenes 154, 155, 157
    photosynthetic unit 210–15
    PQH$_2$ formation **268**
    PufX polypeptide 234
    PufX and quinone-quinol transfer **370–3**
    Q_B cluster residues **33**
    reaction center
      amino acid replacements **17**
      bound 15-cis spheroidene 181
      characterization **11–12**
      crystallization **12–13**

crystal structure **66–7**
near infrared absorption spectra **70**
X-ray crystal form **14, 15, 18**
spheroidene pathway 154–5, 157–66, 168–9, 172–90, 195
stereo pairs **24, 26, 27**
tubular membranes 233
two distinct electron carriers **367**
visible sub-picosecond time-resolved absorption spectroscopy 173
Rhodoblastus acidophilus **361**
Rhodocyclus tenuis **362**
Rhodophyta 110
rhodophyte phycocyanin (R-PC) 270, 274
rhodopin 158, 159, 173, 174
rhodopin glucoside 173, 223–4, 226–7
Rhodopseudomonas spp.
  R. acidophila
    BChl *a* molecule binding 223–5
    ICM morphology 208
    LH2 complex 211, 220–7, 240
    LH2 structure 112
    peripheral complexes 212
    photosynthetic membranes absorption spectra 209
    spirilloxanthin pathway 154, 155
    visible sub-picosecond time-resolved absorption spectroscopy 173
  R. cryptolactis 212
  R. palustris
    ICM morphology 208
    LH complexes **368**
    PufX-like polypeptide in LH1 ring **371**
    RC-LH1 complex three-dimensional structure 235–6
    X-ray crystal forms **16**
  R. viridis see Blastochloris viridis
Rhodospirillaceae **4–45**
Rhodospirillum spp.
  R. molischianum
    BChl *a* molecule binding 223–4
    ICM morphology 208

LH2 complex structure 221
spirilloxanthin pathway 154, 155
visible sub-picosecond time-resolved absorption spectroscopy 173
R. rubrum
  carotenoids singlet energy transfer 175
  core complex EM studies 230–2
  ICM morphology 208
  LH1 complex reconstitution studies 228
  LH complexes **358**
  minor chlorophylls 114
  PSU size 210
  RC-LH1 complexes 2D crystals **370**
  spirilloxanthin 154–5, 157–66, 174–6, 193, 194
Rhodovulvum spp.
  direct electron donors to RC **359**
  R. sulfidophilum **69, 363, 365**
Rieske iron–sulfur protein **403, 433**
ring-like structures 222–3
ring puckering **250**
ring size 231–3
RNA **504**
robustness **476–8**
Roseobacter denitrificans **361, 369**
rotary binding change mechanism **450–1, 464–8**
rotary catalyst F_1 **464–72**
rotary electro-mechanical-chemical transducers **447–81**
rotary electromotor F_O concept **473–6**
rotary engines **170–9**
rotary proton transport **475**
rotational diffusion **174**
rotational molecular motion 180–3
rotation of Earth **494**
rotor portion of ATP synthase **461, 462**
R-PC *see* rhodophyte phycocyanin
RREPs *see* resonance–Raman excitation profiles
Rubrivivax gelatinosus
  carotenoids biosynthetic pathway 155, 156

Subject Index 561

carotenoids chain length binding 156
electron donor determinants 361–2
HiPIP/cyt *c* docking 363, 364
ICM morphology 208
isolated RC membrane studies 359
natural selection of carotenoid structures 154

S^* state 193–4
S_0->S_1 transition 323
S_1->S_2 transition 325
S_2->S_3 transition 325–7
$S_2Y_z^{ox}$ signal 315
S_3 multistate model 331
S_3->->S_4->->S_0 transition 327–30
$S_3Y_z^{ox}$ formation 329
S_4 state 329
S see Huang Rhys factor
SADS *see* species-associated difference spectra
SAFS *see* species-associated fluorescence spectra
SAS *see* species-associated spectra
Scenedesmus 398
Schrödinger equation 49
SDS-PAGE 206–9, 434
secondary electron donor 358–9
secondary electron transfer 72–4, 163–5
secondary endosymbiosis 514–15
secondary processes of photosynthesis *see* Calvin–Benson cycle
secondary quinone acceptor (Q_B)
  acceptor-sided induced photodamage 397
  binding pocket 7, 8, 216–18, 219, 267, 270–1
  cluster in Rhodobacter sphaeroides 33
  cyanobacterial PSIIcc structure 218–20
  diffusion pathway 218–20
  ET steps in anoxygenic bacterial RC 357
  L subunit structure 19
  PQH_2 formation induced by Q_A^- 267–70
  proteobacterial secondary electron transfer reactions 72–4

PSIIcc integral lipids 217, 221
PSII comparison with bacterial RC structure 44–5
PSII difference absorption spectra 242–3
PSII water splitting 240
RC cofactors/inhibitors 11–12
substrate binding sites 29–32
second order cumulant expansions 54, 56–7
second order perturbation theory 44
Sec pathway 131
selective isotope labeling 166
semiclassical harmonic oscillator approach 49–53
sensor kinase component 212
sequence homology
  antenna complexes of purple non-sulfur bacteria 215–17
  Chlorobium limicola RC 81
  cyanobacterial F_x iron–sulfide cluster 121
  cyanobacterial PsaC subunit 126
  green non-sulfur bacterial RCs/proteobacterial RCs 76
  green sulfur bacterial Type I RCs 79
  his in P700 in PSI of oxygen evolving organisms 165
  Lhcb1-Lhcb6 from *Arabidopsis thaliana* 333
  LHCII monomeric minor antenna complexes 352
  light harvesting protein evolution 513
  mitochondrial respiratory chain and cyt c_2/cyt bc_1 366
  mitochondrial respiratory chain and cyt c_y 368
  PEWY in cytochrome b_6f complex 432
  phylogenetic tree inference 496, 504
  plant-type Fds 172
  PsaA/PsaB in cyanobacterial PSI 122, 123
  PsaI subunit 129
  PSII/PSI 401
  purple non-sulfur bacterial LH1/LH2 complexes 215–17, 219, 223

Q_A pocket in anaerobic/aerobic photosynthetic bacteria **369**
serine residues **44**
shaded light 320
shallow antennas 105
Shemin pathway 124
shorter conjugated chains 189–92
sidebands, vibrational 48, 78–81, 114, 115
side-chain distributions **34–6**
sigma-analysis **298**
sigma-coefficients **298**
signaling
  light-regulated 10
  see also trans-membrane signaling
single-heme cytochrome (PscC) **82**
single hit of single target mechanism 401–2
single subunit 16S rRNA **504**
singlet energy transfer 172–6, 352
singlet excited states
  C=C stretching Raman lines 170–1
  carotenoids of purple bacteria 157–64, 193–4
  Chl *a* position in cytochrome b_6f complex **436–9**
  P700 in PSI of oxygen evolving organisms **152–3**, **154**
  Pariser's signs 164, 165, 190
  transition dipole moments 164–7
singlet oxygen
  acceptor-sided induced photodamage 397
  carotenoids in purple bacteria 176
  carotenoid valve 283
  Chl *a* in cytochrome b_6f complex **436–7**, **438**, **439**
  cyanobacterial PSI carotenoids **135**
  luminescence spectroscopy 118–19
  photoinhibitory conditions 402–3
  triplet forming charge recombination 398–9
singlet–singlet annihilation experiments 352
singlet-to-triplet conversion 172
singular-value decomposition (SVD) 159–61, 164, 183–5

S_i states
  activation energies **318–1**
  chloride/bicarbonate ions **311**
  Kok model **295–300**
  lifetimes **297**
  Mn_4O_xCa cluster **307–8**, **316–17**
  transition energetics **301–2**
  transition kinetics **316–20**
  transition probabilities **297–8**
  transition representations in WOC **310**
  WOC substrate water binding **313**
  see also oxidation states; redox states
site-directed mutagenesis
  Arabidopsis 377
  bacterial RC substrate binding sites **31**
  bacterial RC X-ray crystals **17**
  chlorobial RCs **81**
  chlorophyll spectrometry 117
  chromophore binding pockets 116–17
  cyanobacterial chlorophyll A_0 **119**
  cyanobacterial F_x iron–sulfide cluster **121**
  cyt c_2 docking with RC in anoxygenic bacteria **363**, **366**
  fast ET between Fd/Fld and FNR **175–6**
  Mn_4O_xCa cluster protein ligands **314–15**
  modified bacterial RCs **39–44**
  $^1P680^*$ electronic states **247–8**
  P700 in PSI of oxygen evolving organisms **165**
  PsbS protein functions in PSII 378–9
  purple non-sulfur bacterial LH1/LH2 complexes 217
  step-wise deletion in LHCII 342
  two-ET branches of PSI in oxygen evolving organisms **169–71**
site energies 45, 63, 86–8
site interactions 116
slow exchange (W_s) **322**, **326**
slow nanosecond kinetics **264–5**
slow phase 168
  see also A-branch
SLP *see* substrate-level phosphorylation

Subject Index

solar radiation 8, 12–17, 26–30
soluble carriers *see* cytochrome *c*; high-potential iron-sulfur protein
soluble domains 337
soluble lumenal electron carrier **131**
soluble portion (F_1) **451**
solvent extraction **163**
Soret absorption bands 209, **242**, 306–7
'special pair' of chlorophylls **68**, **113**, **245–6**
  see also P700
species-associated difference spectra (SADS) 159–64, 173, 194
species-associated fluorescence spectra (SAFS) 167, 168–9
species-associated spectra (SAS) 183, 185, 187
species differences **152**, **358–9**, **463**
species name revisions **67**
spectral decay kinetics 381–4
spectral density ($J(\omega)$)
  dispersed polaron model 81–2
  EET and optical spectra 77–81
  excitation energy transfer 42–3
  excitonic coupling 46
  pigment–pigment complexes 53
  pigment–protein coupling 42–3
  quantum description of weak coupling limit 56
spectroscopy
  antenna system higher plants' Photosystem I 311–15
  ATP synthase rotation assays **466–8**
  chlorophylls 114–24
  ET in PSI of oxygen evolving organisms **159–65**
  P700 in PSI of oxygen evolving organisms **165–7**
  photon echo **256**
  phylloquinone A_1 characterization **162**
  pigments on biosynthetic pathway to Chl *a* **498**
  resolution/uncertainty principle 192–3
  see also absorption spectra; individual techniques
spherical molecule shape **202–3**

15-cis-spheroidene 180–3, 189, 190, 195
all-trans-spheroidene 180, 181
spheroidene
  15-cis to all-trans isomerization 179–80
  fluorescence quantum yields 166
  near-infrared sub-picosecond time-resolved absorption spectra 160
  quantum efficiency of singlet energy transfer to bacteriochlorophyll 174
  reaction center-bound T_1 spheroidene 183–9
  relaxation scheme 163
  Rhodobacter sphaeroides 154–5, 157–66, 172–90
  singlet state lifetimes 161, 168–9
  structure 159
  sub-picosecond time-resolved fluorescence spectra 169
  triplet-sensitized isomerization 179–80
  visible sub-picosecond time-resolved absorption spectroscopy 162, 173, 175
spheroidenone 179
spinach
  activation energies of S_i state transitions **318–19**
  $C_2S_2M_2$ supercomplex 332
  chloroplasts, dynamic light scattering **201**, **202**
  cytochrome b_6f complex crystallization **422–3**
  FIOPS of dark-adapted thylakoids **296**
  light harvesting chlorophyll I pigment composition 312
  photon counter behavior of photodamage 401
  WOC substrate water binding **313**
  Y_z^{ox} reduction/S_i state oxidation half life times **317–19**
Spinacia oleracea see spinach
spin angular momentum 189
spin density **117**
spin polarization 188
spin–spin coupling 121

spirilloxanthin
　　fluorescence quantum yields 166
　　near-infrared sub-picosecond time-
　　　　resolved absorption spectra 160
　　quantum efficiency of singlet energy
　　　　transfer to bacteriochlorophyll 174
　　relaxation scheme 163
　　Rhodospirillum rubrum 154–5,
　　　　157–66, 174–6, 193
　　singlet lifetimes versus double bond
　　　　numbers 161
　　structure 159
　　visible sub-picosecond time-resolved
　　　　absorption spectroscopy 162, 175
Spirolina platensis **463**
split signals **315**
spring balance effect **469–70**
SQDG *see* sulfoquinoldiacylglycerol
Sr^{2+} **303, 318**
S states **71**, 398–9
stabilization
　　antenna size 309–11
　　Chl *a* position in cytochrome b_6f
　　　　complex **436–7**
　　chlorophyll oligomers 106
　　cyanobacterial PsaD subunit **127**
　　cyanobacterial PsaI subunit **129–30**
　　cyanobacterial PSI **121**
　　LHCII monomers 341–2
stabilized cation–anion radical pairs
　　240, 242
stable charge separation **241–62**, 398–9
stacked grana **198**
stalled actin filament **469–71**
Stark effect **75**
Stark spectroscopy 341, 349
state 1-state 2 transition 310
state transitions (qT) 282–3, 372, 373–5,
　　376
stator portion of ATP synthase **461, 462**
steady-state spectroscopy 346–7, 351,
　　355–6
steady-state terrestrial atmosphere **389**
steep antennas 105
stepper motors **476–80**
stigmatellin **30, 31**

stigmatellin A **12**
STN7 protein kinase 375
stoichiometry
　　anoxygenic bacterial RC
　　　　supercomplexes **372**
　　cyanobacterial Photosystem 285–6
　　cyanobacterial PSIIcc cofactors/
　　　　lipids **204–5, 206**
　　cyt c_t distribution in anoxygenic
　　　　bacterial RC **371**
　　H^+/ATP in thylakoid membranes
　　　　458–9, 463
　　proton-over-ATP in ATP
　　　　synthesis/hydrolysis **453–4**
　　proton release, S_2->S_3 transition in
　　　　WOC **325**
　　RC:cytochrome bc_1 complex ratio
　　　　in PBRC **359**
Stokes–Einstein equation **202**
Stokes shift 316
'storage rings' 240
stored Gibbs energy ($\Delta G_{store}(hv)$) 8, 9
streptactin **470**
streptavidin **467**
stroma, structure **197**
stroma-exposed thylakoids **197**, 373–5,
　　407
stroma lamellae **197, 198**, 315, **455**
stromal hump **123–8**
stromal subunits **126**
strong oxidants **240, 438**
strong pigment–pigment coupling **248–9**
　　density matrix theory 67–73
　　generalized Förster theory 75–7
　　modified Redfield theory 73–5
　　protein–pigment/pigment–pigment
　　　　complexes 62–77
　　site energies 45
structure
　　all-trans β-carotene 13
　　antimycin A **421**
　　ATP **449**
　　ATP synthase **451–2, 461–80**
　　bacterial RCs **7–45**
　　bacteriochlorophylls in anoxygenic
　　　　bacterial RCs **61–2**

bacteriopheophytin **62**
BChl/Chl *a/b* precursors **500**
carotenoid natural selection 189–92
carotenoids in purple bacteria 159
chlorophylls 107–14
chloroplasts **454–5**
cyanobacterial ET carriers **394**, **395**, **399–400**
cyanobacterial PSI **111–38**
cyanobacterial PSIIcc **193–228**
cytochrome b_6f complex **399–400**, **417–39**
DBMIB **421**
di-manganese catalase active center **394**
green non-sulfur bacterial RCs **75–6**
hemi-discoidal phycobilisomes 272–3
iron–sulfur centers **62**
LHCII in higher plants 342–8
menaquinone **62–3**
P680 in PSII **244–52**
P700 in PSI of oxygen evolving organisms 165–7
phycocyanobilin 13
PsbS protein of PSII 377–80
PSII supercomplex **244–52**, 373
PSI in oxygen evolving organisms **149–50**, **165–7**
Q_B site in PSIIcc **270–1**
quinones **62–3**
Rhodopseudomonas acidophila
  carotenoids in LH2 complex 225–7
  spherical molecule shape **202–3**
thylakoid membrane in cyanobacteria/higher plants **196–8**
tridecyl-stigmatellin **421**
Type I/II RCs **63–7**
ubiquinone **62**
vesicles 22–5
WOC 304–17
see also conformation; three-dimensional structure; X-ray diffraction crystallography
sub-picosecond fluorescence up-conversion spectroscopy 165–7
sub-picosecond time-resolved fluorescence spectra 169
sub-picosecond time-resolved Raman spectra 168–9, 170
substrate binding sites **29–34**
substrate-level phosphorylation (SLP) **392**, **397**, **450**
substrate water binding **312–14**
subunits *see* protein subunits
succinate dehydrogenases **395**, **405**
sulfide-supported photosynthesis **9**, **363**, **397**
sulfoquinovosyldiacylglycerol (SQDG) **196**, **215–17**, **271**
sulfur compounds 363
Sun 8, **496**
supercomplexes 372
superexchange mechanism **71**
superoxide dismutases **497**
superradiance (SR) values 350
super-reduced S_i states **303**
supramolecular organization 304–11, **369–73**
SVD *see* singular-value decomposition
symbiotic prokaryotes 109
symmetrical structure **213**, 377–80, **463**
Synechococcus see Thermosynechococcus
Synechocystis 6803 deletion mutants
  absorption spectra 267, 271
  Chl *a* singlet excited state lifetime in cytochrome b_6f complex **437**
  chlorophyllide *a* oxygenase 287–8
  deg genes 408
  donor-side induced photodamage 398
  FtsH proteases 409, 410
  His-tagged PSIIcc **261**
  light-activated heterotrophic growth 397
  non-triplet producing charge recombination 405
  ^{1}P680* electronic states **248**
  P680$^+\cdot$Pheo$_{D1}^{-\cdot}$ formation **253**
  photon counter behavior of photodamage 401

phycobilisome components 270, 272
PsaI subunit **129**
PsaX subunit sequence **132**
PSI mutagenesis studies **119**
triplet state ^{3}P680 in PSII **249**
two-step photodamage mechanism 401
UV photodamage 399
UV photoprotection 411
Y_z^{ox} reduction/S_i state oxidation **318**
synthetic systems 26–30

T_1 state structures *see* triplet states
TA *see* transient absorption
TAKs 375
targeted mutagenesis *see* site-directed mutagenesis
Taylor series 51, 84
TDC *see* transition density cube method
TDS *see* tridecyl-stigmatellin
temperature dependance **155**
terbutryn **31**, **42**
terminal acceptors *see* F_A/F_B
terminal oxo-groups **313–14, 329–30**
terminal respiratory oxidase (TRO) **395–6**
terminology **308, 360, 67**
  ATP synthase **451, 461**
  LHCII chlorophylls 336, 337, 351
  WOC S_i states **308**
terpenoid alcohols 112
tetraheme cytochrome *see* C subunit
tetraheme RC species **359, 360–3**
tetraheme–tetrasulfur ([4Fe-4S]) centers **123–5, 151, 163–5**
tetra-manganese cubane center **506, 507**
tetrapyrroles 114, 115, 124
thermal energy dissipation (qE) 376, 377–9
Thermochromatium tepidum
  C subunit structure **23**
  electron donor substrate binding **33**
  heme-iron site geometries **28**
  H subunit structure **22**
  intramembrane phospholipids **37–9**
  L subunit structure **19**

M subunit structure **20–1**
RC characterization **11**
RC crystallization **13**
RC X-ray crystal form **14, 16**
stereo pairs **24, 26, 27**
tetraheme RC species **360**
thermodynamics
  anoxygenic photosynthetic bacterial RCs **63**
  electron transfer principles **386**
  F_1-ATPase rotating fluorescent actin-filament **468–72**
  F_OF_1 rotary twin engine **480**
  H^+/ATP stoichiometric ratio **458–9**
  oxidative water splitting **300–2**
thermoluminescence 120
thermophilic cyanobacteria **385, 398–400**
Thermosynechococcus spp.
  6803 **172–3**
  7942 405
  PCC 6301 **397, 400**
  PCC 7002 **129, 438**
  primary biomass production **389**
  T. elongatus
    cytochrome b_6f complex X-ray structure **419**
    ET complex crystals **398**
    Photosystem I 275
    Photosystem II 276
    PsaX subunit **132**
    PSI ET chain **151**
    PSIIcc X-ray crystallography **193–228**
    PSII single crystal EXAFS studies **307**
    PSI RC structure **63–5**
    PSI X-ray structure **114–16, 124–6, 136**
  T. lividus, two-ET branches of PSI **168–70**
  T. vulcanus
    activation energies of S_i state transitions **319–20**
    oxygen evolving PSIIcc crystals **200**
    Photosystem II 276
    PsaX subunit structural model **132**

Subject Index

PSIIcc electron density map interpretations **211–12**
Y_z^{ox} reduction/S_i state oxidation half life times **317–19**
thiol-regulation **459–60**
thioredoxin **459**
three-dimensional structure
  cytochrome b_6f complex **424–5**
  Rhodopseudomonas acidophila LH2 complex **220–7**
  Rhodospeudomonas palustris RC-LH1 complex **235–6**
  see also conformation; structure; X-ray diffraction studies
three-electron transport complexes **419–20**
three-pulse photon echo peak shift (3PEPS) experiments 349, 350, 355
three-state model of Gilmore 379
through-bond interactions 122
through-space interactions 121
thylakoids
  bilayer membrane discovery **196**
  circular dichroism 121
  fluorescence emission spectra 315
  lumen, acidification 376, 404
  membranes
    composition in cyanobacteria/plants **196–8**
    cyanobacteria, Photosystems molecular assembly 277–8
    D1 protein rapid turnover 406–11
    FNR in supramolecular organization **174**
    helix D in LHCII 335
    LHCII protein mass 331–2, 334
    PsbS protein of PSII 378
    PSI overview **113**
    vesicle structures 22–5
  structure **454–6**
  WOC substrate water binding **313**
tides, Moon formation **494**
tilted helices 218–19
time-convolution less projection operator technique 66
time-dependent spin polarization changes 188
time ordering operators 54
time-resolved spectroscopy
  CP29 355–6
  electro spray mass spectrometry, Mn–O–Mn bridges in WOC substrate water binding **314**
  EPR spectroscopy 183–6
  fluorescence spectroscopy, LHCII monomers 341
  inter-subunit rotation in F_1 **466**
  LHCII in higher plants 346–7, 349, 351
  optical spectroscopy, A_1^- bidirectional reoxidation kinetics **168–9**
  PsbS protein influence on Lhcbs in PSII 381–4
  Raman spectroscopy, carotenoids in purple bacteria 168–72
timescales
  absorption spectrometry 116
  energy transfer in purple non-sulfur bacterial PSU 241, 242
  evolution **387–8**
  photosynthetic evolution events **509–10**
tomato 312
torque (M) **468–72**
torsional rigidity (C) **478–9**
trans-carotenoids **135**, **136**
transcriptional regulation 212–15
transfer energy 237–42
transfer mechanisms, chlorophylls 104
transfer rates 48
'transfer-to-trap limited' mechanism **160**
transformable cyanobacteria **423**
transformation of energy principles 12–17
transient absorption (TA) 350
transient excitation energy reservoirs 278–9
transition density 85
transition density cube (TDC) method 85
transition dipole moments 164–7, 337
transition rate constant 50
translocon channels 409–10

transmembrane helices (TMH)
  ATP synthase a-subunit **463**
  bound water **36–7**
  cyanobacterial PsaL subunit **128–9**
  cyanobacterial PSIIcc structure
    209, 211–13, 216–17, 219
  cytochrome b_6f complex **425–7**
  HLIP **512**
  H subunit structure **21, 22**
  L & M subunits in proteobacteria **68**
  Lhc complexes of higher plants 331
  LHCII structure 335, 336–7
  M subunit structure **20–1**
  primary electron donor location **21–2**
  protein subunits **18–19**
  PrrBA system 212–14
  PsaA/PsaB in cyanobacterial PSI **122**
  PsbS-protein of PSII 377–9
  PSI in oxygen evolving organisms **150**
  purple bacterial antenna complex 218–20
  RC evolution **502–4**
  see also membrane-spanning helices
transmembrane pH difference (pH_n–pH_p) 17, 21, **453**
transmembrane signaling **422**
transmembrane voltage **475**
transmetalated chlorophylls 113
'trap-limited' mechanism **160**, 334
trapped mixed valence states **308–9**
trapping limited reactions **255**
trapping process see primary charge separation
triads, biomimetic reaction centers 28
triazines **31**
tridecyl-stigmatellin (TDS) **421, 429**
triheme RC species **363–5**
trimeric complexes **114–16, 128–9**, 338, 341, 342, 373
tripartite structure 215
triplet energy 177–9, 183–9, 195
triplet forming charge recombination 398–9
triplet quenching **267**, 345–6
triplet-sensitized isomerization 179–80
triplet states

^{3}P680, electronic configuration in PSII **248–9**
carotenoids of purple bacteria 159–64
cyanobacterial PSI carotenoids **135**
luminescence 120
P700 in PSI of oxygen evolving organisms **165–7**
15-cis-spheroidene conformational changes 190
triplet–triplet energy transfer 154, 343, **436–7, 439**
tri-site binding change mechanisms **464–5, 468, 472**
TRO see terminal respiratory oxidase
tryptophan-rich sensory protein (TspO) 213–14
tubular membranes 233
tunneling nuclei 60–3
tunneling pathway model 86
twisted carotenoids 226, 227
two-channel F_O rotary electromotor model **473, 475**
two-dimensional crystals 229–30, 233, 335–8
two-electron transfer branches **167–71**, **430**
see also A-branch; B-branch
two-photon excitation 345
two-pulse photon echo study 350
two-step mechanism **71**, 401
tyrosine donors 399, 400
tyrosine residues
  chlorophyll a and Tyr105 in cytochrome b_6f complex **438**
  modified bacterial reaction centers **40, 41, 42**
  RC structure comparison with PSII structure **44**
  see also Y_Z

ubi-(mena)-quinone **254**
ubiqionone-2-reconstitution studies **29–31**
ubiquinol **30–2**, 234–6
ubiquinone-10 **402**
ubiquinone **30–2, 62**, 234, 235–6

Subject Index

ultrafast spectroscopy **154**, 165–70, 345, 348–9, 350–1
  see also individual techniques; spectroscopy
ultraviolet (UV) light **205**, **393**, 399–401, 411–12, **498**
uncertainty principle 56, 192–3
unidirectionality **74–5**, **81–2**, **161**, **252**
unitary concept **392**
unitary proton conductance **476**
universe, evolution **387**
unpaired spins 121–2
unsaturated terpenoid alcohols 112
unsaturation, chlorophylls 107
uptake hydrogenase **395**, **401**
uroporphyrinogen 124

V see violaxanthin
van der Waals contact **222–3**, 226, 239
Van Niel equation **389**
variable antenna complex see light harvesting 2 complexes
variant structures **17**, **40–2**
vascular plants 301–22
VDE see violaxanthin deepoxidase
vectorial electron transfer **455–6**
vectorial hydrogen transfer **456**
vesicles 22–5, **457–8**
  see also organelles
vibrational degrees of freedom 42, 43, 48, 68
vibrational Hamiltonian (H_{vib}) 65
vibrational quanta of protein mode 55
vibrational relaxations 167–8, 193
vibrational sidebands 48, 78–80, 81, 114, 115
vibrational spectroscopy 122–3
[8-vinyl]-chlorophylls *a/b* 113
[8-vinyl]-protochlorophyllide *a* 109
violaxanthin deepoxidase (VDE) **374**, **376**, **404**
violaxanthin (V) 340–1, 343, 345, 376
viscous drag **467**, **468**, **470**, **472**
visible sub-picosecond time-resolved spectra 161, 162
vitamin B_{12} 124, 125

Wankel engine, molecular **465–8**
water
  artificial oxidative cleavage catalysts 29–30
  clusters, cyanobacterial PSI A/B branches **120**
  depth, light harvesting pigment evolution **513**
  photosynthetic cleavage 9–10
  see also bound water
water oxidizing complex (WOC)
  artificial systems 29–30
  assembly/structure **302–17**
  chloride/bicarbonate ions **311–12**
  chloroplast structure 25
  cyanobacterial PSIIcc **223–7**
  de novo D1 protein synthesis 410
  electronic structure **308–11**
  evolution **393–4**, **507**
  $P680^{+\cdot}$ reduction by Y_z/oxidative water splitting **263**, **264**, **265**
  photoactivation **302–4**
  PSIIcc **401**
  PSII water splitting **240**
  two-step photodamage mechanism 401
  UV photodamage 399–400
  see also oxidative water splitting
water quality factor (*QualWat*) **36**
water splitting **291–331**
  evolution **497**, **507–9**
  oxidative **195–6**
  PSII overall process **240**
  WOC function **291–331**
  see also water oxidizing complex
water water cycle **404**
W_c state **376–7**, 379
weak coupling limit 48–62
weak pigment–pigment coupling 48–62, 78
W_f see fast exchange
W helix see helix W
Wilkinson Microwave Anisotropy Satellite **387**
WOC see water oxidizing complex
W_s see slow exchange

XANES spectroscopy **309**, **317**, **329**
Xanthophyceae 110
xanthophylls
  cyanobacteria 268
  cycle, PsbS protein functions in PSII 379
  LHCII in higher plants 331, 337, 340–1, 343, 345
  outer antenna Chl *a*/Chl *b*/Xan–protein complexes 331
X_c state 376–7, 379
XES *see* X-ray emission spectroscopy
X-ray diffraction crystallography (XRDC)
  3.0 Å resolution of PSIIcc in cyanobacteria **193–228**
  anoxygenic purple bacteria RCs **13–18**
  ATP synthase **461–6**
  bacterial reaction centers **7–45**
  Blastochloris viridis RC structure **66–7**
  cyanobacterial PSIIcc structure **193–228**
  cytochrome b_6f complex **419**, **420**, **424–8**
  electron density map interpretation problems **211–12**
  ET from Q_A^- to Q_B in PBRCs 268
  LH2 complex from Rhodo-pseudomonas acidophila 221–2
  LHCII structure 335–8, 342–3
  Mn_4O_xCa clusters **305**
  modified bacterial reaction centers **39–44**
  P700 in PSI of oxygen evolving organisms **167**
  peridinin-chlorophyll *a* complex 44, 47
  Photosystem I **151**, **167**, **401**
  Photosysytem II 44, 45, **243–5**, **248**
  phylloquinone A_1 characterization **163**
  plant-type Fds **171–2**
  Prosthecochloris aestuarii FMO-complex 46

Q_A pocket structure in PSIIcc **254**
RC-LH1 complexes in anoxygenic bacteria **370**
resolution increases **211**
Rhodobacter sphaeroides RC structure **66–7**
Synechococcus elongatus PSI **114–16**, **124–6**, **136**
thermophilic cyanobacterial ET complexes **398–400**
X-ray emission spectroscopy (XES) **310**
XRDC *see* X-ray diffraction crystallography

Y_c state 376–7, 379
Y-shaped arrangements **224–5**
Y_z^{ox} formation **329**
$Y_z^{ox}S_3'$ state **328–9**
Y_z tyrosine residue
  $P680^+$ connection 293
  $P680^+$ reduction **262–5**, 299
  reduction kinetics 318
  WOC photoactivation 303
  WOC proton network 315
  Y_z^{ox} reduction kinetics **316–20**

Z *see* zeaxanthin
Zea mays 312, 347
zeaxanthin:chl *a* dimer 383
zeaxanthin deepoxidase 374
zeaxanthin (Z)
  chloroplast thylakoid lumen pH acidification 376
  cyanobacteria 268, 283
  energy dissipation 374
  fluorescence quenching 311
  LHCII organization 340–1, 343
  PsbS protein functions in PSII 379
zero-field splitting parameters 184–6
$zinc^{2+}$ **32**, **72**
zinc chlorophylls 107, 113
Zn-tetrapyrrole (Zn-Proto) 113
Z-scheme **403**